D1218381

THE CARBOHYDRATES

Chemistry, Biochemistry, Physiology

THE CARBOHYDRATES

Chemistry, Biochemistry, Physiology

Edited by
WARD PIGMAN
Department of Biochemistry
University of Alabama Medical Center
Birmingham, Alabama

#41656 2 DLC

1957
ACADEMIC PRESS INC · PUBLISHERS
NEW YORK

COPYRIGHT 1957 BY ACADEMIC PRESS INC.

ALL RIGHTS RESERVED

NO PART OF THIS BOOK MAY BE REPRODUCED IN ANY FORM
BY PHOTOSTAT, MICROFILM, OR ANY OTHER MEANS,
WITHOUT WRITTEN PERMISSION FROM THE PUBLISHERS.

ACADEMIC PRESS INC.
111 FIFTH AVENUE
NEW YORK 3, N. Y.

United Kingdom Edition
Published by
ACADEMIC PRESS INC. (LONDON) LTD.
BERKELEY SQUARE HOUSE, LONDON W. 1

First Printing, 1957
Second Printing, 1962

Library of Congress Catalog Card Number: 57-8379

3/83

PRINTED IN THE UNITED STATES OF AMERICA

QU
75
P62c

CONTRIBUTORS

C. E. BALLOU, *University of California, Department of Plant Biochemistry, Berkeley, California (pp. 172, 478)*

MARY GRACE BLAIR, *University of Alabama, Medical Center, Arthritis and Rheumatism Research Laboratory, Birmingham, Alabama (p. 60)*

HELMUT BAUMANN, *Silikose-Forschungsinstitut der Bergbau-Berufsgenossenschaft, Bochum, Germany (p. 536)*

W. M. CORBETT, *British Rayon Research Organization, Heald Green Laboratories, Wythenshane, Manchester, England (p. 641)*

HARRY G. DAY, *Indiana University, Department of Chemistry. Bloomington, Indiana (p. 779)*

DAVID G. DOHERTY, *Oak Ridge National Laboratory, Biology Division, Oak Ridge, Tennessee (pp. 424, 430, 441)*

JOHN W. GREEN, *Institute of Paper Chemistry, Appleton, Wisconsin (p. 299)*

W. Z. HASSID, *University of California, Department of Plant Biochemistry, Berkeley, California (pp. 172, 478)*

ROLLAND L. LOHMAR, JR., *United States Department of Agriculture, Northern Utilization Research Branch, Peoria, Illinois (p. 241)*

ROBERT W. MOWRY, *University of Alabama, Medical Center, Department of Pathology, Birmingham, Alabama (p. 624)*

G. RAY NOGGLE, *C. F. Kettering Foundation, Yellow Springs, Ohio (pp. 602, 733)*

JANE REID PATTON, *Howard College, Department of Chemistry, Birmingham, Alabama (p. 465)*

WARD PIGMAN, *University of Alabama Medical Center, Biochemistry Department, Birmingham, Alabama (pp. 1, 406, 536, 709, 779)*

DAVID PLATT, *University of Alabama Medical Center, Department of Biochemistry, Birmingham, Alabama (pp. 446, 709)*

JAMES W. PRATT, *National Institute of Arthritis and Metabolic Diseases, Bethesda, Maryland (p. 861)*

LAWRENCE ROSEN, *University of Alabama Medical Center, Department of Biochemistry, Birmingham, Alabama (pp. 407, 452)*

JOHN C. SOWDEN, *Washington University, Department of Chemistry, St. Louis, Missouri (pp. 77, 367)*

ALVA THOMPSON, *The Ohio State University, Department of Chemistry, Columbus, Ohio (pp. 138, 188)*

ELLIOTT VOLKIN, *Oak Ridge National Laboratory, Biology Division, Oak Ridge, Tennessee (pp. 430, 441)*

ROY L. WHISTLER, *Purdue University, Department of Biochemistry, Lafayette, Indiana (p. 641)*

M. L. WOLFROM, *The Ohio State University, Chemistry Department, Columbus, Ohio (pp. 138, 188)*

PREFACE

"The Carbohydrates" is a complete revision and expansion in scope of the earlier "Chemistry of the Carbohydrates."* Two new chapters have been added covering photosynthesis and metabolism (Chapter XIII) and nutritional aspects (Chapter XIV). These additions and the general increase in the coverage of biochemical and physiological aspects reflect the great progress made in biochemistry during the past decade and the important position of the carbohydrates in the processes of life. Marked advances have also been made in recent years especially in reaction mechanisms, stereochemistry of strainless rings, transglycosylation, development of methods for the synthesis of radioactive sugars and their analysis, chromatography and related methods of analysis, identification of tissue carbohydrates *in situ* (histochemistry), and isolation and characterization of animal polysaccharides and their protein complexes. These developments have been brought into the present work.

The vast accumulated literature and the almost terrifying rate of growth create new problems continually. In this volume references are given to about 4500 individual articles, representing the result of the careful examination through much of 1956 of several times this number of articles. In turn, these represent only a small fraction of the actual carbohydrate literature. As a result, considerable selection of material was necessary, and the fullness of the treatment varies. Subjects such as the sugars and their derivatives are discussed in detail, whereas such subjects as the polysaccharides, which have been considered satisfactorily in other monographs, have been condensed. References to more detailed treatments help to increase the coverage.

The relatively scanty general coverage by the current eleven volumes of the "Advances in Carbohydrate Chemistry" is witness to the broad scope and depth of the subject of the carbohydrates. The literature and the available knowledge in the field of carbohydrates, like those of the corresponding fields of the proteins and of the enzymes, are similar in magnitude to those in such broad fields as medicine and dentistry. Preparation of a monograph on starch alone involves dealing with more research material and more basic literature than some specialized branches of medicine.

In order to prevent this new book from being simply an expansion of the old one, considerable borderline material was deleted, and the polysaccha-

* W. W. Pigman and R. M. Goepp, Jr., "Chemistry of the Carbohydrates." Academic Press, New York, 1948.

ride chapters were condensed. The older edition contains additional material of permanent value and should be used in conjunction with the current book.

Presumably this volume will have its main use as a reference work by chemists, biochemists, industrialists, biologists, histochemists, students, and medical and dental research workers. It should be useful as a basic text for graduate courses in the subject. It may have value as a text, with readings assigned to some of the references, for a general advanced course for some departments of biochemistry and microbiology; the integration of the research viewpoint with physical and organic chemistry and biochemistry and with physiology and biology may provide the basis of a useful and practical course, especially for small departments not well prepared for offering advanced courses in special fields of chemistry. The subject cuts across all of these classical disciplines and others such as technology and commerce.

Since the publication of the previous edition, there has been considerable standardization of nomenclature. The new official rules have been followed closely. In areas in which agreement on nomenclature has not been reached, notably nomenclature of some acids (especially ascorbic acids), biologically important nitrogenous compounds, and polysaccharides, arbitrary choices have been made.

The present work has been made possible only by the wholehearted response of some of the important workers in the field who aided in the revision of the material in the previous volume. Acknowledgment of their valuable help is indicated by the authorship of the chapters and some shorter sections. Several associates, including graduate students, cooperated in preparing some sections and gave valuable assistance generally.

The general editorial assistance of Dr. Grace Blair was of great help Doctors James Woods, Robert Teague, and Joseph Volker read some of the material and provided valuable advice. Others who have helped in this or similar ways are B. F. Helferich, J. Goerdeler, M. L. Wolfrom, S. Roseman, C. Ballou, and G. E. McCasland.

The onerous task of preparing the subject index was accepted by Dr. James Pratt to whom special thanks are due. Dr. Hewitt Fletcher gave important assistance in the reading of page proof and in his comments.

The University of Alabama provided indirect support and encouragement essential to the preparation of this book. The whole-hearted cooperation of Academic Press eased the solution of the many editorial and publication problems.

WARD PIGMAN

June 1957
Birmingham, Alabama

CONTENTS

I. Introduction: Structure and Stereochemistry of the Monosaccharides

WARD PIGMAN

1. GENERAL RELATIONS

The carbohydrates comprise one of the major groups of naturally occurring organic materials. They are the basis of many important industries or segments of industries including sugar and sugar products, glucose and starch products, paper and wood pulp, textile fibers, plastics, foods and food processing, fermentation, and, to a less-developed extent, pharmaceuticals, drugs, vitamins, and specialty chemicals.

They are of special significance in plants, the dry substance of which is usually composed of 50 to 80% of carbohydrates. For plants, the structural material is mainly cellulose and the related hemicelluloses accompanied by lesser amounts of a phenolic polymer (lignin). Smaller but important amounts of starch, pectins, and sugars, especially sucrose and D-glucose, are also plant constituents and are obtained commercially from these sources. Many noncarbohydrate organic compounds are found conjugated with sugars in the form of glycosides.

For the higher animals, the principal structural material is protein rather than carbohydrate, and frequently the animal carbohydrates are found in loose or firm combination with proteins, as well as other materials. The amorphous ground substance between cells is composed to a considerable extent of the polysaccharide hyaluronic acid. Other important carbohydrates or carbohydrate-protein complexes are the D-glucose of blood and tissue fluids, the glycogen of liver and muscle particularly, the immuno and blood-group substances, the mucins, and the uronides. Many foreign substances are removed from the body through the intermediary of the formation of glycosides of glucuronic acid. Of special importance to animals are the 2-amino-2-deoxyhexoses, glucosamine and galactosamine. In some of the lower animals a major constituent of the exoskeleton (crab and lobster shells) is a polymer of glucosamine, chitin. Fats, of both animal and plant origin, are fatty acid esters of a sugar alcohol, glycerol.

In all living cells, as far as is known, the carbohydrates are the central pathway for the supply of energy needed for mechanical work and chemical reactions. Phosphate esters of the sugars are important in these transformations, and carbohydrate derivatives, like adenosine triphosphate and related substances, are key substances in energy storage and transfer. Similar polymeric carbohydrate derivatives, the nucleic acids, are essential major cell components. Possibly even more basically, the light energy from the sun is trapped by plants by a mechanism involving chlorophyll and is rapidly stored or transferred to carbohydrate derivatives, sugars, and hydroxy acids. The man-made chemical classifications of cell components have only formal significance in biological systems, and, through common intermediates such as pyruvic acid, serine, and acetate, the proteins, fats, and carbohydrates are interconvertible.

2. SOME DEFINITIONS

Although a term like "carbohydrate" cannot be defined with exactitude, there is value in an examination of its significance and that of related commonly used terms. The carbohydrates comprise several homologous series characterized by a plurality of hydroxyl groups and one or more functional groups, particularly aldehyde or ketone groups, usually in the acetal or hemiacetal forms. Natural polymers of these products with hemiacetal linkages as the polymeric linkage are a very important portion of the carbohydrate group, known as oligo- and polysaccharides.

An oversimplified but possibly acceptable definition of the carbohydrates is that they are composed of the polyhydroxy aldehydes, ketones, alcohols, acids, their simple derivatives, and the polymers having hemiacetal polymeric linkages. (See pages 478 and 641.) The full-fledged nonpolymeric carbohydrates are the five-, six-, and higher-carbon members of the several homologous series. With progressively fewer carbon atoms, the carbohydrate characteristics of the compounds degenerate until the atypical one- and two-carbon compounds, like ethanol, acetaldehyde, and acetic acid, are reached.

Although only one type, the sugars have often been considered as the typical carbohydrates. The sugars (or saccharides) are the monosaccharides and their simple polymers (the oligosaccharides). The monosaccharides are polyhydroxy aldehydes (I) and ketones (IV) which usually exist in an inner hemiacetal form (II or III). The oligosaccharides (VII) contain relatively few combined monosaccharide units (2 to 10) which are connected through acetal glycosidic linkages. When the molecules contain many bound monosaccharide units, the compounds belong to the class of polysaccharides (VII). For the polysaccharides, the relatively diminishing percentage of aldehyde or ketone groups enhances the behavior of the polysaccharides as polyols, except for the acid-labile acetal (glycosidic) linkage (see formula (VII)).

With the historical and frequently practical concept of the monosaccharides as the basic units from which all carbohydrates can be derived, the term glycose is being increasingly used as a basis for class names. A glycose is any monosaccharide, and, by the addition of a suitable ending, various simple derivatives are indicated as classes, such as glycosides (V, VI), glyconic (aldonic) acids (IX), glycaric (aldaric) acids (XI), glycosamines (VIII), glycals, and glycitols (alditols) (XII).

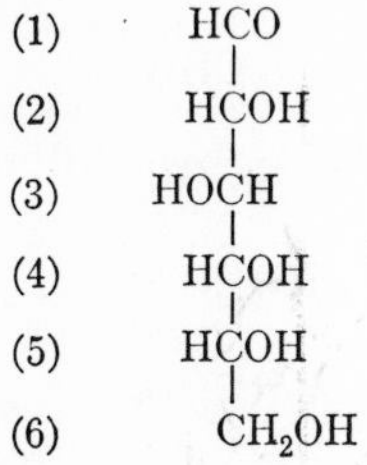
(1)
(2)
(3)
(4)
(5)
(6)
HCO
HCOH
HOCH
HCOH
HCOH
CH2OH

(I)

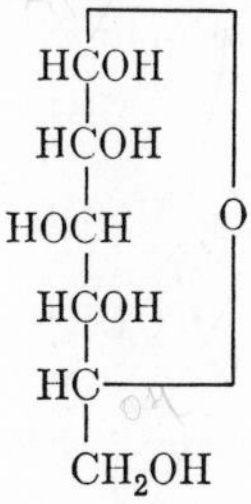
HCOH
HCOH
HOCH
HCOH
HC
CH2OH
O

(II)

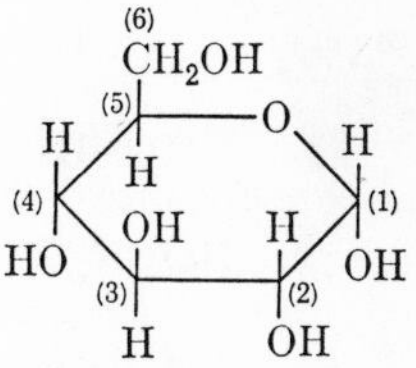
(6)
CH2OH
(5)
O
H
H
H
(4)
(1)
OH
H
HO
OH
(3)
(2)
H
OH

(III)

The aldohexose D-glucose in the open-chain Fischer formula (I), the Fischer-Tollens hemiacetal ring formula (II), and the Haworth formula (III). The numbering system is shown.

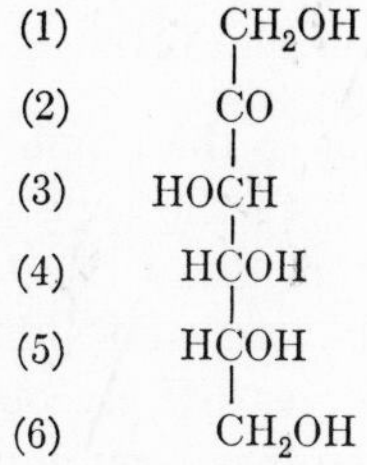
(1)
(2)
(3)
(4)
(5)
(6)
CH2OH
CO
HOCH
HCOH
HCOH
CH2OH

(IV)

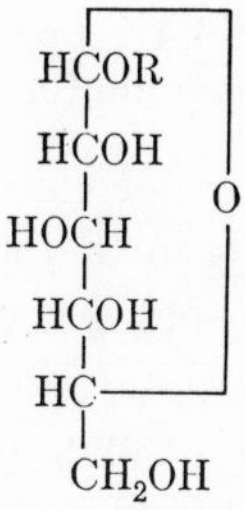
HCOR
HCOH
HOCH
HCOH
HC
CH2OH
O

(V)

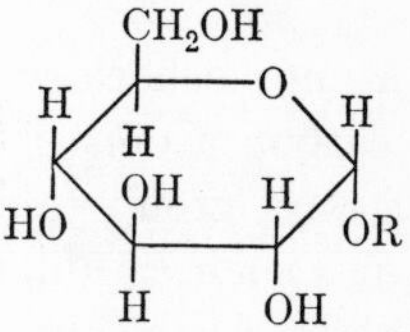
CH2OH
O
H
H
H
OH
H
HO
OR
H
OH

(VI)

A hexulose or ketohexose, fructose (IV). A glycoside with the common mixed full-acetal ring formula (V) and with the Haworth acetal ring formula (VI); R is an alkyl or aryl group.

Oligo and Polysaccharides

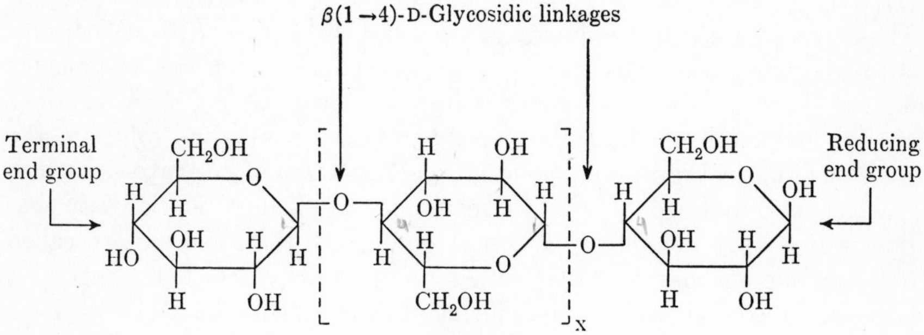
β(1→4)-D-Glycosidic linkages
Terminal end group
Reducing end group
CH2OH
O
H
H
OH
H
HO
H
H
OH
O
H
OH
OH
H
H
H
O
CH2OH
x
O
CH2OH
O
OH
H
H
OH
H
H
H
OH

(VII)

Polysaccharide; X is large (greater than 8 and usually 100 to 2000)
Oligosaccharides; X is small (0 to 8)
- Disaccharide (biose), $X = 0$
- Trisaccharide (triose), $X = 1$
- Tetrasaccharide (tetraose), $X = 2$
- Pentasaccharide (pentaose), $X = 3$

Acids and Amino Sugars

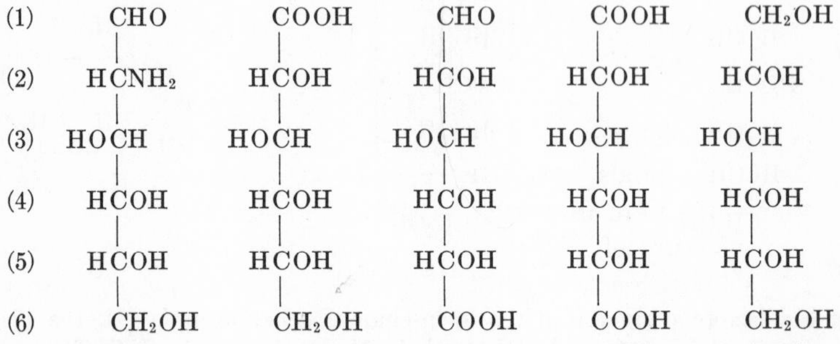

(VIII) (IX) (X) (XI) (XII)

An amino sugar, 2-amino-2-deoxy-D-glucose or glucosamine (VIII); the aldonic acid, gluconic acid (IX); the uronic acid, glucuronic acid (X); the glycaric acid, glucaric or saccharic acid (XI); a glycitol or alditol, sorbitol or D-glucitol (XII).

Monosaccharides usually are further classified according to the number of carbon atoms in the central chain of the molecule and to the type of carbonyl group (aldehyde or ketone) present. This system gives rise to names such as aldotriose, aldotetrose, aldopentose, aldohexose, and aldoheptose. At the one- and two-carbon stage, this series converges into glycolic aldehyde and formaldehyde. The presence of a ketone group has been indicated by names such as ketopentoses and ketohexoses; more recently, the tendency except for some established trivial names is to indicate the presence of a ketone group by the ending "ulose" in names such as pentuloses, hexuloses, and heptuloses.

An aldehyde or ketone group in the free (I, IV) or in the hemiacetal form (II, III) generally is the most reactive of the functional groups present. These groups are called reducing groups, and the sugars with such unsubstituted groups are called reducing sugars. These groups are responsible for the characteristic reactions of reducing sugars. Among such reactions are the reduction of the salts of heavy metals in alkaline solution, the changes of optical rotation in solution, the formation of derivatives such as osazones and hydrazones, and the instability to alkalies. The oligosaccharides which have a reducing group at one end of the molecule are called reducing oligosaccharides (VII). When no free aldehyde or ketone group is present, the compound is a nonreducing oligosaccharide. Disaccharides like maltose and lactose are reducing, whereas sucrose is nonreducing because the aldehyde and ketone groups of the component fructose and glucose have been combined in the formation of the disaccharidic glycosidic linkage. Like the oligosaccharides, the polysaccharides usually have a terminal reducing group (see formula (VII)), but the relative amount of these terminal groups is usually too small to influence the reactions greatly. However, properties like alkali instability may still be determined by the reducing groups (see formula (VII)), although the number is small.

3. NOMENCLATURE

In the early development of carbohydrate chemistry as in that of many other natural materials, special systems of nomenclature were developed which frequently were inconsistent within themselves or with the established nomenclature of organic compounds. Organized efforts have been made to systematize carbohydrate nomenclature, and a considerable area of agreement has been reached by American and English carbohydrate chemists. The recommendations have been embodied in some 35 rules (*1*), which in the present text are followed as closely as possible. The greatest changes from the earlier usage are in the adoption of substitutions as involving parent hydrocarbon radicals, the use of the deoxy system, the establishment of rules for the indication of the configuration of a series of asymmetric carbon atoms, and the systemization of the carbohydrate acids. Old names such as 3-methyl-D-glucose are now written as 3-*O*-methyl-D-glucose. Mucic acid has the systematic name of galactaric acid, and the uronic acid nomenclature has been revised.

4. DEVELOPMENT OF CARBOHYDRATE CHEMISTRY (*2*)

Carbohydrates such as cellulose and sucrose were known to man in very early times in pure or semipure forms. Prehistoric man was acquainted with honey, a fairly pure mixture of the three sugars sucrose, D-fructose, and D-glucose.

The culture of sugar cane and the use of the juices as a sweetening agent appear to have originated in northeastern India. As early as 300 A.D., the crystalline sugar was known and used. Sugar cane culture was extended to China around 400 A.D. and to Egypt around 640 A.D.; from Egypt, the culture and use of the sugar spread gradually over North Africa to Spain

1. Committee on Carbohydrate Nomenclature, *Chem. Eng. News* **31,** 1776 (1953).

2. For more details of the history and earlier work, the reader is referred to the following references from which the present discussion was abstracted: E. O. von Lippmann, "Geschichte des Zuckers," 2nd ed., Berlin, 1929; "Beilsteins Handbuch der organischen Chemie," Vol. 31. Springer, Berlin, 1938; N. Deerr, "The History of Sugar." Chapman & Hall, London, 1949–1950.

and Sicily. The introduction into North America is ascribed to Columbus, who brought the plant to Santo Domingo on his second voyage. Sugar cane cannot be grown well in Europe because it requires a tropical or semitropical climate, but the sugar was known in Europe during the fourteenth and fifteenth centuries and used as a costly sweetening agent. However, by 1600 many sugar refineries had been erected in Europe, and the use of cane sugar had become widespread.

The necessary restriction of the culture of sugar cane to tropical or semitropical lands stimulated the search for sweetening materials which could be obtained from plants native to the temperate region. This search led to the technical development on the European continent of the sugar beet during the latter part of the eighteenth century and especially in the early years of the nineteenth because of the continental blockade during the Napoleonic wars.

The desire to find sweetening agents stimulated the study of known products and of new sources. Honey, grape juice, and raisins were known to contain material which crystallized under some conditions. Marggraf in 1747 described a type of sugar which occurs in raisins. Lowitz (1792) isolated a sugar from honey which he indicated to be different from cane sugar. Proust (1802) claimed that grapes contain a sugar which is different from sucrose. The action of acids on starch was shown to produce a sweet sirup from which a crystalline sugar was isolated by Kirchoff in 1811. Later workers established that the sugar contained in grapes is identical with that in honey, in diabetic urine, and in the acid-hydrolyzates of starch and cellulose; it was given the name of glucose by Dumas (1838) and of dextrose by Kekulé (1866). Emil Fischer revived the name glucose, and it is now used generally in scientific work.

The presence in honey also of a sirupy sugar different frcm glucose and sucrose was recognized by many early workers, but the crystalline material was prepared first by Jungfleisch and Lefranc in 1881. The name of levulose seems to have been applied first by Berthelot (1860), whereas Emil Fischer (1890) suggested the name of fructose for this sugar.

Due to their ease of isolation and purification, sucrose, lactose (milk sugar), starch, cotton cellulose, glucose, and fructose were among the first to be studied, and their empirical composition was found to correspond to the general formula $C_n(H_2O)_x$. Since structural chemistry and the existence of hydroxyl groups and hydrogen as structural elements was unknown at the time, the substances were looked upon quite naturally as compounds of carbon and water, and were termed carbohydrates (French, *hydrates de carbone*).

It was soon learned that acid hydrolysis converted starch and cellulose, $[C_6(H_2O)_5]_x$, into glucose, $C_6(H_2O)_6$, with the uptake of one mole of water per C_6 unit. Cane sugar, $C_{12}(H_2O)_{11}$, took up one mole of water to give two $C_6(H_2O)_6$ sugars (hexoses), glucose and fructose. Lactose, another $C_{12}(H_2O)_{11}$ compound, gave glucose and galactose, both $C_6(H_2O)_6$. Hydrolysis of cherry gum yielded arabinose, $C_5(H_2O)_5$, a pentose. Another C_6 sugar, sorbose, was discovered in an old, fermented sample of sorb apple juice. Further work showed that arabinose, glucose, and galactose were polyhydroxy aldehydes (aldoses) while fructose and sorbose were polyhydroxy ketones (ketoses). Somewhat later a third C_6 aldose (aldohexose), mannose, was synthesized from mannitol and subsequently found in nature. The actual structure of the three natural C_6 aldoses was unknown, but after the development of the Le Bel-van't Hoff theory it was evident that they were stereoisomers, since all were straight-chain compounds.

Meanwhile, the series of naturally occurring, homologous, straight-chain polyhydric alcohols: glycol, glycerol, erythritol (C_4), arabitol (C_5), mannitol, dulcitol, sorbitol, and iditol (C_6), and perseitol (C_7), had been discovered. They had the general formula $C_n(H_2O)_nH_2$, (in modern terms, $HOCH_2(CHOH)_{n-2}CH_2OH$). Erythritol and the higher members were crystalline, sweet tasting, and water soluble. The four hexitols were known to be isomeric, but their relationship to each other and to the five natural C_6 sugars was not known until Emil Fischer's classical work in the early nineties.

Three dibasic acids of the series $HOOC(CHOH)_{n-2}COOH$ were likewise discovered very early, the C_4 tartaric acid from wine lees, and the isomeric C_6 mucic and saccharic acids from the nitric acid oxidation of lactose and of cane sugar.

5. STRUCTURES OF GLUCOSE AND FRUCTOSE (*3*)

The structure of glucose is established by the following evidence. Dumas (1843) determined the empirical formula of the sugar to be CH_2O (when water is taken as H_2O and not as HO as it appears in the early work). Berthelot established the presence of a number of hydroxyl groups by the preparation of an acetate (indicated by him to be a hexaacetate) and formulated glucose as a hexahydric alcohol; however, as a result of additional studies (1862), glucose was formulated as an aldehyde-alcohol with five carbon atoms. The six-carbon nature and the various known properties of glucose were expressed by Fittig and by Baeyer (1868 to 1870) in the formula:

$$(HO)H_2C—CH(OH)—CH(OH)—CH(OH)—CH(OH)—CHO \quad \text{(Fittig, Baeyer)}$$

The Baeyer-Fittig formula is confirmed by molecular weight determinations

3. For references see "Beilsteins Handbuch der organischen Chemie," Vol. 31, p. 83. Springer, Berlin, 1938.

(B. Tollens and Mayer—1888), by the formation of pentaacetates and other esters, and by the exhibition of many aldehyde-type reactions. Thus, the reduction of the sugar produces a hexahydric alcohol (sorbitol), and oxidation with bromine or nitric acid produces a monobasic acid (gluconic acid). These reactions would be anticipated from the presence of an aldehyde group. By reduction (with hydrogen iodide) of the alcohol or acid obtained from glucose, *sec*-hexyl iodide or *n*-hexylic acid is obtained. The formation of the *sec*-hexyl iodide proves that the sugar has a straight chain. These and many other reactions support the Baeyer-Fittig formulation of glucose. However, as will be shown below, the formula does not show the stereochemical relationships of the various groups, and many reactions and properties of the sugar are not fully expressed.

Fructose must be constituted similarly to glucose, for it is reduced to hexahydric alcohols (mannitol and sorbitol). The mannitol has a straight-chain structure as is shown by its conversion to *sec*-hexyl iodide by the action of hydrogen iodide. Oxidation of the sugar with nitric acid yields *meso*-tartaric acid (COOH—CHOH—CHOH—COOH), glycolic acid (CH_2OH—COOH), and oxalic acid and must take place by cleavage of the carbon chain. The formation of tartaric acid and glycolic acid would be expected if a ketone group is present at carbon 2. The existence of a ketone group is shown by the formation of a branched-chain acid when fructose is treated with HCN. The nature of the seven-carbon acid formed by the addition of HCN was shown by Kiliani who reduced it to 2-methylhexanoic acid.

6. STEREOCHEMISTRY

A. General Principles

The sugars with the formula $C_6H_{12}O_6$ known in 1886 were glucose, fructose, galactose, and sorbose. Of the known hexoses, two types of structures were present. These types were the glucose-galactose type with aldehyde structures and the fructose-sorbose type with ketone structures.

The occurrence of structurally identical sugars such as glucose and galactose presented a challenge to the chemists of the later nineteenth century to provide an explanation for the existence of isomers of a type other than structural isomers. The basis for this explanation was developed almost simultaneously by Le Bel and van't Hoff and published in 1874. According to these workers, isomers of a type other than structural isomers should exist for compounds which contain asymmetric carbon atoms. This type of isomerism is illustrated below for glyceraldehyde (CH_2OH—CHOH—CHO). Each of the two isomers is represented by a tetrahedral formula and by a conventional formula.

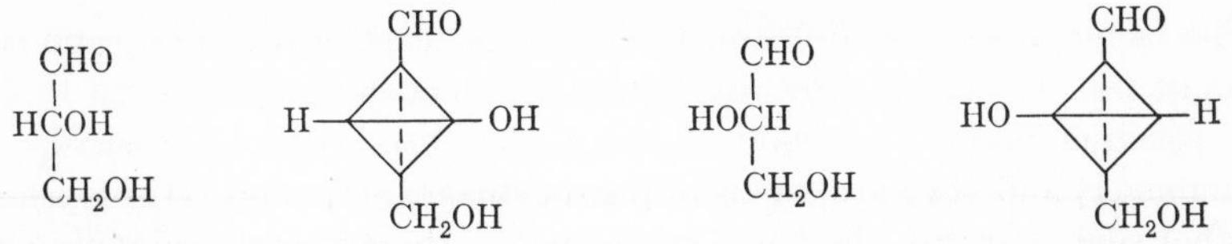

The conventional formulas are derived from the tetrahedral formulas by the use of the convention established by Fischer (*4*). The tetrahedrons are represented as being held so that the dotted lower edge is in the plane of the paper; the H and OH corners are above the plane of the paper with the aldehyde group at the top. The conventional formula represents the projection of the model on the plane of the paper.

The two tetrahedrons differ only in the configuration of the groups in space, and the substances are called stereoisomers. Careful examination of the above figure, or better of models, will show that no matter how the tetrahedrons are turned in space they cannot be made to coincide. However, it should be noted that the two tetrahedrons are related in a fashion like that of an object and its mirror image. When two of the groups attached to the same carbon are identical, isomerism of this type is not possible. The presence of asymmetric carbon atoms in organic compounds was suggested by Le Bel and van't Hoff as the cause of the optical activity of the compounds. Compounds which contain such atoms cause a rotation of the plane of polarization of plane-polarized light when the light is passed through their solutions.

For each of the trioses shown above, there are two related tetroses. The tetroses have two asymmetric carbon atoms; the formulas of the four possible isomers are given below in both the tetrahedral and the ordinary formulas.

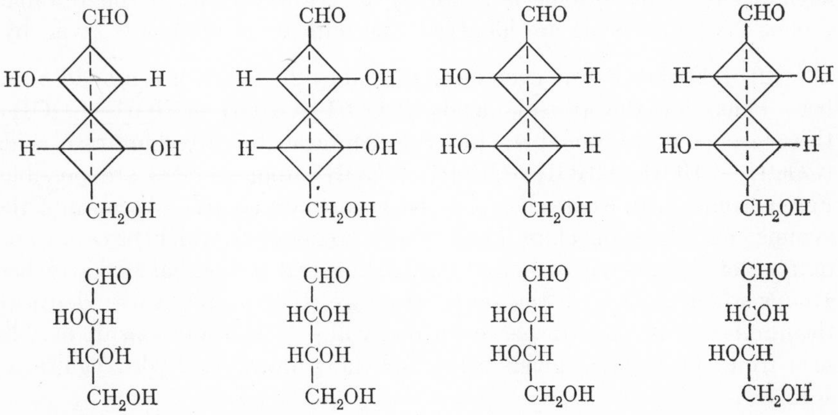

(I) (II) (III) (IV)

4. E. Fischer, *Ber.* **24,** 1836, 2683 (1891); see also C. S. Hudson, *Advances in Carbohydrate Chem.* **3,** 1 (1948).

The isomeric tetroses differ in their spacial relationships and cannot be brought into coincidence by rotation of the models in space even though free rotation about the bond between the tetrahedra is possible. The formulas (I) and (IV) are a pair of mirror images; (II) and (III) represent another such pair. For the four-carbon sugars, there are two pairs of mirror images (enantiomorphs) and four stereoisomers. In the sugar series, substances which differ only in the configuration of the carbon atom immediately adjacent to that carrying the carbonyl or carboxyl group are known as epimers. In the above formulas, (I) and (II) represent a pair of epimers and (III) and (IV) another pair. It may be well to extend the definition of epimers to mean any pair of stereoisomers that differ solely in the configuration of a single asymmetric carbon atom. By this definition compounds (V) and (VI) would be 2-epimers and compounds (V) and (VII) would be 3-epimers.

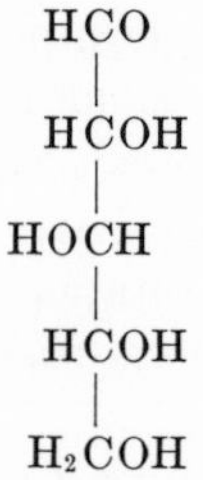

D-Xylose
(V)

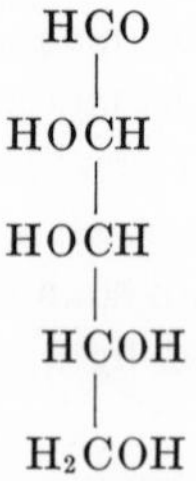

D-Lyxose
(VI)

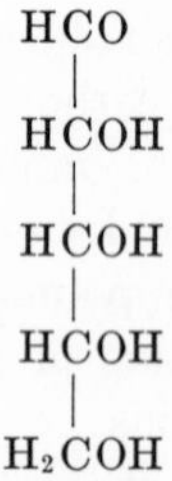

D-Ribose
(VII)

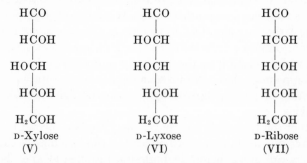

In general, the number of stereoisomers for a structure which involves n asymmetric carbon atoms is given by 2^n. However, when the terminal groups in the molecule are identical, the number of isomers is given by: $2^{\frac{n}{2}-1}(2^{\frac{n}{2}}+1)$ when n is an even number, and by 2^{n-1} when n is an odd number. Thus, for the tartaric acids (COOH—CHOH—CHOH—COOH), three isomers are possible; for the pentaric (hydroxyglutaric) acids (COOH—CHOH—CHOH—CHOH—COOH), four isomers are possible. Fewer isomers can exist when the end groups are identical because of the symmetries which develop. Thus in the compounds which have an odd number of asymmetric carbon atoms, the central carbon has two attached groups which may have the same structure. If two groups are identical, the number of asymmetric centers is really $n - 1$. This relationship may be seen from the formula given below for the pentaric (trihydroxyglutaric) acids.

For the tartaric acids, which have an even number of carbon atoms, the number of isomers is reduced to three because of the symmetry of the molecule. The two formulas represented by (X) are identical. This identity may be shown by moving either of formulas (X) through 180°, keeping it in the plane of the paper. It then becomes identical with the other formula. When formula (VIII) is rotated in the plane of paper through 180°, it does

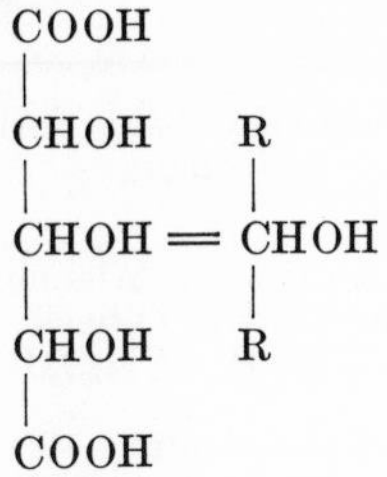

Pentaric acids

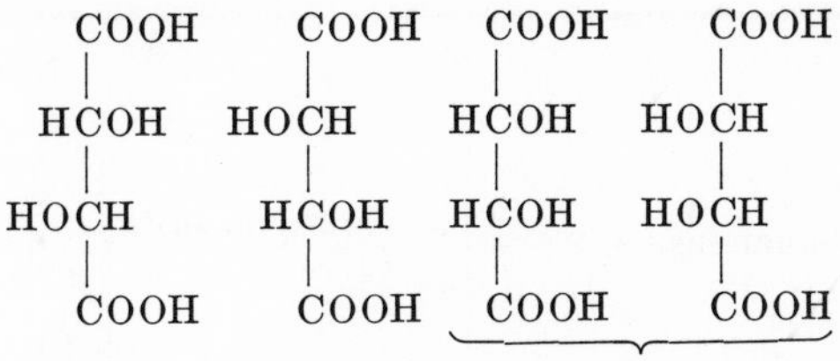

(VIII) (IX) (X)

The isomeric tartaric (tetraric) acids

not become identical with either (IX) or (X). A better test is provided by the construction of the space models; if this is done, it will be found possible to construct only three stereoisomers. Note, however, that any monosubstitution of (X) destroys the *meso* symmetry, giving rise to enantiomorphs.

In general, compounds which contain asymmetric carbon atoms rotate the plane of polarization of plane-polarized light. For this reason they are said to be optically active. When the molecular symmetry is such that the optical activity of one portion of the molecule is cancelled by that of the second portion of the molecule, the compounds are said to be internally compensated and are called *meso* compounds. The tartaric acid with the formula (X) is such a compound and has been known as the *meso*-tartaric acid. The tartaric acids identified as (VIII) and (IX) have been known as *d*-tartaric acid and *l*-tartaric acid because of the sign of their optical rotations (*dextro* and *levo*, respectively). (The nomenclature of these acids is discussed later in this chapter.) The compounds (VIII) and (IX) are nonsuperimposable mirror images, called enantiomorphs. The existence of such pairs of asymmetric isomers is the fundamental basis of optical activity. The asymmetry may be in either the molecular structure or the crystal structure. Asymmetric carbon atoms are not always present in optically active molecules.

Enantiomorphs are identical in most of their properties such as melting points, solubilities, and chemical reactivity. However, when another asymmetric molecule or polarized light is involved, they are markedly different. This behavior is especially pronounced in biological systems, because the enzymes are also asymmetric molecules, and frequently one enantiomorph is handled in biological systems quite differently from the other. D-Glucose is readily utilized by man, whereas its mirror image, L-glucose, is not utilizable.

Mixtures of equal amounts of the tartaric acids (VIII) and (IX) are optically inactive and are termed racemic or D,L-mixtures. Racemic mix-

TABLE I

NUMBER OF STEREOISOMERS OF THE ALDEHYDO-SUGARS AND ALDONIC ACIDS CONTAINING 2 TO 7 CARBONS AND OF THE CORRESPONDING ALCOHOLS AND DIBASIC ACIDS

Parent sugars	No. of asymmetric carbons (n)	Number of possible forms or isomers: Sugars (& Aldonic Acids) CHO (COOH)–$(CHOH)_n$–CH_2OH	Number of possible forms or isomers: Alcohols (& Dibasic Acids)[a] $CH_2OH(COOH)$–$(CHOH)_n$–$CH_2OH(COOH)$
Dioses	0	1	1
Trioses	1	2	1
Tetroses	2	4	3
Pentoses	3	8	4
Hexoses	4	16	10
Heptoses	5	32	16

[a] When n is an odd number, one carbon is not asymmetric.

tures are always formed in the chemical synthesis of potentially optically active substances from inactive materials unless asymmetric substances have been used in the synthesis. Frequently the two components react to form a racemic compound, which has properties (such as solubility and melting point) different from the component isomers. The *meso*-tartaric acid (X) is also optically inactive, because of internal compensation of the asymmetric center, i.e., the two asymmetric carbon atoms have exactly equal but opposite optical rotations.

Because of the extensive use of isotopes in the study of reaction mechanisms, particularly biological mechanisms, a very important special case of an asymmetric carbon atom exists. This is the case of the attachment of two different isotopes of the same element to the same carbon atom. Thus optically active isomers of the type R_1R_2CHD have been obtained (*5*). An optically active *p*-acetyl-α-deuteroethylbenzene was synthesized by Eliel (*6*). The existence of such enantiomorphous isomers, which will be treated differently in biological systems, has tremendously complicated the quantitative significance of the isotope-tracer technique (*7*).

On the basis of the above considerations, which are consequences of the

5. See E. R. Alexander and A. G. Pinkus, *J. Am. Chem. Soc.* **71,** 1786 (1949).

6. E. L. Eliel, *J. Am. Chem. Soc.* **71,** 3970 (1949); A. Streitwieser, *ibid.* **75,** 5014 (1953).

7. A. G. Ogston, *Nature* **162,** 963 (1948).

Le Bel-van't Hoff theory, the number of isomers of each of the sugars having seven or less carbon atoms and of the corresponding dibasic acids and alcohols is given in Table I.

B. Establishment of the Configuration of Glucose and Some Other Sugars

The existence of structurally isomeric sugars was a corollary of the Le Bel-van't Hoff theory. After publication of the theory in the latter part of the nineteenth century, it was soon realized that sugars such as glucose and galactose are stereoisomers. In a series of brilliant researches, Emil Fischer applied the Le Bel-van't Hoff theory to the sugar series and established the configurations of many of the individual sugars.

Fischer's proof was published in two papers which appeared in 1891 (*4*). His proof was expressed in the terminology and conventions of the time. Since the expression of the proof in his original fashion would require a detailed explanation of the older concepts of stereochemistry, it seems better in the present discussion to use the data available to him at the time and to introduce the proof in terms of modern concepts and conventions. The present discussion follows the proof of configuration as outlined (*8*) by C. S. Hudson and in part quotes him.

The following facts were available to Fischer at the time of his establishment of the configuration of glucose.

(1) Three sugars with the formula $C_6H_{12}O_6$ (D-glucose, D-mannose, and D-fructose) react with an excess of phenylhydrazine to give the same

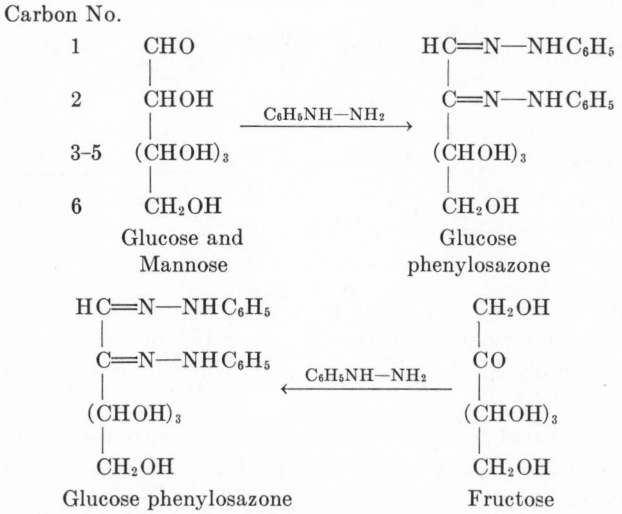
Carbon No.
1
2
3-5
6
CHO
CHOH
(CHOH)3
CH2OH
Glucose and Mannose
C6H5NH—NH2
HC=N—NHC6H5
C=N—NHC6H5
(CHOH)3
CH2OH
Glucose phenylosazone
HC=N—NHC6H5
C=N—NHC6H5
(CHOH)3
CH2OH
Glucose phenylosazone
C6H5NH—NH2
CH2OH
CO
(CHOH)3
CH2OH
Fructose

8. C. S. Hudson, *J. Chem. Educ.* **18,** 353 (1941).

product, glucose phenylosazone. The reactions are illustrated in the accompanying formulas.

The above reactions prove that mannose and glucose are 2-epimers, i.e., they differ only in the configuration of carbon atom 2; also, fructose, glucose, and mannose must have the same configurations for carbon atoms 3, 4, and 5.

(2) Glucose and mannose are oxidized by nitric acid to dibasic acids which are different and which are both optically active.

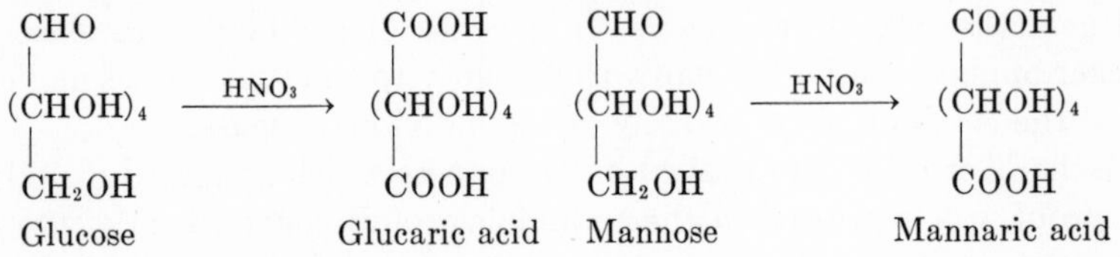
CHO
(CHOH)4
CH2OH
Glucose
HNO3
COOH
(CHOH)4
COOH
Glucaric acid
CHO
(CHOH)4
CH2OH
Mannose
HNO3
COOH
(CHOH)4
COOH
Mannaric acid

The optical activity of the products proves that the configuration of the asymmetric atoms (carbon atoms 2 to 5) cannot be of the type which produces internal compensation.

(3) L-Arabinose, which had been isolated from beet pulp by Scheibler in 1868 and shown to be an aldopentose by Kiliani in 1887, reacts with HCN with the production of a nitrile which hydrolyzes to a six-carbon monobasic acid (I). This acid was shown by Fischer to be the mirror image of the acid (II) produced by the mild oxidation of mannose.

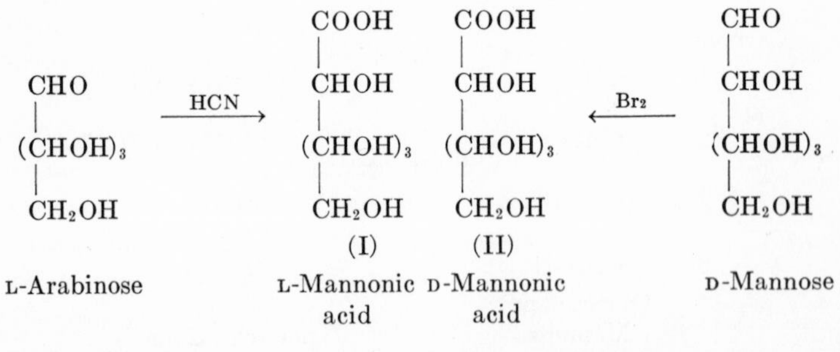
CHO
(CHOH)3
CH2OH
L-Arabinose
HCN
COOH
CHOH
(CHOH)3
CH2OH
(I)
L-Mannonic acid
COOH
CHOH
(CHOH)3
CH2OH
(II)
D-Mannonic acid
Br2
CHO
CHOH
(CHOH)3
CH2OH
D-Mannose

In the synthesis of L-mannonic acid (I), a second acid also is formed which is enantiomorphous with that obtained by the oxidation of glucose. The dibasic acid obtained by the nitric acid oxidation of the arabinose also is optically active.

(4) D-Glucaric acid not only canbe obtained by the oxidation of D-glucose as indicated above, but it is also obtained by the oxidation of another hexose, L-gulose.

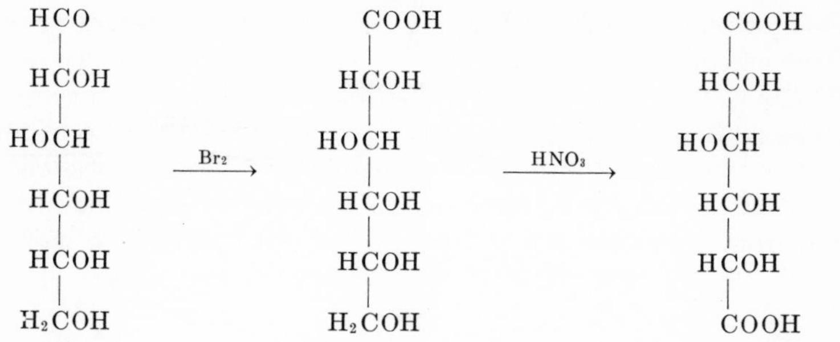

D-Glucose — D-Gluconic acid — D-Glucaric acid

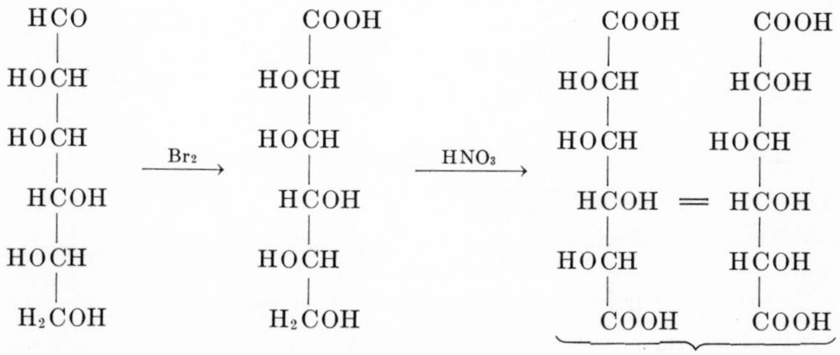

L-Gulose — L-Gulonic acid — D-Glucaric acid

(5) Until recently, no method was available for the establishment of absolute configurations. Fischer's method of assignment, described below, leads finally to a choice between either of a pair of configurations which have a mirror-image relationship. Fischer's solution of this problem consisted in the arbitrary assignment to D-glucaric acid (derived from glucose) of one of two possible formulas. By this action a convention was established which enabled him to make a choice between the enantiomorphous formulas for other substances, once their genetic relationships with D-glucaric acid or glucose had been established. Fischer's concept, although fundamentally correct, has been somewhat modified and made more precise. (See discussion of D,L-usage later in this chapter.) In conformity with the modern concepts, the convention may be expressed by placing the hydroxyl of carbon 5 of glucose on the right side of the carbon chain (see proof below). According to the convention, glucose then will be called D-glucose; because mannose and fructose have the same configurations for carbon 5, they also are known as D-mannose and D-fructose.

Although necessarily purely gratuitous, Fischer's assignment of the absolute configuration of glucose seems to have been correct. A physical method for demonstrating the absolute configuration of tartaric acid shows that the accepted configuration of this compound is the real one (*9*).

The above facts were known at the time of Fischer and, in conjunction with the Le Bel-van't Hoff theory, enabled him to select the configuration of glucose from those for the eight configurations which are possible (when only one of each of the mirror images is considered). The following proof, quoted from a paper by C. S. Hudson, may be said to be a modernized

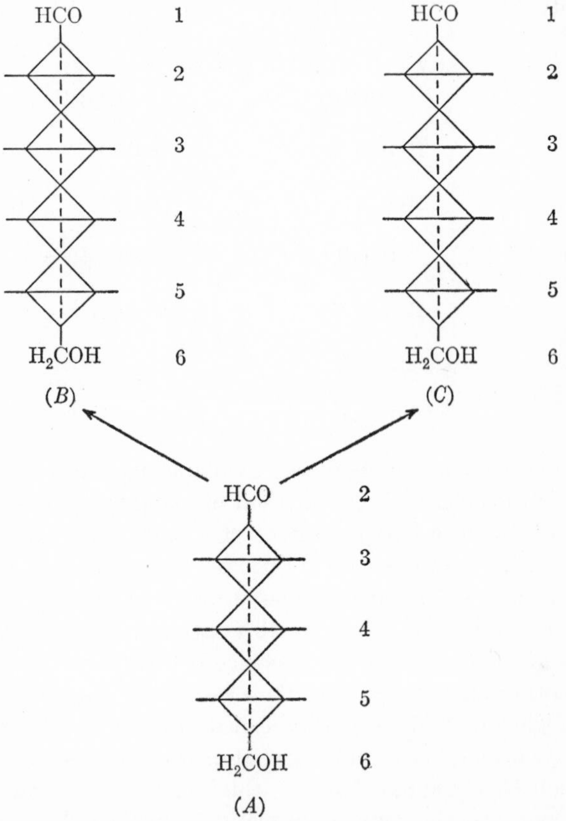
HCO
H2COH
(B)
(C)
(A)

(I)

version of the Fischer proof. Hudson's nomenclature has been modernized in the quotation.

9. J. M. Bijvoet, *Endeavour* **14,** 71 (1955); J. Trommel and J. M. Bijvoet, *Acta Cryst.* **7,** 703 (1954).

"Write the formulas for a pentose (A) and the two hexoses (B and C) which it yields by the Fischer-Kiliani cyanohydrin synthesis as shown in the accompanying diagram (I), using Fischer's convention that the asymmetric carbon atoms (tetrahedra) have the lower edge in the plane of the paper and the corners which carry the H and OH groups lie above this plane. The arrangement of the H and OH groups is then decided through the following steps, in which the pentose is selected to be D-arabinose and in consequence the hexoses become D-glucose and D-mannose."

"Step 1—By convention for the D-configurational series OH is on the right of C-5 (see II).

"Step 2—(D) is optically active hence OH is on the left of C-3 (see II).

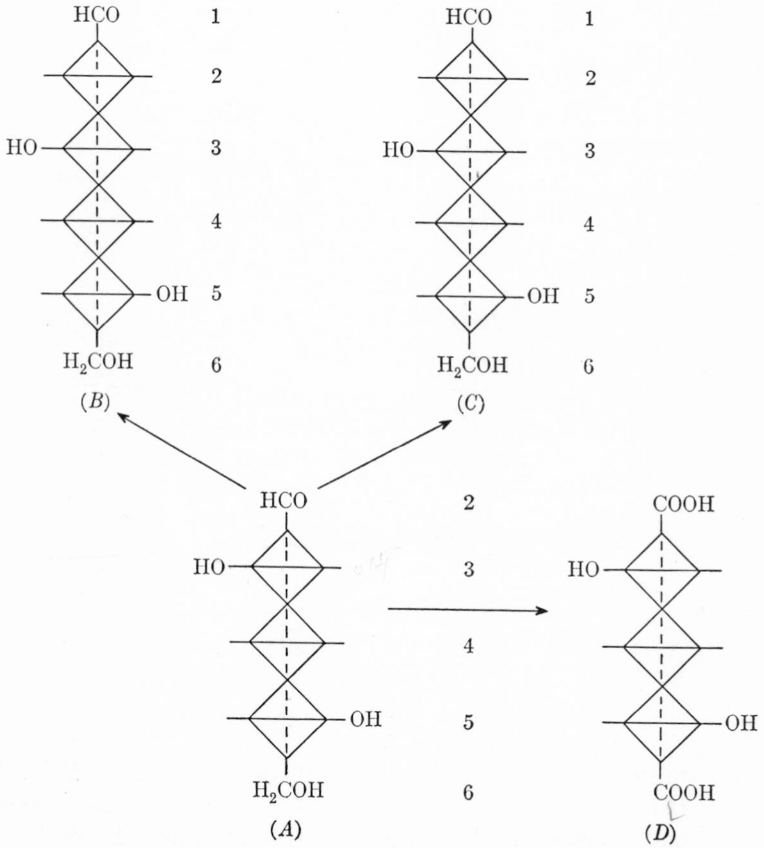
HCO
HO
OH
H_2COH
(B)
HCO
HO
OH
H_2COH
(C)
1
2
3
4
5
6
HCO
HO
OH
H_2COH
(A)
COOH
HO
OH
COOH
(D)

(II)

"Step 3—D-Glucose and D-mannose are epimeric, hence the OH's on C-2 are opposed. Either (B) or (C) may be selected as having OH on the right, without changing the final result; here the OH is placed to the right of C-2 in (B) and consequently to the left in (C) (see III).

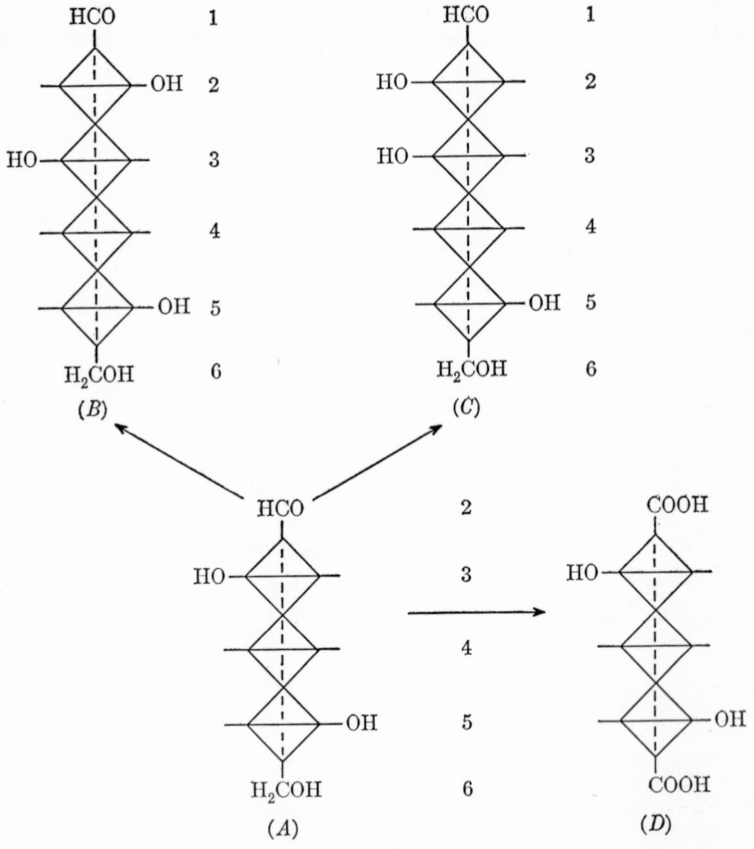
HCO
1
OH
2
HO
3
4
OH
5
H_2COH
6
(B)
HCO
1
HO
2
HO
3
4
OH
5
H_2COH
6
(C)
HCO
2
HO
3
4
OH
5
H_2COH
6
(A)
COOH
HO
OH
COOH
(D)

(III)

"Step 4—Since both D-glucaric and D-mannaric acids (E and F) are optically active, the configuration of neither of them can possess end-to-end symmetry; hence the OH on C-4 must be on the right (see IV). (If it were on the left, (E) would have end-to-end symmetry.)

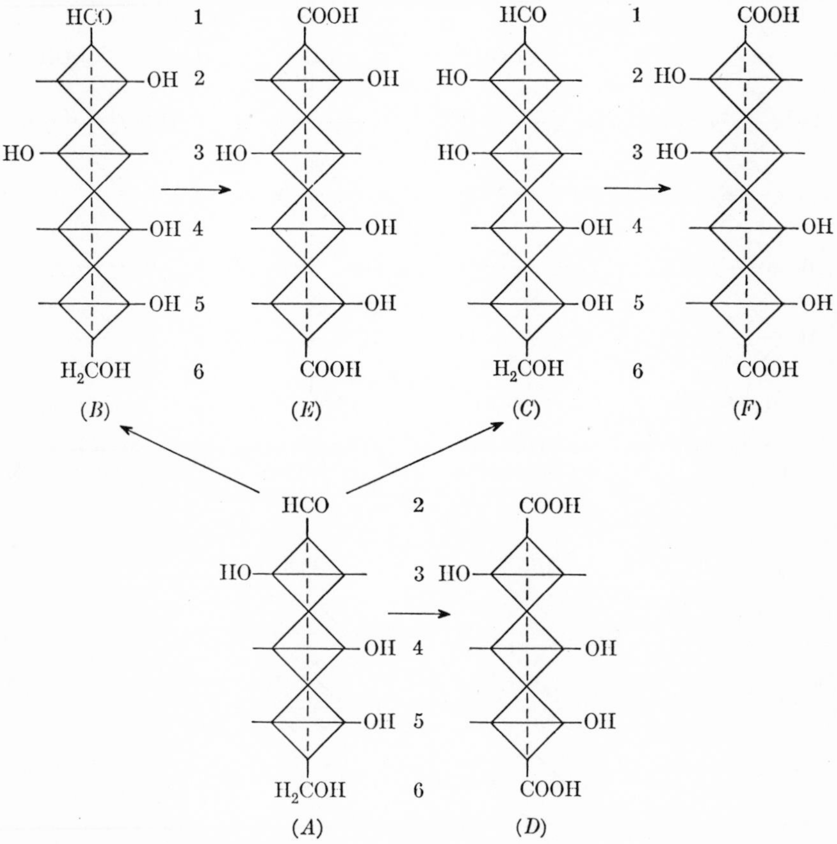
HCO
OH
HO
OH
OH
H_2COH
(B)
1
2
3
4
5
6
COOH
OH
HO
OH
OH
COOH
(E)
HCO
HO
HO
OH
OH
H_2COH
(C)
COOH
HO
HO
OH
OH
COOH
(F)
HCO
HO
OH
OH
H_2COH
(A)
COOH
HO
OH
OH
COOH
(D)

(IV)

At this stage the configuration of D-arabinose (A) and its dibasic acid (D) have become established. D-Glucose and D-mannose have been limited to the configurations (B) and (C), but the correlation within this limit remains to be established. This is done by:

"Step 5—D-Glucaric acid is obtainable from the oxidation of each of two hexoses, namely glucose and gulose. (E) must therefore refer to D-glucaric acid because (F) cannot result from the oxidation of two hexoses. Hence (B) refers to D-glucose, (C) to D-mannose, and (F) to D-mannaric acid."

The proof is now complete and (V) the formulas become:

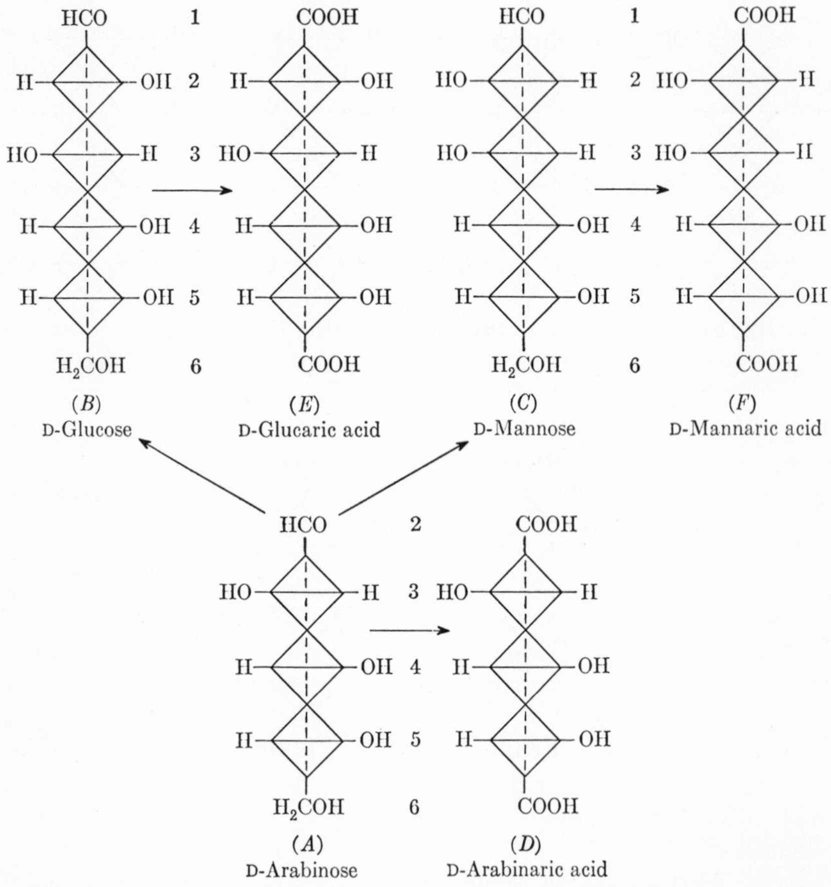
(B) D-Glucose
(E) D-Glucaric acid
(C) D-Mannose
(F) D-Mannaric acid
(A) D-Arabinose
(D) D-Arabinaric acid

(V)

By means of the Fischer convention, the tetrahedral models for glucose, mannose, and arabinose are equivalent to the planar formulas given below. The formula for fructose is derived from the fact that fructose yields the same osazone as glucose when treated with phenylhydrazine (see above); it and glucose must have identical configurations for carbon atoms 3, 4, and 5.

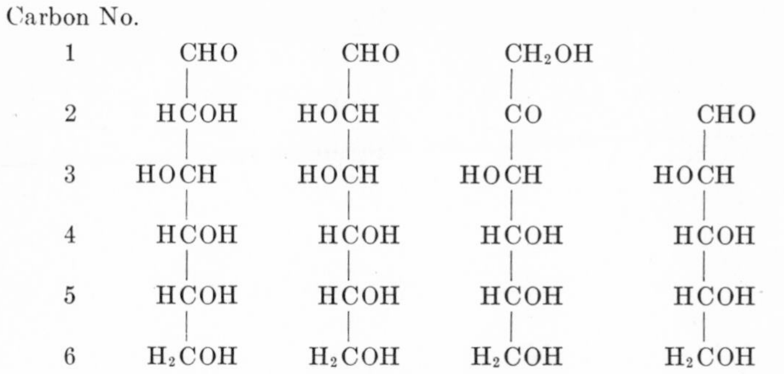
Carbon No.
1
2
3
4
5
6
CHO
HCOH
HOCH
HCOH
HCOH
H_2COH
CHO
HOCH
HOCH
HCOH
HCOH
H_2COH
CH_2OH
CO
HOCH
HCOH
HCOH
H_2COH
CHO
HOCH
HCOH
HCOH
H_2COH

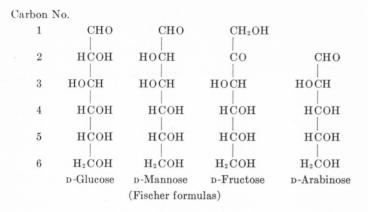

D-Glucose D-Mannose D-Fructose D-Arabinose

(Fischer formulas)

C. D- AND L-NOMENCLATURE

In some types of optically active compounds, it has been customary to distinguish between the enantiomorphous modifications by indicating the sign of their optical rotation as "*d*" (dextrorotatory) or "*l*" (levorotatory). Thus, *d*-tartaric acid (the naturally occurring form) is the isomer which has a dextrorotation. This usage is not followed in carbohydrate chemistry except in very unusual instances. Fischer established the convention of calling ordinary glucose *d*-glucose and employed the prefix *d*- in a configurational sense to mean that a *d*-substance is derivable from *d*-glucose whereas an *l*-substance is derivable from *l*-glucose. Hence, fructose was called *d*-fructose although it exhibits a levorotation.

The Fischer system, however, was modified by Rosanoff (*10*) in order that certain ambiguities would be avoided. Thus, a series of transformations have been carried out as indicated in the formulas on page 22. Either of the enantiomorphous forms of glucaric acid may be produced from ordinary glucose as shown below. Since the transformation of the D-xylose (natural form) to a saccharic acid which is the mirror image of that obtained by the direct oxidation of the glucose was observed first, the natural xylose originally was called *l*-xylose by Fischer; if the conversion of glucose to xylose through glucuronic acid had been observed first, the natural sugar probably would have been termed *d*-xylose.

The system proposed by Rosanoff placed the use of the symbols *d* and *l* (or now D and L) on a logical genetic basis. His system is universally accepted by carbohydrate chemists. It starts with the definition that the

10. M. A. Rosanoff, *J. Am. Chem. Soc.* **28,** 114 (1906); C. S. Hudson, *Advances in Carbohydrate Chem.* **3,** 12 (1948).

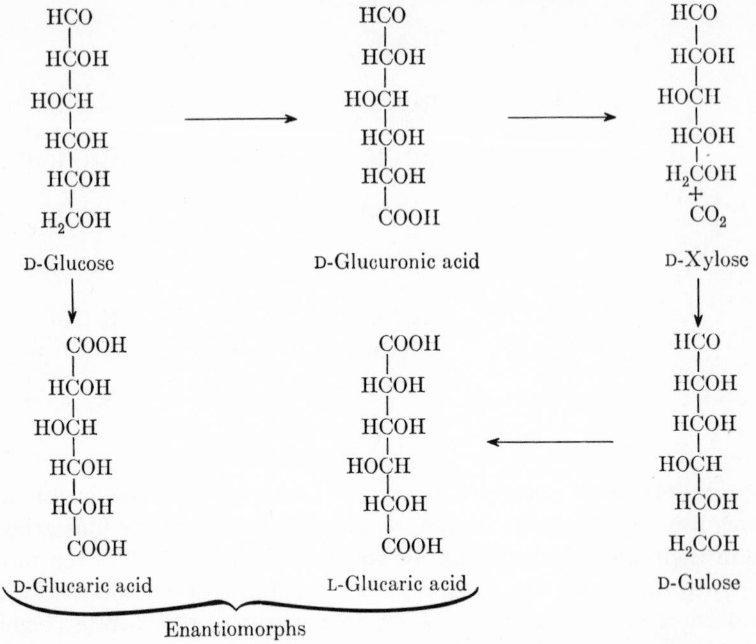
D-Glucose
D-Glucuronic acid
D-Xylose
D-Glucaric acid
L-Glucaric acid
D-Gulose
Enantiomorphs

glycerose which has the formula (I) shall be called D-glyceraldehyde and that with the formula (II) shall be called L-glyceraldehyde.

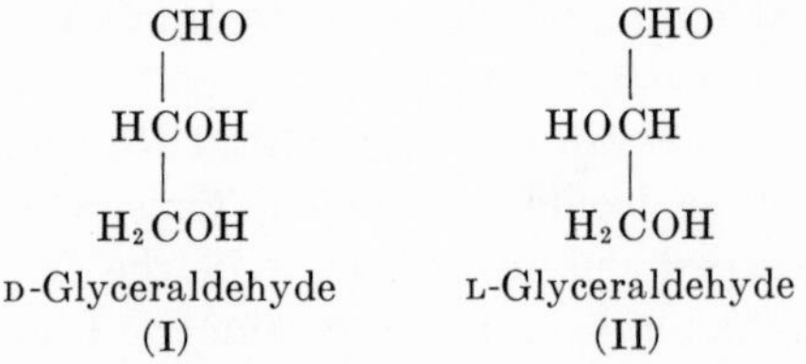
D-Glyceraldehyde
(I)
L-Glyceraldehyde
(II)

According to Rosanoff, all of the higher sugars which conceivably might be derived from D-glyceraldehyde by successive application of the cyanohydrin synthesis shall be called D-sugars. Similarly, all of those obtained in this manner from L-glyceraldehyde shall be called L-sugars.

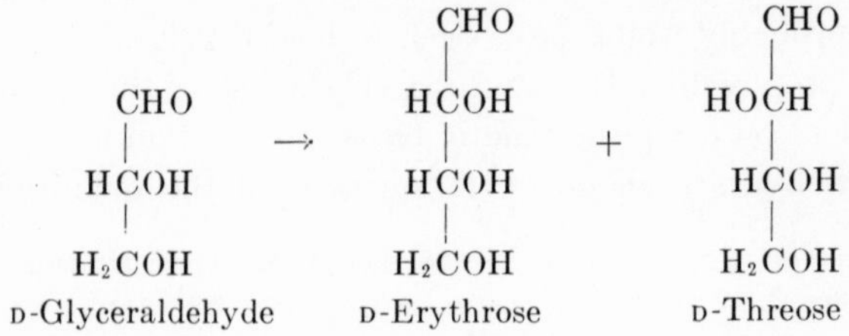
D-Glyceraldehyde
D-Erythrose
D-Threose

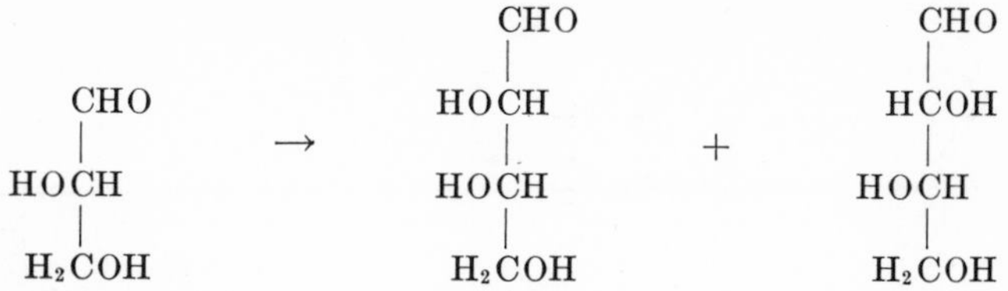

L-Glyceraldehyde L-Erythrose L-Threose

Since a new asymmetric carbon atom is produced in the addition of a carbon atom (through the cyanohydrin synthesis), two epimers are produced from each of the glyceroses. A continuation of this process with each of the four-carbon sugars conceivably would give four D-pentoses and four L-pentoses; application of the cyanohydrin synthesis to the pentoses produces in turn eight D- and eight L-hexoses. Although this entire process has not been carried out experimentally, interconversions have been carried out in number sufficient for the allocation of the configurations of all of the possible sugars through the hexose stage and for many of the higher sugars.

In general, substances may be defined as belonging to the D-family when the asymmetric carbon atom most remote from the reference group (e.g., aldehyde, keto, carboxyl, etc.) has the same configuration as in D-glyceraldehyde; if this carbon has the same configuration as that in L-glyceraldehyde, the substance belongs to the L-family. When the compound is written in the Fischer manner with the reference group towards the top, the allocation to the D- or L- series is made on the basis of the configuration of the bottom-most asymmetric carbon atom, usually the penultimate carbon; substances of the D-series have the hydroxyl group lying on the right and of the L-series on the left. When two possible reference groups are present in the same molecule, the choice of reference group is usually in the following order: CHO, COOH, CO (ketone); for example, in D-glucuronic acid, the reference group is the aldehyde group rather than the carboxyl group.

This classification leads to ambiguous assignment in the case of certain optically active, like-ended compounds wherein the end asymmetric carbons have the same configuration. Such compounds must have a minimum chain length of six carbon atoms, and of those with six carbon atoms only the glucose (sorbitol) configuration leads to ambiguity. Thus, sorbitol might be called D-glucitol or L-gulitol. Since sorbitol is a trivial name (like sucrose or lactose) given to the compound before its configuration was known, it may be used properly without a D- or L- prefix as the name of the naturally occurring isomer.

Like-ended compounds of the type of sorbitol, for which either of the

The D-Family of Aldoses Having 3 to 6 Carbon Atoms

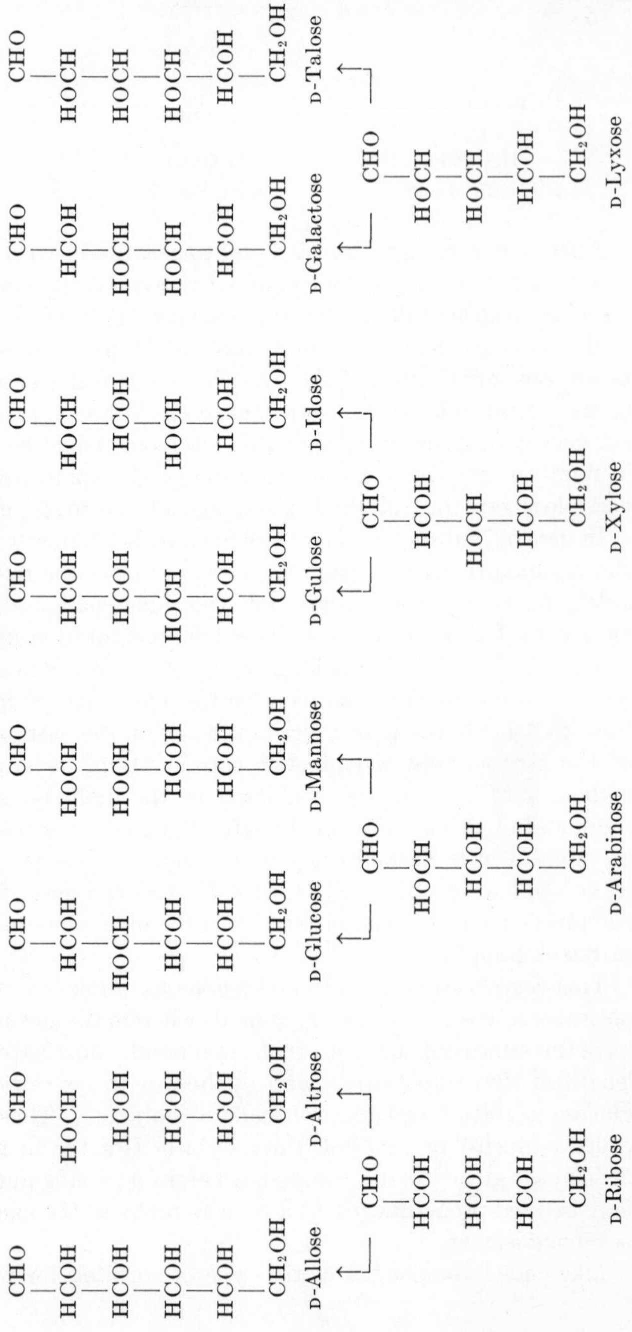
D-Allose
D-Altrose
D-Glucose
D-Mannose
D-Gulose
D-Idose
D-Galactose
D-Talose
D-Ribose
D-Arabinose
D-Xylose
D-Lyxose

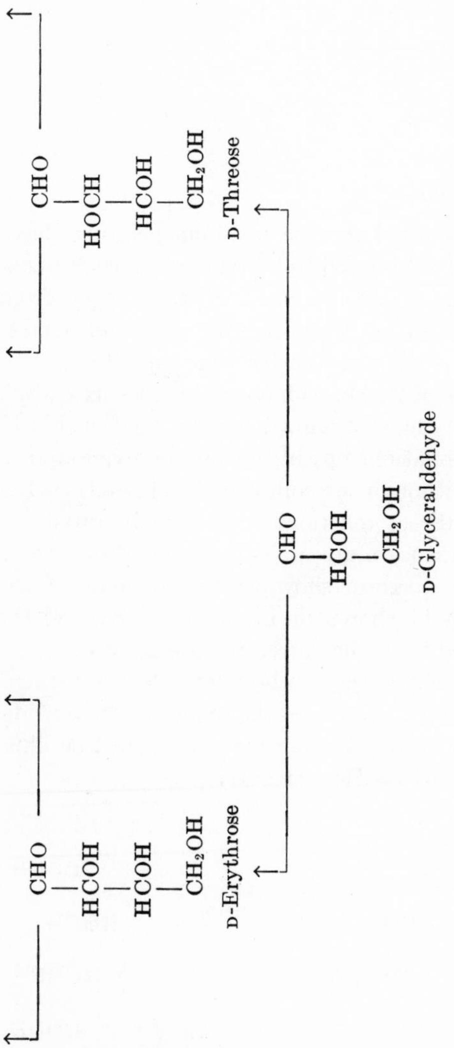
D-Threose
D-Glyceraldehyde
D-Erythrose

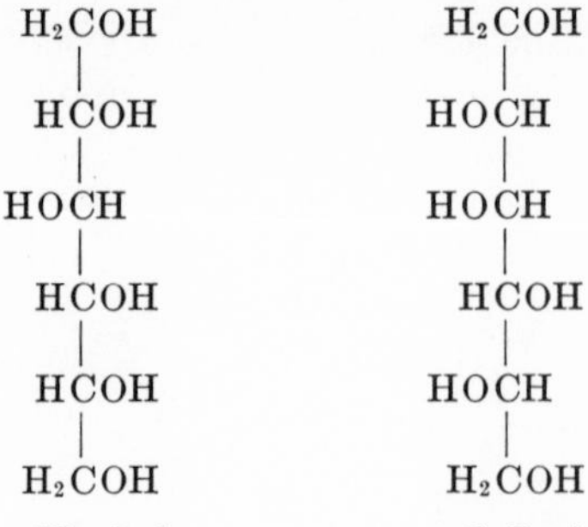

D-Glucitol L-Gulitol

Sorbitol

penultimate carbons atoms can be used for the D,L-nomenclature, have been called *amphi* by Rosanoff and are related to two sugars. In such cases, the most important of the two sugars, usually also the parent sugar from which the compound was first derived, is chosen for the name and D,L-assignment. For sorbitol, the choice is D-glucitol rather than L-gulitol.

The configurations of the family of D-aldoses having three to six carbon atoms are shown in the accompanying diagram. A genetic relationship to D-glyceraldehyde is shown. This relationship, by use of the cyanohydrin synthesis, is chemically feasible. Although the complete set of reactions has not been actually carried out, indirect reactions have demonstrated the validity of the diagram. Dextrorotatory D-glyceraldehyde was shown to be related to D-glucose (*11*). In the diagram showing the formulas of the D-ketoses, the relationships cannot be shown by direct reactions, and the configurations usually were derived from the corresponding aldoses.

Because many optically active substances can be related to the tartaric acids, it is desirable to relate the configurations of the sugars to these acids. This correlation was accomplished first by Fischer (*12*), but it will be illustrated by the conversions carried out by Hockett(*13*):

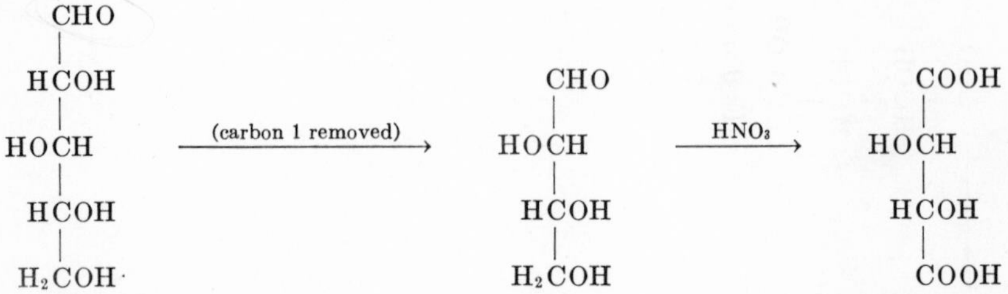
(carbon 1 removed)
HNO_3

D-Xylose D-Threose D-Tartaric acid (levorotatory)

11. A. Wohl and F. Momber, *Ber.* **50**, 455 (1917).
12. E. Fischer, *Ber.* **29**, 1377 (1896).
13. R. C. Hockett, *J. Am. Chem. Soc.* **57**, 2260 (1935).

The configuration of the levorotatory tartaric acid is established by this process. In conformity with the Rosanoff system, it should be known as D-tartaric acid, but it usually is described by its original name of *l*(*levo*)-tartaric acid which was given because of its levorotation. The naturally

D-Family of 2-Ketoses

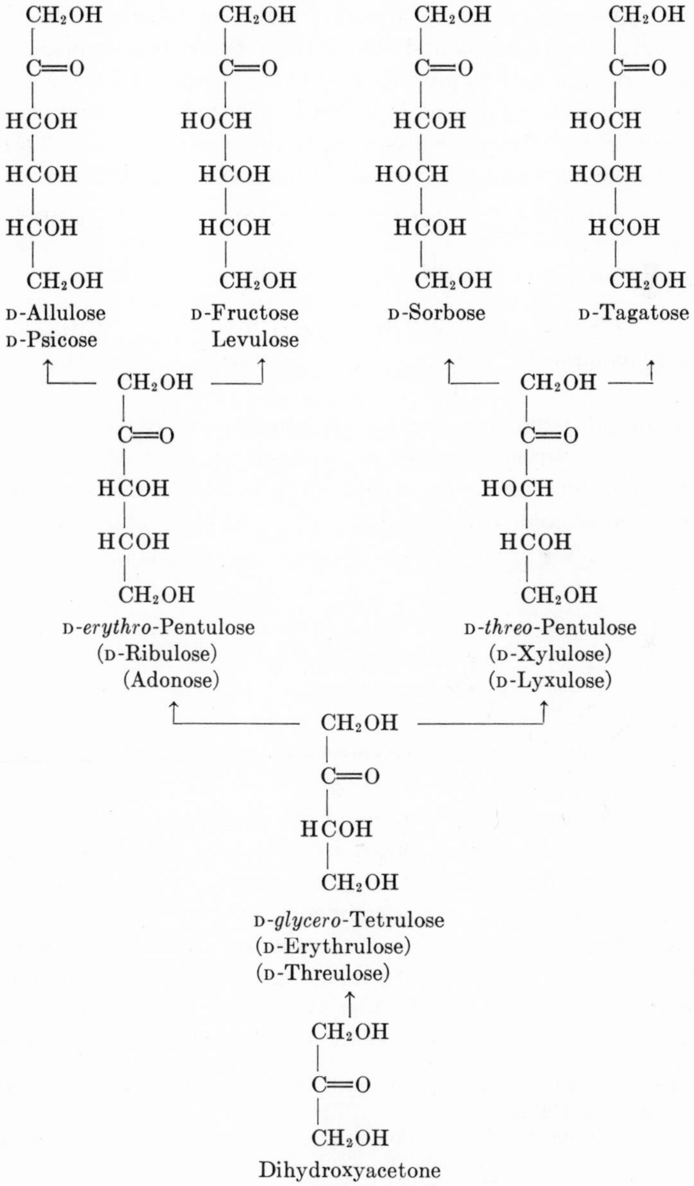
D-Allulose
D-Psicose
D-Fructose
Levulose
D-Sorbose
D-Tagatose
D-*erythro*-Pentulose
(D-Ribulose)
(Adonose)
D-*threo*-Pentulose
(D-Xylulose)
(D-Lyxulose)
D-*glycero*-Tetrulose
(D-Erythrulose)
(D-Threulose)
Dihydroxyacetone

occurring form is the dextrorotatory L-tartaric acid or, earlier, *d*-tartaric acid. This confusion is completely eliminated in the currently accepted nomenclature for these compounds as the D- and L-threaric acids (Chapter VI). The important sarcolactic acid, earlier called *d*-lactic acid from its dextrorotation, is L-lactic acid. The common *l*-malic acid should be termed 2-deoxy-D-*glycero*-tetraric acid.

In the important α-amino acid series, D-glyceraldehyde is also the configurational reference compound. The NH_2 group of serine replaces the OH group at carbon atom 2 in glyceric acid (*14*). The projectional formulas of the amino acids are viewed with the carboxyl at the top, and the assignment of configuration is made according to the position of the α-NH_2 group, D if it is to the right and L if it is to the left. All of the amino acids which

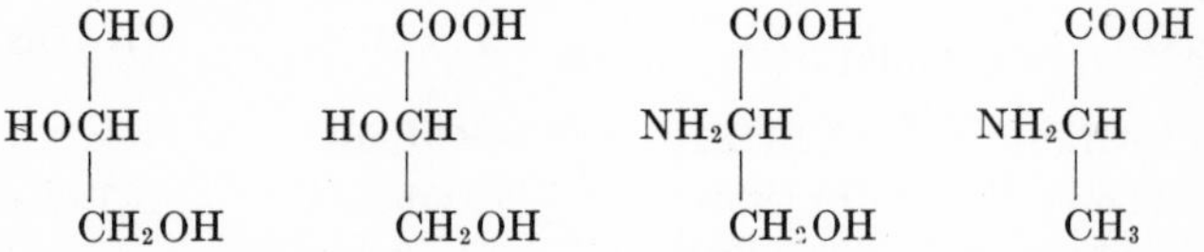

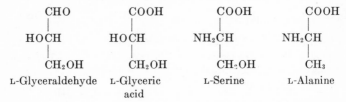

L-Glyceraldehyde L-Glyceric acid L-Serine L-Alanine

occur in normal tissues are now allocated to the L-series, but some of these compounds were earlier indicated as *d*-isomers.

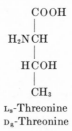

When a second asymmetric carbon atom is in the molecule, such as in threonine, additional considerations are necessary. For example, D_g-

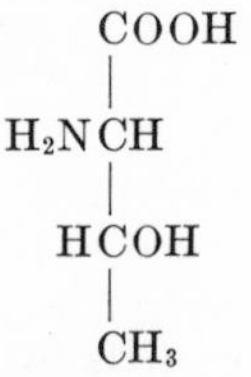

L_s-Threonine
D_g-Threonine

threonine indicates that the compound has been named as a derivative of D-threose in the manner of the sugars from the relationship of D-glyceraldehyde to the configuration of the highest numbered asymmetric carbon. L_s-Threonine indicates the same compound, named in the manner of the amino acids from the relationship of the configuration of the α-carbon to a secondary standard, L-serine; with this usage no system is available for indicating the configuration of the other asymmetric carbon atom.

L-Glyceraldehyde was correlated by Wolfrom, Lemieux, and Olin (*15*)

14. American Chemical Society Committee on Amino Acid Nomenclature, *Chem. Eng. News* **30,** 4522 (1952).

15. M. L. Wolfrom, R. U. Lemieux, and S. M. Olin, *J. Am. Chem. Soc.* **71,** 2870 (1949).

directly with L-alanine, derived from D-glucosamine. The configuration of the amino-bearing carbon in D-glucosamine had already been established through syntheses involving known Walden inversions.

In view of the early confusion in use of the small *d* and *l* for both optical rotations and for configurational relations, it is hoped that the use of D and L will be wholly restricted to a configurational significance based on D-glyceraldehyde. Early *d*- and *l*- prefixes for the hydroxy acids and amino acids, particularly, must be translated to modern nomenclature only after careful consideration of the newly adopted conventions (*14*).

7. RING STRUCTURES OF THE SUGARS

A. Necessity for Ring Structures

Soon after the formulation of glucose as a polyhydroxy aldehyde and of fructose as a polyhydroxy ketone, it became evident that the open-chain formulas would not account for all of the reactions of these sugars. Thus, the sugars give a negative test with the Schiff reagent (fuchsin and sulfurous acid) under the usual conditions of test although, under milder conditions, positive results are obtained (*16*).

The aldehyde and ketone structures also do not account for the change of optical rotation which may be observed for the freshly prepared aqueous solutions of many sugars. This phenomenon, now called mutarotation, was observed by Dubrunfaut in 1846 for glucose solutions.

When the hydroxyl groups of glucose are esterified by treatment with acetic anhydride and a catalyst, two isomeric pentaacetates are formed. Similarly, isomeric methyl glucosides are formed by treatment of glucose with methanol and hydrogen chloride. The existence of two glucosides (*17*) and two pentaacetates (*18*) cannot be predicted on the basis of the aldehyde formula, a conclusion stated by Fischer in the case of the methyl glucosides, which he discovered, and even earlier by Colley and Tollens.

The isolation of crystalline isomers of the sugars provided additional evidence for the inadequacy of the aldehyde formulas. As early as 1856, two crystalline modifications of lactose were prepared by Erdmann (*19*), the forms which are now designated α- and β-lactose; he discovered their mutarotations to the common equilibrium rotation. Tanret (*20*) in 1895 reported the isolation of three forms of glucose which he described as α-,

16. A. Villiers and M. Fayolle, *Bull. soc. chim. France* [3] **11,** 692 (1894); W. C. Tobie, *Ind. Eng. Chem.* **14,** 405 (1942).

17. E. Fischer, *Ber.* **28,** 1145 (1895).

18. E. Erwig and W. Koenigs, *Ber.* **22,** 1464, 2207 (1889).

19. E. O. Erdmann, *Ber.* **13,** 2180 (1880).

20. C. Tanret, *Compt. rend.* **120,** 1060 (1895).

β-, and γ-glucose with the following rotations:

α-Glucose		"β-Glucose"		"γ-Glucose"
+106°	⟶	+52.5°	⟵	+22.5°

When dissolved in water, the α-glucose mutarotated downward and the "γ-glucose" upwards to the same constant specific rotation of 52.5°. Tanret's "β-glucose" exhibited no mutarotation and later was considered to be a mixture of the two other forms in their equilibrium proportions. The name of β-glucose is now given to the form which he named as "γ-glucose." The common form is the α-isomer.

Even before the various isomers of glucose and its derivatives had been isolated, the absence of some typical aldehyde reactions for glucose had been explained by Colley (1870) and by Tollens (1883) as arising from a partial blocking of the aldehyde group by the formation of an inner hemiacetal type of linkage. The formulas proposed by Colley and by Tollens are illustrated below.

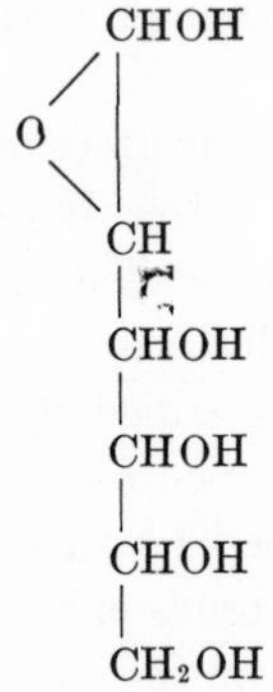
CHOH
O
CH
CHOH
CHOH
CHOH
CH_2OH

Colley formula

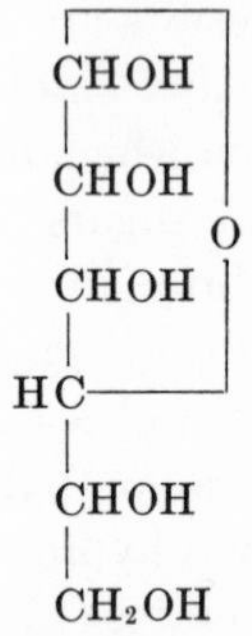
CHOH
CHOH
O
CHOH
HC
CHOH
CH_2OH

Tollens formula

The ring forms of the sugars represent intramolecular hemiacetal derivatives. Aldehydes react with alcohols with the formation of hemiacetals and acetals:

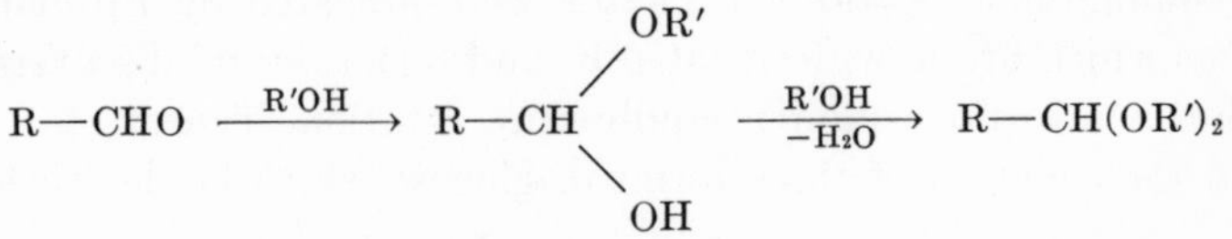
R—CHO
R'OH
R—CH
OR'
OH
R'OH
$-H_2O$
R—CH(OR')$_2$

Hemiacetal Acetal

For the sugar, the hemiacetal (ring) formation takes place by reaction of a hydroxyl with the aldehyde group in the same molecule. Each of the possible ring formulas for glucose allows for two isomers which differ only in the configuration of the hemiacetal group, as carbon 1 is asymmetric in the ring form. Such isomers are distinguished as α- and β-isomers, e.g., α-glucose and β-glucose, and are termed *anomers*. The hemiacetal carbon atom sometimes is known as the *anomeric* or *reducing* carbon atom. The existence of isomeric glucoses, penta-*O*-acetylglucoses and methyl glucosides becomes explicable when the sugar and its derivatives have ring structures.

B. Proof of Ring Structure

Subsequent to the proposal of the ring structures for the sugars and derivatives, acceptance by carbohydrate chemists (*21*) gradually took place. However, it was not until the period 1920 to 1930 that conclusive proof could be offered for the positions of the rings. Prior to this work, the rings usually were considered to be of the 1,4 type shown above in the Tollens formula, i.e., with the ring formation between carbons 1 and 4. This type of structure was based mainly on an analogy with the acid series for which it was known that γ-hydroxy acids could be converted to inner esters (lactones) which have the 1,4- or γ-structure.

Methods now are available for the unequivocal determination of the ring structures of the glycosidic derivatives of the sugars. The glycosides are made by condensing the sugars with alcohols in the presence of acids. (For a detailed discussion of the preparation of glycosides and of the details of the determination of the structures, see Chapter IV.)

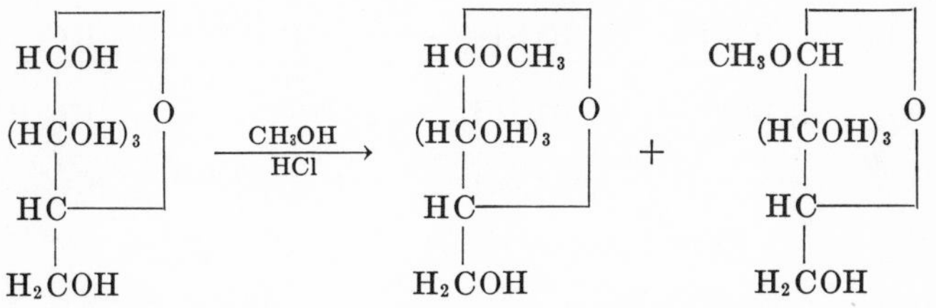
HCOH
(HCOH)₃
HC
H₂COH
O
CH₃OH
HCl
HCOCH₃
(HCOH)₃
HC
H₂COH
O
+
CH₃OCH
(HCOH)₃
HC
H₂COH
O

Originally, the structures of these glycosides were demonstrated by oxidation of the glycosides to fragments which were identified. In order to prevent the oxidation from proceeding too far, the four unsubstituted hydroxyls first were etherified with methyl groups. Details of this method are given later (p. 212). An easier and more direct method involves the periodic acid oxidation of the glycosides. As shown in the formula below, this reagent cleaves the linkage between two adajcent hydroxyl-bearing carbon atoms and removes a hydrogen atom from each carbon. A primary carbinol (CH_2OH) yields formaldehyde; a secondary carbinol (CHOH) gives rise to an aldehyde group or, if flanked by two carbinol groups, to formic acid. The reaction is practically quantitative, and the consumption of periodate

21. See for example E. Fischer and K. Zach, *Ber*. **45,** 456 (1912), footnote on p. 461.

is a direct measure of the number of adjacent hydroxyl groups in a compound. (See Chapter VI.) The structure is determined from the nature of the oxidation products, together with the amount of oxidant that is consumed.

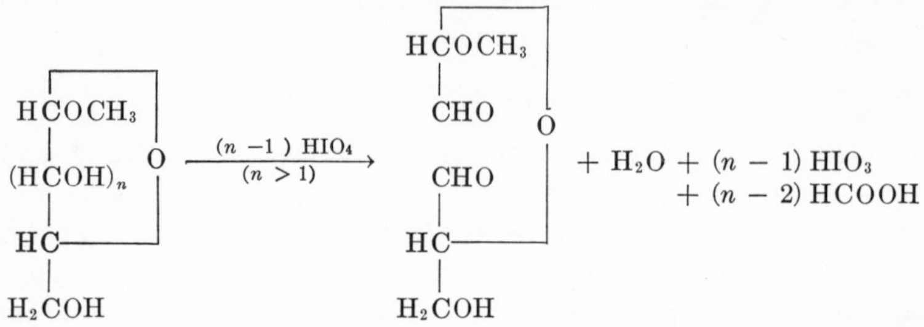

The possible structures for methyl α-D-glucoside are given in formulas (I) to (V). The brackets indicate the adjacent hydroxyl groups.

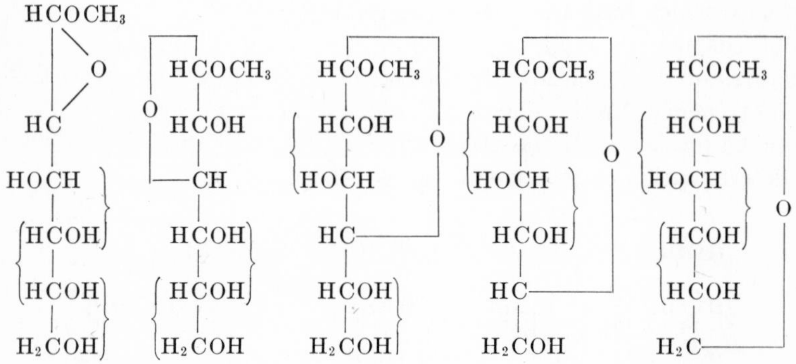

(I)	(II)	(III)	(IV)	(V)	
3	2	2	2	3	Moles oxidant
2	1	0	1	2	Moles HCOOH
1	1	1	0	0	Moles HCHO

The ordinary methyl α-D-glucoside consumes two moles of periodic acid, and no formaldehyde is produced. Hence, the structure must be that represented in (IV), which has a 1,5 oxygen bridge.

The evidence given above and explained in more detail later (p. 212) confirmed in most instances the structures obtained by the earlier methylation-oxidation studies. The periodic acid oxidation method is used widely because of its simplicity. As a result of the application of the methylation-oxidation technique and of the periodic acid method, it is known that the most common ring present in the glycosides is of the six-membered type connecting carbon atoms 1 and 5. However, rings formed between the 1-

and 4-positions are found in some glycosides. Sugars and derivatives which have the 1,5 type of ring may be considered to be derivatives of pyran and those with 1,4-rings to be derivatives of furan. These relations are shown in the accompanying formulas.

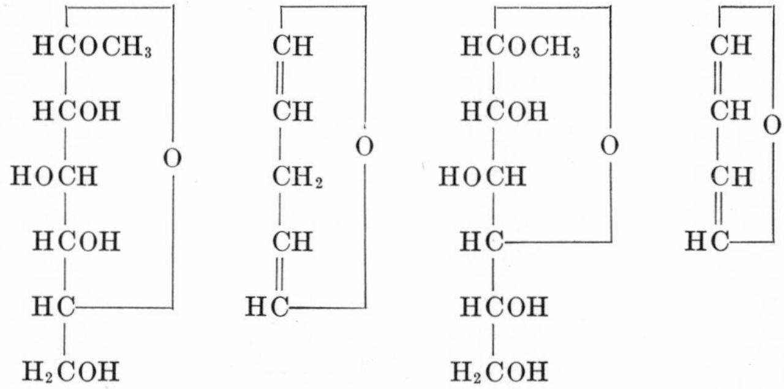

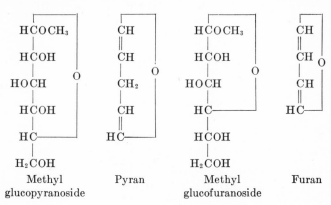

Methyl glucopyranoside — Pyran — Methyl glucofuranoside — Furan

The sugars related to pyran are known as pyranoses, and the corresponding glycosides as pyranosides. Those with furan rings are furanoses and furanosides, respectively.

Although absolute methods are available for the establishment of the ring structures of the glycosides, the corresponding methods for the sugars are indirect. For the glycosides, the rings usually are quite stable under alkaline and neutral conditions. However, in the case of the sugars, difficulties arise from the ease with which ring changes may take place as soon as dissolution of the sugar occurs. The methods which are applicable to the determination of the ring forms of the sugars must be such that ring changes do not precede the necessary reactions. In the following methods, this condition is assumed.

One method for locating the position of the ring in unsubstituted sugars requires oxidation to the corresponding acids or lactones. As shown in the following formulas, the ring compounds should be oxidized (dehydrogenated) by bromine to the corresponding lactones, whereas the free aldehyde forms would give the corresponding acids.

The oxidation reaction takes place in solution, and the nature of the oxidation products establishes the structure of the original sugar unless ring shifts take place prior to the oxidation reaction. By application of this method (*22*), it has been shown that the common form of D-glucose (the α-isomer) gives gluconic δ-lactone. The β-D-glucose gives the same material. Hence, both have pyranose (1,5) rings; otherwise the γ-lactones or the

22. H. S. Isbell and W. W. Pigman, *J. Research Natl. Bur. Standards* **10,** 337 (1933); H. S. Isbell and C. S. Hudson, *ibid.* **8,** 327 (1932); H. S. Isbell, *ibid.* **8,** 615 (1932).

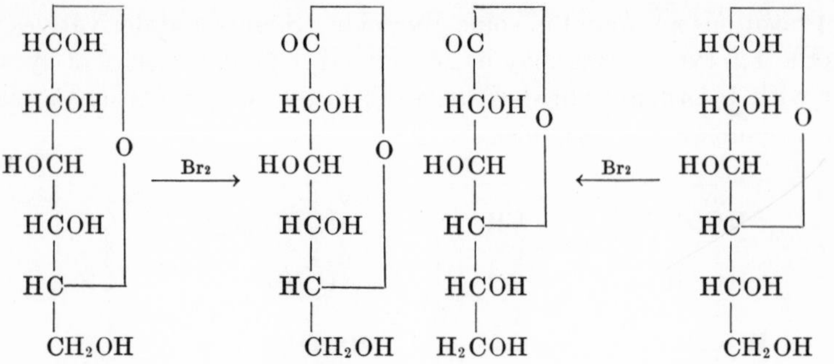

Glucopyranose — Gluconic δ-lactone — Gluconic γ-lactone — Glucofuranose

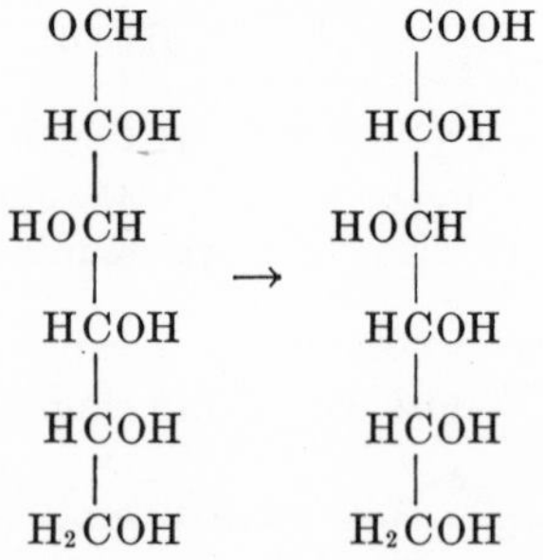

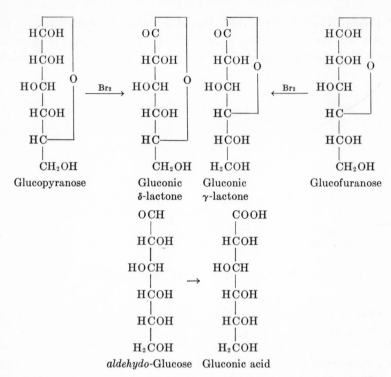

aldehydo-Glucose — Gluconic acid

free acids would be produced. The method has not been widely applied. A crystalline addition compound of mannose and calcium chloride yields mannonic γ-lactone, and appears to have a furanose structure (*23*).

By the bromine oxidation method, the structure of the sugars can be correlated with those of the corresponding lactones and acids. The proof requires that the structures of the lactones be known. In general, the method depends on a correlation of the properties of the lactones with those of the methylated derivatives obtained by methylation and oxidation of the glycosides of known structures.

Another method for the establishment of the ring structures of glucose (and other sugars) involves the correlation of the optical rotations of the sugars with those of the glycosides. This method, although not absolute, was developed and widely applied by C. S. Hudson and has much value for this purpose. It is considered in a later section (p. 70).

The glucosides are hydrolyzed to glucose by certain enzymes (see Chapter X). The identification of the form of the sugar which is released provides a method for the correlation of glycosides with the crystalline forms of the sugar (*24*). The product formed by the enzymic hydrolysis of methyl

23. H. S. Isbell, *J. Am. Chem. Soc.* **55,** 2166 (1933).
24. E. F. Armstrong, *J. Chem. Soc.* **83,** 1305 (1903).

α-glucoside appears to be the ordinary α-isomer; that from methyl β-glucoside appears to be the β-isomer. Hence, unless ring changes take place very rapidly, the α- and β-forms of glucose would appear to have the same pyranose structures as the corresponding glucosides.

The present methods for the determination of the structures of the unsubstituted sugars are rather unsatisfactory as absolute methods because of the possibility of ring shifts. However, the evidence which is available indicates that most of the crystalline sugars have pyranose ring structures. A double compound of mannose with calcium chloride probably has the furanose structure *(23)* and a disaccharide ketose, lactulose, may exist as the furanose modification when in the crystalline state *(25)*. Otherwise crystalline furanose derivatives are known positively to exist only in compounds in which ring shifts are not possible (glycosides, disaccharides, etc.) or in compounds in which the hydroxyl that forms the pyranose ring is blocked by substitution with a stable group.

C. Configuration of the Anomeric Carbon Atom

For each of the ring modifications of the sugars, two isomers can exist, because a new asymmetric carbon atom is created by ring closure at the reducing carbon atom. These isomers are known as α,β-isomers or anomers.

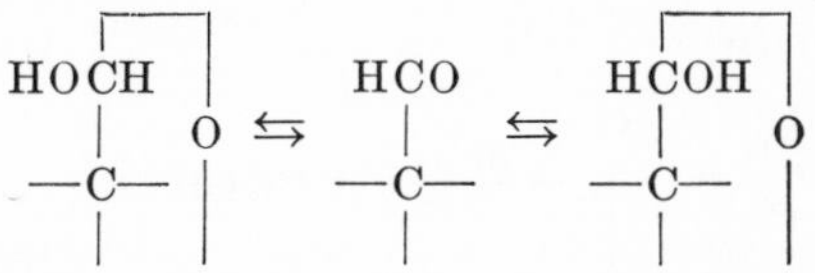
HOCH
O
—C—
HCO
—C—
HCOH
O
—C—

As noted previously, the existence of such isomers was one of the most important reasons for the formulation of ring structures. The isomeric α- and β-glucoses have quite different solubilities, melting points, and rotations. The isomeric pentaacetates and methyl glucosides exhibit similar differences in properties.

The conductivity of sugars freshly dissolved in boric acid solution may give an indication of the relative configuration of the anomeric carbon atom *(26, 27)*. Boric acid forms compounds or complexes, some of an ester structure, with *cis* hydroxyl groups on neighboring carbon atoms (see p. 171 and 262). When α-glucose is dissolved in a boric acid solution, the conductivity of the solution decreases with time until a constant value is reached; on the other hand, the conductivity of β-glucose solutions increases with time. This behavior would be expected for these sugars if α-glucopyranose has a *cis* pair of hydroxyls at carbon atoms 1 and 2, and β-glucopyranose a *trans* pair.

25. H. S. Isbell and W. W. Pigman, *J. Research Natl. Bur. Standards* **20,** 773 (1938).
26. For summary see J. Böeseken and H. Couvert, *Rec. trav. chim.* **40,** 354 (1921).
27. R. Verschuur, *Rec. trav. chim.* **47,** 123, 423 (1928).

The above evidence conforms with the accepted configurations for carbon 1 of the anomeric D-glucoses and played an important part in the acceptance of these configurations. However, Böeseken (*28*) and his co-workers have shown that when adjacent *cis* hydroxyl groups are present in a strainless six-membered ring, boric acid may not react because of the mutual repulsion of such groups, i.e., the adjacent hydroxyl groups will tend to be oriented as far apart as possible. Also, Hückel and co-workers (*29*) have shown that the geometry of six-membered carbon rings of the strainless type is such that *cis* groups may be oriented a maximum of 72° apart, whereas *trans* groups may approach as close as 48°. Additional complications arise, for most sugars other than glucose, in that pairs of contiguous *cis* hydroxyls are present in addition to those at carbons 1 and 2. Also, the furanose form may react preferentially (*30*). (See also discussion on p. 40.)

The periodic acid oxidation provides a means for correlating the configuration of the anomeric carbon atoms of the glycosides (see also p. 218). As shown in the accompanying formulas, representative of the hexosides, carbon 3 is removed in the process (as formic acid), and the asymmetry of carbons 2 and 4 is destroyed.

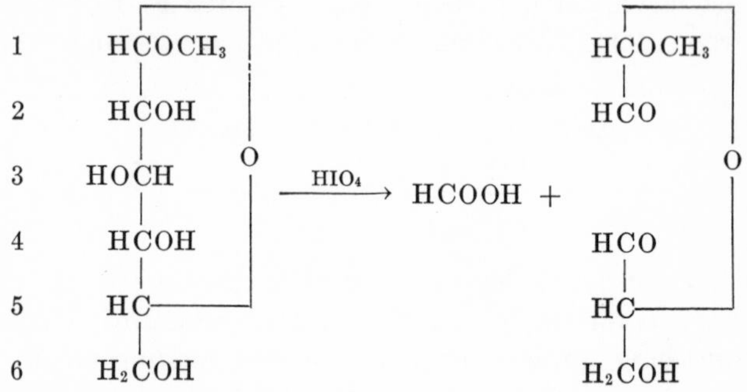
1
2
3
4
5
6
HCOCH₃
HCOH
HOCH
HCOH
HC
H₂COH
O
HIO₄
HCOOH +
HCOCH₃
HCO
O
HCO
HC
H₂COH

Methyl α-D-glucoside
(I)

(II)

In the dialdehyde (II) only two asymmetric carbon atoms remain, and these are derived from carbon atoms 1 and 5 of the original glucoside (I). Hence, all of the D-aldohexosides should yield the same dialdehyde (II) as the corresponding α- or β-D-glucoside. The configuration of carbon 1 of each of the glycosidic derivatives of the hexoses may be correlated with those of the glucosides in this manner (*31*).

28. J. Böeseken, *Advances in Carbohydrate Chem.* **4,** 189 (1949).

29. W. Hückel, H. Havekoss, K. Kumetat, D. Ullmann, and W. Doll, *Ann.* **533,** 128 (1937); *Chem. Abstr.* **32,** 3373 (1938).

30. See J. Böeseken, *Rec. trav. chim.* **61,** 663 (1942); *Chem. Abstr.* **39,** 2054 (1945).

31. E. L. Jackson and C. S. Hudson, *J. Am. Chem. Soc.* **59,** 994 (1937); M. Abdel-Akher, F. Smith, J. E. Cadotte, J. W. Van Cleve, R. Montgomery, and B. A. Lewis, *Nature* **171,** 474 (1953).

The method employing periodic acid oxidation does not allow for an absolute determination of the configuration of the acetal carbon atom of the glycosides, but it provides a method by which the configuration of the acetal carbon of the various hexosides may be correlated with that of the glucosides. By means of comparisons of optical rotation or by a study of the products of enzymic hydrolysis, the relation between the configuration for carbon atom 1 of the glucosides and glucose may be established. However, the development of more absolute methods would be a very desirable undertaking. Such methods are needed particularly for the ketoses.

Evidence for the configuration of carbon atom 1 of some phenyl glucosides has been obtained by the conversion of the β-glucosides to 1,6-anhydro derivatives (see Chapter IV, Glycosans), and by the stability of the α-anomers to strong alkali (*32*).

D. The Representation of the Ring Structures of the Sugars

In the preceding discussion, the structure and configurations of the two isomeric glucoses have been developed. The structure and configuration may be represented by the cyclic form of the Fischer formula as in (I) for α-glucose and as in (II) for methyl α-glucoside.

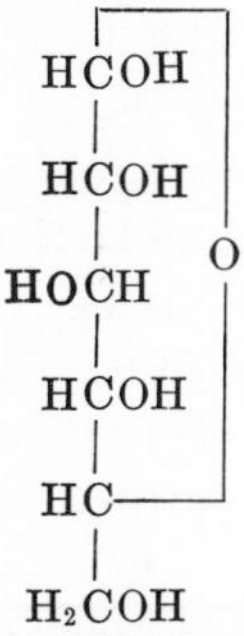
HCOH
HCOH
O
HOCH
HCOH
HC
H₂COH
(I)

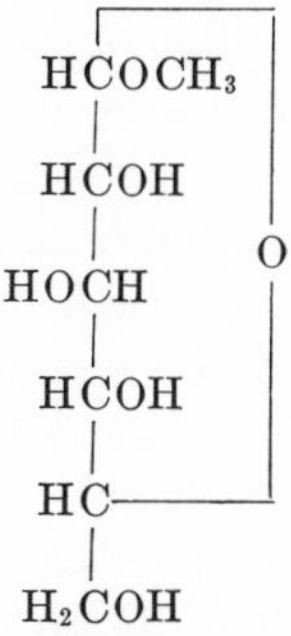
HCOCH₃
HCOH
O
HOCH
HCOH
HC
H₂COH
(II)

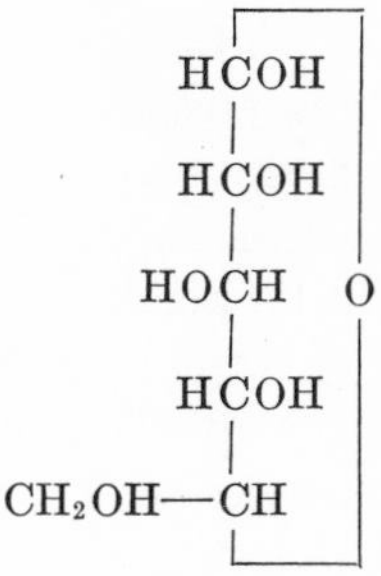
HCOH
HCOH
HOCH
O
HCOH
CH₂OH—CH
(III)

However, the cyclic, Fischer-Tollens formula has several shortcomings. Thus, the molecule is represented as an extended chain of carbon atoms connected by an oxygen bridge between positions 1 and 5. Obviously an extended linear chain is impossible, for carbon atoms 1 and 5 must be close enough for the existence of the oxygen bridge. The configuration of carbon atom 5 as given by the cyclic Fischer formula also does not give a correct picture of the steric relations between the terminal primary hydroxyl group and the hydroxyl groups attached to the ring carbon atoms. A formula of the type of (III) would give a more correct representation of the configura-

32. E. M. Montgomery, N. K. Richtmyer, and C. S. Hudson, *J. Am. Chem. Soc.* **65**, 3 (1943).

tion of carbon atom 5; thus, the primary hydroxyl group is shown to have a *trans* relationship to the hydroxyl groups at carbon atoms 1, 2, and 4.

In order to provide a better picture of the structure and configuration of the glucose molecule, Haworth has proposed a perspective representation. That for α-glucose is shown in formula (IV).

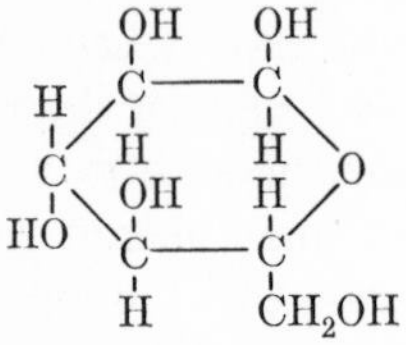

(IV)

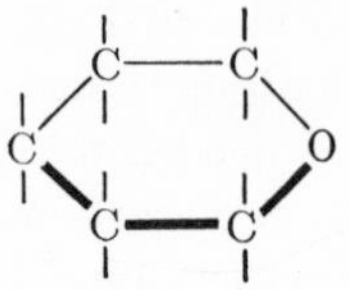

(V)

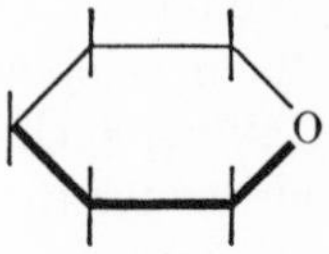

(VI)

The Haworth formula is to be considered as a conventionalized perspective drawing of a three-dimensional model. The basic pyranose ring is represented in (V) and (VI) as a ring in which all of the atoms lie in a single plane. The formulas (IV), (V), and (VI) are to be considered as projections of a hexagonal heterocyclic ring. The hexagon is held so that the observer looks from above; its nearest edge appears as the bottom lines in the above formulas. The edge closest to the observer appears as heavy black lines in (V) and (VI). In formula (V), the valences projecting above the plane are equivalent to a position to the right in the Fischer formula.

In the present volume, a modified form of the Haworth formula will be used in order that an easier transposition from the Fischer to the Haworth formulas will be possible. The transposition from the Fischer to the Haworth type of formula is illustrated below in formulas (VII), (VIII), and (IX). The Haworth formula (IX) is formed from (VIII) by ring closure between carbon atoms 1 and 5. Formula (IX) may be further simplified as in (X) and (XI) by representing the pyranose ring as a hexagon with an oxygen atom at one corner. The side of the ring closest to the observer can be indicated by heavy lines as in (X) although this shading frequently is omitted as in (XI).

The configurations of the asymmetric carbon atoms in the Haworth formula of the type of (IX), (X), and (XI) may be related easily to those in the corresponding Fischer formula (VII). Thus, it can be seen that the hydrogen atoms and hydroxyl groups on carbon atoms 2, 3, and 4 are represented in the same fashion in both types of formulas. The configuration of carbon atom 1, although not represented in the aldehyde structure, is written in the same manner in the ring form of the Fischer formula and in the particular form of the Haworth formula used here. As shown in (VIII), the primary alcoholic group projects above when the hydroxyl group of carbon 5 lies to the right in the Fischer formula. In the D-series of the aldo*hexo*-

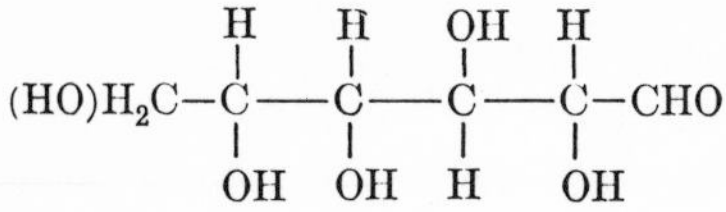

(VII)

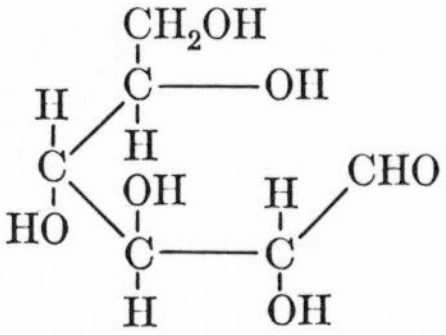

(VIII)

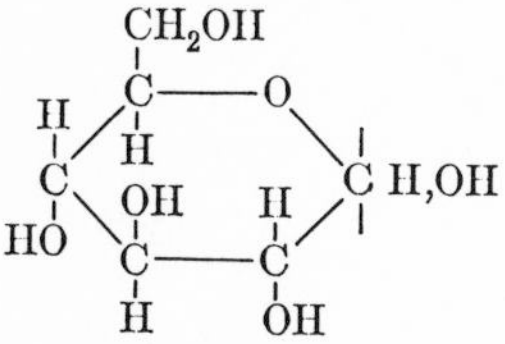

(IX)

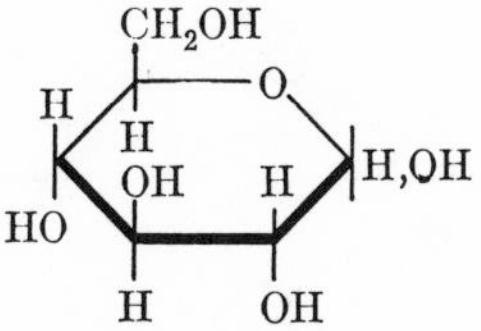

(X)

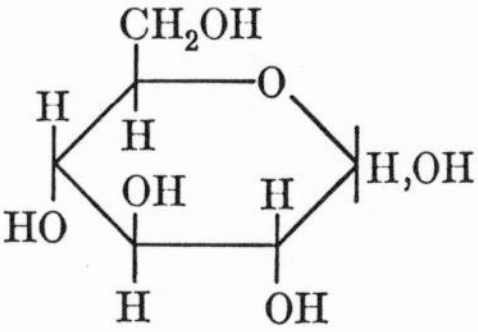

(XI)

pyranoses, the terminal primary hydroxyl group projects above the plane of the ring atoms; in the L-series, it lies below. When the ring is viewed from the opposite side of the model, as in (IV), the configuration of each of the carbon atoms is represented in the opposite manner from that in (IX), (X), and (XI).

Frequently it may be desirable to orient the ring in positions other than that shown in (IX), (X), and (XI). This may be particularly important when bulky groups are present or when linkages between two or more rings are to be represented as for the oligo- and polysaccharides. (Two of the possibilities are given later for each of the pentoses and hexoses, see p. 46.) Since the Haworth formulas are not projections of the Fischer type, they cannot be rotated in the plane of the paper. Reorientations must take place in space.

When the "tail" group attached to the ring contains an asymmetric carbon atom as in the heptopyranoses or the hexofuranoses and the corresponding glycosides, a convention is necessary to represent the configuration of this asymmetric atom. To do this, the Fischer convention may be applied for the "tail" group. Thus, glucofuranose would be:

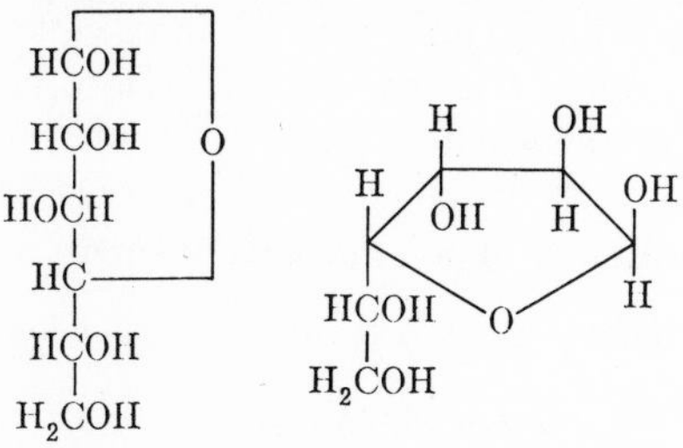

XII

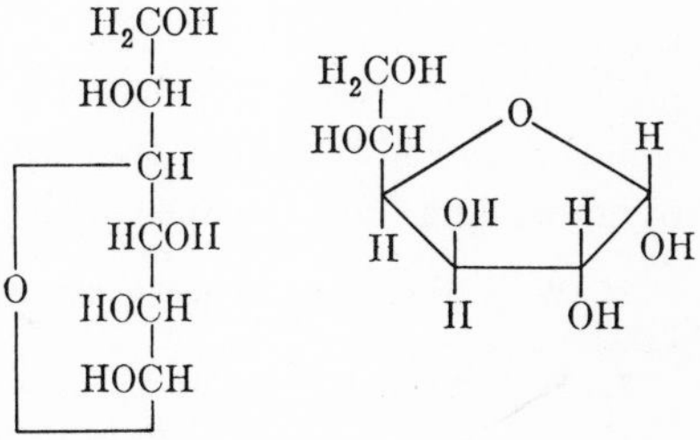

XIII

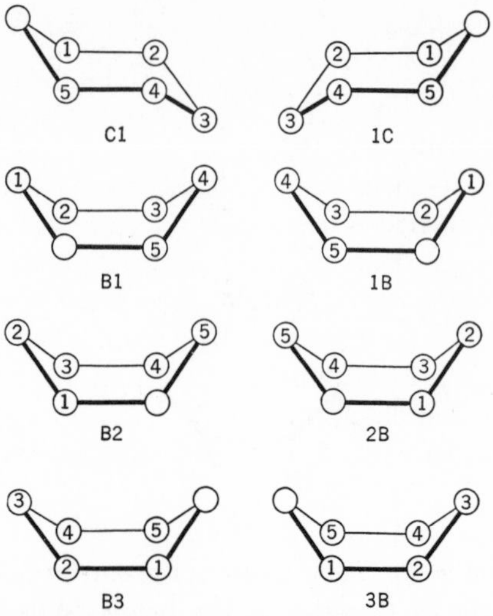
C1
1C
B1
1B
B2
2B
B3
3B

FIG. 1. The eight possible strainless ring forms of the pyranose ring. C1 and 1C are "chair" forms and the others "boat" forms (after Reeves).

The Haworth type of formula represents a considerable improvement over the older cyclic forms of the Fischer formula. Thus, for such formulas it is much clearer that substances might react simultaneously with groups at carbon atoms 4 and 6 or at 1 and 6 to form bridges between these positions. The Haworth formulas, however, are in turn only approximations of the molecular structures. The placement of all atoms in a single plane is an oversimplification. In a single coplanar ring, the valence angles necessarily would be appreciably greater than those in a "strainless" structure having valence angles of 109°.

Although furanoid rings may exist in single coplanar strained rings resembling the Haworth formula, pyranoid rings are puckered strainless rings (*33, 34*). The eight strainless Sachse rings possible for each sugar in each anomeric form are shown in Fig. 1. The forms C1, B1, B2, and B3 differ from 1C, 1B, 2B, and 3B in that the axial and equatorial arrangements are completely reversed in the two series; all axial groups of C1 have equatorial positions in 1C. Bulky or polar groups tend to assume equatorial positions (*35*). Since the chair forms allow the greatest possibilities of true equatorial-axial relations, they appear to be the usual conformations of the pyranose ring (*36*). Because of the large number of polar groups in sugars, it

33. W. N. Haworth, "The Constitution of Sugars," p. 90. Edward Arnold, London, 1929.

34. O. L. Sponsler and W. H. Dore, *Ann. Rev. Biochem.* **5**, 66 (1936).

35. See D. H. R. Barton, *Experientia* **6**, 316 (1950).

36. R. E. Reeves, *Advances in Carbohydrate Chem.* **6**, 123 (1951).

is likely that in solution specific conformations of ring-stabilized compounds are maintained under ordinary conditions, except that a few appear to exist as an equilibrium of the two chair forms. The free energy content of one of the boat forms is probably at least one kilocalorie less than that of the other forms. An energy differential of this much would be necessary to prevent spontaneous interconversions between ring conformations. The free sugars in solution, because of their spontaneous equilibrium with the aldehyde form, act as any of the possible conformations, but derivatives in which the ring is fixed (glycosides, esters, and similar compounds) probably are stabilized usually in the chair forms. A preference for a form with the fewest axial OH groups may be the determining factor for the composition of equilibrated solutions of sugars in solvents. (For additional discussion, see Chapters IV and V.)

True *cis* and *trans* relationships are not probable in the chair form, but exist in some of the boat forms (*36*). When a secondary ring is present, particularly an ethylene oxide ring, the stable form is probably a semi-chair form. Numerous instances of apparently anomolous lack of reactivity to reagents having close steric requirements, such as lead tetraacetate and periodic acid, have been ascribed to the absence of true *cis* relationships in the common chair forms (*36, 36a*).

Many reactions at the anomeric carbon atom, catalyzed by protons, can be explained on the basis of an oxonium ion (XV) in a semi-chair form (*36b*).

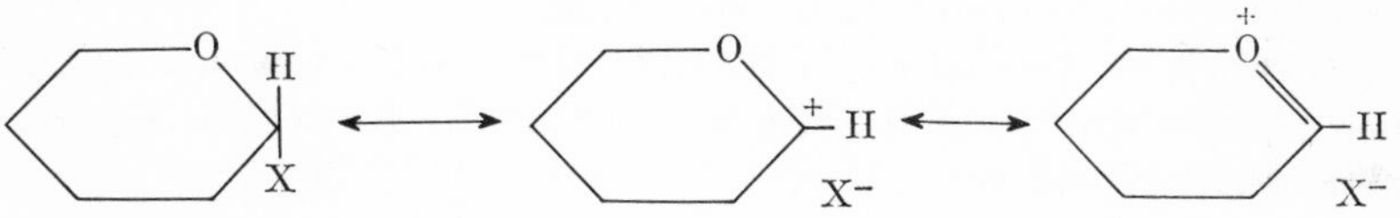
O
H
X
O
+
H
X⁻
+
O
H
X⁻

(XIV) (XV)

The oxonium ion is stabilized by resonance with the carbonium ion (XIV); the resonating bond has double-bond character, and the ring oxygen lies on a line connecting carbon atoms 1 and 5. The ion exists in C1 and 1C forms, with different arrangements of axial and equatorial groups. The two conformations of the ion explain some "neighboring group" effects (Chapter IV).

Of the anomeric forms of the glucopyranoses, the α-isomer probably has the carbon-bound hydrogen in the equatorial position, and the β-isomer has it in the axial position. The corresponding vibrational frequencies for these C—H bonds, 844 (α) and 891 cm.$^{-1}$ (β), are reported to differ enough

36a. See, however, L. P. Kuhn, *J. Am. Chem. Soc.* **76,** 4323 (1954).

36b. G. Huber, *Helv. Chim. Acta* **38,** 1224 (1955); see also R. U. Lemieux, *Advances in Carbohydrate Chem.* **9,** 1 (1954).

so as to permit the identification of the anomers of glycopyranose by infrared absorption measurements (*36c*).

Rings containing seven or more atoms are inescapably puckered and cannot be represented properly in the planar Haworth formulas. In drawing multi-ring compounds, such as 1,6-di-*O*-benzoyl-2,5-*O*-methylene-3,4-*O*-benzylidene-D-mannitol, the best solution probably is to select the most rigid ring as the principal ring for projection and to adjust the more flexible large ring to the smaller ring.

E. Nomenclature of Anomers (α,β Nomenclature)

The system of nomenclature for the anomeric (α, β) isomers of the sugars most commonly employed is that of Hudson (*37*). According to this system, for sugars of the D-series the more dextrorotatory isomer of each α,β pair is known as the α-isomer; the lesser dextrorotatory isomer is the β-isomer. For sugars of the L-series, the converse is true. A correct application of the system requires knowledge that the compounds being considered are truly anomeric, i.e., that they differ only in the configuration of the hemiacetal carbon atoms. If the compounds being considered mutarotate and are of the D-series, usually the α-isomer is the form which mutarotates to a value less positive than the initial value. Particularly in the case of compounds which exhibit complex mutarotations, the mutarotation data must be interpreted with caution, for it can be used for the naming of the sugars only when it represents an α- to β-interconversion.

The structural significance of the rules has been explained by Hudson (*38*), who writes the skeleton stereostructures for the methyl α- and β-pyranosides as follows:

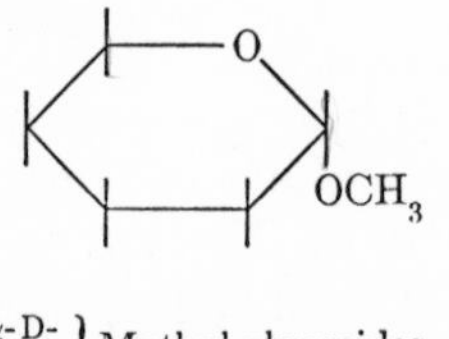
O
OCH3

$\left.\begin{matrix}\alpha\text{-D-}\\\beta\text{-L-}\end{matrix}\right\}$ Methyl glycosides

(Partial rotation of C-1 is *dextro* in sign)

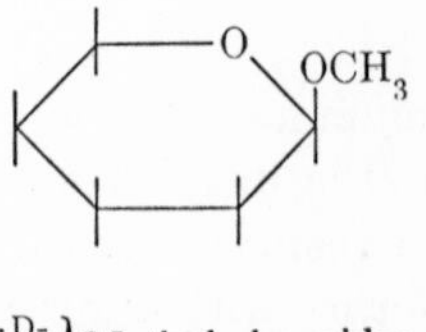
O
OCH3

$\left.\begin{matrix}\beta\text{-D-}\\\alpha\text{-L-}\end{matrix}\right\}$ Methyl glycosides

(Partial rotation of C-1 is *levo* in sign)

36c. S. A. Barker, E. J. Bourne, M. Stacey, and D. H. Whiffen, *J. Chem. Soc.* p. 171 (1954).

37. C. S. Hudson, *J. Am. Chem. Soc.* **31,** 66 (1909); *Advances in Carbohydrate Chem.* **3,** 15 (1948).

38. C. S. Hudson, *J. Am. Chem. Soc.* **60,** 1537 (1938). The Haworth-type formulas which are given have been turned over 180° in space to be in conformity with the formulas as written in the present work. See previous discussion.

The skeleton formulas for the anomeric furanose forms are:

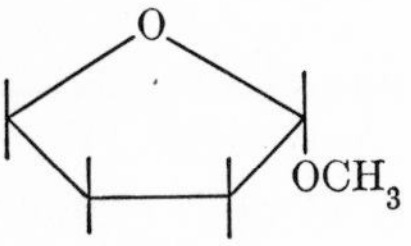
O
OCH3

α-D- } β-L- } Methyl glycosides
(C-1 is dextrorotatory)

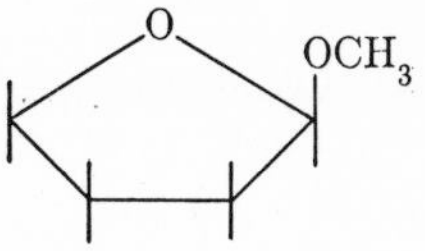
O
OCH3

β-D- } α-L- } Methyl glycosides
(C-1 is levorotatory)

For the pyranosides of the D-aldohexoses and higher-carbon sugars of the D-series, carbon atom 6 is written as projecting above the pyranose ring when written as above; for the corresponding derivatives of the L-series, carbon atom 6 lies below the pyranose ring (see discussion earlier in this chapter).

It should be noted that α-D- and β-L- (also β-D- and α-L-) refer to the same absolute configuration of the anomeric carbon atom. Thus, β-L-arabinose and α-D-galactose have the same absolute configuration at carbon atom 1 and at the other asymmetric atoms and hence exhibit many similarities.

Anomeric modifications of open-chain derivatives of sugars have been prepared. Thus, two 1-chloro-*aldehydo*-D-galactose hexaacetates (I and II) are known (*39*).

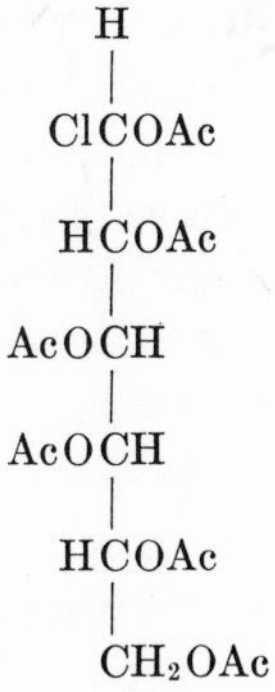
H
ClCOAc
HCOAc
AcOCH
AcOCH
HCOAc
CH2OAc

(I)

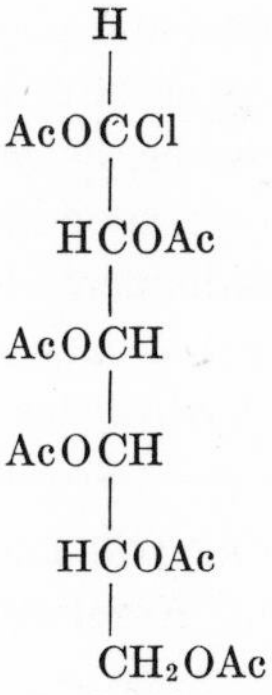
H
AcOCCl
HCOAc
AcOCH
AcOCH
HCOAc
CH2OAc

(II)

These modifications, in analogy to the cyclic forms, have been named α and β according to whether they mutarotate downwards (α) or upwards (β) in acetyl chloride solution containing zinc chloride (*40*).

39. M. L. Wolfrom and R. L. Brown, *J. Am. Chem. Soc.* **63,** 1246 (1941).

40. For a further discussion of the naming of this type of compound see M. L. Wolfrom, M. Konigsberg, and F. B. Moody, *J. Am. Chem. Soc.* **62,** 2343 (1940); R. J. Dimler and K. P. Link, *ibid.* **62,** 1216 (1940).

8. HOMOMORPHOUS SUGARS

A. Homomorphology

Earlier in this chapter, the genetic relationship of the various sugars to D- and L-glyceraldehyde was demonstrated. A relation of considerably more importance for the correlation of the properties and reactions is based on the similarity of substances which have the same configurations for the atoms which compose the pyranose rings. Since for the aldohexoses the number of asymmetric carbons is just sufficient to make each carbon atom in the pyranose ring asymmetric, the aldohexoses may be considered as the basic types for all sugars which can form pyranose rings. The pentoses and higher sugars can be obtained from the hexoses by substitution of the—CH_2OH groups of the hexoses by H or by $(CHOH)_n$—CH_2OH, respectively. The various hexose types are illustrated in the accompanying formulas which also show some of the members of each series. Although 32 hexopyranoses theoretically are possible, only the formulas for the eight D-types are written and the α,β-configuration is not indicated. Because of the lack of asymmetry of carbon atom 5 of the aldopentoses, each of these sugars is related to a pair of hexoses. On the other hand, the basic types of the furanoses are the pentoses.

As would be expected from the identity of the configurations of the pyranose or furanose rings, the members of each homomorphous series show marked chemical and physical similarities (*41*), and it is often possible to predict the properties of unknown members from those of the basic type. The greatest differences, as might be anticipated, are found between the pentoses and the corresponding hexoses. It appears that enzymes which hydrolyze the hexoside members of each series also hydrolyze the glycosides of the other members of each series (*42*). Thus, the enzyme α-mannosidase of almond emulsin hydrolyzes the α-lyxosides as well as the α-mannosides.

B. Nomenclature for Higher Sugars and for Compounds with Numerous Asymmetric Atoms in a Carbon Chain

In the development of the stereochemistry of the sugars, trivial names, as shown on page 24, were assigned to sugars with two, three, and four CH(OH) groups. In earlier usage and recognized in the Carbohydrate Nomenclature Rules of 1953, these names of the C_3 to C_6 sugars have taken on

41. R. M. Hann, A. T. Merrill, and C. S. Hudson, *J. Am. Chem. Soc.* **57,** 2100 (1935); R. M. Hann and C. S. Hudson, *ibid.* **59,** 548 (1937); H. S. Isbell, *J. Research Natl. Bur. Standards* **18,** 505 (1937); H. S. Isbell and W. W. Pigman, *ibid.* **18,** 141 (1937). Many earlier workers had also noticed the resemblances in the structures for the members of the various series.

42. W. W. Pigman, *J. Research Natl. Bur. Standards* **26,** 197 (1941).

D-Idose type

X = —H, L-Xylose
X = $-CH_2OH$, D-Idose
X = $-CH_3$, 6-Deoxy-D-idose
X = $-CHOH-CH_2OH$, (two aldoheptoses)

D-Gulose type

X = —H, L-Lyxose
X = $-CH_2OH$, D-Gulose
X = $-CH_3$, 6-Deoxy-D-gulose
X = $-CHOH-CH_2OH$, (two aldoheptoses)

D-Glucose type

X = —H, D-Xylose
X = $-CH_2OH$, D-Glucose
X = $-CH_3$, D-Quinovose
X = $-CHOH-CH_2OH$, (two aldoheptoses)

D-Mannose type

X = —H, D-Lyxose
X = $-CH_2OH$, D-Mannose
X = $-CH_3$, D-Rhamnose
X = $-CHOH-CH_2OH$, (two aldoheptoses)

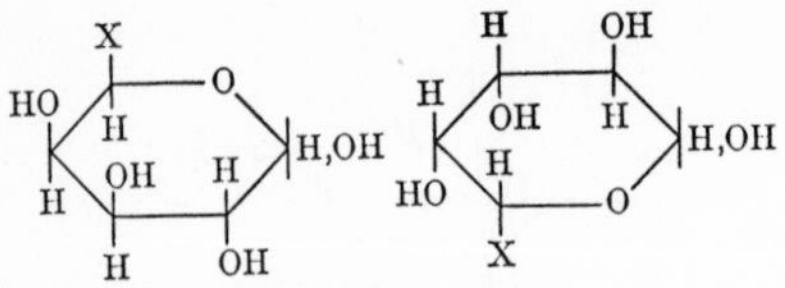

D-Galactose type

$X = -H$, L-Arabinose
$X = -CH_2OH$, D-Galactose
$X = -CH_3$, D-Fucose
$X = -CHOH-CH_2OH$, (two aldoheptoses)

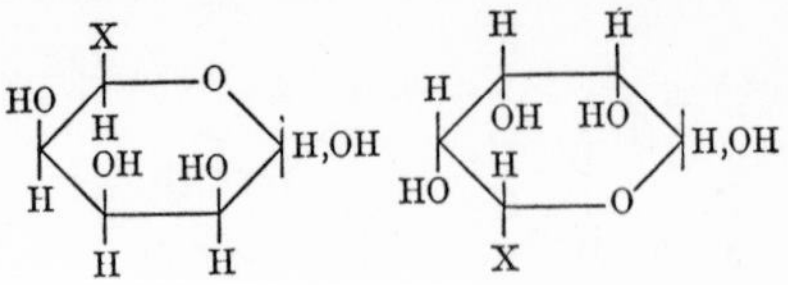

D-Talose type

$X = -H$, L-Ribose
$X = -CH_2OH$, D-Talose
$X = -CH_3$, 6-Deoxy-D-talose
$X = -CHOH-CH_2OH$, (two aldoheptoses)

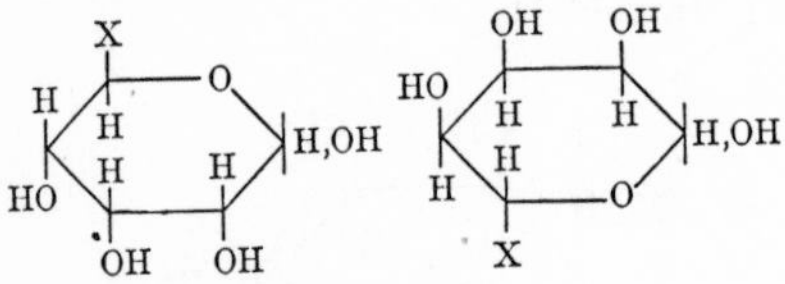

D-Allose type

$X = -H$, D-Ribose
$X = -CH_2OH$, D-Allose
$X = -CH_3$, 6-Deoxy-D-allose
$X = -CHOH-CH_2OH$, (two aldoheptoses)

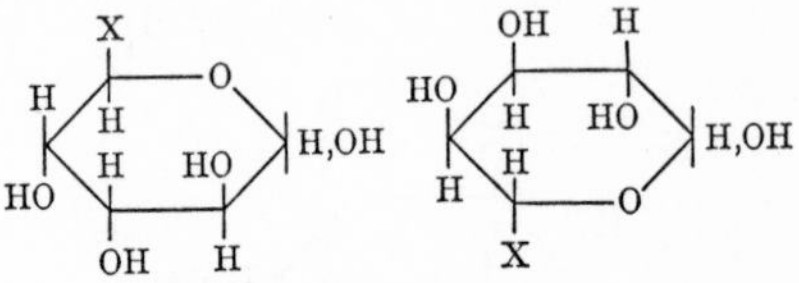

D-Altrose type

$X = -H$, D-Arabinose
$X = -CH_2OH$, D-Altrose
$X = -CH_3$, 6-Deoxy-D-altrose
$X = -CHOH-CH_2OH$, (two aldoheptoses)

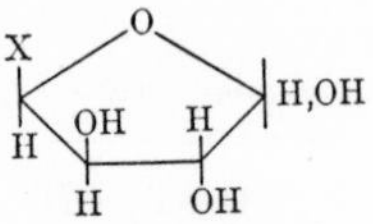

D-Xylose type

$X = -H$, L-Threose
$X = -CH_2OH$, D-Xylose
$X = -CHOH-CH_2OH$, {D-Glucose, L-Idose}

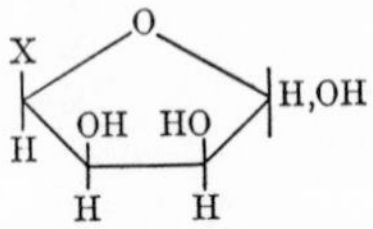

D-Lyxose type

$X = -H$, L-Erythrose
$X = -CH_2OH$, D-Lyxose
$X = -CHOH-CH_2OH$, {D-Mannose, L-Gulose}

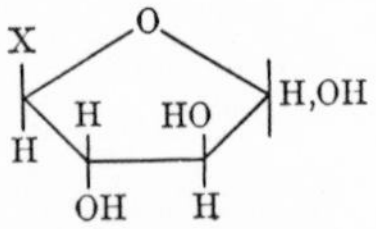

D-Arabinose type

$X = -H$, D-Threose
$X = -CH_2OH$, D-Arabinose
$X = -CHOH-CH_2OH$, {D-Altrose, L-Galactose}

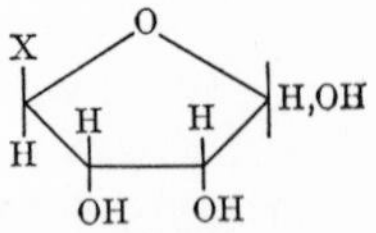

D-Ribose type

$X = -H$, D-Erythrose
$X = -CH_2OH$, D-Ribose
$X = -CHOH-CH_2OH$, {D-Allose, L-Talose}

a more fundamental aspect as the basis for indicating the configuration of consecutive $\overset{|}{\underset{|}{C}}H(OH)$ groups in a chain of carbon atoms. These names and the configurations represented are shown in Table II. The names are used as italicized prefixes before the chemical name as:

$$\text{D-}\textit{gluco}\text{-pentahydroxypentyl, } CH_2OH-\overset{H}{\underset{OH}{C}}-\overset{H}{\underset{OH}{C}}-\overset{OH}{\underset{H}{C}}-\overset{H}{\underset{OH}{C}}-$$

TABLE II

CONFIGURATIONAL PREFIXES

Carbons	Configuration and name[a]		
1	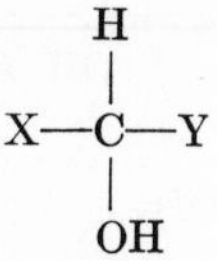 D-*glycero*		
2	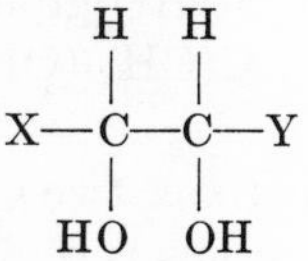 D-*erythro*	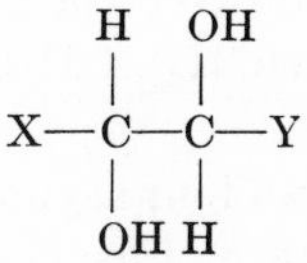 D-*threo*	
3	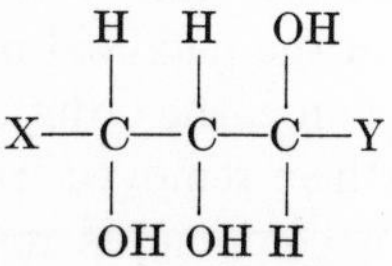 D-*arabino* (*arabo*)	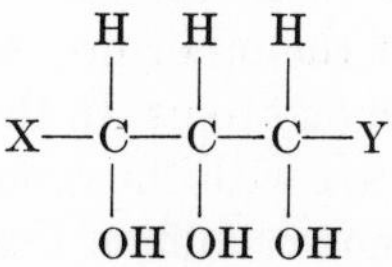 D-*ribo*	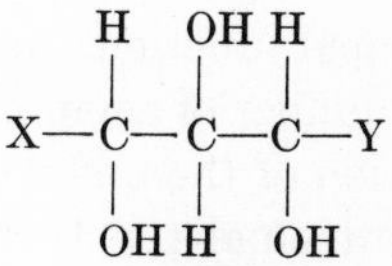 D-*xylo*
	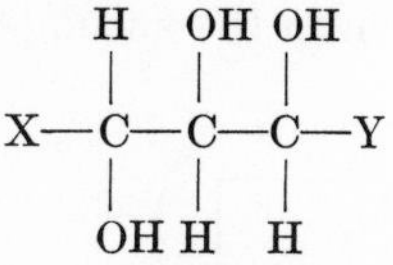 D-*lyxo*		
4	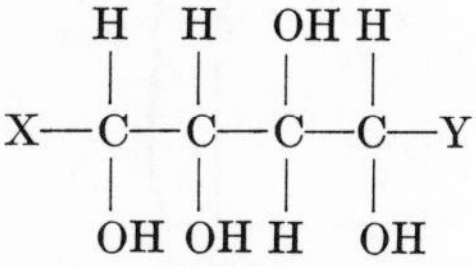 D-*gluco*	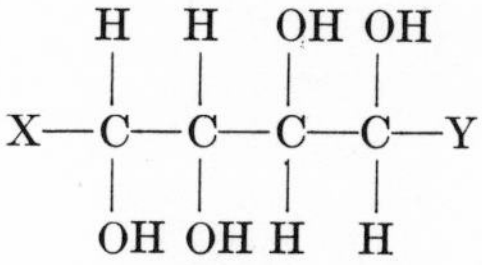 D-*manno*	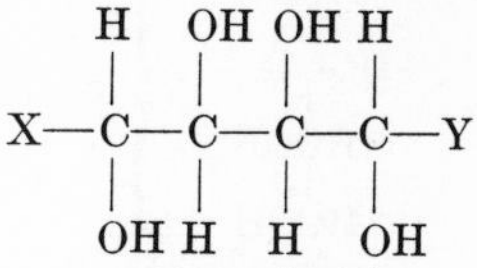 D-*galacto* (*gala*)
	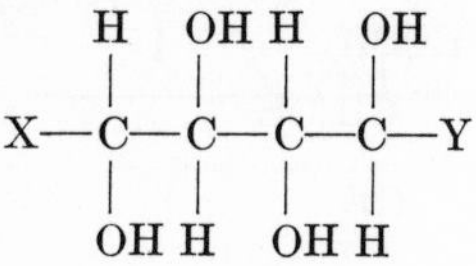 D-*ido*	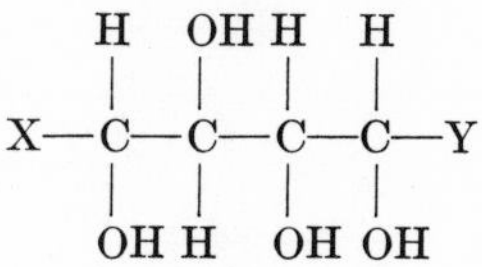 D-*gulo*	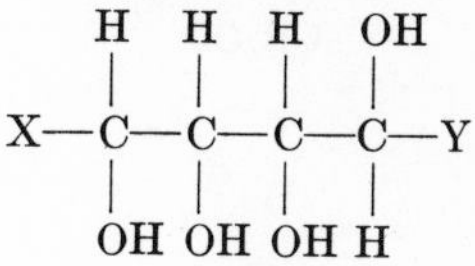 D-*altro*
	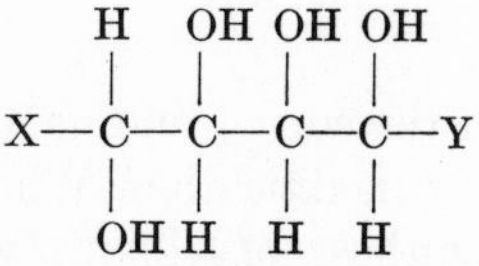 D-*talo*	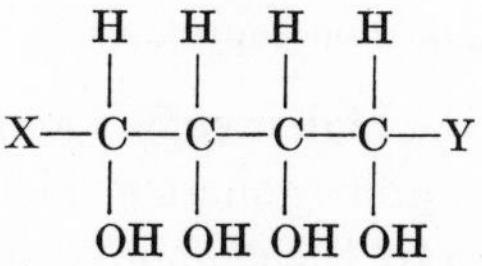 D-*allo*	

[a] The group Y is the main fuctional group such as CHO or COOH. Group Y is written at the top when the carbon chain is vertical. (X and Y cannot be hydrogen.)

If the sequence of asymmetric carbon atoms is broken by a nonasymmetric group, this group is passed over as in:

```
                                          H   H          H
D-ribo-1,3,4,5-tetrahydroxypentyl, CH2OH—C—C—CH2—C—
                                          OH  OH         OH

                                      OH  OH
D-erythro-pentulose, CH2OH—CO—C—C—CH2OH
                                      H   H
```

The same prefixes are used even when one or more CH(OH) groups are replaced by $CH(NH_2)$, $CH(OCH_3)$, CH(Cl), CH(OAc), $C(CH_3)(OH)$ and similar groups.

For a sequence of more than four asymmetric carbon atoms, two or more prefixes are used. The sequence of asymmetric carbon atoms is divided so that there is a four-carbon prefix for the carbon atoms closest to the principal function, and so that the other prefixes contain the maximal possible number of asymmetric carbon atoms. In the actual name, the order of citation of the prefixes is to start with the grouping furthest removed from the principal function. The most common examples of compounds requiring this type of compound prefixes are the sugars and glycitols with seven or more carbon atoms, two examples of which are given in the accompanying formulas.

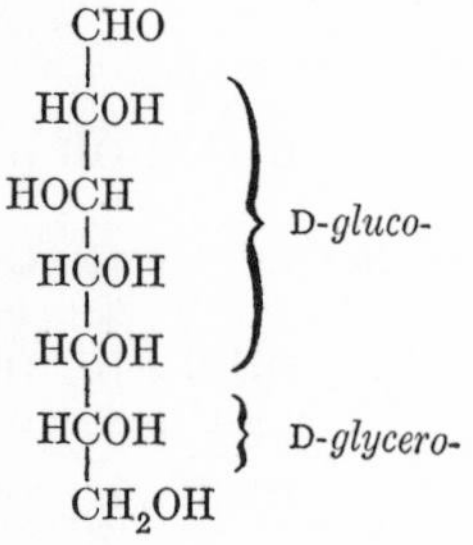

CHO
HCOH
HOCH
HCOH
HCOH
HCOH
CH2OH
D-gluco-
D-glycero-

(I)

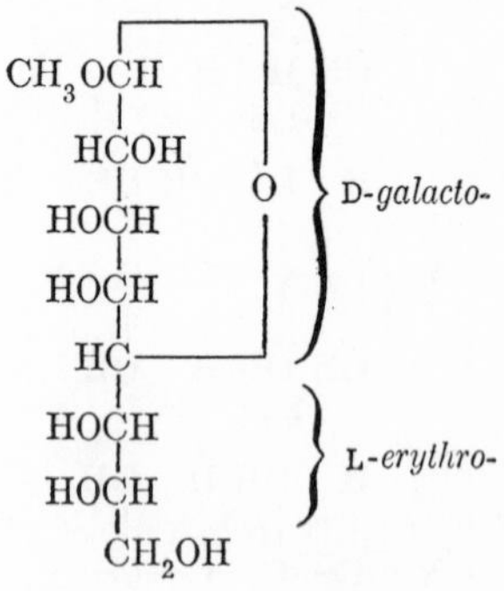

CH3OCH
HCOH
HOCH
HOCH
HC
O
HOCH
HOCH
CH2OH
D-galacto-
L-erythro-

(II)

(I) D-*glycero*-D-*gluco*-heptose (formerly: D-α-altroheptose, D-*gluco*-D-altroheptose)

(II) Methyl L-*erythro*-β-D-*galacto*-octopyranoside

The nomenclature of the higher sugars and of the corresponding alcohols (glycitols) and acids has undergone considerable modification. When synthesized from the hexoses by the cyanohydrin synthesis of Kiliani, two heptoses are derived from each hexose. Emil Fischer adopted the convention of naming the first isomer that was isolated as the α-heptonic acid and the second as the β-heptonic acid. This process gave rise to names like D-α-glucoheptonic and D-β-glucoheptonic acids for the acids derived from D-glucose. Isbell (*43*) later gave this usage a configurational significance, whereas Hudson (*44*) developed a system similar to that given above, except that overlapping prefixes were used.

9. THE SUGARS IN SOLUTION

A. In the Absence of Strong Acids or Alkalies; Mutarotation

Although fairly stable when in the crystalline condition, the sugars undergo many transformations when dissolved in water, particularly in the presence of acids or alkalies. Initially, these changes usually involve the carbon atom carrying the aldehyde or ketone groups. Hence, when these groups are blocked as in the nonreducing compound sugars (e.g., sucrose) or glycosides, the compounds are more stable and do not undergo isomerizations until the blocking groups are removed.

In solution, the polar groups of sugars are highly solvated. With water as the solvent, the hydrogen atom of each hydroxyl group is rapidly exchanged with hydrogen atoms of the solvent. Within a few minutes at room temperature, these hydrogen atoms exchanged completely with the deuterium atoms of heavy water (*45*). The carbon-bound hydrogens and oxygens (except for the "carbonyl" oxygen) are much more firmly bound and require bases, acids, or heat to effect their removal. One oxygen, presumably the carbonyl oxygen or hemiacetal hydroxyl, is much more active than the others. Thus, when glucose is kept in H_2O^{18}, one oxygen atom is exchanged after 100 hours at 55° (*46*).

Interconversions between α,β-isomers and between ring isomers take place under the mildest possible condition of acidity and temperature. Such changes are manifested by the change of optical rotation with time which may be observed for freshly prepared sugar solutions. The change of optical rotation with time is known as mutarotation. Mutarotations may arise from changes other than interconversions between α,β- and ring isomers, but for neutral or slightly acid or slightly alkaline solutions of the sugars they most often arise from such changes. The phenomenon was observed first by Dubrunfaut (1846), who noted that the optical rotation of freshly dissolved glucose changes with time and that after a number of hours the rotation becomes constant. The ordinary form of glucose (α-D-glucose) mutarotates

43. H. S. Isbell, *J. Research Natl. Bur. Standards* **18**, 529 (footnote) (1937).

44. C. S. Hudson, *J. Am. Chem. Soc.* **60**, 1537 (1938); *Advances in Carbohydrate Chem.* **1**, 28 (1945).

45. H. Fredenhagen and K. F. Bonhoeffer, *Z. physik. Chem.* **A181**, 392 (1938).

46. K. Goto and T. Titani, *Bull. Chem. Soc, Japan* **16**, 172, 403 (1941).

downward, and the β-isomer mutarotates upwards; in both cases the same equilibrium value is reached.

$$\begin{array}{ccccc} \alpha\text{-Glucose} & \rightleftarrows & \text{equilibrium} & \rightleftarrows & \beta\text{-Glucose} \\ +112° & \longrightarrow & +52.7° & \longleftarrow & +18.7° \end{array}$$

As mentioned earlier in this chapter, the mutarotation of glucose and other sugars showed that the original aldehyde structure for glucose was not adequate for explaining the properties of the sugar. The separation of isomers of lactose (Erdmann—1880) and of glucose (Tanret—1896) which mutarotated to the same equilibrium value provided good evidence that the observed mutarotations result from an interconversion of the various modifications.

Some glucose oxidase preparations of fungal origin contain an enzyme, mutarotase, which also catalyzes the anomeric interconversions of D-glucose and of D-galactose, and to a lesser degree of maltose and lactose. Mannose and glucosamine are not affected. The enzyme facilitates reactions in which there is stereospecificity for the α,β-isomers, e.g., the actions of glucose oxidase (*46a,b*).

A continuously recording polariscope has been developed (*46b*) which should aid mutarotation measurements.

The mutarotation of α-glucose may be represented by the equation for a first-order reversible reaction.

$$\alpha \underset{k_2}{\overset{k_1}{\rightleftarrows}} \beta \tag{1}$$

$$-\frac{d\alpha}{dt} = k_1[\alpha] - k_2[\beta] \tag{2}$$

Equation (2) gives the rate of change of the α- into the β-form at the time t. The reaction constant for $\alpha \rightarrow \beta$ is k_1, and for $\beta \rightarrow \alpha$ is k_2. The concentrations of the α- and β-form at the time t are represented by $[\alpha]$ and $[\beta]$.

Equation (2) may be integrated and expressed in terms of the optical rotations in the form of equation (3) (*47*).

$$k_1 + k_2 = \frac{1}{t} \log \frac{r_0 - r_\infty}{r_t - r_\infty} \tag{3}$$

In equation (3), r_0 = the rotation at $t = 0$; r_∞ = the final equilibrium rotation; and r_t = the rotation at the time t. The rotations may be expressed as observed or as

46a. D. Keilin and E. F. Hartree, *Biochem. J.* **42,** 221 (1948); A. S. Keston, *Science* **120,** 356 (1954).

46b. G. B. Levy and E. S. Cook, *Biochem. J.* **57,** 50 (1954).

47. T. M. Lowry, *J. Chem. Soc.* **75,** 211 (1899); H. Trey, *Z. physik. Chem.* **18,** 198 (1895).

specific rotations. The specific rotations are calculated from the observed rotations by the relation:

$$\text{Specific Rotation} = [\alpha] = \frac{\alpha \times 100}{l \times c} \quad (4)$$

α = observed rotation.
l = length of column of solution (expressed in decimeters).
c = concentration of active substance as g./100 ml. of solution.
In case the rotations are read on a saccharimeter, the values observed (°S) are multiplied by the factor 0.3462 to give α.

The rotation varies with the wavelength of the light source, and usually the sodium D line is employed. Most rotations are measured at 20°C. The solvents most commonly employed are water and chloroform.

The mutarotation coefficient, $k_1 + k_2$, should be the same for the α- and β-isomers of each sugar. Hudson (*48*) demonstrated that the α- and β-isomers of lactose and of some other sugars give identical values for $k_1 + k_2$ and that the mutarotations follow the first-order equation. Table III lists the mutarotation coefficients for several sugars (*49*).

The mutarotations of the sugars listed in Table III and those for many other sugars follow the first-order equation. The activation energy averages about 17,000 cal./mole; this value corresponds to an increase in rate of 2.5 times for a 10° rise in temperature. The conformity of the mutarotation data to the first-order equation makes it probable that the main constituents of the equilibrium solution are the α- and β-pyranose modifications. The actual composition may be calculated from the optical rotations of the equilibrium solution when the rotations of the pure α- and β-isomers are known. Data of this type are included in Table III. Independent confirmation of the composition of the equilibrium solutions is provided by studies of the rates of bromine oxidation of the sugars, the results of which are also found in Table III.

A number of important sugars exhibit mutarotations which do not follow the first-order equation. (See Fig. 2.) A striking case (*49*) is presented by the pentose ribose; the specific rotation of freshly dissolved L-ribose decreases from an initial value of +23.4° to a minimum of +18.2° and then rises to a constant value of +23.2°. Some other sugars such as α- and β-galactose, α- and β-talose, and α- and β-arabinose exhibit similar but less-striking deviations from the first-order equation. In Fig. 3, log $(r_t - r_\infty)$ vs. time is plotted for α-D-glucose and α-D-talose. Although the curve for α-D-glucose is linear and follows the first-order equation, that for α-D-talose deviates greatly from a straight line during the initial period. This deviation is an

48. C. S. Hudson, *Z. physik. Chem.* **44,** 487 (1903).
49. H. S. Isbell and W. W. Pigman, *J. Research Natl. Bur. Standards* **18,** 141 (1937).

TABLE III

MUTAROTATION COEFFICIENTS AND ACTIVATION ENERGIES FOR SOME SUGARS

Sugar	$k_1 + k_2$ (20°C.)	Q (cal.)	Composition of equilibrium solution (%)	
			From rotations	From oxidation studies
α-D-Glucose	0.00632	17,200	α—36.2	37.4
β-D-Glucose	0.00625	17,200	β—63.8	62.6
α-D-Mannose	0.0173	16,700	α—68.8	68.9
β-D-Mannose	0.0178	17,100	β—31.2	31.1
α-D-Xylose	0.0203	16,800	—	—
α-D-Lyxose	0.0568	15,300	α—76.0	79.7
β-D-Lyxose	0.0591	15,700	β—24.0	20.3
α-Lactose·H_2O	0.00471	17,300	α—36.8	37.5
β-Lactose	0.00466	17,600	β—63.2	62.5
β-Maltose·H_2O	0.00527	17,500	—	—

indication of the lack of the conformity of the talose mutarotation with the first-order equation.

In general, the mutarotations which cannot be expressed by the first-order equation conform to equations derived on the assumption of three components in the equilibrium mixture. The equilibrium involved may be:

$$\alpha \rightleftarrows \mu \rightleftarrows \beta \tag{5}$$

Equations fitting this condition were derived by Riiber and Minsaas (*50*) and by Smith and Lowry (*51*). The Smith and Lowry type of equation is represented by equation (6).

$$[\alpha] = A \times 10^{-m_1 t} + B \times 10^{-m_2 t} + C \tag{6}$$

In this equation, C is the equilibrium rotation, A is the total change in optical rotation due to the slowly mutarotating component, and B is $(r_o - r_\infty) - A$. Methods for applying these equations are described elsewhere (*49*). The constants m_1 and m_2 are functions of the velocity constants for the various reactions represented in equation (*5*).

Changes in other properties such as the solution volume, the refractive index, and the heat content have been shown by Riiber and his associates (*50*) to parallel the changes in rotations.

Mutarotations which cannot be expressed by the first-order equation but which are expressed by equation (6) must represent the establishment of

50. C. N. Riiber and J. Minsaas. *Ber.* **59**, 2266 (1926).

51. G. F. Smith and T. M. Lowry, *J. Chem. Soc.* p. 666 (1928).

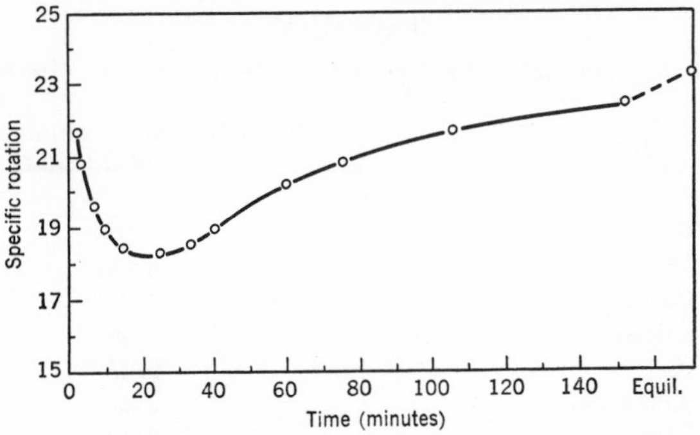
Specific rotation
25
23
21
19
17
15
0
20
40
60
80
100
120
140
Equil.
Time (minutes)

FIG. 2. Mutarotation of L-ribose in water at 0°C.
(Reprinted from: *J. Research Natl. Bur. Standards* **18,** 164 (1937)).

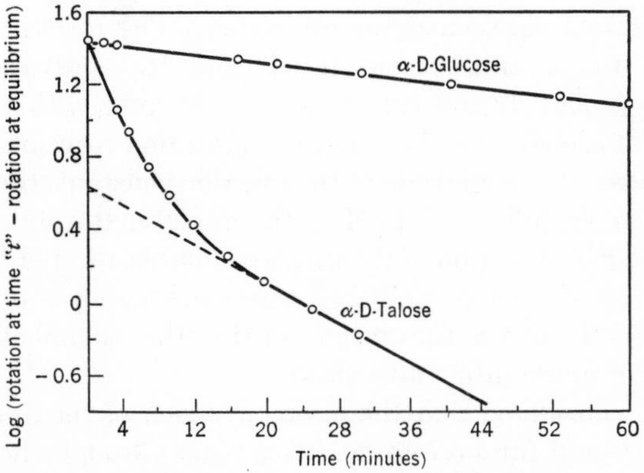
Log (rotation at time "t" – rotation at equilibrium)
1.6
1.2
0.8
0.4
0
– 0.6
α-D-Glucose
α-D-Talose
4
12
20
28
36
44
52
60
Time (minutes)

FIG. 3. "Simple" and "complex" mutarotations.
(Reprinted from "Polarimetry, Saccharimetry and the Sugars"
by F. J. Bates and Associates.)

equilibria in which three or more components are present in appreciable quantities. Hence, equilibrated solutions of sugars such as galactose, arabinose, talose, and, particularly, ribose must have appreciable quantities of isomers other than the pyranose modifications. The ease of conversion of galactopyranose to furanose and free-aldehyde modifications is shown by the formation of appreciable quantities of such isomers in the products of the acetylation (see p. 144).

The mutarotation reactions which follow equation (6) may be considered to consist of two simultaneous or consecutive reactions, one of which is slow and the other of which is rapid. The values of m_1 (which represents the reaction constant for the slowest reaction) are about the same as those for $k_1 + k_2$ for glucose, and the activation energies also have almost the same value as for glucose (*49*). It is probable then that the slower reactions

TABLE IV

QUANTITY OF REDUCIBLE FORM PRESENT IN SOLUTIONS OF SEVERAL SUGARS

Sugar	Reducible forms (mole per cent of total sugar)
Glucose	0.024
Mannose	0.064
Galactose	0.082
Allose	(1.38)
Xylose	0.17
Arabinose	0.28
Lyxose	0.40
Ribose	8.5 (0.1 *M*)

are α,β-conversions between pyranose isomers. The reactions represented by m_2 are 5 to 10 times more rapid, and the activation energy is much smaller (about 13,200 cal./mole as compared with 16,900 for the normal mutarotations). For the rapid mutarotation reactions of galactose, talose, and ribose, the magnitude of the reaction constant, the small activation energy, and the influence of pH on the rate of mutarotation are similar to those for the mutarotation of the furanose modification of fructose. Since the mutarotation of fructose probably represents mainly a pyranose-furanose change (*25*), the fast mutarotations of the other sugars also may represent pyranose-furanose interconversions.

It is usually considered that the interconversion of the α- and β-isomers and of pyranose and furanose forms takes place through the intermediate formation of the *aldehydo* or *keto* forms of the sugars.

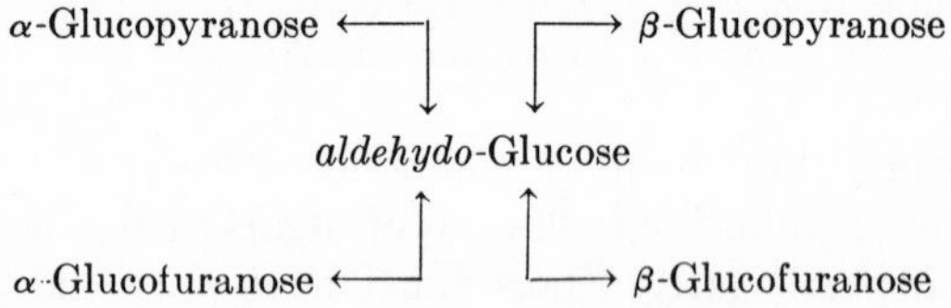
α-Glucopyranose
β-Glucopyranose
aldehydo-Glucose
α-Glucofuranose
β-Glucofuranose

There is no direct proof for the existence of the open-chain forms. However, small quantities of the acetylated open-chain forms are obtained along with the ring forms when some sugars are acetylated (see under Acetyl sugars). Sugar solutions contain isomers which are reducible at the dropping-mercury electrode of the polarograph (*52*). The amounts of the reducible form present in 0.25 *M* solutions of several aldoses at pH 7.0 and 25°C. are shown in Table IV. As may be seen from the table, the amount of the reducible

52. S. M. Cantor and Q. P. Peniston, *J. Am. Chem. Soc.* **62,** 2113 (1940); J. M. Los and K. Wiesner, *ibid.* **75,** 6346 (1953); J. M. Los, L. B. Simpson, and K. Wiesner, *ibid.* **78,** 1564 (1956).

form in glucose solution is very small (0.024 mole per cent). Solutions of other sugars, particularly ribose, contain fairly large amounts. The quantity of reducible material increases rapidly as the pH becomes greater. These data, obtained by Cantor and Peniston, are said to agree with those reported by Lippich (*53*) for the amount of material in solution which reacts "instantaneously" with hydrocyanic acid.

The mutarotation reactions are catalyzed by both hydrogen and hydroxyl ions. The rate of mutarotation of glucose and galactose is at a minimum between the pH limits 3.0 to 7.0. At pH values greater than 7.0 and less than 3.0, the velocity increases rapidly. The curve for mutarotation velocity vs. pH is represented by a catenary. The influence of hydrogen and hydroxyl ions on the rate was found by Hudson to be expressible by equations of the type:

$$k_1 + k_2 = A + B[H^+] + C[OH^-] \tag{7}$$

where A, B, and C are constants. For glucose at 20°C. the equation is (*25*):

$$k_1 + k_2 = 0.0060 + 0.18[H^+] + 16{,}000[OH^-] \tag{8}$$

According to equation (8), glucose mutarotates most slowly at pH 4.61. Acids and alkalies influence the mutarotation of levulose and some other sugars much more markedly than glucose although the minimum for levulose occurs near that for glucose. As may be seen from equations (7) and (8), at pH 4.6 the portion of the catalysis which is due to the water (term A) is much greater than that caused by the hydrogen and hydroxyl ions. In turn, the hydroxyl ions are much more effective catalysts than the hydrogen ions (compare values for B and C).

Equations (7) and (8) are special cases for aqueous solutions of the equation for generalized acid-base catalysis. As shown by Lowry (*54a*), the mutarotations of sugars are reactions involving simultaneous catalysis by both acids and bases, in the generalized concept of acids and bases proposed by Lowry and by Brönsted. Water functions as a complete catalyst because of its amphoteric dissociation into ions: $H_2O \leftrightarrow H^+ + OH^-$. Acids or bases alone are not effective catalysts but in mixture are complete catalysts.

Thus in a mixture of pyridine and cresol, tetra-*O*-methylglucose was found to mutarotate, whereas in either pyridine or cresol, mutarotation was insignificant (*54b*). Lowry, therefore, proposed that the mutarotation of sugars is basically a ternary reaction involving simultaneous acid-base catalysis. The ternary reaction involves the simultaneous transfer of a proton from the acid catalyst to the sugar in the same step that a proton is trans-

53. F. Lippich, *Biochem. Z.* **248,** 280 (1932).
54a. T. M. Lowry and E. M. Richards, *J. Chem. Soc.* **127,** 1385 (1925).
54b. T. M. Lowry and I. J. Faulkner, *J. Chem. Soc.* **127,** 2883 (1925).

ferred from the sugar to the base catalyst yielding the sugar aldehyde (or hydrate) directly (*54c* , *55*).

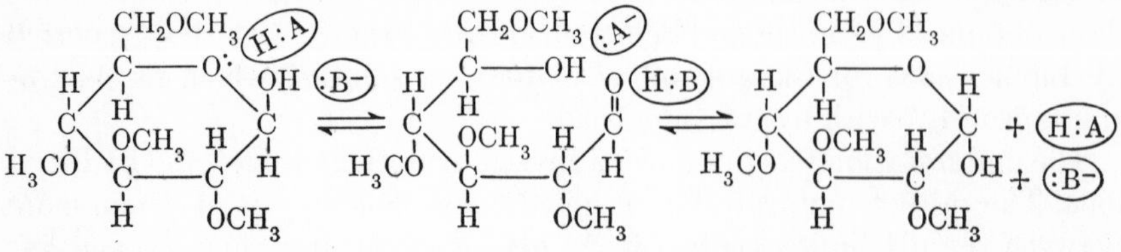

Strong evidence exists for the intermediary role of the free aldehyde in the mutarotation reaction in the observation that no carbon-bound hydrogen atoms and no oxygen atoms exchange with water during the mutarotation reaction. Since one oxygen atom per mole is only slowly exchanged, the possible hydrated aldehyde is formed too slowly to be the intermediate. The dependence of mutarotations on acid and base catalysis accounts for the observation that the rate of mutarotation decreases in aqueous methanol and ethanol solutions as the alcohol concentration is increased (*56*), since the alcohols exhibit less amphoteric properties than does water. In heavy water, the mutarotation of glucose proceeds more slowly than in ordinary water (*45*).

The findings of Swain and Brown (*55*) support the ternary mechanism proposed by Lowry for the mutarotation of tetra-*O*-methylglucose. It was found that the mutarotation of tetra-*O*-methylglucose in benzene in the presence of both an acid (phenol) and a base (pyridine) followed third-order kinetics but was first-order with respect to each component: tetra-*O*-methylglucose, pyridine, and phenol (*55*). 2-Hydroxypyridine was found to be a very effective bifunctional catalyst, and since both acid and base functions were in the same molecule, the mutarotation followed second-order kinetics. Its catalytic action was essentially independent of the other acid and base species present. Although it is a much weaker acid or base than either phenol or pyridine, its catalysis of the mutarotation of tetra-*O*-methylglucose in benzene was much greater than that of either pyridine or phenol, or a mixture of both (*55*).

Although basically a ternary reaction, mutarotation may follow first- or second-order kinetics. As indicated earlier (p. 50), under the usual experimental conditions which involve water as the solvent in large excess and a fixed hydrogen-ion concentration, first-order kinetics are followed. Actually, the reaction usually appears to be second-order in aqueous system when the concentration of the catalyst is taken into consideration. This special situa-

54c. T. M. Lowry, *J. Chem. Soc.* p. 2554 (1927).
55. C. G. Swain and J. F. Brown, Jr., *J. Am. Chem. Soc.* **74,** 2534, 2538 (1952).
56. H. H. Rowley and W. N. Hubbard, *J. Am. Chem. Soc.* **64,** 1010 (1942).

tion has led to the interpretation that two consecutive bimolecular reactions are involved; in one, a proton is added and in the other, a proton is removed in a separate step (*57, 58*).

According to combustion data (*59*) for the crystalline sugars, the complete conversion of α- to β-glucose is accompanied by a heat absorption of 1500 cal./mole and a free energy change of 500 cal./mole.

B. In the Presence of Acids

The mildest type of reaction of the sugars induced by acids is the interconversion between α- and β-isomers or between ring isomers. This type of change has been discussed above under the general subject of mutarotation. Dilute acids at room temperatures have little or no additional action on the sugars, but hot concentrated acids produce profound changes.

The action of acids is that of dehydration. The dehydration may take place by the formation of anhydro rings or of double bonds. The configuration of altrose favors anhydro formation, and the 1,6-anhydroaltropyranose is formed by a brief treatment of the sugar with boiling dilute acids (see under Anhydro sugars). Stronger acids produce furfural, 5-methylfurfural, and 5-hydroxymethylfurfural or levulinic acid from pentoses, 6-deoxyhexoses, and hexoses, respectively. (*60*) The formation of these materials, in particular furfural from the pentoses, proceeds so well that the reaction is used for their estimation (*61, 62*). Although for pentoses furfural is the relatively stable end-product, for hexoses the corresponding 5-hydroxymethylfurfural (I) undergoes further reaction with the formation of formic and levulinic acids (II) (*63*).

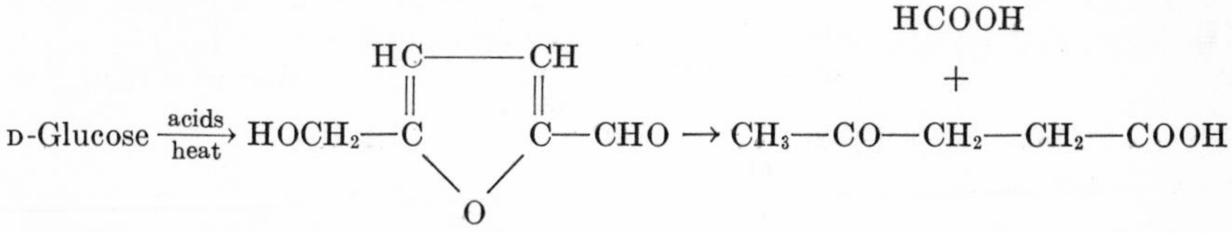
HCOOH
HC——CH
+
D-Glucose
acids
heat
HOCH₂—C
C—CHO → CH₃—CO—CH₂—CH₂—COOH
O

(I) (II)

Yields of hydroxymethylfurfural as high as 54% and of levulinic acid as high as 69 to 79% have been reported by the use of sucrose as the initial

57. K. J. Pedersen, *J. Phys. Chem.* **38,** 581 (1934).

58. C. G. Swain, *J. Am. Chem. Soc.* **72,** 4578 (1950).

59. H. M. Huffman and S. W. Fox, *J. Am. Chem. Soc.* **60,** 1400 (1938).

60. F. H. Newth, *Advances in Carbohydrate Chem.* **6,** 83 (1951).

61. W. E. Stone and B. Tollens, *Ann.* **249,** 227 (1888).

62. C. A. Browne and F. W. Zerban, "Sugar Analysis," p. 904. Wiley, New York, 1941.

63. W. Alberda van Ekenstein and J. J. Blanksma, *Chem. Weekblad* **6,** 717 (1909); **7,** 387 (1910).

material (*64, 65*). Levulinic acid has been prepared commercially from starch by the Moyer patent (*66*) and from wood hydrolyzates. Its ester, salts, and derivatives such as the α- and β-angelica lactones (III, IV) have considerable commercial interest.

(III) (IV)

Ketohexoses react with acids much more rapidly than aldohexoses and, hence, give better yields of 5-hydroxymethylfurfural. The reaction proceeds at an appreciable rate in aqueous solutions of fructose, and even glucose, at 100 to 150° without added acids. Since furfurals readily undergo further reactions with the formation of brown-colored products, it is probable that many of the brown colors produced in food processing and in autoclaved solutions result from the intermediary formation of furfurals (*60*). (See also p. 446). When concentrated hydrochloric or hydrobromic acid is used, the corresponding 5-halogenomethylfurfural is produced.

The enediol (V), as in the alkaline rearrangements, is a likely intermediate. The great difference in the rate of conversion of glucose and fructose to

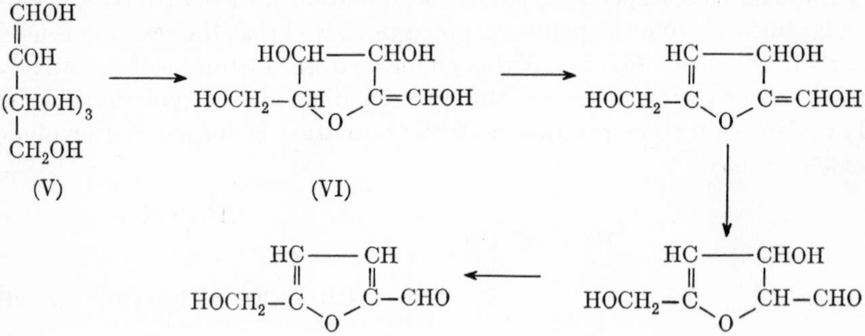

(V) (VI) (I)

hydroxymethylfurfural (I) would, according to this mechanism, indicate that the formation of the enediol is the rate-determining step. Haworth and Jones (*64*) explain the ease of reaction of fructose as a direct conversion of fructofuranose (the ring form) to the anhydro enol (VI), whereas glucose proceeds through the intermediary of the enediol (V). This mechanism is supported by the ease of conversion to furfurals of compounds with 2,5-anhydro rings (*67*).

64. W. N. Haworth and W. G. M. Jones, *J. Chem. Soc.* p. 667 (1944).
65. L. F. Wiggins, *Advances in Carbohydrate Chem.* **4**, 306 (1949).
66. W. W. Moyer, *U. S. Patent* 2,270,328 (January 20, 1942).
67. M. Cifonelli, J. A. Cifonelli, R. Montgomery, and F. Smith, *J. Am. Chem. Soc.* **77**, 121 (1955).

On the other hand, mechanisms differing from the above in the order of dehydration have been proposed by Hurd and Isenhour, by Isbell (*68*), and by Wolfrom, Schuetz, and Cavalieri (*69*). The mechanism of the latter involves in the first two dehydrations the production of α,β double bonds in a manner generally characteristic of β-hydroxy carbonyl compounds. To be noted also is the apparent greater ease of dehydration (indicated by the Dische diphenylamine test, presumably a measure of the hydroxylevulinic aldehyde formed) of arabinal and xylal as compared to 2-deoxyribose (*70*), although the former are known to have pyranose rings.

According to Pummerer and Gump (*71*), levulinic acid is formed as a result of the following series of reactions:

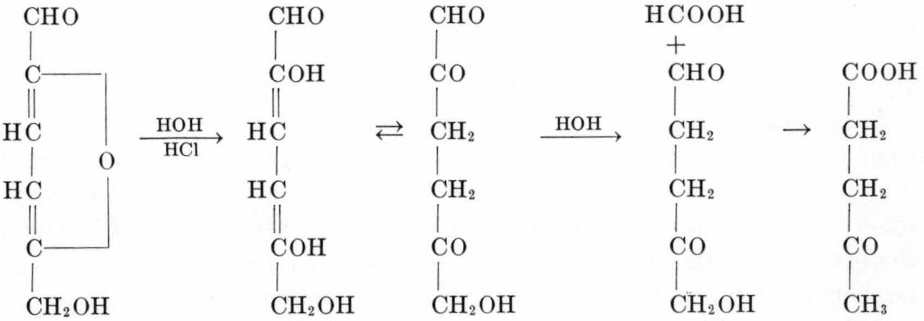
CHO
C
HC
HC
C
CH₂OH
O
HOH
HCl
CHO
COH
HC
HC
COH
CH₂OH
⇄
CHO
CO
CH₂
CH₂
CO
CH₂OH
HOH
HCOOH
+
CHO
CH₂
CH₂
CO
CH₂OH
→
COOH
CH₂
CH₂
CO
CH₃

The first step, ring opening, is a characteristic reaction of furan derivatives. The final step is an intermolecular oxidation-reduction reaction. Evidence for this mechanism (*71*) is given by the isolation under similar conditions of the acetal derivative of the intermediate five-carbon keto aldehyde, and by the high yield of levulinic acid produced from it by the action of acids. Yields as high as 80 % of levulinic acid have been obtained from 5-hydroxymethylfurfural. Furthermore, radioactive formic acid is derived by this reaction from D-glucose-1-C^{14} whereas the accompanying levulinic acid is devoid of activity (*72*).

Acids also catalyze the condensation of two sugar molecules to form disaccharides and products (oligosaccharides) of a greater degree of polymerization. In the presence of alcohols, the condensation takes place with formation of the glycosides of the alcohols. A true equilibrium is approached and condensation is favored by a high concentration of the reactants. Condensa-

68. See H. S. Isbell, *J. Research Natl. Bur. Standards* **32,** 45 (1944).

69. M. L. Wolfrom, R. D. Schuetz, and L. F. Cavalieri, *J. Am. Chem. Soc.* **70,** 514 (1948); **71,** 3518 (1949).

70. R. E. Deriaz, M. Stacey, E. G. Teece, and L. F. Wiggins, *J. Chem. Soc.* p. 1222 (1949).

71. R. Pummerer and W. Gump, *Ber.* **56,** 999 (1923); R. Pummerer, O. Guyot, and L. Birkofer, *Ber.* **68,** 480 (1935).

72. J. C. Sowden, *J. Am. Chem. Soc.* **71,** 3568 (1949).

tion takes place preferentially between the primary hydroxyl group of one molecule and the reducing group of another molecule, but small amounts of the products from the condensation of the reducing group with most of the secondary hydroxyls have been isolated (*73*). This process is known as "reversion." Combined with carbon chromatography, it is suitable for the

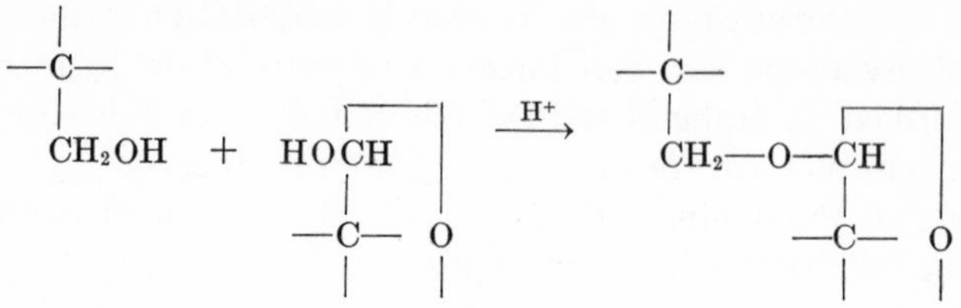
H+

preparation of gentiobiose and "isomaltose" (see under Isomaltose).

C. In the Presence of Alkalies*

Although the sugars exhibit moderate stability to acids, particularly at room temperature, they are profoundly affected (*74*) by alkalies even under very mild conditions. Contrary to what might be expected, the sugars exhibit their maximum stability at acid conditions rather than at pH 7. Thus, the optimal pH for the stability of D-fructose (*75*) and for D-glucose (*76*) lies between pH 3 and 4. When methylglyoxal production is used as a measure of the stability, the optimal pH is around 1 (*77*).

The action of alkalies follows three general courses: isomerizations mainly at the reducing end of the molecule, fragmentation into substances that have fewer carbon atoms than the original sugar, and internal oxidations and reductions.

The simplest isomerization reaction of the reducing sugars is the Lobry de Bruyn and Alberda van Ekenstein transformation (*78*). Thus, when glucose is treated with dilute alkalies at room temperature, the optical rotation decreases, and from the products of reaction, glucose, mannose, and fructose can be separated. The treatment of sugars with alkalies has considerable value for preparatory purposes, particularly for obtaining ketoses.

* Prepared by Mary Grace Blair.

73. A. Thompson, K. Anno, M. L. Wolfrom, and M. Inatome, *J. Am. Chem. Soc.* **76,** 1309 (1954); J. C. Sowden and A. S. Spriggs, *ibid.* **78,** 2503 (1956); J. H. Pazur and T. Budovich, *ibid.* **78,** 1885 (1956).

74. For summary see W. L. Evans, *Chem. Revs.* **31,** 537 (1942); **6,** 281 (1929).

75. J. A. Mathews and R. F. Jackson, *Bur. Standards J. Research* **11,** 619 (1933).

76. W. Kröner and H. Kothe, *Ind. Eng. Chem.* **31,** 248 (1939); E. J. McDonald, *J. Research Natl. Bur. Standards* **45,** 200 (1950).

77. C. Enders, *Biochem. Z.* **312,** 349 (1942).

78. C. A. Lobry de Bruyn and W. Alberda van Ekenstein, *Rec. trav. chim.* **14,** 156, 203 (1895); **15,** 92 (1896); **16,** 241, 257, 262, 274, 282 (1897); **18,** 147 (1899); **19,** 1 (1900); W. Alberda van Ekenstein and J. J. Blanksma, *ibid.* **27,** 1 (1908).

Disaccharides undergo similar isomerizations, also useful for the preparation of the ketoses (p. 481), but some cleavage of the glycosidic linkage occurs (*79*).

On the basis of the usual methods of analysis, which involve the determination of reducing sugars, ketoses, and mannose, Wolfrom and Lewis (*80*) concluded that very few side reactions take place if the glucose is treated with lime water saturated at 35°C. After about five days, the equilibrated mixture had the following composition:

	Per cent
Glucose	63.5
"Fructose" (ketoses)	31.0
Mannose	2.5
Other substances (probably saccharinic acids)	3

However, analyses by isotopic dilution (*81*) reveal that with 0.035 *N* sodium hydroxide at 35° (hence, presumably also with lime water) more deep-seated changes are slowly occurring, which ordinarily are undetected. A neutral nonfermentable fraction, which is predominantly ketose, is accumulating. The apparent equilibrium reached under mild conditions is probably dependent upon the neutralization of the original alkali by the acidic products formed.

For the interpretation of the mechanism of the Lobry de Bruyn-Alberda van Ekenstein transformation, the formation of an intermediate enediol usually is postulated. In the formation of the double bond, the asymmetry of carbon atom 2 is destroyed, and the two epimeric aldoses and the corresponding ketose will be in equilibrium.

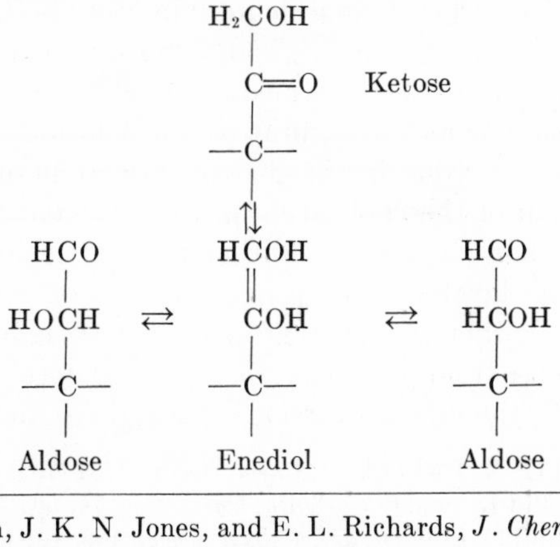
H2COH
C=O
Ketose
HCO
HOCH
HCOH
COH
HCO
HCOH
Aldose
Enediol
Aldose

79. See L. Hough, J. K. N. Jones, and E. L. Richards, *J. Chem. Soc.* p. 295 (1954); W. M. Corbett and J. Kenner, *ibid.* p. 1789 (1954).

80. M. L. Wolfrom and W. L. Lewis, *J. Am. Chem. Soc.* **50**, 837 (1928).

81. J. C. Sowden and R. Schaffer, *J. Am. Chem. Soc.* **74**, 499 (1952).

The enediol shown in the illustration would be expected to exist in ionic form in an alkaline solution. Each of the enol ions should be stabilized as a resonance hybrid:

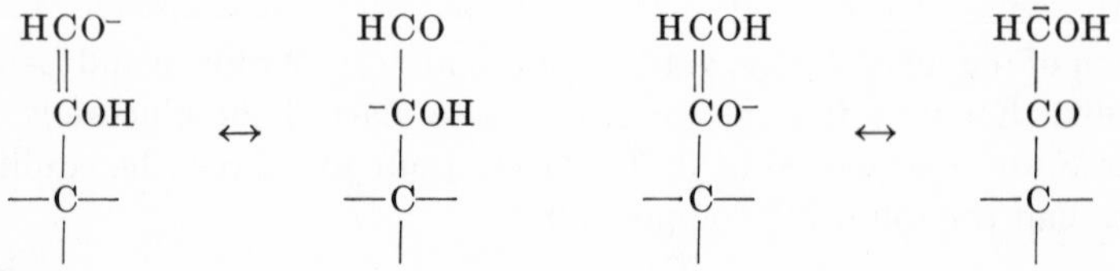

As would be expected from this mechanism, 2,3,4,6-tetra-*O*-methylglucose gives only 2,3,4,6-tetra-*O*-methylmannose when treated with alkali (saturated lime solutions). The same equilibrium point is reached from tetra-*O*-methylmannose (*80*). In this instance, ketose formation is precluded because of the absence of an ionizable hydrogen atom on carbon 2

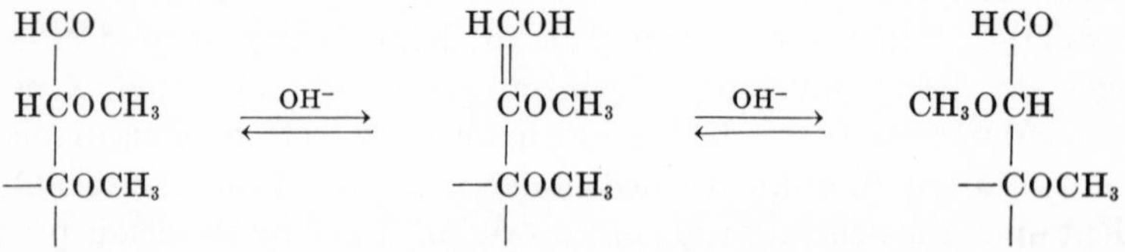

of the enol form. However, the enolic methoxyl group is relatively unstable, and the 1-*O*-methyl group attached to fructose is removed under similar conditions (*82*).

The ready removal of the hydrogen atom next to the carbonyl group is consistent with the expected activities of such atoms in alkaline solutions, as in the aldol condensations. Experimental evidence is provided by the observation that one carbon-bound deuterium atom is formed when tetra-*O*-methylglucose (*45*) or glucose (*83*) is dissolved in alkaline heavy water.

Further confirmation of the intermediary enediol has been obtained by studies of the rearrangement in saturated lime solutions of 1-deuterio-glucose (*84*) made by the reduction of gluconic γ-lactone in D_2O.

By a continuation of the enolization process, the enediol grouping may move along the carbon chain and additional isomerizations are possible.

Epimerization at the third carbon or formation of ketoses that have a carbonyl group at carbon 3 may take place. These reactions explain the formation of D-psicose from D-glucose (*85*), D-*gluco*-heptulose from D-*glycero*-D-*gala*-heptose (*86*), the interconversions of D-sorbose and D-galactose (*78*),

82. J. Kenner and G. N. Richards, *J. Chem. Soc.* p. 1784 (1954).
83. J. C. Sowden and R. Schaffer, *J. Am. Chem. Soc.* **74,** 505 (1952).
84. Y. J. Topper and D. Stetten, Jr., *J. Biol. Chem.* **189,** 191 (1951).
85. L. Hough, J. K. N. Jones, and E. L. Richards, *J. Chem. Soc.* p. 2005 (1953).
86. E. M. Montgomery and C. S. Hudson, *J. Am. Chem. Soc.* **61,** 1654 (1939).

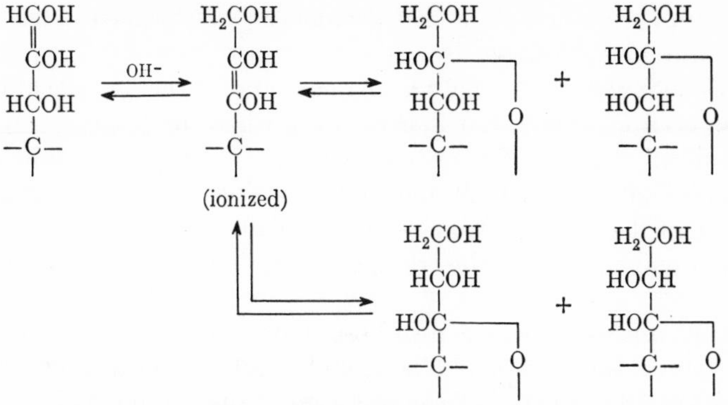
HCOH
COH
HCOH
OH-
H2COH
COH
(ionized)
HOC
HOCH
O
+

and the occurrence of allitol among the products of the electrolytic reduction of D-glucose in mildly alkaline solution (*87*). Lobry de Bruyn and Alberda van Ekenstein (*78*) considered that they had obtained a nearly pure 3-ketose, which they called galtose, from the action of lead hydroxide on galactose, and the same product in lower purity from the action of other bases. A corresponding fraction, glutose, from glucose could not be freed completely from contaminants, but it was obtained in supposedly high purity from the action of lead hydroxide on fructose. Glutose was described as the acid-labile nonfermentable component of the isomerization mixture (contrary to later work, psicose was considered to be fermentable) and was said to be identical with the corresponding fraction of sugar-cane molasses.

Often, later workers have used the term glutose as synonymous with the nonfermentable reducing fraction of the alkali-isomerization mixture from D-glucose or molasses. Much of the nonfermentable reducing fraction of sugar-cane molasses was shown later to be composed of complex substances from a browning (Maillard) reaction (Chapter VIII) involving the interaction of sugars and amino acids (*88*). A trace of psicose from distillery "slop" has been reported (*89*).

On the other hand, the product from glucose is an exceedingly complex mixture, the composition of which varies with the conditions of treatment. D-Psicose (from treatment with ammonia)(*85*) and (DL + D)-sorbose (from treatment with a strong base resin) (*90*) have been identified definitely in the mixture. D-Glucose is readily converted to D-fructose. From the latter has been isolated after treatment with potassium hydroxide (DL + D)-sor-

87. M. L. Wolfrom, B. W. Lew, and R. M. Goepp, Jr., *J. Am. Chem. Soc.* **68,** 1443 (1946).

88. W. W. Binkley and M. L. Wolfrom, *J. Am. Chem. Soc.* **72,** 4778 (1950); C. Erb and F. W. Zerban, *Ind. Eng. Chem.* **39,** 1597 (1947).

89. F. W. Zerban and L. Sattler, *Ind. Eng. Chem.* **34,** 1180 (1942).

90. M. G. Blair and J. C. Sowden, *J. Am. Chem. Soc.* **77,** 3323 (1955).

bose and (DL + D or L)-allose (*91*). Evidence was obtained indicating the presence of D- and L-psicose also.

In any one investigation, only a small amount of the unfermentable material has been identified, but it is evident, when the fragmentary results are assembled, that any hexose may be expected from any other hexose among the products under suitable conditions of treatment by alkali. For completion of the sequence from D-glucose to all D- and L-hexoses, only the isolation of one member of the trio L-glucose, L-mannose, and L-fructose is needed.

The mechanisms by which D-sorbose and L-sugars are formed are not known. Conceivably 3,4- and 4,5-enediols might be formed. On the other hand, the possibility exists of the cleavage of the carbon chain through a reversed aldol condensation. If a hexose was cleaved to two glyceraldehyde molecules, they would be expected partially to isomerize immediately to dihydroxyacetone. A very rapid aldol condensation of glyceraldehyde and dihydroxyacetone occurs (p. 113) with the formation of fructose and sorbose. These ketohexoses have a *trans* arrangement of the hydroxyls at the new asymmetric centers (*92*, *93*).

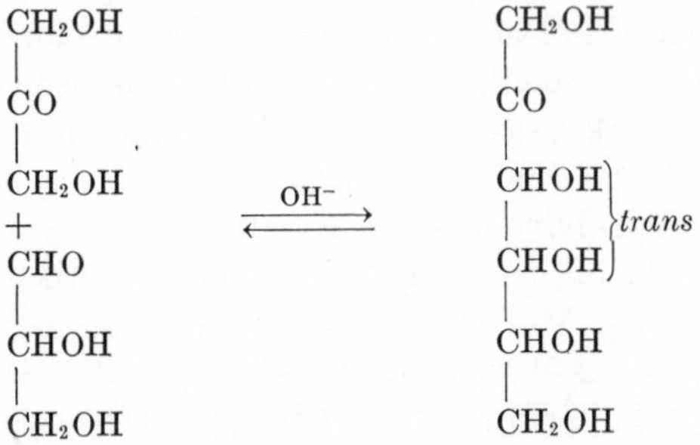
CH₂OH
CO
CH₂OH
+
CHO
CHOH
CH₂OH
OH⁻
CH₂OH
CO
CHOH
trans
CHOH
CHOH
CH₂OH

In the reaction mixtures of the action of alkali on hexoses, small amounts of methylglyoxal (pyruvic aldehyde) and much lactic acid appear; this is proof that the molecule is sensitive to a cleavage of some kind at the center of the chain. These products also occur in the alkali-treated solutions of trioses, along with traces of acetol, lactic aldehyde, and pyruvic acid (*74*, *93*). However, the trioses so rapidly condense to sugars that the appearance of common reaction products does not establish the sequence of reactions. If trioses deliberately are added to an alkaline hexose solution

91. M. L. Wolfrom and J. N. Schumacher, *J. Am. Chem. Soc.* **77**, 3318 (1955).

92. H. O. L. Fischer and E. Baer, *Helv. Chim. Acta* **19**, 519 (1936); W. G. Berl and C. E. Feazel, *J. Am. Chem. Soc.* **73**, 2054 (1951).

93. E. Waldmann and V. Prey, *Monatsh.* **82**, 856 (1951); **83**, 65 (1952); V. Prey, E. Waldmann, H. Berbalk, and F. Ludwig, *ibid.* **84**, 551 (1953); V. Prey, E. Waldmann, H. Berbalk, and F. Sommer, *ibid.* **85**, 1186 (1954).

to check on proposed procedures of isolation, they rapidly disappear (*93*). (See also Acrose, Chapter II).

Similar cleavages between carbons 1 and 2 to give formaldehyde and an aldopentose or between carbons 2 and 3 to give glycolaldehyde and a tetrose should not be excluded from consideration, although the bulk of the sugar fraction is hexose. Compounds having one or two carbon atoms are found (formic and acetic acids), but these are also products of the trioses. The quantities produced from hexoses and from trioses are similarly affected by changes in temperature and in concentration of alkali (*74*). Schmidt (*94*) has offered a theoretical argument for cleavage of hexoses mostly to trioses, which assumes that in the 1,2-enediol the 3–4 bond is weakened by the presence of the double bond.

If fragmentation and recombination of trioses is occurring during the alkaline isomerization of the hexoses, branched-chain hexoses (not yet isolated) are also to be expected. Dihydroxyacetone undergoes aldol condensation with itself under the influence of dilute sodium hydroxide to, among other products, "dendroketose" (*95*).

In addition to the isomerizations to other sugars, internal oxidations and reductions and migrations of groups occur (see below) and make impossible the establishment of a true equilibrium. In the presence of excess alkali the reaction eventually proceeds almost completely to nonreducing substances. In carbonate buffer at pH 10 and at 100°, reducing power is lost very rapidly and the reaction is reported to be first-order with respect to both sugar and hydroxyl-ion concentrations (*96*).

Some workers have reported a cation dependence and others an independence. Any differences, if noted, were attributed usually to the strength of the base. Thus, Lobry de Bruyn and Alberda van Ekenstein (*78*) reported the reaction products of lead hydroxide to be different from those of numerous other bases which they studied. Notably, with lead hydroxide the ketose of the 1,2-enediol "equilibrium" was missing. This was attributed to its very rapid conversion to the supposed "3-ketose." Kusin (*97*) recorded a similar observation with calcium hydroxide as compared to sodium hydroxide, but he believed the ketose was never formed. Under the conditions studied, lime acting on glucose gave mannose but no detectable amounts of fructose, whereas sodium hydroxide gave a measurable amount of fructose but only a trace of mannose. Sowden and Schaffer (*81*) found no differences in the initial "mutarotation" of D-mannose in the presence of 0.035 *N* sodium and calcium hydroxides at 35°, but differences in the direction of

94. O. Schmidt, *Chem. Revs.* **17**, 137 (1935).

95. L. M. Utkin, *Doklady Akad. Nauk S.S.S.R.*, **67**, 301 (1949); *Chem. Abstr.* **44**, 3910 (1950).

96. L. J. Heidt and C. M. Colman, *J. Am. Chem. Soc.* **74**, 4711 (1952).

97. A. Kusin, *Ber.* **69**, 1041 (1936).

"mutarotation" were observed for 0.5 N solutions. They obtained 29% D-fructose from D-glucose and 20% from D-mannose with 0.035 N sodium hydroxide at 35°. Gottfried and Benjamin (*98*), working at high temperatures, could find no important difference in the glucose, fructose, mannose "equilibrium" with a variety of bases: sodium hydroxide, sodium carbonate, calcium hydroxide, magnesium hydroxide, trisodium phosphate, and sodium sulfite. They obtained a maximum conversion of D-glucose to true D-fructose (as fermentable ketose) of about 21%, although the apparent ketose content was as high as 31%.

Lactic acid occurs amongst the products of the action of alkali on hexoses. From 1 mole of D-glucose, treated at 25°C. with benzyltrimethylammonium hydroxide, Evans reported the production of 1.2 moles of racemic lactic acid (60% of a theory of 2 moles per mole hexose). The substance apparently can be obtained by the action of alkali on any sugar (inclusive of trioses, pentoses, disaccharides, etc.) (*99*). Its preparation from sucrose under conditions of high temperature and pressure has been extensively studied from the viewpoint of potential industrial application. Lactic acid may be considered as the saccharinic acid (see below) related to glyceraldehyde and may arise from the rearrangement of a triose fragment.

Internal oxidations and reductions and migrations of groups occur which result also in the formation of a group of saccharinic acids isomeric with the sugars, and the corresponding lactones (saccharins). After Peligot (1839) and other workers had isolated acidic materials from among the products of the action of alkalies on glucose, Scheibler and Kiliani (*100*, *101*) identified one of the products, saccharinic acid, as an isomer of D-glucose with the empirical formula $C_6H_{12}O_6$. The saccharinic acid loses a molecule of water to form saccharin. The formulas of these substances resulting from the researches of Scheibler and Kiliani are shown below.

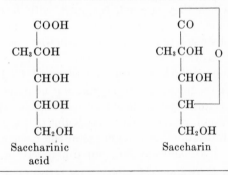

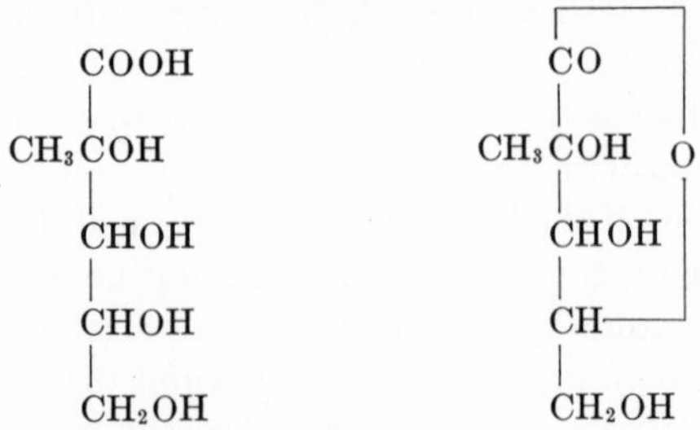
COOH
CH₃COH
CHOH
CHOH
CH₂OH
CO
CH₃COH
O
CHOH
CH
CH₂OH

Saccharinic acid   Saccharin

98. J. B. Gottfried and D. G. Benjamin, *Ind. Eng. Chem.* **44,** 141 (1952).

99. R. Montgomery, "The Chemical Production of Lactic Acid from Sugars," Scientific Report Series, No. 11. Sugar Research Foundation, New York, 1949.

100. C. Scheibler, *Ber.* **13,** 2212 (1880).

101. H. Kiliani, *Ber.* **15,** 701, 2953 (1882).

The branched-chain structure of saccharinic acid is demonstrated by the reduction of the acid by hydrogen iodide (and phosphorus) to 2-methylpentanoic acid:

$$CH_3{-}CH_2{-}CH_2{-}\overset{\overset{\displaystyle CH_3}{|}}{C}H{-}COOH$$

Nitric acid oxidizes the saccharinic acid to a dibasic acid which by reduction with hydrogen iodide is converted to 2-methylglutaric acid:

$$CH_2OH{-}CHOH{-}CHOH{-}\underset{\underset{\displaystyle OH}{|}}{\overset{\overset{\displaystyle CH_3}{|}}{C}}{-}COOH \xrightarrow{HNO_3}$$

$$COOH{-}CHOH{-}CHOH{-}\underset{\underset{\displaystyle OH}{|}}{\overset{\overset{\displaystyle CH_3}{|}}{C}}{-}COOH \xrightarrow[P]{HI}$$

$$COOH{-}CH_2{-}CH_2{-}\overset{\overset{\displaystyle CH_3}{|}}{C}H{-}COOH$$

The presence of the new carboxyl group in the terminal position rather than in the 2-position proves that the primary alcohol group is located at the terminal carbon atom and the methyl group is at carbon atom 2.

Cuisinier found among the products of the action of lime on maltose and lactose a substance with the formula $C_6H_{12}O_6$ which was termed isosaccharinic acid. Kiliani prepared the same material from galactose. The corresponding lactone was termed isosaccharin. As a result of the work of Kiliani (*102*) the isosaccharinic acids may be formulated as:

$$CH_2OH{-}CHOH{-}CH_2{-}\overset{\overset{\displaystyle CH_2OH}{|}}{C}OH{-}COOH$$

Only two D- and two L-stereoisomers of such a structure are possible, for only the penultimate ("D,L") carbon atom and carbon atom 2 are asymmetric. The isomers in the D-series are distinguished as α-isosaccharinic acid and β-isosaccharinic acid according to the configuration of carbon atom 2.

Still a third type of product was isolated by Kiliani (*103*) from the products of the action of alkalies on galactose and lactose. This material, isomeric

102. H. Kiliani, *Ber.* **18**, 2514 (1885).
103. H. Kiliani and H. Naegell, *Ber.* **35**, 3528 (1902).

with saccharinic acid, was termed metasaccharinic acid and is a 3-deoxy-aldohexonic acid:

$$CH_2OH—CHOH—CHOH—CH_2—CHOH—COOH$$

Metasaccharinic acid

Two metasaccharinic acids have been obtained from glucose. These have retained the original configuration of the carbon atoms at 4 and 5, since they give 2-deoxy-D-ribose upon degradation and since one is identical with the synthetic 3-deoxy-D-*arabino*-hexonic acid (*104*, *105*). (See Chapter II, also.)

The mechanism of the formation of the saccharinic acids and their derivatives remains unclear. Nef has suggested that the reaction proceeds through the diketone produced by removal of a molecule of water. This suggestion was combined by Isbell (*68*) with current concepts of the benzilic acid rearrangement. Benzilic acid rearrangements of the diketones would produce the saccharinic acids, the nature of the acid being determined by the position of dehydration.

Dehydration appears to be facilitated by the presence of a substituent methoxy or glycosyl group (*106*). The distribution of activity in the metasaccharinic acid from D-galactose-1-C^{14} is in agreement with the Nef-Isbell mechanism (*107*). However, a distribution of C^{14} between carbon atom 2 and the methyl group (in the ratio of 3:2) found in the saccharinic acid from D-mannose-1-C^{14} demands another or additional explanation. A recombination of fragments seems necessary to account for the appearance of C^{14} at the tertiary position (*107*).

Kenner and Richards (*82*) have found that the relative yields of metasaccharinic and isosaccharinic acids from glucose increase at the expense of saccharinic acid as the concentration of alkali is increased. This is interpreted on the basis of the necessity of doubly charged ions as intermediates in the formation of the meta and iso acids and of singly charged ions in the saccharinic acid formation. High concentrations of alkali would favor the formation of doubly charged ions. Accompanying small amounts of 2,4-dihydroxybutyric acid could have been formed by a "meta" rearrangement of a tetrose formed by cleavage of glucose at the 2,3-position.

Nef (*108*) after a long series of researches described the still more complicated mixture obtained in the presence of oxidizing agents as a "furchtbares

104. J. C. Sowden, *J. Am. Chem. Soc.* **76,** 3541 (1954).

105. G. N. Richards, *ibid.* **76,** 3277, 3638 (1954).

106. J. Kenner and G. N. Richards, *J. Chem. Soc.* p. 278 (1954); W. M. Corbett and J. Kenner, *ibid.* p. 1431 (1955).

107. J. C. Sowden and D. J. Kuenne, *J. Am. Chem. Soc.* **75,** 2788 (1953).

108. J. U. Nef, *Ann.* **357,** 294 (1907); **376,** 1 (1910); **403,** 204 (1913).

Gemisch," but it would seem that the term could be applied aptly to the mixture obtained without the additional complication of oxidative reactions. Even a methylcyclopentenolone was obtained in a yield of 1 to 2% by the action of 1.8% sodium hydroxide on galactose at 100° (*109*).

As is evident from the above discussion, the action of alkalies on the sugars is a complicated and still little understood process in spite of the extensive and excellent work by Nef, Evans, and many other workers. Very dilute alkalies catalyze the α,β and presumably the furanose-pyranose conversions. In greater amounts, they bring about isomerization between the epimeric aldoses and the corresponding ketoses, probably through the formation of a 1,2-enediol. Higher concentrations of alkalies bring about conversions between all of the various sugars of the same chain length, probably partially as a result of the formation of 2,3- and 3,4-enediols and partially as a result of the recombination of the cleavage fragments of the carbon chain. Rearrangements occur in which saccharinic acids are formed from the original sugars and from their isomerization and cleavage products (*109a*). Finally, as shown by Nef, polymerization takes place with the formation of resins and "polysaccharides" of unknown composition.

D. Behavior of the Sugars with Short Carbon Chains

The foregoing discussions of the sugars in solution mainly was devoted to the hexoses. The aldopentoses and the higher-carbon sugars may be expected to exhibit similar reactions because they can form pyranose and furanose rings and enediols similar to those for the hexoses. As the number of carbon atoms decreases, pyranose and finally furanose rings become impossible. Thus, the ketopentoses and the aldotetroses can form only furanose rings; the trioses and glycolaldehyde cannot form even a furanose ring. Ring formation appears to take place when possible as is demonstrated by the mutarotation (*110*) of crystalline D-threose ($[\alpha]_D$ + 29.1° → + 19.6°) and by the normal molecular weight of erythrose in solution (*111*). The lower sugars with two and three carbon atoms form dimers easily; for some of the substances both the monomeric and the dimeric forms have been isolated (*112*). The dimers of glycolaldehyde and of glyceraldehyde have

109. T. Enkvist, *Acta Chem. Scand.* **8,** 51 (1954).

109a. See also: J. W. Green, *J. Am. Chem. Soc.* **78,** 1894 (1956); R. L. Whistler and W. M. Corbett, *ibid.* **78,** 1003 (1956); J. C. Sowden, *Advances in Carbohydrate Chem.* (in press).

110. W. Freudenberg, *Ber.* **65,** 168 (1932).

111. V. Deulofeu, *J. Chem. Soc.* p. 2973 (1932).

112. For example, see results for dihydroxyacetone as reported by H. O. L. Fischer and H. Mildbrand, *Ber.* **57,** 707 (1924).

been formulated (*113*) as the products of an extramolecular acetal formation analogous to the formation of pyranose and furanose rings by the higher sugars:

$$
\begin{array}{ccc}
\text{H}_2\text{C}-\text{CHO} & & \text{H}_2\text{C}-\text{CH(OH)} \\
| & & |\quad| \\
\text{OH OH} & \rightleftharpoons & \text{O}\quad\text{O} \\
| & & |\quad| \\
\text{OHC}-\text{CH}_2 & & \text{(HO)HC}-\text{CH}_2
\end{array}
$$

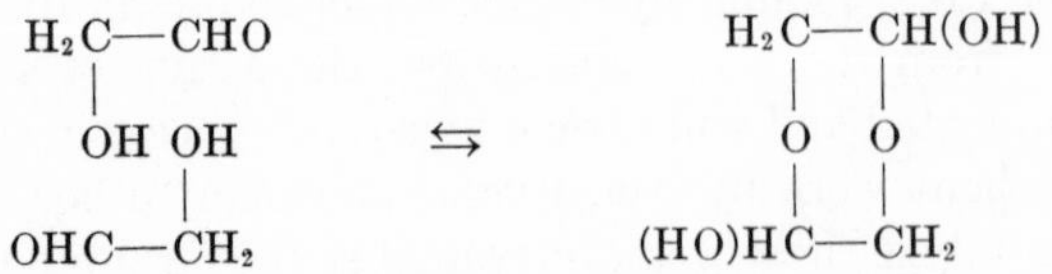

In conformity with the conversion of glucose to mannose and fructose, glyceraldehyde is converted partially to dihydroxyacetone in the presence of pyridine or dilute alkalies (*114*).

$$
\begin{array}{ccc}
\text{CHO} & & \text{CH}_2\text{OH} \\
| & & | \\
\text{CHOH} & \xrightleftharpoons{\text{OH}^-} & \text{CO} \\
| & & | \\
\text{CH}_2\text{OH} & & \text{CH}_2\text{OH}
\end{array}
$$

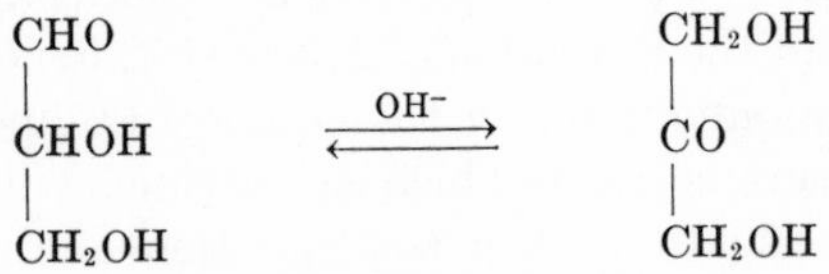

At 25°C. to 50°C., potassium hydroxide (0.2 to 6 N) converts glyceraldehyde to formic, acetic, and lactic acids (*115*).

10. OPTICAL SUPERPOSITION, THE ISOROTATION RULES, AND THE INFLUENCE OF STRUCTURE ON OPTICAL ROTATION

In optically active compounds that have more than one asymmetric center, the rotation of each compound might be considered as the sum of the partial rotations of the asymmetric centers. Thus, for the isomeric compounds:

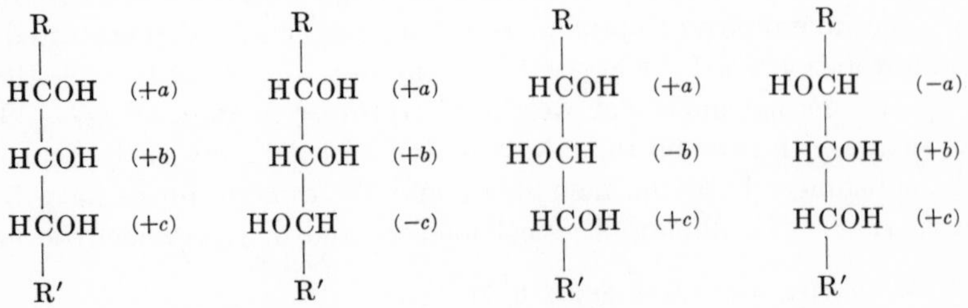

$$
\begin{array}{cccc}
\text{R} & \text{R} & \text{R} & \text{R} \\
| & | & | & | \\
\text{HCOH}\ (+a) & \text{HCOH}\ (+a) & \text{HCOH}\ (+a) & \text{HOCH}\ (-a) \\
| & | & | & | \\
\text{HCOH}\ (+b) & \text{HCOH}\ (+b) & \text{HOCH}\ (-b) & \text{HCOH}\ (+b) \\
| & | & | & | \\
\text{HCOH}\ (+c) & \text{HOCH}\ (-c) & \text{HCOH}\ (+c) & \text{HCOH}\ (+c) \\
| & | & | & | \\
\text{R}' & \text{R}' & \text{R}' & \text{R}' \\
\text{(I)} & \text{(II)} & \text{(III)} & \text{(IV)}
\end{array}
$$

113. M. Bergmann and A. Miekeley, *Ber.* **62,** 2297 (1929); **64,** 802 (1931); R. K. Summerbell and L. K. Rochen, *J. Am. Chem. Soc.* **63,** 3241 (1941); E. Baer and H. O. L. Fischer, *J. Biol. Chem.* **150,** 213 (1943); A. Wohl and C. Neuberg, *Ber.* **33,** 3095 (1900).

114. H. O. L. Fischer, C. Taube, and E. Baer, *Ber.* **60,** 480 (1927).

115. W. L. Evans and H. B. Hass, *J. Am. Chem. Soc.* **48,** 2703 (1926).

the partial rotations contributed by the individual asymmetric carbon atoms might be represented as $\pm a$, b, and c. If in all of the above stereoisomers, the rotatory contribution of each asymmetric center remains the same and differs only in sign according to its configuration, the sum of the rotations of compounds (II), (III), and (IV) should be equal to that of the compound (I). Thus,

For compound (I), the rotation is $+ a + b + c$
For compound (II), the rotation is $+ a + b - c$
For compound (III), the rotation is $+ a - b + c$
For compound (IV), the rotation is $- a + b + c$

Sum (II + III + IV) is $(+ a + b + c)$

The hypothesis of the additive nature of the rotatory contributions of the individual asymmetric centers of steroisomers in making up the total rotation of each isomer was formulated by van't Hoff and has been known as the "principle of optical superposition." In its full generalization as applied to all substances, the hypothesis of optical superposition is definitely unsound and thus it is not a "principle"; nevertheless, it has been shown by Hudson *(116)* that the hypothesis holds in first approximation for a large number of carbohydrates, and the approximation is sufficiently close to permit valuable inferences concerning structure and configuration to be drawn from comparisons of the rotations of carbohydrates through the application of his Isorotation Rules.

According to these rules, the rotation of a glycoside or other sugar derivative may be considered to be composed of two parts: A, the partial rotation of the anomeric carbon atom, and B, the rotatory contribution of the other active centers. According to the configuration of the active centers, A and B may be positive or negative.

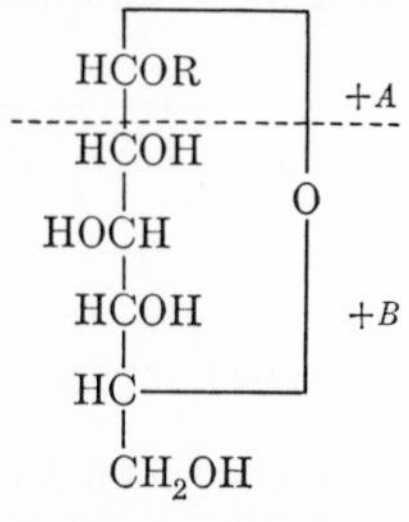
HCOR
+A
HCOH
O
HOCH
HCOH
+B
HC
CH2OH

Alkyl α-D-glucoside
$[M]_\alpha = + A + B$

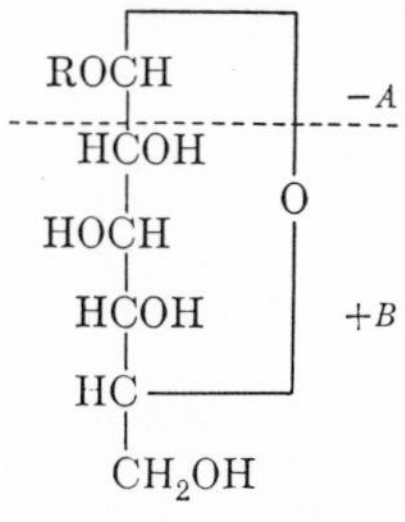
ROCH
−A
HCOH
O
HOCH
HCOH
+B
HC
CH2OH

Alkyl β-D-glucoside
$[M]_\beta = - A + B$

116. C. S. Hudson, *J. Am. Chem. Soc.* **31,** 66 (1909); see also F. J. Bates and Associates, *Natl. Bur. Standards Circ.* **C440,** 411 (1942).

The application of the optical superposition principle permits of the calculation of the partial rotations A and B. Thus, $M_\alpha - M_\beta = A + B + A - B = 2A$ and $M_\alpha + M_\beta = A + B - A + B = 2B$. Hence, the partial rotations may be obtained by adding the molecular rotations of anomers to give $2B$ and by subtracting the molecular rotation of the β-isomer from that of the α-isomer to give $2A$. The partial rotations are one-half of each of these sums and differences. As a result of the measurement of the rotation of many α-β pairs in the sugar series, Hudson was able to formulate the two Rules of Isorotation:

Rule 1: "The rotation of carbon 1 in the case of many substances of the sugar group is affected in only a minor degree by changes in the structure of the remainder of the molecule."

Rule 2: "Changes in the structure of carbon 1 in the case of many substances of the sugar group affect in only a minor degree the rotation of the remainder of the molecule."

According to the first rule, changes in the structure of a sugar or glycoside molecule at carbon atoms 2, 3, 4, 5, and 6 should have little influence on the partial rotation (A) of carbon atom 1. In Table V, the effects of substitutions in the pyranose ring of glucosides on the rotatory contribution of the anomeric carbon atom (A) are indicated. As a first approximation, the substitution of methyl groups at carbon atoms 2 and 3 and of large glucosyl groups at carbon atoms 4 and 6 appear to affect the rotation of carbon atom 1 only to a minor degree. Even a difference in ring structure has but little influence.

Although the first rule does not mention configurational changes, it is of interest to investigate the influence of variations in the configuration of the remaining carbon atoms on the rotatory contribution of carbon 1. For this purpose, the $2A$ values of a number of glycosides are given in Table VI. It will be noted that the $2A$ values for the upper four pairs of glycosides agree very well but that the values for the mannosides and rhamnosides differ

TABLE V

TEST OF RULE 1.—$2A$ VALUES FOR SUBSTITUTED GLUCOSIDES

Glucopyranoside		Molecular rotation		$2A$ $(M_\alpha - M_\beta)$
		α-isomer	β-isomer	
Methyl		30,860	−6,640	37,500
Methyl 2,3-di-O-methyl-		31,690	−8,130	39,800
Methyl 6-β-O-glucosyl-	(methyl gentiobiosides)	23,340	−12,800	36,100
Methyl 4-β-O-glucosyl-	(methyl cellobiosides)	34,490	−6,810	41,300
Ethyl (pyranosides)		31,700	−7,600	39,300
Ethyl (furanosides)		20,400	−17,900	38,300

TABLE VI

2*A* Values for Glycosides

Methyl glycosides of:	±2*A*
L-Arabinose	37,460
D-Galactose	38,220
D-Glucose	37,500
D-Gulose	39,390
D-Mannose	28,930
L-Rhamnose	28,140

appreciably from those for the other glycosides. The latter two pairs differ from the others in the configuration of *carbon 2* which is immediately adjacent to carbon atom 1. The observed differences probably are to be ascribed to interaction between the groups attached to carbon 2 and those at carbon 1. As is shown by the 2*A* values for glucosides, galactosides, and gulosides, configurational changes at carbon atoms more distant from carbon 1 than carbon 2 have only a secondary influence on the partial rotation of carbon 1. It would be expected that the unknown idosides, altrosides, and talosides (which have the same configuration for carbon atom 2 as mannose) would have 2*A* values similar to those for the mannosides, whereas the rotational differences for the allosides should be similar to those for the glucosides. The interaction between groups should become less as the temperature is increased. Actually at 80°C., the difference between the 2*A* values for mannose and glucose derivatives is much less (*117*) than at 20°C.

The second Rule of Isorotation requires for each sugar type that the total rotatory contribution (*B*) of all carbon atoms except that of the anomeric carbon atom (*A*) be independent of the structure of the groups attached to the latter. Data for testing this rule are given in Table VII by a comparison of the 2*B* values for glucose and the glucosides. For the aliphatic glucosides, there is good agreement between the various 2*B* values. But, as pointed out by several writers, the phenyl glucosides exhibit appreciably larger 2*B* values (*118*). The average 2*B* value for the aliphatic glucosides is 23,200 (B = 11,600) and for the aromatic glucosides is 32,200 (B = 16,100). Other sugars exhibit similar differences. These data prove the general validity of the second rule but indicate that the rule should be modified to allow for the differences between the *B* values for the aromatic and the aliphatic glycosides.

117. W. Kauzmann, *J. Am. Chem. Soc.* **64,** 1626 (1942).

118. E. F. and K. F. Armstrong, "The Carbohydrates," p. 41. Longmans, Green, New York, 1934; W. W. Pigman and H. S. Isbell, *J. Research Natl. Bur. Standards* **27,** 9 (1941). See also W. A. Bonner, M. J. Kubitshek, and R. W. Drisko, *J. Am. Chem. Soc.* **74,** 5082 (1952).

TABLE VII

TEST OF RULE 2.—2*B* VALUES FOR GLUCOSIDES

Glucoside	$2B$ ($M_\alpha + M_\beta$)
H (glucose)	23,600
Methyl	24,200
Ethyl	24,000
Propyl	22,700
Ethylene glycol	23,500
Allyl	19,700
Cyclohexyl	24,100
Benzyl	21,000
Phenyl	31,400
p-Nitrophenyl	33,700
p-Hydroxyphenyl	31,300

TABLE VIII

2*B* VALUES FOR GLUCOPYRANOSIDES AND GLUCOFURANOSIDES

	$[M]_D$	$2B$
α-D-Glucose	20,200	23,600
β-D-Glucose	3,400	
Ethyl α-glucofuranoside	20,400	2,500
Ethyl β-glucofuranoside	−17,900	
Ethyl α-glucopyranoside	31,700	24,100
Ethyl β-glucopyranoside	−7,600	

The second Rule of Isorotation has considerable value for the determination of the structure of the sugars. As mentioned elsewhere (p. 31), the structures of the glycosides can be determined by reliable methods, but the corresponding methods for the sugars are less trustworthy. However, if by application of the second rule the sugar is found to have the same *B* value as a glycoside of known structure, it usually may be assumed that the sugar has the same structure as the glycoside. As an example, the *B* value for the crystalline forms of glucose may be compared to those for the ethyl glucopyranosides and the ethyl glucofuranosides (Table VIII). The agreement of the 2*B* value for the crystalline forms of glucose with that for the ethyl glucopyranosides provides strong evidence that the known isomers of glucose are pyranose modifications.In the case of glucose, the pyranose structure also is confirmed by other methods (p. 33).

In a similar fashion, application of the Isorotation Rules led to the inference (*119*) that the biose constituent of the glycoside amygdalin is gentio-

119. C. S. Hudson, *J. Am. Chem. Soc.* **46,** 483 (1924).

biose; this structure was established shortly afterwards by chemical synthesis.

The calculation of the A and B values requires that the rotations of both the α- and β-isomers be known. However, a direct correlation between the molecular rotations of β-glucosides and the corresponding rotatory contributions (A) of the anomeric carbon atom has been shown. This correlation would be expected, for according to the Isorotation Principle, the molecular rotation of a β-glucoside is represented as $[M]_\beta = -A + B$; $[M]_\beta$ should vary directly with A since B is a constant. It is possible then to investigate the effect of the structure of the aglycon group of a glucoside on the partial rotation of the carbon atom 1 by a direct comparison of the molecular rotations of the β-glucosides. The molecular rotations are calculated from the specific rotations by multiplication by the molecular weights ($[M]_\beta = [\alpha]_D \times$ M.W.). They represent the influences of variations in the structure of the aglycon group (group R) on the total molecular rotation and probably on A.

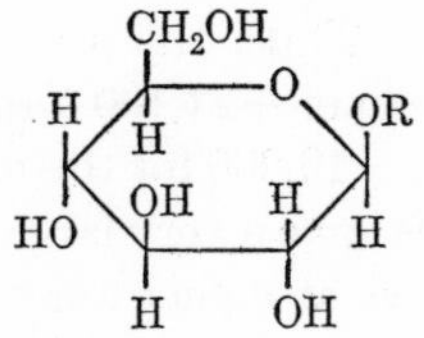
CH₂OH
O
H
OR
H
OH
H
HO
H
H
OH

Although the β-glucosides of the primary and secondary alcohols have rotations usually falling in the interval −6,500 to −10,000, those derived from phenols exhibit molecular rotations greater than −17,000. The corresponding derivatives of the tertiary alcohols have molecular rotations near

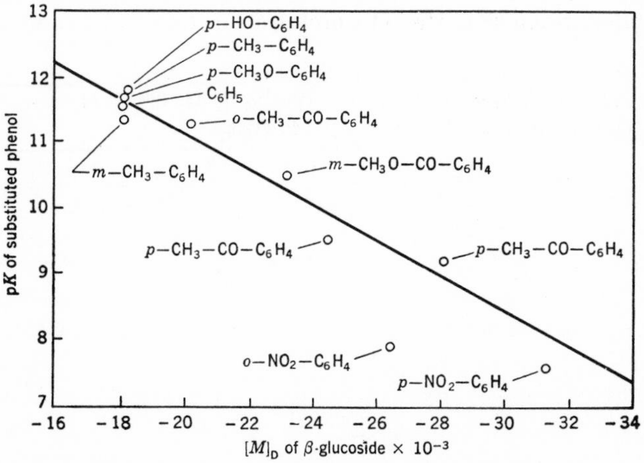
p—HO—C6H4
p—CH3—C6H4
p—CH3O—C6H4
C6H5
o—CH3—CO—C6H4
m—CH3—C6H4
m—CH3O—CO—C6H4
p—CH3—CO—C6H4
p—CH3—CO—C6H4
o—NO2—C6H4
p—NO2—C6H4
pK of substituted phenol
13
12
11
10
9
8
7
-16
-18
-20
-22
-24
-26
-28
-30
-32
-34
[M]D of β-glucoside × 10−3

FIG. 4. Relationship between the pK values of phenols and the molecular rotations of the corresponding β-glucosides.

−4,000. For the aromatic glucosides, there is an interesting correlation between the effect of substituent groups present in the phenyl nucleus on the rotations and the influence of the same groups on substitution reactions of benzene derivatives. The "ortho-para directing groups" when substituted in the aromatic nucleus of phenyl β-glucoside have little or no effect on the rotation. However, "meta-directing groups" in positions meta and para to the glucosidic connection cause the rotation of the glucoside to become appreciably more negative than for phenyl β-glucoside. Thus, the value of −31,000 for *p*-nitrophenyl β-glucoside compares to that of −18,200 for the phenyl β-glucoside. Diortho-substituted derivatives have anomalously low molecular rotations which are near those of the tertiary-alkyl β-glucosides (−4,000 to −5,000).

As shown in Fig. 4, the influence of substituents in the aromatic nucleus of phenyl β-glucoside parallels the effect of the same groups on the acidity of the corresponding substituted phenols.

Many of the ortho-substituted phenyl β-glucoside tetraacetates have anomalous positive rotations. Thus, the *o*-nitrophenyl β-glucoside tetraacetate has a molecular rotation of +21,100 ($[\alpha]_D$ = 45) as compared to the negative values −17,400 and −19,200 for the meta- and para-isomers. The positively rotating derivatives have a very large temperature coefficient and their rotations become negative at higher temperatures, although the rotations of the *m*- and *p*-isomers are affected only to a minor degree by an increase of temperature. This and other evidence makes it probable that the positive rotation of certain of the *o*-substituted phenyl β-glucoside tetraacetates is due to a bonding of the group in the ortho-position with an acetyl group in the sugar portion of the molecule (*120*).

The relation of ring conformations to the optical rotations of sugar derivatives offers promise in the interpretation of fine features of the structures (*121*).

120. W. W. Pigman, *J. Research Natl. Bur. Standards* **33,** 129 (1944).
121. D. H. Wiffen, *Chemistry & Industry* p. 946 (1956).

II. OCCURRENCE, PROPERTIES, AND SYNTHESIS OF THE MONOSACCHARIDES

John C. Sowden

1. NATURALLY OCCURRING MONOSACCHARIDES

A. Introduction

Many sugars and deoxysugars are found free or combined in naturally occurring materials. These sugars are of particular importance because of the interest in their biological function and in their present or potential industrial application. To the sugar chemist, these sugars are of value in providing, along with the natural sugar alcohols and uronic acids, starting materials for the preparation of the synthetic sugars. The list of known naturally occurring sugars and deoxysugars gradually is being expanded as isolation procedures are developed and improved. The biosynthesis of many is discussed in Chapter XIII and their nutritional aspects in Chapter XIV.

D-Glucose, free or combined, undoubtedly is the most widely distributed of the sugars. Other aldohexoses found in natural products are D-mannose and D- and L-galactose. D-Fructose is the only abundant natural ketose. The occurrence of another hexulose, D-tagatose, has been established (*1*), but the reported isolation (*2*) of L-sorbose needs further substantiation. Of the pentoses, D-xylose, D-ribose, and D- and L-arabinose are of biological origin. L-*threo*-Pentulose (L-xylulose) is excreted in the urine of patients with pentosuria and D-*erythro*-pentulose (D-ribulose) has been recognized as an intermediate in carbohydrate metabolism and photosynthesis. Both of these ketopentoses have been reported to occur in minor amounts in normal human urine. The aldotetrose ester, D-erythrose 4-phosphate, is an intermediate in several natural enzymic transformations. The three-carbon sugar series is represented by glyceraldehyde and dihydroxyacetone, which occur as their phosphate derivatives in the intermediate stages of cellular metabolism as well as in many other related biological processes. Two heptuloses, two aldoheptoses (*2a*) and two heptitols have been isolated from natural products.

1. E. L. Hirst, L. Hough, and J. K. N. Jones, *Nature* **163,** 177 (1949).

2. C. M. Martin and F. H. Reuter, *Nature* **164,** 407 (1949).

2a. M. W. Slein and G. W. Schnell, *Proc. Soc. Exptl. Biol. Med.* **82,** 734 (1953); W. Weidel, *Z. physiol. Chem.* **299,** 253 (1955); A. P. Maclennan and D. A. L. Davies, *Biochem. J.* **63,** 31p (1956).

Sedoheptulose occurs as an intermediate in photosynthesis and carbohydrate metabolism (Chapter XIII).

The presence in plant materials of L-glucose, the enantiomorph of the ubiquitous D-glucose, has been reported (*3*) but needs confirmation. However, the natural occurrence of 2-deoxy-2-*N*-methylamino-L-glucose in streptomycin and of 6-deoxy-3-*O*-methyl-L-glucose (L-thevetose) in certain cardiac glycosides has been established.

Many deoxysugars, formally derived from ordinary sugars by the replacement of a hydroxyl group by a hydrogen atom, are of biological origin. The sugars with a terminal methyl rather than a primary alcohol group are the most common deoxysugars. All of the aldohexoses mentioned above are represented in the D- or L-form by naturally occurring 6-deoxy-D-glucose, 6-deoxy-D- and -L-galactose (D- and L-fucose), and 6-deoxy-L-mannose (L-rhamnose). 2-Deoxy-D-*erythro*-pentose (2-deoxy-D-ribose) is widely distributed in cellular materials as the sugar component of the deoxynucleic acids. A large variety of 6-deoxy- and 2,6-dideoxy-aldohexoses and their 3-*O*-methyl ethers are found as constituents of the cardiac glycosides (Chapter X).

Sugars and deoxysugars with branched carbon chains also occur in nature (Chapter X). These include apiose (*4*) and hamamelose (*5*), found in plant sources, and streptose (*6*), cordycepose (*7*), mycarose (*8*), and cladinose (*8a*), which occur as constituents of antibiotic substances.

The natural sugars may exist free, or combined as components of larger molecules such as oligosaccharides, polysaccharides, glycosides, etc. The better-defined polysaccharides are usually homopolymers of monosaccharides: cellulose, starch, and glycogen are D-glucose polymers; inulin gives D-fructose; and pectins yield mainly D-galacturonic acid on hydrolysis. Other polysaccharides (gums, hemicelluloses, and many animal polysaccharides) are heteropolymers of simple sugars, uronic acids, and amino sugars (Chapter XII).

3. F. B. Power and F. Tutin, *Chem. Zentr.* **77,** Part II, 1623 (1906); H. Saha and and K. N. Choudhury, *J. Chem. Soc.* **121,** 1044 (1922).

4. See C. S. Hudson, *Advances in Carbohydrate Chem.* **4,** 57 (1949).

5. See O. T. Schmidt, *Ann.* **476,** 250 (1929); O. T. Schmidt and K. Heintz, *ibid.* **515,** 77 (1934).

6. F. A. Kuehl, Jr., M. N. Bishop, E. H. Flynn, and K. Folkers, *J. Am. Chem. Soc.* **70,** 2613 (1948); M. L. Wolfrom and C. W. DeWalt, *ibid.* **70,** 3148 (1948).

7. K. G. Cunningham, S. A. Hutchinson, W. Manson, and F. S. Spring, *J. Chem. Soc.* p. 2299 (1951); H. R. Bentley, K. G. Cunningham, and F. S. Spring, *ibid.* p. 2301 (1951).

8. P. P. Regna, F. A. Hochstein, R. L. Wagner, Jr., and R. B. Woodward, *J. Am. Chem. Soc.* **75,** 4625 (1953).

8a. P. F. Wiley and O. Weaver, *J. Am. Chem. Soc.* **77,** 3422 (1955); **78,** 808 (1956).

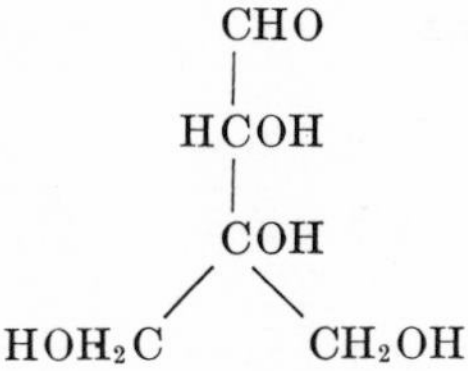
Apiose

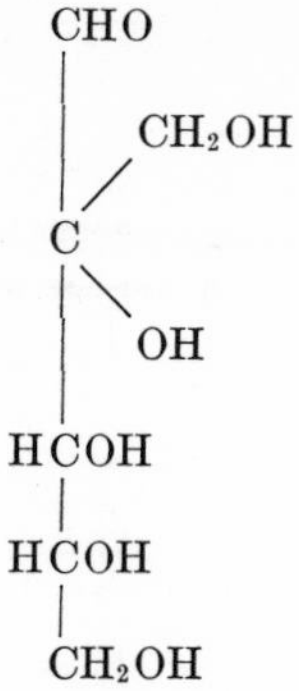
Hamamelose

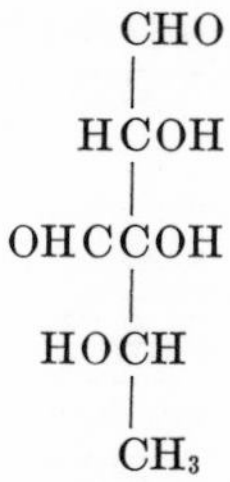
Streptose

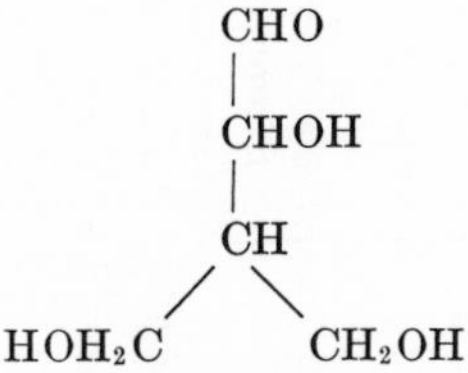
Cordycepose

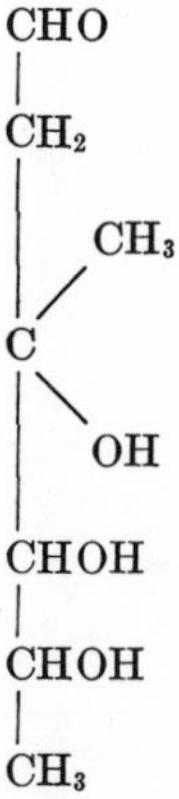
Mycarose

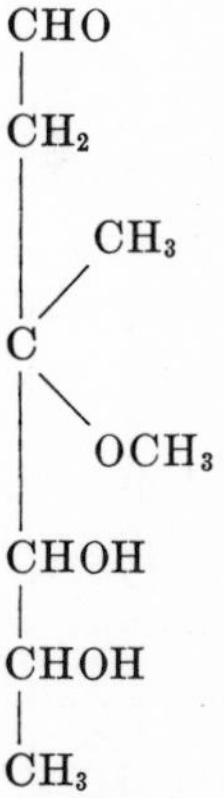
Cladinose

B. Origin and Preparation of Some Naturally Occurring Monosaccharides

a. Pentoses

L-Arabinose

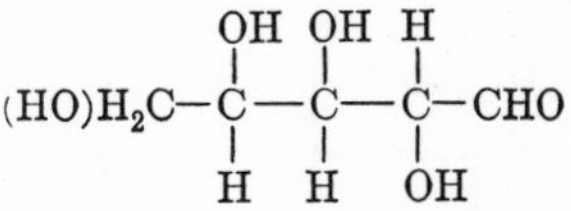
aldehydo-L-Arabinose

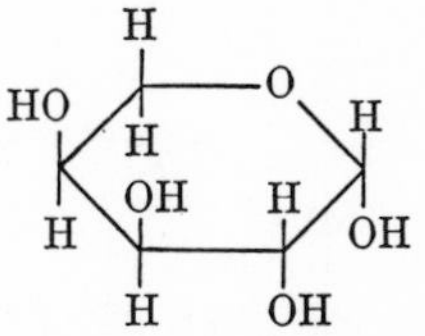
β-L-Arabopyranose

Occurrence. The sugar occurs in the free state in the heartwood of many coniferous trees. In a combined state, it is very widely distributed in plant

TABLE I

PHYSICAL PROPERTIES AND DERIVATIVES OF SOME NATURAL MONOSACCHARIDES[a]

Sugar	M.p.[b] (°C.)	$[\alpha]_D^{20-25}$ (final in H_2O)	Characteristic derivative[a]	Reference	M.p. (°C.)	$[\alpha]_D$ (final)
Aldopentose						
L-Arabinose[c]	160	105°	Benzylphenylhydrazone	*(9)*	174	−14.6° (CH_3OH)
			Diphenylhydrazone	*(10)*	204–5	14.9° (C_5H_5N)
D-Ribose	87	−23.7°	*p*-Bromophenylhydrazone	*(11)*	164–5	10.3° (C_2H_5OH)
D-Xylose	145	19°	Benzylphenylhydrazone	*(12)*	95	−20.3° (CH_3OH)
			Cd Xylonate–$CdBr_2$ double salt	*(13)*	—	8.8° (H_2O)
Ketopentose						
D-*erythro*-Pentulose (D-Ribulose)	Sirup	−16.3°	*o*-Nitrophenylhydrazone	*(14)*	168–9	−48° (CH_3OH)
L-*threo*-Pentulose (L-Xylulose)	Sirup	34.8°	*p*-Bromophenylhydrazone	*(15)*	128	31.5° (C_5H_5N)
Deoxypentose						
2-Deoxy-D-*erythro*-pentose (2-Deoxy-D-ribose)	92–5	−58°	Benzylphenylhydrazone	*(16)*	128	−17.5° (C_5H_5N)
			Anilide	*(17)*	174	46° (C_5H_5N)
Aldohexose						
D-Galactose[c]	167	80.2°	Benzylphenylhydrazone	*(18)*	157–8	−14.3° (C_5H_5N)
	118–20 (monohydrate)		Oxidation to mucic acid	*(19)*	210–20	0°
D-Glucose[c]	146	52.7°	Benzylphenylhydrazone	*(18)*	163–4	−48° (C_5H_5N)
	83–6 (monohydrate)		*p*-Bromophenylhydrazone	*(18)*	164–6	18° (C_5H_5N)
			Oxidation to D-glucaric acid	*(20)*		
D-Mannose	132	14.6°	Phenylhydrazone	*(18, 21)*	199–200	33.8° (C_5H_5N)
			Anhydro-phenylhydrazone tetraacetate	*(22)*	123–4	12° (C_5H_5N)
Ketohexose						
D-Fructose	102–4	−92.4°	2,5-Dichlorophenylhydrazone	*(23)*	154	5.3° (C_5H_5N)
L-Sorbose	159–61	−43°	2,5-Dichlorophenylhydrazone	*(23)*	117	−32.7° (C_5H_5N)

D-Tagatose	134–5	−5°	1,2:3,4-Di-*O*-isopropylidene-D-tagatose	(*24*)	65–6	72° (H_2O)
			D-Tagatopyranose penta-acetate	(*25*)	132	30.2° ($CHCl_3$)
<u>6-Deoxyaldohexose</u>[d]						
L-Fucose[c] (6-Deoxy-L-galactose)	145	−76°	Benzylphenylhydrazone	(*12, 26*)	178	14.9° (CH_3OH)
			Diphenylhydrazone	(*26, 27*)	198	−15.8° (C_5H_5N)
D-Quinovose (6-Deoxy-D-glucose)	139–45	29.7°	Phenylosazone[e]	(*28*)	186–7	−95° (C_5H_5N, white light)
L-Rhamnose (6-Deoxy-L-mannose)	93–4 (monohydrate)	8.9°	Phenylhydrazone	(*29*)	160	27° (80% C_2H_5OH)
			Phenylosazone[f]	(*28*)	189	94° (C_5H_5N, white light)
<u>Ketoheptose</u>						
D-*manno*-Heptulose	152	29.4°	*p*-Bromophenylhydrazone	(*30*)	179	—
			α-Hexaacetate	(*31*)	110	39° ($CHCl_3$)
Sedoheptulose (D-*altro*-Heptulose)	Sirup	2–3°	Sedoheptulosan	(*32*)	155	−146° (H_2O)
			Sedoheptulosan monohydrate	(*33*)	102	−134° (H_2O)
			Sedoheptulosan tetrabenzoate	(*34*)	166	−188° ($CHCl_3$)

[a] For additional information and details, it is suggested that the following references in particular be consulted:

H. Vogel and A. Georg, "Tabellen der Zucker und ihrer Derivate." Springer, Berlin, 1931.

Tollens-Elsner, "Kurzes Handbuch der Kohlenhydrate," 4th ed. Barth, Leipzig, 1935. (Photo-Lithoprint Reproduction, Edwards Brothers, Inc., Ann Arbor, 1943.)

"Beilsteins Handbuch der organischen Chemie," Vol. 31. Springer, Berlin, 1938.

F. J. Bates and Associates, *Natl. Bur. Standards Circ.* **C440** (1942).

[b] Melting points of usual crystalline modifications.

[c] D-Arabinose, L-galactose, D-fucose, and possibly L-glucose also occur in nature. The physical properties of these sugars and their derivatives are identical with those of the corresponding enantiomorphs listed above except for the sign of the optical rotation.

[d] In addition to the more common 6-deoxyaldohexoses listed here, 6-deoxy-L-talose [J. Schmutz, *Helv. Chim. Acta* **31,** 1719 (1948)] and 6-deoxy-D-allose [M. Keller and T. Reichstein, *ibid.* **32,** 1607 (1949)] have been identified as constituents of cardiac glycosides (see Chapter X).

[e] Enantiomorph of L-rhamnose phenylosazone.

[f] Enantiomorph of D-quinovose phenylosazone.

TABLE I—*Continued*

9. W. Alberda van Ekenstein and C. A. Lobry de Bruyn, *Rec. trav. chim.* **15,** 225 (1896); O. Ruff and G. Ollendorf, *Ber.* **32,** 3234 (1899).

10. C. Neuberg, *Ber.* **33,** 2253 (1900); A. Müther and B. Tollens, *Ber.* **37,** 311 (1904).

11. P. A. Levene and W. A. Jacobs, *Ber.* **42,** 2104, 2472, 2476, 3247 (1909); P. A. Levene and R. S. Tipson, *J. Biol. Chem.* **115,** 731 (1936).

12. O. Ruff and G. Ollendorf, *Ber.* **32,** 3235 (1899); E. Votoček, F. Valentin, and O. Leminger, *Collection Czechoslov. Chem. Communs.* **3,** 252 (1931).

13. G. Bertrand, *Bull. soc. chim.* [3] **5,** 554 (1891); **19,** 1001 (1898); C. S. Hudson and H. S. Isbell, *J. Am. Chem. Soc.* **51,** 2225 (1929).

14. C. Glatthaar and T. Reichstein, *Helv. Chim. Acta* **18,** 80 (1935).

15. P. A. Levene and F. B. LaForge, *J. Biol. Chem.* **18,** 319 (1914); I. Greenwald, *ibid.* **88,** 1 (1930); **89,** 501 (1930); L. von Vargha *Ber.* **68,** 24 (1935).

16. P. A. Levene and T. Mori, *J. Biol. Chem.* **83,** 803 (1939), P. A. Levene, L. A. Mikeska, and T. Mori, *ibid.* **85,** 785 (1930); R. E. Deriaz, W. G. Overend, M. Stacey, E. G. Teece, and L. F. Wiggins, *J. Chem. Soc.* 1879 (1949).

17. P. W. Kent, M. Stacey, and L. F. Wiggins, *J. Chem. Soc.* 1232 (1949); W. G. Overend, M. Stacey, and L. F. Wiggins, *ibid.* 1358 (1949); P. A. J. Gorin and J. K. N. Jones, *Nature* **172,** 1051 (1953).

18. A. Hoffman, *Ann.* **366,** 277 (1909).

19. W. H. Kent and B. Tollens, *Ann.* **227,** 221 (1885); "Beilstein's Handbuch der Organischen Chemie," Vol. 3, p. 581. Springer, Berlin, 1921; *ibid.* Vol. 31, p. 303, 1938.

20. R. Gans and B. Tollens, *Ann.* **249,** 219 (1888); Tollens-Elsner "*Kurzes Handbuch der Kohlenhydrate,*" p. 199. Barth, Leipzig, 1935.

21. C. L. Butler and L. H. Cretcher, *J. Am. Chem. Soc.* **53,** 4358 (1931).

22. M. L. Wolfrom and M. G. Blair, *J. Am. Chem. Soc.* **68,** 2110 (1946).

23. I. Mandl and C. Neuberg, *Arch. Biochem. and Biophys.* **35,** 326 (1952).

24. T. Reichstein and W. Bosshard, *Helv. Chim. Acta* **17,** 753 (1934).

25. Y. Khouvine and Y. Tomada, *Compt. rend.* **205,** 736 (1937); Y. Khouvine, G. Arragon, and Y. Tomada, *Bull. soc. chim. France* [5] **6,** 354 (1939).

26. A. Müther and B. Tollens, *Ber.* **37,** 306 (1904).

27. A. Müther, Dissertation, Göttingen, p. 21, 1903.

28. E. Fischer and K. Zach, *Ber.* **45,** 3761 (1912); K. Freudenberg and K. Raschig, *ibid.* **62,** 373 (1929).

29. E. Fischer and J. Tafel, *Ber.* **20,** 2566 (1887); C. Tanret, *Bull. soc. chim. France* [3] **27,** 395 (1902).

30. F. B. LaForge, *J. Biol. Chem.* **28,** 511 (1917).

31. E. M. Montgomery and C. S. Hudson, *J. Am. Chem. Soc.* **61,** 1654 (1939).

32. F. B. LaForge and C. S. Hudson, *J. Biol. Chem.* **30,** 61 (1917).

33. J. W. Pratt, N. K. Richtmyer, and C. S. Hudson, *J. Am. Chem. Soc.* **74,** 2200 (1952).

products, being found in gums, hemicelluloses, pectic materials, and bacterial polysaccharides. Several glycosides yield the sugar on hydrolysis.

Preparation (*35*). Mesquite gum, from a plant (*Prosopis juliflora* and related species) common in the southwestern United States, and cherry gum are utilized. Mesquite gum consists of L-arabinose, D-galactose, and 4-*O*-methyl-D-glucuronic acid in combination, and cherry gum in addition has some D-xylose and D-mannose. By controlled hydrolysis most of the pentose is removed without hydrolyzing the other constituents to any great extent. The L-arabinose is then partially purified by dialysis (*36*) or ion-exchange procedures (*37*) and crystallized from ethyl alcohol. Wheat and rye bran, peach gum, Australian black wattle gum, and spent beet pulp have been utilized for the preparation of L-arabinose.

General Discussion. Although calcium chloride compounds of both the α- and β-anomers have been crystallized (*38*), only one crystalline anomer of the sugar itself is known, and this has been usually designated as the β-anomer, following the nomenclature of Hudson.

Neither L- nor D-arabinose is fermentable by yeasts.

D-Arabinose

Occurrence. The sugar is encountered infrequently. Cathartic-acting glycosides (aloins) such as barbaloin, isobarbaloin, nataloin, and homonataloin from plants of the genus *Aloe* (*A. barbadensis*) yield D-arabinose (*39*). The glycosidic union is very resistant to hydrolysis. The sugar occurs in the furanose modification as a constituent of the polysaccharide fraction of tubercle bacilli (*40*).

Preparation. The D-arabinose has the same configuration as the lower five carbon atoms of D-glucose. Therefore, any of the methods for removing carbon 1 from D-glucose leads to D-arabinose or a derivative. Probably the most convenient method is the oxidation of the easily obtained calcium gluconate by hydrogen peroxide and ferric acetate (*41*).

35. T. S. Harding, *Sugar* **24,** 656 (1922); E. Anderson and L. Sands, *J. Am. Chem. Soc.* **48,** 3172 (1926); *Org. Syntheses Collective Vol.* **1,** 60 (1932).

36. E. V. White, *J. Am. Chem. Soc.* **69,** 715 (1947).

37. C. S. Hudson, *J. Am. Chem. Soc.* **73,** 4038 (1951); F. B. Cramer, *J. Franklin Inst.* **256,** 93 (1953).

38. W. C. Austin and J. P. Walsh, *J. Am. Chem. Soc.* **56,** 934 (1934); J. K. Dale, *ibid.* **56,** 932 (1934); H. S. Isbell and W. W. Pigman, *J. Research Natl. Bur. Standards* **18.** 141 (1937).

39. M. E. Léger, *Ann. chim.* [9] **8,** 265 (1917); C. S. Gibson and J. L. Simonsen, *J. Chem. Soc.* p. 553 (1930).

40. M. Maxim, *Biochem. Z.* **223,** 404 (1930); E. Chargaff and R. J. Anderson, *Z. physiol. Chem.* **191,** 172 (1930); W. N. Haworth, P. W. Kent, and M. Stacey, *J. Chem. Soc.* p. 1211, 1220 (1948).

41. R. C. Hockett and C. S. Hudson, *J. Am. Chem. Soc.* **56,** 1632 (1934); H. G. Fletcher, Jr., H. W. Diehl, and C. S. Hudson, *ibid.* **72,** 4546 (1950).

D-Ribose

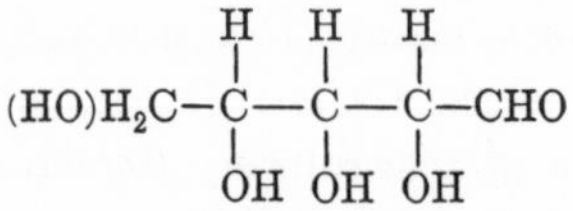

aldehydo-D-Ribose

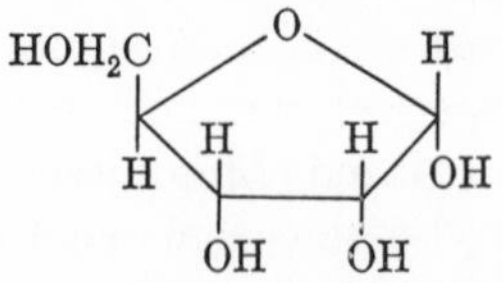

α-D-Ribofuranose

Occurrence. D-Ribose and 2-deoxy-D-ribose comprise the carbohydrate constituents of nucleic acids, which are found in all plant and animal cells. In general, the ribonucleic acids are found in the cytoplasm and the deoxyribonucleic acids in the nucleus (Chapter VIII). The 5-thiomethyl analog of D-ribose also is a constituent of yeast nucleic acid.

Preparation (*42*, *43*). D-Ribose may be synthesized from D-arabinose by alkaline isomerization, by the glycal synthesis, or through the pyridine-catalyzed epimerization of D-arabonic acid followed by reduction. The sugar also has been prepared by the oxidative degradation of calcium D-altronate (*44*) and by the nitromethane synthesis from D-erythrose (*45*).

The best methods for laboratory preparations involve the stepwise hydrolysis of yeast nucleic acid. The original procedure of Levene and Clark which requires the action of ammonia at elevated temperatures and pressures has been greatly improved by Phelps, who uses magnesium oxide as the hydrolytic agent. The hydrolytic products, consisting of a mixture of nucleosides, then are further hydrolyzed by acid to produce D-ribose.

A similar method is based on the enzymic hydrolysis of the yeast nucleic acid (*46*). Emulsins prepared from sweet almonds, alfalfa seeds, and many sprouted seeds hydrolyze polynucleotides (nucleic acids) to the nucleosides. Guanosine (*N*-ribosyl-guanine) is produced almost quantitatively and adenosine picrate (picrate of *N*-ribosyl-adenine) is likewise obtained in high yield. As in the earlier methods, the nucleosides are hydrolyzed by acids to give D-ribose.

General Discussion (*47a*). The universal occurrence of D-ribose in all living cells makes this sugar of the greatest interest to biochemists and biologists.

42. F. J. Bates and Associates, *Nat. Bur. Standards, Circ.* **C440** (1942).

43. P. A. Levene and E. P. Clark, *J. Biol. Chem.* **46**, 19 (1921); F. P. Phelps, *U. S. Patent* 2,152,662 (1939); L. Laufer and J. Charney, *U. S. Patents* 2,379,913 and 2,379,914 (1945).

44. C. S. Hudson and N. K. Richtmyer, *U. S. Patent* 2,162,721 (1939).

45. J. C. Sowden, J. Am. Chem. Soc. **72**, 808 (1950).

46. H. Bredereck, M. Köthnig, and E. Berger, *Ber.* **73**, 956 (1940).

47. See: R. W. Jeanloz and H. G. Fletcher, Jr., *Advances in Carbohydrate Chem.* **6**, 135 (1951).

47a. W. G. Overend and M. Stacey *in* "The Nucleic Acids" (E. Chargaff and J. N. Davidson, eds.), p. 9. Academic Press, New York, 1955.

Not only is it a constituent of the nucleic acids but also of several vitamins and coenzymes (Chapters VIII and XIII). The sugar occurs in these natural products in the furanose modification. Solutions of ribose probably contain considerable quantities of the furanose form, and the mutarotation is complex and exhibits a minimum. Its metabolism is discussed in Chapters XIII and XIV.

D-Ribose is not fermentable by ordinary yeasts.

D-Xylose

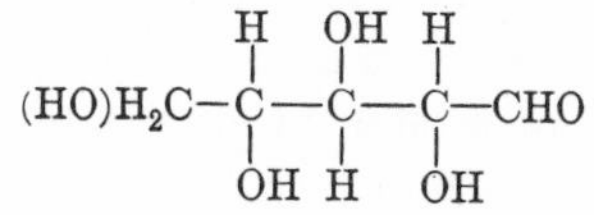
H OH H
(HO)H₂C—C—C—C—CHO
OH H OH

aldehydo-D-Xylose

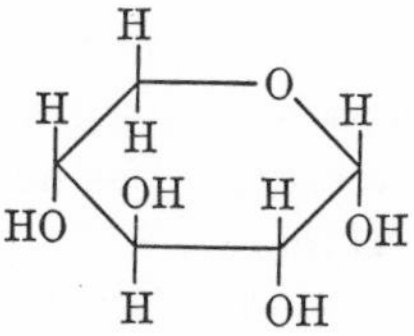
H
O
H
H
H
OH
H
HO
OH
H
OH

α-D-Xylopyranose

Synonyms. Wood sugar; in earlier literature *l*-xylose.

Preparation (*42*, *48*). The sugar is prepared from corn-cobs (or many other woody materials) by boiling with acids, fermenting out the glucose with yeasts, and crystallizing the D-xylose from the evaporated solution.

General Discussion. The presence of combined D-xylose in considerable quantities in many important agricultural wastes has stimulated interest in this sugar and its preparation. Cottonseed hulls, pecan shells, corn-cobs and straw have been investigated as sources of the sugar, and several large-scale preparations (*49*, *50*) have been carried out. The sugar crystallizes fairly easily and could be made cheaply, but insufficient uses have been developed to make the manufacture of the sugar of commercial interest. Since it is not fermentable by ordinary yeasts or utilizable by many animals, the value of the sugar is considerably limited. Sheep are able to make use of 94 to 100% of ingested xylose although hogs eliminate 30% in the urine. The assimilation is greater when the sugar is fed along with large amounts of other materials (*50*). This pentose is cataractogenic to young rats when fed in large quantities (see under D-Galactose and in Chapter XIV). Many bacteria and certain yeasts are able to ferment the sugar with the formation of important substances. Lactic and acetic acids in yields of 85 to 96% are formed (*51*) by the action of certain *Lactobacilli* on D-xylose. *Torula* and

48. T. S. Harding, *Sugar* **25,** 124 (1923); C. S. Hudson and T. S. Harding, *J. Am. Chem. Soc.* **40,** 1601 (1918); K. P. Monroe, *ibid.* **41,** 1002 (1919).

49. W. T. Schreiber, N. V. Geib, B. Wingfield, and S. F. Acree, *Ind. Eng. Chem.* **22,** 497 (1930).

50. N. A. Sytchev, *Compt. rend. acad. sci. U.S.S.R.* **29,** 384 (1940).

51. M. Iwasaki, *J. Agr. Chem. Soc. Japan* **16,** 148 (1940).

Monilia yeasts grow well on hydrolyzed straw and corn-cobs and provide a good cattle feed (*50*).

D-*erythro*-Pentulose

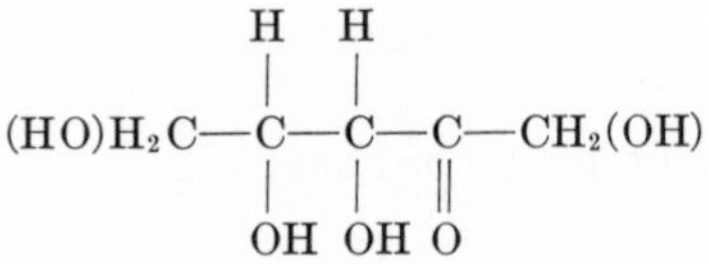

Synonyms. D-Ribulose, D-riboketose.

Occurrence. Phosphorylated D-*erythro*-pentulose is an intermediate in the oxidative pathway of glucose metabolism by yeast or animal tissue and has been recognized as an early product of photosynthesis in plants (see Chapter XIII).

Preparation (*52*). The ketopentose has been synthesized from D-arabinose by isomerization with pyridine followed by isolation as the crystalline *o*-nitrophenylhydrazone. The free sugar has not been crystallized. The D-*erythro*-pentulose 5-phosphate may be obtained by treatment of D-gluconic acid 6-phosphate with yeast enzymes (Chapter XIII).

L-*threo*-Pentulose

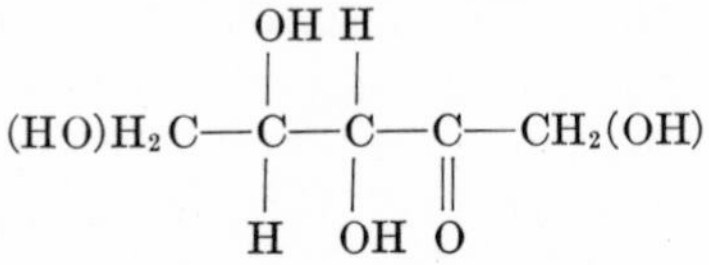

Synonyms. L-Xylulose, L-xyloketose, urine pentose.

Occurrence. In urine of many cases of pentosuria.

Preparation (*53*). The sugar has been synthesized by boiling L-xylose with pyridine, removing unchanged L-xylose by crystallization, and isolating the L-*threo*-pentulose as the *p*-bromophenylhydrazone.

General Discussion. The occasional presence of pentoses in urine was known for a considerable time before the identification of the sugar as L-*threo*-pentulose by Levene and LaForge (*54*). The precursor of the pentose is believed to be D-glucuronic acid since administration of this substance induces the appearance of the ketopentose in the urine (*55*). Rats exhibit a significant increase of liver glycogen when fed D-*threo*-pentulose but not

52. C. Glatthaar and T. Reichstein, *Helv. Chim. Acta* **18,** 80 (1935).

53. L. von Vargha, *Ber.* **68,** 18 (1935); cf. O. T. Schmidt and R. Treiber, *Ber.* **66,** 1765 (1933).

54. P. A. Levene and F. B. LaForge, *J. Biol. Chem.* **18,** 319 (1914); I. Greenwald, *ibid.* **88,** 1 (1930).

55. M. Enklewitz and M. Lasker, *J. Biol. Chem.* **110,** 443 (1935).

when fed the natural L-isomer. The natural isomer is partially utilized by dogs, however (*56*). (See also Chapter XIV.)

2-Deoxy-D-*erythro*-Pentose

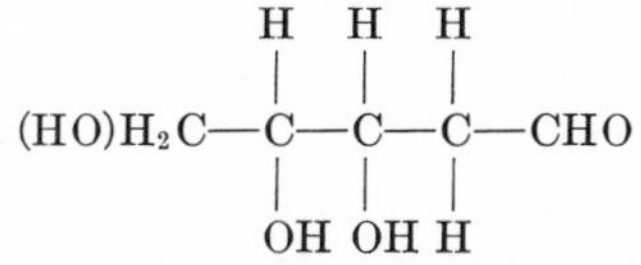

Synonyms. 2-Deoxy-D-ribose, ribodesose, thyminose.

Occurrence. In furanosidic combination with purines and pyrimidines in the nucleic acids of plant and animal cells.

Preparation. The preparation of 2-deoxy-D-*erythro*-pentose by hydrolysis of the natural deoxypentosenucleic acids is tedious and the yields are low. The nucleic acids first are hydrolyzed enzymatically to deoxyribonucleosides (*N*-deoxyribofuranosyl purines and pyrimidines). Further mild acidic hydrolysis then liberates the sugar from the purine bases (*57*). The sugar–pyrimidine linkage, however, is more stable and its hydrolysis by stronger acid is accompanied by destruction of the deoxypentose to levulinic acid. Direct mercaptanolysis of deoxyribosenucleic acids has been employed to obtain the dibenzyl mercaptal of the deoxysugar (*58*).

2-Deoxy-D-*erythro*-pentose may be prepared from D-arabinose by the glycal method (*59*) or from D-erythrose by the nitroolefin synthesis (*60*). The two most convenient methods, however, start from D-glucose. In one of these (*61*), D-glucose is isomerized by alkali (Chapter I) to a mixture of 3-deoxy-D-*arabo*- and 3-deoxy-D-*ribo*-hexonic acids (the D-glucometasaccharinic acids) and the latter are converted to the deoxypentose by oxidative degradation. The D-glucometasaccharinic acids also are readily prepared by alkaline degradation of the disaccharide laminaribiose or its parent polysaccharide laminarin (*62*). The second method based on D-glucose

56. H. W. Larson, N. R. Blatherwick, P. J. Bradshaw, and S. D. Sawyer, *J. Biol. Chem.* **117,** 719 (1937); H. W. Larson, W. H. Chambers, N. R. Blatherwick, M. E. Ewing, and S. D. Sawyer, *ibid.* **129,** 701 (1939).

57. P. A. Levene and E. S. London, *J. Biol. Chem.* **83,** 793 (1929); P. A. Levene and T. Mori, *ibid.* **83,** 803 (1929); P. A. Levene, L. A. Mikeska, and T. Mori, *ibid.* **85,** 785 (1930); O. Schindler, *Helv. Chim. Acta* **32,** 979 (1949); P. Reichard and B. Estborn, *Acta Chem. Scand.* **4,** 1047 (1950).

58. P. W. Kent, *Nature* **166,** 442 (1950).

59. A. M. Gakhokidze, *J. Gen. Chem.* (*U.S.S.R.*) **15,** 539 (1945); R. E. Deriaz, W. G. Overend, M. Stacey, E. G. Teece, and L. F. Wiggins, *J. Chem. Soc.* p. 1879 (1949).

60. J. C. Sowden, *J. Am. Chem. Soc.* **71,** 1897 (1949); **72,** 808 (1950).

61. J. C. Sowden, *J. Am. Chem. Soc.* **76,** 3541 (1954).

62. W. M. Corbett and J. Kenner, *J. Chem. Soc.* p. 3274 (1954).

involves the preparation of the 3-*O*-methylsulfonyl-D-glucose and the direct degradation of the latter by alkali to the deoxypentose (*62a*).

General Discussion (*47a, 63*). The biosynthesis of 2-deoxy-D-*erythro*-pentose is believed to occur by aldol condensation between D-glyceraldehyde 3-phosphate and acetaldehyde (Chapter XIII). However, an alternative route, that involves the direct *in vivo* reduction of D-ribose to its 2-deoxy analog, also has some support (*63a*).

A remarkable difference between normal sugars and 2-deoxysugars is the extreme ease with which the latter undergo glycoside formation. In further contrast to the normal sugars, 2-deoxy-D-*erythro*-pentose is readily destroyed by aqueous mineral acids which convert it to levulinic acid.

b. Hexoses

D-Galactose

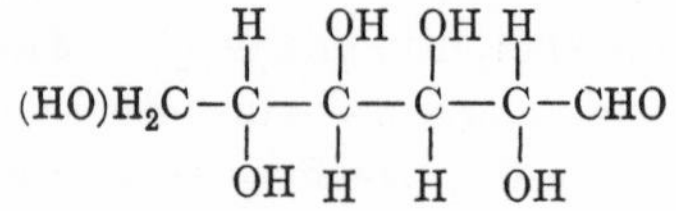

aldehydo-D-Galactose

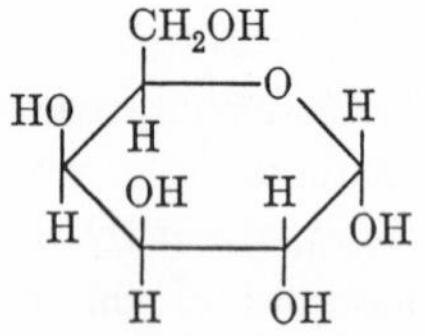

α-D-Galactopyranose

Synonyms. "Cerebrose," "brain sugar."

Occurrence. The sugar is a frequent constituent of oligosaccharides, notably lactose, melibiose, and raffinose. Polysaccharides which yield galactose on hydrolysis include agar, gum arabic, mesquite gum, western larch gum, and many other plant gums and mucilages. A few glycosides have also been reported to yield galactose on hydrolysis (idaein, myrtillin, the cerebrosides, etc.). D-Galactose occurs in glycosidic combination with *myo*-inositol (*64*) in sugar beets and with glycerol (*65*) in certain algae. Crystalline galactose has been observed on ivy berries.

Galactose polysaccharides from animal sources include the galactogens of the albumin gland of the snail (*Helix pomatia*), frog spawn, and beef lung (Chapter XII). The cerebrosides and gangliosides, occurring in con-

62a. D.C.C. Smith, *Chemistry & Industry* p. 92 (1955).

63. For a general discussion of the chemistry of 2-deoxysugars, including 2-deoxy-D-*erythro*-pentose, see W. G. Overend and M. Stacey, *Advances in Carbohydrate Chem.* **8,** 45 (1953).

63a. M. C. Lanning and S. S. Cohen, *J. Biol. Chem.* **216,** 413 (1955).

64. R. J. Brown and R. F. Serro, *J. Am. Chem. Soc.* **75,** 1040 (1953); E. A. Kabat, D. L. MacDonald, C. E. Ballou, and H. O. L. Fischer, *ibid.* **75,** 4507 (1953).

65. H. Colin and E. Guéguen, *Compt. rend.* **191,** 163 (1930); R. C. Bean, E. W. Putman, R. E. Trucco, and W. Z. Hassid, *J. Biol. Chem.* **204,** 169 (1953).

siderable amounts in brain and nerve tissue, are principally galactosides (Chapter X).

Preparation (*66*). The most frequently used method requires the hydrolysis of lactose by acids and the direct fractional crystallization of the galactose. A modification of the method involves the removal of the glucose by fermentation with yeasts and the crystallization of the remaining galactose. Water-soluble gums extractable from the western or eastern larch may serve as sources for the sugar (*67*).

General Discussion. The usual crystalline modification of the sugar is the α-D-galactopyranose, although the β-anomer is obtained by crystallization from cold alcoholic solution (*68*). Galactose and glucose differ only in the configuration of carbon 4, and this difference is accompanied by a greater tendency for galactose to give furanose derivatives. As a result, the mutarotation of the galactose isomers does not follow the first-order equation, and considerable quantities of furanose isomers are formed when the sugar is directly acetylated.

Galactose is one of the few sugars other than D-glucose which is found distributed to any great extent in the animal kingdom. In combination with glucose as the disaccharide lactose, it is an important constituent of the milk of mammals. Radioactive tracer experiments have demonstrated that the mammary gland of the cow will convert D-glucose-1-C^{14} to D-galactose-1-C^{14} during lactose production (*69*). Similarly, when D-galactose-1-C^{14} is ingested by rats, D-glucose-1-C^{14} can be isolated subsequently from the liver glycogen (*70*). In relation to the mechanism of configurational inversion at carbon 4 that results in the interconversion of glucose and galactose, the hydrolysis of glucose 4-phosphate by acid or alkaline phosphatase, or by aqueous acid, produces the original glucose and not galactose (*71*). The configurational interconversion *in vivo* now is known to be achieved enzymically, through the agency of uridine-5′-pyrophosphoric acid, as described below for lactose-fermenting yeasts.

D-Galactose, like D-xylose, produces cataracts when introduced into the diet of experimental animals (*72*). Large amounts of D-galactose in the diet

66. T. S. Harding, *Sugar* **25,** 175 (1923); E. P. Clark, *Bur. Standards Sci. Papers* **17,** 228 (1922); G. Mougne, *Bull. soc. chim. biol.* **4,** 206 (1922).

67. A. W. Schorger and D. F. Smith, *J. Ind. Eng. Chem.* **8,** 494 (1916); L. E. Wise, P. L. Hamer, and F. C. Peterson, *Ind. Eng. Chem.* **25,** 184 (1933).

68. C. S. Hudson and E. Yanovsky, *J. Am. Chem. Soc.* **39,** 1021 (1917).

69. E.Dimant, V. R. Smith, and H. A. Lardy, *J. Biol. Chem.* **201,** 85 (1953).

70. Y. J. Topper and D. Stetten, Jr., *J. Biol. Chem.* **193,** 149 (1951).

71. H. R. Dursch and F. J. Reithel, *J. Am. Chem. Soc.* **74,** 830 (1952).

72. See: H. S. Mitchell and G. M. Cook, *Proc. Soc. Exptl. Biol. Med.* **43,** 85 (1940); A. M. Yudkin and H. A. Geer, *Arch. Opthalmol.* **23,** 28 (1940).

of chickens results in violent spasms and eventual death (*73*). Similar effects are noted in humans who are afflicted with galactosemia due to an inability to assimilate the galactose portion of lactose in milk.

The fermentation of D-galactose by galactose-adapted and lactose-fermenting yeasts has received much study. Leloir (*74*) and his associates demonstrated that galactose enters the main glycolytic pathways by a direct interconversion of galactose 1-phosphate and glucose 1-phosphate promoted by an enzyme, "galactowaldenase," in the yeast. (See Chapter XIII.)

L-Galactose; DL-Galactose

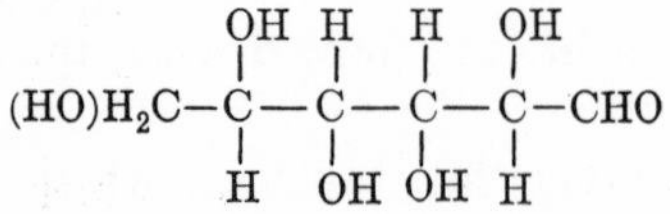
OH H H OH
(HO)H2C—C—C—C—C—CHO
H OH OH H

aldehydo-L-Galactose

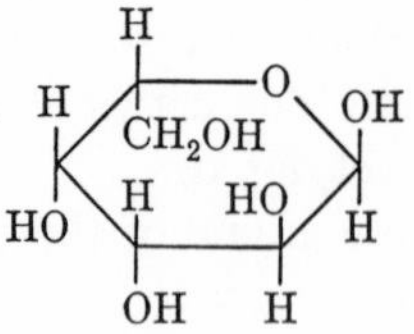
H
H
O
OH
CH2OH
H
HO
HO
H
OH
H

α-L-Galactopyranose

Occurrence. Several polysaccharides including chagual gum, agar-agar, and flaxseed mucilage produce L-galactose on hydrolysis, and, since D-galactose is usually present, the DL-galactose is obtained. Galactogen from snails also gives D- and L-galactose on hydrolysis (*75*).

Preparation. The synthetic methods are the most convenient although the preparation from flaxseed mucilage and agar has been described (*76*). The separation of L-galactose from natural or synthetic DL-mixtures is accomplished by the fermentation of the D-galactose by galactose-adapted yeasts or by resolution of the hydrazones formed from optically active 1-amyl-1-phenylhydrazine (*77*).

The reduction of the readily available D-galacturonic acid to L-galactonic acid and finally to L-galactose may be recommended for the preparation of this sugar. More details are given later in this chapter (p. 128).

73. H. Dam, *Proc. Soc. Exptl. Biol. Med.* **55,** 57 (1944).

74. R. Caputto, L. F. Leloir, C. E. Cardini, and A. C. Paladini, *J. Biol. Chem.* **184,** 333 (1950); L. F. Leloir and C. E. Cardini, *Ann. Rev. Biochem.* **22,** 179 (1953).

75. D. J. Bell and E. Baldwin, *Nature* **146,** 559 (1940).

76. E. Anderson, *J. Biol. Chem.* **100,** 249 (1933); E. Anderson and H. J. Lowe, *ibid.* **168,** 289 (1947); C. Araki, *J. Chem. Soc. Japan* **59,** 424 (1938).

77. C. Neuberg and M. Federer, *Ber.* **38,** 872 (1905).

D-Glucose

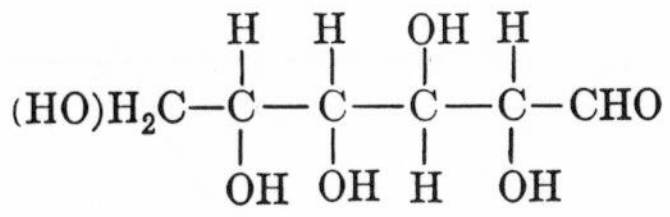

aldehydo-D-Glucose

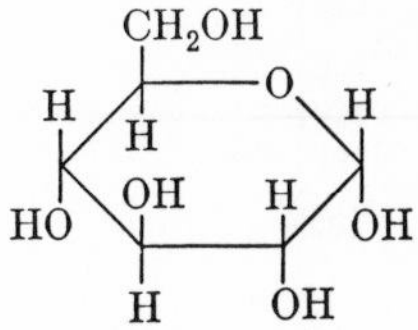

α-D-Glucopyranose

Synonyms. Dextrose, blood sugar, grape sugar, corn sugar.

Occurrence. This sugar, in a free or combined form, is not only the most common of the sugars but also is probably the most abundant organic compound. It occurs free in fruits, plant juices, honey, blood, lymph, cerebrospinal fluid, and urine and is a major component of many oligosaccharides (notably of sucrose), polysaccharides (particularly cellulose, starch, and glycogen) and glucosides.

Preparation (*78*). D-Glucose (usually called dextrose commercially because of its dextrorotation) is manufactured on a large scale from starch. Potato starch (Europe) and corn starch (America) are utilized.

Starch, in aqueous suspension, and 0.25 to 0.5% of hydrochloric acid (by weight of starch) are put in a converter. Steam is passed into the converter and a pressure of about 40 pounds per square inch is maintained until a 90 to 91% conversion to glucose has been attained. The acid solution is then passed into tubs and neutralized to a pH of 4.8 with sodium carbonate. Fatty materials originating from the starch are removed by centrifugals, and protein and insoluble carbohydrates subsequently by filtration. Alternatively, fats and proteins are removed from the initial acid hydrolyzate by coagulation with bentonite and the clarified solution is further purified by ion exchange. A cation-exchanger first removes metal ions; then acid is removed by passage over an anion-exchanger. The sugar solution from either process is decolorized and purified by passage through bone black (animal charcoal) and after evaporation to approximately 30°Bé. (*ca.* 55% by weight) is filtered again through bone black. The final filtrate is then evaporated in a vacuum pan. The subsequent treatment depends upon the product desired.

The last stage in the process is the most difficult to carry out on a large scale because the crystallization should take place from aqueous solution (cheapness), the crystals should be homogeneous (at least three forms are possible), and the particular crystals obtained should be easily centrifuged

78. W. B. Newkirk, *Ind. Eng. Chem.* **16**, 1173 (1924); **28**, 760 (1936); **31**, 18 (1939); G. R. Dean and J. B. Gottfried, *Advances in Carbohydrate Chem.* **5**, 127 (1950).

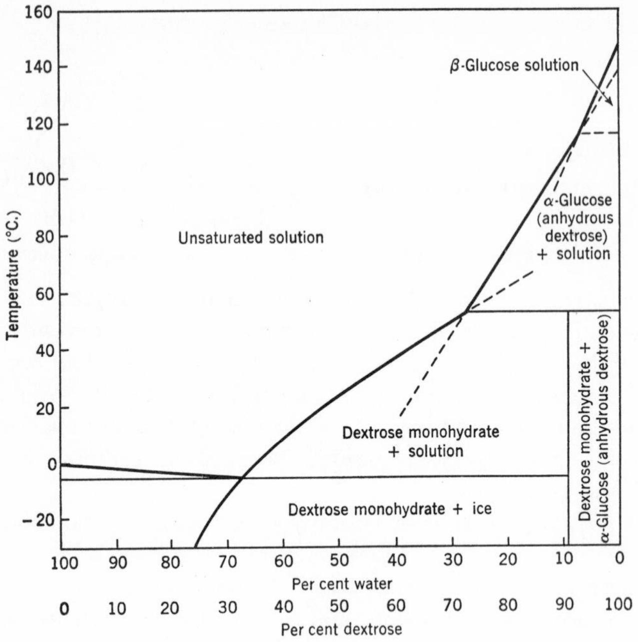
160
140
120
100
80
60
40
20
0
-20
Temperature (°C.)
β-Glucose solution
α-Glucose
(anhydrous
dextrose)
+ solution
Unsaturated solution
Dextrose monohydrate
+ solution
Dextrose monohydrate + ice
Dextrose monohydrate +
α-Glucose (anhydrous dextrose)
100 90 80 70 60 50 40 30 20 10 0
Per cent water
0 10 20 30 40 50 60 70 80 90 100
Per cent dextrose

FIG. 1

and washed. The conditions under which the various pyranose forms of D-glucose are stable are illustrated in the above phase diagram (*79*) of the system D-glucose–water (Fig. 1).

Below 50°C., α-D-glucose·H_2O is the stable crystalline phase, but above 50°C. the anhydrous form is obtained. At still higher temperatures, the β-D-glucose forms the solid phase. Although at any temperature it is usually possible to obtain any form by the addition of the proper seed crystals, this is usually not desirable since the introduction of seed crystals of the more stable modification will result in a change to the latter if equilibrium conditions are attained. In the commercial process these conditions are met for the hydrate by cooling the liquid at a concentration of about 40°Bé. (about 77% by weight) to a temperature of about 50°C., and after seeding heavily with the hydrate allowing it to crystallize while the mass is stirred and slowly cooled. The crystals are then separated by centrifugation and passed through driers.

For the preparation of the anhydrous material, the crystals are developed at higher temperatures in the vacuum pan while the evaporation is taking place. This is done by first evaporating about 15 to 20% of the total batch to a thick sirup (90% dry substance) and allowing crystals to form spon-

79. W. B. Newkirk, *Ind. Eng. Chem.* **28,** 764 (1936).

taneously. The remainder of the batch is then used to dilute the seed formed and the evaporation is continued. When the crystals have developed to the desired point, the mass is passed into a centrifuge and the mother liquors removed. During this final stage and during the washing, the proper temperatures are maintained to prevent spontaneous formation of the hydrate. The crystals are finally dried by filtered, warm air.

The β-D-glucose has proved of some technical interest because of its greater initial solubility. It has been prepared (*80*) by dissolution in hot pyridine and crystallization at 0°C. The accompanying molecule of pyridine is removed at 105°C. The β-isomer is also prepared (*81*) by crystallization from hot acetic acid and recrystallization from water and alcohol at lower temperatures. At temperatures greater than about 115°C., the β-D-glucose is the stable form in contact with a saturated aqueous solution (see Fig. 1). Because of the high solubility at these temperatures very concentrated solutions must be used. It is possible to work at somewhat lower temperatures (100°C.) if seed of the α-isomer is excluded. The β-D-glucose may be prepared by seeding a concentrated glucose solution at 100°C. with β-glucose and then evaporating it at this temperature to a solid mass (*82*). Spray-drying of a hot concentrated glucose solution produces a mixture of the α- and β-sugar (*83*).

In industrial circles, the term "glucose" is used to describe a partially hydrolyzed starch product that consists of dextrins, oligosaccharides, maltose, and D-glucose. The material is also designated as C.S.U. (corn sirup, unmixed). The commercial material is made by autoclaving aqueous starch suspensions with acids. It has a reducing power usually in the range 40 to 45% of the same weight of D-glucose; the concentration of solid material lies in the range 78 to 85%.

"Hydrol" is the mother liquor remaining from the preparation of D-glucose and corresponding to the "molasses" of cane-sugar refining. The sugar content of a typical hydrol consists of about 65% of D-glucose and 35% of disaccharides and higher oligosaccharides. Disaccharides that have been identified (*84*) in hydrol include gentiobiose, maltose, 6-*O*-α-D-glucopyranosyl-D-glucose ("isomaltose," "brachiose"), α,α-trehalose, cellobiose,

80. R. Behrend, *Ann.* **377,** 220 (1910); A. W. Mangam and S. F. Acree, *J. Am. Chem. Soc.* **39,** 965 (1917).

81. C. S. Hudson and J. K. Dale, *J. Am. Chem. Soc.* **39,** 323 (1917).

82. R. L. Whistler and B. F. Buchanan, *J. Biol. Chem.* **125,** 557 (1938); C. Tanret, *Bull. soc. chim. France* [3] **13,** 733 (1895).

83. A. T. Harding, *U. S. Patent* 2,369,231 (1945).

84. H. Berlin, *J. Am. Chem. Soc.* **48,** 1107, 2627 (1926); E. M. Montgomery and F. B. Weakley, *J. Assoc. Offic. Agr. Chemists* **36,** 1096 (1953); J. C. Sowden and A. S. Spriggs, *J. Am. Chem. Soc.* **76,** 3539 (1954); J. C. Sowden and A. S. Spriggs, *J. Am. Chem. Soc.* **78,** 2503 (1956).

and 5-*O*-β-D-glucopyranosyl-D-glucose. The 6-*O*-α-D-glucopyranosyl-D-glucose arises principally as a residuum of the original starch structure (*85*), whereas the other disaccharides are formed mainly by acid reversion of the dextrose (*86*). From amylopectin, hydrolyzed under conditions leading to negligible reversion, 3-*O*-α-D-glucopyranosyl-D-glucose also has been isolated, thus indicating the preformation of this linkage in starch (*86a*).

D-Mannose

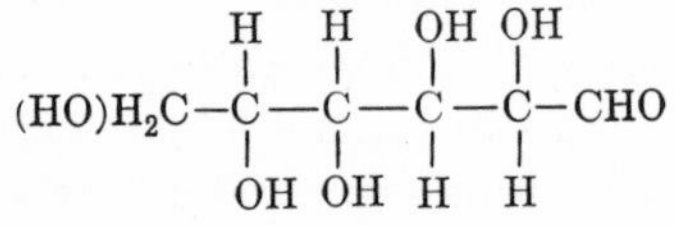

aldehydo-D-Mannose

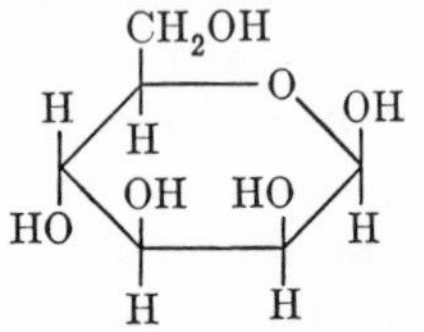

β-D-Mannopyranose

Synonyms. "Seminose."

Occurrence. Authentic instances of the presence of the free sugar in natural products are lacking, but polysaccharides yielding D-mannose on hydrolysis are frequently encountered. For preparatory purposes, the most important source is the seed of the tagua palm (*87*), *Phytelephas macrocarpa*, also known as vegetable ivory. Salep mucilage from tubers of Orchidaceae, white spruce hemicellulose, and *Phoenix canariensis* are rich enough sources of D-mannose that they have been used for the preparation of this sugar. Other mannans are proliferated by yeasts and by the red alga *Porphyra umbilicalis* (*88*). D-Mannose has also been reported as a constituent of ovomucoid, of blood serum globulins, and of tubercle bacilli (Chapter XII).

Preparation (*89*). Shavings obtained as by-products from the preparation of buttons from the ivory nut (*Phytelephas macrocarpa*) are considered the best source. The vegetable-ivory shavings are hydrolyzed with acids, and, by a fractionation employing alcohols, the D-mannose formed is separated from other substances and crystallized directly from alcoholic solution or,

85. A. Thompson, M. L. Wolfrom, and E. J. Quinn, *J. Am. Chem. Soc.*, **75,** 3003 (1953).

86. W. R. Fetzer, E. K. Crosby, C. E. Engel, and L. C. Kirst, *Ind. Eng. Chem.* **45,** 1075 (1953); A. Thompson, K. Anno, M. L. Wolfrom, and M. Inatome, *J. Am. Chem. Soc.* **76,** 1309 (1954).

86a. M. L. Wolfrom and A. Thompson, *J. Am. Chem. Soc.* **77,** 6403 (1955).

87. R. Reiss, *Ber.* **22,** 609 (1889).

88. J. K. N. Jones, *J. Chem. Soc.* p. 3292 (1950).

89. T. S. Harding, *Sugar* **25,** 583 (1923); E. P. Clark, *J. Biol. Chem.* **51,** 1 (1922); C. S. Hudson and E. L. Jackson, *J. Am. Chem. Soc.* **56,** 958 (1934); H. S. Isbell, *J. Research Natl. Bur. Standards* **26,** 47 (1941).

alternatively, is converted to the easily crystallizable methyl α-D-mannoside. The direct crystallization of D-mannose is a considerable improvement over the earlier methods which separated the sugar as the phenylhydrazone.

General Discussion. Both pyranose anomers of the sugar are known, and either may be obtained from aqueous solution by adding seed crystals of the desired form to a supersaturated solution. The importance of having seed crystals is well illustrated by this sugar. The single anomer known for many years was the β-D-mannose, but in laboratories in which the α-anomer had been obtained, it became very difficult to obtain the more-soluble β-form. The β-D-mannose now can be obtained only by very careful exclusion of the seed of the α-anomer.

D-Mannose forms an easily crystallizable compound (*90*) with calcium chloride of the formula $C_6H_{12}O_6 \cdot CaCl_2 \cdot 4H_2O$, which exhibits a complex mutarotation with a maximum and which appears to contain the furanose modification of the sugar.

D-Mannose is absorbed by rats at only about 12% of the rate of D-glucose, and, even after allowance for this difference in absorption, the glycogen deposition in the liver is much smaller for D-mannose than for D-glucose. This sugar is also much less effective than D-glucose in lowering an existing ketonuria (*91*). (See also Chapter XIV.)

sym-D-Mannosylguanosine 5′-pyrophosphoric acid has been isolated from yeast where it is presumed to act as a D-mannose donor in the formation of the yeast mannan (*92*).

D-Fructose

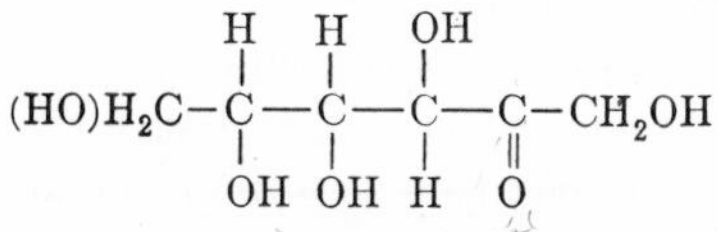
H H OH
(HO)H₂C—C—C—C—C—CH₂OH
OH OH H O

keto-D-Fructose

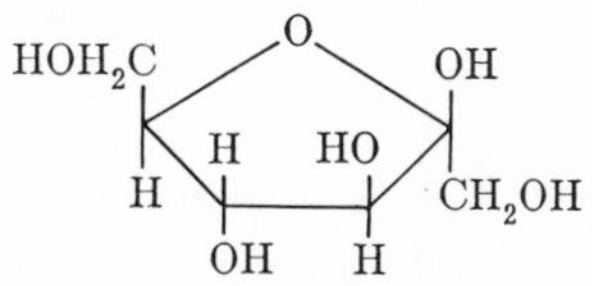
HOH₂C
O
OH
H
HO
H
CH₂OH
OH
H

β(?)-D-Fructofuranose

Synonyms. Levulose, fruit sugar.

Occurrence (*93*). D-Fructose is found, usually accompanied by sucrose, in an uncombined form in fruit juices and honey. Apples and tomatoes are

90. J. K. Dale, *Bur. Standards J. Research* **3,** 459 (1929); H. S. Isbell, *J. Am. Chem. Soc.* **55,** 2166 (1933); H. S. Isbell and W. W. Pigman, *J. Research Natl. Bur. Standards* **18,** 141 (1937).

91. H. J. Deuel, Jr., L. F. Hallman, S. Murray, and J. Hilliard, *J. Biol. Chem.* **125,** 79 (1938).

92. E. Cabib and L. F. Leloir, *J. Biol. Chem.* **206,** 779 (1954).

93. For a review of the chemistry of D-fructose, see C. P. Barry and J. Honeyman, *Advances in Carbohydrate Chem.* **7,** 53 (1952).

said to have particularly large quantities of the sugar. Sucrose consists of D-fructose and D-glucose in glycosidic union. Plants of the family Compositae contain large amounts of levulose polysaccharides (inulins) (Chapter XII). It is of interest that many common weeds, e.g., Jerusalem artichoke, burdock, goldenrod, and dandelion, as well as dahlias and chicory utilize inulins as reserve polysaccharides. The sugar is a frequent constituent of oligosaccharides, often combined with glucose as a sucrose unit, but it rarely occurs in glycosides other than oligosaccharides.

Preparation (*42*). The abundance and wide distribution of D-fructose in natural products, its sweetness, and its resistance to crystallization have stimulated considerable experimental work on methods of preparation. Most methods depend for the isolation of the sugar on the formation of a difficultly soluble calcium levulate or fructosate in which one mole of the sugar is combined with one of lime. The compound is washed free from impurities, such as other sugars and inorganic salts, and decomposed to D-fructose and insoluble calcium carbonate by carbonation.

The best source of D-fructose for large-scale purposes is probably the inversion of sucrose by acids or invertase. The separation of the ketose from the concomitant D-glucose then may be accomplished by direct crystallization, by removal of the D-glucose after oxidation with bromine to D-gluconic acid (ketoses are not affected), or by precipitation of the calcium fructosate. Hydrolysis of the natural inulins mentioned above also may serve for the preparation of D-fructose, which is isolated from the hydrolyzate by precipitation of the lime complex. Conditions are patented for preparing D-fructose by the action of alkali on D-glucose (*94*).

General Discussion. Only one crystalline isomer of the sugar is known, and this is probably a pyranose form. In solution, however, as indicated by evidence obtained from mutarotation studies, a considerable amount of the furanose modification is present. There is no evidence for a true equilibrium between α- and β-anomers although this condition may be a result of the presence of only a small quantity of the unknown anomer rather than of its complete absence. Upon acetylation, the acetylated acyclic modification is obtained accompanied by the cyclic forms. In natural products the sugar, when combined, is always found as the furanose modification.

Most tests have shown D-fructose to be the sweetest of the sugars, although the actual ratios between the various sugars depend to a considerable extent on the methods and conditions adopted for the comparison. Compared to a sweetness value for sucrose of 100, that for D-fructose has been reported as varying from 103 to 173. (See also Chapter XIV.) In Table II are given the relative sweetnesses of some sugars and other organic compounds.

94. S. M. Cantor and K. C. Hobbs, *U. S. Patent* 2,354,664 (1944).

TABLE II

RELATIVE SWEETNESS OF SOME ORGANIC COMPOUNDS (*95*)

Compound	Relative sweetness
Cane sugar (sucrose)	1
D-Fructose	1.0–1.5
D-Glucose	0.5–0.6
Lactose	0.27
Maltose	0.60
Sorbitol	0.48
Glycerol	0.48
Invert sugar	0.8–0.9
Saccharin (D-benzosulfimide)	200–700
Perillaldehyde-α-*anti*-oxime	2000
2-Amino-4-nitrophenyl *n*-propyl ether (*96*)	4000

Intravenously injected D-fructose is assimilated much more rapidly than D-glucose and can be accepted safely at higher rates than the latter without causing undue diuresis, hyperglycemia, or carbohydrate spillage through the urine (*97*). In the absence of ketosis, diabetics can utilize D-fructose without insulin more efficiently than D-glucose, presumably due to differences in the mechanism of initial phosphorylation of the two sugars (*98*). (See Chapter XIV for further discussion.)

L-Sorbose

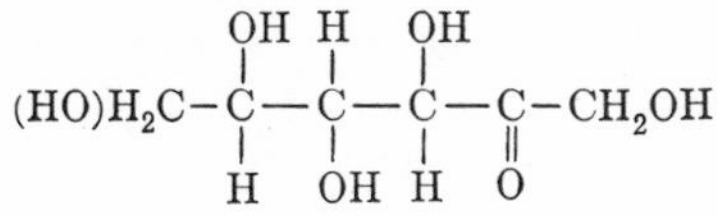
OH H OH
(HO)H2C-C—C—C—C-CH2OH
H OH H O

keto-L-Sorbose

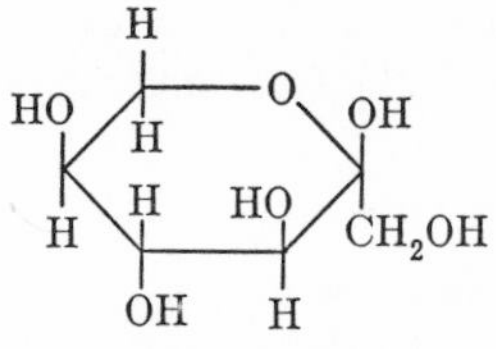
H
HO
O
OH
H
H
HO
H
CH2OH
OH
H

α(?)-L-Sorbopyranose

Synonyms. Sorbinose; also in earlier literature *d*-sorbose.

Occurrence (*99*). L-Sorbose has been reported in the enzymic hydrolyzate

95. C. F. Walton, "International Critical Tables," Vol. 1, p. 357 (1926).

96. J. J. Blanksma and P. W. M. Van der Weyden, *Rec. trav. chim.* **59,** 629 (1940); P. E. Verkade, C. P. van Dijk, and W. Meerburg, *ibid.* **65,** 346 (1946).

97. T. Weichselbaum, R. Elman, and R. H. Lund, *Proc. Soc. Exptl. Biol. Med.* **75,** 816 (1950).

98. M. Miller, W. R. Drucker, J. E. Owens, J. W. Craig, and H. Woodward, Jr., *J. Clin. Invest.* **31,** 115 (1952).

99. For a review of the chemistry of L-sorbose and D-tagatose, see J. V. Karabinos, *Advances in Carbohydrate Chem.* **7,** 99 (1952).

of a pectin from the skin of the passion fruit (*Passiflora edulis*) (*2*). Although L-sorbose is found in the fermented juice of mountain-ash berries (*Sorbus aucuparia* L.), it has been shown to be a secondary product formed by the oxidation of sorbitol (D-glucitol) by bacteria such as *Acetobacter xylinum.*

Preparation. The biochemical oxidation of sorbitol is the most convenient source of this sugar, which, as an intermediate in the commercial synthesis of ascorbic acid, is prepared in large quantities by this method. The early researches by Bertrand (*100*) showed that sorbitol may be oxidized by sorbose bacteria (*Acetobacter xylinum* Adrian Brown) to L-sorbose. Yields of 50 to 75% are reported. By carrying out the fermentation with *Acetobacter suboxydans* in rotating drums instead of utilizing surface cultures of Bertrand's organism, yields of over 90% are obtained (*101*).

D-Tagatose

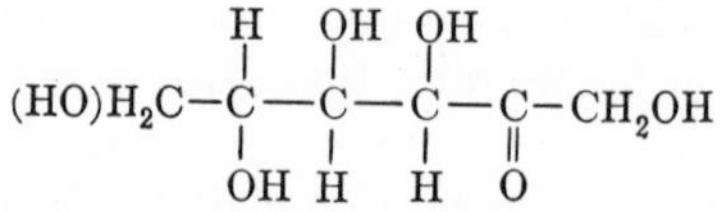

keto-D-Tagatose

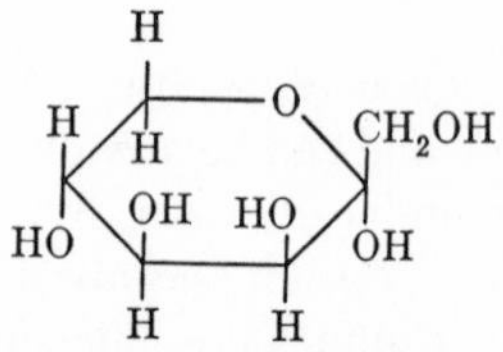

α(?)-D-Tagatopyranose

Occurrence (*99*). D-Tagatose has been obtained as a hydrolytic product from a gum exudate of the tropical tree *Sterculia setigera* (*1*).

Preparation. D-Tagatose has been prepared by the isomerization of D-galactose (*102*) with aqueous alkali or pyridine and by the oxidation of D-talitol with *Acetobacter suboxydans* (*103*).

L-Fucose

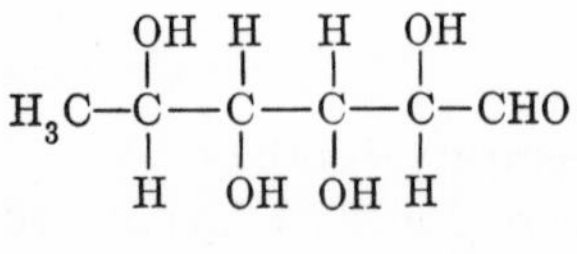

aldehydo-L-Fucose

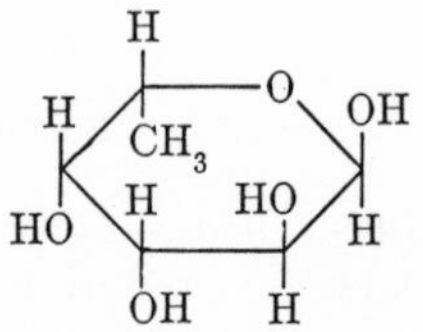

α-L-Fucopyranose

Synonyms. 6-Deoxy-L-galactose, L-galactomethylose, L-rhodeose.

Occurrence. The sugar is found as a constituent of the cell walls of marine

100. G. Bertrand, *Compt. rend.* **126,** 762 (1898).

101. P. A. Wells, J. J. Stubbs, L. B. Lockwood, and E. T. Roe, *Ind. Eng. Chem.* **29,** 1385 (1937).

102. C. A. Lobry de Bruyn and W. Alberda van Ekenstein, *Rec. trav. chim.* **16,** 265 (1897); T. Reichstein and W. Bosshard, *Helv. Chim. Acta* **17,** 753 (1934).

103. E. L. Totton and H. A. Lardy, *J. Am. Chem. Soc.* **71,** 3076 (1949).

algae (seaweed) and of a few gums. It also has been identified in the polysaccharides of blood group – specific substances from both animal and human sources (*104*). This sugar seems to be a fairly common constituent of zoöpolysaccharides (Chapter XII).

Preparation (*42*, *105*). Seaweed (*Fucus* species or *Ascophyllum nodosum*) is hydrolyzed by acids and the neutralized hydrolyzate fermented by galactose-acclimatized yeasts. The solution after evaporation is extracted with alcohol; after removal of the alcohol, the extracted material is converted to the difficulty soluble phenylhydrazone. The hydrazine groups are then removed by reaction with benzaldehyde and the sugar is crystallized from the liquid. The fermentation removes the mannose and galactose which often accompany the L-fucose in seaweeds. The mannose is particularly objectionable since it also forms a difficultly soluble phenylhydrazone.

D-Fucose

Synonyms. 6-Deoxy-D-galactose, D-galactomethylose, rhodeose.

Occurrence and Preparation (*106*). This rare sugar is occasionally found in the hydrolytic products of glycosides. The roots of certain South and Central American plants (Convolvulaceae), used as purgatives, give resins of a glycosidic nature. Jalap resin (convolvulin) and Scammonium or Tampico jalap (jalapin) are obtained from *Tubera jalapae* and *Ipomoea orizabensis*, respectively. Jalapin yields D-glucose, L-rhamnose, D-fucose, and (*dextro*)-11-hydroxyhexadecanoic acid on hydrolysis. Convolvulin on the other hand gives among other products, 3,12-dihydroxyhexadecanoic acid, D-glucose, L-rhamnose, and the 6-deoxy-D-glucose rather than D-fucose.

D-Quinovose

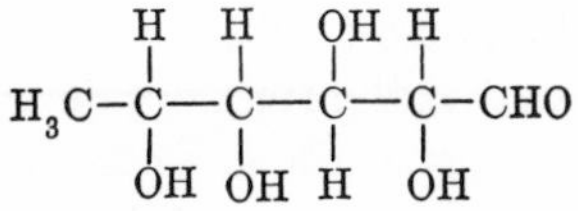
H H OH H
H3C–C–C–C–C–CHO
OH OH H OH

aldehydo-D-Quinovose

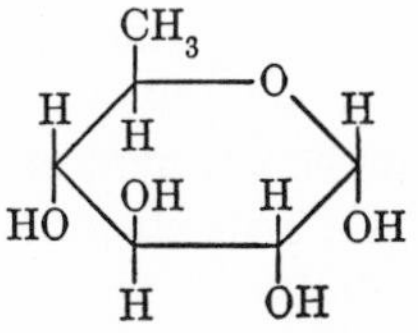
CH3
O
H
H
H
HO
OH
H
OH
H
OH

α-D-Quinovopyranose

Synonyms. 6-Deoxy-D-glucose, D-glucomethylose, D-isorhamnose, D-epirhamnose, isorhodeose, chinovose.

104. H. G. Bray, H. Henry, and M. Stacey, *Biochem. J.* **40,** 124 (1946); E. A. Kabat, H. Baer, A. E. Bezer, and V. Knaub, *J. Exptl. Med.* **88,** 43 (1948).

105. E. P. Clark, *J. Biol. Chem.* **54,** 65 (1922); R. C. Hockett, F. P. Phelps, and C. S. Hudson, *J. Am. Chem. Soc.* **61,** 1658 (1939).

106. E. Votoček and F. Valentin, *Collection Czechoslov. Chem. Communs.* **1,** 46, 606 (1929); F. B. Power and H. Rogerson, *J. Chem. Soc.* **101,** 1 (1912); L. A. Davies and R. Adams, *J. Am. Chem. Soc.* **50,** 1749 (1928); C. Mannich and P. Schumann, *Arch. Pharm.* **276,** 211 (1938).

Occurrence and Preparation (*107*). The bark of many species of *Cinchona* contains a glycoside (quinovin or chinovin) which is extracted with the quinine alkaloids. Upon treatment with alcoholic hydrogen chloride, the ethyl 6-deoxyglucoside is obtained. Convolvulin is a mixture of glycosides, one of which yields 6-deoxy-D-glucose on hydrolysis (*108*) (see under D-Fucose), as does purginic acid.

L-Rhamnose

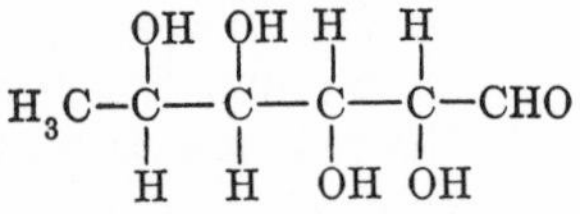

aldehydo-L-Rhamnose

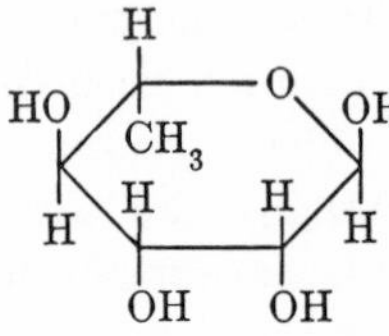

α-L-Rhamnopyranose

Synonyms. 6-Deoxy-L-mannose, L-mannomethylose, "isodulcit."

Occurrence (*109*). The sugar is a frequent constituent of glycosides, which provide its best source. It may occur (*110*) in the free state in the leaves and blossoms of the poison ivy, *Rhus toxicodendron* L. Some polysaccharides of gums and mucilages contain L-rhamnose. The sugar also has been detected in various immunological polysaccharides of bacterial origin (*111*).

Preparation (*42*, *112*). "Lemon flavin," a khaki dyestuff obtained from the bark of an oak species (*Quercus tinctoria* Mich.), provides an excellent source of the sugar. The "lemon flavin" is hydrolyzed by boiling it with acids, and, after neutralization of the solution and treatment with a considerable quantity of decolorizing carbon, the sugar crystallizes from the evaporated solution.

The glycoside naringin, prepared easily from grapefruit canning wastes, has also been suggested as a source of L-rhamnose (*113*).

The main constituent of the "lemon flavin" is the rhamnoside quercitrin (Chapter X). This glycoside yields after hydrolysis the aglycon (quercetin) and L-rhamnose.

General Discussion. The sugar is known in both α- and β-forms. Under ordinary conditions, the α-L-rhamnose · H_2O crystallizes. Anhydrous acetone

107. C. Liebermann and F. Giesel, *Ber.* **16,** 935 (1883); E. Fischer and C. Liebermann, *ibid.* **26,** 2415 (1893); K. Freudenberg, *ibid.* **62,** 373 (1929).

108. E. Votoček, *Ber.* **43,** 476 (1910).

109. See: C. Liebermann and O. Hörmann, *Ann.* **196,** 299 (1879).

110. S. F. Acree and W. A. Syme, *Am. Chem. J.* **36,** 309 (1906).

111. S. M. Partridge, *Biochem. J.* **42,** 251 (1948); G. Pon and A. M. Staub, *Bull. soc. chim. biol.* **34,** 1132 (1952); M. McCarty, *J. Exptl. Med.* **96,** 569 (1952).

112. T. S. Harding, *Sugar* **25,** 23, 82 (1923); C. F. Walton, *J. Am. Chem. Soc.* **43,** 127 (1921).

113. G. N. Pulley and H. W. von Loesecke, *J. Am. Chem. Soc.* **61,** 175 (1939).

solutions, seeded with crystals of the β-anomer, crystallize giving β-L-rhamnose (anhydrous). Seed crystals of the β-anomer are obtained by melting the rhamnose hydrate and allowing the melt to crystallize at high temperatures. A molecular compound, β-rhamnose α-rhamnose, is reported (*114*).

c. Heptoses

D-*manno*-Heptulose

$$\text{(HO)H}_2\text{C}\underset{\overset{|}{\text{OH}}}{\overset{\overset{H}{|}}{-}}\text{C}\underset{\overset{|}{\text{OH}}}{\overset{\overset{H}{|}}{-}}\text{C}\underset{\overset{|}{\text{H}}}{\overset{\overset{OH}{|}}{-}}\text{C}\underset{\overset{|}{\text{H}}}{\overset{\overset{OH}{|}}{-}}\text{C}\underset{\overset{||}{\text{O}}}{-}\text{CH}_2\text{(OH)}$$

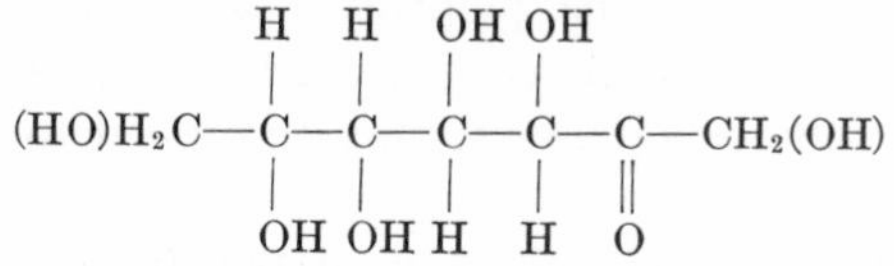

Synonyms. D-Mannoketoheptose.

Occurrence. The sugar is found free accompanied by one of the two corresponding alcohols, perseitol (D-*glycero*-D-*gala*-heptitol), in the avocado or alligator pear (*Persea gratissima*).

Preparation (115). Ground avocados are extracted with water and the extracts evaporated to a thick sirup from which the sugar and perseitol are extracted with alcohol. The process may be repeated several times. The perseitol crystallizes from the alcoholic solution and the D-*manno*-heptulose is separated as the *p*-bromophenylhydrazone, which is converted to the sugar by treatment with benzaldehyde. When crystals are once available, the sugar may be crystallized directly from the extracts.

D-*manno*-Heptulose also may be prepared readily from D-arabinose by the nitroethanol synthesis (see p. 111).

General Discussion. Studies of the physiological availability of the sugar exhibit an interesting species difference. Rabbits can utilize D-*manno*-heptulose but rats cannot. The related aldoheptose D-*glycero*-D-*gala*-heptose is not utilized by either species (*116*).

The constitution of the sugar was shown by conversion to an osazone which is identical with that obtained from the aldoheptoses produced from D-mannose by the cyanohydrin synthesis.

Sedoheptulose

$$\text{(HO)H}_2\text{C}\underset{\overset{|}{\text{OH}}}{\overset{\overset{H}{|}}{-}}\text{C}\underset{\overset{|}{\text{OH}}}{\overset{\overset{H}{|}}{-}}\text{C}\underset{\overset{|}{\text{OH}}}{\overset{\overset{H}{|}}{-}}\text{C}\underset{\overset{|}{\text{H}}}{\overset{\overset{OH}{|}}{-}}\text{C}\underset{\overset{||}{\text{O}}}{-}\text{CH}_2\text{(OH)}$$

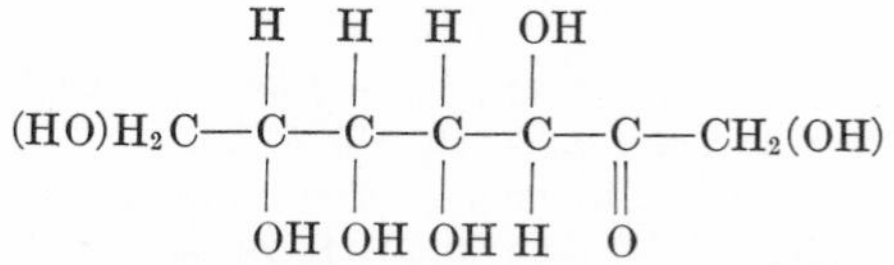

114. E. L. Jackson and C. S. Hudson, *J. Am. Chem. Soc.* **59**, 1076 (1937); E. Fischer, *Ber.* **28**, 1162 (1895); T. Purdie and C. R. Young, *J. Chem. Soc.* **89**, 1194 (1906).

115. F. B. LaForge, *J. Biol. Chem.* **28**, 517 (1916); E. M. Montgomery and C. S. Hudson, *J. Am. Chem. Soc.* **61**, 1654 (1939).

116. J. H. Roe and C. S. Hudson, *J. Biol. Chem.* **121**, 37 (1937).

Synonyms. D-*altro*-Heptulose. "Volemulose" (*117*), obtained by the oxidation of natural volemitol (D-*glycero*-D-*talo*-heptitol) with *Acetobacter xylinum*, has been identified as sedoheptulose (*118*), possibly contaminated with D-*manno*-heptulose (*119*). "Volemose," obtained by hypobromite oxidation of volemitol, is a complex mixture containing mainly the predictable aldoheptoses; the name should be abandoned (*120*).

Occurrence. Sedoheptulose was found originally in *Sedum spectabile*, Bor., a common, herbaceous, perennial plant used for decorative purposes (*121*). It has since been detected in many of the succulent plants, and, indeed, as an intermediate of photosynthesis, it may be present to some extent in all green plants.

Preparation (*121*, *122*). The sugar is extracted by water from ground *Sedum* leaves and stems and the extracts are evaporated to a thick sirup. The sedoheptulose is extracted by alcohol which is removed by evaporation. An aqueous solution of the sirup is purified with lead acetate. After removal of the excess lead by precipitation with hydrogen sulfide, a crude solution of the sugar is obtained.

General Discussion. Sedoheptulose plays an important role in the formation of hexose sugars from lower-carbon fragments both in photosynthesis and in carbohydrate metabolism by animal tissues (Chapter XIII).

Sedoheptulose itself has not been crystallized. However, on being heated with dilute mineral acid, it forms an equilibrium mixture containing about 20% of the sugar and 80% of a readily crystalline, nonreducing anhydride (*121*). The structure of the anhydride has been established as 2,7-anhydro-β-D-*altro*-heptulopyranose (*123*).

The sugar has been suggested as a source for D-altrose and D-ribose since it is easily oxidized by oxygen in alkaline solution to D-altronic acid; calcium D-altronate is oxidized by hydrogen peroxide and ferric acetate to D-ribose. These reactions also provide proof for the assignment of the D-altrose configuration to the sugar (*122*).

117. G. Bertrand, *Bull. soc. chim. France* [3], **19**, 348 (1898).

118. L. C. Stewart, N. K. Richtmyer, and C. S. Hudson, *J. Am. Chem. Soc.* **71**, 3532 (1949).

119. V. Ettel, J. Liebster, M. Tadra and M. Kulhánek, *Collection Czechoslov. Chem. Communs.* **16**, 696 (1951).

120. W. T. Haskins and C. S. Hudson, *J. Am. Chem. Soc.* **69**, 1370 (1947); V. Ettel, J. Liebster, and M. Tadra, *Chem. Listy* **46**, 445 (1952).

121. F. B. LaForge and C. S. Hudson, *J. Biol. Chem.* **30**, 61 (1917).

122. N. K. Richtmyer, R. M. Hann, and C. S. Hudson, *J. Am. Chem. Soc.* **61**, 343 (1939).

123. J. W. Pratt, N. K. Richtmyer, and C. S. Hudson, *J. Am. Chem. Soc.* **73**, 1876 (1951); **74**, 2200 (1952).

2. SYNTHETIC SUGARS

Synthetic sugars are obtained by two main routes. For the completely synthetic sugars, the starting materials are simple, nonsugar organic substances, and, since the latter are either racemic or nonasymmetric, the sugars produced are racemic. The most widely applied and important methods depend upon transformations of available natural sugars or their derivatives to other, synthetic sugars. These transformations may utilize increases or decreases in chain length, isomerizations, or inversions of configuration.

A. COMPLETE SYNTHESIS OF THE SUGARS

a. Formose and Related Products

Formaldehyde condenses in the presence of weak bases to form a complex mixture of sugars called formose or methose (*124*). The polymerization undoubtedly proceeds through a combination of acyloin and aldol condensations. Fischer and Tafel (*125*) obtained a similar sugar mixture by the action of dilute alkali on acrolein dibromide. Presumably, the reaction sequence is the following (Chapter I):

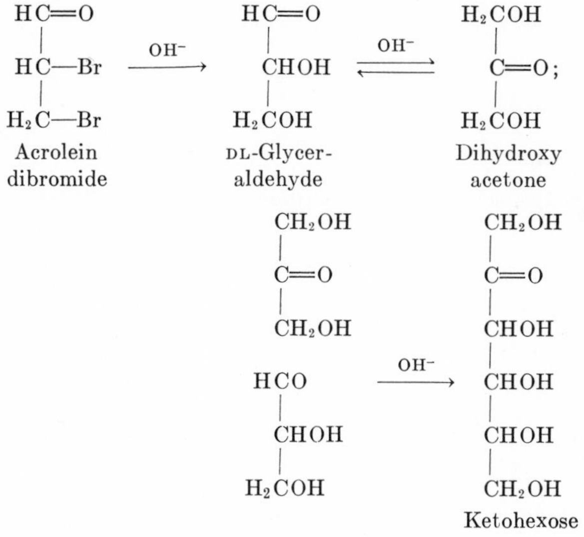

$$
\begin{array}{ccccc}
\text{HC}{=}\text{O} & & \text{HC}{=}\text{O} & & \text{H}_2\text{COH} \\
| & \xrightarrow{\text{OH}^-} & | & \xrightleftharpoons{\text{OH}^-} & | \\
\text{HC—Br} & & \text{CHOH} & & \text{C}{=}\text{O}; \\
| & & | & & | \\
\text{H}_2\text{C—Br} & & \text{H}_2\text{COH} & & \text{H}_2\text{COH} \\
\text{Acrolein} & & \text{DL-Glycer-} & & \text{Dihydroxy} \\
\text{dibromide} & & \text{aldehyde} & & \text{acetone}
\end{array}
$$

$$
\begin{array}{ccc}
\text{CH}_2\text{OH} & & \text{CH}_2\text{OH} \\
| & & | \\
\text{C}{=}\text{O} & & \text{C}{=}\text{O} \\
| & & | \\
\text{CH}_2\text{OH} & & \text{CHOH} \\
& & | \\
\text{HCO} & \xrightarrow{\text{OH}^-} & \text{CHOH} \\
| & & | \\
\text{CHOH} & & \text{CHOH} \\
| & & | \\
\text{H}_2\text{COH} & & \text{CH}_2\text{OH} \\
& & \text{Ketohexose}
\end{array}
$$

Treatment of the reaction product with phenylhydrazine gave two crystalline hexosazones in yields of about 13 % (*125, 126*). The two osazones were

---

124. A. Butlerow, *Ann.* **120**, 295 (1861); O. Loew, *J. prakt. Chem.* [2], **33**, 321 (1886).
125. E. Fischer and J. Tafel, *Ber.* **20**, 1088, 2566 (1887).
126. W. Küster and F. Schoder, *Z. physiol. Chem.* **141**, 110 (1924).

given the names α-acrosazone and β-acrosazone; the corresponding sugar components are α-acrose and β-acrose. The constitution of these products was demonstrated in an outstanding series of researches by Fischer and Tafel (*127*), which also led to the complete synthesis of D-glucose, D-mannose, and D-fructose:

Fischer and Tafel's Complete Synthesis of Hexose Sugars

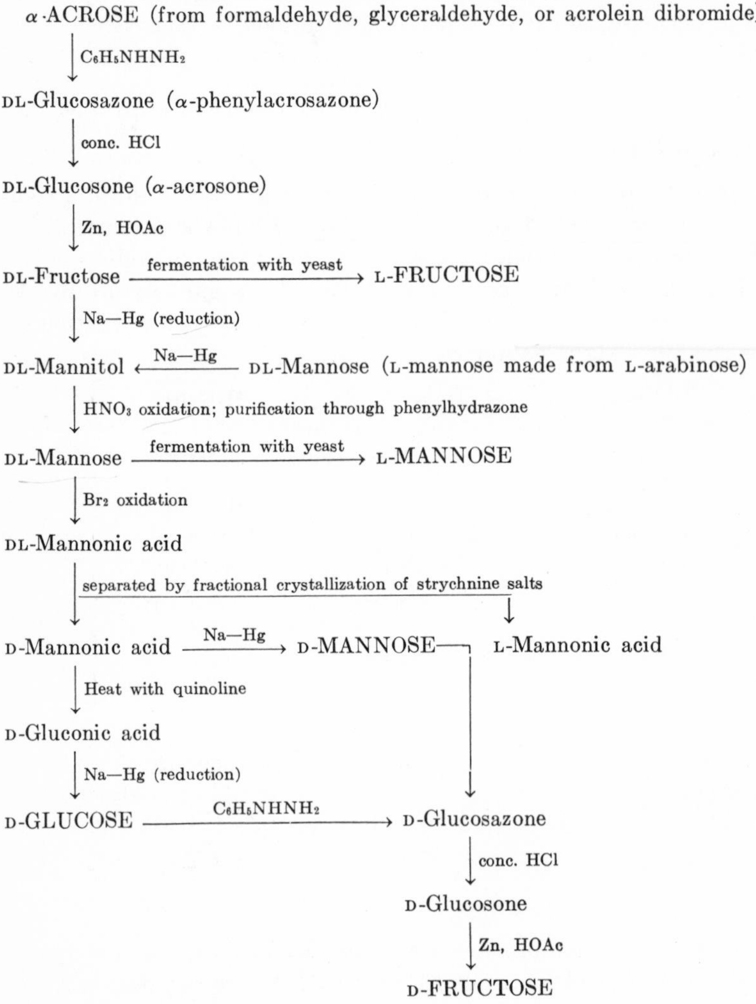
α-ACROSE (from formaldehyde, glyceraldehyde, or acrolein dibromide)
$C_6H_5NHNH_2$
DL-Glucosazone (α-phenylacrosazone)
conc. HCl
DL-Glucosone (α-acrosone)
Zn, HOAc
DL-Fructose
fermentation with yeast
L-FRUCTOSE
Na—Hg (reduction)
DL-Mannitol
Na—Hg
DL-Mannose (L-mannose made from L-arabinose)
HNO_3 oxidation; purification through phenylhydrazone
DL-Mannose
fermentation with yeast
L-MANNOSE
Br_2 oxidation
DL-Mannonic acid
separated by fractional crystallization of strychnine salts
D-Mannonic acid
Na—Hg
D-MANNOSE
L-Mannonic acid
Heat with quinoline
D-Gluconic acid
Na—Hg (reduction)
D-GLUCOSE
$C_6H_5NHNH_2$
D-Glucosazone
conc. HCl
D-Glucosone
Zn, HOAc
D-FRUCTOSE

---

127. See summary by E. Fischer, *Ber.* **23,** 2114 (1890).

From this evidence, particularly the identification of the DL-mannitol from natural sources with that from the α-acrosazone, the α-acrose could be any (or all) of the three DL-sugars which yields the DL-glucosazone: glucose, mannose, and fructose. The β-acrosazone has been shown to be DL-sorbosazone, which could be produced from gulose and idose as well as sorbose (*126*, *128*). Considerations of the mechanism of the reaction indicate that only the ketoses can result as straight-chain products from the reactions of the glyceraldehyde and of the acrolein dibromide, and the resistance of formose to bromine oxidation supports this view. The condensations to these products are undoubtedly aldol condensations which take place between the carbonyl groups and hydrogen atoms *adjacent* to carbonyl groups (Chapter I). If two molecules of glyceraldehyde reacted in this fashion, the product would have a branched chain and not a straight chain. However, in alkaline solution glyceraldehyde is in equilibrium with dihydroxyacetone, and these substances could condense to form ketoses. This mechanism is substantiated by the direct isolation from the acrose mixture of DL-sorbose (*128*). Thus, of the four possible ketohexoses which should be formed since no asymmetric reagents are involved, two have been identified as DL-fructose (α-acrose) and DL-sorbose (β-acrose). The other isomers may be present in minor amounts in the condensation products along with many other substances. Kinetic studies have indicated that the final yield of straight-chain ketohexoses is 75 to 90% when dilute sodium hydroxide is used to condense DL-glyceraldehyde (*129*).

A further discussion of the aldol condensation as a synthetic method for the sugars appears on page 113.

b. Direct Chemical Syntheses

By the application of a series of standard organic reactions (*130*), DL-threose has been prepared from 1,3-dichloro-2-propanol and from γ-bromocrotonaldehyde, while DL-erythrose has been obtained from allyl alcohol.

A number of racemic and *meso* hexitols and pentitols have been prepared by Lespieau and Wiemann (*131*) from simpler, unsaturated, organic start-

128. E. Schmitz, *Ber.* **46,** 2327 (1913).

129. W. G. Berl and C. E. Feazel, *J. Am. Chem. Soc.* **73,** 2054 (1951).

130. W. W. Lake and J. W. E. Glattfeld, *J. Am. Chem. Soc.* **66,** 1091 (1944); J. W. E. Glattfeld and B. D. Kribben, *ibid.* **61,** 1721 (1939); G. Braun, *ibid.* **52,** 3167, 3176 (1930); **54,** 1133 (1932); H. Schmid and E. Grob, *Helv. Chim. Acta* **32,** 77 (1949).

131. R. Lespieau, *Advances in Carbohydrate Chem.* **2,** 107 (1946).

ing materials. The following synthesis of allitol and galactitol is typical:

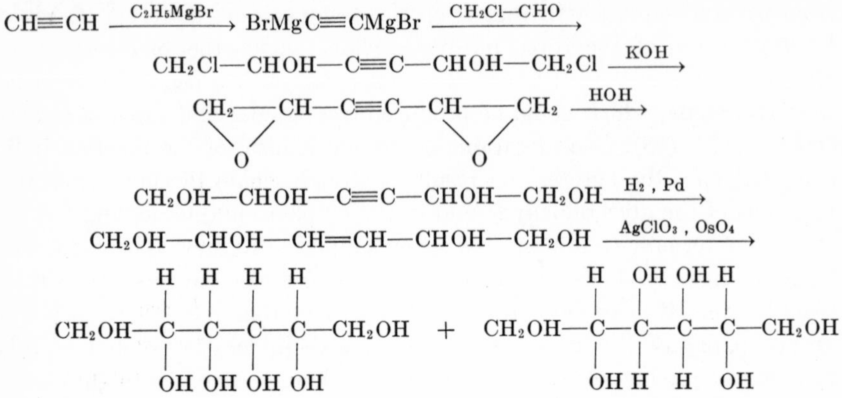

Allitol Galactitol

B. Methods for Lengthening the Carbon Chain of the Sugars

a. The Cyanohydrin Synthesis (Kiliani-Fischer)

One of the earliest and most useful methods of increasing the length of the carbon chain of the sugars takes advantage of the well-known addition of hydrocyanic acid to aldehydes or ketones:

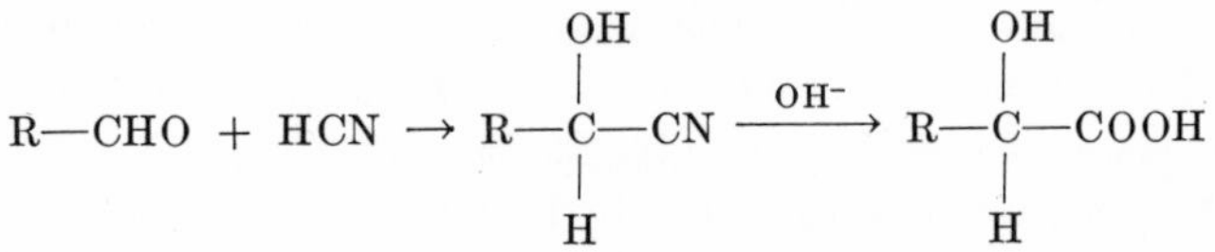

Cyanohydrin

The original procedure devised by Kiliani (*132*) for the sugars involved the reaction of the sugar with an aqueous solution of hydrogen cyanide in the presence of a little ammonia. This has been simplified and improved by adding the sugar to a solution of sodium cyanide and calcium chloride (*133*). In solutions buffered at pH 9.0–9.1, the addition reaction apparently goes to completion with all simple sugars (*134*). The cyanohydrins, which normally are not isolated, are hydrolyzed with alkali, and the resulting acids are obtained by appropriate means as their lactones.

Inasmuch as a new asymmetric center is created, two isomers are formed, but, since the original substance is optically active, the amounts of the two isomers will usually not be equal (asymmetric synthesis). The proportions

132. H. Kiliani, *Ber.* **18,** 3066 (1885); **19,** 221, 772 (1886), (fructose); **19,** 767, 1128 (1886), (glucose); **19,** 3029 (1886); **20,** 282, 339 (1887), (arabinose); **21,** 915 (1888); **22,** 521 (1889), (galactose).

133. C. S. Hudson, O. Hartley, and C. B. Purves, *J. Am. Chem. Soc.* **56,** 1248 (1934).

134. W. Militzer, *Arch. Biochem.* **21,** 143 (1949).

vary from about equal amounts (ribose and HCN) to almost entirely one isomer (mannose and HCN) under the original conditions of Kiliani. The generalization has been made (*135*) that the product formed in largest quantity by the cyanohydrin synthesis has a *trans* configuration for carbons 2 and 4. However, the important observation was made later that the proportions of epimers formed can be varied over a wide range depending upon whether the condensation is performed under conditions of acid or base catalysis (*136*, *137*). Thus, the arabinoses under base catalysis give mainly the products with gluconic configuration whereas acid catalysis produces mainly the mannonic isomers.

The method of choice for separating the epimeric acids usually is unique for each individual starting sugar and is based on fractional crystallizations of the lactones, metallic or alkaloidal salts, the phenylhydrazides, amides, double salts, benzylidene derivatives, etc.

The cyanohydrin synthesis of higher-carbon aldose sugars was completed with the observation by Emil Fischer (*138*) that the sugar acid lactones can be reduced to the corresponding sugars with sodium amalgam, in slightly acid solution. When conducted in alkaline solutions, the reductions proceed further to the sugar alcohols. The fact that the lactones, but not the aldonic acids, are reduced by this treatment is analogous to the relatively easy reduction of simple organic esters in contrast to the stability of the related free acids towards reduction. Control of the pH at 3–3.5 during the reduction of the lactones is the most important factor for obtaining maximum yields of the sugars (*139*). The use of the slightly soluble sodium acid oxalate or benzoic acid in the reduction mixture gives more effective pH control than the stepwise addition of mineral acids (*137*).

Reduction of the sugar acid lactones to aldose sugars also may be accomplished by catalytic hydrogenation (*140*) or, very conveniently, with sodium borohydride in aqueous solution (*141*). Other methods of reduction include the catalytic hydrogenation of the acetylated aldonyl chlorides (*142*) or thio esters (*143*).

135. See: C. S. Hudson, *Advances in Carbohydrate Chem.* **1,** 26 (1945).

136. C. S. Hudson, *J. Am. Chem. Soc.* **73,** 4498 (1951).

137. H. S. Isbell, J. V. Karabinos, H. L. Frush, N. B. Holt, A. Schwebel, and T. T. Galkowski, *J. Research Natl. Bur. Standards* **48,** 163 (1952).

138. E. Fischer, *Ber.* **22,** 2204 (1889).

139. N. Sperber, H. E. Zaugg, and W. M. Sandstrom, *J. Am. Chem. Soc.* **69,** 915 (1947).

140. J. W. E. Glattfeld and E. M. Shaver, *J. Am. Chem. Soc.* **49,** 2305 (1927); J. W. E. Glattfeld and G. W. Schimpff, *ibid.* **57,** 2204 (1935).

141. M. L. Wolfrom and H. B. Wood, *J. Am. Chem. Soc.* **73,** 2933 (1951).

142. E. W. Cook and R. T. Major, *J. Am. Chem. Soc.* **58,** 2410 (1936); J. W. E. Glattfeld and B. D. Kribben, *ibid.* **61,** 1720 (1939).

143. M. L. Wolfrom and J. V. Karabinos, *J. Am. Chem. Soc.* **68,** 1455 (1946).

The cyanohydrin synthesis is illustrated by the preparation of the heptoses from D-mannose (*144*).

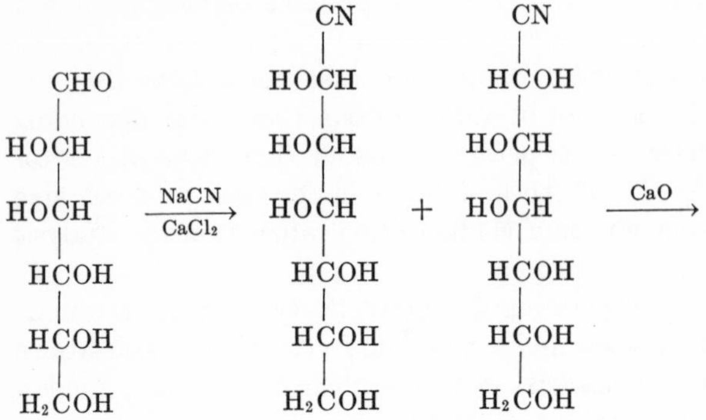
CHO
HOCH
HOCH
HCOH
HCOH
H2COH
NaCN
CaCl2
CN
HOCH
HOCH
HOCH
HCOH
HCOH
H2COH
+
CN
HCOH
HOCH
HOCH
HCOH
HCOH
H2COH
CaO

D-Mannose   Epimeric D-mannoheptonic nitriles

Crystalline mixture of basic calcium salts, $Ca(C_7H_{13}O_8)_2 \cdot 2CaO \xrightarrow{CO_2}$

Normal calcium salts, $Ca(C_7H_{13}O_8)_2$

By direct crystallization of the calcium salts one isomer is obtained in fairly pure form. The mother liquors which contain both isomers are converted to the free acids by treatment with sulfuric acid and finally to the lead salts by neutralization of the acids with lead oxide. Fractional crystallization of these lead salts leads to separation of the two isomers. These are converted to the lactones, (I, II), which in turn are reduced to the sugars (III, IV) by sodium amalgam in slightly acid solution.

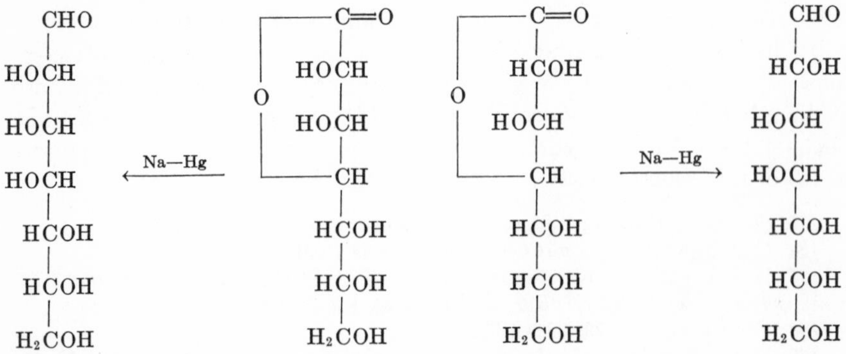
CHO
HOCH
HOCH
HOCH
HCOH
HCOH
H2COH
Na—Hg
C=O
HOCH
O
HOCH
CH
HCOH
HCOH
H2COH
C=O
HCOH
O
HOCH
CH
HCOH
HCOH
H2COH
Na—Hg
CHO
HCOH
HOCH
HOCH
HCOH
HCOH
H2COH

(IV) (I) (II) (III)

The cyanohydrin synthesis should make it possible to go from the simplest members of the sugar series to all of the higher sugars. Synthetic

144. H. S. Isbell, *J. Research Natl. Bur. Standards* **20,** 97 (1938).

sugars with as many as ten carbons in a straight chain (e.g., a D-glucodecose) have been prepared from the hexoses by this method (*145*).

b. The Nitromethane Synthesis (*Sowden-Fischer*)

The nitromethane synthesis of higher-carbon aldose sugars utilizes two well-known general reactions of the nitroparaffins. These are the base-catalyzed condensation of nitromethane with an aldehyde to produce a *C*-nitroalcohol (*146*), and the decomposition of the sodium salt of the latter with cold, moderately concentrated mineral acid to produce an aldehyde (*147*) containing one more carbon atom than the original aldehyde.

$$R{-}CHO + CH_3NO_2 \xrightarrow{Na^+OH^-} R{-}CHOH{-}CH{=}NO_2{\cdot}Na + H_2O$$

$$2\ R{-}CHOH{-}CH{=}NO_2{\cdot}Na + 2\ H_2SO_4 \rightarrow$$

$$2\ R{-}CHOH{-}CHO + 2\ NaHSO_4 + N_2O + H_2O$$

Under the conditions explored so far for conducting this synthesis in the sugar series (*148*), it is not as widely applicable, with regard to starting sugar, as is the cyanohydrin synthesis. However, for certain selected syntheses the nitromethane synthesis has the advantage of simplicity combined with satisfactory yields.

Although the sugars condense with nitromethane in aqueous alkali (*148a*), the reaction usually is carried out in methanol solution (or suspension) with sodium methoxide acting as the basic catalyst. In the most favorable examples of the condensation reaction, the sodium salts of the *C*-nitroalcohols precipitate from this solution and can be isolated simply by filtration. As in the cyanohydrin condensation, two epimeric products are formed, usually in unequal amounts. After removal of the sodium by ion exchange, the epimeric *C*-nitroalcohols frequently can be separated by fractional crystallization. For some syntheses, partially substituted sugars, such as the benzylidene derivatives, may be used to advantage.

The decomposition of the sodium *C*-nitroalcohols with aqueous sulfuric acid to give the corresponding higher-carbon aldose sugars proceeds smoothly, and the resulting sugars are either crystallized directly or isolated as a convenient derivative.

The nitromethane synthesis is illustrated by the preparation of L-glucose and L-mannose from L-arabinose (*149*).

145. L. H. Philippe, *Ann. chim. phys.* [8] **26,** 393 (1912).
146. L. Henry, *Compt. rend.* **120,** 1265 (1895).
147. J. U. Nef, *Ann.* **280,** 263 (1894).
148. See: J. C. Sowden, *Advances in Carbohydrate Chem.* **6,** 291 (1951).
148a. J. C. Sowden and R. R. Thompson, *J. Am. Chem. Soc.* **77,** 3160 (1955).
149. J. C. Sowden and H. O. L. Fischer, *J. Am. Chem. Soc.* **69,** 1963 (1947).

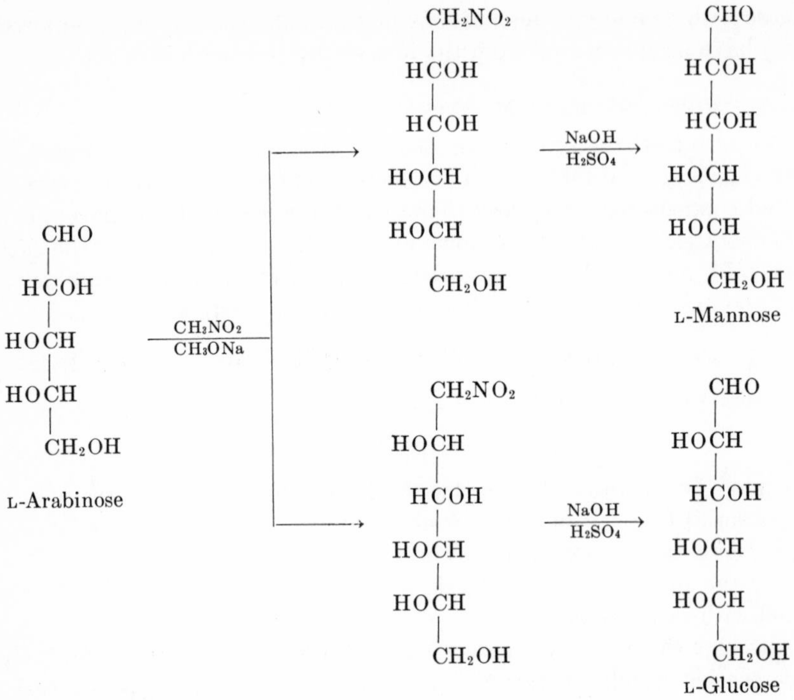
CH_3NO_2
CH_3ONa
NaOH
H_2SO_4
L-Arabinose
L-Mannose
L-Glucose

The mixed, epimeric *C*-nitroalcohols, obtained in nearly equal amounts in a combined yield of approximately 50%, are readily separated by fractional crystallization. Decomposition of the individual sodium *C*-nitroalcohols with aqueous sulfuric acid then affords the hexoses in good yield. The L-glucose may be crystallized directly, and the L-mannose is isolated conveniently via the phenylhydrazone.

In addition to L-glucose and L-mannose, other sugars that have been prepared conveniently by the nitromethane synthesis include L-gulose (*150*), the aldoheptoses from D-mannose (*151*), and D-*erythro*-L-*manno*-octose (*152*).

A double condensation of nitromethane with a pentose dialdehyde has been applied to effect ring closure, yielding a mixture of *C*-nitrodeoxyinositols. The sodium salts of these cyclic *C*-nitroalcohols, in contrast to the straight-chain analogs, were found to be stable to aqueous sulfuric acid when attempts were made to convert them to the corresponding ketoses (inososes) (*153*).

150. J. C. Sowden and H. O. L. Fischer, *J. Am. Chem. Soc.* **67,** 1713 (1945).
151. J. C. Sowden and R. Schaffer, *J. Am. Chem. Soc.* **73,** 4662 (1951).
152. J. V. Karabinos and C. S. Hudson, *J. Am. Chem. Soc.* **75,** 4324 (1953).
153. J. M. Grosheintz and H. O. L. Fischer, *J. Am. Chem. Soc.* **70,** 1476, 1479 (1948); B. Iselin and H. O. L. Fischer, *ibid.* **70,** 3946 (1948).

An adaptation of the nitromethane synthesis to the preparation of higher-carbon ketose sugars involves the use of nitroethanol in place of nitromethane. Two carbons, thus, are added to an aldose sugar to give a mixture of two ketose sugars. An example is the conversion of D-arabinose to a mixture of D-*manno*-heptulose and D-*gluco*-heptulose (*154*). The intermediate secondary nitroalcohols may be obtained, alternatively, by condensing the aldose successively with nitromethane and formaldehyde (*154a*).

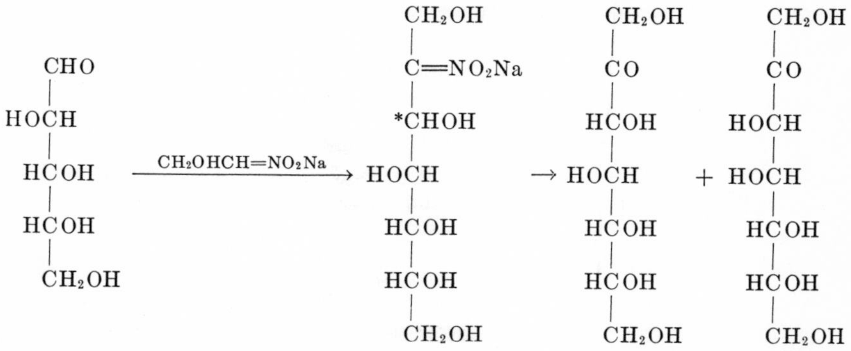
CHO
HOCH
HCOH
HCOH
CH₂OH
CH₂OHCH=NO₂Na
CH₂OH
C=NO₂Na
*CHOH
HOCH
HCOH
HCOH
CH₂OH
CH₂OH
CO
HCOH
HOCH
HCOH
HCOH
CH₂OH
CH₂OH
CO
HOCH
HOCH
HCOH
HCOH
CH₂OH

D-Arabinose D-*gluco*-Heptulose D-*manno*-Heptulose

c. The Diazomethane Synthesis

The action of diazomethane on an acid chloride to give a diazomethyl ketone (*155*) and the hydrolysis or acetolysis of the latter is applicable as a method of synthesis for higher-carbon ketoses (*156a–d*).

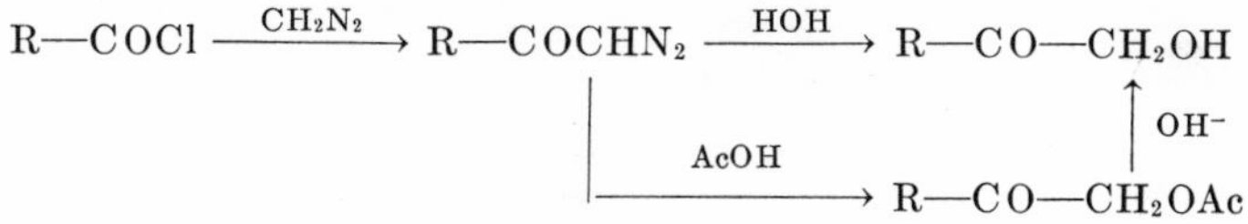
R—COCl
CH₂N₂
R—COCHN₂
HOH
R—CO—CH₂OH
OH⁻
AcOH
R—CO—CH₂OAc

The fully acetylated (or acetonated) intermediates are employed in the sugar series, so that the complete sequence of synthesis is:

Aldose → acetylated aldonic acid → acetylated aldonyl chloride → acetylated diazomethyl ketose → acetylated ketose → ketose

154. J. C. Sowden, *J. Am. Chem. Soc.* **72,** 3325 (1950).

154a. J. K. N. Jones, *J. Chem. Soc.* p. 3643 (1954).

155. F. Arndt, B. Eistert, and W. Partale, *Ber.* **60,** 1364 (1927); F. Arndt and J. Amende, *ibid.* **61,** 1122 (1928).

156a. K. Gätzi and T. Reichstein, *Helv. Chim. Acta* **21,** 186 (1938).

156b. K. Iwadare, *Bull. Chem. Soc. Japan* **14,** 131 (1939).

156c. M. L. Wolfrom, D. I. Weisblat, W. H. Zophy, and S. W. Waisbrot, *J. Am. Chem. Soc.* **63,** 201 (1941).

156d. M. L. Wolfrom, S. W. Waisbrot, and R. L. Brown, *J. Am. Chem. Soc.* **64,** 2329 (1942).

The acetylated aldonic acids may be prepared by oxidation of the *aldehydo*-sugar acetates (*157*), by the direct acetylation of certain aldonic salts (*158*), or by the sequence (*159*):

Aldose → aldose oxime → acetylated aldononitrile →

acetylated aldonamide → acetylated aldonic acid

In only a few instances are the fully acetylated acids available by direct acetylation of the free acids, the acetylated lactones being the more usual products (see Chapter VI, also).

The diazomethane synthesis of ketoses has been widely applied by Wolfrom and his co-workers. Among the ketose sugars that have been prepared from lower-carbon aldose sugars by this method are: D- and L-sorbose, D- and L-fructose, L-*gala*-heptulose (perseulose) and its enantiomorph, L-*manno*-heptulose (the enantiomorph of the naturally occurring sugar from the avocado), and sedoheptulose, as well as several ketooctoses and two ketononoses (*156a*, *156d*, *160–165*).

The method is illustrated by the synthesis of D-*gala*-heptulose (*162*):

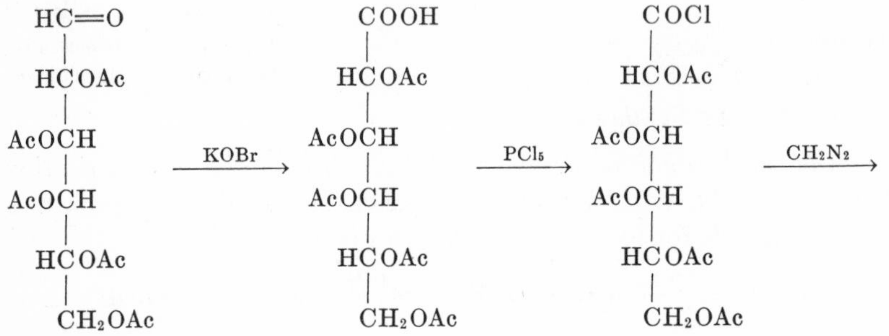

aldehydo-D-Galactose pentaacetate

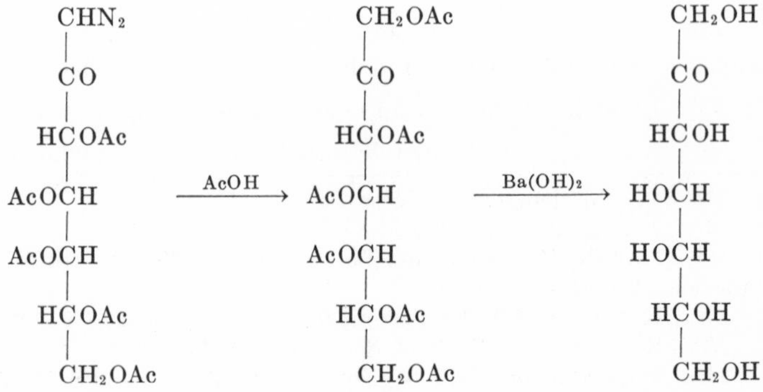

D-*gala*-Heptulose

157. R. T. Major and E. W. Cook, *J. Am. Chem. Soc.* **58**, 2410, 2474 (1936).

The versatility of diazomethane as a synthetic tool in the open-chain sugar series is evident in the following applications:

The reaction with an *aldehydo*-sugar acetate leads to a deoxyketose (*156c*).

$$R{-}CHOAc{-}CHO + CH_2N_2 \rightarrow R{-}CHOAc{-}CO{-}CH_3 + N_2$$

The acetylated diazomethyl ketoses undergo the Wolff rearrangement (*166*) when treated in water with silver oxide to give a mixture of 2-deoxyaldonic lactones (*167*).

$$R{-}CHOAc{-}CHOAc{-}CHOAc{-}CO{-}CHN_2 \xrightarrow[H_2O]{Ag_2O}$$

$$\underbrace{R{-}CH{-}CHOAc{-}CHOAc{-}CH_2{-}C}_{O}{=}O$$

When treated with dry hydrogen halides, the acetylated diazomethyl ketoses yield the halogenated deoxyketoses (*167*).

$$R{-}CHOAc{-}CO{-}CHN_2 + HX \rightarrow R{-}CHOAc{-}CO{-}CH_2X + N_2$$

d. Miscellaneous Syntheses

The alkali-catalyzed aldol condensations of lower-carbon sugars as a means of increasing the chain length are of particular interest in view of the importance in biological systems of similar condensations catalyzed by enzymes (aldolases) and also in view of the mechanism of the alkaline rearrangements of sugars (Chapter I).

The earlier aldol condensations of racemic glyceraldehyde to give racemic hexose sugars (p. 103) have been repeated with the pure enantiomorph, D-glyceraldehyde, and dihydroxyacetone (*168*). When these substances are condensed by 0.01 *M* barium hydroxide solution, a mixture of nearly

---

158. K. Ladenburg, M. Tishler, J. W. Wellman, and R. D. Babson, *J. Am. Chem. Soc.* **66,** 1217 (1944).

159. C. D. Hurd and J. C. Sowden, *J. Am. Chem. Soc.* **60,** 235 (1938); see also G. B. Robbins and F. W. Upson, *ibid.* **60,** 1788 (1938); **62,** 1074 (1940).

160. M. L. Wolfrom, S. M. Olin, and E. F. Evans, *J. Am. Chem. Soc.* **66,** 204 (1944).

161. M. L. Wolfrom and A. Thompson, *J. Am. Chem. Soc.* **68,** 791 (1946).

162. M. L. Wolfrom, J. M. Berkebile, and A. Thompson, *J. Am. Chem. Soc.* **71,** 2360 (1949); M. L. Wolfrom, R. L. Brown, and E. F. Evans, *ibid.* **65,** 1021 (1943).

163. M. L. Wolfrom and H. B. Wood, *J. Am. Chem. Soc.* **73,** 730 (1951).

164. M. L. Wolfrom, J. M. Berkebile, and A. Thompson, *J. Am. Chem. Soc.* **74,** 2197 (1952).

165. M. L. Wolfrom and A. Thompson, *J. Am. Chem. Soc.* **68,** 1453 (1946); M. L. Wolfrom and P. W. Cooper, *ibid.* **71,** 2668 (1949); **72,** 1345 (1950); M. L. Wolfrom and H. B. Wood, *ibid.* **77,** 3096 (1955).

166. L. Wolff, *Ann.* **394,** 23 (1912).

167. M. L. Wolfrom, S. W. Waisbrot, and R. L. Brown, *J. Am. Chem. Soc.* **64,** 1701 (1942).

168. H. O. L. Fischer and E. Baer, *Helv. Chim. Acta* **19,** 519 (1936).

equal parts of D-fructose and D-sorbose is obtained in 90 to 95% yield. The other two possible ketohexoses (D-tagatose and D-psicose) were not detected. The asymmetric synthesis favors the formation of *trans* hydroxyl groups for the two new asymmetric centers (carbons 3 and 4). Similarly, when

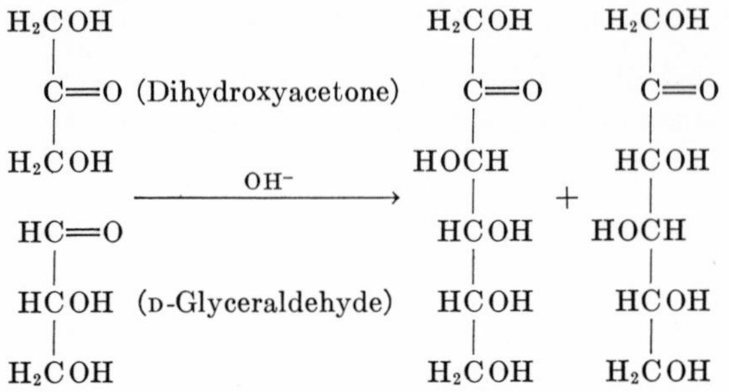

$$
\begin{array}{cccc}
\text{H}_2\text{COH} & & \text{H}_2\text{COH} & \text{H}_2\text{COH} \\
| & & | & | \\
\text{C}=\text{O} \ (\text{Dihydroxyacetone}) & & \text{C}=\text{O} & \text{C}=\text{O} \\
| & & | & | \\
\text{H}_2\text{COH} & \xrightarrow[]{\text{OH}^-} & \text{HOCH} & \text{HCOH} \\
& & | & \quad | \\
\text{HC}=\text{O} & & \text{HCOH} \ + \ \text{HOCH} \\
| & & | & | \\
\text{HCOH} \ (\text{D-Glyceraldehyde}) & & \text{HCOH} & \text{HCOH} \\
| & & | & | \\
\text{H}_2\text{COH} & & \text{H}_2\text{COH} & \text{H}_2\text{COH} \\
& & \text{D-Fructose} & \text{D-Sorbose}
\end{array}
$$

D-glyceraldehyde is condensed with glycolaldehyde, all four D-aldopentoses result with arabinose and xylose (2,3-*trans* hydroxyls) predominating over ribose and lyxose (2,3-*cis* hydroxyls) (*169*). Branched-chain sugars, presumably aldohexoses, are formed from 2,3-O-isopropylidene-D-glyceraldehyde in the presence of alkali (*170*), and a racemic branched-chain ketohexose can be isolated from dihydroxyacetone under similar conditions (*171*). The employment of an asymmetric catalyst (enzyme) directs the course of the reaction so that fewer isomers are formed. Thus, D-glyceraldehyde and dihydroxyacetone 1-phosphate condense in the presence of an aldolase from yeast and muscle extracts, giving D-fructose 1-phosphate as the sole reaction product (*172*). In close analogy to its biological synthesis (Chapter XIII) is the preparation of 2-deoxy-D-ribose by the aldol condensation of 2,3-O-isopropylidene-D-glyceraldehyde with acetaldehyde (*173*).

Partially methylated sugars may be prepared from the corresponding methylated polymerizing substances. Thus, methoxyacetaldehyde, prepared by chromic acid oxidation of methoxyethanol, polymerizes in the presence of potassium carbonate to 2,4-di-O-methylaldotetrose (*174*).

$$2\text{CH}_3\text{OCH}_2\text{—CHO} \xrightarrow{\text{K}_2\text{CO}_3} \text{CH}_3\text{OCH}_2\text{—CH(OH)—CH(OCH}_3\text{)—CHO}$$

A condensation reaction (*175*) of particular value for the preparation of ascorbic acid and related substances depends on the coupling of sugars with

169. L. Hough and J. K. N. Jones, *Nature* **167**, 180 (1951).
170. H. O. L. Fischer and E. Baer, *Ber.* **63**, 1749 (1930).
171. L. M. Utkin, *Doklady Akad. Nauk S.S.S.R.* **67**, 301 (1950).
172. O. Meyerhof, K. Lohmann, and P. Schuster, *Biochem. Z.* **286**, 319 (1936).
173. W. G. Overend and M. Stacey, *J. Sci. Food Agr.* **1**, 168 (1950).
174. C. D. Hurd and J. L. Abernethy, *J. Am. Chem. Soc.* **63**, 1966 (1941).
175. B. Helferich and O. Peters, *Ber.* **70**, 465 (1937).

the ethyl ester of glyoxylic acid ($CHO—COOC_2H_5$) in the presence of cyanides. The reaction is similar to the well-known benzoin condensation, and two carbons are added to the sugar carbon chain.

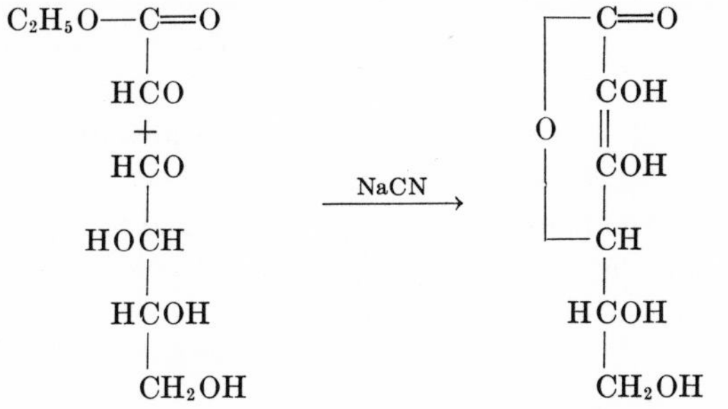

D-Threose D-Ascorbic Acid

By the action of Grignard reagents on suitably blocked esters or similar derivatives of the sugar acids, alkyl or aryl groups may be added to the sugars with the formation of carbon–carbon bonds (*176*).

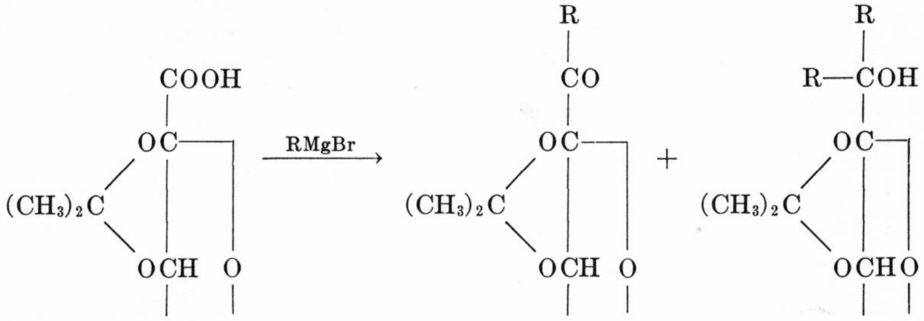

Di-*O*-isopropylidene-2-*keto*-D-gluconic acid

Aldehydo derivatives of the sugars in which the hydroxyls are blocked react with the Grignard reagent to give *C*-substituted alditols (*176*, *177*).

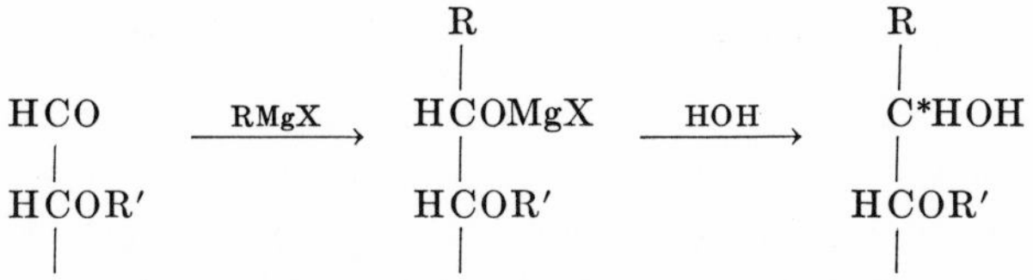

($R = CH_3$, cyclohexyl, phenyl, α-naphthyl)

176. C. Paal, *Ber.* **49,** 1583 (1916); H. Ohle and O. Hecht, *Ann.* **481,** 233 (1930); H. Ohle and C. Dambergis, *ibid.* **481,** 255 (1930); H. Ohle and I. Blell, *ibid.* **492,** 1 (1931).

177. K. Gätzi and T. Reichstein, *Helv. Chim. Acta* **21,** 914 (1938); J. English, Jr., and P. H. Griswald, Jr., *J. Am. Chem. Soc.* **67,** 2039 (1945).

The stereochemical configuration at the new asymmetric center* has been established for certain of the phenyl derivatives through degradation to known derivatives of the enantiomorphic mandelic acids (C_6H_5—CHOH—COOH) (*178*).

When acetylated glycosyl halides react with an excess of Grignard reagent, glycosylation of the aromatic or aliphatic group of the latter occurs by metathesis (*179*). The excess of reagent must include two moles for each ester function of the acetylated glycosyl halide since these react even more readily than does the halogen function (*180*). Grignard reagents that have been employed include the phenyl, *p*-tolyl, 1-naphthyl, butyl, isopropyl, benzyl, 2-thienyl, and 5-bromo-2-thienyl.

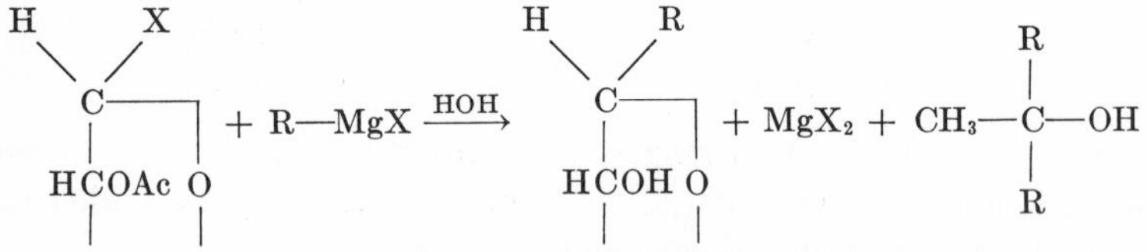

(mixture of anomers)

An interesting application of the Grignard reaction leads to 2-deoxy-D-ribose from 2,3-*O*-isopropylidene-D-glyceraldehyde and allylmagnesium bromide (*181*).

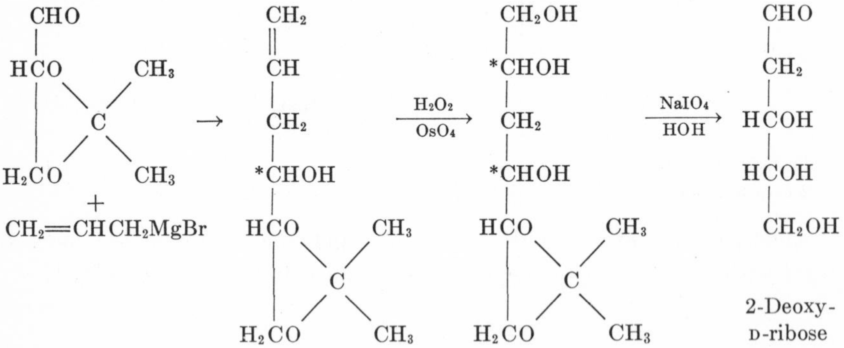

2-Deoxy-D-ribose

The Friedel-Crafts reaction also has been applied to the acetylated glycosyl halides, and by this method it is possible to proceed further and add two hydrocarbon radicals to the carbon chain of the glycosyl halides. Thus,

178. W. A. Bonner, *J. Am. Chem. Soc.* **73,** 3126 (1951).
179. C. D. Hurd and W. A. Bonner, *J. Am. Chem. Soc.* **67,** 1972 (1945); C. D. Hurd and R. P. Holysz, *ibid.* **72,** 1732 (1950); for a review of the Grignard and Friedel-Crafts processes in the sugar series, see W. A. Bonner, *Advances in Carbohydrate Chem.* **6,** 251 (1951).
180. W. A. Bonner, *J. Am. Chem. Soc.* **68,** 1711 (1946).
181. L. Hough, *Chemistry & Industry* p. 406 (1951).

Hurd and Bonner (*179, 182*) found that aluminum chloride catalyzes a reaction between tetra-*O*-acetyl-α-D-glucosyl chloride and benzene to yield 1-deoxy-1-phenyl-D-glucose (I) and 1-deoxy-1,1-diphenyl-D-glucitol (II). This represents a new application of the Friedel-Crafts reaction and involves glucosylation (by the tetra-*O*-acetyl-α-D-glucosyl chloride) of the aromatic nucleus. Because of the cleavage of the ester groups and subsequent formation of acetophenone, more than catalytic quantities of aluminum chloride are needed. The amount of catalyst present influences the composition of the reaction products; five moles favors the formation of the monosubstituted product whereas eight moles of aluminum chloride enhances the yield of the disubstituted product. This reaction

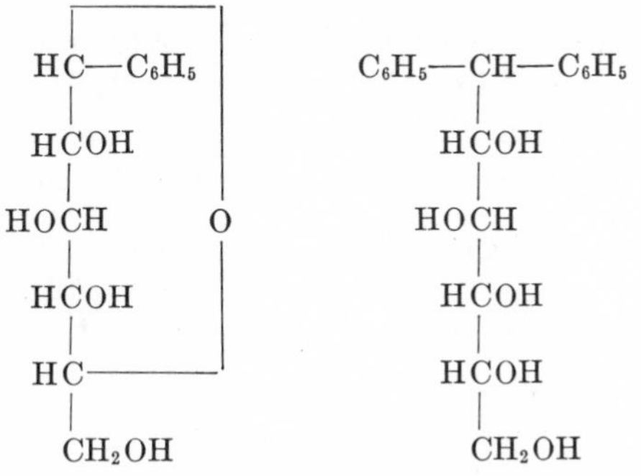

(I) (II)

was further extended to toluene, from which the disubstituted product was the only pure compound isolated. Usually reacetylation of the products is necessary to obtain crystallizable materials.

The monosubstituted derivative (I) yields the disubstituted derivative (II) upon acetylation and treatment with benzene and aluminum chloride. By treatment of the acetylated monosubstituted compounds with an aromatic hydrocarbon different from that used originally, a new asymmetric center is created and two isomers are possible:

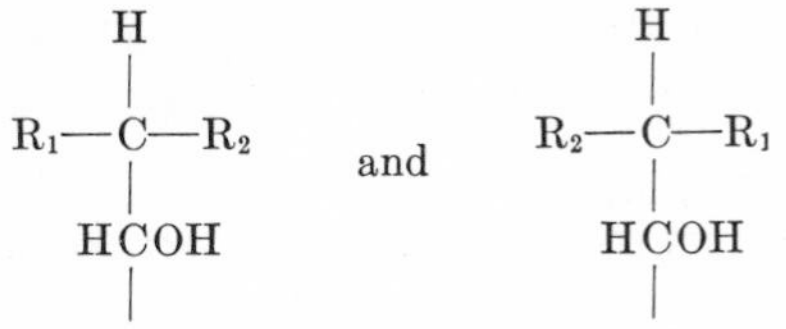

Compounds of this type have been prepared in which R_1 = *p*-tolyl and R_2 = phenyl groups.

The acetylated glycosyl halides also have been used to effect glycosyla-

182. C. D. Hurd and W. A. Bonner, *J. Am. Chem. Soc.* **67**, 1664, 1759, 1977 (1945).

tion by reaction with phenyllithium, butyllithium and diphenylcadmium (*183*). With the latter reagent, coupling occurs without deacetylation of the carbohydrate moiety.

C. Methods for Shortening the Carbon Chain of Sugars

a. The Ruff Degradation

One of the most useful methods for shortening the carbon chain of a sugar involves oxidation of a soluble salt of the aldonic acid with hydrogen peroxide in the presence of *ferric* acetate (*184*). Prior to the development of this method by Ruff, H. J. H. Fenton had shown that tartaric acid is oxidized by hydrogen peroxide in the presence of *ferrous* salts, but apparently no oxidative cleavage of carbon–carbon bonds was noted. The *ferrous* ion–catalyzed oxidation was extended to many carbohydrates by associates of Fenton (Chapter VI) and by other workers (*185*). The *ferric* ions used as the catalyst in the Ruff method permit the oxidation of aldonic acids but are inactive with respect to sugars. *Ferrous* ions are much less selective.

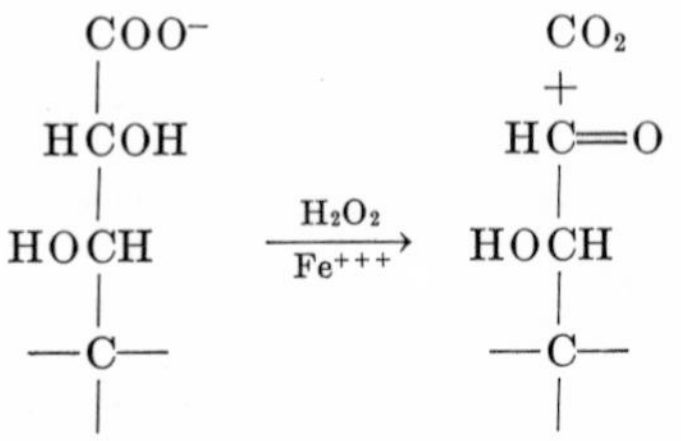
COO⁻
HCOH
HOCH
—C—
H2O2
Fe+++
CO2
+
HC=O
HOCH
—C—
Calcium D-gluconate D-Arabinose

Ruff applied the reaction to the easily available salts of the aldonic acids and showed that the oxidation takes place by the cleavage of carbon–carbon bonds and the direct formation of sugars. The yields are modest, but the sugars usually crystallize readily. D-Arabinose is produced from calcium D-gluconate in 50% of the theoretical quantity. The use of ion-exchange resins to remove ionic materials from the reaction mixture prior to isolation of the sugar is beneficial. By this technique, the yield of D-lyxose from calcium D-galactonate is increased from 17 to 41% (*186*). Salts other than the

183. C. D. Hurd and R. P. Holysz, *J. Am. Chem. Soc.* **72,** 1735, 2005 (1950).

184. O. Ruff, *Ber.* **31,** 1573 (1898); **34,** 1362 (1901); O. Ruff and G. Ollendorf, *ibid.* **33,** 1798 (1900).

185. For a discussion of the development of the reaction see C. F. Cross, E. J. Bevan, and T. Heiberg, *J. Chem. Soc.* **75,** 747 (1899); R. S. Morrell and J. M. Crofts, *ibid.* **75,** 786 (1899).

186. H. G. Fletcher, Jr., H. W. Diehl, and C. S. Hudson, *J. Am. Chem. Soc.* **72,** 4546 (1950).

calcium salts may be employed, e.g., strontium D-xylonate is oxidized to D-threose (*187*).

b. The Wohl Degradation

The degradation procedure devised by Wohl (*188*) is essentially the reverse of the cyanohydrin synthesis. It involves the removal of the cyanide group from the acetylated nitriles, which in turn are formed from the oximes by application of the usual acetylation procedures. In the original process, the cyanide group was eliminated by the action of ammoniacal silver oxide. Under these conditions, the diacetamide compound of the lower sugar results, and the free sugar is obtained from it by acid hydrolysis.

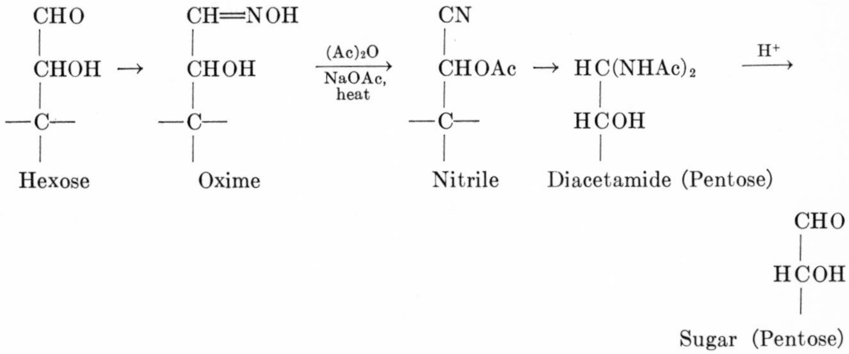
CHO
CHOH
—C—
Hexose
CH=NOH
CHOH
—C—
Oxime
(Ac)2O
NaOAc, heat
CN
CHOAc
—C—
Nitrile
HC(NHAc)2
HCOH
Diacetamide (Pentose)
H+
CHO
HCOH
Sugar (Pentose)

Since acetamide, which results from ammonolysis of the ester functions, does not itself condense with free sugars (*189*) or acetylated aldehydo-sugars (*190*), the mechanism of formation of the diacetamide derivatives has received considerable study. A possible mechanism (*191*) is based on intramolecular migration of acetyl groups from oxygen to nitrogen, according to the scheme:

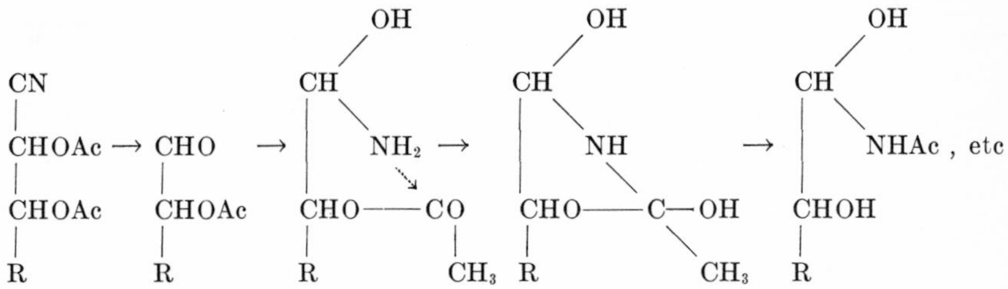
CN
CHOAc
CHOAc
R
CHO
CHOAc
R
OH
CH
NH2
CHO
CO
R
CH3
OH
CH
NH
CHO
C—OH
R
CH3
OH
CH
NHAc, etc
CHOH
R

187. R. C. Hockett, *J. Am. Chem. Soc.* **57,** 2260 (1935).
188. A. Wohl, *Ber.* **26,** 730 (1893).
189. P. Brigl, H. Mühlschlegel, and R. Schinle, *Ber.* **64,** 2921 (1931).
190. R. C. Hockett and L. R. Chandler, *J. Am. Chem. Soc.* **66,** 957 (1944).
191. H. S. Isbell and H. L. Frush, *J. Am. Chem. Soc.* **71,** 1579 (1949).

Partial substantiation for such a mechanism has been obtained by isotopic tracer studies (*192*), and direct chemical evidence is available that only the acetyl groups on carbons 2 and 3 of the aldehydo-sugar acetate are involved in forming the diacetamide derivative (*193*).

In later variations of the degradation, strong aqueous ammonia without added silver oxide (*194*), and sodium methoxide (*195*) in chloroform solution have been employed. The latter method gives the free, lower aldose sugar directly.

D-Gluconic nitrile, which can be obtained in 55% yield by the action of hydroxylamine acetate on D-glucose in acetic acid solution, is degraded quantitatively to D-arabinose simply by the action of hot water (*196*). However, the usual Wohl degradation via the acetylated nitriles (*197*), even in the most favorable instances, gives over-all (aldose → aldose) yields of only 30 to 35%.

c. The Weerman Degradation

The Hofmann method for the degradation of amides to the amines of one less carbon was applied by Weerman (*198*) to the amides of α-hydroxy acids and led to the production of aldehydes with one carbon less than the original acid:

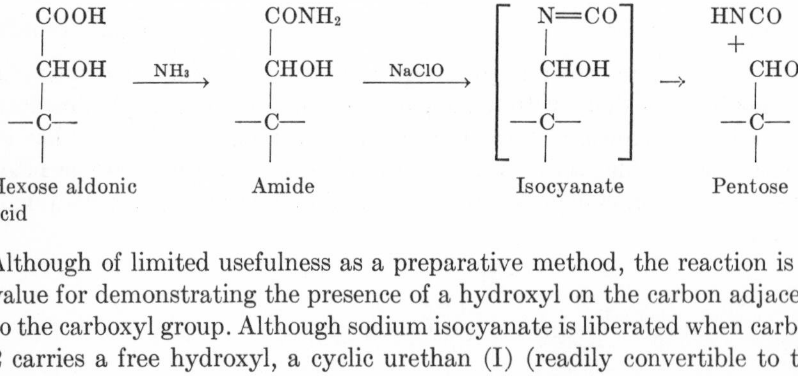
COOH
CHOH
NH₃
CONH₂
CHOH
NaClO
N=CO
CHOH
HNCO
+
CHO

Hexose aldonic acid — Amide — Isocyanate — Pentose

Although of limited usefulness as a preparative method, the reaction is of value for demonstrating the presence of a hydroxyl on the carbon adjacent to the carboxyl group. Although sodium isocyanate is liberated when carbon 2 carries a free hydroxyl, a cyclic urethan (I) (readily convertible to the

192. R. C. Hockett, V. Deulofeu, and J. O. Deferrari, *J. Am. Chem. Soc.* **72,** 1840 (1950).

193. R. Allerton and W. G. Overend, *J. Chem. Soc.* p. 35 (1952).

194. L. Maquenne, *Compt. rend.* **130,** 1402 (1900); R. C. Hockett, *J. Am. Chem. Soc.* **57,** 2265 (1935); R. C. Hockett, V. Deulofeu, A. L. Sedoff, and J. R. Mendive, *ibid.* **60,** 278 (1938).

195. G. Zemplén and D. Kiss, *Ber.* **60,** 165 (1927).

196. A. Wohl and O. Wollenberg, *Ann.* **500,** 281 (1933).

197. For a review of the method, see V. Deulofeu, *Advances in Carbohydrate Chem.* **4,** 119 (1949).

198. R. A. Weerman, *Rec. trav. chim.* **37,** 16 (1917).

lower sugar (II)), is formed when this carbon carries a methoxyl group (*199*):

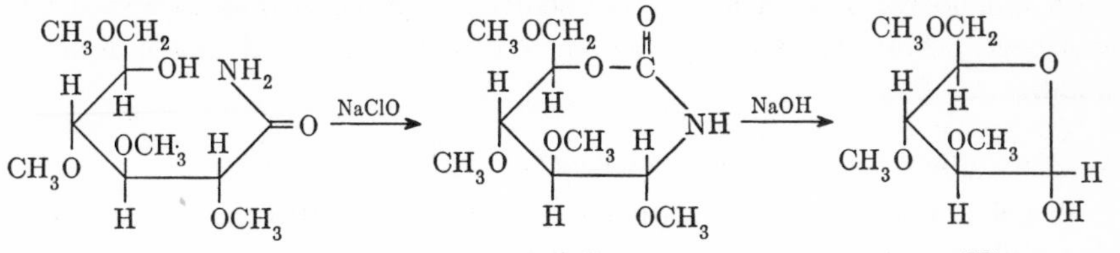

(I) (II)

d. Degradation of Sugars via *the Disulfones* (*MacDonald-Fischer*)

A method of degradation with excellent preparative possibilities has been devised by MacDonald and Fischer (*200*). The higher-carbon sugar first is condensed with ethyl mercaptan to form the bis(ethylthio)acetal (mercaptal) (I) (Chapter IV). Oxidation of the mercaptal with perpropionic acid then leads to the bis(ethylsulfonyl) compound (II), which is smoothly degraded by aqueous ammonia to the next lower aldose and bis(ethylsulfonyl)methane.

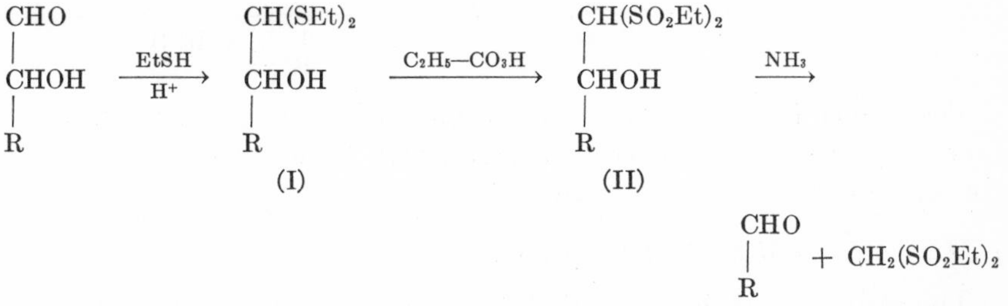

In addition to the saturated disulfone (II), unsaturated (III) and anhydro (IV) disulfones have been identified as products of the oxidation with certain of the mercaptals (*200, 201*). Both of the latter modifications of the disulfone, however, also degrade smoothly to the lower-carbon aldose.

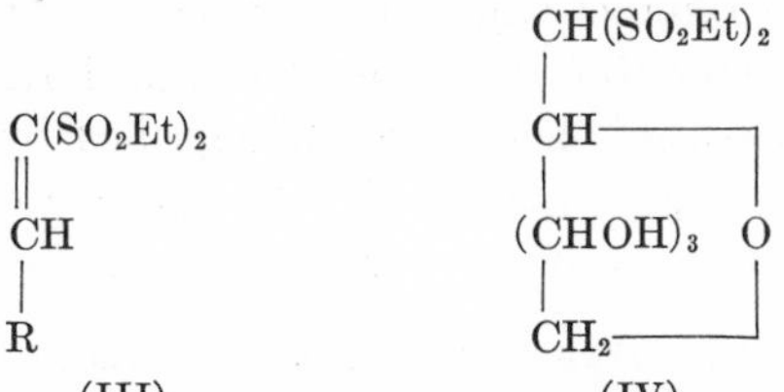

(III) (IV)

199. W. N. Haworth, S. Peat, and J. Whetstone, *J. Chem. Soc.* p. 1975 (1938).

200. D. L. MacDonald and H. O. L. Fischer, *J. Am. Chem. Soc.* **74,** 2087 (1952); *Biochim. et Biophys. Acta* **12,** 203 (1953); *J. Am. Chem. Soc.* **77,** 4348 (1955); C. E. Ballou, H. O. L. Fischer, and D. L. MacDonald, *J. Am. Chem. Soc.* **77,** 5967 (1947).

201. L. Hough and T. J. Taylor, *Chemistry & Industry* p. 575, 1018 (1954); H. Zinner and K.-H. Falk, *Ber.* **88,** 566 (1955).

The oxidation step also has been applied to the acetylated mercaptals with monoperphthalic acid in ether solution, and the degradation step also has been performed with hydrazine, hydroxylamine, and dilute aqueous alkali.

e. Degradation of Sugars via *the Oximes (Weygand-Löwenfeld)*

When a sugar oxime in aqueous bicarbonate solution is treated with 2,4-dinitrofluorobenzene, degradation to the next lower sugar occurs with the liberation of hydrocyanic acid and 2,4-dinitrophenol (*202*). The degradation apparently is analogous, in its final stage, to the Wohl degradation.

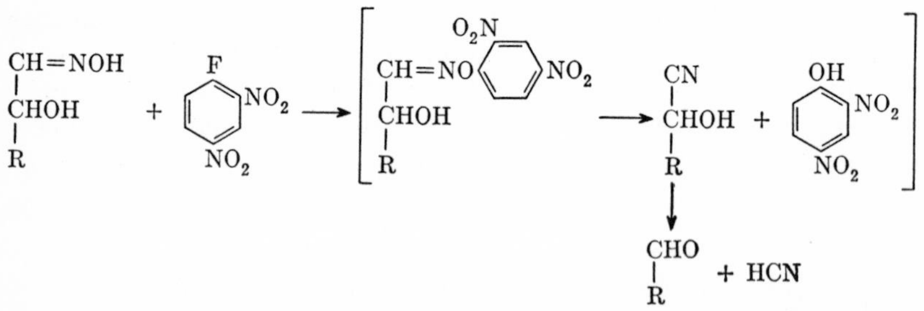

The method has been applied successfully for the preparation of D-arabinose, D-lyxose, 5-thiomethyl-D-arabinose, and 2-deoxy-D-xylose from the corresponding higher-carbon sugars (*203*).

f. Miscellaneous Methods of Degradation

The early work of Kiliani and of Nef demonstrated that the sugars are oxidized by air in alkaline solution with the formation of aldonic and other acids which have fewer carbons in the molecule. Spengler and Pfannenstiel (*204*) found that the yields of the aldonic acids with one carbon less than the original sugar can be improved by the use of oxygen rather than air. This oxidation is often of value for elucidating configurational relationships as well as for preparatory purposes. Thus, the formulation of the structure of perseulose as L-*gala*-heptulose is confirmed by its degradation to L-galactonic acid by oxygen and alkali (*205*). An extensive study (*206*) of the reaction reveals that for many sugars the difference between the use of

202. F. Weygand and R. Löwenfeld, *Ber.* **83,** 559 (1950).

203. F. Weygand, O. Trauth, and R. Löwenfeld, *Ber.* **83,** 563 (1950); F. Weygand and H. Wolz, *ibid.* **85,** 256 (1952).

204. O. Spengler and A. Pfannenstiel, *Z. Wirtschaftsgruppe Zuckerind.* **85,** 547 (1935).

205. N. K. Richtmyer, R. M. Hann, and C. S. Hudson, *J. Am. Chem. Soc.* **61,** 340 (1939).

206. H. S. Isbell, *J. Research Natl. Bur. Standards* **29,** 227 (1942).

air and oxygen may not be as great as originally thought. In addition to monosaccharides, the degradation has been applied successfully to the disaccharides cellobiose, maltose, and lactose (*207*).

The oxidation of the double bonds of glycals by ozone furnishes an additional method for shortening the carbon chains of the sugars (*208*). The oxidation of L-arabinal to L-erythrose provides an example (*209*).

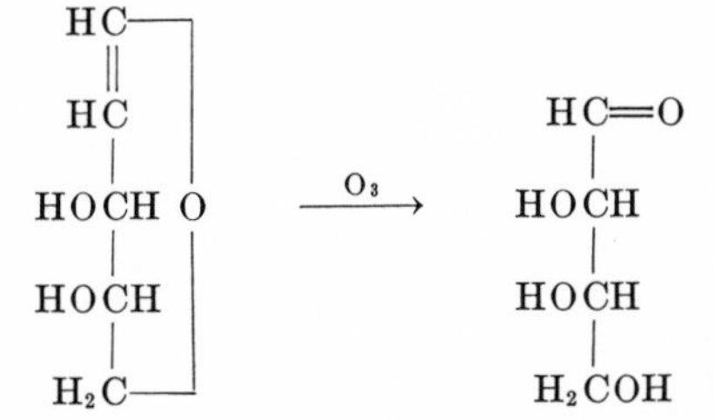
HC
HC
HOCH O
HOCH
H_2C
O_3
HC=O
HOCH
HOCH
H_2COH

L-Arabinal L-Erythrose

The α-glycol–cleaving oxidants (see Chapter VI) lead tetraacetate, periodic acid, and sodium metaperiodate, in addition to their extensive applications in structural studies, are valuable for the preparation of certain lower-carbon sugars. With these oxidants, the linkage between adjacent carbons carrying hydroxyl groups is ruptured, and sugars with shorter carbon chains may result. If more than two neighboring hydroxyl groups are available, the oxidation proceeds further so that it is usually desirable to block certain of the hydroxyls of the original substance with groups such as isopropylidene, benzylidene, etc. Sorbitol forms 1,3:2,4-di-*O*-ethylidene-D-glucitol when treated with paraldehyde and acid. The ethylidene derivative is oxidized by lead tetraacetate to di-*O*-ethylidene-L-xylose, which on acid hydrolysis gives L-xylose (*210*). The procedure has particular value for the preparation of the lower sugars. The 1,3-*O*-benzylidene-D-arabitol may be used for the preparation of D-threose (*211*), whereas D-erythrose results from 4,6-*O*-benzylidene-D-glucitol (*212*).

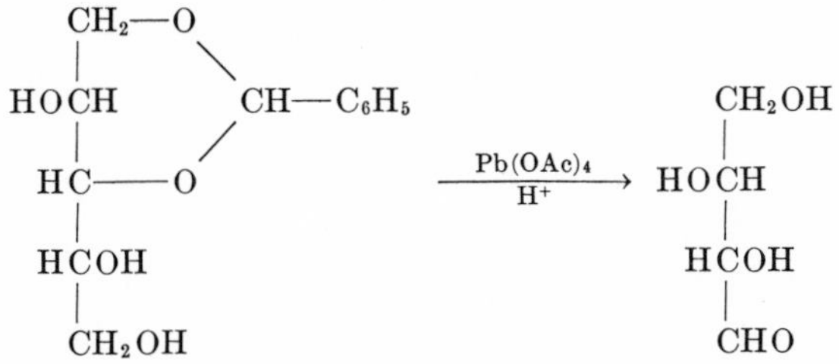
CH_2—O
HOCH
CH—C_6H_5
HC—O
HCOH
CH_2OH
$Pb(OAc)_4$
H^+
CH_2OH
HOCH
HCOH
CHO

D-Threose

207. E. Hardegger, K. Kreis, and H. El Khadem, *Helv. Chim. Acta* **35,** 618 (1952).
208. E. Fischer, M. Bergmann, and H. Schotte, *Ber.* **53,** 509 (1920).
209. G. E. Felton and W. Freudenberg, *J. Am. Chem. Soc.* **57,** 1637 (1935).

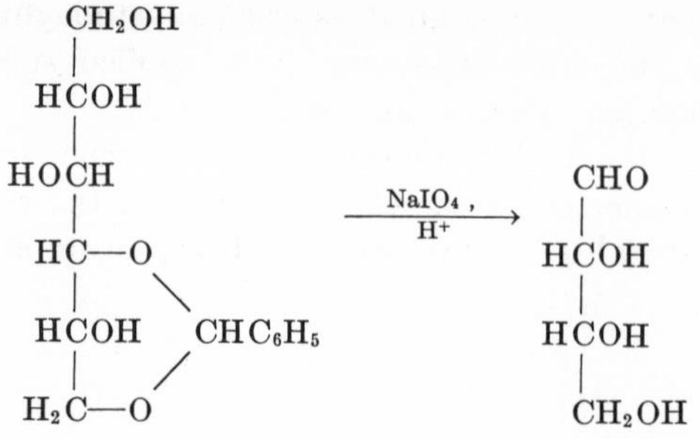

D-Erythrose

The important D- and L-glyceraldehyde may be obtained from the 1,2:5,6-di-*O*-isopropylidene-D- and -L-mannitol (I) (*213*).

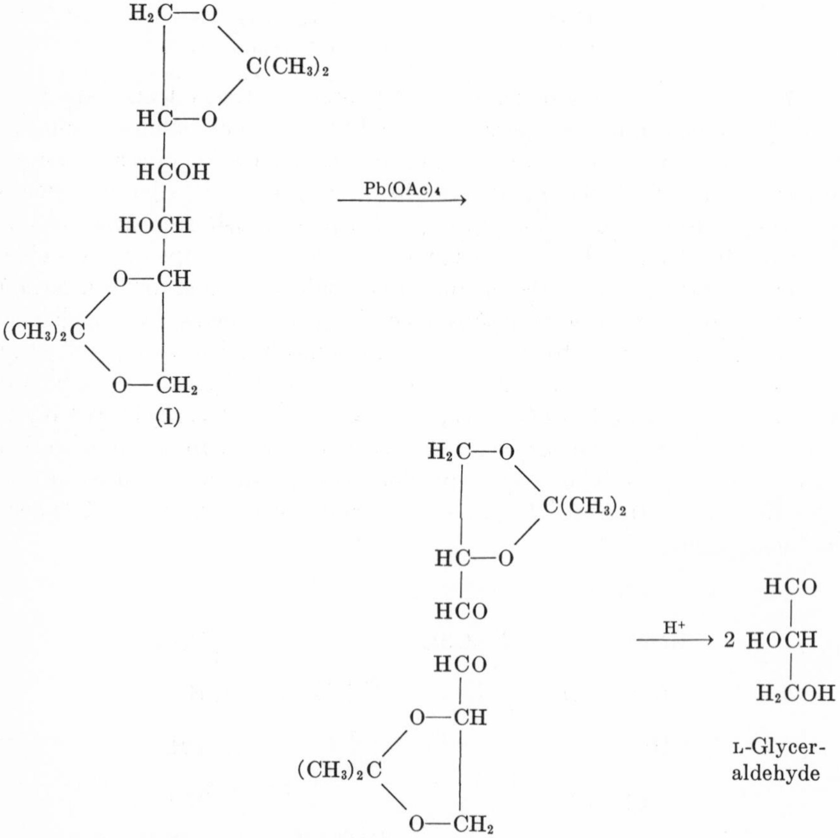

(I)

L-Glyceraldehyde

210. H. Appel, *J. Chem. Soc.* p. 425 (1935); R. C. Hockett and F. C. Schaeffer, *J. Am. Chem. Soc.* **69,** 849 (1947); R. K. Ness and H. G. Fletcher, Jr., *J. Am. Chem. Soc.* **74,** 5341 (1952).

211. M. Steiger and T. Reichstein, *Helv. Chim. Acta* **19,** 1016 (1936).

By controlling the amount of glycol-cleaving oxidant, even the free sugars may be selectively degraded to practical amounts of the related lower sugars. Thus, D-glucose may be oxidized alternatively to D-arabinose, D-erythrose, or D-glyceraldehyde with increasing amounts of oxidant (*213a*).

D. Methods Based on Changing the Configuration of Other Sugars

A number of methods utilized for the synthesis of sugars depend upon changing the configuration of one or more carbon atoms of other sugars. Especially when the configuration of carbon 2 of the aldoses is changed, the process is termed an epimerization.

a. Pyridine and Alkaline Rearrangements

In the presence of alkalies or tertiary amines, the sugars (or the aldonic acids) which differ in the configuration of carbon 2 (2-epimers) establish a pseudo equilibrium. The effect of alkali is more profound for the free sugars than for the acids, and the ketoses are in equilibrium with the 2-epimeric aldoses. (See Chapter I.) The action may proceed still further and involve carbon 3, and under more drastic conditions the reaction mixture assumes an exceedingly complex composition. The large number of isomers produced from sugars by alkali limits the general application of this method for purposes of synthesis because of the difficulties in the separation of the mixtures and in controlling the reaction.

The reaction brought about by alkalies, called the Lobry de Bruyn-Alberda van Ekenstein transformation (Chapter I), has its major application for obtaining synthetic ketoses which are usually the principal components of the equilibrium. By the reaction of weak alkali on D-glucose, two ketoses (D-fructose and D-psicose) and two aldoses (D-mannose and D-glucose) are formed. Galactose gives analogous products under the same conditions; two ketoses, sorbose and tagatose, and two aldoses, talose and galactose, have been identified (*214*). The ketoses lactulose (from lactose) and D-*gluco*-heptulose are easily prepared by this method (*215*, *42*).

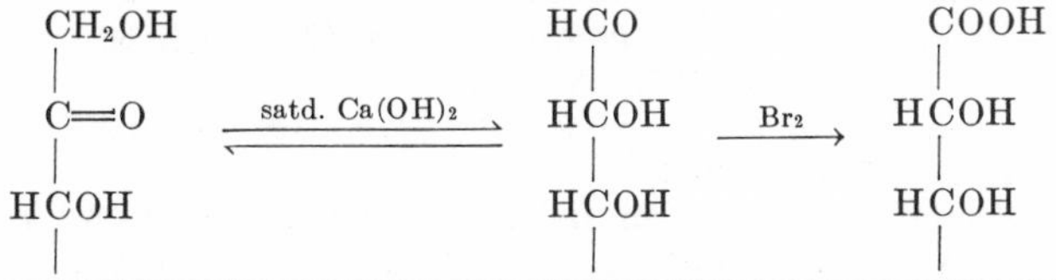
CH₂OH
C=O
HCOH
satd. Ca(OH)₂
HCO
HCOH
HCOH
Br₂
COOH
HCOH
HCOH

212. J. C. Sowden, *J. Am. Chem. Soc.* **72,** 808 (1950).

213. H. O. L. Fischer and E. Baer, *Helv. Chim. Acta* **19,** 519 (1936); E. Baer and H. O. L. Fischer, *J. Am. Chem. Soc.* **61,** 761 (1939); W. T. Haskins, R. M. Hann, and C. S. Hudson, *ibid.* **65,** 1663 (1943).

213a. A. S. Perlin, *J. Am. Chem. Soc.* **76,** 2595 (1954); C. Schöpf and H. Wild, *Ber.* **87,** 1571 (1954); A. S. Perlin and C. Brice, *Can. J. Chem.* **33,** 1216 (1955).

The aldoses in such mixtures may be oxidized by bromine, which has no action on the ketoses. The aldonic acids formed in this manner are conveniently separated from the ketoses by ion-exchange resins.

The isomerizing action of hot pyridine also has considerable value for the preparation of ketoses from aldoses (*216*). The two possible D-ketopentoses are prepared by heating the corresponding pentoses with pyridine and fractionally distilling the acetone derivatives of the reaction products. From D-xylose and D-ribose (or D-arabinose), the amorphous D-*threo*-pentulose and D-*erythro*-pentulose are obtained (*52*, *53*, *217*). D-*ribo*-Hexulose (D-psicose) and D-tagatose also have been prepared from the corresponding aldohexoses by the action of pyridine (*218*).

The direct action of alkali or pyridine on the sugars is of particular value for the preparation of the ketoses, but the action of pyridine on the aldonic acids is solely an epimerization. The action of hot tertiary amines (particularly aqueous pyridine and quinoline), as well as of alkali, on the aldonic acids and their methylated derivatives results in the establishment of an equilibrium between the two epimeric acids (*219*).

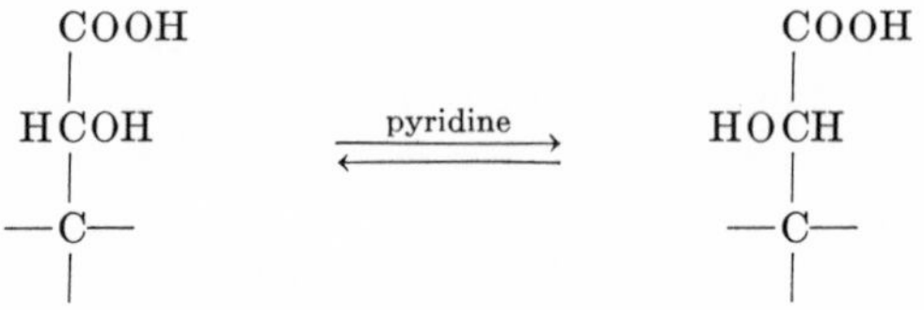
COOH
HCOH
—C—
pyridine
COOH
HOCH
—C—

D-Gluconic acid D-Mannonic acid

The sugars are prepared by reduction of the corresponding lactones. From D-arabonic acid, D-ribose (*220*) is obtained by this procedure, and from D- and L-galactonic acids, D- and L-talose (*221*) are prepared.

214. C. A. Lobry de Bruyn and W. Alberda van Ekenstein, *Rec. trav. chim.* **16,** 241, 245, 256 (1897); J. U. Nef, *Ann.* **403,** 342, 362 (1914).

215. E. M. Montgomery and C. S. Hudson, *J. Am. Chem. Soc.* **52,** 2101 (1930); W. C. Austin, C. J. Smalley, and M. I. Sankstone, *ibid.* **54,** 1933 (1932).

216. H. O. L. Fischer, C. Taube, and E. Baer, *Ber.* **60,** 479 (1927); S. N. Danilov, E. D. Venus-Danilova, and P. Shantarovich, *ibid.* **63,** 2269 (1930); P. A. Levene and D. W. Hill, *J. Biol. Chem.* **102,** 563 (1933).

217. P. A. Levene and R. S. Tipson, *J. Biol. Chem.* **115,** 731 (1936); O. T. Schmidt and K. Heintz, *Ann.* **515,** 77 (1934).

218. M. Steiger and T. Reichstein, *Helv. Chim. Acta* **19,** 184 (1936); Y. Khouvine, G. Arragon, and Y. Tomoda, *Bull. soc. chim. France* [5] **6,** 354 (1939).

219. E. Fischer, *Ber.* **23,** 799 (1890); W. N. Haworth and C. W. Long, *J. Chem. Soc.* p. 345 (1929).

220. M. Steiger, *Helv. Chim. Acta* **19,** 189 (1936).

221. W. Bosshard, *Helv. Chim. Acta* **18,** 482 (1935); C. Glatthaar and T. Reichstein, *ibid.* **21,** 3 (1938); O. F. Hedenburg and L. H. Cretcher, *J. Am. Chem. Soc.* **49,** 478 (1927).

b. Glycal Synthesis

By the oxidation of the glycals with perbenzoic acid or hydrogen peroxide (the latter in *t*-butyl alcohol in the presence of OsO_4) two hydroxyl groups are added, and the two corresponding 2-epimeric sugars are produced (*222*). The acetylated glycals are obtained by the reduction of the acetylglycosyl bromides (see Glycals).

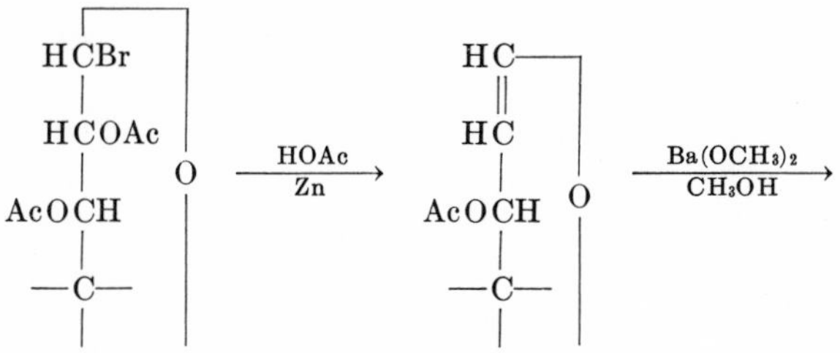
HCBr
HCOAc
AcOCH
—C—
O
HOAc
Zn
HC
HC
AcOCH
—C—
O
Ba(OCH₃)₂
CH₃OH

Tetra-*O*-acetyl-D-galactosyl bromide — Tri-*O*-acetyl-D-galactal

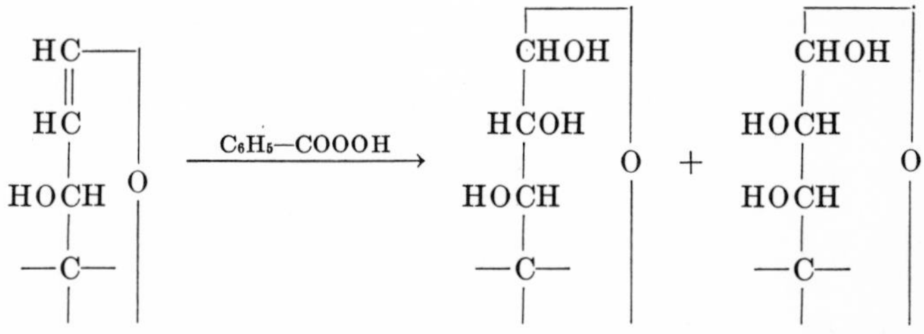
HC
HC
HOCH
—C—
O
C₆H₅—COOOH
CHOH
HCOH
HOCH
—C—
O
+
CHOH
HOCH
HOCH
—C—
O

D-Galactal — D-Galactose — D-Talose

This method often is better than the pyridine rearrangement for bringing about epimerization, and the resulting sugars crystallize more easily than the sugar obtained by the reduction of an aldonic acid. The hexose, D-talose, has been prepared as a sirup a number of times by the pyridine rearrangement of D-galactonic acid, but crystalline material was first obtained through the glycal synthesis (*223*). From seed crystals prepared in this way, D-talose could then be crystallized from the sirupy product obtained by the reduction of D-talonic lactone (*221*).

c. Inversion of All of the Asymmetric Carbons by Transfer of the Aldehyde or Hemiacetal Group

By a transfer of the aldehyde or hemiacetal group from carbon 1 to the terminal atom of the carbon chain, a formal reversal of the configuration of

222. M. Bergmann and H. Schotte, *Ber.* **54,** 440 (1921); R. C. Hockett, A. C. Sapp, and S. R. Millman, *J. Am. Chem. Soc.* **63,** 2051 (1941).

223. P. A. Levene and R. S. Tipson, *J. Biol. Chem.* **93,** 631 (1931); W. W. Pigman and H. S. Isbell, *J. Research Natl. Bur. Standards* **19,** 189 (1937).

all of the asymmetric centers of the molecule results. The intermediates for this method are the uronic acids, which may be synthesized by a number of methods from the sugars, dibasic acids, and alcohols (Chapter VI). The method (*224*) depends on the reduction of the aldehyde group of uronic acids; the resulting aldonic acids are converted to lactones and reduced to the sugars. The naturally occurring uronic acids are useful intermediates, particularly the easily prepared D-galacturonic acid which may be reduced to L-galactose. Since D-galactose may be converted to D-galacturonic acid by oxidation of the di-*O*-isopropylidene-D-galactose with alkaline permanganate, the procedure provides a means for transforming D-galactose to its enantiomorph (*225*). The conversion of a sugar into its enantiomorph by this procedure is not the usual result but only occurs for sugars related to inactive dibasic acids. From D-glucose through the intermediate D-glucuronic acid, L-gulose (earlier *d*-gulose) is obtained. Of the fifteen D- (or L-) aldoses up to and including the hexoses, six would be changed to the enantiomorph by the transfer of the aldehyde group, three would be unchanged, and six would be converted to other sugars.

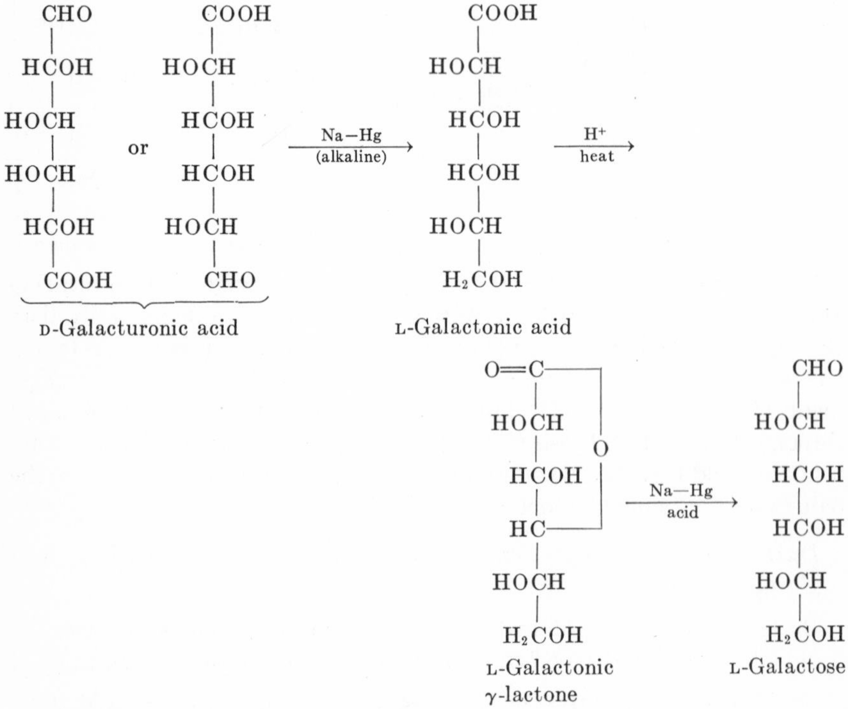
or
Na—Hg
(alkaline)
H+
heat
Na—Hg
acid

D-Galacturonic acid

L-Galactonic acid

L-Galactonic γ-lactone

L-Galactose

---

224. E. Fischer and O. Piloty, *Ber.* **24,** 521 (1891); H. Thierfelder, *Z. physiol. Chem.* **15,** 71 (1891).

225. C. Glatthaar and T. Reichstein, *Helv. Chim. Acta,* *20,* 1537 (1937); K. Iwadare *d. Methods Depending on Walden Inversions*

p-Toluenesulfonyl (tosyl) esters and other sulfate esters of the sugars readily form epoxide rings on treatment with alkali, provided that a free, *trans*-hydroxyl group is present on a carbon atom contiguous with the ester grouping. (See Chapter III.) The displacement of the tosyloxy group is accomplished with a rearward approach, nucleophilic attack by the neighboring *trans*-OH, and the process involves Walden inversion on the sugar carbon of the original ester grouping. Moreover, the epoxide ring can be opened by more vigorous treatment with alkali. This intermolecular reaction also involves rearward approach, with the displacing anion being OH^- or a similar base ion. Again Walden inversion occurs on the carbon atom under nucleophilic attack and, since two similar carbon atoms are available in the epoxide grouping, a mixture of two products results. One will have the configuration of the original tosyl ester, whereas the other will have undergone a double Walden inversion (*226*). (See p. 167).

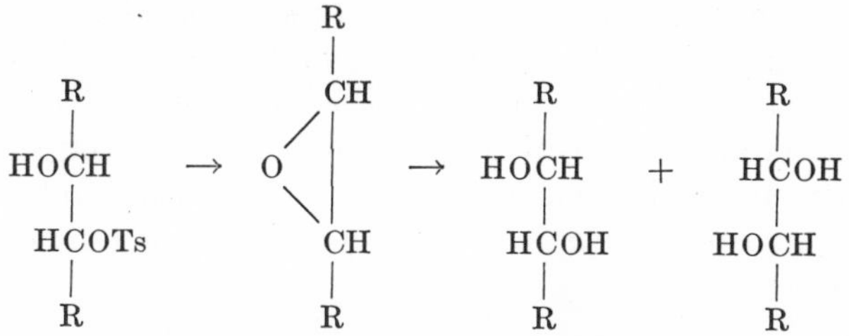
R
HOCH
HCOTs
R
→
R
CH
O
CH
R
→
R
HOCH
HCOH
R
+
R
HCOH
HOCH
R

When the hemiacetal hydroxyl of a 2-*O*-tosyl or 2-*O*-mesyl aldose is unsubstituted, titration with dilute alkali at room temperature eliminates the sulfonic ester grouping and provides the related epimeric sugar in good yield (*62a*, *226a*). The epimerization presumably proceeds through an intermediate 1,2-epoxide.

Several other methods result in inversions of configuration probably as the result of Walden inversions taking place during the decomposition of intermediate compounds. Thus, the action of $AlCl_3$ and PCl_5 on octa-*O*-acetylcellobiose produces a derivative of the new disaccharide celtrobiose. The process results in a change from the D-glucose to the D-altrose configuration. Although the latter method has value for the production of D-altrose, the principal utility of these procedures is for the production of the rarer disaccharides and more details are given in the section on disaccharide synthesis.

---

and B. Kubota, *Sci. Papers Inst. Phys. Chem. Research (Tokyo)* **34,** 183 (1937–38); R. A. Pizzarello and W. Freudenberg, *J. Am. Chem. Soc.* **61,** 611 (1939); H. S. Isbell, *J. Research Natl. Bur. Standards* **33,** 45 (1944).

226. For a review of these reactions, see S. Peat, *Advances in Carbohydrate Chem.* **2,** 38 (1946).

226a. J. K. N. Jones and W. H. Nicholson, *J. Chem. Soc.* p. 3050 (1955).

E. Methods for the Synthesis of Deoxysugars

a. Terminal Deoxysugars

The synthesis of 6-deoxy-D-glucose (see D-Quinovose, p. 99) is carried out from 2,3,4-tri-*O*-acetyl-6-bromo-6-deoxy-α-D-glucosyl bromide. The dihalide is converted to the methyl 2,3,4-tri-*O*-acetyl-6-bromo-6-deoxy-β-D-glucoside by treatment with silver carbonate and methyl alcohol, and the bromine is exchanged for a hydrogen atom by reduction with zinc and acetic acid (*227*).

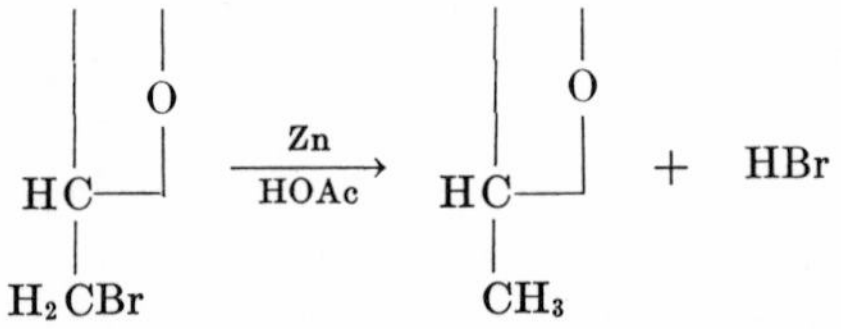
O
HC
H₂CBr
Zn
HOAc
O
HC
CH₃
+ HBr

A method of more general application depends on the reduction of iodo derivatives in which the iodine has replaced the hydroxyl of a primary alcoholic group. These are easily obtained by treatment of the tosyl derivatives with sodium iodide in acetone solution (sealed tube) or in refluxing acetonylacetone (*228*) or acetic anhydride (*229*). The reduction is often carried out by catalytic methods. The 5-deoxy-D-xylose is synthesized from D-xylose by this method, and by application of the cyanohydrin synthesis 6-deoxy-D-gulose is prepared (*230*).

D-Xylose $\longrightarrow$ mono-*O*-isopropylidene-5-*O*-tosyl-D-xylose $\xrightarrow{\text{NaI}}$

5-deoxy-5-iodo-mono-*O*-isopropylidene-D-xylose $\xrightarrow[\text{NaOH}]{H_2\text{, Ni}}$

5-deoxy-mono-*O*-isopropylidene-D-xylose $\xrightarrow{H^+}$ 5-deoxy-D-xylose $\xrightarrow{\text{NaCN}}$

6-deoxy-D-gulonic lactone $\xrightarrow{\text{Na—Hg}}$ 6-deoxy-D-gulose

The tosyloxy group also may be replaced by the thiocyanate group and the latter then removed reductively to give the deoxysugar (*231*).

The simplest conversion of the tosyl ester to the deoxysugar is by reductive cleavage. Although reduction with sodium amalgam or Raney nickel regenerates the primary hydroxyl group, the use of lithium aluminum hy-

227. E. Fischer and K. Zach, *Ber.* **45,** 3761 (1912).

228. G. E. Murray and C. B. Purves, *J. Am. Chem. Soc.* **62,** 3195 (1940); T. S. Gardner and C. B. Purves, *ibid.* **64,** 1539 (1942).

229. W. T. Haskins, R. M. Hann, and C. S. Hudson, *J. Am. Chem. Soc.* **64,** 137 (1942).

230. P. A. Levene and J. Compton, *J. Biol. Chem.* **111,** 325, 335 (1935).

231. R. M. Hann, N. K. Richtmyer, H. W. Diehl, and C. S. Hudson, *J. Am. Chem. Soc.* **71,** 561 (1950).

dride with *primary* tosyl esters leads to the deoxysugar (*232*). An exception is the di-*O*-isopropylidene-1-*O*-tosyl-D-fructose which, like the secondary tosyl esters, undergoes simple detosylation on treatment with lithium aluminum hydride.

The 1-deoxyketoses are prepared from the aldehydo-sugar acetates via the diazomethane synthesis (p. 113) (*156c*).

b. *Nonterminal Deoxysugars*

In addition to their use in epimerization (p. 127), the glycals are valuable intermediates for the preparation of 2-deoxyaldoses (*233*). The elements of water are added by treatment of the glycal with sulfuric acid at low temperature, possibly with the formation of the sulfuric acid ester, and then neutralization with barium carbonate:

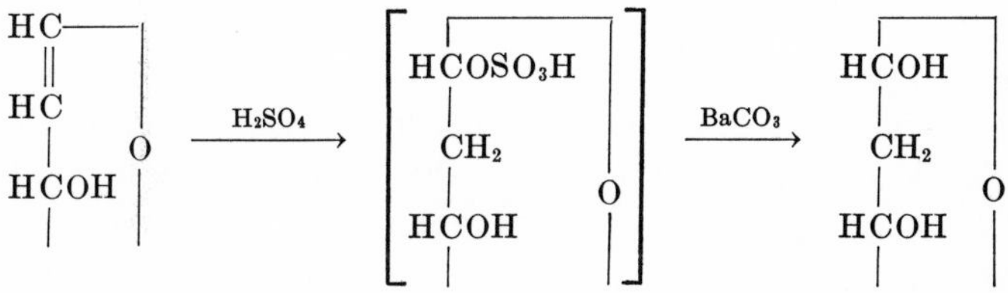
HC
HC
O
HCOH
H2SO4
HCOSO3H
CH2
O
HCOH
BaCO3
HCOH
CH2
O
HCOH

D-Ribal 2-Deoxy-D-ribose

A large number of 2-deoxyaldoses have been obtained by this method (*63*). The yields, especially in the preparation of the glycals, vary widely among the different sugars.

Another general method for the 2-deoxyaldoses utilizes the *C*-nitroalcohols (p. 109). When the acetylated *C*-nitroalcohols are refluxed in benzene or ether solution with sodium bicarbonate, the α-acetoxy group is eliminated (*234*) to produce an acetylated *C*-nitroolefin. Selective reduction of the double bond, deacetylation, and decomposition of the *aci*-nitro salt with aqueous sulfuric acid then gives the 2-deoxysugar (*148*, *235*).

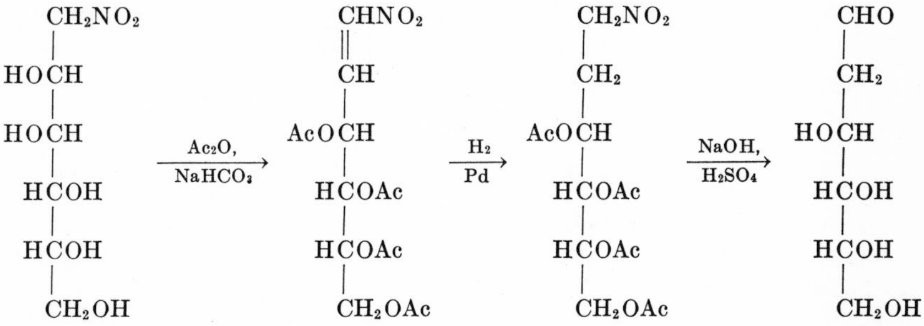
CH2NO2
HOCH
HOCH
HCOH
HCOH
CH2OH
Ac2O,
NaHCO3
CHNO2
CH
AcOCH
HCOAc
HCOAc
CH2OAc
H2
Pd
CH2NO2
CH2
AcOCH
HCOAc
HCOAc
CH2OAc
NaOH,
H2SO4
CHO
CH2
HOCH
HCOH
HCOH
CH2OH

1-Deoxy-1-nitro-D-mannitol 2-Deoxy-D-*arabo*-hexose

The sugar epoxides (p. 393) have been used extensively to obtain deoxysugars. The epoxide ring may be opened with sodium methylmercaptide to yield the methylthio derivatives. Reductive desulfurization then gives the deoxysugar (*236*). Alternatively, the epoxide grouping may be reductively opened by catalytic hydrogenation or with lithium aluminum hydride to give the deoxysugars directly (*237*).

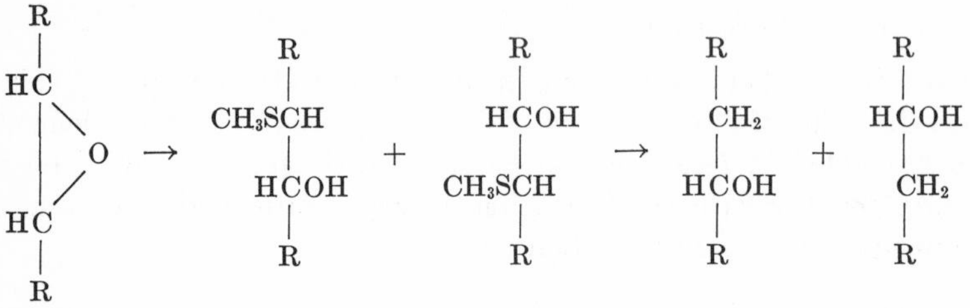

Since the deoxy function may be introduced at either of the carbon atoms of the original epoxide, a mixture of two products usually results.

The Wolff rearrangement of diazomethyl ketoses leads to the 2-deoxyaldonic acids (*167*) which may serve as sources of the 2-deoxysugars (p. 113).

The synthesis of deoxysugars, both terminal and nonterminal, has been widely studied and applied by Reichstein and his associates in connection with their studies of the sugar components of the cardiac glycosides (Chapter X).

F. Preparation of Ketoses by Biochemical Oxidation of Alcohols

Of considerable importance for the preparation of the ketose sugars is the oxidation of the sugar alcohols by bacteria. It was first observed that the occurrence of L-sorbose in the juice of the mountain ash (*Sorbus aucuparia*) is due to the bacterial oxidation of the precursor, sorbitol. The bacteria responsible were isolated and their oxidizing action on a series of polyhydric alcohols was extensively studied by Bertrand (*238*). The active organism was shown to be identical with *Acetobacter xylinum* previously

232. H. Schmid and P. Karrer, *Helv. Chim. Acta* **32,** 1371 (1949).

233. M. Bergmann, H. Schotte, and W. Lechinsky, *Ber.* **55,** 158 (1922); **56,** 1052 (1923).

234. G. Schmidt and G. Rutz, *Ber.* **61,** 2142 (1928).

235. J. C. Sowden and H. O. L. Fischer, *J. Am. Chem. Soc.* **69,** 1048 (1947); J. C. Sowden, *ibid.* **71,** 1897 (1949); **72,** 808 (1950).

236. R. Jeanloz, D. A. Prins, and T. Reichstein, *Helv. Chim. Acta* **29,** 371 (1946).

237. D. A. Prins, *Helv. Chim. Acta* **29,** 1 (1946); D. A. Prins, *J. Am. Chem. Soc.* **70,** 3955 (1948).

238. G. Bertrand, *Ann. chim.* [8] **3,** 181 (1904).

isolated from vinegar by Adrian Brown. According to the generalization of Bertrand, the oxidation of alcohols by *A. xylinum* is favored by a *cis* relationship of two secondary hydroxyl groups adjacent to a primary alcoholic group. The secondary hydroxyl adjacent to the primary hydroxyl is then oxidized to a ketone group by the organism. Glycerol is oxidized to dihydroxyacetone.

$$(HO)H_2C—CH(OH)—CH_2(OH) \rightarrow (HO)H_2C—CO—CH_2(OH)$$

Another organism, *Acetobacter suboxydans*, found originally in spoiled beer, gives better results than *A. xylinum*. It has been found particularly effective for manufacturing L-sorbose from sorbitol and has made this sugar available at low cost (*239*). The organism gives L-erythrulose by oxidation

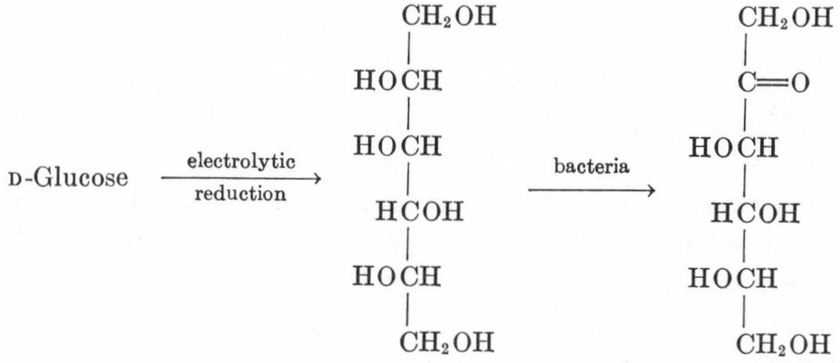
D-Glucose
electrolytic
reduction
bacteria
Sorbitol L-Sorbose

of *meso*-erythritol, and dihydroxyacetone by oxidation of glycerol (*240*). The presence of a small amount of glucose (0.05 %) as well as aeration and agitation promotes the oxidation of perseitol to perseulose and seems to provide optimal conditions for the oxidation of other alcohols (*241*).

The action of *A. suboxydans* is more specific than that of *A. xylinum* as demonstrated by studies of the action of the former on a number of sugar alcohols (*242*). Although the same groupings are necessary, there is a marked difference between the actions of *A. suboxydans* on enantiomorphs. For this organism to act, it appears that the glycol grouping adjacent to the primary alcohol grouping must be not only *cis* but also of the D-configuration. This modified Bertrand rule may also be applied to the terminal deoxysugars if the methyl group is considered as just a hydrogen atom. Thus,

239. E. I. Fulmer, J. W. Dunning, J. F. Guymon, and L. A. Underkofler, *J. Am. Chem. Soc.* **58,** 1012 (1936); P. A. Wells, L. B. Lockwood, J. J. Stubbs, E. T. Roe, N. Porges, and E. A. Gastrock, *Ind. Eng. Chem.*, **31,** 1518 (1939); *U. S. Patent* 2,121,533 (1938); A. J. Kluyver and F. J. de Leeuw, *Tijdschr. Vergelijk. Geneesk.* **10,** 170 (1924).

240. See R. L. Whistler and L. A. Underkofler, *J. Am. Chem. Soc.* **60,** 2507 (1938); K. R. Butlin, *J. Soc. Chem. Ind.* **57,** T468 (1938).

241. E. B. Tilden, *J. Bacteriol.* **37,** 629 (1939).

242. R. M. Hann, E. B. Tilden, and C. S. Hudson, *J. Am. Chem. Soc.* **60,** 1201 (1938).

L-fucitol (6-deoxy-L-galactitol) is oxidized by *A. suboxydans* to 1-deoxy-D-*xylo*-3-hexulose (*243*).

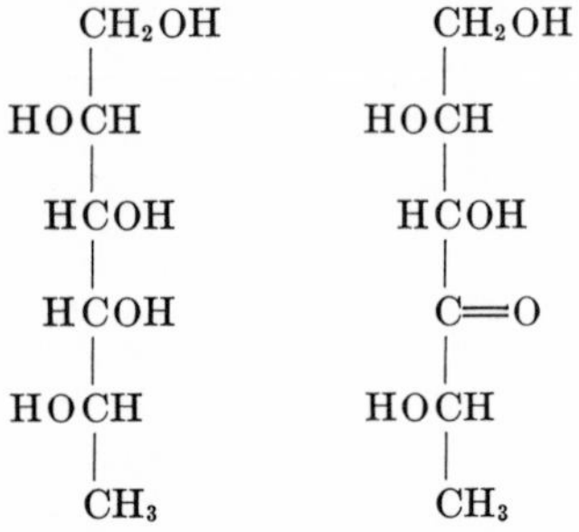

L-Fucitol 1-Deoxy-D-*xylo*-3-hexulose

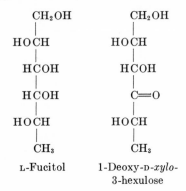

The action of the organism is not limited to the sugar series since the closely analogous *myo*-inositol, a cyclic alcohol, yields a pentahydroxycyclohexanone called inosose (*244*) (Chapter V). The biological oxidation of *meso-glycero-gulo*-heptitol to L-*gluco*-heptulose provides a method of passing from D-glucose to L-glucose. The heptitol is obtained by the reduction of the product of the cyanohydrin synthesis from D-glucose, and the L-*gluco*-heptulose yields L-gluconic acid (and other acids) when subjected to the action of oxygen in alkaline solution (*79*, *245*).

The chemical oxidation of sugar alcohols to ketoses may be successful when only one unsubstituted hydroxyl group is present. Thus, 6-*O*-benzoyl-1,3:2,4-di-*O*-ethylidene-D-glucitol is oxidized to the corresponding L-sorbose derivative by the action of chromic acid dissolved in glacial acetic acid (*246*).

G. Aldose to Ketose Conversion Utilizing the Osones

A method of considerable historical interest is the transformation of the aldoses to the ketoses through the osazones and osones (*247*). In his classical work which led to the synthesis of the isomeric sugars, Fischer utilized this procedure. Although better preparative methods are now available, the method still is important for demonstrating structural relationships. The

243. N. K. Richtmyer, L. C. Stewart, and C. S. Hudson, *J. Am. Chem. Soc.* **72,** 4934 (1950).

244. A. J. Kluyver and A. G. J. Boezaardt, *Rec. trav. chim.* **58,** 956 (1939); T. Posternak, *Helv. Chim. Acta* **24,** 1045 (1941).

245. W. D. Maclay, R. M. Hann, and C. S. Hudson, *J. Am. Chem. Soc.* **64,** 1606 (1942); N. K. Richtmyer and C. S. Hudson, *ibid.* **64,** 1609 (1942).

246. W. R. Sullivan, *J. Am. Chem. Soc.* **67,** 837 (1945).

247. E. Fischer, *Ber.* **22,** 87 (1889).

osazones are transformed to the osones by treatment with concentrated hydrochloric acid or aldehydes. The reduction of the osone to the ketose is brought about by the action of zinc and acetic acid.

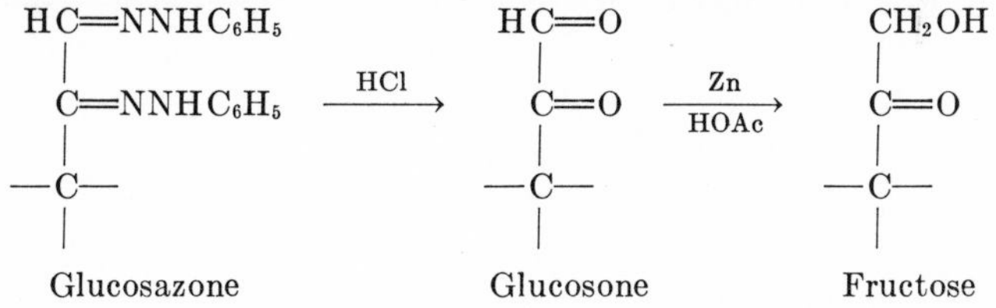
HC=NNHC6H5
C=NNHC6H5
—C—
HCl
HC=O
C=O
—C—
Zn
HOAc
CH2OH
C=O
—C—
Glucosazone
Glucosone
Fructose

The Amadori rearrangement of aldosyl amines to aminodeoxyketoses (Chapter VIII), which is an intermediate reaction during osazone formation, also provides a means of passing from aldose to ketose structures.

H. Methods for Isotope-Labeled Sugars

The preparation of sugars containing isotopic carbon, either uniformly distributed or in specific positions of the carbon chain, is a comparatively recent development in carbohydrate synthesis. Certain of the known synthetic methods have been applied for isotopic labeling and, in addition, certain new synthetic methods have been developed solely for the introduction of the isotope.

Uniformly labeled D-glucose, D-fructose, and sucrose are prepared by photosynthesis using an appropriate plant and isotopic carbon dioxide (*248*). Similarly, uniformly labeled D-galactose is obtained by photosynthesis with $C^{14}O_2$ and the red alga *Irideae laminarioides*, where it occurs as a 2-glycerol D-galactopyranoside (*65*).

D-Glucose labeled only at carbons 3 and 4 is isolated by the hydrolysis of the liver glycogen of animals after injection of isotopic bicarbonate (*249*).

Any of the chain-lengthening synthetic methods are, of course, applicable for the introduction of isotopic carbon. Of these, the cyanohydrin (*250*) and nitromethane (*251*) syntheses have proved useful for the preparation of 1-labeled aldoses. The addition of hydrogen cyanide to an aldose is essentially quantitative even with only stoichiometric amounts, whereas the

248. L. G. Livingston and G. J. Medes, *J. Gen. Physiol.* **31,** 75 (1947); S. Aronoff, A. Benson, W. Z. Hassid, and M. Calvin, *Science* **105,** 664 (1947); E. W. Putman, W. Z. Hassid, G. Krotkov, and H. A. Barker, *J. Biol. Chem.* **173,** 785 (1948).

249. A. K. Solomon, B. Vennesland, F. W. Klemperer, J. M. Buchanan, and A. B. Hastings, *J. Biol. Chem.* **140,** 171 (1941); H. G. Wood, N. Lifson, and V. Lorber, *ibid.* **159,** 475 (1945); D. B. Zilversmit, I. L. Chaikoff, D. D. Feller, and E. J. Masoro, *ibid.* **176,** 389 (1948).

250. D. E. Koshland, Jr., and F. H. Westheimer, *J. Am. Chem. Soc.* **71,** 1139 (1949); **72,** 3383 (1950).

251. J. C. Sowden, *Science* **109,** 229 (1949); *J. Biol. Chem.* **180,** 55 (1950).

addition of nitromethane proceeds best in the presence of an excess of the nitroparaffin. Accordingly, the improved cyanohydrin synthesis (*137*), particularly in view of the possibility of controlling the ratio of epimeric products, is the preferred method for isotopic synthesis. Isbell and his associates (*137*, *252*) have prepared a number of 1-labeled aldoses by this method including D-ribose, D-arabinose, D-lyxose, D-xylose, D-glucose, D-mannose, D-galactose, D-talose, and the disaccharides maltose and lactose. 1-Labeled D-mannonic γ-lactone also has been converted to 1,6-labeled D-fructose by reduction to D-mannitol and oxidation of the latter to D-fructose with *A. suboxydans* (*253*).

The incorporation of isotope into carbon 6 of D-glucose is accomplished by the reaction sequence (*254*):

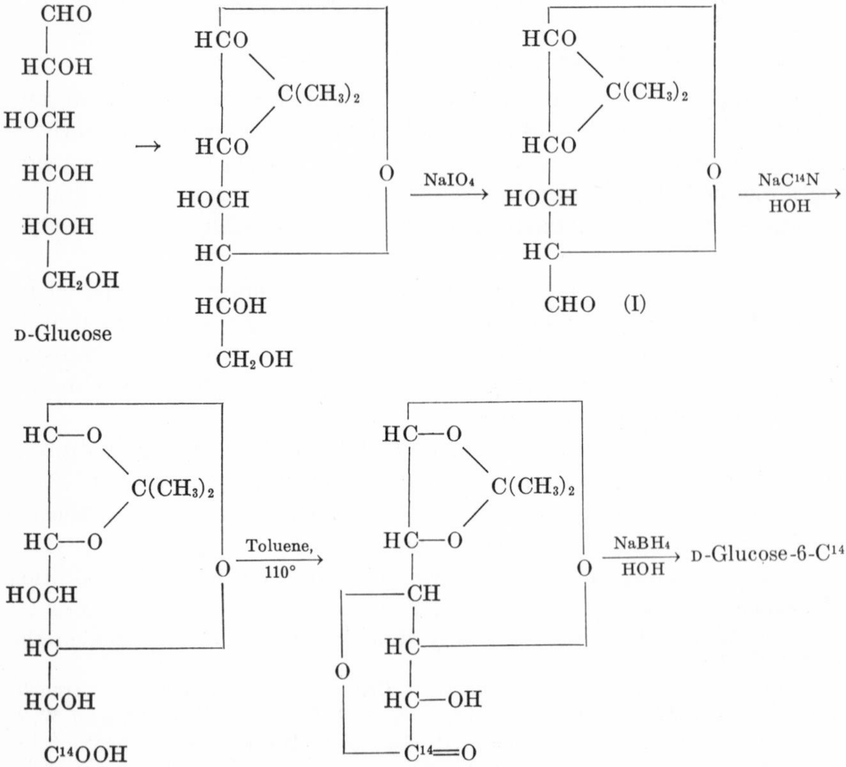
D-Glucose
NaIO₄
(I)
NaC¹⁴N
HOH
Toluene,
110°
NaBH₄
HOH
D-Glucose-6-C¹⁴

252. H. L. Frush and H. S. Isbell, *J. Research Natl. Bur. Standards* **50,** 133 (1953); **51,** 307 (1953); H. S. Isbell, H. L. Frush, and N. B. Holt, *ibid.* **53,** 217, 325 (1954).

253. H. S. Isbell and J. V. Karabinos, *J. Research Natl. Bur. Standards* **48,** 438 (1952).

254. J. C. Sowden, *J. Am. Chem. Soc.* **74,** 4377 (1952).

The intermediate 6-labeled D-glucuronic acid also is a valuable biochemical tool.

When D-glucose-1-C^{14} is converted to the acetonated pentose dialdehyde (I), reduction of the latter and subsequent hydrolysis affords D-xylose-1-C^{14} (*255*).

255. J. C. Sowden, *J. Am. Chem. Soc.* **73,** 5496 (1951).

III. ESTERS

A. THOMPSON AND M. L. WOLFROM*

In the carbohydrate group as a whole, including polysaccharides, the dominant functional group is the hydroxyl group, particularly if the hemiacetal group is considered as a hydroxyl. The normal sugar alcohols (alditols), glycosides, and polysaccharides (glycans) have primary and secondary alcoholic groups, and the sugars, these groups and also carbonyl or hemiacetal groups.

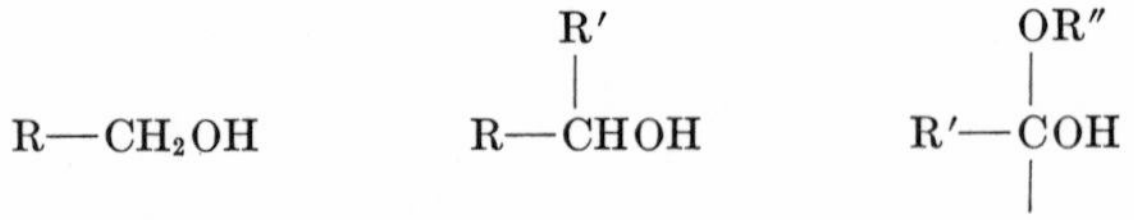

Primary alcohol Secondary alcohol Hemiacetal

One of the most common reactions of hydroxyl groups is that of esterification. The present chapter covers the ester derivatives of carbohydrates other than polysaccharides. Since the esters of the sugars have received the most study, the discussion will be centered about them.

Some of the ester derivatives of polysaccharides, such as cellulose acetates or nitrates, are of considerable industrial importance (Chapter XII). Those of the sugars have not been commercialized to any great extent, with the possible exception of sucrose octaacetate. An important series of surface-active materials are provided by alditols and their anhydro derivatives partially esterified with long-chain fatty acids (Chapter VII). For the latter derivatives, increased solubility in water is provided by reaction with ethylene oxide.

A few esters of the sugars occur in natural products (Chapter X). Vaccinin (mono-*O*-benzoyl-D-glucose) is found in the juice of blueberries; populin (salicin 6-benzoate) occurs in *Populus* species; sugar-beet pectin contains an *O*-acetyl group. Phosphate esters of hexoses, trioses, and hydroxy acids act as intermediates in the biological synthesis of polysaccharides, ethyl alcohol (alcoholic fermentation), and lactic acid (glycolysis). An ester of crocetin and gentiobiose is known (Chapter X).

* The section on "Phosphate Esters" (pp. 172–187) was prepared by W. Z. Hassid and C. E. Ballou.

Esterification is accomplished by reaction of the carbohydrate with an acyl halide or an acid anhydride and catalyst. The catalyst may be an acid, as perchloric, sulfuric, trifluoroacetic acid, or zinc chloride, or a base, like pyridine or sodium acetate. Acids may hydrolyze glycosidic bonds if present, whereas bases may cause rearrangements if reducing sugars are used. In common with other organic esters, these derivatives are hydrolyzed by both acids and alkalies, with alkalies being particularly effective. The fully substituted organic esters are soluble in organic solvents, particularly well in the chlorinated hydrocarbons. If fully esterified, the products generally are well crystallized and are obtained in good yield.

The ease of reactivity of the sugar hydroxyl groups is usually in the order: hemiacetal hydroxyl, primary alcohol, secondary alcohol. The presence of ring structures, however, has a great influence on the reactivity. For the sugars, cyclic esters (usually pyranoses) are the principal products obtained on esterification, but sometimes small amounts of acyclic esters (derivatives of the *aldehydo-* or *keto-*form) are among the reaction products. *aldehydo-*Forms seem to be encountered especially among the higher-carbon aldoses, whereas ketoses (*1*) are very prone to yield acyclic esters.

Part I

Acyl Derivatives

1. ACETATE ESTERS

A. Cyclic Acetates with Pyranose and Furanose Rings

The acetyl derivatives of the sugars have been extensively employed as intermediates in sugar synthesis and for the isolation and identification of the sugars. Their value for these purposes arises from their ease of preparation and crystallization and because the acetyl groups are easily removed. The sugars are highly tautomeric and their numerous tautomeric phases may be captured and studied in their acetate esters. As early as 1860, Berthelot (*2*) obtained a sirupy ester by reacting D-glucose with acetic acid. Liebermann (*3*) introduced the use of anhydrous sodium acetate and acetic anhydride, and Franchimont (*3a*) obtained from D-glucose, sodium acetate, and acetic anhydride a crystalline ester which was probably β-D-glucopyranose pentaacetate. The use of zinc chloride as a catalyst in place of sodium acetate gave the α-D-anomer (*4*), although, because of difficulties

1. E. M. Montgomery and C. S. Hudson, *J. Am. Chem. Soc.* **56,** 2463 (1934); C. S. Hudson and D. H. Brauns, *ibid.* **37,** 2736 (1915); E. Pacsu and F. V. Rich, *ibid.* **55,** 3018 (1933); M. L. Wolfrom and A. Thompson, *ibid.* **56,** 880 (1934).

2. M. Berthelot, *Ann. chim. phys.* [3] **60,** 93 (1860).

3. C. Liebermann and O. Hörmann, *Ber.* **11,** 1618 (1878).

3a. A. P. N. Franchimont, *Ber.* **12,** 1940 (1879).

4. E. Erwig and W. Koenigs, *Ber.* **22,** 1464 (1889).

in analysis, the two pentaacetates were not recognized at the time as being

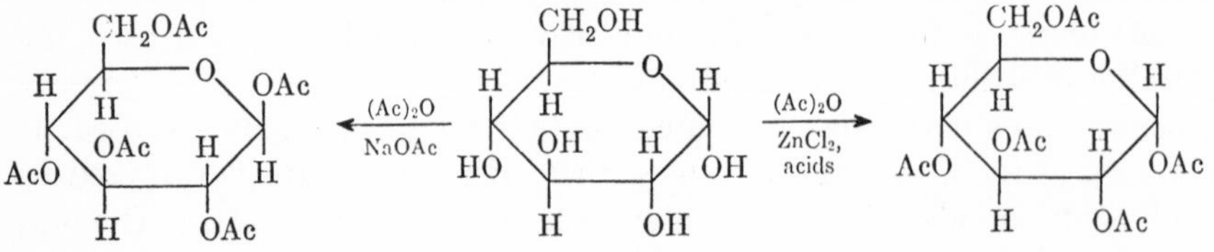

β-D-Glucopyranose pentaacetate α-D-Glucose α-D-Glucopyranose pentaacetate

isomers. These two catalysts are still used extensively for acetylation, but pyridine, sulfuric acid, perchloric acid, and trifluoroacetic anhydride have advantages as catalysts in many instances (*5*). The catalytic efficiencies of perchloric acid, phosphoric acid, and zinc chloride are related to their relative proton affinities (relative acidities) in the acetylating medium (*6*).

For the acetylation of β-naphthol, the reaction has been shown to be subject to both acidic and basic catalysis (*7*). The rate of acetylation is slowest between pH 1 and 3 (in glacial acetic acid, acetic anhydride) and increases at both higher and lower acidities. These results may apply to the acetylation of carbohydrates.

The acetylation reaction has been adapted to the analytical assay of hydroxyl groups (*8*).

The acetylation of the nonreducing sugars and other derivatives which consist of a single modification can be carried out by almost any method which does not affect glycosidic linkages, but the acetylation of the reducing sugars is complicated by the existence of tautomers. For this reason it is necessary to select a method which will give the desired product. The isomer obtained depends upon the catalyst used in the acetylation and upon the temperature. The following general scheme (*9*) illustrates the effect of these factors on the acetylation of D-glucose. At low temperatures (0°C.) the equilibriums represented by reactions (I) and (II) are only slowly established and the acetylation reactions (III) or (IV) take place without isomerization. By the use of pyridine and a low temperature, the α-D-aldohexose yields the α-D pentaacetate, and the β-D-aldohexose yields the β-D pentaacetate. Behrend and Roth found that under these conditions acetyla-

5. A. Verley and F. Bölsing, *Ber.* **34,** 3354 (1901); R. Behrend and P. Roth, *Ann.* **331,** 362 (1904); A. P. N. Franchimont, *Compt. rend.* **92,** 1053 (1881); D. Krüger and A. Roman, *Ber.* **69,** 1830 (1936).

6. D. Krüger, *Nitrocellulose* **9,** 175 (1938).

7. J. B. Conant and G. M. Bramann, *J. Am. Chem. Soc.* **50,** 2305 (1928).

8. M. Freed and A. M. Wynne, *Ind. Eng. Chem. Anal. Ed.* **8,** 278 (1936); B. E. Christensen and R. A. Clarke, *ibid.* **17,** 265 (1945).

9. C. S. Hudson, *Ind. Eng. Chem.* **8,** 380 (1916).

IV

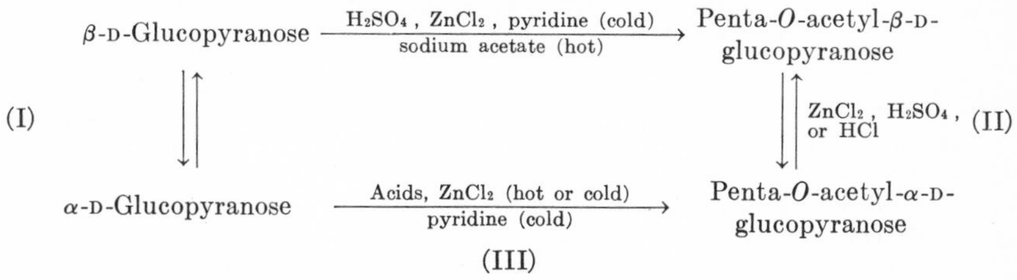
β-D-Glucopyranose
H2SO4 , ZnCl2 , pyridine (cold)
sodium acetate (hot)
Penta-O-acetyl-β-D-glucopyranose
(I)
ZnCl2 , H2SO4 , or HCl
(II)
α-D-Glucopyranose
Acids, ZnCl2 (hot or cold)
pyridine (cold)
Penta-O-acetyl-α-D-glucopyranose
(III)

tion is faster than anomerization. At higher temperatures, in the presence of acid catalysts, isomerization between the acetates takes place, and the products obtained depend upon the position of the equilibrium represented by the reaction (II). In the case of D-glucose, the equilibrium mixture of the pentaacetates consists of 90% of the alpha and 10% of the beta penta-*O*-acetyl-D-glucopyranose (*10*). For many sugars the α-D-acetates predominate in the equilibrium mixture and consequently the use of acid catalysts, such as zinc chloride, and a relatively high temperature (20 to 110°C.) produces the α-D acetate from either the α-D- or β-D-sugar. With sodium acetate as a catalyst at a high temperature, the equilibrium (I) between the α-D- and β-D-sugars is established, whereas the equilibrium (II) between the acetates is not. Since the β-D-sugar is acetylated more rapidly than the α-D-, the principal product is then the acetylated β-D-sugar.

The diagram also illustrates how the α-D acetates may be prepared from the β-D acetates. For this purpose, a mixture of sulfuric acid, acetic acid, and acetic anhydride has certain advantages over zinc chloride (*1*). This reagent also brings about the transformation of acetylated glycosides to the corresponding *O*-acetyl-α-D-aldoses. In contradiction to the general belief that the reaction is only catalyzed by acid catalysts, solid sodium hydroxide in an inert solvent also catalyzes the transformation of the beta to the alpha *O*-acetyl-D-sugars (*11*). In the case of D-galactose, a considerable proportion of the β-D-galactofuranose pentaacetate is produced by the hot acetylation with the sodium acetate catalyst (*12*); even more is formed on hot acetylation with pyridine (*13*). The acetylation of ketoses is a special problem with low temperatures and acid catalysts being favored, especially with fructose. Ketene is not a useful acetylating agent for the sugars (*14*).

Reflecting the greater numbers of tautomers in solution, the number and types of crystalline isomers of the sugar acetates is generally greater than

10. C. L. Jungius, *Z. physik. Chem.* **52,** 97 (1905).

11. M. L. Wolfrom and D. R. Husted, *J. Am. Chem. Soc.* **59,** 364 (1937).

12. C. S. Hudson, *J. Am. Chem. Soc.* **37,** 1591 (1915).

13. H. H. Schlubach and V. Prochownick, *Ber.* **63,** 2298 (1930); R. K. Ness, H. G. Fletcher, Jr., and C. S. Hudson, *J. Am. Chem. Soc.* **73,** 3742 (1951).

14. C. D. Hurd, S. M. Cantor, and A. S. Roe, *J. Am. Chem. Soc.* **61,** 426 (1939).

TABLE I

Properties of Penta-*O*-acetyl-D-Galactoses

Substance	M.p. (°C.)	$[\alpha]_D^{20}$ ($CHCl_3$)
Penta-*O*-acetyl-α-D-galactopyranose	96	+106.7°
Penta-*O*-acetyl-β-D-galactopyranose	142	+25°
Penta-*O*-acetyl-α-D-galactofuranose	87	+61.2°
Penta-*O*-acetyl-β-D-galactofuranose	98	−41.6°
Penta-*O*-acetyl-α-D-galactoseptanose	128	−11.0°
Penta-*O*-acetyl-β-D-galactoseptanose	101	−78.3° (18°C.)
Penta-*O*-acetyl-*aldehydo*-D-galactose	121	−25° (26°C.)

for the parent sugar. Thus, seven isomeric pentaacetates of D-galactose are known (Table I). Dimeric acetates of the trioses and dioses are established (*15*). These are cyclic acetals derived from the dioxane ring.

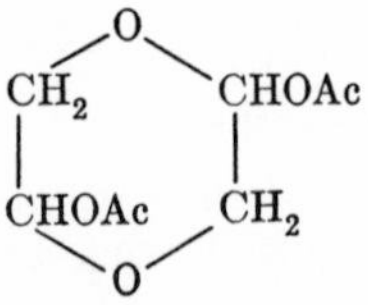
O
CH2
CHOAc
CHOAc
CH2
O

Glycolaldehyde diacetate

(cyclic dimer)

B. Acyclic Acetates

The open-chain forms of the sugars are presumed to be the intermediates in certain reactions, such as mutarotation, oxidation to aldonic acids, or reduction to alditols, but, so far as is known, crystalline sugars always exist in one of the ring forms. In aqueous solutions, there is considerable evidence that appreciable amounts of the open-chain (*aldehydo* or *keto*; probably hydrated in water) form may exist in solutions of sugars such as ribose and fructose. (See Chapter I.) As noted before (p. 139), acyclic esters are occasionally obtained by direct acetylation methods, especially with the ketoses and the higher-carbon aldoses. In general, the ring of an aldose can be opened by the action of hydrochloric acid and ethanethiol (ethyl mercaptan) to form the acyclic diethyl dithioacetal (*16*) (mercaptal). Amorphous penta-*O*-methyl-*aldehydo*-D-glucose, prepared (*17*) by the methylation of D-glucose diethyl dithioacetal (I) with subsequent removal of the dithioacetal group, has an acyclic structure. Demercaptalation of the acetylated di-

15. R. K. Summerbell and L. K. Rochen, *J. Am. Chem. Soc.* **63,** 3241 (1941).
16. E. Fischer, *Ber.* **27,** 673 (1894).
17. P. A. Levene and G. M. Meyer, *J. Biol. Chem.* **69,** 175 (1926).

thioacetal (II) in the presence of cadmium carbonate allowed the isolation of crystalline *aldehydo*-D-glucose pentaacetate (III) (*18*). The acetyl and benzoyl derivatives of the free aldehyde and ketone (*aldehydo* and *keto*) forms of the sugars are in general well-characterized crystalline substances and have been extensively investigated by Wolfrom and by Brigl and their co-workers. The sugar dithioacetals (I), oximes (IV), and semicarbazones

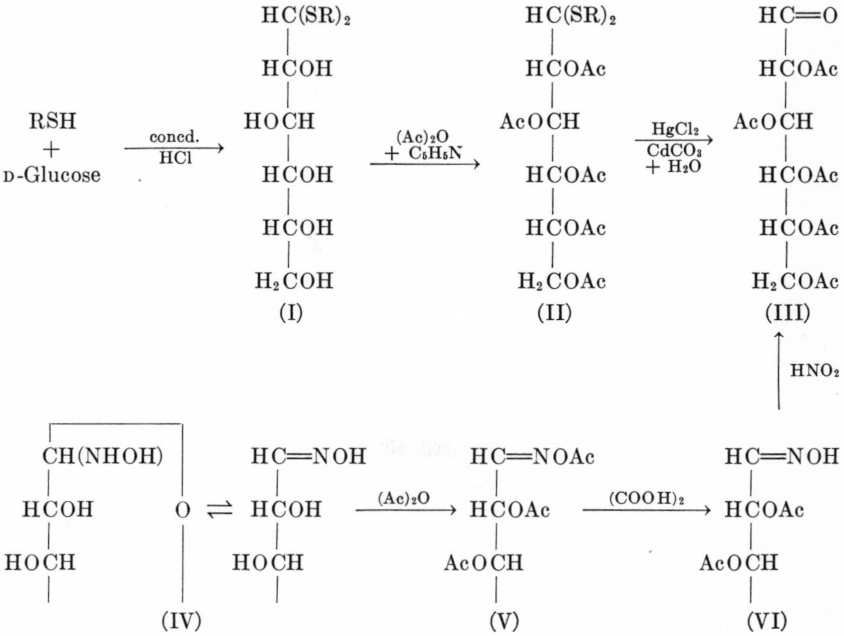

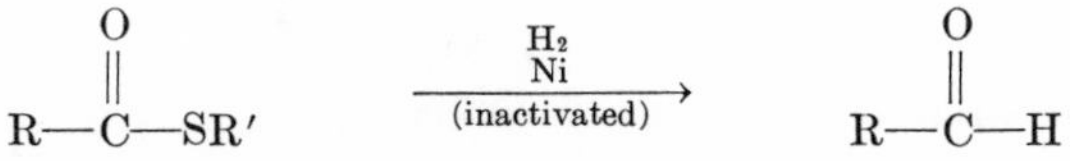

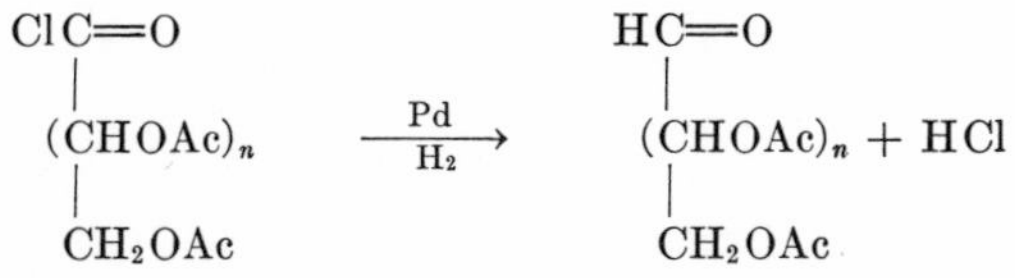

18. M. L. Wolfrom, *J. Am. Chem. Soc.* **51**, 2188 (1929).

have been applied to their preparation. The nitrogen condensation products of the reducing sugars exhibit ring-chain tautomerism (IV), and acyclic derivatives (V) are sometimes obtained by direct acylation methods (*19*). *aldehydo*-Acetates may also be prepared by the reduction of the acetylated aldonic acid chlorides or aldonate thiol esters (see formulas). Tetra-*O*-acetyl-*aldehydo*-D-ribose (*20*) has been prepared by the two latter methods.

The sugar dithioacetals are perhaps the best intermediates except that the reaction conditions may be too severe for some sugars, such as the disaccharides, which may be hydrolyzed (*21*). The ketoses are too acid-sensitive for direct mercaptalation; D-fructose diethyl dithioacetal has been prepared by Wolfrom and Thompson only by an indirect method (*1*). The reduction of the acid chloride has not been extensively used but should be limited only by the availability of the acetylated acids (p. 309) (*22*).

As noted above, the ketoses are especially prone to produce acyclic acetates by methods of direct acetylation, as exemplified by D-fructose (*1*) and D-sorbose (*23*). It has been demonstrated by Pacsu (*1*) and by Wolfrom and Thompson (*1*) that the long known penta-*O*-acetyl-"α"-D-fructose of Hudson and Brauns (*1*) has a free ketonic group. A general method, involving the action of diazomethane on *O*-acetylated aldonic acid chlorides, has been developed for the synthesis of *O*-acetyl-*keto*-sugars (*24*) (see formulas).

The acylic esters are true aldehydes or ketones and exhibit the reactions typical of these compounds. The *aldehydo* esters give positive tests with Schiff's reagent, whereas the unsubstituted aldoses do not. Oxidation of *O*-acetyl-*aldehydo*-sugars by hypobromite produces the corresponding *O*-acetylated aldonic acids (*25*).

The reaction of the acetyl and benzoyl sugars with ethanethiol in the presence of zinc chloride (*26*) is of value in distinguishing between cyclic

19. M. L. Wolfrom and A. Thompson, *J. Am. Chem. Soc.* **53,** 622 (1931); V. Deulofeu and J. O. Deferrari, *J. Org. Chem.* **17,** 1087 (1952).

20. M. L. Wolfrom and J. V. Karabinos, *J. Am. Chem. Soc.* **68,** 724 (1946); R. Pasternack and E. V. Brown, U. S. Patent 2,237,263 (1941).

21. M. L. Wolfrom, L. W. Georges, and S. Soltzberg, *J. Am. Chem. Soc.* **56,** 1794 (1934).

22. G. B. Robbins and F. W. Upson, *J. Am. Chem. Soc.* **62,** 1074 (1940); C. D. Hurd and J. C. Sowden, *ibid.*, **60,** 235 (1938); M. L. Wolfrom, M. Konigsberg, and D. I. Weisblat, *ibid.* **61,** 574 (1939); K. Ladenburg, M. Tishler, J. W. Wellman, and R. D. Babson, *ibid.* **66,** 1217 (1944).

23. G. Arragon, *Compt. rend.* **196,** 1733 (1933); H. H. Schlubach and J. Vorwerk, *Ber.* **66,** 1251 (1933); Y. Khouvine and G. Arragon, *Bull. soc. chim. France* [5] **5,** 1404 (1938); M. L. Wolfrom, S. M. Olin, and E. F. Evans, *J. Am. Chem. Soc.* **66,** 204 (1944).

24. M. L. Wolfrom, S. W. Waisbrot, and R. L. Brown, *J. Am. Chem. Soc.* **64,** 2329 (1942).

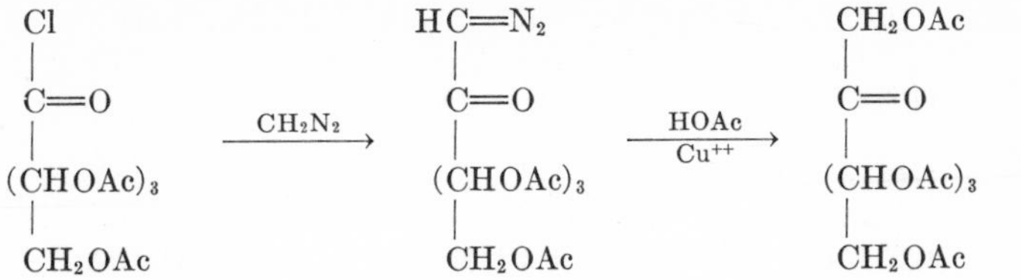
Cl
C=O
(CHOAc)₃
CH₂OAc
CH₂N₂
HC=N₂
C=O
(CHOAc)₃
CH₂OAc
HOAc
Cu⁺⁺
CH₂OAc
C=O
(CHOAc)₃
CH₂OAc

Tetra-*O*-acetyl-D-arabonyl chloride — 1-Deoxy-1-diazo-tetra-*O*-acetyl-D-fructose — Penta-*O*-acetyl-*keto*-D-fructose

and acyclic forms, acetates of the *aldehydo*- and *keto*-form producing dithioacetals without acetyl loss. The fully acetylated esters of β-D-glucopyranose, β-D-galactopyranose, β-D-fructopyranose, and D-*glycero*-β-D-*gulo*-heptopyranose, lose one acetyl group and produce thioethyl β-D-glycosides, whereas the α-anomers of the D-glucopyranose and D-galactopyranose acetates are unaffected.

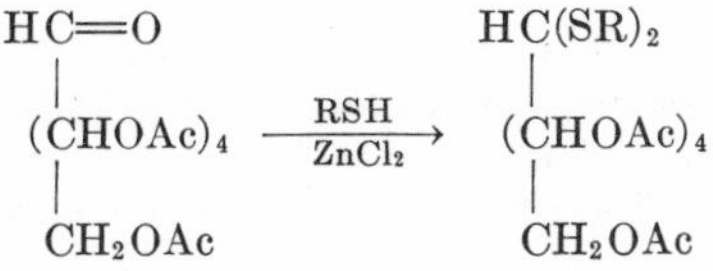
HC=O
(CHOAc)₄
CH₂OAc
RSH
ZnCl₂
HC(SR)₂
(CHOAc)₄
CH₂OAc

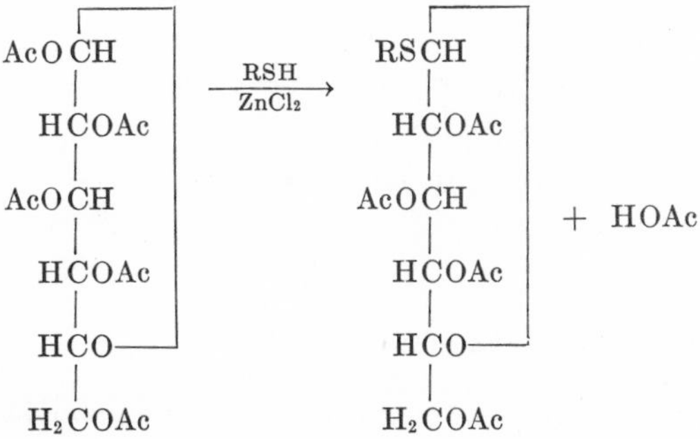
AcOCH
HCOAc
AcOCH
HCOAc
HCO
H₂COAc
RSH
ZnCl₂
RSCH
HCOAc
AcOCH
HCOAc
HCO
H₂COAc
+ HOAc

The *O*-acetyl-*aldehydo*-sugars mutarotate in aqueous and alcoholic solutions and some form crystalline hydrates and alcoholates which have been shown to be aldehydrol and hemiacetal derivatives (*27*), respectively. Further acetylation of an *aldehydo*-aldohexose pentaacetate yields the

25. R. T. Major and E. W. Cook, *J. Am. Chem. Soc.* **58,** 2474 (1936).

26. M. L. Wolfrom and A. Thompson, *J. Am. Chem. Soc.* **56,** 1804 (1934); P. Brigl and R. Schinle, *Ber.* **66,** 325 (1933); R. U. Lemieux, *Can. J. Chem.* **29,** 1079 (1951).

27. M. L. Wolfrom, *J. Am. Chem. Soc.* **53,** 2275 (1931); M. L. Wolfrom and W. M. Morgan, *ibid.* **54,** 3390 (1932); R. J. Dimler and K. P. Link, *ibid.* **62,** 1216 (1940).

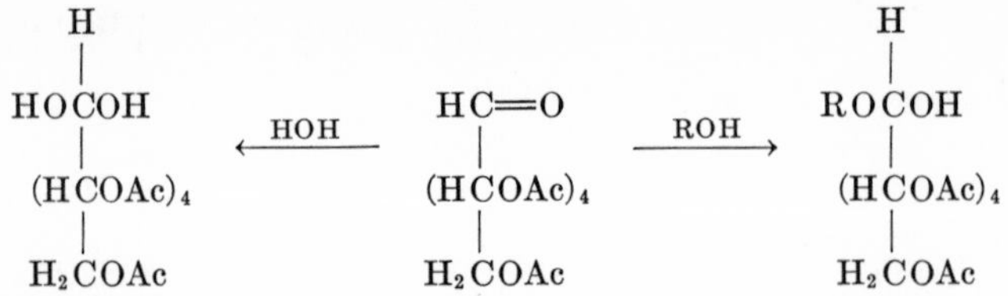

Aldehydrol Hemiacetal

heptaacetate, $AcOH_2C—(CHOAc)_4—CH(OAc)_2$ (*28*) also obtained on acetolysis of glycosides (*29*).

C. Cyclic Acetates with a Septanose Ring

By a special series of reactions, a pair of cyclic penta-*O*-acetyl-D-galactoses with seven-atom rings (septanose rings) have been synthesized by Micheel with Suckfüll and with Spruck (*30*). The synthetic reaction sequence employed was:

D-galactose diethyl dithioacetal → 2,3,4,5-tetra-*O*-acetyl-6-*O*-trityl-D-galactose diethyl dithioacetal → 2,3,4,5-tetra-*O*-acetyl-6-*O*-trityl-D-galactose hydrate → 2,3,4,5-tetra-*O*-acetyl-D-galactose hydrate → 1,2,3,4,5-penta-*O*-acetyl-α- and -β-D-galactoseptanose (Table I)

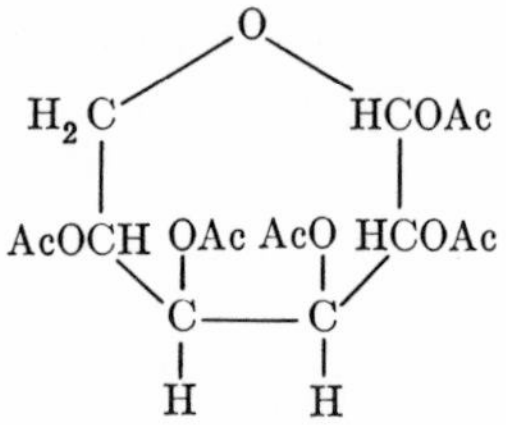

Penta-*O*-acetyl-α-D-galactoseptanose

The septanose structure was confirmed (*31*) by conversion of the penta-acetate to a methyl tetra-*O*-methyl-D-galactoseptanoside which upon oxidation with nitric acid gave tetra-*O*-methylgalactaric acid, $COOH—(CHOCH_3)_4COOH$.

28. M. L. Wolfrom, *J. Am. Chem. Soc.* **57,** 2498 (1935); F. Micheel, F. Ruhkopf, and F. Suckfüll, *Ber.* **68,** 1523 (1935).

29. E. M. Montgomery, R. M. Hann, and C. S. Hudson, *J. Am. Chem. Soc.* **59,** 1124 (1937); K. Freudenberg and K. Soff, *Ber.* **70,** 264 (1937); B. Lindberg, *Acta Chem. Scand.* **3,** 1153 (1949); L. Asp and B. Lindberg, *ibid.* **4,** 1386, 1446 (1950).

30. F. Micheel and F. Suckfüll, *Ann.* **502,** 85 (1933); F. Micheel and W. Spruck, *Ber.* **67,** 1665 (1934).

31. F. Micheel and F. Suckfüll, *Ann.* **507,** 138 (1933).

D. Acetyl Migration

In the presence of dilute alkali, acyl groups attached to sugars which also contain free hydroxyls may wander and occupy new positions (*32*). Helferich and Klein (*33*, *34*) observed a mutarotation to take place for solutions of 1,2,3,4-tetra-*O*-acetyl-β-D-glucose and found that the soft-glass container catalyzed the transfer of an acetyl group, probably from the fourth to the sixth carbon atom. When the resulting 1,2,3,6-tetra-*O*-acetyl-β-D-glucose was methylated by methyl iodide and silver oxide, a second migration of an acetyl group from carbon 1 to carbon 4 took place (*34*). Such migrations (*35*) have been observed frequently (see also under Phosphate Esters) and are considered to take place through an intermediate orthoester as suggested by Fischer (*36*), rather than by an actual hydrolysis and recombination of the wandering group. It should be noted that the geometry of the pyranose rings is such that groups attached to carbons 1, 4, and 6 can approach each other quite closely and that the postulated six-membered orthoacetic structures are strainless even when the two linkages are *trans* to the ring. In all known instances of acetyl migration, the acetyl group moves in a direction away from the carbonyl group. Methods suit-

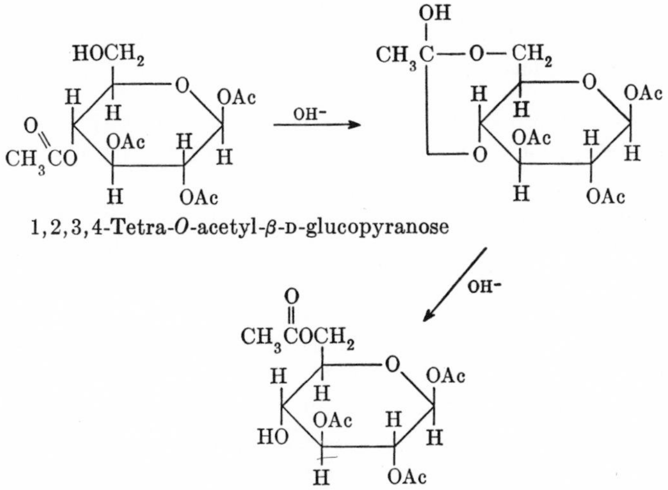
HOCH2
O
OAc
H
H
O
CH3CO
OAc
H
H
H
OAc
OH-
OH
CH3C—O—CH2
O
OAc
OH-
CH3COCH2
HO

1,2,3,4-Tetra-*O*-acetyl-β-D-glucopyranose

1,2,3,6-Tetra-*O*-acetyl-β-D-glucopyranose

---

32. E. Fischer, M. Bergmann, and A. Rabe, *Ber.* **53,** 2362 (1920).

33. B. Helferich and W. Klein, *Ann.* **450,** 219 (1926); **455,** 173 (1927).

34. W. N. Haworth, E. L. Hirst, and E. G. Teece, *J. Chem. Soc.* p. 1408 (1930).

35. See review by E. L. Hirst and S. Peat, *Ann. Repts. Chem. Soc.* **31,** 172 (1934); J. M. Sugihara, *Advances in Carbohydrate Chem.* **8,** 1 (1953).

36. E. Fischer, *Ber.* **53,** 1621 (1920).

able for the preparation of partially esterified sugar structures are reviewed in a succeeding section (p. 158).

2. BENZOATE ESTERS

The Schotten-Baumann reaction (action of benzoyl chloride and sodium hydroxide) has been used for benzoylating the hydroxyl groups of carbohydrates (*37*). On benzoylating D-fructose, Brigl and Schinle (*26*, *38*) obtained simultaneously the 1,3,4,5-pyranose tetrabenzoate, 1,3,4,6-furanose tetrabenzoate, and 1,3,4,5,6-*keto*-pentabenzoate, thus demonstrating the highly tautomeric nature of this ketohexose. To obtain completely benzoylated sugars, the method ordinarily is modified by the use of benzoyl chloride and pyridine or quinoline (*39*). Benzoylation takes place with more difficulty than acetylation, and considerably longer reaction periods are required.

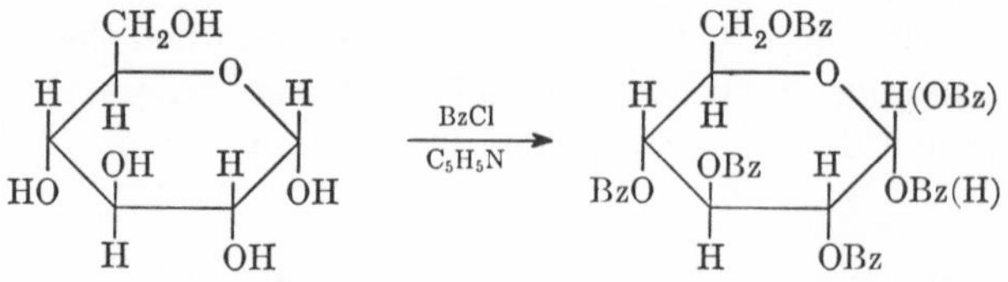
CH2OH
O
H
H
H
OH
H
HO
OH
H
OH
BzCl
C5H5N
CH2OBz
O
H
H
H(OBz)
OBz
H
BzO
OBz(H)
H
OBz

α-D-Glucose Penta-*O*-benzoyl-D-glucoses (alpha and beta)

By the use of substituted benzoyl chlorides, derivatives such as the penta-*O*-(*p*-bromobenzoyl)- and penta-*O*-(*p*-nitrobenzoyl)-D-glucoses have been prepared.

The sugar benzoates are quite similar in their properties and reactions to the sugar acetates, and it frequently happens that, when a desired acetate ester cannot be obtained in a crystalline condition, the benzoate ester may crystallize. This has been especially true in the aldopentose series. Furthermore, the anomeric penta-*O*-acyl-D-glucofuranoses are characterized only in the benzoate series. They may be converted to *O*-benzoylglycosyl halides by methods similar to those for the *O*-acetylglycosyl halides (see below), and the halogen may be replaced by R—O— groups (R = alkyl, aryl, and acyl groups) as for the *O*-acetyl analogs. As the compounds have not received the same amount of attention that has been devoted to the acetate esters, many problems remain uninvestigated. Recent work has

37. Z. H. Skraup, *Monatsh.* **10,** 389 (1889); L. Kueny, *Z. physiol. Chem.* **14,** 330 (1890).

38. P. Brigl and R. Schinle, *Ber.* **67,** 127 (1934).

39. E. Fischer and H. Noth, *Ber.* **51,** 321 (1918); P. A. Levene and G. M. Meyer, *J. Biol. Chem.* **76,** 513 (1928).

shown that mono-*O*-benzoyl-D-talose does not have an orthobenzoic acid structure (*40*) but other orthobenzoates are now known.

Wandering of *O*-acyl groups from an esterified to an unesterified hydroxyl occurs (*41*) for *O*-benzoyl as well as *O*-acetyl groups. For example, DL-1,4-di-*O*-benzoylgalactitol melts at 171°C., but if held at this temperature the product solidifies to an isomer melting at 202° which is 1,6-di-*O*-benzoylgalactitol (*42*). But, in general, *O*-benzoyl groups are more stable than *O*-acetyl groups. The *O*-benzoyl derivatives of the free-aldehyde form of D-glucose have been investigated by Brigl and associate (*43*); they are similar to the *O*-acetyl analog.

The use of boric acid has been suggested by Brigl for the preparation of partially *O*-benzoylated sugars (*41*, *44*). Unimolar *O*-benzoylation of glycosides and mercaptals results usually in preferential esterification of the primary hydroxyl (*45*).

Several partially *O*-benzoylated sugars and glycosides are naturally occurring. Griebel isolated a mono-*O*-benzoyl-D-glucose (vaccinin) from the juice of blueberries (*Vaccinium vitisidaea* L.) It was shown by Ohle (*46*) probably to be 6-mono-*O*-benzoyl-D-glucose. Populin, which is found in the bark of a species of poplar, was demonstrated by Richtmyer and Yeakel (*45*) to be salicyl 6-*O*-benzoyl-β-D-glucopyranoside.

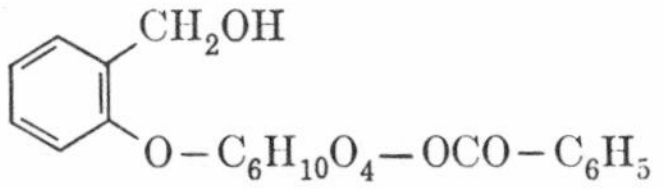
CH2OH
O−C6H10O4−OCO−C6H5

Populin (6-*O*-Benzoylsalicin)

A nonreducing di-*O*-benzoyldisaccharide containing D-glucose and D-xylose residues has been reported (*47*) as occurring in *Daviesia latifolia*, an Australian shrub.

From the biological standpoint, 1-mono-*O*-benzoyl-D-glucuronic acid is the most important benzoyl derivative. This compound occurs in the urine of dogs fed benzoic acid. Its structure was shown by the following evidence

40. W. W. Pigman and H. S. Isbell, *J. Research Natl. Bur. Standards* **19,** 189 (1937).

41. H. Ohle, *Ber.* **57,** 403 (1924); P. Brigl and H. Grüner, *Ann.* **495,** 67 (1932).

42. R. M. Hann, W. D. Maclay, and C. S. Hudson, *J. Am. Chem. Soc.* **61,** 2432 (1939).

43. P. Brigl and H. Mühlschlegel, *Ber.* **63,** 1551 (1930).

44. P. Brigl and H. Grüner, *Ber.* **67,** 1969 (1934).

45. T. Lieser and R. Schweizer, *Ann.* **519,** 271 (1935); N. K. Richtmyer and E. Yeakel, *J. Am. Chem. Soc.* **56,** 2495 (1934).

46. H. Ohle, *Biochem. Z.* **131,** 611 (1922).

47. F. B. Power and A. H. Salway, *J. Chem. Soc.* **105,** 767, 1062 (1914).

(*48*). Upon acetylation and esterification, the natural product gives a tri-*O*-acetyl methyl ester. This product is identical with that obtained by the reaction of 1-bromotetra-*O*-acetyl-D-glucuronic acid methyl ester with silver benzoate and must have the *O*-benzoyl group at carbon 1.

3. *O*-ACYLGLYCOSYL HALIDES

In the cyclic forms of the sugars, the hemiacetal hydroxyl group on the reducing carbon (carbon 1 in the aldoses and carbon 2 in the known ketoses) has a greatly enhanced reactivity over that exhibited by the simple alcoholic functions of the sugar stem. This reactivity is influenced by the spatial asymmetry and by the nature and relative positions of the groups on the neighboring carbon atoms. These considerations account for marked differences observable in sugar ester behavior. Such groups as the hydroxyl, halogen, acoxy, alkoxy, nitrate, phosphate, or sulfate, may be substituted for each other, by the proper choice of reagents, on the reducing carbon of

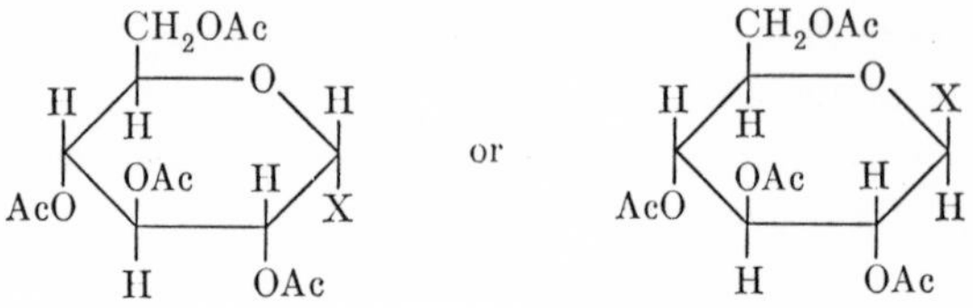
CH2OAc
O
H
H
OAc
AcO
X
OAc
or
CH2OAc
O
X
H
OAc
AcO
H
OAc

$$X{=}OH, F, Cl, Br, I, O{-}\overset{O}{\overset{\|}{C}}{-}R, OR, ONO_2, OPO(OH)_2, OSO_2OH$$

the acetylated sugars. The acetoxy group on the reducing carbon of the acetylated sugars can be replaced by halogen or by nitrate groups (*49*). The resulting compounds, especially the *O*-acetyl-α-D-glycopyranosyl chlorides and bromides, are important intermediates in synthesis. The first compound of this type (tetra-*O*-acetylglucopyranosyl chloride) was prepared by Colley by the action of acetyl chloride on D-glucose (*50*). To prepare an acylglycosyl halide, an *O*-acetylated or *O*-benzoylated sugar is (*51*) most commonly treated with a solution of a halogen acid in acetic acid. Addition of acetic anhydride to the mixture is generally made and offers the advantage of a lower freezing point, the possibility of obtaining a higher concentration of halogen acid, the exclusion of moisture from the mixture, and prevention of incidental deacetylation.

48. W. F. Goebel, *J. Biol. Chem.* **122,** 649 (1937–38).

49. W. Koenigs and E. Knorr, *Ber.* **34,** 957 (1901).

50. A. Colley, *Ann. chim. phys.* [4] **21,** 363 (1870); D. H. Brauns, *J. Am. Chem. Soc.* **44,** 401 (1922).

51. A. Bodart, *Monatsh.* **23,** 1 (1902); E. Fischer and H. Fischer, *Ber.* **43,** 2521 (1910).

Liquid hydrogen halide has been used as a reagent on the acetylated sugar (*52*). This method is especially valuable for obtaining the *O*-acetylglycosyl fluorides, a reaction investigated particularly by Brauns (*53*). In some instances (cellobiose, see p. 482), the hydrogen fluoride causes rearrangements to take place with the production of derivatives of new sugars. Prolonged action of hydrogen bromide on D-glucopyranose pentaacetate produces dibromides by replacement of the acetoxy groups at carbons 1 and 6 (anomeric and primary-alcohol groups).

A mixture of phosphorus pentachloride and aluminum chloride has been used for preparing the *O*-acetylglycosyl chlorides from the acetylated sugars in chloroform solution (*54*). Titanium tetrachloride may be used in place of the mixture of aluminum and phosphorus chlorides (*55*). Lemieux and Brice (*56*) have shown that penta-*O*-acetyl-β-D-glucopyranose, but not its α-anomer, reacts rapidly with titanium chloride to form tetra-*O*-acetyl-β-D-glucopyranosyl chloride, which quickly rearranges to its α-anomer. Some sugars (the reducing disaccharides cellobiose and lactose) undergo inversion at carbons 2 and 3 of the reducing moiety during the reaction with phosphorus and aluminum chlorides and yield the halides of new sugars.

Colley's method, using acetyl chloride, is not widely employed because of the difficulty in controlling the reaction. The first method is the best for most preparations although for the fluorides the second method is particularly valuable. The stability of the *O*-acetylglycosyl halides follows the order: fluorides > chlorides > bromides > iodides. The iodides decompose rapidly even at 0°C., whereas the fluorides may be kept for long periods without decomposition.

As the carbon atom carrying the halogen is asymmetric, two anomeric isomers are possible. Application of the isorotation rules of Hudson indicates that most of the compounds in the aldohexose structures belong to a single series which is assigned the α-D-configuration. With some of the aldopentoses, the stable form isolated is of the β-D-configuration. Schlubach, however, has reported that tetra-*O*-acetyl-α-D-glucopyranosyl bromide (dextrorotatory) can be converted into the anomeric tetra-*O*-acetyl-β-D-glucopyranosyl chloride (levorotatory) by treatment with silver chloride. This β-D-isomer was very unstable and was transformed rapidly into the α-D-anomer. Like instability has been detected in other β-D-anomers of the

52. E. Fischer and E. F. Armstrong, *Ber.* **34,** 2885 (1901).

53. D. H. Brauns, *J. Am. Chem. Soc.* **45,** 833 (1923); D. H. Brauns and H. L. Frush, *Bur. Standards J. Research* **6,** 449 (1931).

54. F. von Arlt, *Monatsh.* **22,** 144 (1901); Z. H. Skraup and R. Kremann, *ibid.* **22,** 375 (1901).

55. E. Paçsu, *Ber.* **61,** 1508 (1928).

56. R. U. Lemieux and C. Brice, *Can. J. Chem.* **30,** 295 (1952).

hexose series (*57*) and makes these substances in general useless for the synthesis of α-D-glycosides by the Koenigs-Knorr reaction (see below).

On the basis of conformational studies, Hassel and Ottar (*58*) have advanced a theory to explain the greater stability of one or the other of the two anomeric *O*-acetyl-D-glycopyranosyl halides. It is considered that the pyranose ring is theoretically capable of eight strainless ring conformations, six boat and two staggered or chair forms. (See also Chapter I.) The evi-

a
e
4
a
e
O
2
5
3
e
a
1
e
e
a
a
a
e
5
a
1
O
e
4
3
2
a
e
e
a

C1 1C

dence indicates that one of the two chair forms will be favored and that for most purposes the boat forms can be neglected. In the hexopyranoses the anomer in which the relative position of the halogen and the large group substituted on carbon 5 can be represented in the two chair forms by the equation

$$-X_a\ ,\ -CH_2OAc_e \rightleftharpoons -X_e\ ,\ -CH_2OAc_a$$

is more stable, while the less-stable anomer can be represented by

$$-X_e\ ,\ -CH_2OAc_e \rightleftharpoons -X_a\ ,\ -CH_2OAc_a$$

The values *e* and *a* refer to the equatorial or axial positions of the substituents. In the absence of the $-CH_2OAc$ group, as in the aldopentopyranose ring, the interaction between the groups on carbons 1 and 3 becomes of importance and determines the stable isomer. This behavior is known as the *Hassel-Ottar effect* governing the stability of anomeric halides.

Alkalies remove halogen and acetyl groups from the *O*-acetyl-D-glycosyl iodides, bromides, and chlorides. However, the fluorine atom in tetra-*O*-acetyl-D-glucosyl fluoride is more stable than the acetyl groups, which may be removed by alkali leaving D-glucosyl fluoride (*59*). The fluorine is more easily removed by acids than by bases, a relation which is the reverse of that for other halogens and most acyl groups. By heating gentiobiosyl fluoride with water and calcium carbonate, the free sugar is regenerated.

The importance of the *O*-acetylglycopyranosyl halides lies in the ease

57. E. Fischer, *Ber.* **44,** 1898 (1911); H. Schlubach, *ibid.* **59,** 840 (1926); P. Brigl and H. Keppler, *ibid.* **59,** 1588 (1926); D. H. Brauns, *J. Am. Chem. Soc.* **49,** 3170 (1927); H. Schlubach and R. Gilbert, *Ber.* **63,** 2292 (1930).

58. O. Hassel and B. Ottar, *Acta Chem. Scand.* **1,** 929 (1947).

59. B. Helferich, K. Bäuerlein, and F. Wiegand, *Ann.* **447,** 27 (1926).

with which the halogen atom may be replaced by many acoxyl, aroxyl, and alkoxyl groups. Ordinarily the reaction is carried out at room temperature in an anhydrous, inert solvent (such as benzene or ether) with alcohols or with the salts of phenols or acids and in the presence of silver carbonate, silver oxide, or an organic base such as pyridine or quinoline. These latter substances probably function by removing the halide ion as AgX or the hydrogen halide as the salt of the organic base. When water is formed in the reaction, the presence of a desiccant in the reaction mixture is desirable. The reactivity of the *O*-acetylglycopyranosyl halides is in the order: I > Br > Cl > F. Since the iodides decompose too easily to be kept for any time and since the fluorides react with too much difficulty, the bromides and chlorides are most commonly employed.

Some of the many ester or halide groups which have been introduced into the sugar molecule by this means are: I (*60*), Cl (*61*), F (*60*), ONO_2 (*49*), OH (*62*), CH_3CO (*49, 63*), Cl_3CCO (*60*), *p*-CH_3—$C_6H_4SO_2$(tosyl) (*60*).

A few of the alkyl or aryl groups which may be substituted in this way are: CH_3—, C_2H_5—, *n*-$C_{16}H_{33}$—, CH_2OH—CH_2—, C_6H_5—, benzyl, α-naphthyl, menthyl, and D-glucopyranosyl (*64*).

Anomerization of α- and β-isomers, formation of *O*-acetyl-D-glycopyranosyl halides, replacement of the halides by other groups, and the formation of glycosides and orthoacetates are closely related reactions and follow similar patterns. This substitution appears to be a first-order reaction (*65*), in which an ion from the environment moves in as the rate-controlling dissociation of the departing group occurs, resulting in inversion of the

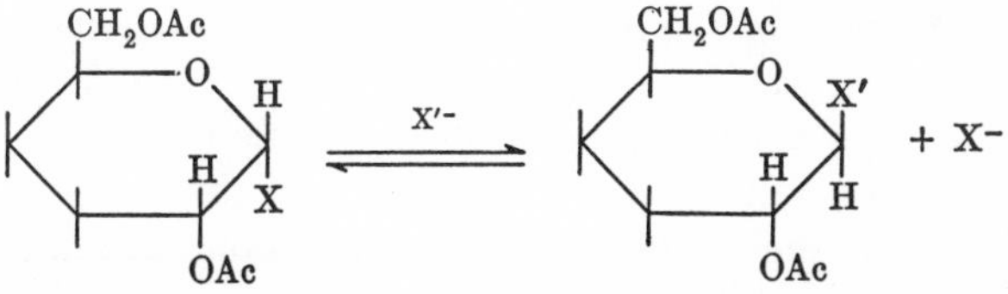
CH2OAc
O
H
H
X
OAc
X'-
CH2OAc
O
X'
H
H
OAc
+ X-

optical form of carbon 1. However, when an acetyl group on carbon 2 occurs *trans* to the departing group on carbon 1, a complication arises. The *trans* acetyl group attacks the back side of carbon 1 as the departing group

60. B. Helferich and R. Gootz, *Ber.* **62**, 2505, 2789 (1929).

61. H. H. Schlubach, P. Stadler, and I. Wolf, *Ber.* **61**, 287 (1928).

62. E. Fischer and K. Delbrück, *Ber.* **42**, 2776 (1909); E. Fischer and K. Hess, *Ber.* **45**, 912 (1912); B. Lindberg, *Acta Chem. Scand.* **1**, 710 (1947).

63. B. Lindberg, *Acta Chem. Scand.* **3**, 1355 (1949).

64. See Chapters IV and IX, under individual oligosaccharides.

65. F. H. Newth and G. O. Phillips, *J. Chem. Soc.* pp. 2896, 2900, 2904 (1953); N. B. Chapman and W. E. Laird, *Chemistry & Industry* p. 20 (1954); R. U. Lemieux and G. Huber, *Can. J. Chem.* **33**, 128 (1955).

dissociates, forming an orthoester type of ion which is open to attack by nucleophilic groups.

Winstein and co-workers (*66*) have determined that the relative rates of acetolysis of *cis*- and *trans*-2-acetoxycyclohexyl *p*-toluenesulfonates are: unsubstituted, 1.00 > *trans*-2-OAc, 0.30 ≫ *cis*-2-OAc, 4.5×10^{-4}. The course of these reactions are discussed and the deductions appear to be applicable to the sugars. Related interpretations have also been made for the series by Isbell and Frush, by Post, and by Pacsu (*67*).

Lemieux and Brice (*56*, *68*) introduced C^{14}-labeled acetate ion into an anomerization reaction catalyzed by an aprotic acid and involving β-D-glucopyranose pentaacetate as the initial material. This substance, a 1,2-*trans*-isomer, has been reported to give, under the reaction conditions, an equilibrium mixture of 90% of the α-D- and 10% of the β-D-anomer (*10*, *69*). Lemieux and Brice found that a very rapid initial reaction occurred, in which the β-D-glucopyranose pentaacetate became labeled, followed by a much slower formation of similarly labeled α-D-anomer. They believed that the starting material (VII) equilibrates very rapidly with an orthoester ion (VIII) and the labeled acetate ion to yield labeled starting material. This is followed by a slower rate-controlling reaction to form a second intermediate such as a 1,6-orthoester ion (XII) or a carbonium ion (XIII or XIV). This new intermediate can then combine with labeled acetate ion to form a labeled α-D-glucopyranose pentaacetate (XV). Anomerization of α-D-glucopyranose pentaacetate, a 1,2-*cis*-isomer, would involve either the reverse course or a direct replacement with inversion and without neighboring group participation. In either case it would proceed only to a limited extent because of the high stability of the α-D-anomer under these acidic conditions.

The above scheme may be applied to substitution reactions, in general, under three types of conditions: first, as above, in the presence of a strong aprotic acid such as the halides of zinc, tin, boron, titanium, or of an anhydrous hydrogen halide; second, in a weakly basic solution containing an excess of anions as would exist in a solution of silver or mercuric acetate in acetic acid; and, third, in alkaline solution containing strongly basic anions such as hydroxyl or alkoxyl.

66. S. Winstein, C. Hanson, and E. Grunwald, *J. Am. Chem. Soc.* **70,** 812 (1948); S. Winstein, E. Grunwald, R. E. Buckles, and C. Hanson, *ibid.* **70,** 816 (1948).

67. H. L. Frush and H. S. Isbell, *J. Research Natl. Bur. Standards* **27,** 413 (1941); H. W. Post "The Chemistry of the Aliphatic Orthoesters," p. 106. Reinhold, New York, 1943; E. Pacsu, *Advances in Carbohydrate Chem.* **1,** 78 (1945).

68. R. U. Lemieux, *Advances in Carbohydrate Chem.* **9,** 1 (1954); R. U. Lemieux and C. Brice, *Can. J. Chem.* **33,** 109 (1955).

69. K. Freudenberg and K. Soff, *Ber.* **69,** 1245 (1936); E. P. Painter, *J. Am. Chem. Soc.* **75,** 1137 (1953).

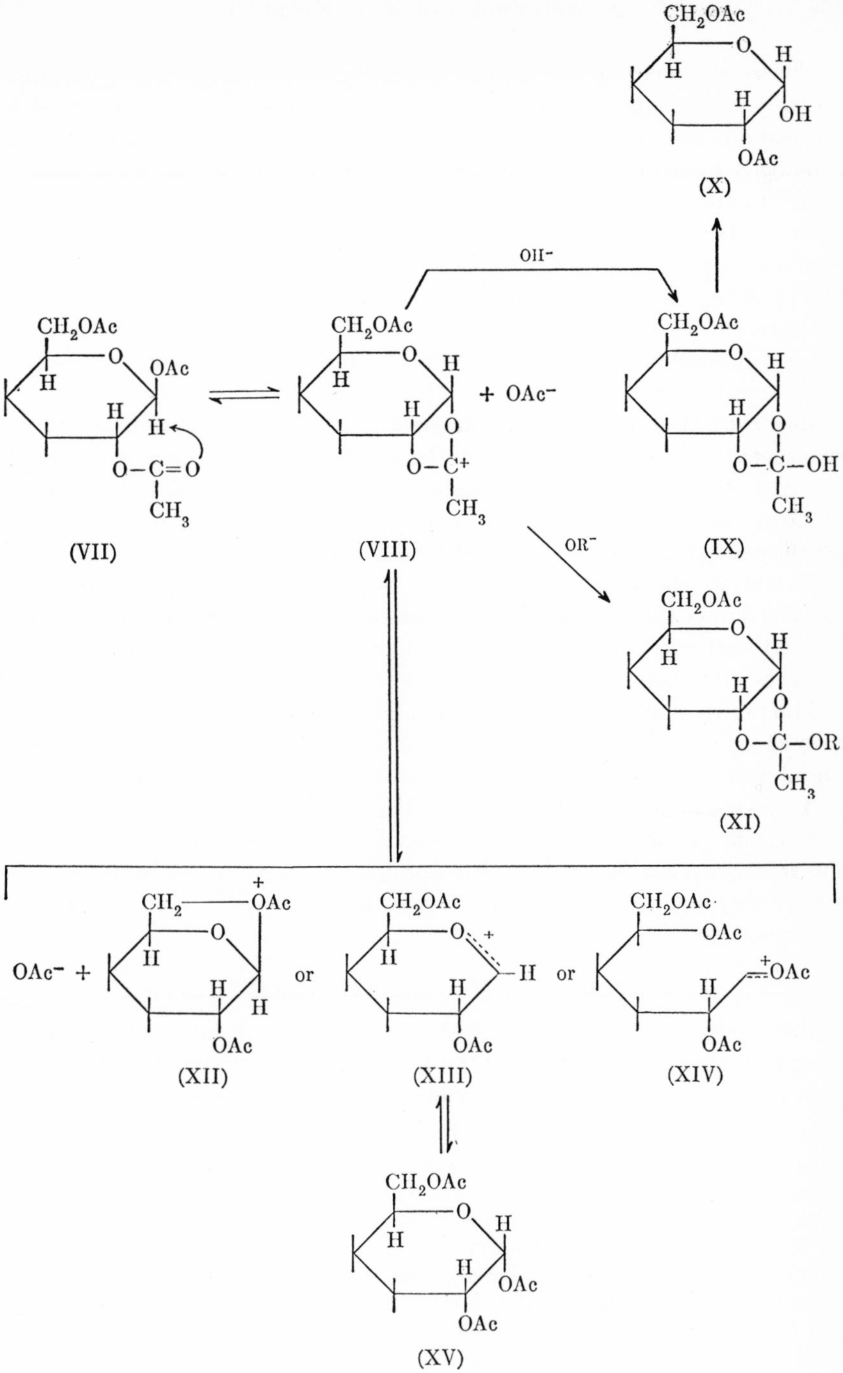
CH2OAc
OAc
(X)
OH-
(VII)
(VIII)
+ OAc-
(IX)
OR-
(XI)
OAc- +
or
(XII)
(XIII)
(XIV)
(XV)

The replacement of a hemiacetal acetate group by a halogen requires strongly acid conditions under which anomerization readily occurs and the more stable anomeric form will appear in the product. The replacement of a halogen by acetate is carried out under milder, nonanomerizing conditions. In the 1,2-*cis*-isomer, the reaction is largely a simple replacement with inversion at the reducing carbon. In a 1,2-*trans*-isomer, the halogen would dissociate to form the orthoacetate ion (VIII) which would combine with acetate ion to form (VII) without inversion. Thus, tetra-*O*-acetyl-α-D-glucopyranosyl bromide (a *cis* form) and tetra-*O*-acetyl-α-D-mannopyranosyl bromide (a *trans* form), when treated with silver acetate in acetic acid, both yield the β-D-anomer (*49*, *70*).

In a neutral or alkaline medium containing water, a 1,2-*cis* halide is replaced by hydroxyl with inversion. In the 1,2-*trans* situation, a hydroxyl ion can combine with the orthoester ion (VIII) to give a 1,2-hydrogen orthoacetate (IX) (*66*) which then isomerizes to a 2,3,4,6-tetra-*O*-D-glycopyranosyl acetate (X) without inversion of the carbon atom at position 1. In alcohol the situation is the same except that the alkyl orthoacetate (XI) is stable (*67*). Additional support for these speculations is given by Ness, Fletcher, and Hudson (*71*) in their work on replacement reactions with the tri-*O*-benzoylaldopentopyranosyl halides (see p. 198).

Most of the known *O*-acylglycosyl halides are pyranose in ring structure. One which was later shown to be a furanose form was described by Hudson and Johnson (*72*) and has been utilized to synthesize β-D-galactofuranose 2,3,5,6-tetraacetate (*72*, *73*) and ethyl β-D-galactofuranoside (*74*). A 1,3,4,6-tetra-*O*-acetyl-D-fructofuranosyl bromide was undoubtedly an intermediate (not isolated) in the conversion of inulin triacetate to the sirupy 1,3,4,6-tetra-*O*-acetyl-D-fructose utilized in the synthesis of isosucrose (*75*).

4. TRIHALOGENOACETATE DERIVATIVES

Brigl (*76*) has obtained (*77*) a stable 3,4,6-tri-*O*-acetyl-2-*O*-(trichloroacetyl)-β-D-glucosyl chloride by the action of solid phosphorus pentachloride on β-D-glucopyranose pentaacetate. This compound yields 1,3,4,6-

70. P. A. Levene and R. S. Tipson, *J. Biol. Chem.* **90,** 89 (1931).

71. R. K. Ness, H. G. Fletcher, Jr., and C. S. Hudson, *J. Am. Chem. Soc.* **72,** 2200 (1950); **73,** 959 (1951); H. G. Fletcher, Jr., and C. S. Hudson, *ibid.* **72,** 4173 (1950).

72. C. S. Hudson and J. M. Johnson, *J. Am. Chem. Soc.* **38,** 1223 (1916).

73. J. Compton and M. L. Wolfrom, *J. Am. Chem. Soc.* **56,** 1157 (1934).

74. H. H. Schlubach and K. Meisenheimer, *Ber.* **67,** 429 (1934).

75. J. C. Irvine and E. T. Stiller, *J. Am. Chem. Soc.* **54,** 1079 (1932); W. W. Binkley and M. L. Wolfrom, *ibid.* **68,** 2171 (1946).

76. P. Brigl, *Z. physiol. Chem.* **116,** 1 (1921); **122,** 245 (1922).

77. W. J. Hickinbottom, *J. Chem. Soc.* p. 1676 (1929).

tetra-*O*-acetyl-2-*O*-(trichloroacetyl)-α-D-glucose upon treatment with silver acetate in acetic acid (*78*). Because of the strong electron-attracting ability of the three chlorine atoms, the *trans* trichloroacetyl group apparently does not participate in this replacement reaction. The Brigl β-chloro derivative is also of interest because it was used to prepare 3,4,6-tri-*O*-acetyl-1,2-anhydro-D-glucose (*76*), an intermediate in the synthesis of sucrose (*79*).

Trifluoroacetates of carbohydrates have been prepared (*80*). These substances, which are quite sensitive to hydrolysis, show some promise as intermediates in synthetic work. Trifluoroacetic anhydride is a powerful impelling reagent for the acetylation of polysaccharides (*80*).

5. ACYLGLYCOSYL HALIDES OF ACYCLIC STRUCTURE

The free-aldehyde form of *O*-acetylated hexoses was shown by Wolfrom (*28*) to react with acyl halides to form products of the type R—CH(OAc)X, isolable in the two forms (*81*) predictable on stereochemical grounds. A product of this structure has been obtained in low yield by the direct action of acetic anhydride and hydrogen bromide upon L-arabinose (*82*). Phosphorus pentachloride reacts with ordinary aldehydes to produce the 1,1-dihalides. It reacts similarly with *aldehydo*-penta-*O*-acetyl-D-galactose to give the 1,1-dichloride (*83*).

A useful halide was encountered by Hudson and co-workers (*29*) in the partial acetolysis of methyl tri-*O*-acetyl-β-D-arabinopyranoside and was shown to have the structure R—CH(OMe)Cl. It was obtainable in two forms and its halogen was replaceable by methoxyl and acetoxyl groups. Other and more general methods for preparing these halides were devised by Wolfrom and co-workers (*84*) and the products were utilized in the preparation of acetals and thioacetals, as shown below (*85*).

$$\mathrm{R{-}}\overset{\displaystyle \mathrm{H} \atop |}{\mathrm{C}}\mathrm{{=}O} + \mathrm{EtSH} \rightarrow \mathrm{R{-}CH(SEt)(OH)} \rightarrow \mathrm{R{-}CH(SEt)(OAc)} \rightarrow$$

$$\mathrm{R{-}CH(SEt)Cl} \rightarrow \mathrm{R{-}CH(SEt)(OEt)}$$

---

78. R. U. Lemieux and G. Huber, *Can. J. Chem.* **31,** 1040 (1953).

79. R. U. Lemieux and G. Huber, *J. Am. Chem. Soc.* **75,** 4118 (1953); **78,** 4117 (1956).

80. E. J. Bourne, C. E. M. Tatlow, and J. C. Tatlow, *J. Chem. Soc.* p. 1367 (1950); M. Stacey, E. J. Bourne, J. C. Tatlow, and J. M. Tedder, *Nature* **164,** 705 (1949).

81. M. L. Wolfrom and R. L. Brown, *J. Am. Chem. Soc.* **63,** 1246 (1941).

82. G. E. Felton and W. Freudenberg, *J. Am. Chem. Soc.* **57,** 1637 (1935).

83. M. L. Wolfrom and D. I. Weisblat, *J. Am. Chem. Soc.* **62,** 1149 (1940).

84. M. L. Wolfrom, M. Konigsberg, and F. B. Moody, *J. Am. Chem. Soc.* **62,** 2343 (1940).

85. M. L. Wolfrom, D. I. Weisblat, and A. R. Hanze, *J. Am. Chem. Soc.* **62,** 3246 (1940).

6. PARTIALLY ESTERIFIED SUGAR STRUCTURES

When 2,3,4,6-tetra-*O*-methyl-D-glucose was synthesized by Purdie and Irvine (*86*), Fischer and Delbrück countered by preparing a corresponding acetate through the controlled hydrolysis (*62*) of the halogen in penta-*O*-acetyl-D-glucopyranosyl bromide. Fischer then obtained other partially esterified D-glucose structures through the use of blocking groups, employing for this purpose the mono- and diisopropylidene cyclic acetals of D-glucose. These were benzoylated and, on removal of the isopropylidene groups, there resulted a monobenzoate and a tribenzoate of D-glucose (*39*, *87*). The benzoate groups are now known to have entered the 3- and the 3,5,6-positions, respectively. Exact structure assignment is complicated by the possibility of acyl migration (see p. 147). A useful blocking group was introduced by Helferich in the triphenylmethyl (trityl) ether (Chapter VII) formed by the action of trityl chloride on the sugar or substituted sugar in pyridine solution, the reagent reacting preferentially with the primary alcoholic functions (*88*). Further substitution, as by acetylation, may then be made and the trityl ether group is removed subsequently by mild acidity; in this manner 1,2,3,4-tetra-*O*-acetyl-β-D-glucopyranose was made available (*33*) and was employed in the synthesis of gentiobiose (*33*). Partial benzoylation of D-glucose diethyl dithioacetal with subsequent demercaptalation yielded 3,4,5,6-tetra-*O*-benzoyl-*aldehydo*-D-glucose (*89*). The 3,4,6-triacetate of D-glucopyranose was obtained by the partial hydrolysis of 3,4,6-tri-*O*-acetyl-2-*O*-(trichloroacetyl)-β-D-glucosyl chloride (*76*, *90*). Other methods for obtaining partially esterified sugar structures are known, but such esters have not been as useful as the corresponding methyl ethers because of the greater lability of the ester function.

7. CARBONATES, XANTHATES, CARBANILATES

The sugars react with methyl (or ethyl) chloroformate at 0°C. in the presence of alkali to give a mixture of cyclic carbonate and acyclic *O*-methoxycarbonyl (or *O*-ethoxycarbonyl) derivatives (*91*). The cyclic carbonate structures resemble those of the isopropylidene cyclic acetals as shown in the formulas.

In the presence of pyridine and methyl or ethyl chloroformate, the sugars are converted to fully acylated *O*-methoxycarbonyl or *O*-ethoxycarbonyl derivatives (*92*).

86. T. Purdie and J. C. Irvine, *J. Chem. Soc.* **83,** 1021 (1903); **85,** 1049 (1904).
87. E. Fischer and C. Rund, *Ber.* **49,** 88 (1916).
88. B. Helferich, *Advances in Carbohydrate Chem.* **3,** 79 (1948).
89. P. Brigl, H. Mühlschlegel, and R. Schinle, *Ber.* **64,** 2921 (1931).
90. P. Brigl and R. Schinle, *Ber.* **62,** 1717 (1929).
91. C. F. Allpress and W. N. Haworth, *J. Chem. Soc.* **125,** 1223 (1924).
92. G. Zemplén and E. D. László, *Ber.* **48,** 915 (1915).

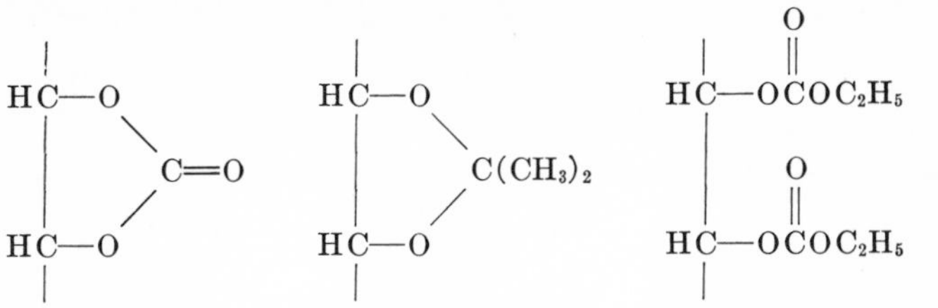
HC—O
C=O
HC—O
HC—O
C(CH3)2
HC—O
O
HC—OCOC2H5
O
HC—OCOC2H5

Carbonate structure — Isopropylidene structure — *O*-Ethoxycarbonyl structure

A better method for the preparation of the carbonates utilizes the action of carbonyl chloride (phosgene) at 0°C. on pyridine solutions of the sugars. By this method, D-glucose, D-fructose, D-mannose, and L-arabinose dicarbonates have been obtained (*93*).

The carbonate groups, similarly to other acyl groups, are hydrolyzed easily by alkalies and with more difficulty by acids. This difference from the properties of sugar cyclic acetals (the isopropylidene sugars) is used advantageously for the preparation of the glucofuranosides. Because of the hydrolytic action of hydroxyl ions, the methylation procedures cannot be used for the elucidation of the structures of these compounds, but it is usually considered that the sugar carbonates are analogous in structure to isopropylidene sugars. The dicarbonates of several common sugars have been given the following structures: D-glucofuranose 1,2:5,6-dicarbonate, D-mannofuranose 2,3:5,6-dicarbonate, D-galacto- and L-arabinopyranose 1,2:3,4-dicarbonate, D-fructopyranose 1,2:4,5-dicarbonate.

A carbonate group and an isopropylidene group may be introduced into a sugar molecule in a single step by carrying out the reaction with carbonyl chloride in dry acetone solution. D-Xylose under these conditions gives 1,2-*O*-isopropylidene-D-xylose 3,5-carbonate although D-galactose yields di-*O*-isopropylidene-6-*O*-(chloroformyl)-D-galactopyranose (*94*). Treatment of the D-mannofuranose dicarbonate with thionyl chloride gives the D-mannofuranosyl chloride dicarbonate.

When the sugar molecule contains only one free hydroxyl group, two moles of the sugar derivative may react with one mole of carbonyl chloride (*95*). The following formulas illustrate the reaction of 1,2,3,4-tetra-*O*-acetyl-D-glucopyranose and phosgene to form bis(1,2,3,4-tetra-*O*-acetyl-D-glucopyranose) 6-carbonate.

The xanthates, or dithiocarbonates, are important substances in cellulose technology. They have been studied to some extent with the simple sugars. Their sodium salts are formed from the alcohol, carbon disulfide, and alkali and may be converted to the alkyl esters.

93. W. N. Haworth and C. R. Porter, *J. Chem. Soc.* p. 151 (1930); p. 2796 (1929).
94. W. N. Haworth, C. R. Porter, and A. C. Waine, *Rec. trav. chim.* **57,** 541 (1938).
95. D. D. Reynolds and W. O. Kenyon, *J. Am. Chem. Soc.* **64,** 1110 (1942).

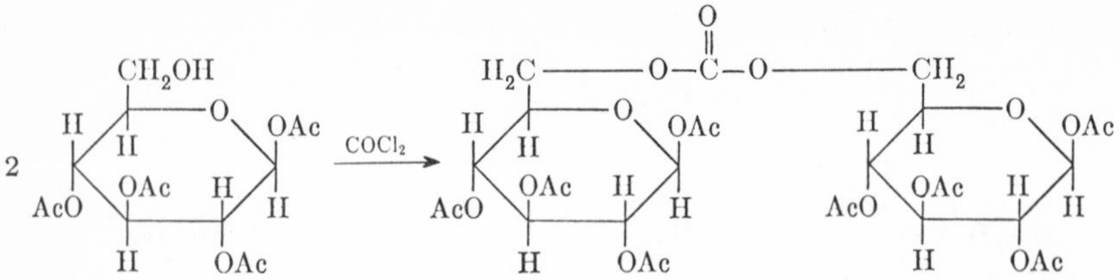

These esters are not useful in the formation of olefins by the Tschugaev reaction. Evidence exists that position 2 in aldoses is favored in xanthation.

$$ROH + CS_2 + NaOH \rightarrow RO\text{—}CS\text{—}S^{-}Na^{+} + HOH$$

$$RO\text{—}CS\text{—}S^{-}Na^{+} + R'X \rightarrow RO\text{—}CS\text{—}SR' + Na^{+} + X^{-}$$

The ease of crystallization and the stability under mild conditions of hydrolysis has created interest in the sugar carbanilates. These derivatives are made by the reaction of carbohydrates with phenyl isocyanate in pyridine solution (*96*).

$$\text{HCOH} \xrightarrow{C_6H_5\text{—}N{=}C{=}O} \text{HCOC}(=O)\text{—NH—}C_6H_5$$

8. GALLOYL DERIVATIVES AND TANNINS

Certain tannins are probably gallic acid and digallic acid esters of D-glucose and of other sugars and derivatives. In order to provide evidence for the structure of the gallotannins, Fischer, Freudenberg, and Bergmann (*97*) synthesized a number of these derivatives by the action of tri-*O*-acetylgalloyl chloride or penta-*O*-acetyl-*m*-digalloyl chloride on D-glucose. The acetyl groups were subsequently removed. These substances may be represented as shown below.

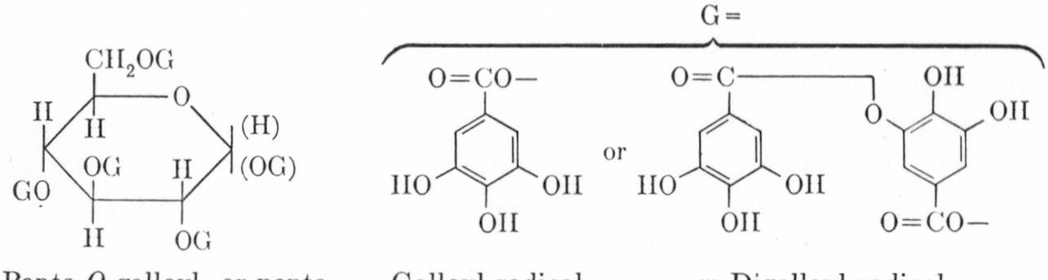

Penta-*O*-galloyl- or penta-*O*-digalloyl-D-glucose (galloyltannins) — Galloyl radical — *m*-Digalloyl radical

96. H. Tessmer, *Ber.* **18,** 968, 2606 (1885); W. M. Hearon, G. D. Hiatt, and C. R. Fordyce, *J. Am. Chem. Soc.* **66,** 995 (1944); M. L. Wolfrom and D. E. Pletcher, *ibid.* **62,** 1151 (1940).

97. E. Fischer, *Ber.* **52,** 809 (1919); K. Freudenberg, "Tannin, Cellulose and Lignin." Springer, Berlin, 1933.

The synthetic galloyl and digalloyl esters were not demonstrated absolutely as identical with the natural gallotannins, but the natural substances may be mixed esters of *O*-galloyl- and *O*-digalloyl-D-glucose, in which case the number of isomers would be so great as to make the synthesis extremely difficult. In addition, tri-, tetra-, and poly-galloyl radicals might also be present in the molecule. Karrer, Salomon, and Peyer (*98*) suggest that the Chinese gallotannin from the leaf galls of *Rhus semialata* is a mixture. Certain fractions have the average composition of a nonagalloyl-D-glucose with the nine galloyl groups attached together or to the sugar residue, possibly as four digallic acid and one gallic acid although other combinations may occur. For the Turkish gallotannin, obtained from gall nuts of certain oaks, the problem appears simpler since the molecule contains only five molecules of gallic acid; the tannin is, presumably, the penta-*O*-galloyl-D-glucose. However, the substances are difficult to purify, and the natural substances are clearly mixtures. The tanning properties of synthetic galloyl esters of the sugars are very similar to those of natural gallotannins (*99*).

Glucogallin obtained from the Chinese rhubarb by Gilson has been identified (*100*) through synthesis as 1-*O*-galloyl-β-D-glucose.

The bark of the North American shrub *Hamamelis virginica* contains in addition to other tannins, about 1 to 2% of crystalline hamameli-tannin (XVI) (*97*). The substance has the composition of a di-*O*-galloylhexose, and on acid or enzyme hydrolysis, it gives two moles of gallic acid and one mole of an unusual hexose, hamamelose (XVII), whose structure has been established as 2-*C*-(hydroxymethyl)-D-ribose (XVII) (*101*).

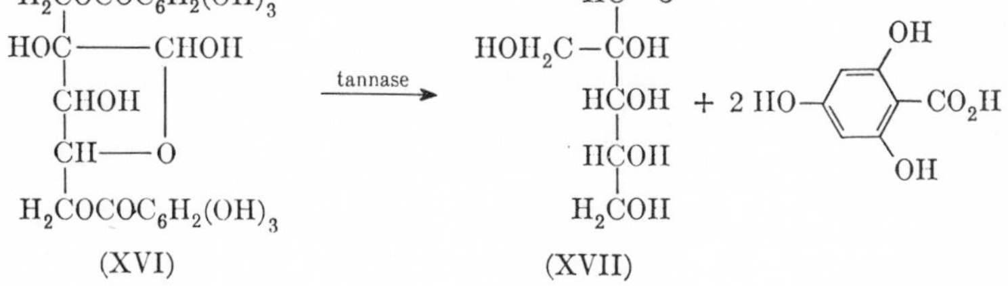
tannase

(XVI) (XVII)

Hamamelose

98. P. Karrer, H. R. Salomon, and J. Peyer, *Helv. Chim. Acta* **6,** 3 (1923).

99. A. Russell, W. G. Tebbens, and W. F. Arey, *J. Am. Chem. Soc.* **65,** 1472 (1943); A. Russell and W. G. Tebbens, *ibid.* **66,** 1866 (1944).

100. E. Fischer and M. Bergmann, *Ber,* **51,** 1760 (1918).

101. O. T. Schmidt, *Ann.* **476,** 250 (1929); O. T. Schmidt and K. Heintz, *ibid.* **515,** 77 (1934).

9. ALDONATE ESTERS

Simple esters of the sugar acids, as ethyl D-mannonate (*102*) and diethyl galactarate (*103*), have long been known (Chapter VI). D-Galacturonic acid occurs in pectins largely esterified with methanol (*104*). Many of the methyl esters of the *O*-acetyl aldonic acids have been obtained by the action of diazomethane upon the fully acetylated aldonic acids. Penta-*O*-acetyl-D-gluconates of some of the alditols (XVIII) and of cellulose have been described (*105*). The methyl acid ester of di-*O*-acetyl-L-(*dextro*)-

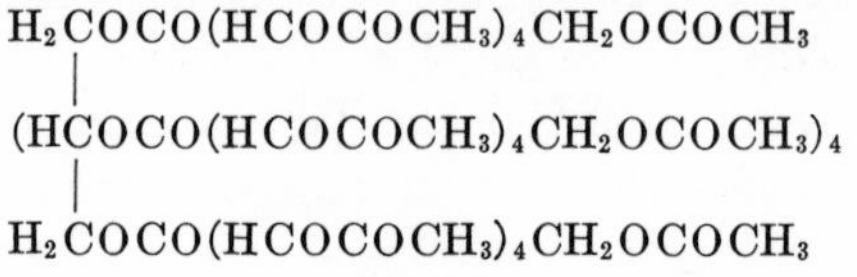
H₂COCO(HCOCOCH₃)₄CH₂OCOCH₃
(HCOCO(HCOCOCH₃)₄CH₂OCOCH₃)₄
H₂COCO(HCOCOCH₃)₄CH₂OCOCH₃

(XVIII)

threaric (tartaric) acid (XIX) is known. An ester condensation polymer (XX) of low molecular weight has been prepared from D-gluconic acid (*106*).

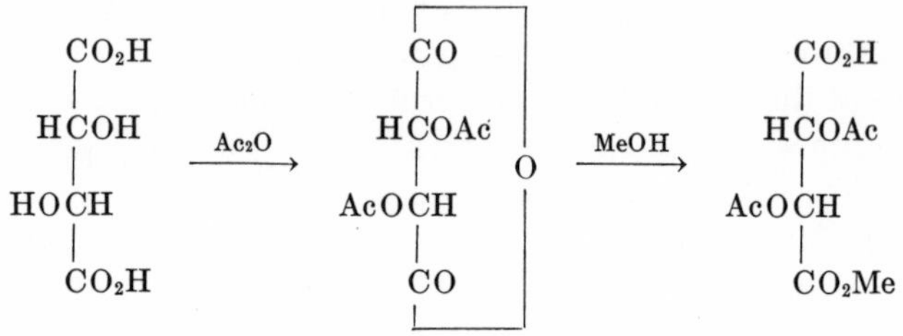
CO₂H
HCOH
HOCH
CO₂H
Ac₂O
CO
HCOAc
AcOCH
CO
O
MeOH
CO₂H
HCOAc
AcOCH
CO₂Me

(XIX)

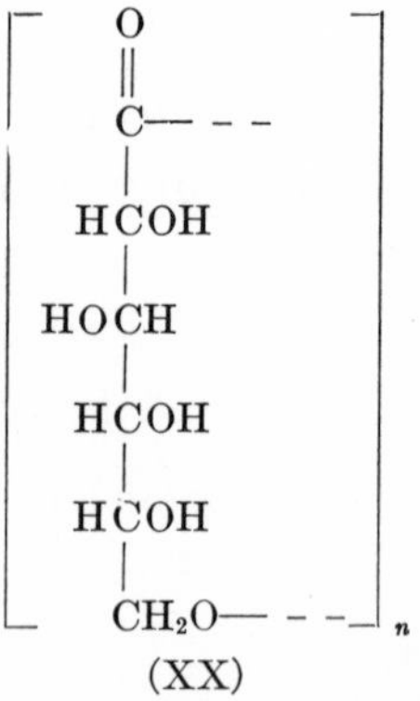
O
C
HCOH
HOCH
HCOH
HCOH
CH₂O
n

(XX)

102. O. F. Hedenburg, *J. Am. Chem. Soc.* **37,** 345 (1915).

103. J. Malaguti, *Ann. chim. phys.* [2] **63,** 86 (1836); E. Fischer and A. Speier, *Ber.* **28,** 3252 (1895).

104. Z. I. Kertesz, "The Pectic Substances," p. 68. Interscience, New York, (1951).

105. M. L. Wolfrom and P. W. Morgan, *J. Am. Chem. Soc.* **64,** 2026 (1942).

106. C. L. Mehltretter and R. L. Mellies, *J. Am. Chem. Soc,* **77,** 427 (1955).

10. OTHER ESTERS OF CARBOXYLIC ACIDS

The sugars and their derivatives have been esterified with many other organic acids. Among these are the fatty acids and cinnamic acid (*92*, *107*). Most of the products have been made by the action of acyl halides and pyridine on sugars. The fatty acid esters are similar in properties to the natural fats, the glycerol esters.

Considerable interest has been shown in the partially esterified esters of the sugar alcohols and their anhydrides because of their surface-active properties. For this reason, the methods of preparation have received much study (see p. 397) (*108*).

The monopalmitate of ascorbic acid (*109*) has been prepared by a method (*110*) that has been applied only to a few other carbohydrates. The method consists of reacting ascorbic acid and fatty acid in 95% sulfuric acid at room temperature. Since the esterification is reported to take place for primary alcohol groups, the method may have value in the preparation of other pure monoesters. The monoesters of ascorbic acid offer promise as antioxidants for edible fats and oils (*111*).

Polymerizable esters of sugars are made by treatment of sugars with methacrylic anhydride and pyridine (*112*).

$$\begin{array}{l} \;\;| \\ \mathrm{HCOH} \\ \;\;| \\ \mathrm{HCOH} \\ \;\;| \end{array} + (\mathrm{CH_2{=}CCH_3CO})_2\mathrm{O} \rightarrow \begin{array}{l} \;\;| \\ \mathrm{HCOCO{-}C(CH_3){=}CH_2} \\ \;\;| \\ \mathrm{HCOCO{-}C(CH_3){=}CH_2} \\ \;\;| \end{array}$$

Solutions of glucose pentamethacrylate gel in the presence of cobalt naphthenate or of benzoyl peroxide.

11. TOSYLATES AND MESYLATES

p-Toluenesulfonic (*113*) (tosyl), methanesulfonic (*114*) (mesyl), and other organic sulfonic esters have been prepared and are discussed in detail by Tipson (*115*). The tosyl esters, which have been particularly well

107. K. Hess and E. Messmer, *Ber.* **54,** 499 (1921); S. Oden, *Arkiv Kemi Mineral. Geol.* **7,** No. 15 (1918).

108. H. A. Goldsmith, *Chem. Revs.* **33,** 257 (1943).

109. D. Swern, A. J. Stirton, J. Turer, and P. A. Wells, *Oil and Soap* **20,** 224 (1943).

110. W. R. Bloor, *J. Biol. Chem.* **7,** 427 (1910); **11,** 141, 421 (1912).

111. R. W. Riemenschneider and J. Turer, U. S. Patents 2,375,250; 2,383,815–16 (1945).

112. R. H. Treadway and E. Yanovsky, *J. Am. Chem. Soc.* **67,** 1038 (1945); W. N. Haworth, H. Gregory, and L. F. Wiggins, *J. Chem. Soc.* p. 488 (1946).

113. K. Freudenberg, O. Burkhart, and E. Braun, *Ber.* **59,** 714 (1926).

114. B. Helferich and A. Gnüchtel, *Ber.* **71,** 712 (1938); B. Helferich and H. Jochinke, *Ber.* **73,** 1049 (1940).

115. R. S. Tipson, *Advances in Carbohydrate Chem.* **8,** 107 (1953).

studied, exhibit certain unique characteristics which make them of great importance in synthetic and analytical organic chemistry. Presumably, the other sulfonate esters should have analogous properties, but they have not received enough study to make this certain.

Preparation of sulfonate esters is accomplished by treatment of a carbohydrate with a pyridine solution of an aryl or alkyl sulfonyl chloride (RSO_2Cl) or with 50% sodium hydroxide and the sulfonyl chloride at room temperature. Under these conditions, all of the hydroxyl groups may be esterified except those on the reducing (anomeric) carbons which are replaced by halide atoms. Thus, D-glucose gives tetra-*O*-tosyl-D-glucopyranosyl chloride. The primary hydroxyl group seems to be more easily esterified than the secondary hydroxyls (*116*).

The tosyloxy groups which esterify primary hydroxyl groups may be replaced by an iodine atom when the ester is heated with an acetone or acetonylacetone solution of sodium iodide. Tosyloxy groups esterified with secondary hydroxyls usually remain unaffected by this treatment unless contiguous to a similar group esterified with a primary hydroxyl (*117*). When the latter condition exists, both groups may be removed with the formation of a double bond, erythritol tetratosylate forming butadiene (*118*).

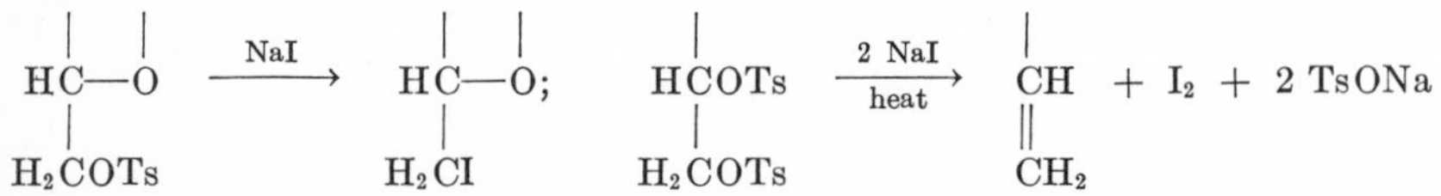

Creation of a double bond also may occur when there is a free hydroxyl adjacent to a tosyl group at a primary alcohol grouping as in 6-*O*-tosyl-D-glucofuranosides (*119*). Exceptions to the rule are the tosyl esters of "isomannide" and "isosorbide"; the tosyloxy groups of these compounds, although esterifying secondary hydroxyl groups, are replaced with iodine under the above conditions (see p. 397).

The difference in ease of replacement of tosyloxy groups esterified with primary and secondary alcoholic groups is used to measure quantitatively the primary groups in a compound (*120*). This is done by tosylation of the material; treatment of the ester with sodium iodide replaces the *O*-tosyl groups esterified with primary alcoholic groups; the iodo compound is treated with silver nitrate, and the iodine atoms are replaced quantitatively with nitrate groups; the liberated iodide precipitates as silver iodide which

116. A. Bernoulli and H. Stauffer, *Helv. Chim. Acta* **23**, 615 (1940); J. Compton, *J. Am. Chem. Soc.* **60**, 395 (1938).

117. R. M. Hann, A. T. Ness, and C. S. Hudson, *J. Am. Chem. Soc.* **66**, 73 (1944); A. B. Foster and W. G. Overend, *J. Chem. Soc.* p. 3452 (1951).

118. R. S. Tipson and L. H. Cretcher, *J. Org. Chem.* **8**, 95 (1943).

119. D. J. Bell, E. Friedmann, and S. Williamson, *J. Chem. Soc.* p. 252 (1937).

120. J. W. H. Oldham and J. K. Rutherford, *J. Am. Chem. Soc.* **54**, 366 (1932).

may be determined quantitatively.

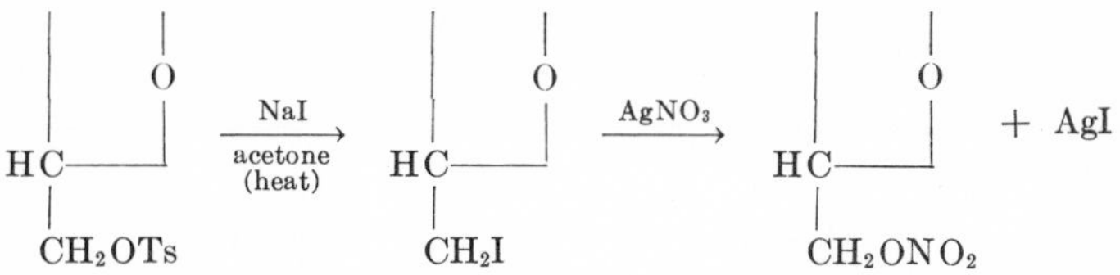

The yield of the iodo compound or of the *p*-toluenesulfonic acid is high and has been used for the determination of the nature of the alcoholic group in the parent compound (*121*). The replacement of a tosyloxy by a nitrate group is also brought about directly by heating the ester with silver nitrate in acetonitrile solution. Since the nitrate group can be removed with the formation of a free hydroxyl group by reduction with iron dust and acetic acid, mixed *O*-acyl derivatives may be prepared (see p. 169). The mesyl esters (CH_3SO_2OR) may be carried through a similar series of replacement reactions, and for these esters it is also possible to replace with iodine some of the mesyl groups which esterify secondary hydroxyls.

p-Toluenesulfonate groups, in otherwise completely substituted sugar derivatives, are extremely difficult to saponify but are removed without Walden inversion; thus boiling a 5% solution of 1,2:5,6-di-*O*-isopropylidene-3-*O*-tosyl-D-glucose in 2.5 *N* potassium hydroxide (in 50% ethanol) for seven hours afforded an almost quantitative yield of 1,2:5,6-di-*O*-isopropylidene-D-glucose (*122*). They are more readily removed by reductive detosylation with sodium amalgam in aqueous ethanol, the above alcohol being so regenerated without Walden inversion and with the production of sodium *p*-toluenesulfinate (*123*). Other reducing agents may be employed and, if the tosylate is primary, reductive cleavage to a methyl group can be effected.

$$-CH_2OTs \xrightarrow{[H]} -CH_3$$

Tosyl esters of the carbohydrates occuring within the rings, are not replaceable by acetate ion under vigorous conditions.

If the sulfonate is attached to a ring hydroxyl which is adjacent to an unsubstituted hydroxyl, and if the two groups are configurationally *trans*, epoxy ring closure is effected by alkaline (though not by acid) treatment with a concomitant Walden inversion at the carbon which originally bore the sulfonate ester. If the two asymmetric centers are configurationally *cis*, the original ester may be recovered unchanged under conditions which

121. W. T. Haskins, R. M. Hann, and C. S. Hudson, *J. Am. Chem. Soc.* **64,** 132 (1942).

122. J. W. H. Oldham and G. J. Robertson, *J. Chem. Soc.* p. 685 (1935); P. A. Levene and J. Compton, *J. Am. Chem. Soc.* **57,** 777 (1935).

123. K. Freudenberg and F. Brauns, *Ber.* **55,** 3233 (1922).

lead readily to epoxide formation in the former (*124*) (see also Chapter VII).

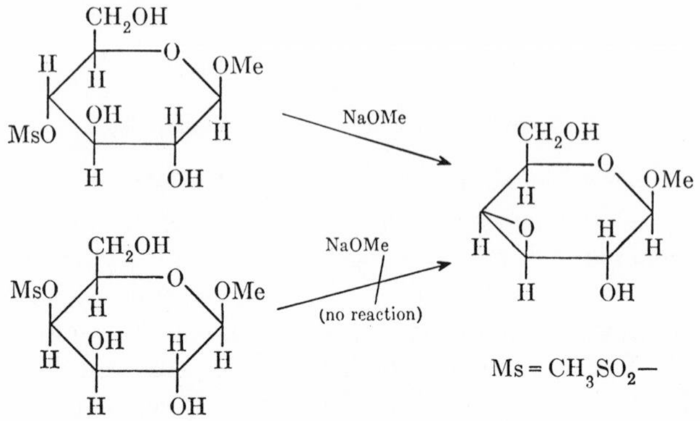
NaOMe
NaOMe
(no reaction)
Ms = CH3SO2—

Such an epoxy ring as the above may be hydrolyzed under acidic or basic conditions (more vigorous than is required for their formation) with Walden inversion at the carbon undergoing carbon-to-oxygen scission (Chapter VII). Two products are therefore formed, with one being gen-

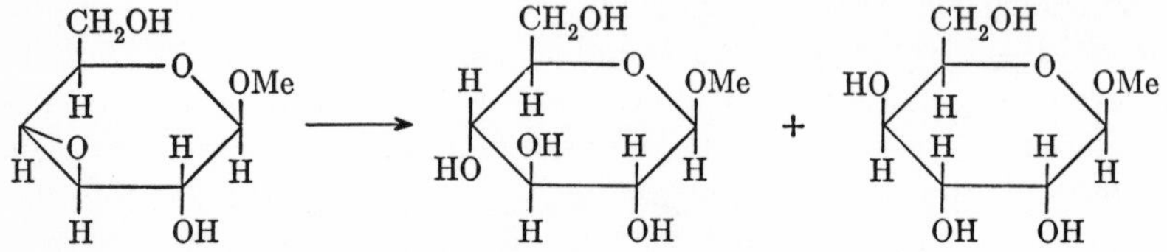

erally preferred, depending upon the configuration of the anhydro sugar as a whole, on the substituent groups in it, and upon the nature of the reagent used (*124*). The new glycol groupings necessarily appear in the two possible *trans* configurations (see also p. 390).

Application of the above principles concerned with the opening and clos-

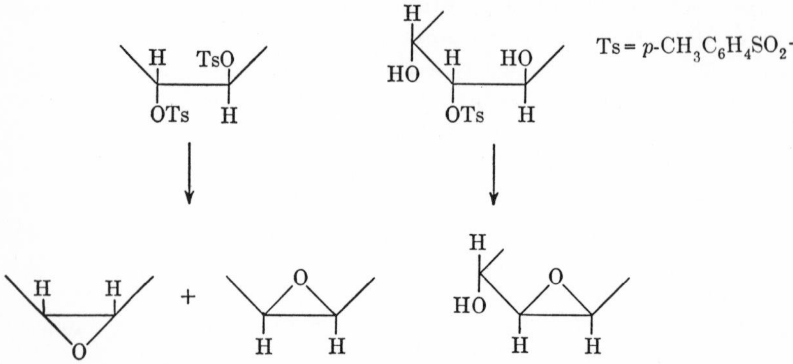
Ts = p-CH3C6H4SO2—

ing of epoxy rings fixed in another sugar ring, will lead to the prediction of the possible products obtainable if a disulfonate ester is present or if a monosulfonate ester is present and is flanked on either side by a hydroxyl group.

The transformations from one sugar to another which result from the above reactions are of considerable importance for the preparation of the

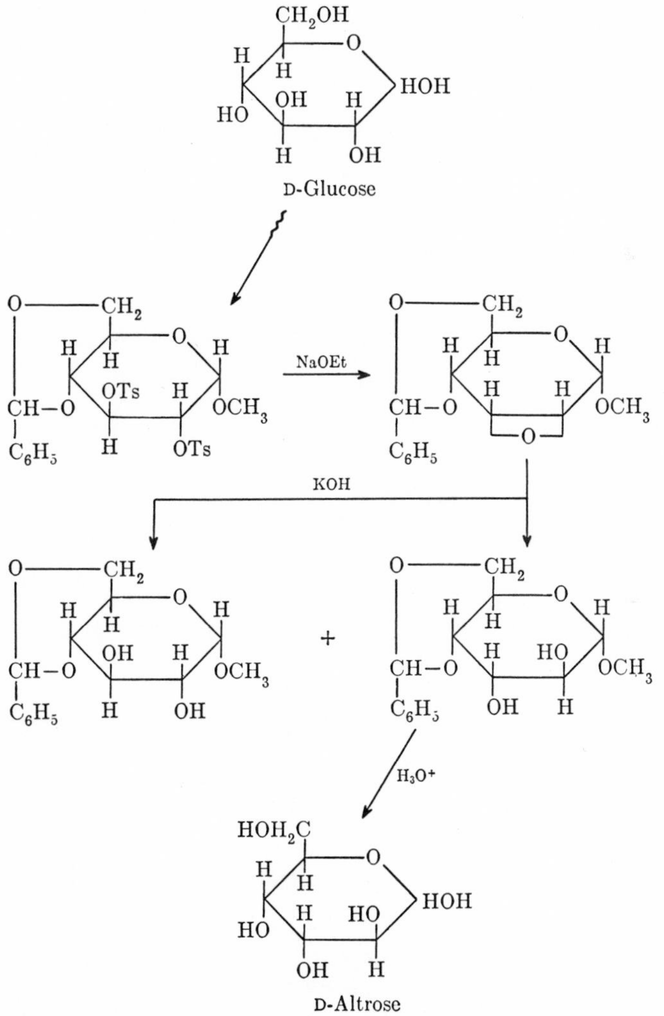
D-Glucose
NaOEt
KOH
+
H₃O⁺
D-Altrose

---

124. S. Peat, *Advances in Carbohydrate Chem.* **2,** 37 (1946); A. Müller, M. Moricz, and G. Verner, *Ber.* **72,** 745 (1939); D. J. Bell and S. Williamson, *J. Chem. Soc.* p. 1196 (1938).

rare sugars. The rare sugar D-altrose may be prepared from D-glucose by the series of reactions shown (*125*).

Although the epoxy or ethylene oxide ring is the usual ring formed, other types have been reported. (See Chapter VII, also.) By treating methyl 3-*O*-tosyltri-*O*-acetyl-β-D-glucopyranoside (XXI) with sodium methoxide, Peat and Wiggins (*126*) obtained, in addition to methyl 2,3-anhydro- and 3,4-anhydro-β-D-allopyranoside (XXIII and XXII), the methyl 3,6-anhydro-β-D-glucofuranoside (XXIV). The furanoside is considered to have been formed from (XXII) by reaction of the primary hydroxyl group with

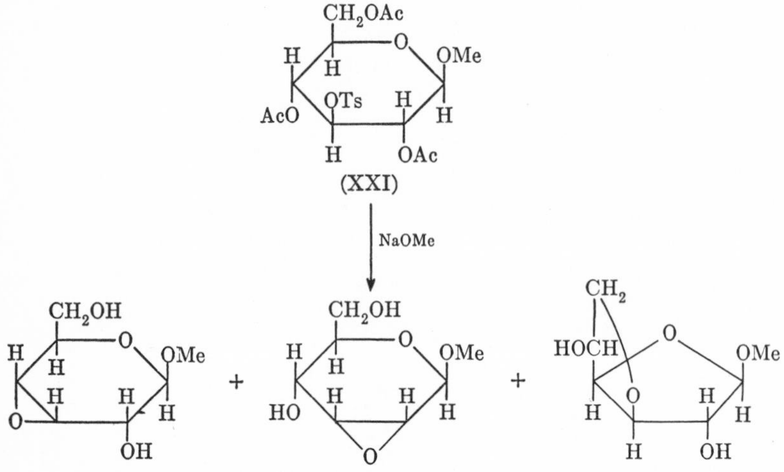
CH2OAc
O
H
H
OMe
OTs
H
AcO
H
H
OAc
NaOMe
CH2OH
O
H
H
OMe
H
H
H
O
OH
+
CH2OH
O
H
H
OMe
H
H
HO
H
O
+
CH2
HOCH
O
OMe
O
H
H
H
H
OH

(XXI) (XXII) (XXIII) (XXIV)

the epoxy ring and subsequent shifting of the pyranose ring to the more stable furanoside.

Part II

Inorganic Esters

1. NITRATE ESTERS

Carbohydrate nitrates have considerable importance as explosives (*127*). Cellulose nitrate, of a high degree of nitration (approximately 2.5 groups per anhydro-D-glucose unit), plasticized with glycerol trinitrate, is cur-

125. G. J. Robertson and C. F. Griffith, *J. Chem. Soc.* p. 1193 (1935); N. K. Richtmyer and C. S. Hudson, *J. Am. Chem. Soc.* **63,** 1727 (1941).

126. S. Peat and L. F. Wiggins, *J. Chem. Soc.* pp. 1088, 1810 (1938); W. N. Haworth, L. N. Owen, and F. Smith, *ibid.* p. 88 (1941).

127. For a general discussion, see T. L. Davis, "Chemistry of Powder and Explosives," Vol. II, p. 191. Wiley, New York, 1943.

rently the only useful gun propellant, being utilized to expel the shell from the gun barrel. It is stabilized with diphenylamine. Highly nitrated starch is also utilized as an explosive, especially for grenades. The nitrate esters of ethylene glycol, glycerol, and D-mannitol are useful explosives. Many nitrates of simple sugars and glycosides have been prepared by Will and Lenze (*128*). They are unstable to heat and storage.

Nitration can be effected at low temperatures by mixed acids (sulfuric and nitric); by nitric acid of high concentration; by nitric acid and acetic anhydride (acetyl nitrate is formed in such mixtures and they must not be concentrated); and by nitrogen pentoxide in halogenated hydrocarbon solvents with or without the addition of sodium fluoride to complex with the nitric acid formed (*129*):

$$ROH + N_2O_5 \rightarrow RONO_2 + HNO_3$$

Nitration of an aldose can be effected without change in anomeric form; thus, α-D-glucopyranose yields α-D-glucopyranose pentanitrate and β-D-glucopyranose gives β-D-glucopyranose pentanitrate.

The halogen atoms of *O*-acetylglycopyranosyl halides may be replaced by nitrate ester groups with the production of *O*-acetylglycopyranosyl nitrates, which can also be made from the acetate by the action of concentrated nitric acid in chloroform (*49*, *130*). Halogen atoms or tosyloxy groups esterifying primary alcoholic groups are substituted by nitrate groups on reaction with silver nitrate. The amount of silver halide produced has been used for the estimation of primary alcohol groups (see p. 165). Since the nitrate may be converted to a hydroxyl by reduction with iron dust and acetic acid, the nitrates are often useful for the preparation of partially substituted sugar derivatives (*131*).

Nitrate esters undergo rapid decomposition on detonation or on thermal ignition (*132*); gaseous oxides of carbon and nitrogen are formed. Work with the simple nitrate esters of monohydric alcohols indicates that the first step in the thermal decomposition is homolytic cleavage to produce

128. W. Will and F. Lenze, *Ber*. **31,** 68 (1898); J. A. Wyler, U. S. Patents 2,039,045, 2,039,046 (1936).

129. G. V. Caesar and M. Goldfrank, *J. Am. Chem. Soc.* **68,** 372 (1946); L. Brissaud, *Mém. services chim. état*, **30,** 120 (1943), *Chem. Abstr.*, **41,** 715 (1947); J. Honeyman and J. W. W. Morgan, *Advances in Carbohydrate Chem.* **12** in press (1957).

130. Z. H. Skraup and R. Kremann, *Monatsh.* **22,** 1037 (1901); A. Colley, *Compt. rend.* **76,** 436 (1873).

131. D. J. Bell and R. L. Synge, *J. Chem. Soc.* p. 1711 (1937); 833, 836 (1938); J. Dewar and G. Fort, *ibid.* p. 492, 496 (1944); J. W. H. Oldham, *ibid.* p. 2840 (1925); J. Dewar, G. Fort, and N. McArthur, *ibid.* p. 499 (1944).

132. M. L. Wolfrom, J. H. Frazer, L. P. Kuhn, E. E. Dickey, S. M. Olin, D. O. Hoffman, R. S. Bower, A. Chaney, E. Carpenter, and P. McWain, *J. Am. Chem. Soc.* **77,** 6573 (1955).

nitrogen dioxide and a radical which is stabilized by the formation of a carbonyl group.

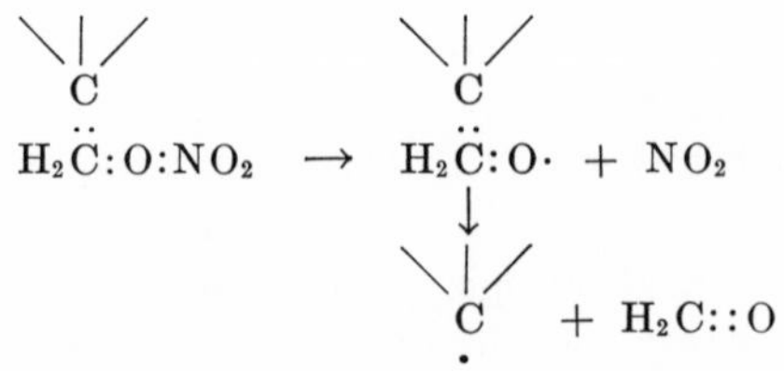

Nitrate esters generally do not undergo simple saponification on treatment with alkali but instead undergo extensive decomposition with the production of nitrite ion, carbonyl groups, and anhydro compounds. The last reaction can be favored in sterically suitable situations; thus, a high yield of methyl 3,6-anhydro-α-D-glucopyranoside was obtained on treating methyl α-D-glucopyranoside 6-nitrate with alkali (*133*).

Denitration can be effected by chemical reducing agents (*134*). For monomolecular nitrates, reductive denitration with hydrogen and Raney nickel (*135*) is preferable. Ammonium hydrogen sulfide effectively denitrates the nitrated polysaccharides.

2. SULFATE ESTERS

Chlorosulfonic acid, $HOSO_2Cl$, reacts with D-glucose to form the following ester.

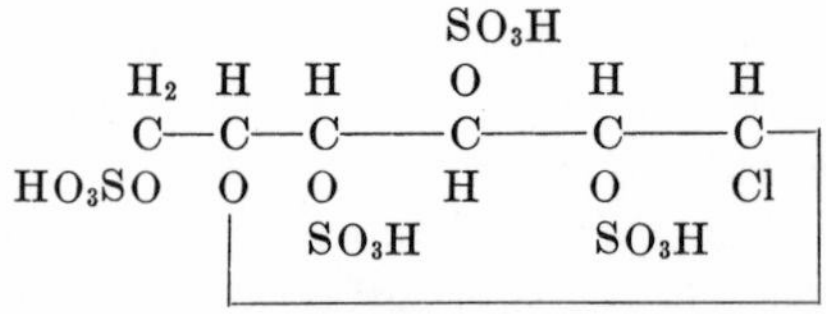

In pyridine and with a suitably blocked derivative, the same reagent can be used selectively to introduce sulfate acid ester groups; thus, 1,2:5,6-di-*O*-isopropylidene-D-glucose can be sulfated, and, on removal of the cyclic acetal groups, D-glucose 3-sulfate can be obtained as a suitable salt. Sulfur trioxide or chlorosulfonic acid in liquid sulfur dioxide, and sulfur trioxide in halogenated hydrocarbon solvents, pyridine, or *N*,*N*-dimethylformamide, can also be employed for sulfation.

Desulfation can be effected without Walden inversion, through acetolysis performed by solution of the salts in absolute hydrogen sulfate at low

133. E. K. Gladding and C. B. Purves, *J. Am. Chem. Soc.* **66,** 76 (1944).

134. D. O. Hoffman, R. S. Bower, and M. L. Wolfrom, *J. Am. Chem. Soc.* **69,** 249 (1947).

135. L. P. Kuhn, *J. Am. Chem. Soc.* **68,** 1761 (1946).

temperature followed by the addition of acetic anhydride (*136*). Removal of sulfate acid esters can be carried out also by hydrolysis with acid or alkali; in the latter case, anhydro-ring formation is occasionally encountered. Thus 1,2-*O*-isopropylidene-D-glucofuranose 6-sulfate is stated to form the 3,6-anhydro derivative, whereas the 3-sulfate of the same structure is hydrolyzed to the parent D-glucose derivative without anhydride formation or Walden inversion (*137*).

Natural sulfate acid esters occur as salts in many seaweed polysaccharides (*138*). They are also found widely distributed in the polysaccharides (*139*) of animal tissues (Chapter XII), such as those in skin, cartilage, cornea, and gastric mucin. Heparin (p. 720) (*140*), the natural blood anticoagulant, is a highly sulfated polysaccharide of this type and contains both sulfate acid ester groups and a sulfamic acid function, $RNHSO_2OH$.

3. BORIC ACID ESTERS (*140a*)

Boric acid esters of the sugars are rather ill-defined, but v. Vargha reported that when D-glucose is shaken in an acetone solution containing sulfuric acid and orthoboric acid (H_3BO_3), a crystalline 1,2-*O*-isopropylidene-D-glucofuranose 3,5-orthoborate separates (*141*). In the main, however, these esters are used for special purposes. They have been employed for the preparation of partially benzoylated sugar derivatives. In the presence of aqueous borax, the alditols and sugars have rotations quite different from those for the aqueous solutions (*142*).

The ionization of boric acid is enhanced in solutions containing carbohydrates (*143*). This effect is variable, apparently depending upon the individual complexing ability of the sugar. Khym and Zill (*144*) have used this effect to separate sugars by removing their borate complexes from ion-exchange resins in columns by differential elution with acid developers

136. M. L. Wolfrom and R. Montgomery, *J. Am. Chem. Soc.* **72,** 2859 (1950).

137. E. G. V. Percival, *J. Chem. Soc.* p. 119 (1945).

138. T. Mori, *Advances in Carbohydrate Chem.* **8,** 316 (1953).

139. P. A. Levene, "Hexosamines and Mucoproteins." Longmans, Green, London, 1925; M. Stacey, *Advances in Carbohydrate Chem.* **2,** 161 (1946).

140. A. B. Foster and A. J. Huggard, *Advances in Carbohydrate Chem.* **10,** 335 (1955).

140a. For additional discussion, see Chapters I and V.

141. L. von Vargha, *Ber.* **66,** 704 (1933).

142. L. Vignon, *Compt. rend.* **77,** 1191 (1873); **78,** 148 (1874); M. Murgier and M. E. Darmois, *Atti 10th congr. intern. chim.* **2,** 737 (1938).

143. G. Magnanini, *Z. physik. Chem.* **6,** 58 (1890); H. Schäfer, *Z. anorg. Chem.* **247,** 96 (1941); M. G. Mellon and V. N. Norris, *Ind. Eng. Chem.* **16,** 123 (1924); L. S. Weatherby and H. H. Chesney, *ibid.* **18,** 820 (1926); J. Böeseken, *Advances in Carbohydrate Chem.*, **4,** 189 (1949).

144. J. X. Khym and L. P. Zill, *J. Am. Chem. Soc.* **73,** 2399 (1951); **74,** 2090 (1952).

of successively increasing strength. Foster (*145*) has used the effect to separate sugars by paper ionophoresis. The borate complexes formed by the various mono-*O*-methylhexopyranoses or D-glucopyranosyl-D-glucopyranoses display rates of movement highly characteristic of their structures.

Crystalline esters of alditols and aldoses completely esterified with phenylboronic acid, $C_6H_5B(OH)_2$, have been reported (*146*).

4. HALOGENO ESTERS

Halogeno esters, other than the *O*-acetylglycosyl halides (p. 150), are known wherein a halogen has replaced one or more of the primary hydroxyl functions in aldoses, alditols (p. 261), and ketoses. Generally, these derivatives are known in otherwise substituted (mainly esterified) structures. They can be made by the prolonged action of hydrogen bromide, either the liquid alone or in acetic acid solution, on the acetates; and by replacement with iodine of primary tosyl or nitrate groups with sodium iodide in acetone or acetonylacetone solution (p. 164). The iodide (or other halide) can be exchanged for other halides by heating with the desired sodium halide in acetone solution. Scission of the 1,6-ring of 1,6-anhydro-β-D-glucopyranose with phosphorus pentabromide gave tri-*O*-acetyl-6-bromo-6-deoxy-D-glucopyranosyl bromide (*147*). Treatment of the *O*-acyl-1-deoxy-1-diazo-*keto*-glycoses (*148*) with dry hydrogen chloride or bromide in ether produces the *O*-acyl-1-deoxy-1-halogeno-*keto*-glycose.

Secondary halogen esters are also known. The addition of bromine to D-glucal 3,4,6-triacetate (p. 401) produces 3,4,6-tri-*O*-acetyl-2-bromo-2-deoxy-D-glucopyranosyl bromide (*149*). Methyl 4,6-dichloro-4,6-dideoxy-α-D-glucopyranoside 2,3-sulfate was obtained by the action of sulfuryl chloride on methyl α-D-glucopyranoside (*150*).

Helferich and Gnüchtel (*114*) state that iodide replacement by the action of sodium iodide in acetone is not confined exclusively to the 6-*O*-mesyl group but also took place with an *O*-mesyl group substituted at carbon 4.

5. PHOSPHATE ESTERS* (*151*)

The naturally occurring phosphate esters are products of intermediary metabolism and are of great metabolic importance (Chapter XIII). They

* This section was prepared by W. Z. Hassid and C. E. Ballou.

145. A. B. Foster, *J. Chem. Soc.* p. 982 (1953); R. Consden and W. M. Stanier, *Nature* **169**, 783 (1952).

146. H. G. Kuivila, A. H. Keough, and E. J. Soboczenski, *J. Org. Chem.* **19**, 780 (1954); M. L. Wolfrom and J. Solms, *ibid.* **21**, 815 (1956).

147. P. Karrer and A. P. Smirnoff, *Helv. Chim. Acta* **5**, 124 (1922).

148. M. L. Wolfrom and R. L. Brown, *J. Am. Chem. Soc.* **65**, 1517 (1943); M. L. Wolfrom, A. Thompson, and E. F. Evans, *ibid.* **67**, 1793 (1945).

149. E. Fischer, M. Bergmann, and H. Schotte, *Ber.* **53**, 509 (1920).

150. B. Helferich, G. Sprock, and E. Besler, *Ber.* **58**, 886 (1925).

TABLE II

DISSOCIATION CONSTANTS OF SOME SUGAR PHOSPHATES[a]

[Compiled by L. F. Leloir (*151*)]

Compound	pK_1'	pK_2'	Reference
Phosphoric acid	1.95–2.00	6.83–6.93	(*153, 154*)
D-Xylose 1-phosphate	1.25	6.15	(*155*)
D-Glucose 1-phosphate	1.10	6.13	(*154*)
D-Glucose 3-phosphate	0.84	5.67	(*156*)
D-Glucose 6-phosphate	0.94	6.11	(*156*)
D-Fructose 6-phosphate	0.97	6.11	(*156*)
D-Fructose 1,6-diphosphate	1.48	6.29[b]	(*157*)
D-Galactose 1-phosphate	1.00	6.17	(*158, 159*)
Maltose 1-phosphate	1.52	5.89	(*155*)

[a] The values are those calculated with the formula: $K_1' = \frac{H^+ [B + H^+]}{C - [B + H^+]}$ and $pK_2' = pH - \log \frac{B}{C - B}$ where H^+ represents the hydrogen-ion concentration, B the amount of alkali added to the acid, and C the concentration of the acid.

[b] The pK values for fructose diphosphate are average values of the constants of the two phosphate groups. Meyerhof and Lohman calculated the values of each of the secondary dissociation constants as $pK_{2a}' = 6.1$ and $pK_{2b}' = 6.5$.

serve as intermediates in the synthesis and degradation of starch, glycogen, and sucrose. They also function as substrates in the processes of glycolysis, fermentation of sugars to alcohol and other products, photosynthetic fixation of carbon dioxide, and in most oxidative biological processes. Phosphate esters occur as constituents of nucleic acids and of coenzymes which are closely related to vitamins of the B complex (Chapter VIII).

The phosphoric mono- and diesters of the sugars are strongly acidic substances isolated often as crystalline barium, calcium, lead, sodium, cyclohexylammonium, or alkaloid salts. They are usually stronger acids than free orthophosphoric acid (Table II), a fact which has been rationalized according to modern theory (*152*).

151. For an excellent detailed review see L. F. Leloir, *in* "Progress in the Chemistry of Organic Natural Products" (L. Zechmeister, ed.), Vol. 8; p. 47. Springer, Vienna, 1951.

152. W. D. Kumler and J. J. Eiler, *J. Am. Chem. Soc.* **65**, 2355 (1943).

153. D. D. Van Slyke, *J. Biol. Chem.* **52**, 525 (1922); H. T. S. Britton and R. A. Robinson, *Trans. Faraday Soc.* **28**, 531 (1932).

154. C. F. Cori, S. P. Colowick, and G. T. Cori, *J. Biol. Chem.* **121**, 465 (1937).

155. W. R. Meagher and W. Z. Hassid, *J. Am. Chem. Soc.* **68**, 2135 (1946).

156. O. Meyerhof and K. Lohmann, *Biochem. Z.* **185**, 113 (1927).

157. O. Meyerhof and J. Suranyi, *Biochem. Z.* **286**, 319 (1936).

158. H. W. Kosterlitz, *Biochem. J.* **37**, 321 (1943).

159. S. P. Colowick, *J. Biol. Chem.* **124**, 557 (1938).

A. Synthesis of Phosphate Esters

The use of phosphorus oxychloride for the synthesis of phosphate esters of sugars (*160*) has been largely replaced by dibenzyl (*161*) and diphenyl phosphorochloridates (*162*). The latter reagent may be prepared in a pure, stable form which reacts readily with an alcohol in pyridine at low temperature. The phenyl groups may be removed from the resulting di-*O*-phenyl phosphate derivative of the alcohol by catalytic hydrogenation employing a platinum catalyst.

Phenyl phosphorodichloridate (*163*) is useful in the synthesis of asymmetric phosphate diesters such as that of the phosphatide shown below.

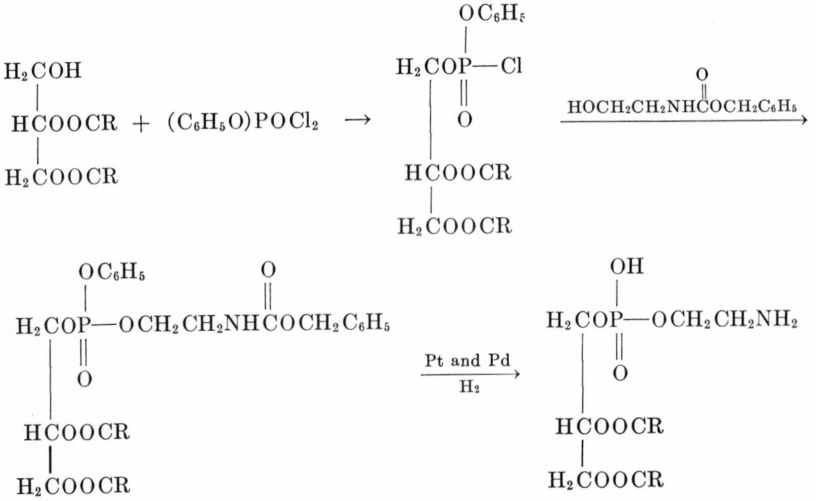

Inorganic phosphate reacts with epoxides to give phosphate esters. This method (*164*) is particularly useful for the preparation of D-glucose 6-phosphate labeled with the isotope P^{32}.

Glycose 1-phosphates may be prepared by reacting the poly-*O*-acetylglycosyl bromide with trisilver phosphate (*154*). The resulting phosphate triester is simultaneously deacetylated and hydrolyzed under controlled conditions to give the α-D-glycose 1-phosphate. By this procedure α-D-glucose (*165*), α-D-mannose (*166*), and α-D-galactose 1-phosphates (*167*)

160. E. Fischer, *Ber.* **47,** 3193 (1914); C. Neuberg and H. Pollak, *Ber.* **43,** 2060 (1910); E. Baer, *Biochem. Preparations.* **2,** 25, 31 (1952).

161. F. R. Atherton, H. T. Openshaw, and A. R. Todd. *J. Chem. Soc.* p. 382 (1945).

162. P. Brigl and H. Müller, *Ber.* **72,** 2121 (1939); H. A. Lardy and H. O. L. Fischer, *Biochem. Preparations.* **2,** 39 (1952).

163. E. Baer, J. Maurukas, and M. Russell, *J. Am. Chem. Soc.* **74,** 152 (1952).

164. G. P. Lampson and H. A. Lardy, *J. Biol. Chem.* **181,** 693 (1949).

165. M. E. Krahl and C. F. Cori, *Biochem. Preparations.* **1,** 33 (1949).

166. S. P. Colowick, *J. Biol. Chem.* **124,** 557 (1938).

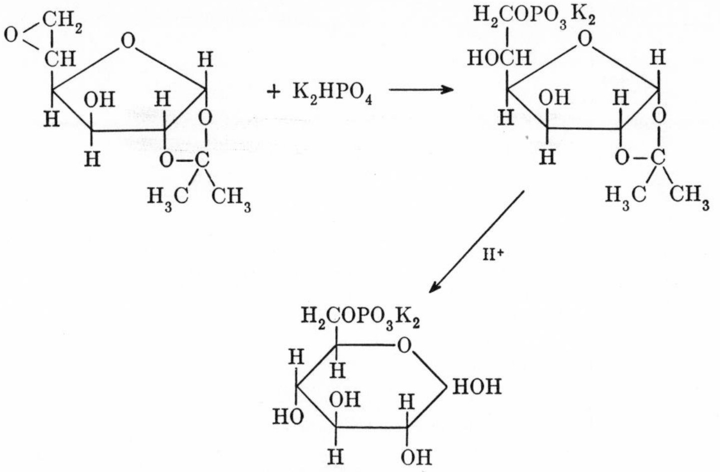

have been prepared. The β-isomers are prepared by reacting the poly-*O*-acetylglycosyl bromide with diphenyl silver phosphate, followed by catalytic hydrogenation to remove the phenyl groups and saponification of the acetyl groups (*168*).

They also can be synthesized by coupling the poly-*O*-acetylglycosyl bromide with monosilver phosphate as the phosphorylating agent (*168a*).

Enzymic syntheses of α-D-glucose 1-phosphate from starch by the action of phosphorylase (*169*) and of D-glucose 6-phosphate from readily available D-fructose 1,6-diphosphate have been described (*170*).

B. Phosphate Migration

Phosphate esters readily undergo intramolecular migration from one hydroxyl group to another under the influence of acid (*171*). (See Fig. 1, *172*.) This migration probably proceeds through a cyclic compound similar to the orthoester structure proposed in acyl group migration (p. 147 and 433):

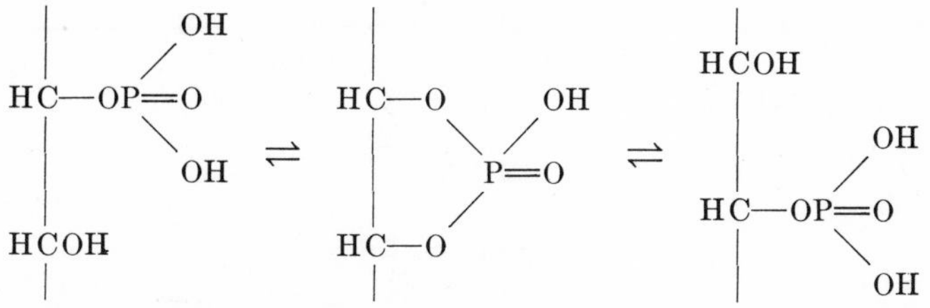

Any procedure of isolation or preparation that involves treatment with hot

167. H. W. Kosterlitz, *Biochem. J.* **33,** 1087 (1939).

168. L. Zervas, *Naturwissenschaften* **27,** 317 (1939); M. L. Wolfrom, C. S. Smith, D. E. Pletcher, and A. E. Brown, *J. Am. Chem. Soc.* **64,** 23 (1942).

168a. F. J. Reithel, *J. Am. Chem. Soc.* **67,** 1056 (1945).

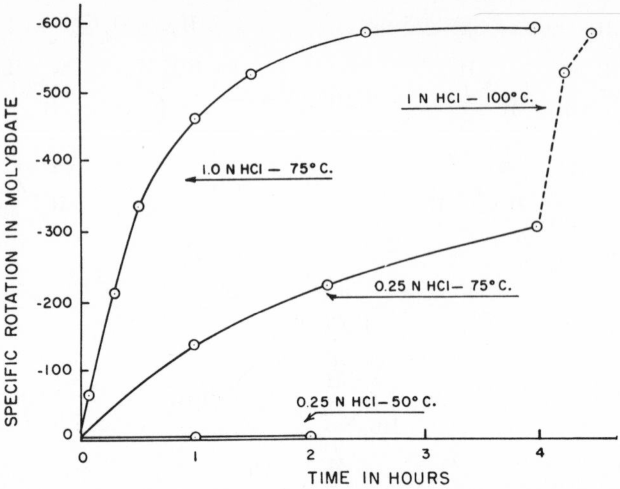

SPECIFIC ROTATION IN MOLYBDATE
TIME IN HOURS
-600
-500
-400
-300
-200
-100
0
0
1
2
3
4
1 N HCl — 100° C.
1.0 N HCl — 75° C.
0.25 N HCl— 75° C.
0.25 N HCl—50° C.

FIG. 1. Acid catalyzed phosphate migration of D-glyceric acid 2-phosphate to the 3-phosphate.

acid will likely bring about such migrations, resulting in an equilibrium mixture, which in the case of the glyceric acid phosphates is four parts of the 3-isomer and one part of the 2-isomer (*172*).

Compounds possessing the cyclic phosphate structure may be prepared by the action of phosphorus oxychloride or phenyl phosphorodichloridate on a glycol, or by treating phosphate monoesters with trifluoroacetic anhydride (*173*) or a carbodiimide reagent (*174*). The latter is the preferred reagent since it may be used in the presence of water and usually gives a good yield of a pure product. The reaction is formulated as follows:

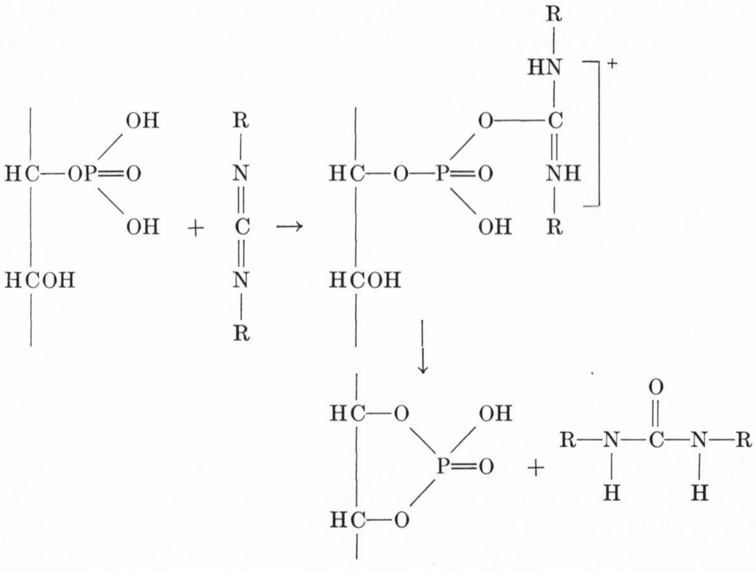

The resulting cyclic phosphate diester is hydrolyzed readily in acid or alkali to the phosphate monoester.

These cyclic phosphates are intermediates in the enzymic and alkaline degradation of ribonucleic acids, and may be the activated intermediates for the enzymic synthesis of ribonucleic acids from the nucleotides (*175*). Enzymes specific for the hydrolysis of nucleoside 2,3-cyclic phosphates to the monoesters have been prepared from snake venom, spleen, and intestinal mucosa. (See Chapter VIII.)

C. Hydrolysis of Phosphate Esters

The ease of hydrolysis of phosphate monoesters by acid or alkali varies greatly with the structure. The rate of hydrolysis actually measured may be the result of secondary changes in the sugar portion brought about by the acid or alkali, or it may represent the hydrolysis of the phosphate group after it has migrated to another position, since the rate of phosphate migration in acid solution is greater than that of its hydrolysis (*176*). In some compounds the phosphate group probably leaves by an elimination mechanism rather than by hydrolysis, with the result that the removal of phosphate is particularly enhanced.

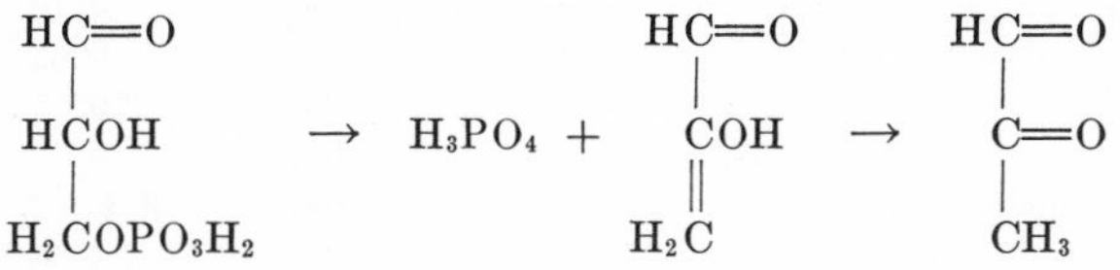

Table III lists the rates of hydrolysis in acid of some pentose and hexose phosphates. In general, the glycosyl phosphates hydrolyze readily in acid, due to their glycosidic structure. Phosphates located α- or β- to carbonyl functions are also easily removed.

The primary esters, such as D-glucose 6-phosphate, are much more resistant to acid hydrolysis, whereas phosphate esters of glyceric acid or

---

169. R. M. McCready and W. Z. Hassid, *J. Am. Chem. Soc.* **66,** 560 (1944); *Biochem. Preparations* **4,** 63 (1955).

170. W. A. Wood, *Biochem. Preparations.* **3,** 71 (1953).

171. P. A. Levene and A. L. Raymond, *J. Biol. Chem.* **107,** 75 (1934); E. Chargaff, *ibid.* **144,** 455 (1942); E. Baer and M. Kates, *ibid.* **185,** 615 (1950).

172. Taken from C. E. Ballou and H. O. L. Fischer, *J. Am. Chem. Soc.* **76,** 3188 (1954).

173. D. M. Brown, D. I. Magrath, and A. R. Todd, *J. Chem. Soc.* p. 2708 (1952).

174. H. G. Khorana, *Chem. Revs.* **53,** 145 (1953); C. A. Dekker and H. G. Khorana, *J. Am. Chem. Soc.* **76,** 3522 (1954).

175. L. A. Heppel, *in* "Chemical Pathways of Metabolism" (D. M. Greenberg, ed.), Vol. II, p. 263. Academic Press, New York, 1954.

176. K. R. Farrar, *J. Chem. Soc.* p. 3131 (1949).

TABLE III

OBSERVED HYDROLYSIS CONSTANTS OF SOME SUGAR PHOSPHATES

[Compiled by L. F. Leloir (*151*)]

Compound	Normality of acid	Temperature (°C.)	$k \times 10^{3a}$	Reference
D-Ribose 1-phosphate	0.5	25	1200	(*177*)
D-Ribose 3-phosphate	0.01	100	~1.7	(*178*)
	0.25	100	~4.5	(*179*)
D-Ribose 5-phosphate	0.01	100	~0.3	(*178*)
	0.25	100	~0.5	(*179*)
D-Xylose 1-phosphate	0.1	36	6.21	(*155*)
D-Xylose 5-phosphate	1	100	3–4	(*180*)
α-D-Glucose 1-phosphate	0.1	36	4.36	(*155*)
	0.25	37	1.30	(*154*)
	1	33	5.0	(*181*)
β-D-Glucose 1-phosphate	1	33	15.0	(*181*)
D-Glucose 2-phosphate	0.1	100	2.18	(*182*)
D-Gluconic acid 2-phosphate	1	100	0.3	(*183*)
D-Glucose 6-phosphate	0.1	100	0.13	(*184*)
	OA[b]	100	0.167	(*184*)
	1	100	0.23	(*185*)
	OA[b]	100	0.28	(*185*)
D-Gluconic acid 6-phosphate	1	100	0.15–0.26	(*186*)
α-D-Glucose 1,6-diphosphate	0.25	37	0.31	(*187*)
	1	30	0.78	(*188*)
β-D-Glucose 1,6-diphosphate	1	30	3.15	(*188*)
D-Fructose 1-phosphate	OA[b]	100	0.62	(*189*)
	1	100	70	(*189*)
	0.1	100	9	(*189*)
D-Fructose 6-phosphate	OA[b]	100	0.4–0.5	(*185*)
	1	100	4.36	(*185*)
			52	(*190*)
D-Fructose 1,6-diphosphate	1	100	4.2	
α-D-Galactose 1-phosphate	0.25	25	0.90	(*191*)
	0.25	37	5.9	(*191*)
β-D-Galactose 1-phosphate	0.25	37	5.6	(*192*)
D-Mannose 6-phosphate	0.1	100	0.13	(*185*)
	1	100	0.29	(*185*)
	OA[b]	100	0.28	(*185*)
D-Mannonic acid 6-phosphate	1	100	0.13–0.20	(*186*)
D-Mannonic γ-lactone 6-phosphate	1	100	0.12	(*186*)
L-Sorbose 6-phosphate	1	100	4.8	(*193*)
Maltose 1-phosphate	0.1	36	3.21	(*155*)
Ketoheptose monophosphate	1	100	4	(*194*)

[a] The constants are calculated with the formula $k = \frac{1}{t} \log_{10} \frac{a}{a - x}$, or more usually, $k = \frac{1}{t_2 - t_1} \log_{10} \frac{a - x_1}{a - x_2}$. The time is in minutes, and a is the initial concentration of the substance. The time for 50% hydrolysis, $t_{1/2} = \frac{0.30}{k}$, the time for 98% hydrolysis, $t = \frac{1.7}{k}$.

[b] OA means that the free acid was heated at its own acidity.

glycerol require prolonged heating at 100°C. in 1 *N* acid for complete hydrolysis (*195*).

The mechanism of alkaline hydrolysis of phosphate esters (rupture of P → O bond) is such that inversion during hydrolysis is unlikely (*196*). Acid hydrolysis on the other hand catalyzes cleavage of the C → O bond (*197*).

D. Naturally Occurring Hexose Phosphates

A number of hexose phosphates have been isolated from natural sources. Of these D-fructose 1,6-diphosphate (Harden-Young ester) (I), D-fructose 6-phosphate (Neuberg ester) (II), D-glucose 6-phosphate (Robison ester) (III), and α-D-glucose 1-phosphate (IV) are of particular biochemical importance in the processes of fermentation and glycolysis. These hexose phosphates are interconvertible in the presence of the proper enzymes and cofactors.

The work on phosphorylated sugars was initiated by Harden and Young (*198*), who first discovered D-fructose 1,6-diphosphate in fermenting yeast.

---

177. H. M. Kalckar, *J. Biol. Chem.* **167,** 477 (1947).

178. P. A. Levene and E. T. Stiller, *J. Biol. Chem.* **104,** 299 (1934).

179. H. G. Albaum and W. W. Umbreit. *J. Biol. Chem.* **167,** 369 (1947).

180. P. A. Levene and A. L. Raymond, *J. Biol. Chem.* **102,** 347 (1933).

181. M. L. Wolfrom, C. S. Smith, D. E. Pletcher, and A. E. Brown, *J. Am. Chem. Soc.* **64,** 23 (1942).

182. K. R. Farrar, *J. Chem. Soc.* p. 3131 (1949).

183. J. Courtois and M. Ramet, *Bull. soc. chim. France* **11,** 539 (1944).

184. R. Robison and E. J. King, *Biochem. J.* **25,** 323 (1931).

185. R. Robison, *Biochem. J.* **26,** 2191 (1932).

186. V. R. Patwardhan, *Biochem. J.* **28,** 1854 (1934).

187. C. E. Cardini, A. C. Paladini, R. Caputto, L. F. Leloir, and R. E. Trucco, *Arch. Biochem.* **22,** 87 (1949).

188. T. Posternak, *J. Biol. Chem.* **180,** 1269 (1949).

189. B. Tanko and R. Robison, *Biochem. J.* **29,** 961 (1935).

190. M. Macleod and R. Robison, *Biochem. J.* **27,** 286 (1933).

191. H. W. Kosterlitz, *Biochem. J.* **37,** 318 (1943).

192. F. J. Reithel, *J. Am. Chem. Soc.* **67,** 1056 (1945).

193. K. M. Mann and H. A. Lardy, *J. Biol. Chem.* **187,** 339 (1950).

194. R. Robison and M. G. Macfarlane, *in* "Methoden der Fermentforschung," (Bamann-Myrbäck, eds.), p. 296. Georg Thieme, Leipzig, 1941.

195. W. Kiessling, *Ber.* **68,** 243 (1935).

196. E. Blumenthal and J. B. M. Herbert, *Trans. Faraday Soc.* **41,** 611 (1945); see also D. M. Brown and A. R. Todd, *J. Chem. Soc.* p. 2040 (1953); D. Lipkin and P. T. Talbert, *Chemistry & Industry* p. 143 (1955).

197. M. Cohen, *J. Biol. Chem.* **180,** 771 (1949).

198. A. Harden and W. J. Young, *J. Chem. Soc.* **21,** 189 (1905); A. Harden, "Alcoholic Fermentation," 4th ed. Longmans, Green, London, 1932.

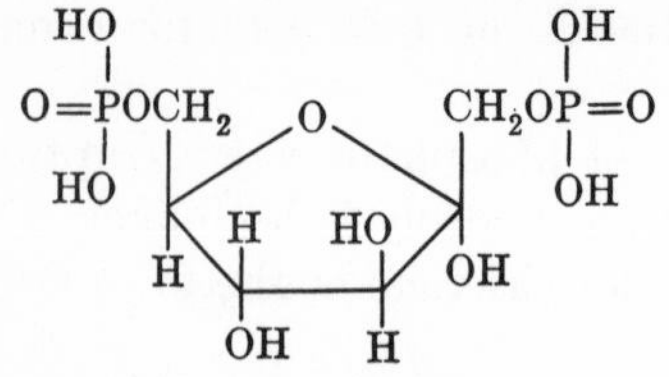

D-Fructofuranose 1,6-diphosphate
(I)

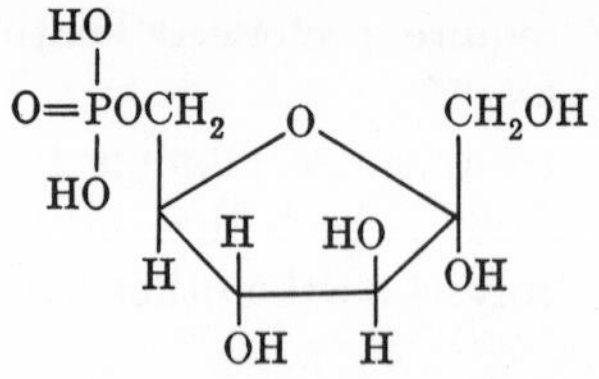

D-Fructofuranose 6-phosphate
(II)

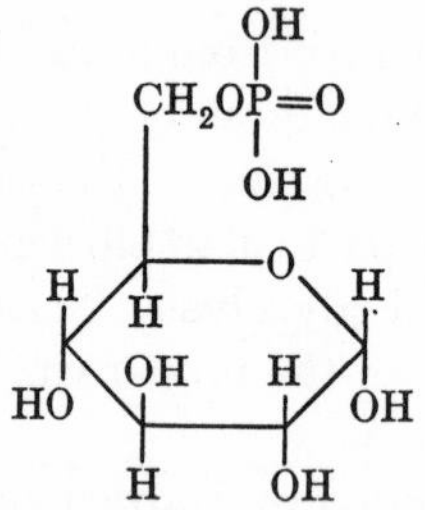

D-Glucopyranose 6-phosphate
(III)

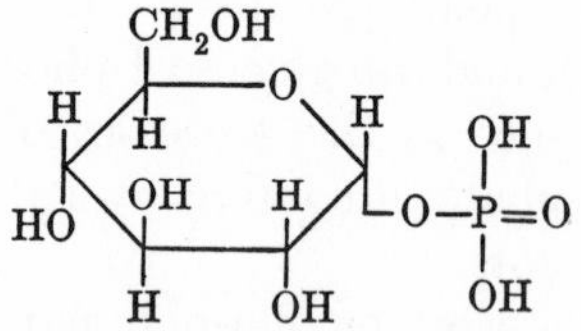

α-D-Glucopyranose 1-phosphate
(IV)

The procedure consisted in allowing air- or acetone-dried yeast or yeast juice to ferment sugar in the presence of phosphate. Under these conditions phosphate becomes esterified according to the following equation:

$$2 \text{ Hexose} + 2 \text{ phosphate} \rightarrow \text{hexose diphosphate} + 2 \text{ ethanol} + 2\ CO_2$$

According to the conditions, hexose monophosphate and trehalose phosphate also accumulate in varying amounts. Separation of the fructose diphosphate from the monophosphate can be effected by precipitating the diphosphate with neutral lead acetate or barium ions, followed by precipitation of the monophosphate from the supernatant liquid with basic lead acetate or barium ions in 50% or stronger ethanol (*199*). The separation of the different monophosphates was carried out by fractional crystallization (*200*). Chromatographic methods have also been used (Chapter XI).

Besides the many esters isolated from yeast and muscle tissue, Levene and his associates prepared ribose 3- and 5-phosphates by hydrolysis of nucleotides (*201*). α-D-Glucose 1-phosphate was isolated by Cori, Colowick, and Cori (*202*) as a product of the phosphorolysis of glycogen. Leloir and

199. R. Robison and W. T. J. Morgan, *Biochem. J.* **24,** 119 (1930).

200. R. Robison and E. J. King, *Biochem. J.* **25,** 323 (1931); also see W. W. Umbreit, R. H. Burris, and J. F. Stauffer "Manometric Techniques and Tissue Metabolism," Burgess, Minneapolis, 1949.

201. P. A. Levene and E. Jorpes, *J. Biol. Chem.* **81,** 575 (1929); P. A. Levene and W. A. Jacobs, *Ber.* **44,** 746 (1911).

202. C. F. Cori, S. P. Colowick, and G. T. Cori, *J. Biol. Chem.* **121,** 465 (1937).

co-workers (*203*) showed that α-D-glucose 1,6-diphosphate is present in animal tissues and yeast and possesses properties of a coenzyme. α-D-Galactose 1-phosphate was found by Kosterlitz (*204*) in the liver of a rabbit which had been fed D-galactose. D-Ribose 1-phosphate and deoxyribose 1-phosphate were obtained by Kalckar (*205*, *206*) by the phosphorolysis of nucleosides.

E. D-Fructose 1,6-Diphosphate (Harden-Young Ester)

The fact that hexose diphosphate forms an osazone with simultaneous elimination of one phosphate group when treated with hydrazine shows that one of the phosphate groups in the molecule is attached to carbon 1 (*207*). Determination of the rates of hydrolysis of the methyl α,β-D-fructoside diphosphate derivatives showed them to be very high (*208*). This high rate was taken as proof that the glycosides possess a furanose ring. Elimination of the phosphate groups from these compounds by phosphatase produced the corresponding methyl α- and β-D-fructosides. The specific rotations and ease of hydrolysis of the latter showed that they were D-fructofuranosides. In addition, methylation and subsequent hydrolysis of these glycosides yielded tetra-*O*-methyl-D-fructofuranose. The structure of the ester was, thus, established as D-fructofuranose 1,6-diphosphate.

F. Fructose 6-Phosphate (Neuberg Ester)

This ester was first prepared (*209*) by partial hydrolysis of D-fructose diphosphate and later isolated by Robison (*210*) from the hexose monophosphate fraction obtained by yeast juice fermentation.

The phosphate group at carbon 1 of D-fructose 1,6-diphosphate is hydrolyzed in 1 *N* acid, at 100°C., approximately 12 times as fast as that at carbon 6. Although at this temperature some destruction of the D-fructose occurs, a fairly good yield of the ester can be obtained by this method. An improved procedure whereby the hydrolysis is carried out at a lower temperature is given by Neuberg, Lustig, and Rothenberg (*211*).

203. L. E. Leloir, R. E. Trucco, C. E. Cardini, A. C. Paladini, and R. Caputto, *Arch. Biochem.* **19,** 339 (1948).

204. H. W. Kosterlitz, *Biochem. J.* **31,** 2217 (1937).

205. H. M. Kalckar, *J. Biol. Chem.* **167,** 477 (1947).

206. M. Friedkin and H. M. Kalckar, *J. Biol. Chem.* **184,** 437 (1950); M. Friedkin, H. M. Kalckar, and E. Hoff-Jörgensen, *J. Biol. Chem.* **178,** 527 (1949); see also M. Friedkin and D. Roberts, *ibid.* **207,** 257 (1954).

207. W. J. Young, *Biochem. Z.* **32,** 178 (1911).

208. W. T. J. Morgan, *Biochem. J.* **21,** 675 (1927); H. H. Schlubach and H. E. Bartels, *Ann.* **541,** 76 (1939); P. A. Levene and A. L. Raymond, *J. Biol. Chem.* **79,** 621 (1928).

209. C. Neuberg, *Biochem. Z.* **88,** 432 (1918).

210. R. Robison, *Biochem. J.* **26,** 2191 (1932).

211. C. Neuberg, H. Lustig, and M. A. Rothenberg, *Arch. Biochem.* **3,** 33 (1944).

G. D-Glucose 6-Phosphate (Robison Ester)

This hexose phosphate was detected by Harden and Robison (*212*) in the products of yeast juice fermentation and recognized only as a mixture of an aldose and D-fructose. Later Robison and King (*213*) were able to prepare D-glucose 6-phosphate in pure form. The assignment of position of the phosphate group in the D-glucose was adduced from the following: Positions 1 and 2 were eliminated because the osazone contained phosphate. Inasmuch as the synthetically prepared D-glucose 3-phosphate (*214*) was found to have properties different from the natural substance, position 3 was also excluded. Positions 4 and 5 were eliminated on the ground that two methyl glycosides could be prepared from this ester, one of which behaved, on acid hydrolysis, as a furanoside and the other as a pyranoside (*215*). Levene and Raymond (*216*) finally synthesized a hexose monophosphate, known to contain the phosphate at carbon 6, and which had chemical and biological properties similar to those of the Robison ester. Robison and King (*217*) also prepared an osazone from their purified natural ester which was identical with that given by D-fructose 6-phosphate.

H. α-D-Glucose 1-Phosphate (Cori Ester)

This ester was first isolated as a crude product by Cori, Colowick, and Cori (*218*) as a result of the action of frog muscle enzymes on glycogen and inorganic phosphate. A pure product was obtained when rabbit muscle extracts were dialyzed and then incubated with glycogen, phosphate buffer, and adenylic acid. The latter served as an activator of the enzyme (phosphorylase).

α-D-Glucose 1-phosphate was prepared synthetically (*218*) by treatment of tetra-*O*-acetyl-D-glucosyl bromide with silver phosphate in benzene. The tri-(tetra-*O*-acetyl-D-glucose) 1-phosphate produced was converted into D-glucose 1-phosphate by hydrolysis with acidic methanol and was obtained as an amorphous barium salt. The crystalline dipotassium salt was described by Kiessling (*219*).

Since the ester is alkali-stable and non-reducing and liberates D-glucose on hydrolysis, the phosphate must be attached to carbon 1 in the D-glucose. Cori, Colowick, and Cori (*218*) suggested that the hexose phosphate

212. A. Harden and R. Robison, *Proc. Chem. Soc.* **30,** 16 (1914).
213. R. Robison and E. J. King, *Biochem. J.* **25,** 323 (1931).
214. P. A. Levene and A. L. Raymond, *J. Biol. Chem.* **89,** 479 (1930).
215. E. J. King, R. R. McLaughlin, and W. T. J. Morgan, *Biochem. J.* **25,** 310 (1931).
216. P. A. Levene and A. L. Raymond, *J. Biol. Chem.* **91,** 751 (1931); **92,** 757 (1931).
217. R. Robison and E. J. King, *Biochem. J.* **25,** 323 (1931).
218. C. F. Cori, S. P. Colowick, and G. T. Cori, *J. Biol. Chem.* **121,** 465 (1937).
219. W. Kiessling, *Biochem. Z.* **298,** 421 (1938).

had the α-type linkage and the pyranose configuration. Wolfrom and Pletcher (*220*) confirmed this structure by showing that when the ester was oxidized with periodate, two moles of this reagent were consumed, with liberation of one mole of formic acid but of no formaldehyde. This evidence is consistent with a hexopyranose 1-phosphate structure. The α-linkage was adduced from the high dextrorotation and from a comparison with the synthetic β-D-glucose 1-phosphate.

I. Miscellaneous Phosphate Esters

D-Ribulose 5-phosphate is found together with D-ribose 5-phosphate as an oxidation product of D-gluconic acid 6-phosphate with a purified yeast enzyme (*221–223*). The D-ribulose 5-phosphate was identified as the *o*-nitrophenylhydrazone derivative, having a specific rotation in methanol of 50 ± 5°. D-Ribulose 5-phosphate appears to be the precursor of D-ribose in yeast and rat liver. A D-ribulose diphosphate was detected in the products formed during the first few seconds of photosynthesis (*224*).

An extract has been prepared from spinach leaves which catalyzes the formation of D-ribulose diphosphate from adenosine triphosphate and D-ribose 5-phosphate (*225*). The D-ribulose diphosphate appears to be an intermediate in a carbon dioxide fixation system in which D-ribose 5-phosphate was the added substrate (*226*).

The action of an enzyme, transketolase, from rat liver or from spinach, on pentose 5-phosphate results in the formation of a triose phosphate and an ester of sedoheptulose, which is presumably sedoheptulose 7-phosphate. The heptulose has been identified by the preparation of sedoheptulosan tetrabenzoate (*227*).

Sedoheptulose diphosphate is formed from sedoheptulose 7-phosphate and D-fructose 1,6-diphosphate in the presence of the enzymes aldolase and transaldolase (*228*). One of its two phosphate groups is relatively labile

220. M. L. Wolfrom and D. E. Pletcher, *J. Am. Chem. Soc.* **63,** 1050 (1941).

221. B. L. Horecker and P. Z. Smyrniotis, *J. Biol. Chem.* **196,** 135 (1952).

222. B. L. Horecker, P. Z. Smyrniotis, and J. E. Seegmiller, *J. Biol. Chem.* **193,** 383 (1951).

223. J. E. Seegmiller and B. L. Horecker, *J. Biol. Chem.* **194,** 261 (1952).

224. A. A. Benson, *J. Am. Chem. Soc.* **74,** 2123 (1952); J. R. Quayle, R. C. Fuller, A. A. Benson, and M. Calvin, *ibid.* **76,** 3610 (1954).

225. A. Weissbach, P. Z. Smyrniotis, and B. L. Horecker, *J. Am. Chem. Soc.*, **76,** 5572 (1954).

226. A. Weissbach, P. Z. Smyrniotis, and B. L. Horecker, *J. Am. Chem. Soc.* **76,** 3611 (1954).

227. B. L. Horecker, P. Z. Smyrniotis, and H. Klenow, *J. Biol. Chem.* **205,** 661 (1953).

228. B. L. Horecker, P. Z. Smyrniotis, H. H. Hiatt, and P. A. Marks, *J. Biol. Chem.* **212,** 827 (1955).

to acid hydrolysis. The sedoheptulose diphosphate is cleaved by aldolase to yield one mole of dihydroxyacetone phosphate and presumably D-erythrose phosphate. The ester is probably sedoheptulose 1,7-diphosphate. The free sugar has been identified by conversion to sedoheptulosan tetrabenzoate.

D-Erythrose 4-phosphate has been synthesized and shown to condense with dihydroxyacetone phosphate in the presence of aldolase to give a heptulose diphosphate with properties similar to the one described above (*229*). The synthetic tetrose phosphate is optically inactive, and is decomposed by acid at a rate similar to glyceraldehyde 3-phosphate.

Both the α- and β-forms of lactose 1-phosphate have been prepared (*230*). The α-lactose 1-phosphate was synthesized by phosphorylating hepta-*O*-acetyl-α-lactosyl bromide with silver diphenyl phosphate. For the preparation of the β-form of this ester monosilver phosphate was used as a phosphorylating agent (*192*).

α-D-Mannose 1,6-diphosphate was made from 2,3,4-tri-*O*-acetyl-6-diphenylphosphonyl-α-D-mannosyl bromide and silver diphenyl phosphate (*231*). The specific rotation of the potassium salt of the ester in water is $[\alpha]_D^{21}$ +29.9°.

The specific rotations of the various hexose phosphates are given in Table IV.

J. Phosphate Esters of 3-Carbon Sugars

These compounds, listed in Table V, are all intermediates in the metabolism of D-glucose. (See Chapter XIII.) Although all have been isolated from natural sources, they are most readily available in pure form by synthetic procedures. The phosphates of glyceraldehyde and dihydroxyacetone are very sensitive to decomposition by alkali with the liberation of inorganic phosphate, a characteristic on which their determination in the presence of other alkali-stable phosphate esters is based (*231a*). They are also decomposed by hot dilute acid.

229. C. E. Ballou, H. O. L. Fischer, and D. L. MacDonald, *J. Am. Chem. Soc.* **77,** 2658, 5967 (1955).

230. F. J. Reithel and R. C. Young, *J. Am. Chem. Soc.* **74,** 4210 (1952).

231. T. Posternak and J. P. Rosselet, *Helv. Chim. Acta* **36,** 1614 (1953).

231a. K. Lohmann, *Ann. Rev. Biochem.* **7,** 125 (1938).

TABLE IV

THE SPECIFIC ROTATION OF SOME SUGAR PHOSPHATES

[Compiled by L. F. Leloir (*151*)]

Compound	Salt	Solvent	Light source	[α]	Reference
D-Ribose 3-phosphate	Na_2	Water	D	−9.7°	(*232*)
	Na_2	Half satd. boric acid	D	+38°	(*232*)
D-Ribose 5-phosphate	Free acid	Water	D	+16.5°	(*232*)
	Ba	Water	D	+5°	(*233*)
D-Arabinose 5-phosphate	Ba	Water	D	−18.8°	(*234*)
	Brucine	50% Pyridine	D	−48.6°	(*234*)
D-Xylose 1-phosphate	Ba	Water	D	+65°	(*155*)
	K_2	Water	D	+76°	(*155*)
D-Xylose 5-phosphate	Na_2	50% Pyridine	D	+3.2°	(*180*)
	Na_2	Half satd. Borax	D	+4°	(*180*)
α-D-Glucose 1-phosphate	Free acid	Water	D	+120°	(*154*)
	K_2	Water	D	+78.5°	(*220*)
	K_2	Water	5461	+90°	(*220*)
	Ba	Water	D	+75°	(*154*)
	Brucine	Water	D	+0.5°	(*220*)
β-D-Glucose 1-phosphate	Brucine	Water	D	−20°	(*220*)
α-L-Glucose 1-phosphate	Ba	Water	D	−73.2°	(*235*)
	K_2	Water	D	−78.2°	(*235*)
D-Glucose 2-phosphate	K_2	Water	D	+15°	(*182*)
	K_2	0.1*N* Sulfuric acid	D	+35°	(*182*)
D-Glucose 3-phosphate	Free acid	Water	5461	+39°	(*236*)
	Free acid	Water	D	+39.5°	(*237*)
	Brucine	50% Pyridine	D	−14.5°	(*238*)
	Ba	Water	D	+26.5°	(*237*)
	Ba	Water	5461	+27°	(*236*)
D-Glucose 4-phosphate	Brucine	Pyridine	D	−45.3°	(*239*)
	Brucine	20% Ethanol	D	−9.8°	
D-Glucose 5-phosphate	Ba	Water	D	+15°	(*240*)
D-Glucose 6-phosphate	Free acid	Water	D	+35.1°	(*241*)
	Free acid	Water	5461	+41.4°	(*241*)
	Ba	Water	D	+18°	(*241*)
	Ba	Water	5461	+21.2°	(*241*)
	K_2	Water	D	+21.2°	(*242*)
D-Gluconic acid 6-phosphate	Ba	Water	5461	−1.5°	(*241*)
	Free acid	Water	5461	+0.2°	(*241*)
D-Gluconic lactone 6-phosphate	—	Water	5461	+21°	(*241*)
α-D-Glucose 1,6-diphosphate	Free acid	Water	D	+83°	(*188*)
β-D-Glucose 1,6-diphosphate	Free acid	Water	D	−19°	(*188*)

TABLE IV—*Continued*

Compound	Salt	Solvent	Light source	[α]	Reference
D-Fructose 1-phosphate	Free acid	Water	5461	−64.2°	(*189*)
	Ba	Water	5461	−39°	(*189*)
	Brucine	Water	5461	−52.1°	(*189*)
D-Fructose 6-phosphate	Ba	Water	D	+3.6°	(*243*)
D-Fructose 1,6-diphosphate	Free acid	Water	D	+4.1°	(*243*)
α-D-Galactose 1-phosphate	Free acid	Water	D	+148.5°	(*191*)
	K_2	Water	D	+108°	(*191*)
	Ba	Water	5461	+113°	(*191*)
	Ba	Water	D	+92°	(*191*)
β-D-Galactose 1-phosphate	Ba	Water	D	+31.3°	(*192*)
D-Mannose 1-phosphate	Free acid	Water	D	+58°	(*244*)
	Ba	Water	D	+36°	
D-Mannose 6-phosphate	Free acid	Water	5461	+15.1°	(*185*)
	Ba	Water	5461	+3.5°	
D-Mannonic γ-lactone 6-phosphate	—	Water	5461	+54.1°	(*186*)
D-Mannonic δ-lactone 6-phosphate	—	Water	5461	+60.6°	(*186*)
D-Tagatose 6-phosphate	Ba	Water	D	+5.6°	(*245*)
L-Sorbose 1-phosphate	K_2	Water	D	−16.5°	(*193*)
L-Sorbose 6-phosphate	Ba	Water	D	−12.0°	(*193*)
Trehalose monophosphate	Free acid	Water	5461	+185°	(*246*)
	Ba	Water	5461	+132°	(*246*)
	Brucine	Water	5461	+31°	(*246*)
Ketoheptose monophosphate	Ba	Water	5461	+8°	(*247*)

(Compiled by W. Z. Hassid and C. E. Ballou)

Compound	Salt	Solvent	Light source	[α]	Reference
α-L-Arabinose 1-phosphate	Cyclohexylamine	Water	D	+30.8°	(*248*)
β-L-Arabinose 1-phosphate	Cyclohexylamine	Water	D	+91°	(*248*)
α-D-Xylose 1-phosphate	Cyclohexylamine	Water	D	+58°	(*248*)
β-D-Xylose 1-phosphate	Cyclohexylamine	Water	D	+0.8°	(*248*)
β-D-Ribofuranose 1-phosphate	Ba	5% acetic acid	D	−47.1°	(*249*)
α-D-Ribofuranose 1-phosphate	Cyclohexylamine	Water	D	+40.3°	(*250*)
D-Xylose 3-phosphate	Cyclohexylamine	Water	D	+14.1°	(*251*)
	Ba	Water	D	+1.27°	

232. P. Levene and S. A. Harris, *J. Biol. Chem.* **101**, 419 (1933).
233. A. M. Nichelson and A. R. Todd, *J. Chem. Soc.* p. 2476 (1949).

TABLE IV—*Continued*

234. P. A. Levene and C. C. Christman, *J. Biol. Chem.* **123,** 607 (1938).
235. A. L. Potter, J. C. Sowden, W. Z. Hassid, and M. Doudoroff, *J. Am. Chem. Soc.* **70,** 1751 (1948).
236. K. Josephson and S. Proffe, *Ann.* **481,** 91 (1930).
237. P. A. Levene and A. L. Raymond, *J. Biol. Chem.* **89,** 479 (1930).
238. P. A. Levene and A. L. Raymond, *J. Biol. Chem.* **91,** 751 (1931).
239. A. L. Raymond, *J. Biol. Chem.* **113,** 375 (1936).
240. K. Josephson and S. Potter, *Biochem. Z.* **258,** 147 (1933).
241. R. Robison and E. J. King, *Biochem. J.* **25,** 323 (1931).
242. H. A. Lardy and H. O. L. Fischer, *J. Biol. Chem.* **164,** 513 (1946).
243. C. Neuberg, H. Lustig, and M. A. Rothenberg, *Arch. Biochem.* **3,** 33 (1944).
244. S. P. Colowick, *J. Biol. Chem.* **124,** 557 (1938).
245. E. L. Totton and H. A. Lardy, *J. Biol. Chem.* **181,** 701 (1949).
246. R. Robison and W. T. J. Morgan, *Biochem. J.* **22,** 1277 (1928).
247. R. Robison, M. G. Macfarlane, and A. Tazelaar, *Nature* **142,** 114 (1938).
248. E. W. Putman and W. Z. Hassid, *J. Am. Chem. Soc.* in press.
249. R. S. Wright and H. G. Khorana, *J. Am. Chem. Soc.* **78,** 811 (1956).
250. G. M. Tenner, R. S. Wright and H. G. Khorana, *J. Am. Chem. Soc.* **78,** 506 (1956).
251. J. G. Moffatt and H. G. Khorana, *J. Am. Chem. Soc.* **78,** 883 (1956).

TABLE V

PHOSPHORYLATED 3-CARBON INTERMEDIATES OF CARBOHYDRATE METABOLISM

Compound	$[\alpha]_D$	References
D-Glyceraldehyde 3-phosphate	+14° (free acid in water)	*(254)*
Dihydroxyacetone phosphate	—	*(255)*
D-Glyceric acid 3-phosphate	−14.5° (1 *N* HCl)	*(256)*
	−745° (neutral molybdate)	
D-Glyceric acid 2-phosphate	+13° (1 *N* HCl)	*(257)*
	+5° (neutral molybdate)	
D-Glyceric acid 1,3-diphosphate	−2.3° (free acid in water)	*(258)*
D-Glyceric acid 2,3-diphosphate	−2.3° (free acid in water)	*(259)*
L-Glycerol 1-phosphate	−1.45° (2 *N* HCl)	*(260)*
Enolpyruvate phosphate	—	*(261)*

254. O. Meyerhof and R. Junowicz-Kocholaty, *J. Biol. Chem.* **149,** 71 (1943); C. E. Ballou and H. O. L. Fischer, *J. Am. Chem. Soc.* **77,** 3329 (1955).
255. W. Kiessling, *Ber.* **67,** 869 (1934).
256. O. Meyerhof and W. Schulz, *Biochem. Z.* **297,** 60 (1938); C. E. Ballou and H. O. L. Fischer, Abstract 7D, 126th Meeting, American Chemical Society, 1954.
257. C. E. Ballou and H. O. L. Fischer, *J. Am. Chem. Soc.* **76,** 3188 (1954).
258. E. Negelein and H. Brömel, *Biochem. Z.* **303,** 132 (1939).
259. E. Baer, *J. Biol. Chem.* **185,** 763 (1950).
260. E. Baer and H. O. L. Fischer, *J. Biol. Chem.* **128,** 491 (1939).
261. E. Baer and H. O. L. Fischer, *J. Biol. Chem.* **180,** 145 (1949).

IV. GLYCOSIDES, SIMPLE ACETALS, AND THIOACETALS

M. L. Wolfrom and A. Thompson

The carbonyl group of aldoses (I) and ketoses (IX) may react externally, under acid catalysis, with alcohols to form glycosides (mixed monocyclic acetals, II, III) and under special conditions and in the presence of suitable blocking groups, to form acyclic acetals (VIII). Dithioacetals ("mercaptals", V) and 1-thioglycosides (VI) are formed when thiols ("mercaptans") are employed instead of alcohols. The dithioacetals are obtainable from the aldoses directly. If the condensation is internal, glycosans (internal bicyclic acetals, IV) are formed from aldoses; ketohexoses form bimolecular dianhydrides (X) containing a central dioxane ring.

The carbonyl groups of aldehydes or ketones condense with pairs of hydroxyls provided by a carbohydrate to produce alkylidene or arylidene derivatives. These resulting compounds are cyclic acetals, which differ

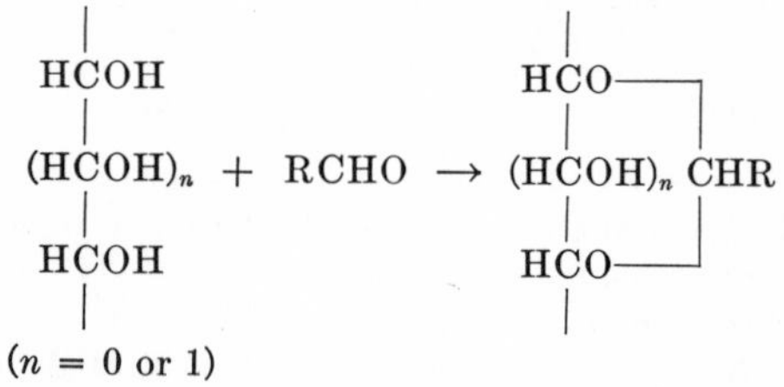
HCOH
(HCOH)n + RCHO → (HCOH)n CHR
HCOH
HCO
HCO

(n = 0 or 1)

from glycosides and glycosans in that the carbonyl group is supplied by a noncarbohydrate.

Anhydro derivatives may be considered to be of two general types: (1) glycosans (inner glycosides, IV) for which water is split out between an anomeric hydroxyl group and a primary or secondary alcohol group, (2) anhydrides (ethers, XI), treated under "Ethers" in a subsequent chapter, which may be considered to be derived by the removal of water between hydroxyl groups, neither of which is on the reducing carbon.

The glycosides are widely distributed in plants and to a lesser extent in animals. Because the chemistry of the natural glycosides resides to a considerable degree in the noncarbohydrate portion and in biochemical aspects, the natural glycosides are discussed in a later chapter in connection with enzymes (Chapter X).

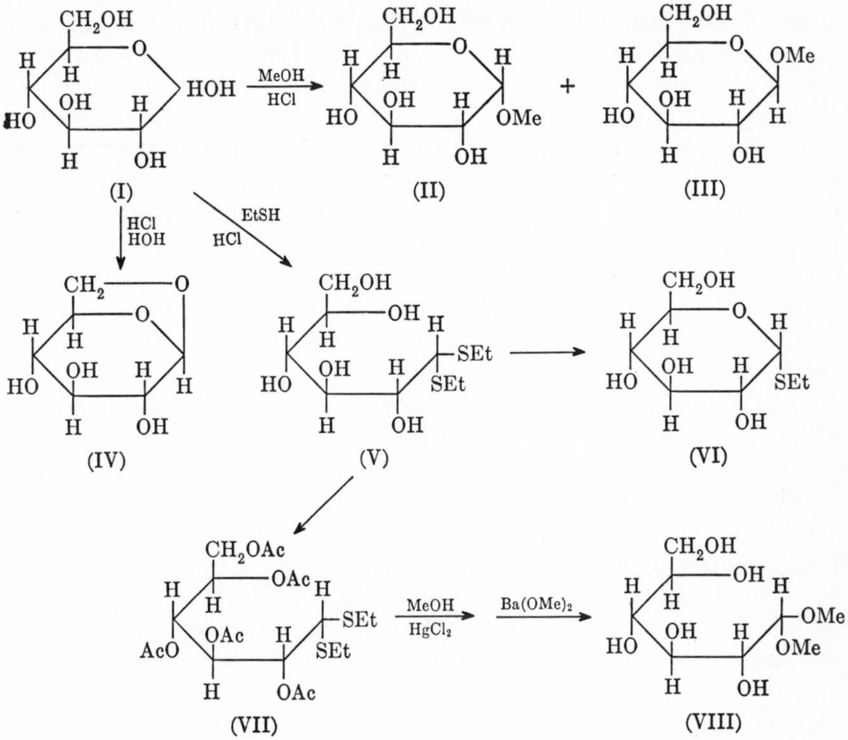

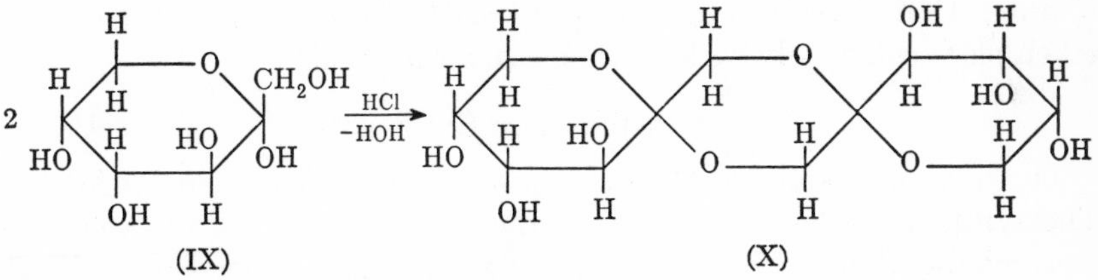

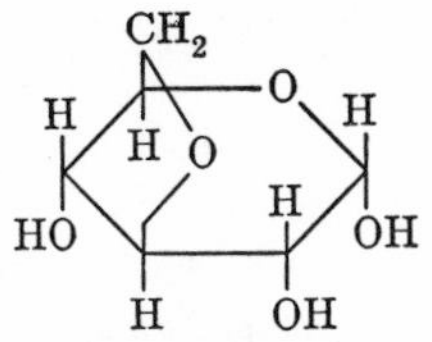

(XI)

3,6-Anhydro-α-D-glucopyranose

1. GLYCOSIDES

The glycosides may be defined as acetal derivatives of the cyclic forms of the sugars (normally pyranoses and furanoses) in which the hydrogens of the hemiacetal hydroxyls have been replaced by alkyl or aryl groups and which on complete hydrolysis yield a mono- or polyhydric alcohol or phenol and one or more monosaccharides. In the older literature the term "glucoside" was used generically for all such derivatives and was not confined to glucose derivatives. Present usage restricts "D-glucosides" to the D-glucose derivatives whereas "glycosides" is used in the generic sense. Specific glycosides are named by replacing the ending "ose" of the parent sugar by "oside" and by adding the name of the alkyl or aryl radical and the symbol α or β to designate the configuration of the glycosidic (anomeric) carbon, as methyl β-D-glucopyranoside. For more complex groups, it is sometimes more convenient to use the name of the alcohol or phenol rather than the radical, as hydroquinone α-D-galactopyranoside.

Many phytochemical names such as salicin and helicin are in use for natural glycosides although chemical names usually are to be preferred since they indicate the structure and facilitate classification. However, the trivial names offer the advantage of brevity and frequently indicate the source of the glycoside, as salicin from *Salix*. For convenience, the alkyl or aryl group is often referred to as the "aglycon group" (less preferably as the "aglucone group") and the corresponding free phenol or alcohol as the "aglycon." The sugar radical is the "glycosyl" (glycofuranosyl, glycopyranosyl) group and is obtained by removing the hydroxyl of the anomeric carbon (carbon 1 of aldoses).

Di-, oligo-, and poly-saccharides have glycosidic linkages. For these compounds, the aglycon group is a sugar radical (see under Oligosaccharides, Chapter IX). Glycosans are inner glycosides for which acetalation has taken place completely within a single sugar molecule.

A. Methods for Synthesis

The first successful synthesis of glycosides was carried out by Michael. The synthesis was accomplished by the interaction of tetra-*O*-acetyl-α-D-glucopyranosyl chloride (I) and the potassium salts of phenols (*1*). Under the conditions of the reaction, acetyl groups were also removed, and the glycoside was produced.

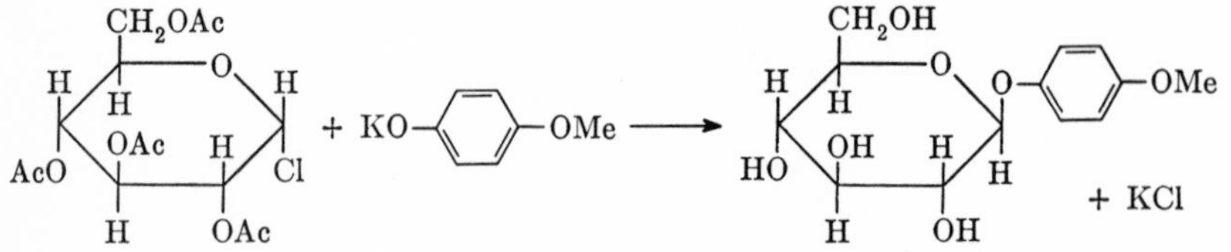
CH2OAc
O
H
H
OAc
H
AcO
Cl
H
OAc
+ KO
OMe
CH2OH
O
O
OMe
H
H
OH
H
HO
H
H
OH
+ KCl

(I)

Methylarbutin

1. A. Michael, *Am. Chem. J.* **1,** 305 (1879); **6,** 336 (1885); *Compt. rend.* **89,** 355 (1879).

Fischer, in an attempt to synthesize the acetals of the sugars by the action of methyl alcohol and hydrogen chloride, found that only one methyl group was introduced per mole of sugar and that he had obtained the methyl analog of the natural glycosides (*2*, *2a*). The Michael synthesis can be applied only to condensations with phenols and the Fischer synthesis applies only to alcohols. Koenigs and Knorr, however, by utilizing their tetra-*O*-acetyl-α-D-glucopyranosyl bromide, silver carbonate, and an alcohol or phenol (under anhydrous conditions) provided a procedure applicable to the preparation of both alkyl and aryl glycosides (*3*). The above methods, their modifications, and new methods have been widely applied to the preparation of glycosides. These methods are considered separately below in more detail.

a. Fischer Method

Aldehydes and ketones react in anhydrous alcoholic solutions of hydrogen chloride with the formation of acetals, and the simplest members of the sugar series, glycolaldehyde and glyceraldehyde, react similarly. The cyclic sugars, which are already hemiacetals, under these conditions establish an equilibrium in which the anomeric pyranosides and furanosides predominate. γ-Hydroxy aldehydes, such as γ-hydroxyvaleraldehyde, act similarly and create oxygen rings by intramolecular acetal formation (*4*). The furanose forms of the sugars seem to react the most readily, but the pyranosides generally are the principal constituents under equilibrium conditions. Hence, if the furanosides are particularly desired, the reaction is carried out under the milder conditions. At the boiling temperature of the solvent, equilibrium is usually attained after 3 to 24 hours for hydrogen chloride concentrations of 0.5 to 1.5%.

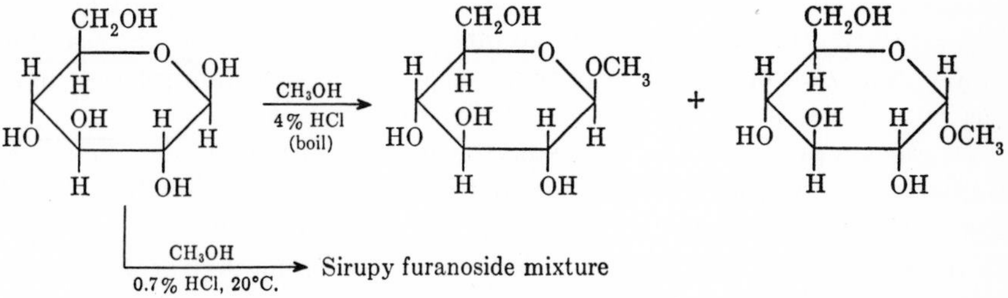

CH₂OH
CH₃OH
4% HCl
(boil)
OCH₃
CH₃OH
0.7% HCl, 20°C.
Sirupy furanoside mixture

Levene, Raymond, and Dillon (*5*) have made a detailed study of the

2. E. Fischer, *Ber.* **26**, 2400 (1893).
2a. E. Fischer, *Ber.* **28**, 1145 (1895).
3. W. Koenigs and E. Knorr, *Ber.* **34**, 957 (1901).
4. B. Helferich and F. A. Fries, *Ber.* **58**, 1246 (1925).
5. P. A. Levene, A. L. Raymond, and R. T. Dillon, *J. Biol. Chem.* **95**, 699 (1932).

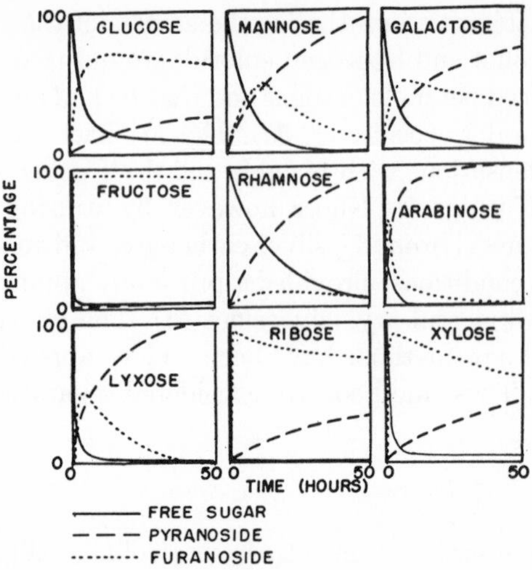
GLUCOSE
MANNOSE
GALACTOSE
FRUCTOSE
RHAMNOSE
ARABINOSE
LYXOSE
RIBOSE
XYLOSE
PERCENTAGE
100
0
50
TIME (HOURS)
FREE SUGAR
PYRANOSIDE
FURANOSIDE

FIG. 1. Composition of solution during glycoside formation at 25° in methanol containing 0.5 per cent hydrogen chloride.

changes which take place during methyl glycoside formation, and their data are summarized for a number of common sugars in Fig. 1.

The composition of the reaction mixture was determined by analysis for reducing sugars before and after hydrolysis under strongly acidic conditions (pyranosides and furanosides hydrolyzed) and under weakly acidic conditions (furanosides hydrolyzed).

As will be noted from Fig. 1, furanosides appear to be formed in the first stages of the reaction, but their quantity decreases in the later stages. On the other hand, the proportion of pyranosides increases progressively with time. The quantity of furanoside varies greatly with the nature of the sugar and seems to be particularly great for ribose. The values for fructose, and possibly other sugars, should be interpreted with caution because the difference in ease of hydrolysis of some furanosides and pyranosides is small (see later discussion of the ease of hydrolysis of glycosides).

It appears probable that the dialkyl acetals are formed under the same conditions as for the glycosides but that the equilibrium favors the formation of the mixed acetals (the glycosides). In methyl alcohol which contains hydrogen chloride, the D-glucose and D-galactose dimethyl acetals yield the corresponding pyranosides (*6*). For the D-glucosides, D-mannosides, and D-galactosides, the alpha pyranose form predominates over the beta in the equilibrium mixture. The glycosidation of D-galactose with methanol and hydrogen chloride has been investigated (*7*) by modern chromatographic

6. H. A. Campbell and K. P. Link, *J. Biol. Chem.* **122,** 635 (1938); M. L. Wolfrom and S. W. Waisbrot. *J. Am. Chem. Soc.* **61,** 1408 (1939).

7. D. F. Mowery, Jr., and G. F. Ferrante, *J. Am. Chem. Soc.* **76,** 4103 (1954).

TABLE I (*7*)
METHYL GLYCOSIDATION OF D-GALACTOSE

Reaction conditions	Time (hr.)	Furanose (%)		Pyranose (%)	
		α-D-	β-D-	α-D-	β-D-
25°C., 0.5% HCl, *c* 0.75	6	17	33	0	50
	940	30	7	49	14
64°C., 4% HCl, *c* 1.5	3	73	4	9	14
	20	39	5	40	16

isolative methods and it has been shown that a mixture of β-D-furanosides and -pyranosides is first formed which then shifts to a mixture of the α-D-anomers (Table I). The furanoside assay employed was again based upon the relative ease of hydrolysis of this ring structure. Although Micheel and Suckfüll (*8*) have shown that methyl β-D-galactoseptanoside has the same low stability toward acid hydrolysis as the corresponding furanoside, such a septanoside was not encountered by Mowery and Ferrante (*7*) in their isolative work effected by clay-column chromatographic techniques.

The Fischer procedure is particularly good for the preparation of the alkyl pyranosides although a few crystalline furanosides have been obtained in this manner (*9*). Better methods for the furanosides are described later. The disaccharides are partially hydrolyzed under the conditions of glycoside formation as are also the acetyl groups of acetylated sugars.

The use of ion-exchange resins makes possible the commercial continuous process for the preparation of methyl α-D-glucopyranoside.

The introduction of acid catalysis effected by the acid form of a suitable ion-exchange resin, has also led to the synthesis of the anomeric methyl glycosides of D-glucurono-γ-lactone (*10*). As these glycosides were known to be furanoid (*11*), reduction of the lactone (*12*) with sodium borohydride (*13*) yielded the anomeric forms of methyl D-glucofuranoside.

8. F. Micheel and F. Suckfüll, *Ber.* **66,** 1957 (1933).

9. W. N. Haworth, E. L. Hirst, and J. I. Webb, *J. Chem. Soc.* p. 651 (1930); C. B. Purves and C. S. Hudson, *J. Am. Chem. Soc.* **56,** 708 (1934); E. M. Montgomery and C. S. Hudson, *ibid.* **59,** 992 (1937); R. K. Ness, H. W. Diehl and H. G. Fletcher, Jr., *ibid.*, **76,** 763 (1954); I. Augestad and E. Berner, *Acta Chem. Scand.* **8,** 251 (1954).

10. J. E. Cadotte, F. Smith, and D. Spriestersbach, *J. Am. Chem. Soc.* **74,** 1501 (1952); E. M. Osman, K. C. Hobbs, and W. E. Walston, *J. Am. Chem. Soc.* **73,** 2726 (1951).

11. F. Smith, *J. Chem. Soc.* p. 584 (1944).

12. D. D. Phillips, *J. Am. Chem. Soc.* **76,** 3598 (1954).

13. M. L. Wolfrom and H. B. Wood, *J. Am. Chem. Soc.* **73,** 2933 (1951).

b. Anomeric Replacement

The preparation of a glycoside by the Koenigs-Knorr reaction involves treatment of an *O*-acetylglycosyl halide with the corresponding alcohol or phenol, in certain inert solvents when necessary, and in the presence of excess silver carbonate or silver oxide.

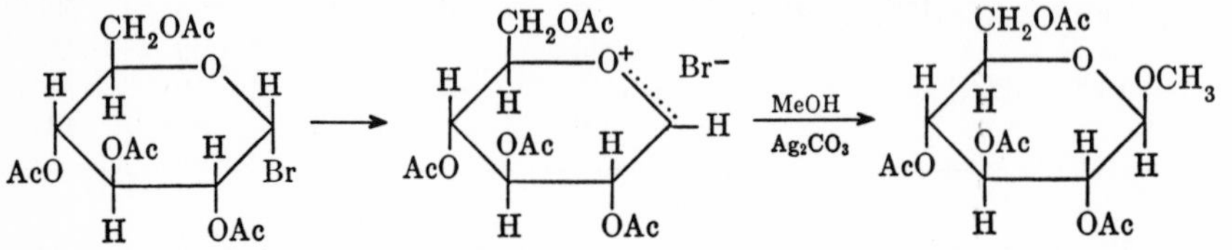
MeOH
Ag_2CO_3

Tetra-*O*-acetyl-α-D-glucopyranosyl bromide — Methyl tetra-*O*-acetyl-β-D-glucopyranoside

The substitution follows first-order kinetics with inversion of the anomeric carbon, the dissociation of the halide being the rate-controlling step (*14*). However, when a *trans* situation exists between the 1-halogen and the 2-*O*-acetyl group, the *O*-acetyl group may attack the back face of carbon 1 as the halogen departs, forming an orthoester carbonium ion. Frush and Isbell (*15*), Pacsu (*15a*), and Lemieux (*16*) have discussed this in detail. Under the slightly basic conditions of the Koenigs-Knorr reaction an alkoxy radical can then attack this carbonium ion to form a stable orthoester.

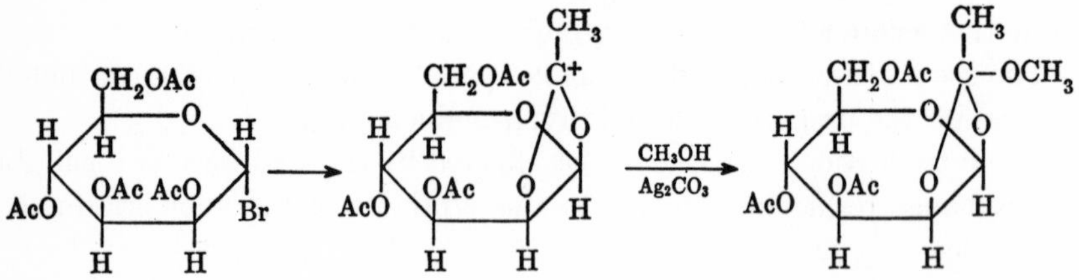
CH_3OH
Ag_2CO_3

Tetra-*O*-acetyl-α-D-mannopyranosyl bromide — Tri-*O*-acetyl-α-D-mannopyranose 1,2-(methyl orthoacetate)

The halogen of the *trans*-isomer may also be replaced, with inversion of the carbon atom, without participation of the 2-*O*-acetyl group to form an alkyl glycoside. However, the dissociation of the halogen, the rate-controlling step, is many times faster when aided by the 2-*O*-acetyl group. The

14. E. P. Painter, *J. Am. Chem. Soc.* **75,** 1137 (1953); F. H. Newth and G. O. Phillips, *J. Chem. Soc.* pp. 2896, 2900, 2904 (1953); L. J. Haynes and F. H. Newth, *Advances in Carbohydrate Chem.* **10,** 207 (1955).

15. H. L. Frush and H. S. Isbell, *J. Research Natl. Bur. Standards* **27,** 413 (1941).

15a. E. Pacsu, *Advances in Carbohydrate Chem.* **1,** 78 (1945).

16. R. U. Lemieux, *ibid.* **9,** 1 (1954).

major product of the Koenigs-Knorr reaction in which a 2-*O*-acetyl group is in the *trans*-position to the 1-halogen in the starting material, is, therefore, the alkyl orthoacetate, with a small amount of the alkyl β-D-glycopyranoside.

An interesting reaction useful in testing for the orthoester structure is that which takes place with hydrogen chloride in chloroform. Under these conditions, the orthoester derivatives are converted to the normal *O*-acetylglycosyl chlorides.

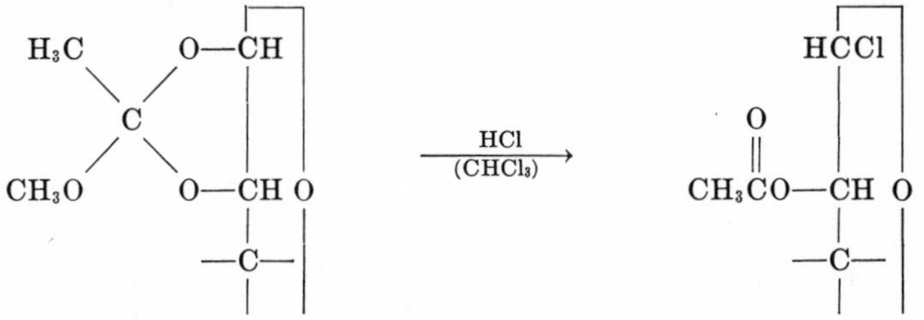
HCl
(CHCl3)

Aldose methyl orthoacetate — *O*-Acetylglycosyl chloride

Derivatives having an orthoacetic acid structure (with a free hydroxyl rather than a methoxyl group) have been described (*17*), but no direct proof of structure was provided. The orthoacetic acid and ester structures call for a new asymmetric carbon, and in one instance the two forms have been isolated. Talley, Reynolds, and Evans (*18*) isolated two isomeric orthoacetate forms (I, II) of the product obtained by condensing tetra-*O*-acetyl-α-D-mannopyranosyl bromide with 1,2,3,4-tetra-*O*-acetyl-β-D-glucose.

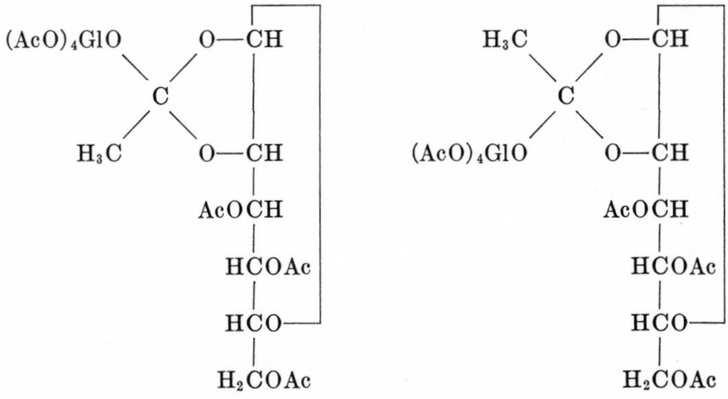

(I) (II)

17. W. N. Haworth, E. L. Hirst, and E. G. Teece, *J. Chem. Soc.* p. 1408 (1930); N. K. Richtmyer and C. S. Hudson, *J. Am. Chem. Soc.* **58**, 2534 (1936).

18. E. A. Talley, D. D. Reynolds, and W. L. Evans, *J. Am. Chem. Soc.* **65**, 575 (1943).

The first representative of the orthoester type was prepared by Fischer, Bergmann, and Rabe (*19*), who, by reacting tri-*O*-acetyl-α-L-rhamnosyl bromide with methyl alcohol in the presence of silver carbonate, obtained a compound with the same analysis as an acetylated methyl L-rhamnoside but which exhibited the unique property of having one acetyl group resistant to alkaline hydrolysis. A similar derivative of D-mannose was then reported by Dale (*20*).

An explanation for this behavior was arrived at simultaneously by Freudenberg and Braun and by Bott, Haworth, and Hirst (*21*). The evidence adduced by the latter workers for the structure of the D-mannose derivative (III) follows.

Substance with analysis corresponding to that for methyl tetra-*O*-acetyl-D-mannoside (III) $\xrightarrow{OH^-}$ Substance with analysis corresponding to that for methyl mono-*O*-acetyl-D-mannoside (IV) $\xrightarrow[NaOH]{(CH_3)_2SO_4}$ Tri-*O*-methyl derivative of (IV) $\xrightarrow{2\%\ HCl}$ Tri-*O*-methyl-D-mannose $\xrightarrow{OBr^-}$ 3,4,6-Tri-*O*-methyl-D-mannono-δ-lactone

The structure of the lactone was demonstrated by synthesis. Eliminating a three-atom ethylene oxide ring as improbable, the position of the alkali-resistant *O*-acetyl group is located by this evidence as carbon 2. The resistance of this group to alkaline hydrolysis is indicative of an unusual structure. An orthoester structure agrees with this resistance as well as with the ease with which the acetyl and methyl groups are hydrolyzed by acids. The ordinary alkyl orthoacetates exhibit similar properties.

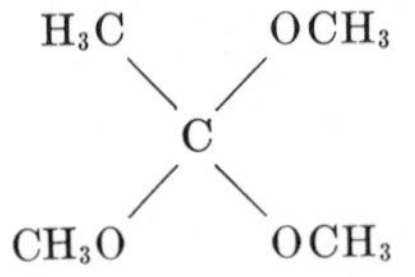
H₃C
OCH₃
C
CH₃O
OCH₃
Methyl orthoacetate

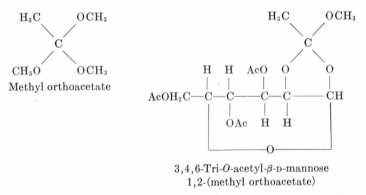

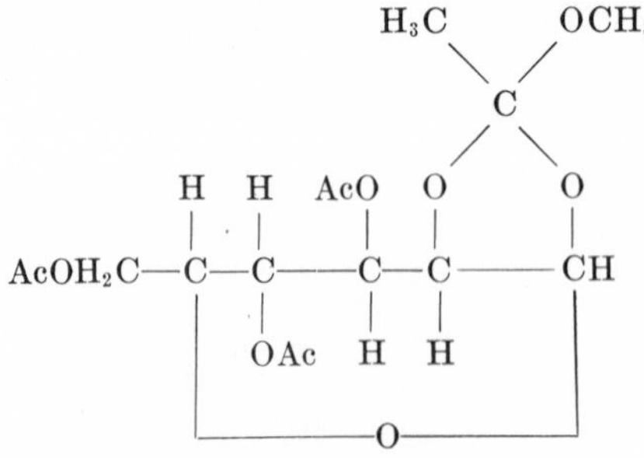
H₃C
OCH₃
C
H H AcO O O
AcOH₂C—C—C—C—C—CH
OAc H H
O
3,4,6-Tri-*O*-acetyl-β-D-mannose 1,2-(methyl orthoacetate)

---

19. E. Fischer, M. Bergmann, and A. Rabe, *Ber.* **53,** 2362 (1920).

20. J. K. Dale, *J. Am. Chem. Soc.* **46,** 1046 (1924).

21. K. Freudenberg and E. Braun, *Naturwissenschaften* **18,** 393 (1930); H. G. Bott, W. N. Haworth, and E. L. Hirst, *J. Chem. Soc.* p. 1395 (1930).

These compounds were called originally "gamma" glycosides (a term used for furanosides at the time) because of their ease of hydrolysis by acids. Sugars for which orthoacetate derivatives have been reported are: L-rhamnose, D-mannose, D-lyxose, 4-*O*-β-D-glucopyranosyl-D-mannose, D-talose, D-ribose, D-*glycero*-D-*gulo*-heptose, turanose, maltose, D-fructose, neolactose, D-*glycero*-L-*talo*-heptose (*15*), D-glucose (*22*), and an acyclic orthoacetate of D-galactose (*23*).

Since the Koenigs-Knorr reaction takes place with inversion, it would seem possible to prepare some of the more difficultly obtainable α-D-glycosides by starting with the *O*-acetyl-β-D-glycopyranosyl halides rather than with the common α-D-anomers. The notable instances in which this procedure has succeeded was accomplished (*24*) with 3,4,6-tri-*O*-acetyl-2-*O*-trichloroacetyl-β-D-glucopyranosyl chloride and 3,4,6-tri-*O*-acetyl-β-D-glucopyranosyl chloride. Apparently neither the *O*-trichloroacetyl group nor the hydroxyl group on carbon 2 (*15*, *15a*, *16*, *25*) can participate in a substitution reaction which allows simple replacement to occur without the formation of orthoesters. The instability of ordinary *O*-acetyl-β-D-glycopyranosyl halides limits its application. When the α-D-glycopyranoside is not obtained by this procedure, it is probable that interconversion of the isomeric halides took place more rapidly than the replacement reaction (see *O*-Acetyl-D-glycopyranosyl Halides, Chapter III).

Many improvements in the original method, in special instances, are particularly valuable (*26*). The use of "Drierite" (anhydrous calcium sulfate) is often beneficial. The presence of iodine may improve the yields. The *O*-acetylglycosyl bromides react at a lower temperature than the corresponding chlorides and are to be preferred for most reactions; the longer-chain aliphatic alcohols do not react with the chlorides under the usual conditions. If the aglycons are valuable substances, the use of an excess of the glycosyl halide is advisable (*27*). The *O*-benzoylglycosyl bromides often may be used advantageously in place of the acetyl analogs (*28*).

As mentioned above, Michael in his original synthesis of the aromatic glycosides utilized the reaction between tetra-*O*-acetyl-D-glucopyranosyl chloride and the potassium salts of phenols. The utility of the method has

22. R. U. Lemieux and C. Brice, *Can. J. Chem.* **33,** 109 (1955).

23. M. L. Wolfrom and D. I. Weisblat, *J. Am. Chem. Soc.* **66,** 805 (1944).

24. W. J. Hickinbottom, *J. Chem. Soc.* p. 1676 (1929); W. F. Goebel, F. H. Babers, and O. T. Avery, *J. Exptl. Med.* **55,** 761 (1932).

25. R. U. Lemieux, C. Brice, and G. Huber, *Can. J. Chem.* **33,** 134 (1955).

26. D. D. Reynolds and W. L. Evans, *J. Am. Chem. Soc.* **60,** 2559 (1938); B. Helferich and J. Goerdeler, *Ber.* **73,** 532 (1940); C. M. McCloskey, R. Pyle, and G. H. Coleman, *J. Am. Chem. Soc.* **66,** 349 (1944).

27. A. Robertson and R. B. Waters, *J. Chem. Soc.* p. 2730 (1930).

28. J. W. H. Oldham, *J. Am. Chem. Soc.* **56,** 1360 (1934); H. G. Fletcher, Jr., R. K. Ness, and C. S. Hudson, *J. Am. Chem. Soc.* **73,** 3698 (1951).

been greatly increased by using the more reactive tetra-*O*-acetyl-D-glucopyranosyl bromide and by carrying out the reaction in an alkaline aqueous-acetone solution of the phenol (*29*). This method is a convenient one for the preparation of phenyl glycosides and takes place with inversion of the anomeric carbon atom. Under the conditions of the modified procedure, the acetyl groups are not saponified, and the acetylated glycosides are obtained.

When weakly acidic catalysts are used, orthoester formation stops, and simple replacement occurs with retention of configuration in 1,2-*trans* and, with inversion, in a 1,2-*cis* situation (*28*, *30*). When still stronger acid catalysts are used, anomerizing equilibria prevail in which the major product is the most structurally stable anomer (see Transglycosidation (*31*), below). The identity of the more stable halogen anomer is determined by the Hassel-Ottar effect (*32*), and is the α-anomer in the *O*-acetyl-D-aldohexopyranose series, while in the *O*-acetyl-aldopentopyranose series, the β-anomers of D-ribose and L-arabinose and the α-anomers of D-xylose and D-lyxose are the stable forms (p. 152).

Zemplén and Csürös (*33*) have been able to prepare some of the α-D-glycosides by the use of the more acid catalysts mercuric acetate or ferric chloride, in place of silver carbonate, and by fixing the ratio of D-glucosyl halide to the catalyst.

The acetoxy group on the first carbon of the acetylated aldoses is more labile than the other acetoxy groups and, as previously discussed (p. 150), is easily replaced by a halogen atom to form the *O*-acetylglycosyl halides. It is also replaceable, as discovered by Helferich and Schmitz-Hillebrecht

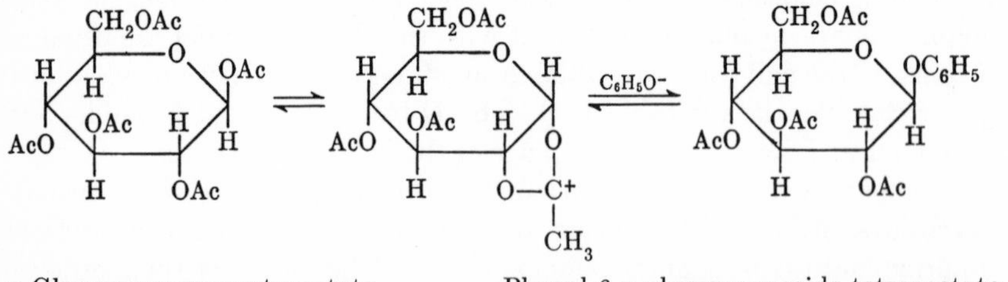
CH2OAc
H
OAc
AcO
H
OAc
O
CH3
C6H5O−
OC6H5

β-D-Glucopyranose pentaacetate   Phenyl β-D-glucopyranoside tetraacetate

29. C. Mannich, *Ann.* **394,** 223 (1912); E. Fischer and E. F. Armstrong, *Ber.* **34,** 2885 (1901); **35,** 833 (1902); J. H. Fisher, W. L. Hawkins, and H. Hibbert, *J. Am. Chem. Soc.* **62,** 1412 (1940).

30. R. K. Ness, H. G. Fletcher, Jr., and C. S. Hudson, *J. Am. Chem. Soc.* **73,** 959 (1951); H. G. Fletcher, Jr., and R. K. Ness, *ibid.* **76,** 760 (1954).

31. M. Doudoroff, H. A. Barker, and W. Z. Hassid, *J. Biol. Chem.* **168,** 725 (1947).

32. O. Hassel and B. Ottar, *Acta Chem. Scand.* **1,** 929 (1947); see Chapter III of this volume.

33. G. Zemplén and Z. Csürös, *Ber.* **64,** 993 (1931); G. Zemplén, *Fortschr. Chem. org. Naturstoffe* **1,** 1 (1938); *Ber.* **74A,** 75 (1941).

(*34*), by a phenoxy group when the acetylated sugar is heated with a phenol in the presence of an acid catalyst (zinc chloride or *p*-toluenesulfonic acid). The weak *p*-toluenesulfonic acid catalyst and a short heating time favors replacement with retention of configuration, but, unless optimal conditions are found, considerable anomerization occurs and both isomers are produced. The stronger aprotic acid zinc chloride, and a longer heating time favor anomerization (see Transglycosidation, below) and the production of the stable isomer. The yields may be improved by removing the acetic acid by vacuum distillation during the reaction (*35*). The phenyl tetra-*O*-acetyl-α-D-glucopyranoside is the main product when equilibrium is established in the presence of zinc chloride and phenol. It has been demonstrated that the utilization of quinoline at 100°C. instead of silver carbonate favors the formation of the phenyl α-D-glycosides (*36*).

While the above methods have been cited for the preparation of pyranosides, it is apparent that they might also serve for the synthesis of other ring structures should the reactants have nonpyranoid rings preformed in them. Thus, tetra-*O*-acetyl-α-D-galactofuranosyl chloride and tetra-*O*-acetyl-α-D-galactoseptanosyl chloride have been utilized in the synthesis of ethyl β-D-galactofuranoside (*37*) and methyl β-D-galactoseptanoside (*8*), respectively.

c. *From Dithioacetals*

Through variation of the conditions employed for the hydrolysis, in the presence of mercuric compounds, of the thioalkyl groups from aldose or ketose dithioacetals (mercaptals), pyranosides, furanosides, 1-thioglycosides, or acetals may be obtained (*6*, *38–40*). Several natural 1-thioglyco-

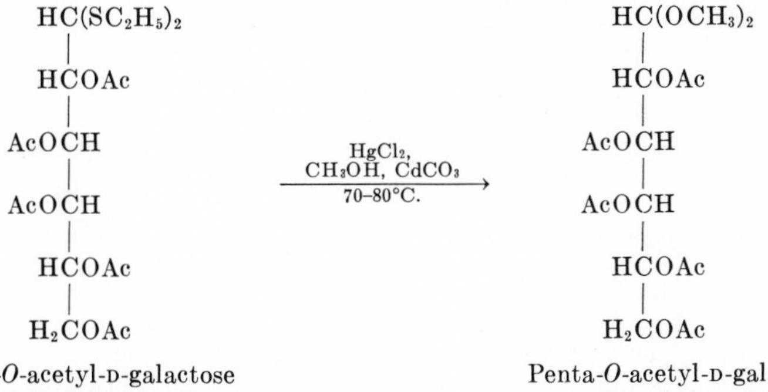

HC(SC2H5)2
HCOAc
AcOCH
AcOCH
HCOAc
H2COAc
HgCl2,
CH3OH, CdCO3
70–80°C.
HC(OCH3)2
HCOAc
AcOCH
AcOCH
HCOAc
H2COAc

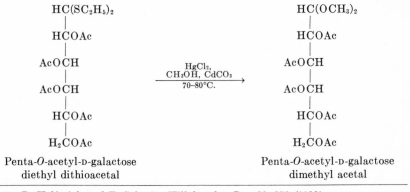

Penta-*O*-acetyl-D-galactose diethyl dithioacetal — Penta-*O*-acetyl-D-galactose dimethyl acetal

34. B. Helferich and E. Schmitz-Hillebrecht, *Ber.* **66**, 378 (1933).
35. K. Sisido, *J. Soc. Chem. Ind. Japan* **39**, 217B (1936).
36. E. Fischer and L. von Mechel, *Ber.* **49**, 2813 (1916).
37. H. H. Schlubach and K. Meisenheimer, *Ber.* **67**, 429 (1934).
38. W. Schneider and J. Sepp, *Ber.* **49**, 2054 (1916); W. Schneider, J. Sepp, and O. Stiehler, *ibid.* **51**, 220 (1918).

sides are known (Chapter X). Mixed monothioacetals have been synthesized (*41*); they are probable intermediates in these reactions (*42, 43*). The products obtainable vary with the sugar structure and the reaction conditions. The method is particularly suitable for obtaining furanosides which may be formed, especially in the presence of mercuric oxide (*39*). In aqueous

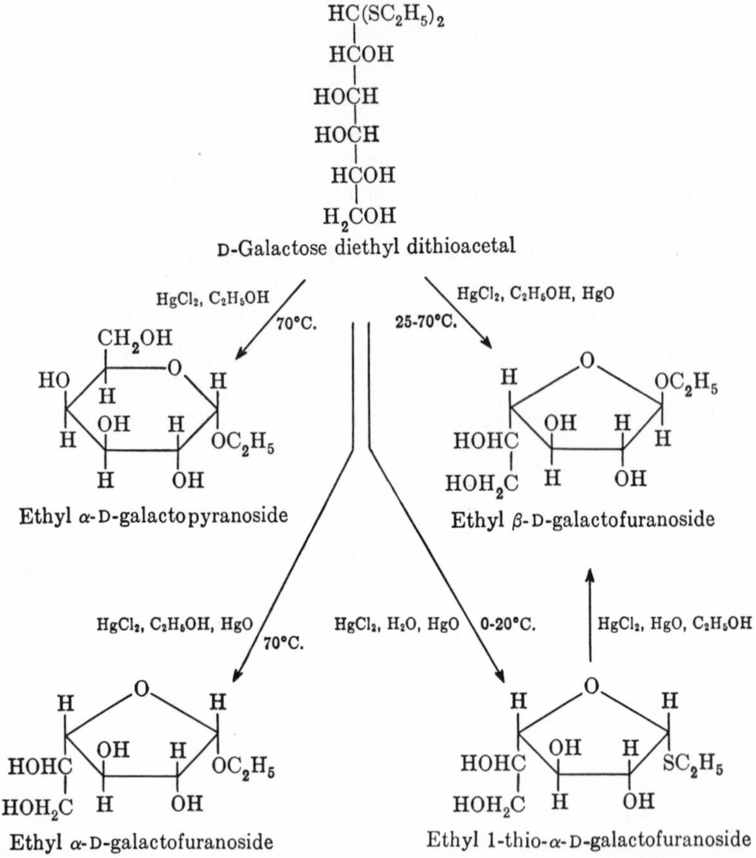
D-Galactose diethyl dithioacetal
HgCl₂, C₂H₅OH 70°C.
HgCl₂, C₂H₅OH, HgO 25-70°C.
Ethyl α-D-galactopyranoside
Ethyl β-D-galactofuranoside
HgCl₂, C₂H₅OH, HgO 70°C.
HgCl₂, H₂O, HgO 0-20°C.
HgCl₂, HgO, C₂H₅OH
Ethyl α-D-galactofuranoside
Ethyl 1-thio-α-D-galactofuranoside

39. E. Pacsu, *Ber.* **58,** 509 (1925); E. Pacsu and N. Ticharich, *ibid.* **62,** 3008 (1929); J. W. Green and E. Pacsu, *J. Am. Chem. Soc.* **59,** 1205, 2569 (1937); **60,** 2056, 2288 (1938); E. Pacsu and E. J. Wilson, Jr., *ibid.* **61,** 1450, 1930 (1939).

40. M. L. Wolfrom, L. J. Tanghe, R. W. George, and S. W. Waisbrot, *J. Am. Chem. Soc.* **60,** 132 (1938); M. L. Wolfrom and S. W. Waisbrot, *ibid.* **60,** 854 (1938); M. L. Wolfrom, S. W. Waisbrot, D. I. Weisblat, and A. Thompson, *ibid.* **66,** 2063 (1944).

41. M. L. Wolfrom and D. I. Weisblat. *J. Am. Chem. Soc.* **62,** 878 (1940); M. L. Wolfrom, D. I. Weisblat, and A. R. Hanze, *ibid.* **62,** 3246 (1940).

42. E. Pacsu, *J. Am. Chem. Soc.* **61,** 1671 (1939).

43. M. L. Wolfrom, D. I. Weisblat, and A. R. Hanze, *J. Am. Chem. Soc.* **66,** 2065 (1944).

solution, the removal of a single thioalkyl group can produce 1-thioglycosides. The acetals are formed when the hydroxyl groups are acetylated or otherwise blocked; in the case of D-fructose, the acetal is obtained in the absence of any blocking groups (*42*). The accompanying diagram illustrates the conditions employed for obtaining some of the possible products from D-galactose diethyl dithioacetal. The ethyl 1-thio-α-D-galactofuranoside was not isolated, but the corresponding D-glucose derivative was made by the procedure shown. In some cases the dibenzyl and not the diethyl dithioacetal was actually employed.

Ethanethiolysis (mercaptolysis) of methyl α- or β-D-mannopyranoside with concentrated hydrochloric acid and ethanethiol for eighteen hours, at room temperature, yields ethyl 1-thio-β-D-mannopyranoside (I), a small amount of the α-D-isomer, and none of the dithioacetal (*44*). Better results were obtained with free D-mannose, using the same reaction conditions. It

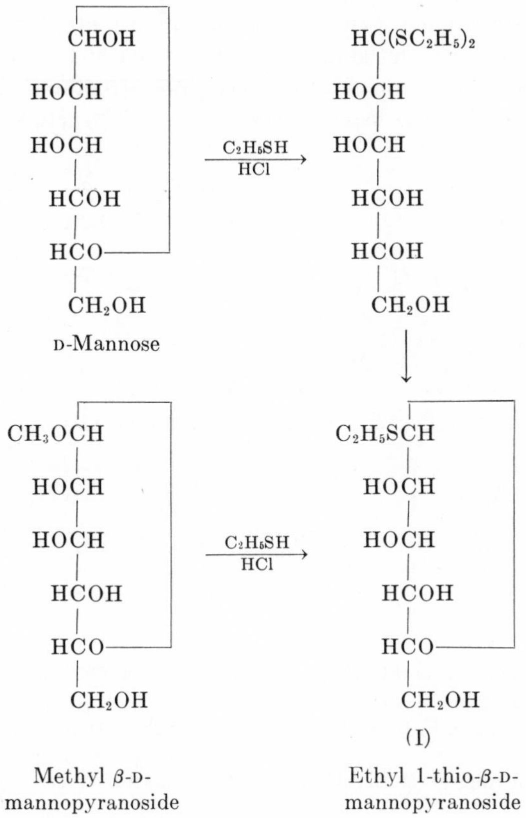
CHOH
HOCH
HOCH
HCOH
HCO
CH_2OH
D-Mannose
C_2H_5SH
HCl
$HC(SC_2H_5)_2$
HOCH
HOCH
HCOH
HCOH
CH_2OH
CH_3OCH
HOCH
HOCH
HCOH
HCO
CH_2OH
C_2H_5SH
HCl
C_2H_5SCH
HOCH
HOCH
HCOH
HCO
CH_2OH
(I)
Methyl β-D-mannopyranoside
Ethyl 1-thio-β-D-mannopyranoside

44. J. Fried and D. E. Walz, *J. Am. Chem. Soc.* **71,** 140 (1949).

is known that these conditions produce D-mannose diethyl dithioacetal in five minutes (*45*). It is therefore obvious that the dithioacetal is an intermediate in the reaction.

Similar prolonged ethanethiolysis of D-mannopyranosylstreptomycin (*46*) produced ethyl 1-thio-α- and -β-D-mannopyranosides, isolated as acetates. Likewise, streptomycin was cleaved with ethanethiol and hydrochloric acid (*47*) to produce ethyl 1-thiostreptobiosaminide diethyl dithioacetal hydrochloride. This type of cleavage is useful in structure determination since the carbonyls are protected with thioacetal groups as they are released (*48*). It was by means of this reaction that the nature of the acid-sensitive streptose portion of streptomycin was elucidated. (See Chapter X.)

d. Direct Alkylation

The glycosidic hydroxyl undergoes preferential alkylation when the sugar is alkylated with one equivalent of dimethyl sulfate and alkali (*49, 49a*). The procedure is particularly valuable for obtaining methyl glycosides of the D-mannose type for which the Koenigs-Knorr reaction fails because of orthoester formation. Alkylation of tetra-*O*-acetyl-β-D-fructopyranose with silver oxide and methyl iodide leads to the methyl β-D-fructopyranoside tetraacetate (*50*).

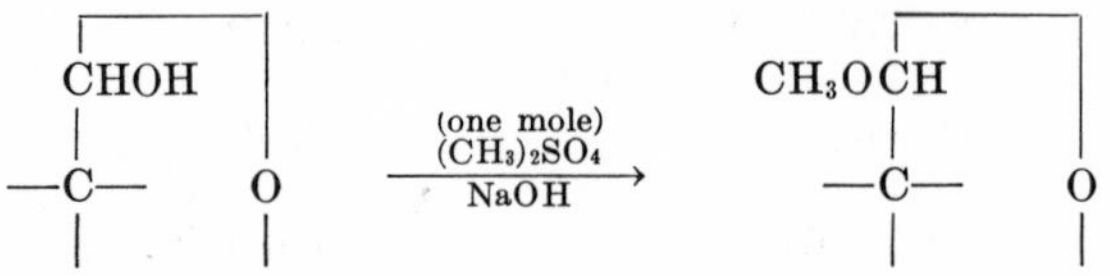
CHOH
(one mole)
(CH3)2SO4
NaOH
CH3OCH
—C—
O

e. From Glycals

Alcohols in the presence of perbenzoic acid add to the double bond of glycals to give glycosides of two sugars (see under Glycals) since two new

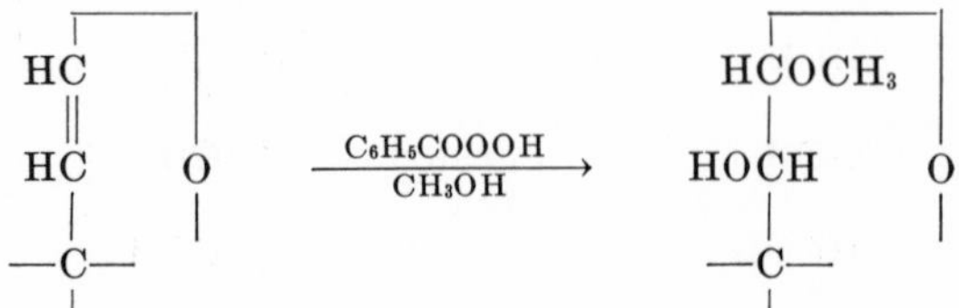
HC
HC
O
—C—
C6H5COOOH
CH3OH
HCOCH3
HOCH

45. P. A. Levene and G. M. Meyer, *J. Biol. Chem.* **74,** 695 (1927).

46. H. E. Stavely and J. Fried, *J. Am. Chem. Soc.* **71,** 135 (1949).

47. F. A. Kuehl, Jr., E. H. Flynn, N. G. Brink, and K. Folkers, *J. Am. Chem. Soc.* **68,** 2096 (1946).

48. M. L. Wolfrom, D. R. Myers, and E. N. Lassettre, *J. Am. Chem. Soc.* **61,** 2172 (1939).

49. L. Maquenne, *Bull. soc. chim. France* [3]**33,** 469 (1905).

49a. H. S. Isbell and H. L. Frush, *J. Research Natl. Bur. Standards* **24,** 125 (1940).

asymmetric carbons are produced (1 and 2). For the addition of methyl alcohol to D-glucal, the principal product is the methyl α-D-mannopyranoside (*51*).

f. Glycofuranosides and Glycofuranoses from Carbonates

Haworth, Porter, and Waine (*52*) utilized the stability of the carbonates to acids and instability to bases (see p. 159) for the preparation of crystalline furanosides and furanoses as illustrated below.

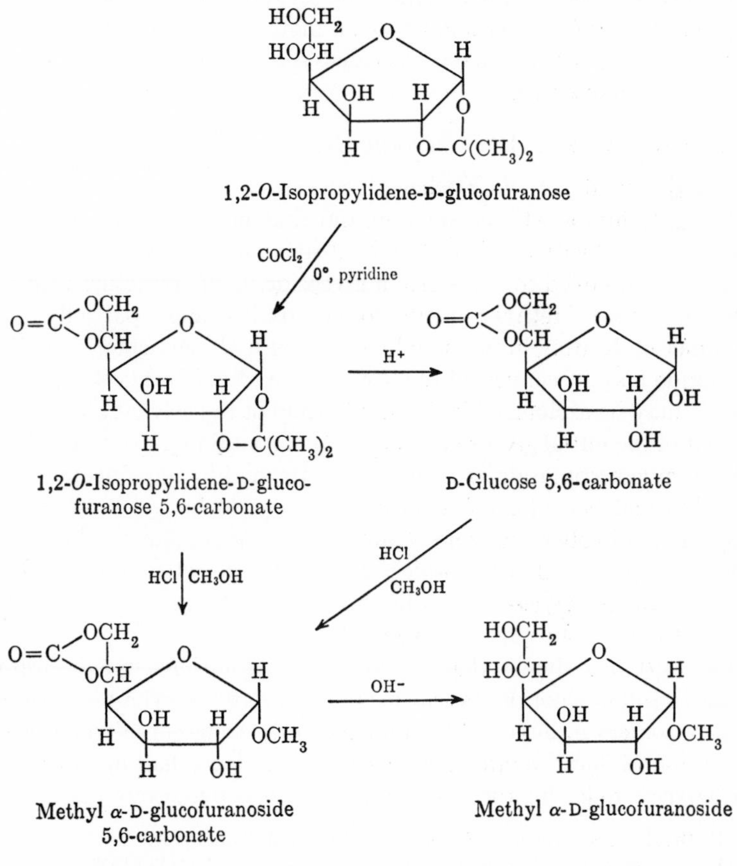
1,2-O-Isopropylidene-D-glucofuranose
COCl₂
0°, pyridine
1,2-O-Isopropylidene-D-glucofuranose 5,6-carbonate
H⁺
D-Glucose 5,6-carbonate
HCl
CH₃OH
HCl
CH₃OH
OH⁻
Methyl α-D-glucofuranoside 5,6-carbonate
Methyl α-D-glucofuranoside

g. Enzymic Synthesis

In the Fischer method for the synthesis of glycosides, an alcohol and a sugar are condensed by the use of an acid as the catalyst. As has been shown

50. C. S. Hudson and D. H. Brauns, *J. Am. Chem. Soc.* **38,** 1216 (1916).
51. M. Bergmann and H. Schotte, *Ber.* **54,** 1564 (1921).
52. W. N. Haworth, C. R. Porter, and A. C. Waine, *J. Chem. Soc.* p. 2254 (1932).

in the work of Bourquelot and associates, enzymes may be utilized in place of the acid to catalyze the formation of glycosides. Recently much excellent work has been done on the synthesis of oligo- and poly-saccharides by means of enzymic action. For further discussion see Chapters IX, X, and XII.

h. From 1,2-Anhydrides

The reaction of 1,2-anhydro sugars with alcohols promises to be a useful method for the preparation of glycosides. Brigl (*53*) prepared methyl β-D-glucopyranoside 3,4,6-triacetate by evaporating a solution of 1,2-anhydro-3,4,6-tri-*O*-acetyl-D-glucose in methanol to dryness. Recently, Lemieux and Huber (*54*) have extended the method to the synthesis of sucrose (see Chapter IX).

i. Transglycosidation (31) by Chemical Methods

In the discussion of the Fischer glycosidation reaction (p. 191), it was noted that equilibria between anomers and ring forms arose when a reducing sugar was treated with an alcohol under acid catalysis. This type of reaction can then be employed to transform a glycoside of one structure into one of another structure. Methyl β-D-galactopyranoside changes partially into the α-D-anomer on heating in methanol containing hydrogen chloride (*55*), and a furanoside may be converted to a pyranoside (*39*). The alkyl group of the glycoside may be exchanged if the alkyl group of the solvent alcohol differs from that of the initial glycoside. In methanol containing hydrogen chloride, ethyl α-D-glucopyranoside is transformed to methyl α-D-glucopyranoside; the methyl and benzyl α-D-fructofuranosides yield benzyl β-D-fructopyranoside when dissolved in benzyl alcohol under similar conditions (*56*). Acetylated methyl aldopyranosides have been converted to the analogous acetylated phenyl glycosides by heating with a phenol and zinc chloride (*57*) or with moist phosphorus oxychloride (*58*).

Pacsu (*59*) has shown that in chloroform solution (free of water or ethanol) titanium chloride transforms the acetylated alkyl β-D-glycosides to their α-D-isomers in high yield. Lindberg (*60*), using boron trifluoride as a catalyst, found that the rate of anomerization is dependent upon the nature of the aglycon, following the order *t*-butyl > isopropyl > ethyl > methyl >

53. P. Brigl, *Hoppe Seyler's Z. physiol. Chem.* **122,** 245 (1922).
54. R. U. Lemieux and G. Huber, *J. Am. Chem. Soc.* **75,** 4118 (1953).
55. C. L. Jungius, *Z. physik. Chem.* **52,** 97 (1905).
56. C. B. Purves and C. S. Hudson, *J. Am. Chem. Soc.* **59,** 1170 (1937).
57. E. M. Montgomery, N. K. Richtmyer, and C. S. Hudson, *J. Am. Chem. Soc.* **64,** 690 (1942).
58. T. H. Bembry and G. Powell, *J. Am. Chem. Soc.* **64,** 2419 (1942).
59. E. Pacsu, *J. Am. Chem. Soc.* **52,** 2563, 2568, 2571 (1930).
60. B. Lindberg, *Acta Chem. Scand.* **2,** 426, 534 (1948).

allyl, benzyl. Although Pacsu had shown that the glycosidic linkage of a (1 → 4)-linked disaccharide was resistant to these conditions, Lindberg (*61*) anomerized the disaccharide linkage of the β-D-(1 → 6)-linked gentiobiose and converted it to isomaltose, α-D-(1 → 6). Lindberg found that in the anomerization of acetylated alkyl aldopyranosides with strong acid catalysts in an acetylating medium, some *aldehydo*-1,1-diacetate of the acetylated sugar structure (I) used was always formed as a by-product.

When one aglycon is exchanged for another, the reaction is obviously intermolecular and can probably be explained by the postulations already discussed (see Anomeric Replacement). However, when anomerization occurs, especially in an environment free of the aglycon obtained by the hydrolysis of the glycoside, the reaction is probably intramolecular and takes place without dissociation of the aglycon from the glycoside. In view of these considerations, Lindberg (*62*) suggests a reaction course for the anomerization of glycosides in strong acid which is supported by Painter (*14*) and is not in conflict with previous proposals.

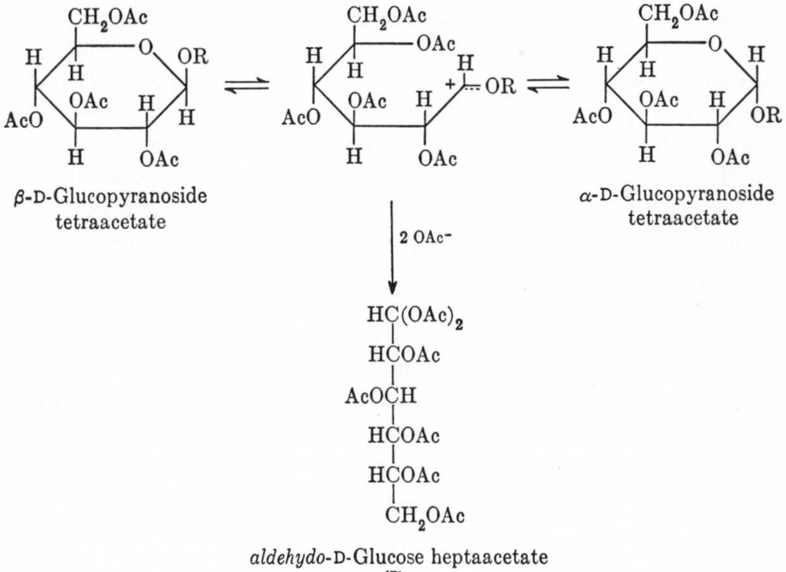
CH₂OAc
H
O
OR
H
OAc
H
AcO
H
H
OAc
β-D-Glucopyranoside tetraacetate
CH₂OAc
OAc
H
H
H
+
OR
OAc
H
AcO
H
OAc
CH₂OAc
O
H
H
H
OAc
H
AcO
OR
H
OAc
α-D-Glucopyranoside tetraacetate
2 OAc⁻
HC(OAc)₂
HCOAc
AcOCH
HCOAc
HCOAc
CH₂OAc

aldehydo-D-Glucose heptaacetate
(I)

B. Properties of Glycosides

The glycosides are water-soluble substances except when the hydrocarbon aglycon becomes large enough to dominate the physical behavior of the com-

61. B. Lindberg, *Acta Chem. Scand.* **3,** 1350, 1355 (1949).
62. B. Lindberg, *Acta Chem. Scand.* **3,** 1153 (1949).

pound. In the *n*-alkyl β-D-glucopyranoside series, the glucopyranosides become quite difficultly soluble in water when the aglycon has more than nine carbon atoms. The higher members of the *n*-alkyl series of β-D-glucosides are surface active and form liquid crystals at the melting point (*63*). The solubility of the surface-active materials in water is improved by treating the glycosides with alkylene oxides (as ethylene oxide) in the presence of catalysts such as sodium hydroxide or an amine (*64*). The increased solubility of glycosides as compared with the free aglycon has been utilized to enhance the effect of many pharmaceutical substances; the glycosides of 2-alkyl-1,4-naphthohydroquinones (antihemorrhagic agents) provide an example (*65*).

a. Sensitivity to Alkaline Hydrolysis

It is usually considered that the glycosidic linkage is stable to the action of alkalies and consequently that glycosides exhibit no reducing action on Fehling solution. However, some do reduce Fehling solution. The first alkali-sensitive glycoside reported is apparently the 2,4,6-tribromophenyl β-glycoside of Fischer and Strauss (*66*).

The alkali-sensitive glycosides may be classified (*67*) into three types: (1) glycosides of phenols, (2) glycosides of enols conjugated with a carbonyl group, and (3) glycosides of alcohols substituted in the "β"-position by a negative group. As a matter of fact, the first two classifications could be put under the third, which is therefore the significant structural detail (*68*).

The sensitivity of the phenyl glycosides to alkali has long been known, but Tanret (*69*) was the first to recognize that the degradation of phenyl β-D-glucopyranoside yields 1,6-anhydro-β-D-glucopyranose (see Glycosans, p. 221).

An early example of the alkaline degradation of an *enol* glycoside is that of theobromine β-D-glucopyranoside tetraacetate, discovered by Fischer and Helferich (*70*). The alkali lability of glycosides with enols of the type

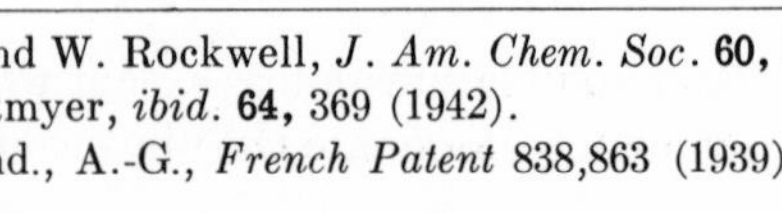
CH2OAc
O
H
H
OAc
H
AcO
H
H
OAc
O–C=C–C–CH3
H H
O

(I)

63. C. R. Noller and W. Rockwell, *J. Am. Chem. Soc.* **60,** 2076 (1938); W. W. Pigman and N. K. Richtmyer, *ibid.* **64,** 369 (1942).

64. I. G. Farbenind., A.-G., *French Patent* 838,863 (1939); *Chem. Abstr.* **33,** 6996 (1939).

65. B. Riegel and P. G. Smith, *U. S. Patent* 2,336,890 (1943); *Chem. Abstr.* **38,** 3420 (1944).

shown in (I), may be associated with the activating conjugated carbonyl structure of the aglycon (*71*).

Kuhn and Löw (*72*) described a third type of alkali-sensitive glycoside, picrocrocin (II), which was observed to decompose in aqueous alkali to D-glucose and the aglycon safranal (III). (See Chapter X.)

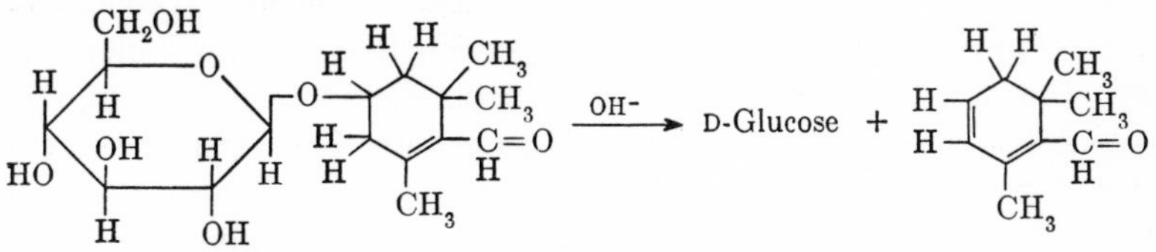
OH-
D-Glucose +

(II) Picrocrocin

(III) Safranal

Other alkali-sensitive glycosides of alcohols substituted in the "β"-position by a negative group and having structures similar to picrocrocin may be allocated to this third class.

$$Gl(OAc)_4 \xrightarrow{\beta-D} O—CH_2—CH_2—\overset{O}{\overset{\|}{C}}—CH_3$$

$$Gl(OAc)_4 \xrightarrow{\beta-D} O—CH_2—CH_2—SO_2—OC_2H_5$$

$$Gl(OAc)_4 \xrightarrow{\beta-D} O—CH_2—CH_2—NO_2$$

[Gl(OAc)$_4$ = Tetra-*O*-acetyl-D-glucopyranosyl—]

b. Hydrogenolysis of Aralkyl and Aromatic Glycosides

Catalytic hydrogenolysis in the sugar series was first applied to the benzyl ethers by Freudenberg and associates (*73*), who found that these substances were cleaved by hydrogenolysis with sodium amalgam and with hydrogen and platinum metals in glacial acetic acid solution. Kariyone and Kondo (*74*) using colloidal platinum and hydrogen, cleaved D-glucose from the aryl glycosides aucubin and arbutin, but not from salicin. The benzyl

66. E. Fischer and H. Strauss, *Ber.* **45,** 2467 (1912).

67. C. E. Ballou, *Advances in Carbohydrate Chem.* **9,** 59 (1954).

68. See also W. M. Corbett and J. Kenner, *J. Chem. Soc.* p. 2245 (1953); *ibid.* p. 3274 (1954).

69. C. Tanret, *Compt. rend.* **119,** 158 (1894).

70. E. Fischer and B. Helferich, *Ber.* **47,** 210 (1914).

71. C. E. Ballou and K. P. Link, *J. Am. Chem. Soc.* **72,** 3147 (1950).

72. R. Kuhn and I. Löw, *Ber.* **74,** 219 (1941).

73. K. Freudenberg, W. Dürr, H. von Hochstetter, W. Jacobi, H. vom Hove, A. Noë, and E. Gärtner, *Ber.* **61,** 1735 (1928).

74. T. Kariyone and K. Kondo, *J. Pharm. Soc. Japan* **48,** 679, 684 (1928); *Chem. Abstr.* **23,** 393 (1929).

β-D-glycosides are cleaved by hydrogen with the aid of palladium catalysts (in the presence of hydrogen ions at room temperature and atmospheric pressure) to toluene and the sugar (*75*). The use of this catalyst provides a method for the conversion of aromatic to cyclohexyl glucosides (*75*). By the use of the palladium catalyst the following transformations are carried out: phenyl to cyclohexyl β-D-glucopyranoside, and phenylpropyl to 3-cyclohexylpropyl β-D-glucopyranoside (but salicin to *o*-cresyl β-D-glucopyranoside). Catalytic hydrogenation has also been employed for the preparation of gentiobiose from amygdalin (*76*). Because of the great reactivity of the ethylenic linkage, this linkage may be preferentially hydrogenated even when an aromatic ring is present (*77*). The benzyl β-D-glycosides are also split by hydrogen with the aid of a platinum catalyst. The hydrogenation of aromatic β-D-glycosides with platinum (*75*) follows two paths, either reductive cleavage of the glycosidic link or hydrogenation of the phenyl to cyclohexyl β-D-glycoside. When the latter occurs first the glycoside is not cleaved. Under optimal conditions, phenyl compounds have been cleaved to a maximum of 70%.

c. *Hydrolysis by Acids*

The rates of hydrolysis of many glycosides have been measured and provide excellent though incomplete data for investigations of the influence of structural and configurational changes on the stability of the glycosidic linkage. Such comparisons can only be made in a qualitative fashion since the activation energies differ somewhat for the various glycosides, and comparisons made at one temperature may not always agree with those at another temperature.

Effect of Variations in the Aglycon Structure. As a rule, the glycosides with aliphatic aglycon groups (methyl and mandelonitrile glucosides) are more resistant to acid hydrolysis than those with aromatic aglycon groups. Although there is a considerable difference in the activation energies for the various glycosides, this difference does not seem to be related entirely to the aromatic or aliphatic character of the aglycon group. The ease of hydrolysis of the D-glucopyranosides, of the same anomeric configuration, increases in the order ethyl, methyl, benzyl, phenyl (*78*). The β-D-anomer is in most cases more readily hydrolyzed than is the α-D-anomer. The reverse is true for: the phenyl group as aglycon, the methyl D-gulopyranosides, and the (1 → 4)- and (1 → 6)-linked disaccharides of D-glucose.

75. N. K. Richtmyer, *J. Am. Chem. Soc.* **56,** 1633 (1934).
76. M. Bergmann and W. Freudenberg, *Ber.* **62,** 2785 (1929).
77. N. K. Richtmyer and R. M. Hann, *J. Am. Chem. Soc.* **57,** 227 (1935).
78. L. J. Heidt and C. B. Purves, *J. Am. Chem. Soc.* **66,** 1385 (1944); K. Butler, S. Laland, W. G. Overend, and M. Stacey, *J. Chem. Soc.* p. 1433 (1950).

TABLE II

CONFORMATIONAL STABILITY AND RELATIVE RATES OF HYDROLYSIS OF THE METHYL GLYCOPYRANOSIDES[a]

Methyl glycopyranoside of:	k/k'[b]	Instability factors[c]	
		C1	1C
α-D-Xylose	4.5	1[d]	Δ2, 3, 4[d]
β-D-Xylose	9.0	A	A, 1, 2, 3, 4
α-D-Glucose	1.0	1	Δ2, 3, 4, 5
β-D-Glucose	1.9	A	A, 1, 2, 3, 4, 5
D-*glycero*-α-L-*gluco*-Heptose	0.76[e]	1	Δ2, 3, 4, 5
α-D-Lyxose	14.5	1, 2	3, 4
β-D-Lyxose	46.4	A, Δ2	A, 1, 3, 4
α-D-Rhamnose[e]	9.5[e]	1, 2	3, 4, 5
β-D-Rhamnose[e]	21.9[e]	A, Δ2	A, 1, 3, 4, 5
α-D-Mannose	2.4	1, 2	3, 4, 5
β-D-Mannose	5.7	A, Δ2	A, 1, 3, 4, 5
D-*glycero*-α-L-*manno*-Heptose	1.3[e]	1, 2	3, 4, 5
D-*glycero*-β-L-*manno*-Heptose	3.0[e]	A, Δ2	A, 1, 3, 4, 5
α-D-Gulose	58.1	1, 3, 4	Δ2, 5
β-D-Gulose	19.0	A, 3, 4	A, 1, 2, 5
D-*glycero*-α-D-*gulo*-Heptose	20.9	1, 3, 4	Δ2, 5
D-*glycero*-β-D-*gulo*-Heptose	6.7	A, 3, 4	A, 1, 2, 5
α-D-Arabinose[e]	13.1	A, 1, 2, 3	A, 4
β-D-Arabinose[e]	9.0	Δ2, 3	1, 4
α-D-Galactose	5.2	1, 4	Δ2, 3, 5
β-D-Galactose	9.3	A, 4	A, 1, 2, 3, 5

[a] Material in this table was calculated from data in publications of Isbell and Frush (*49a*) and Riiber and Sørensen (*79*) and from a theoretical consideration of conformational structures [see Reeves (*82*); Shafizadeh and Thompson, *J. Org. Chem.* **21,** 1059 (1956).]

[b] Ratio of the rate constant for the hydrolysis of the methyl glycopyranoside to that of methyl α-D-glucopyranoside in 0.5 *N* hydrochloric acid at 75°C.

[c] A, refers to the Hassel-Ottar (*32*) rule regarding anomeric configurations, Δ2 refers to the exalted influence of an axial group on carbon 2 in the particular orientation illustrated in Fig. 3; C1 and 1C refer to the two chair forms of the pyranose ring, Fig. 2.

[d] The arabic numerals refer to those carbon positions on the pyranose ring possessing an instability factor.

[e] Values found on enantiomorph or calculated indirectly because of incomplete data.

Structure of the Pyranose Ring in Relation to Hydrolysis of the Glycosides. The relative rates of hydrolysis of a number of methyl glycosides have been determined (*49a, 79*), and are recorded in Table II. It has been shown by

79. C. N. Riiber and N. A. Sørensen, *Kgl. Norske Videnskab. Selskabs Skrifter* **No. 1** (1938). See also first edition of this book.

Paul (*80*) that 2-*O*-methyl tetrahydropyran (methyl 2,3,4-trideoxyaldo-pentopyranoside) is rapidly hydrolyzed by dilute acid at room temperature. The rates of hydrolysis of the ethyl 2,3-dideoxy-, ethyl 2-deoxy-, and ethyl α-D-glucopyranoside decrease in the order named (*81*). It is, therefore, obvious that the substitution of hydroxyl groups in the tetrahydropyran structure greatly decreases the ease of hydrolysis of the glycosidic linkage. A considerable variation in the behavior of the sugars within the pyranose series indicates that the hydroxyl or other groups exert a somewhat less than maximal stabilizing influence in some positions.

Reducing sugars, their glycosides, and other derivatives, are capable of a type of transient isomerism which involves changes in the ring shape (conformation) and vastly alters the relative position of various groups within the same molecule. A study of this type of isomerism is of considerable value in rationalizing the varying sensitivity of the glycopyranosides toward acid hydrolysis. It is considered that the pyranose ring of any individual sugar is theoretically capable of eight strainless ring conformations, six boat and two staggered or chair forms (Fig. 2). (See also Chapter I, p. 40.) The evidence indicates that one of the two chair forms will be favored and that the boat forms can for most purposes be neglected (*32*, *82*).

Half the substituents lie approximately in the plane of the ring and these positions are designated equatorial (*e*); the other half are perpendicular and are designated axial (*a*). Reeves (*82*) states that any axial substituent, other than hydrogen, on the pyranose ring introduces an element of instability into the ring conformation. An enhanced unstabilizing effect is noted when the oxygen atom on carbon 2 is axial and its C—O valence bisects the tetrahedral angle of the two C—O valences of carbon 1 as shown in Fig. 3. The rule of Hassel and Ottar (*32*) concerning *O*-acetyl-D-glycopyranosyl halides can be applied to the glycopyranosides. In the aldohexopyranosides, that anomer which can be represented in the two chair forms by

$$—OR_e\ ,\ —CH_2OH_a \rightleftharpoons —OR_a\ ,\ —CH_2OH_e$$

is the more stable; the less stable anomer can be represented by

$$—OR_a\ ,\ —CH_2OH_a \rightleftharpoons —OR_e\ ,\ —CH_2OH_e.$$

In the absence of the —CH_2OH group in the aldopentopyranosides, the same rule may be applied to the substituents on carbons 1 and 3. A conformational analysis of a number of methyl D-glycopyranosides and the

80. R. Paul, *Bull. soc. chim. France* [5] **1,** 971 (1934); *Compt. rend.* **197,** 1652 (1933).

81. W. G. Overend, M. Stacey, and J. Staněk, *J. Chem. Soc.* p. 2841 (1949); G. N. Richards, *Chemistry & Industry* p. 228 (1955); A. B. Foster and W. G. Overend, *ibid.* p. 566 (1955).

82. R. E. Reeves, *J. Am. Chem. Soc.* **72,** 1499 (1950); *Advances in Carbohydrate Chem.* **6,** 107 (1951); A. Scattergood and E. Pacsu, *J. Am. Chem. Soc.* **62,** 903 (1940).

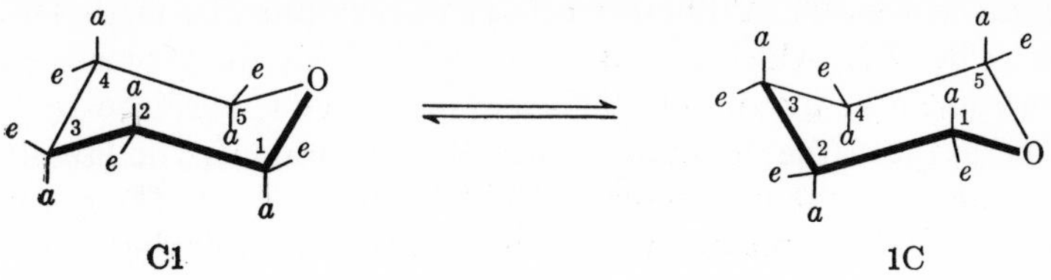
a
e
4
a
e
O
e
3
2
5
a
1
e
e
a
a
C1
a
a
e
e
e
5
e
3
4
a
1
2
a
O
e
e
a
1C

FIG. 2

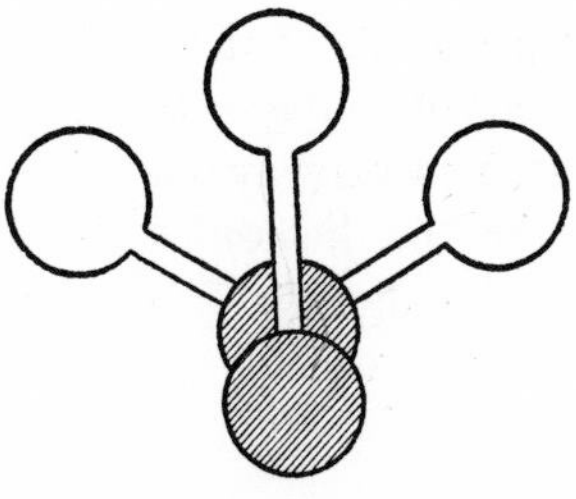

FIG. 3

instability factors to be found in the two chair forms discussed above are listed in Table II. Inspection of these data reveals that the rate of hydrolysis of the methyl D-glycopyranosides increases with the conformational instability of the most favored chair form.

Reeves (*82*) has been able to explain the rotational and conductometric behavior of a large number of glycopyranosides in cuprammonium solution by means of conformational considerations, and to obtain experimental evidence confirming the predicted favored conformational forms.

Methyl α-D-glucopyranoside, which has the most stable conformational structure of the hexopyranosides, is also the most slowly hydrolyzed, the resistance to hydrolysis in members of the series becoming less marked as more instability factors are introduced. The stabilizing effect of substitution on carbon 5 is illustrated by the increasing resistance to hydrolysis of the series of methyl glycosides of α-D-lyxose, α-L-rhamnose, α-D-mannose, and D-*glycero*-α-D-*manno*-heptose, having the α-D-mannopyranose structure in which the substituted groups on carbon 5 are: —H, —CH_3, —CH_2OH, and —CHOH—CH_2OH. In anomeric pairs, the more stable form, as predicted by the Hassel-Ottar rule concerning anomers, is usually the more difficult to hydrolyze. In some instances, as in the α- and β-D-gulopyranose and α- and β-L-arabinopyranose glycosidic structures, the anomer-directing effect may be reversed by a preponderance of opposing factors.

The aldofuranosides are hydrolyzed slightly faster than the aldoseptanosides (*8*) and from 50 to 200 times more rapidly than the corresponding aldopyranosides (*83*). A different behavior is exhibited by methyl α-D-fructofuranoside (*56*), which is hydrolyzed only about three times as fast as the corresponding pyranoside. This may possibly be explained by the fact that methyl α-D-fructopyranoside has the α-D-arabinopyranose structure with an added instability factor (—CH_2OH) on carbon 1. The rules of conformation are not applicable to the furanosides, since this ring is essentially planar.

C. Determination of Glycoside Structure

The determination of glycoside structure involves ascertainment of the ring size and the assignment of configuration to the anomeric carbon. There are no chemical methods presently available for the determination of the anomeric configuration of the ketosides. Structural establishment was effected for those glycosides derived from the methyl or simplest alkyl group. Correlations to other glycosides were then made through the *O*-acetylglycosyl halides (p. 194).

a. Determination of Ring Size by Methylation and Oxidation

The ring size of the glycosides was first determined by methylation and oxidation procedures. Methylation (p. 369) of either anomer of methyl D-glucopyranoside (I, IV) with subsequent hydrolytic scission of the glycosidic methyl group, led to the same crystalline tetra-*O*-methyl-D-glucose (III), and this on nitric acid oxidation yielded tri-*O*-methylxylaric acid (V), characterized as its diamide or bis(*N*-alkylamide). This type of oxidative proof of ring structure was first established with D-xylose by Hirst and Purves (*84*) and was later extended to D-glucose (*85*). Before this work it had been considered, by analogy with the lactones, that the more stable or "normal" ring form was the 1,4 or furanose. Similar treatment of the crystalline methyl α-D-glucofuranoside (VI) led to the identification of di-*O*-methyl-L-threaric acid (VIII) as the final oxidation product (*86*). The intermediate methylated lactones (II, VII) exhibited the hydrolytic behavior characteristic of δ- and γ-lactones, respectively. These established facts, along with others, have been incorporated in a general postulation to the effect that exo double bonds stabilize a 5-membered ring and destabilize a 6-membered ring, an oxygen atom being considered as essentially conformationally equivalent to a methylene group (*87*).

A similar type of oxidative degradation was employed by Micheel and

83. W. N. Haworth, *Ber.* **65A,** 43 (1932).
84. E. L. Hirst and C. B. Purves, *J. Chem. Soc.* p. 1352 (1923).
85. E. L. Hirst, *J. Chem. Soc.* p. 350 (1926).
86. W. N. Haworth, E. L. Hirst, and E. J. Miller, *J. Chem. Soc.* p. 2436 (1927).
87. H. C. Brown, J. H. Brewster, and H. Shechter, *J. Am. Chem. Soc.* **76,** 467 (1954).

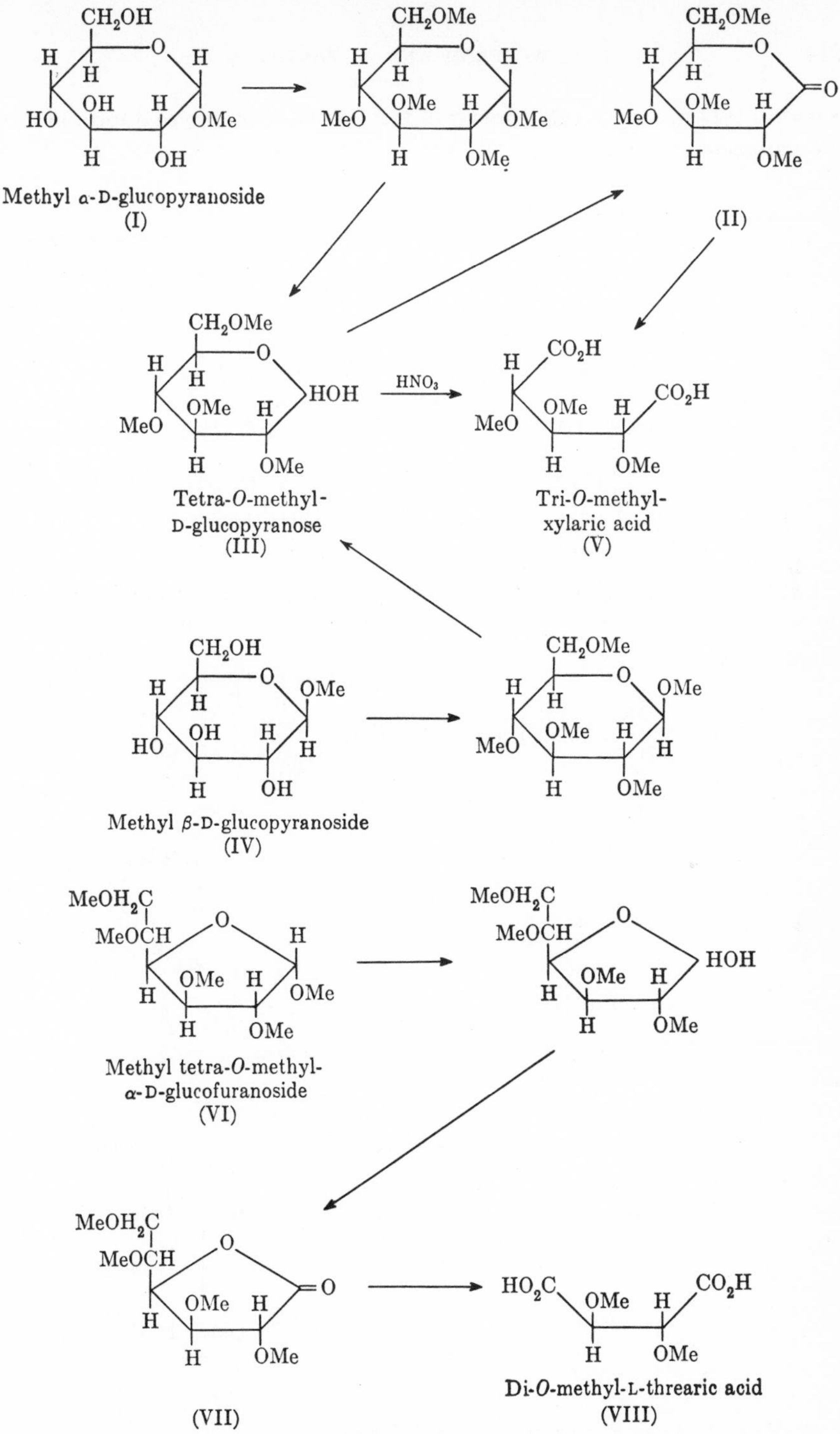
Methyl α-D-glucopyranoside
(I)
(II)
Tetra-O-methyl-
D-glucopyranose
(III)
HNO3
Tri-O-methyl-
xylaric acid
(V)
Methyl β-D-glucopyranoside
(IV)
Methyl tetra-O-methyl-
α-D-glucofuranoside
(VI)
(VII)
Di-O-methyl-L-threaric acid
(VIII)

Suckfüll (*88*) in their establishment of the 1,6 or septanose ring form in the β-D-galactose structure.

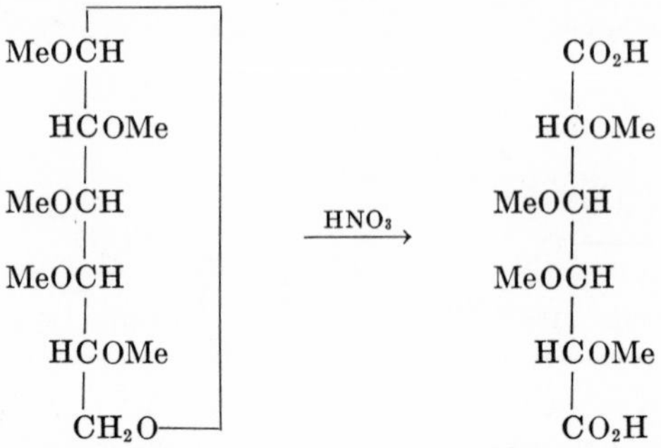
MeOCH
HCOMe
MeOCH
MeOCH
HCOMe
CH_2O
HNO_3
CO_2H
HCOMe
MeOCH
MeOCH
HCOMe
CO_2H

Methyl tetra-*O*-methyl-β-D-galactoseptanoside — Tetra-*O*-methyl-galactaric acid

Oxidative degradation of methyl ethers has been utilized in establishing the ring structures in pyranosides of D-fructose (*89*) and L-sorbose (*90*)

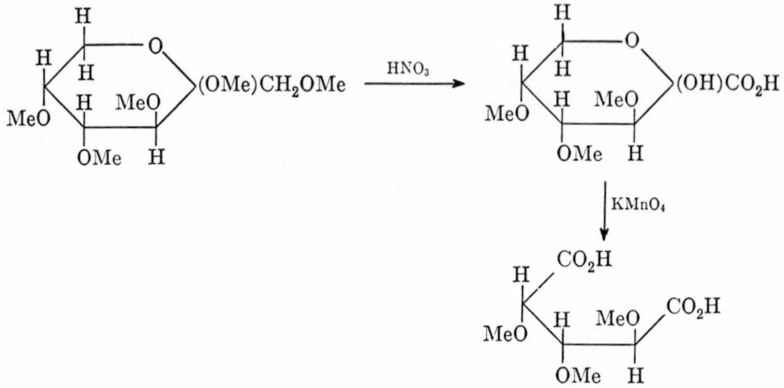
$(OMe)CH_2OMe$
HNO_3
$(OH)CO_2H$
$KMnO_4$
CO_2H
MeO
OMe

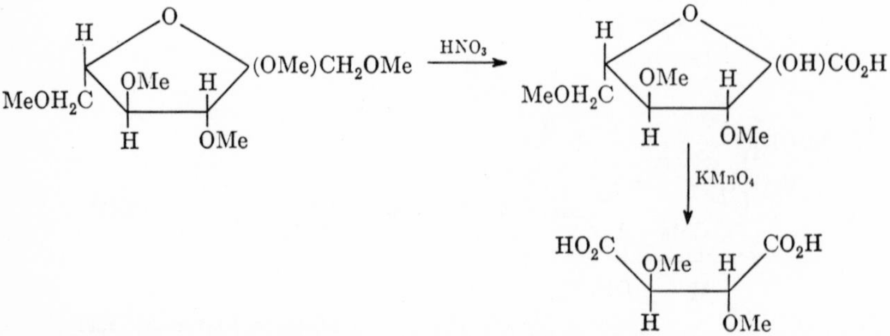
$MeOH_2C$
$(OMe)CH_2OMe$
HNO_3
$(OH)CO_2H$
$KMnO_4$
HO_2C
CO_2H
OMe

88. F. Micheel and F. Suckfüll, *Ann.* **507,** 138 (1933).
89. W. N. Haworth, E. L. Hirst, and A. Learner, *J. Chem. Soc.* p. 1040, 2432 (1927).

and in furanosides of the former (*91*); the ring form of an α-keto acid is an intermediate. (The reactions are shown on p. 214.)

b. Determination of Ring Size by Glycol Cleavage; Periodate Ion as an Oxidant

Glycol cleavage by oxidation with sodium periodate, lead tetraacetate, or sodium bismuthate, is a useful method for determination of the ring size of glycosides as well as for the assignment of anomeric configuration and position of substituents on the ring. (See Chapters VI and I.)

After the discovery by Malaprade (*92*) that polyhydroxy compounds were oxidized by periodate ion, Fleury and co-workers (*93*) pointed out that the reaction is selective for hydroxyl groups on adjacent carbon atoms and results in chain scission. Hudson and co-workers (*94*) developed periodate oxidation into an extremely convenient method for structural studies in carbohydrates (*95*). Because of the masking effect of the aglycon on the reducing carbon, the methyl glycosides are particularly suitable materials for this type of analysis. The method involves the determination of the molar ratios of oxidant consumed and of formic acid and formaldehyde produced. D-Mannitol, for example, consumes five moles of oxidant and produces four moles of formic acid and two moles of formaldehyde.

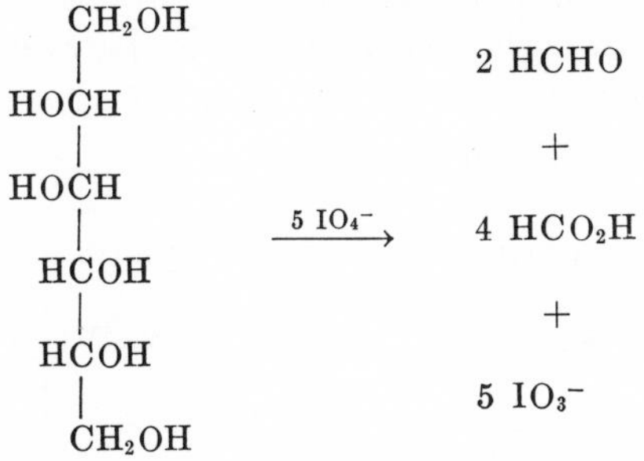

CH₂OH
HOCH
HOCH
HCOH
HCOH
CH₂OH
5 IO₄⁻
2 HCHO
+
4 HCO₂H
+
5 IO₃⁻

The periodate method affords a simple means for the determination of the ring structure of a glycoside. The number of moles of periodate consumed, of formic acid and formaldehyde produced, by the most common types of rings are: tetrofuranoside or pentofuranoside, one mole of periodate, no formic acid, no formaldehyde; pentopyranosides, two moles of periodate,

90. R. L. Whistler and R. M. Hixon, *J. Am. Chem. Soc.* **59**, 2047 (1937).

91. J. Avery, W. N. Haworth, and E. L. Hirst, *J. Chem. Soc.* p. 2308 (1927).

92. L. Malaprade, *Bull. soc. chim. France* [4] **39**, 325 (1926); [4] **43**, 683 (1928); *Compt. rend.* **186**, 382 (1928).

93. P. Fleury and J. Lange, *Compt. rend.* **195**, 1395 (1932); *J. pharm. chim.* **17**, 107 (1933); **17**, 196 (1933); H. Hérissey, P. Fleury, and M. Joly, *ibid.* **20**, 149 (1934).

94. E. L. Jackson and C. S. Hudson, *J. Am. Chem. Soc.* **59**, 994 (1937); **61**, 959 (1939); W. D. Maclay, R. M. Hann, and C. S. Hudson, *ibid.* **61**, 1660 (1939); E. L. Jackson, *Org. Reactions* **2**, 341 (1944).

95. J. M. Bobbitt, *Advances in Carbohydrate Chem.* **11**, 1 (1956).

one mole of formic acid, no formaldehyde; hexopyranoside, two moles of periodate, one mole of formic acid, no formaldehyde. The dialdehydes obtained can be stabilized by oxidation to dibasic acids (*94*) or by reduction to primary alcohols (*96*); the products so obtained can be employed for further characterization and differentiation.

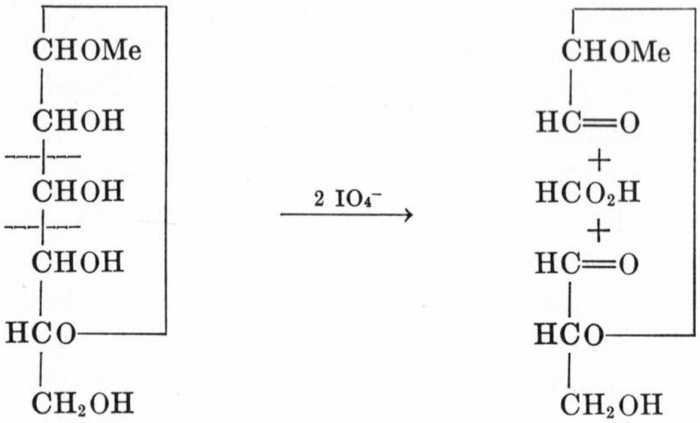

Aldohexopyranoside

Glycosides containing the group —$(CHOH)_nCH_2OH$ outside the ring, where n is 1 or more, may undergo a more extensive type of oxidation. The malondialdehyde acetal intermediate (see formulas) is further oxidized (*97*, *98*) without showing a critical point in the rate curve (*99*). Many cyclic β-diketones and some keto acids and deoxy sugars are oxidized at the methylene groups. (See Chapter VI.)

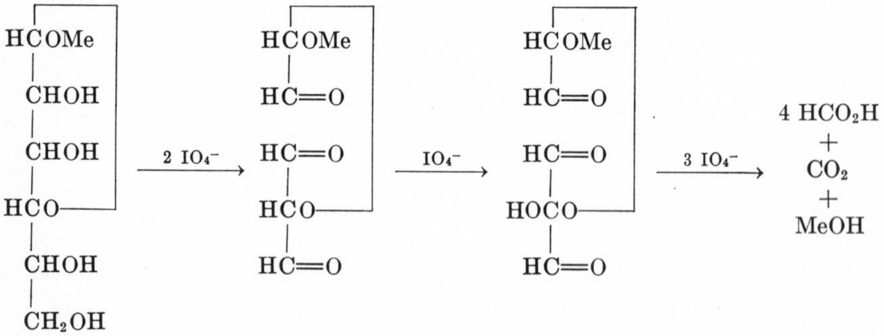

The periodate glycol oxidation reaction is pH-dependent and proceeds

96. A. T. Ness, R. M. Hann, and C. S. Hudson, *J. Am. Chem. Soc.* **66,** 665, 670 (1944); M. Abdel-Akher, J. K. Hamilton, R. Montgomery, and F. Smith, *ibid.*, **74,** 4970 (1952); F. Smith and J. W. Van Cleve, *ibid.* **77,** 3091 (1955).

97. C. F. Huebner, S. R. Ames, and E. C. Bubl, *J. Am. Chem. Soc.* **68,** 1621 (1946).

98. R. K. Ness, H. G. Fletcher, Jr., and C. S. Hudson, *J. Am. Chem. Soc.* **73,** 3742 (1951).

99. M. L. Wolfrom, A. Thompson, A. N. O'Neill, and T. T. Galkowski, *J. Am. Chem. Soc.* **74,** 1062 (1952).

best in the pH range 3–5. Periodate shows some tendency to act as a general rather than as a specific oxidant, and rate curves, determined at room temperature and below, are desirable. An α-glycol group contained in a ring and adjacent to an acetamido function, is attacked only slowly by periodate (*100*). Bicyclic structures are known which contain α-glycol groups that are completely resistant to periodate attack (*101*). These substances are the 1,6-anhydrohexofuranoses (see the succeeding section). In some types of periodate oxidation, formate esters of considerable stability may be formed (*102*).

The periodate oxidation reaction can often be used to determine the location of a substituted hydroxyl in a molecule. Methyl β-D-glucopyranoside, substituted by *O*-methyl on carbon 2 or 4, on 3, or on 6, consumes one, none, and two moles of oxidant, respectively, per mole of substance. The method has been extended to the determination of the types of linkages present in oligosaccharides (*99*) and to the determination of the degree of branching and of the types of linkages present in polysaccharides (*103*). (See Chapters IX and XII.)

Lead tetraacetate is another useful α-glycol–cleaving reagent and has the advantage that it may be employed in organic solvents (*104*). It may also be used in aqueous solution (*105*) in which case any formic acid produced is oxidized to carbon dioxide (*106*). Even in anhydrous acetic acid, formic acid is oxidized slowly (*107*). Criegee and associates (*108*) have shown that the rate of lead tetraacetate oxidation is very much lower in anhydrous acetic acid than in other organic solvents and that in this solvent the oxidant cleaves cyclic structures bearing *cis*-α-glycols more rapidly than correspondingly situated *trans*-α-glycols. This difference has been utilized by

100. M. L. Wolfrom, R. K. Madison, and M. J. Cron, *J. Am. Chem. Soc.* **74,** 1491 (1952).

101. R. J. Dimler, *Advances in Carbohydrate Chem.* **7,** 37 (1952).

102. K. H. Meyer and P. Rathgeb, *Helv. Chim. Acta* **31,** 1540, 1545 (1948); **32,** 1102 (1949); G. R. Barker and D. C. C. Smith, *Chemistry & Industry* p. 30, 1035 (1952); F. S. H. Head and G. Hughes, *J. Chem. Soc.* p. 603 (1954).

103. T. G. Halsall, E. L. Hirst, and J. K. N. Jones, *J. Chem. Soc.* p. 1399 (1947); A. Jeanes, W. C. Haynes, C. A. Wilham, J. C. Rankin, E. H. Melvin, M. J. Austin, J. E. Cluskey, B. E. Fisher, H. M. Tsuchiya, and C. E. Rist, *J. Am. Chem. Soc.* **76,** 5041 (1954).

104. R. Criegee, *Ann.* **481,** 275 (1930); *Ber.* **64,** 260 (1931); *Angew. Chem.* **50,** 153 (1937).

105. E. Baer, J. M. Grosheintz, and H. O. L. Fischer, *J. Am. Chem. Soc.* **61,** 2607 (1939).

106. J. M. Grosheintz, *J. Am. Chem. Soc.* **61,** 3379 (1939).

107. R. C. Hockett, M. T. Dienes, H. G. Fletcher, Jr., and H. E. Ramsden, *J. Am. Chem. Soc.* **66,** 467 (1944).

108. R. Criegee, *Ber.* **65,** 1770 (1932); R. Criegee, L. Kraft, and B. Rank, *Ann.* **507,** 159 (1933).

Hockett and co-workers in a series of studies applied to sugar structures wherein the rate of oxidant consumption was accurately measured. Working with pyranosides, it was demonstrated that their vicinal triols are oxidized more rapidly if at least two of the hydroxyl groups are *cis*-oriented and that an α-hydroxy aldehyde will be relatively rapidly oxidized if a hydroxyl group is sterically available for hemiacetal formation with the carbonyl group (*109*). They showed further that the hydroxy-malonaldehyde derivative formed in the oxidation of hexofuranosides was susceptible to further oxidation by attack on hydrogen (*110*). No effect of configuration on the oxidation behavior of acyclic alditols was noted since no fixed space relations exist among the various hydroxyl groups because of the possibility of free rotation around the carbon-to-carbon single bonds (*107*).

Sodium perbismuthate, $NaBiO_3$, and argentic ion, Ag^{+++}, have been shown to effect α-glycol cleavage (*111*); they have been studied in some detail (*112*).

Oxidation, by atmospheric oxygen, of solutions of methyl α-D-glucopyranoside in cuprammonium solution is stated to proceed with cleavage of carbon bonds similar to that for periodic acid (*113*).

c. *Determination of Anomeric Configuration*

The use of the terms α and β for anomeric forms of the glycosides was first systematized by Hudson (*114*), who stated that "the names should be so selected that for all sugars which are genetically related to D-glucose the subtraction of the rotation of the β form from that of the α form gives a positive difference, and for all sugars which are genetically related to L-glucose a negative difference." This rule, based upon the isorotation rules of Hudson, is more generally expressed by stating that the more dextrorotatory anomer, in the D-series, is assigned the prefix α and the hydroxyl, or substituted hydroxyl, of the anomeric carbon is written to the right in the Fischer projection formula. (See Chapter I.)

The actual configuration of the anomeric carbon in the methyl D-gluco-

109. W. S. McClenahan and R. C. Hockett, *J. Am. Chem. Soc.* **60,** 2061 (1938); R. C. Hockett and W. S. McClenahan, *ibid.* **61,** 1667 (1939); R. C. Hockett, M. T. Dienes, and H. E. Ramsden, *ibid.* **65,** 1474 (1943).

110. R. C. Hockett, M. H. Nickerson, and W. H. Reeder, III, *J. Am. Chem. Soc.* **66,** 472 (1944).

111. L. J. Heidt, E. K. Gladding, and C. B. Purves, *Paper Trade J.* **121,** No. 9, 35 (1945).

112. W. Rigby, *J. Chem. Soc.* p. 1907 (1950); F. P. Greenspan and H. M. Woodburn, *J. Am. Chem. Soc.* **76,** 6345 (1954).

113. V. I. Ivanov and K. M. Sokova, *Compt. rend. acad. sci. U. R. S. S.* **42,** 175 (1944); *Chem. Abstr.* **39,** 281 (1945).

114. C. S. Hudson, *J. Am. Chem. Soc.* **31,** 66 (1909).

pyranosides was determined by the reaction of methanol with 1,2-anhydro-α-D-glucopyranose 3,4,6-triacetate to give methyl β-D-glucopyranoside 3,4,6-triacetate (*53*). It is known (*115*) that solvolysis of *cis*-epoxide rings occurs with Walden inversion, at the point of carbon–oxygen scission, to produce *trans*-glycol derivatives. This principle was first established with carbohydrate derivatives (*116*). Therefore, the methoxyl group in the methyl D-glucopyranosides bears a *trans* relation to the hydroxyl on carbon 2 in the β-anomer and a *cis* relation in the α-anomer. For D-mannose, the reverse is true.

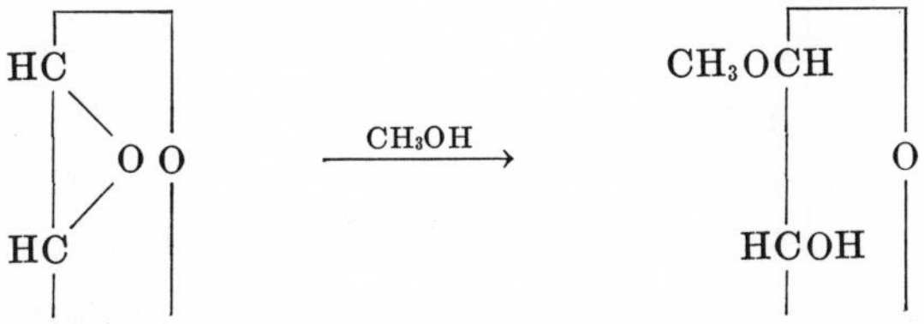
HC
O O
HC
CH_3OH
CH_3OCH
O
HCOH

The dialdehydes obtained in the periodate oxidation of glycosides and utilized for the determination of ring size (p. 32, 216), were also employed by Jackson and Hudson (*94*) for the configurational correlation of the anomeric carbons of aldohexopyranosides and aldopentopyranosides. The dialdehydes were oxidized to the dibasic acids and these were isolated as

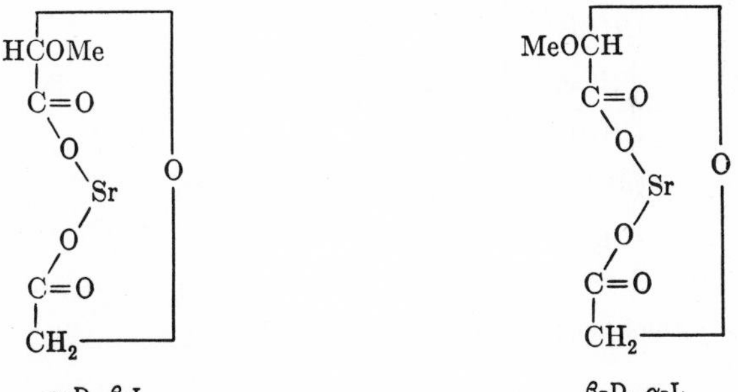
HCOMe
C=O
O
Sr
O
O
C=O
CH_2
MeOCH
C=O
O
Sr
O
O
C=O
CH_2

α-D, β-L (I) β-D, α-L (II)

their crystalline hydrated strontium salts. The products from the aldopentopyranosides contained the residual anomeric center as the only optically active group. Of the numerous derivatives investigated, all of the anomers classified as α-D by the Hudson isorotation rules gave the same product while those classified as β-D gave the enantiomorph. It is of interest to note that the products (I, II) from the α-D-anomers are identical with those

115. S. Winstein and R. B. Henderson, *J. Am. Chem. Soc.* **65**, 2196 (1943); S. Winstein and R. B. Henderson *in* "Heterocyclic Compounds" (R. C. Elderfield, ed.), Vol. I, p. 22. Wiley, New York, 1950.

116. S. Peat, *Advances in Carbohydrate Chem.* **2**, 37 (1946).

from the β-L-anomers. This illustrates the fact that the configurations about carbon 1 of the α-D- and β-L-sugars are identical.

The dibasic acids obtained by Jackson and Hudson from the aldohexopyranosides were stereoisomeric and retained the asymmetry of the penultimate carbon center. All of the anomers investigated that were classified

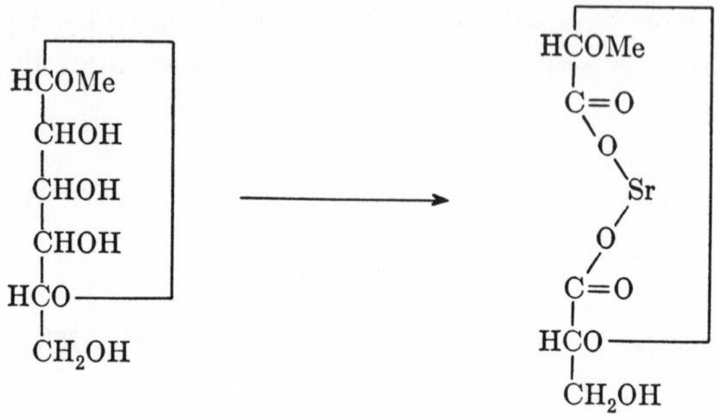

α-D-Aldohexopyranoside (III)

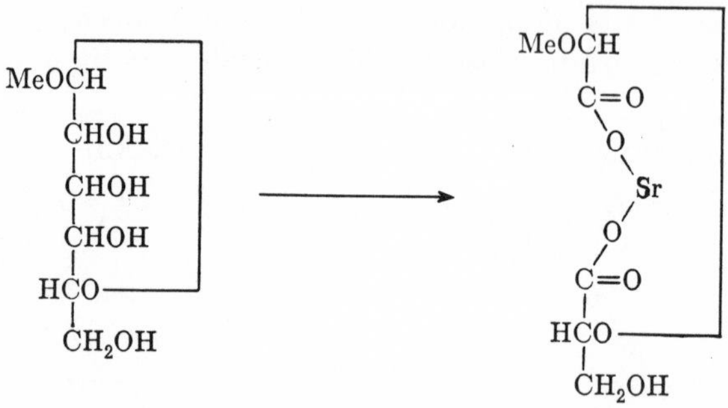

β-D-Aldohexopyranoside (IV)

as α-D, on the basis of the Hudson isorotation rules, gave the same substance (III) and those so classified as β-D, gave the other stereoisomer (IV).

2. GLYCOSANS

Condensation of a hemiacetal hydroxyl with another hydroxyl group in the same molecule produces an anhydro sugar (glycosan) which can be considered as an intramolecular glycoside. The most common glycosans may be classified, by their skeletal structures, as 1,2-anhydro- and 1,6-anhydro-pyranoses, and 1,6-anhydrofuranoses. The ether anhydro derivatives are considered in Chapter VII.

A. PREPARATION

1,2-Anhydro-D-glucopyranose is obtained as its triacetate by the action of ammonia in benzene on 3,4,6-tri-*O*-acetyl-2-*O*-trichloroacetyl-β-D-glucopyranosyl chloride (*53*).

Pyrolysis of sugars and polysaccharides under reduced pressure causes dehydration with the formation of anhydro sugars of the glycosan type. Dry distillation of cellulose, starch, and glucosides (*117*) gives 1,6-anhydro-β-D-glucopyranose ("levoglucosan"). The pyrolysis of lactose leads to the same 1,6-anhydro-β-D-glucopyranose as well as to the corresponding 1,6-anhydro-β-D-galactopyranose. The polysaccharide agar gives small yields of the same anhydro-D-galactose under similar conditions (*118*). The direct pyrolysis of α-D-galactose produces the above isomer and 1,6-anhydro-α-D-galactofuranose (*119*). The 1,6-anhydro-β-D-mannopyranose ("levomannosan") is obtained in a similar manner from the seeds of the ivory nut palm (*Phytelephas macrocarpa*). The glycosans are found in the distillates from these pyrolyses, and as shown by Hann and Hudson, the preparation of *O*-isopropylidene derivatives increases the yields and facilitates the crystallization of many of the compounds.

Treatment of aromatic β-D-glucopyranosides with alkali at 100°C. provides an excellent method for the preparation of 1,6-anhydro-β-D-glucopyranose ("levoglucosan") (*69*, *120*). Even after long periods of heating, aromatic and alkyl α-D-glucopyranosides and alkyl β-D-glucopyranosides remain virtually unaffected. The corresponding 1,6-anhydro-β-D-galactopyranose is produced under similar conditions from both the phenyl α- and β-D-galactopyranosides. Although the reaction takes place in a few hours for the β-D isomer, several weeks are required for the α-D isomer.

The mechanism of the reaction has been studied by McCloskey and Coleman (*121*). It appears that a 1,2-anhydride may be an intermediate in the formation of 1,6-anhydro-β-D-glucopyranose because the reaction is blocked by the presence of a methoxyl group at carbon 2 whereas the presence of methoxyl groups at carbons 3 and 4 does not prevent the reaction. This reaction course does not explain the formation of 1,6-anhydro-β-D-mannopyranose from the phenyl β-D-anomer and the corresponding

117. A. Pictet and J. Sarasin, *Helv. Chim. Acta* **1**, 87 (1918); J. C. Irvine and J. W. H. Oldham, *J. Chem. Soc.* **127**, 2729 (1925).

118. R. M. Hann and C. S. Hudson, *J. Am. Chem. Soc.* **63**, 1484 (1941).

119. R. M. Hann and C. S. Hudson, *J. Am. Chem. Soc.* **63**, 2241 (1941); B. H. Alexander, R. J. Dimler, and C. L. Mehltretter, *ibid.* **73**, 4658 (1951).

120. E. M. Montgomery, N. K. Richtmyer, and C. S. Hudson, *J. Am. Chem. Soc.* **65**, 3 (1943); *J. Org. Chem.* **10**, 194 (1945); G. H. Coleman, C. M. McCloskey, and R. Kirby, *Ind. Eng. Chem.* **36**, 1040 (1944).

121. C. M. McCloskey and G. H. Coleman, *J. Org. Chem.* **10**, 184 (1945).

D-galactose derivative from the phenyl α-D-anomer. The reaction is discussed by Lemieux (*16*) who suggests other possible reaction paths.

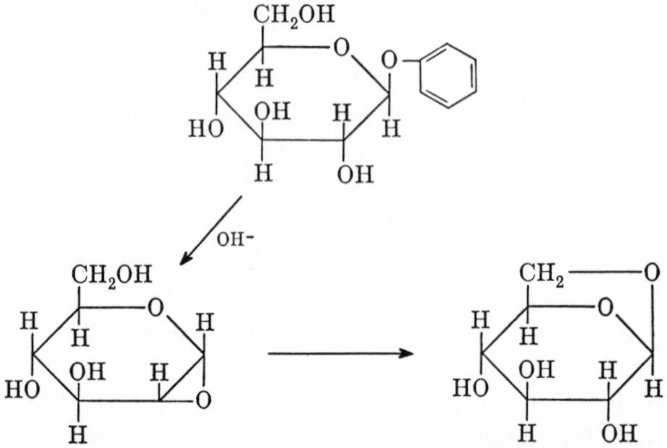

CH_2OH
O
O
H
H
OH
HO
H
H
H
OH
OH-
CH_2OH
O
H
H
H
OH
H
HO
O
H
CH_2
O
O
H
H
OH
H
HO
H
H
OH

The quaternary salt formed from tetra-*O*-acetyl-α-D-galactopyranosyl bromide and trimethylamine yields 1,6-anhydro-β-D-galactopyranose on treatment with barium hydroxide (*122*). During treatment of tri-*O*-acetyl-5-*O*-trityl-D-ribofuranose with hydrogen bromide, a trityl and an acetyl group are removed with the formation of 2,3-di-*O*-acetyl-1,5-anhydro-D-ribofuranose (*123*) (shown by other workers to be dimeric).

A number of aldohexoses and aldo- and keto-heptoses, having a pyranose structure, tend to produce 1,6-anhydro-β-D-glycopyranoses upon heating with dilute hydrochloric acid. The reaction has been studied extensively by Hudson, Richtmyer, and their associates (*124*), who have prepared and characterized a number of 1,6-anhydropyranoses by this method. It is of interest to compare the conformational relationships of the parent sugars with their ability to form anhydrides. Reeves (*82*) states that the anhydride-forming tendency of altrose and idose may be explained by their capability to exist in the 1C form (Fig. 2). The anhydride-forming tendency of the other sugars studied supports this theory.

B. Structures

The determination of the structures of the glycosans, and anhydro sugars in general, is of particular importance because the preparative methods give little direct information concerning the structures and because Walden inversions may take place. Methylation, followed by hydrolysis of the anhy-

122. F. Micheel, *Ber.* **62,** 687 (1929); P. Karrer and A. P. Smirnoff, *Helv. Chim. Acta* **4,** 817 (1921).

123. H. Bredereck, M. Köthnig, and E. Berger, *Ber.* **73,** 956 (1940).

124. N. K. Richtmyer and C. S. Hudson, *J. Am. Chem. Soc.* **57,** 1716 (1935); J. W. Pratt, N. K. Richtmyer, and C. S. Hudson, *ibid.* **75,** 4503 (1953); L. C. Stewart and N. K. Richtmyer, *ibid.* **77,** 424, 1021 (1955).

dro ring, gives partially methylated sugars which may be identified by nitric acid oxidation or by comparison with compounds of known structure.

The periodic acid oxidation is well adapted to the determination of most of the rings present, and the principle is the same as that described for the glycosides. For the purpose of illustrating the method, the arguments cited by Jackson and Hudson (*125*) for the structure of 1,6-anhydro-β-D-glucopyranose are given. This substance upon oxidation by periodic acid or sodium metaperiodate produces one mole of formic acid and consumes two moles of the oxidant. This evidence demands that the compound have three contiguous hydroxyl groups and limits the possible structures to two types: 1,2-anhydro-D-glucoseptanose and 1,6-anhydro-D-glucopyranose. The dialdehyde upon oxidation by hypobromite followed by acid hydrolysis gives strontium oxalate and strontium D-glyceronate. As the formation of these products agrees only with the latter structure, "levoglucosan" is properly described as 1,6-anhydro-D-glucopyranose. From the *cis* relationship of the hydroxyl of carbon 1 of β-D-glucose to the $—CH_2OH$ group, it is considered that the anhydro ring has the β-configuration since the connection is bebetween carbon 1 and carbon 6. The crystalline strontium salt of the dibasic acid which was isolated serves as a reference compound for the determination of the structure of any anhydro hexose with similar structure, since the asymmetry of all carbon atoms except carbon 1 and carbon 5 is destroyed.

C. Reactions

The cleavage of anhydro rings of the glycosan type occurs in a manner similar to that for the inner ethers (see p. 166, 388). Acetolysis of 1,6-anhydro-β-D-glucopyranose produced a mixture of anomeric penta-*O*-acetyl-D-glucopyranoses in which the α-D form predominated (88%) (*126*). The larger ring is cleaved also by the action of titanium tetrachloride in chloroform solution to produce 2,3,4-tri-*O*-acetyl-α-D-glucopyranosyl chloride (*127*).

1,2-Anhydro-α-D-glucopyranose 3,4,6-triacetate reacts with acetic anhydride (*53*) to give a mixture containing α-D-glucopyranose pentaacetate. It is opened by water to give primarily β-D-glucopyranose 3,4,6-triacetate and with methanol to give methyl β-D-glucopyranoside 3,4,6-triacetate.

The furanose ring is stabilized markedly toward acid hydrolysis by the 1,6-anhydro ring (*128*). The conditions required for the hydrolysis of the 1,6-anhydrofuranoses are comparable with those for 1,6-anhydropyranoses.

125. E. L. Jackson and C. S. Hudson, *J. Am. Chem. Soc.* **62,** 958 (1940).

126. K. Freudenberg and K. Soff, *Ber.* **69,** 1245 (1936).

127. G. Zemplén and Z. Csürös, *Ber.* **62,** 993 (1929); G. Zemplén and A. Gerecs, *ibid.* **64,** 1545 (1931).

128. R. J. Dimler, H. A. Davis, and G. E. Hilbert, *J. Am. Chem. Soc.* **68,** 1377 (1946).

D. Diketohexose Dianhydrides

D-Fructose is known to form bimolecular dianhydrides containing a central dioxane ring, when acted upon by aqueous acids. Six such substances have been described (*129*). A high degree of polymorphism is characteristic of these substances and their derivatives. The first of these

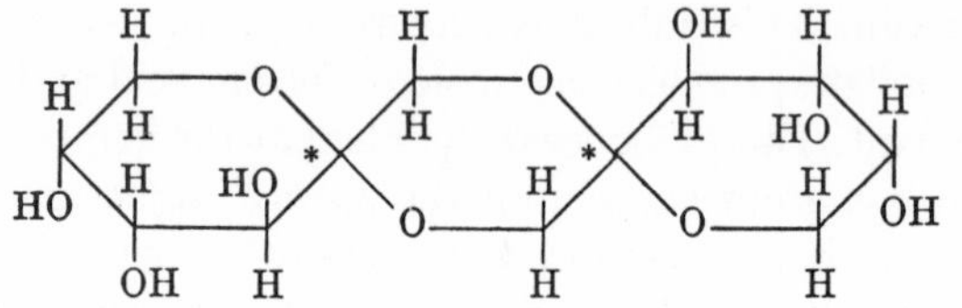

"Diheterolevulosan I"
(Di-D-fructopyranose 1,2′:2,1′-dianhydride)
(I)

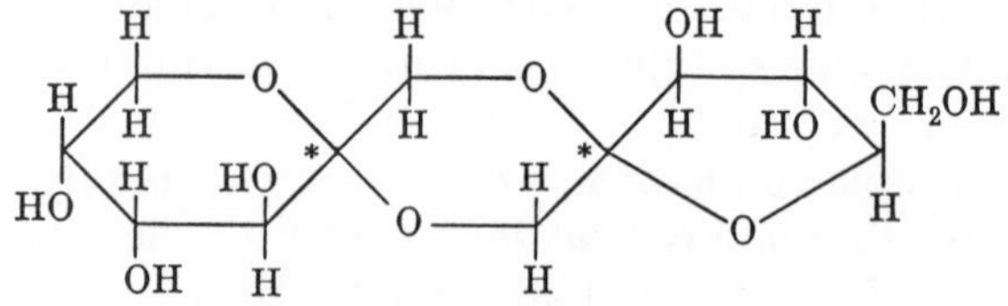

"Diheterolevulosan II"
(D-Fructopyranose-D-fructofuranose 1,2′:2,1′-dianhydride)
(II)

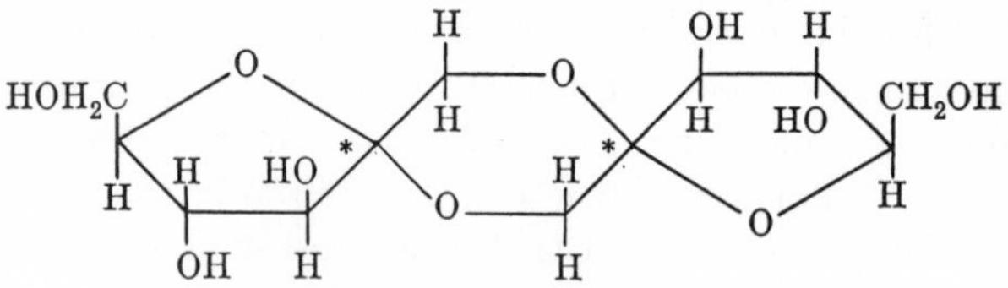

"Difructose anhydride I"
(Di-D-fructofuranose 1,2′:2,1′-dianhydride)
(III)

*Anomeric configuration unknown.

("diheterolevulosan I") was isolated by Pictet and Chavan (*130*) and was subsequently shown (*131*) to be di-D-fructopyranose 1,2′:2,1′-dianhydride (I).

Another dianhydride of D-fructose was isolated by Wolfrom and Blair

129. M. L. Wolfrom, H. W. Hilton, and W. W. Binkley, *J. Am. Chem. Soc.* **74,** 2867 (1952).
130. A. Pictet and J. Chavan, *Helv. Chim. Acta* **9,** 809 (1926).

(*131*), and the structure (II) was established for it (*132*). Wolfrom, Hilton, and Binkley (*129*) isolated an isomer which they believed to be either di-D-fructopyranose 1,2′:2,3′-dianhydride or an anomeric form of (II).

Jackson and Goergen (*133*) and Jackson and McDonald (*134*) have isolated three dianhydrides of D-fructose from the nonreducing residue that remains after the removal of D-fructose from the acid hydrolyzate of inulin (*135*). On the basis of methylation data (*136*), structure (III) was assigned to "difructose anhydride I." "Difructose anhydride III" was considered (*135*) to be di-D-fructofuranose 1,2′:2,3′-dianhydride. Wolfrom, Hilton, and Binkley (*129*) believe, on the basis of rotational data, that "difructose anhydrides II and III" are structural units differing only in the configuration of one of the asymmetric centers on the substituted dioxane ring.

Two dianhydrides of L-sorbose have been isolated by Wolfrom and Hilton (*137*). The first of these substances was established by periodate oxidation to be di-L-sorbopyranose 2,1′:2′,1-dianhydride and the second as probably L-sorbofuranose-L-sorbopyranose 2,1′:2′,1-dianhydride.

No monomolecular anhydride of a ketohexose has been established; they are known in the ketoheptose series. An interesting bicyclic structure containing a "meta" or "1,3" dioxane ring has been established by Stewart

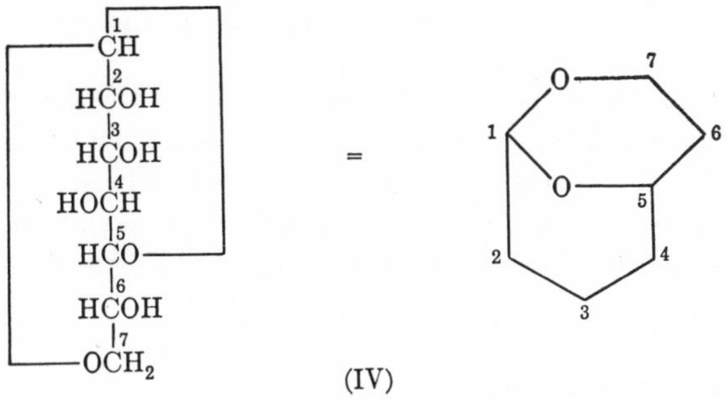

(IV)

and Richtmyer (*124*) in the substance 1,7-anhydro-D-*glycero*-*β*-D-*gulo*-heptopyranose (IV).

131. H. H. Schlubach and C. Behre, *Ann.* **508,** 16 (1934); E. J. McDonald and R. F. Jackson, *J. Research Natl. Bur. Standards* **35,** 497 (1945); M. L. Wolfrom and M. G. Blair, *J. Am. Chem. Soc.* **70,** 2406 (1948).

132. M. L. Wolfrom, W. W. Binkley, W. L. Shilling, and H. W. Hilton, *J. Am. Chem. Soc.* **73,** 3553 (1951).

133. R. F. Jackson and S. M. Goergen, *Bur. Standards J. Research* **3,** 27 (1929).

134. R. F. Jackson and E. J. McDonald, *Bur. Standards J. Research* **6,** 709 (1931).

135. E. J. McDonald, *Advances in Carbohydrate Chem.* **2,** 253 (1946).

136. W. N. Haworth and H. R. L. Streight, *Helv. Chim. Acta* **15,** 693 (1932).

137. M. L. Wolfrom and H. W. Hilton, *J. Am. Chem. Soc.* **74,** 5334 (1952).

3. ACETAL AND DITHIOACETAL DERIVATIVES OF ACYCLIC SUGARS

A. Dithioacetals

In their reaction with alcohols under acid catalysis, the aldoses differ from the simple, or unhydroxylated, aldehydes in forming mixed monocylic acetals (glycosides) rather than acyclic dialkyl acetals. However, Fischer (*138*) found that, on shaking a cold solution of an aldose in concentrated hydrochloric acid with a thiol, a crystalline product separated which was the dithioacetal (mercaptal) of the acyclic structure. These substances have

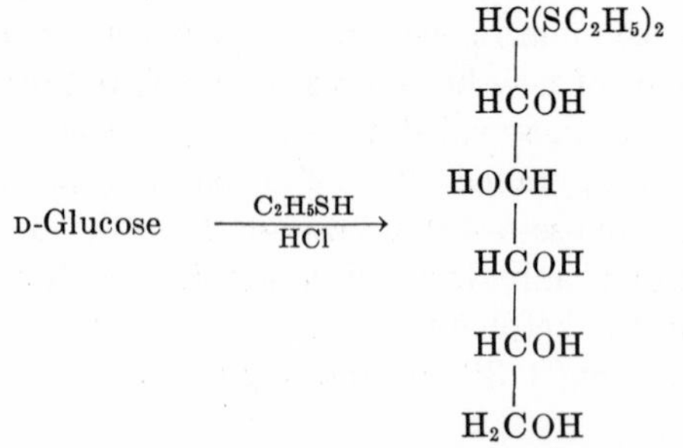
D-Glucose
C2H5SH
HCl
HC(SC2H5)2
HCOH
HOCH
HCOH
HCOH
H2COH

D-Glucose diethyl dithioacetal

served as useful intermediates for the preparation of the acyclic derivatives of the sugars (see p. 142). Fructose is too acid-sensitive for direct mercaptalation but its dithioacetal was obtained indirectly from the acylated *keto*-D-fructose, formed from the ketose by direct acylation, by reaction with the thiol and an acid (*139*) with subsequent removal of the ester-blocking groups.

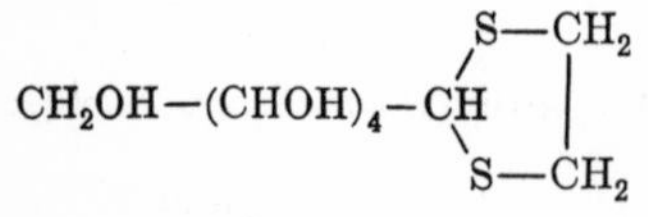
S—CH2
CH2OH—(CHOH)4—CH
S—CH2

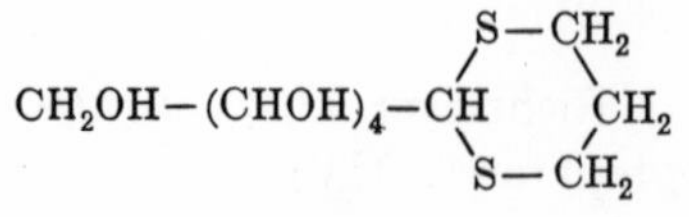
S—CH2
CH2OH—(CHOH)4—CH
CH2
S—CH2

An interesting type of dithioacetal, very stable to hydrolysis by acids, is that made from dithioglycol or 1,3-propanedithiol (*140*).

In addition to their use for the preparation of acyclic sugar derivatives, the sugar dithioacetals are of value in the preparation of deoxyalditols by

138. E. Fischer, *Ber.* **27,** 673 (1894).

139. M. L. Wolfrom and A. Thompson, *J. Am. Chem. Soc.* **56,** 880 (1934); P. Brigl and R. Schinle, *Ber.* **66,** 325 (1933).

140. W. T. Lawrence, *Ber.* **29,** 547 (1896).

reductive desulfuration (*141*), the carbonyl group being thereby reduced to the hydrocarbon stage.

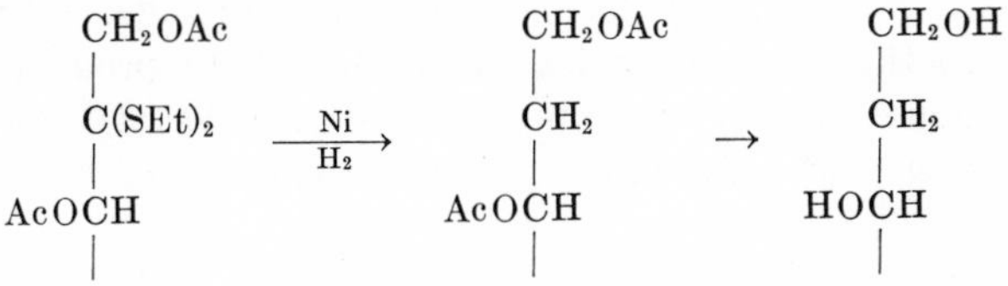

As shown earlier in this chapter, the thioalkyl groups may be removed from the sugar dithioacetals, and, according to the conditions employed, furanosides, pyranosides, thioglycosides, or acetals may be obtained.

The stability of the dithioacetals and their ease of preparation make them significant for the identification of the monosaccharides (*142*).

The reactive carbonyl of an *aldehydo*-sugar acetate adds thiols and from such adducts have been obtained mixed acetal and thioacetal derivatives (*41*, *43*) which are the probable intermediates in the conversion of dithioacetals to furanosides (p. 199).

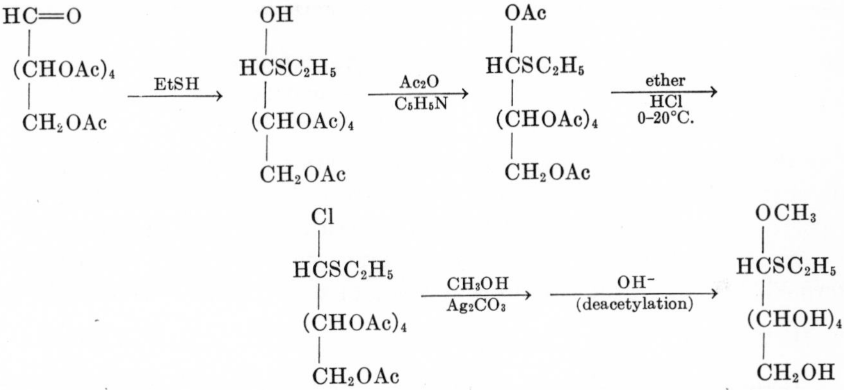

B. Acetals

Acetal derivatives of simple acyclic sugars (glycolaldehyde and glyceraldehyde) have long been known, but special reactions are required to prepare the acetals of the tetroses and higher sugars since the glycosides (mixed acetals) are formed preferably. Several methylated sugar dimethyl acetals have been reported (*45*), but the first unsubstituted acetal in the sugar series was the D-arabinose dimethyl acetal of Montgomery, Hann, and

141. M. L. Wolfrom and J. V. Karabinos, *J. Am. Chem. Soc.* **66**, 909 (1944); J. Bougault, E. Cattelain, and P. Chabrier, *Bull. soc. chim. France* [5] **5**, 1699 (1938); [5] **7**, 780, 781 (1940).

142. M. L. Wolfrom and J. V. Karabinos, *J. Am. Chem. Soc.* **67**, 500 (1945).

Hudson (*143*). The specific and unusual method used for the preparation (see formulas below) depends on the action of zinc chloride, under acetylating conditions, in rupturing the oxygen–carbon linkage of the pyranose ring of the methyl D-arabinosides. As intermediate products, the fully acetylated hemiacetal (I) and the chloro derivative (II) are produced. Deacetylation of the final product gives D-arabinose dimethyl acetal.

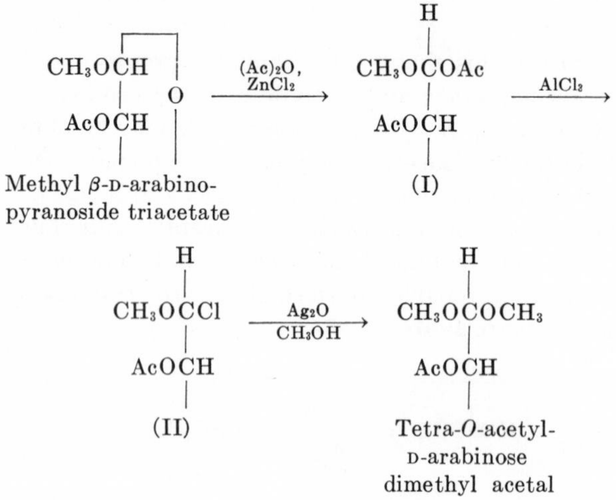
CH₃OCH
O
AcOCH
(Ac)₂O, ZnCl₂
H
CH₃OCOAc
AcOCH
AlCl₃
Methyl β-D-arabino-pyranoside triacetate
(I)
H
CH₃OCCl
AcOCH
Ag₂O
CH₃OH
H
CH₃OCOCH₃
AcOCH
(II)
Tetra-O-acetyl-D-arabinose dimethyl acetal

A direct and general method for the preparation of sugar acetals depends on acetal exchange of the thioalkyl radicals of dithioacetals in which ring closure is blocked by the presence of substituent groups such as acetyl groups (*6*, *40*). If ring closure is not prevented, glycosides are usually formed. Fructose dithioacetals and those of a few other sugars, particu-

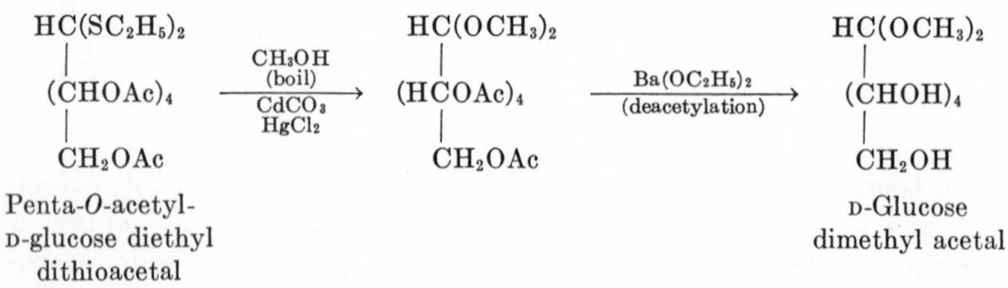
HC(SC₂H₅)₂
(CHOAc)₄
CH₂OAc
CH₃OH (boil)
CdCO₃ HgCl₂
HC(OCH₃)₂
(HCOAc)₄
CH₂OAc
Ba(OC₂H₅)₂ (deacetylation)
HC(OCH₃)₂
(CHOH)₄
CH₂OH
Penta-O-acetyl-D-glucose diethyl dithioacetal
D-Glucose dimethyl acetal

larly at low temperatures, may form acetals by this method even when ring closure is possible (*42*).

The acetals are converted to the corresponding pyranosides in alcoholic hydrogen chloride (Fischer conditions for preparation of glycosides) and, hence, are in equilibrium with the glycosides, but the equilibrium favors the glycosides.

Acyclic hemiacetals of the *aldehydo*-sugar acetates are formed in solution and account for the mutarotation of these derivatives in alcohol; those in the galactose structure are isolable (*144*). Two isomeric hemiacetals are possible for each sugar, for carbon 1 becomes asymmetric. The two forms of the ethyl hemiacetal of methyl tetra-*O*-acetyl-*aldehydo*-D-galacturonate have been isolated by Dimler and Link (*145*) and have been designated as α and β, following the usage of Hudson (*114*), in which that derivative in the D-series having the more positive rotation is assigned the prefix alpha.

Derivatives of aldose hemiacetals with the hydroxyl replaced by halogen or acetate have been described and, in many cases, isolated in the two forms demanded by stereochemical theory (*143*, *146*).

4. REACTIONS OF CARBOHYDRATES WITH ALDEHYDES AND KETONES

Aldehydes react with alcohols to form acetals.

$$RCHO + 2R'OH \rightarrow RCH(OR')_2 + H_2O$$

Two hydroxyls of a carbohydrate molecule may react with an aldehyde with the formation of a cyclic acetal. These products are known as *O*-arylidene or *O*-alkylidene derivatives of sugars. Acetone condenses similarly to give *O*-isopropylidene (acetone) derivatives (*2a*).

The first cyclic acetals of this type were prepared by Wurtz (*147*), who showed that ethylene glycol and acetaldehyde react when heated together and that one mole of water is lost. Mineral acids, zinc chloride, and copper sulfate greatly accelerate the reaction.

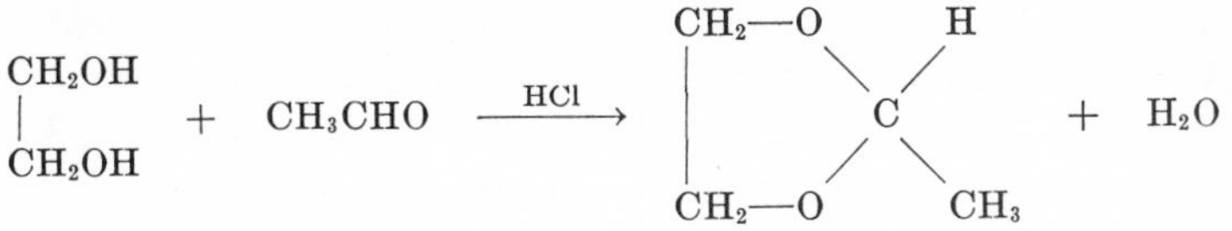
CH₂OH
CH₂OH
+
CH₃CHO
HCl
CH₂—O
H
C
CH₂—O
CH₃
+
H₂O

Other aldehydes (benzaldehyde, formaldehyde) (*148*), condense with alditols and sugars to form cyclic acetals (*149*). The analogous reaction of

143. E. M. Montgomery, R. M. Hann, and C. S. Hudson, *J. Am. Chem. Soc.* **59,** 1124 (1937).

144. M. L. Wolfrom, *J. Am. Chem. Soc.* **52,** 2464 (1930); **53,** 2275 (1931); M. L. Wolfrom and W. M. Morgan, *ibid.* **54,** 3390 (1932).

145. R. J. Dimler and K. P. Link, *J. Am. Chem. Soc.* **62,** 1216 (1940).

146. M. L. Wolfrom, M. Konigsberg, and F. B. Moody, *J. Am. Chem. Soc.* **62,** 2343 (1940).

147. A. Wurtz, *Compt. rend.* **53,** 378 (1861); *Ann.* **120,** 328 (1861).

148. M. Schulz and B. Tollens, *Ann.* **289,** 20 (1896); B. Tollens, *Ber.* **32,** 2585 (1899).

149. J. Meunier, *Compt. rend.* **106,** 1425, 1732 (1888); *Ann. chim. phys.* [6] **22,** 412 (1891); E. Fischer, *Ber.* **27,** 1524 (1894).

acetone with alditols to yield crystalline products was described by Fischer (*150*).

In *O*-ethylideneglycol, a five-membered ring is present, but, in the acetal derivatives of 1,3-propanediol, a six-membered ring must be present. In alditols and sugars, these and other types of rings are possible. This subject was investigated for the lower polyhydric alcohols particularly by Hibbert and associates.

Hibbert's method depended upon studying the nature and amounts of the reaction products when alternate courses of reaction were possible. Thus, when equimolar quantities of acetaldehyde (actually, acetylene with mercuric sulfate was used instead of acetaldehyde; see below under Ethylidene Derivatives), glycol and glycerol were allowed to react, the major product (1,3-*O*-ethylideneglycerol) had a six-membered ring and the minor product (*O*-ethylideneglycol) a five-membered ring (*151*). Hence, a preference for the larger ring is indicated.

In a similar manner, the reaction of trimethylacetaldehyde with glycerol was studied.

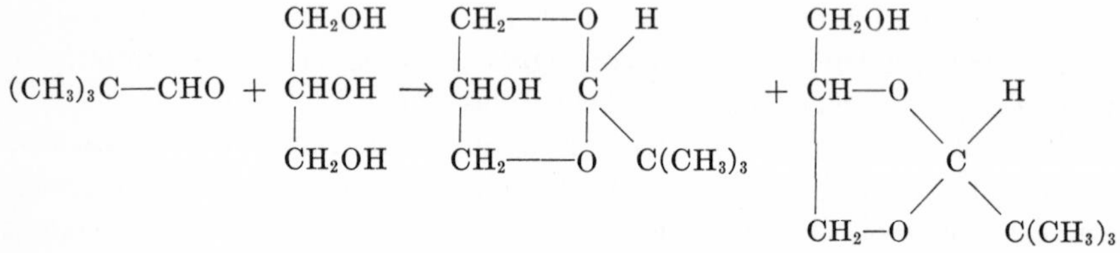

(I) (II)

The distribution of the products between six- and five-membered rings (I and II) was in the ratio 2:3. The nature of the substitution was shown by methylation of the products, hydrolysis of the acetal residues, and identification of the monomethyl ethers (*152*). In general, for glycerol, it was shown that such condensations reach a reversible equilibrium between the various possible isomers. Chloral and acetone formed five-membered rings exclusively.

Ring shifts have been observed for the *O*-isopropylidene derivatives of galactitol when benzoylation was attempted with benzoyl chloride and pyridine. The 2,3:5,6-di-*O*-isopropylidene-D,L-galactitol is converted to 1,6-di-*O*-benzoyl-2,3:4,5-di-*O*-isopropylidenegalactitol (*153*).

It is probable that these condensations take place through the inter-

150. E. Fischer, *Ber.* **28,** 1167 (1895).

151. H. S. Hill and H. Hibbert, *J. Am. Chem. Soc.* **45,** 3117 (1923).

152. S. M. Trister and H. Hibbert, *Can. J. Research* **B14,** 415 (1936).

153. R. M. Hann, W. D. Maclay, and C. S. Hudson, *J. Am. Chem. Soc.* **61,** 2432 (1939).

mediate formation of an acyclic hemiacetal (*154*). In fact, the intermediate product was isolated in the case of chloral and ethylene glycol (*155*).

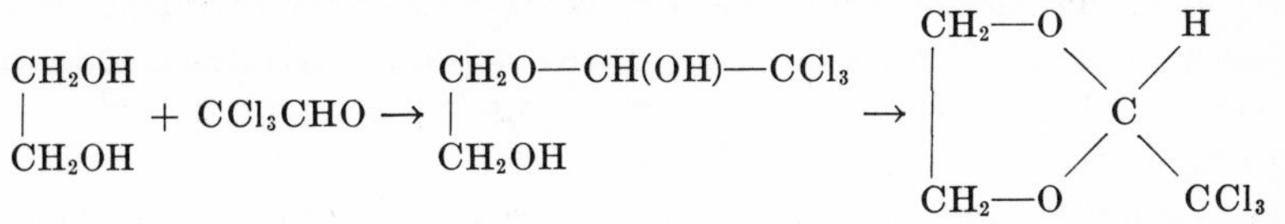

The general types of ring found in acetal derivatives are the six- and five-membered dioxolane rings, respectively. Sometimes, seven-membered rings are formed, as with 1,4-butanediol.

A study of methylene acetals derived from galactitol (dulcitol), D-mannitol and D-glucitol (sorbitol), and ribitol (adonitol) enabled Hann and Hudson (*156*) to reach certain conclusions concerning the manner in which substitutions of these groups in alditols occur. On the basis of these conclusions and from a consideration of new relevant information, Barker and Bourne (*157*) have set up an amended set of rules to cover virtually all known cases of the formation of benzylidene, ethylidene, and methylene derivatives. In order to simplify the presentation of these rules, the Greek letters α, β, and γ will be used to signify the relative positions of the two hydroxyl groups engaged in cyclization, along the carbon chain of the polyhydric alcohol, and C and T will indicate whether these groups are disposed *cis* or *trans* in the usual Fischer projectional formula; C and T will be required only when both alcohol groups are secondary.

The extended rules are: (1) the first preference is for a βC-ring; (2)

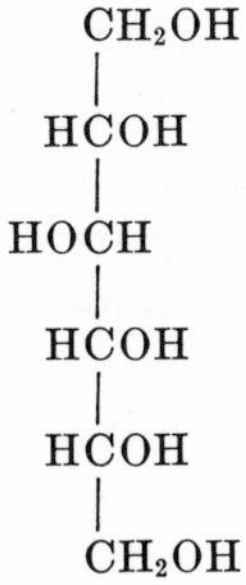

D-Glucitol

(1st, βC) 2,4-*O*-Benzylidene-
(2nd, βC, β) 1,3:2,4-di-*O*-Benzylidene-
(3rd, βC, β, α) 1,3:2,4:5,6-tri-*O*-Benzylidene-

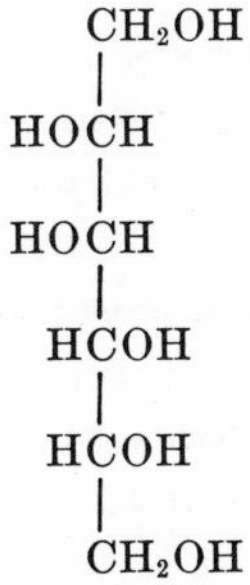

D-Mannitol

(1st, β, β) 1,3:4,6-di-*O*-Methylene-
(2nd, β, β, γT) 1,3:2,5:4,6-tri-*O*-Methylene-

154. H. Adkins and A. E. Broderick, *J. Am. Chem. Soc.* **50,** 499 (1928).
155. de Forcrand, *Compt. rend.* **108,** 618 (1889).
156. R. M. Hann and C. S. Hudson, *J. Am. Chem. Soc.* **66,** 1909 (1944).
157. S. A. Barker and E. J. Bourne, *J. Chem. Soc.* p. 905 (1952).

second, for a β-ring; (3) third, for an α-, αT-, βT-, or γT-ring; (4) in *O*-methylenation a βT-ring takes precedence over an αT- or a γT-ring; (5) in *O*-benzylidenation and *O*-ethylidenation, an αT-ring takes precedence over a βT- or a γT-ring; (6) rules (4) and (5) may not apply when one or both of the carbon atoms carrying the hydroxyl groups concerned is already a part of a ring system.

An alternative way of assessing the relative stabilities of acetal groups in substituted alditols of different types is to consider the products resulting when di- and tri-acetals are submitted to partial hydrolysis with aqueous acid. The order of stability is: βC > β > α and γT.

Knowledge regarding favored ring types in isopropylidene structures is meager and somewhat contradictory. Nevertheless, it is clear that the above rules do not apply and that there is a marked preference for five-membered rings.

After their structures were established, these cyclic acetals became very important in the synthesis of partially substituted carbohydrates of known structure. Their use for this purpose arises from their stability under alkaline conditions and their ease of hydrolysis under mild conditions of acidity. Thus, free hydroxyl groups in *O*-isopropylidenated sugars can be esterified or alkylated, and the blocking isopropylidene groups subsequently can be removed by treatment with acid. Although benzylidene groups are relatively stable to acids, they may be removed easily by catalytic hydrogenation; *O*-methylene groups are extremely resistant to acid hydrolysis.

A. Methylene (Formal) Derivatives

Sugars, alditols, and aldonic acids react with formaldehyde in the presence of acids to yield mono- or di-*O*-methylene derivatives or, in the case of hexitols, tri-*O*-methylene derivatives (*148*). Crystalline mono-*O*-methylene-D-glucose made by this method has a free reducing group. A sirupy di-*O*-methylene-D-glucose, made by melting D-glucose and trioxymethylene together, has no reducing properties (*158*).

The structures of many methylene sugar derivatives have not been determined, but those of many of the alditol derivatives are known. The greater ease of acetolysis of methylene groups attached to primary hydroxyls over those attached to secondary hydroxyls, has been of considerable value in the elucidation of the structures of these compounds by Hudson and co-workers (*96*). Thus the linkages at carbons 1 and 6 of 1,3:2,4:5,6-tri-*O*-methylene-D-glucitol are cleaved with sulfuric acid in acetic anhydride and acetic acid as shown in the formulas. The structure of the mono-*O*-methylene-D-glucitol is demonstrated by its oxidation with periodic acid

158. C. A. Lobry de Bruyn and W. Alberda van Ekenstein, *Rec. trav. chim.* **22,** 159 (1903).

to a mono-*O*-methylene-L-xylose which is reduced to mono-*O*-methylene-xylitol. The latter must have the 2,4-structure with no neighboring pairs of hydroxyl groups, because it is not attacked by periodic acid.

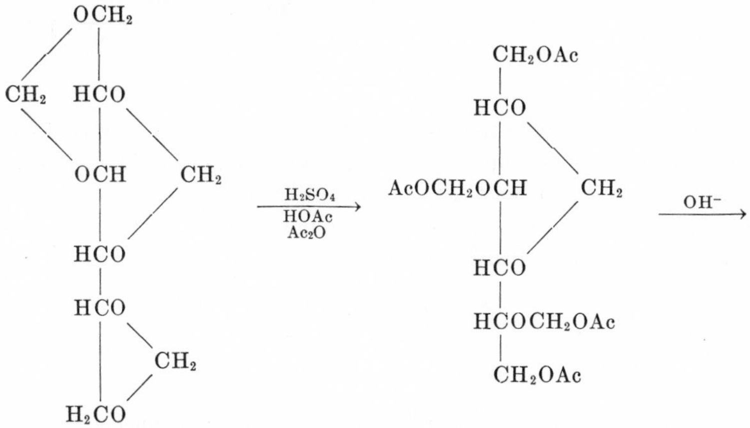

OCH_2
CH_2
HCO
OCH
CH_2
HCO
HCO
CH_2
H_2CO
H_2SO_4
HOAc
Ac_2O
CH_2OAc
HCO
$AcOCH_2OCH$
CH_2
HCO
$HCOCH_2OAc$
CH_2OAc
OH^-

Tri-*O*-methylene D-glucitol

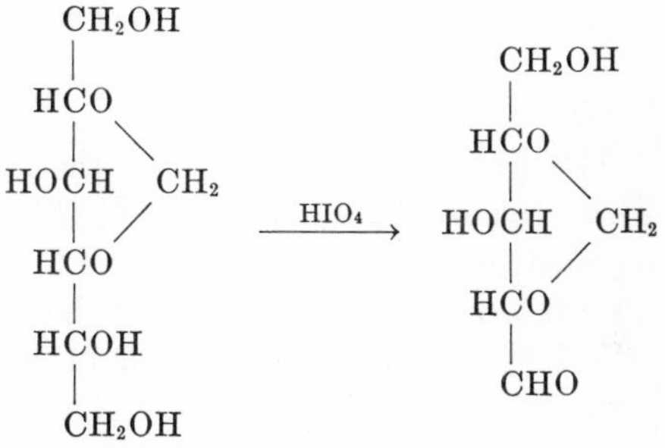

CH_2OH
HCO
HOCH
CH_2
HCO
HCOH
CH_2OH
HIO_4
CH_2OH
HCO
HOCH
CH_2
HCO
CHO

Mono-*O*-methylene-D-glucitol   Mono-*O*-methylene-L-xylose

B. Benzylidene Derivatives

Benzaldehyde reacts (*159*) with D-glucose and with methyl α- and β-D-glucopyranosides to form the 4,6-*O*-benzylidene derivatives. In the *O*-benzylidene and related compounds, the acetal carbon is asymmetric and should give rise to two isomers. Evidence has been evinced that such isomers exist and that some are relatively unstable (*160*).

159. L. Zervas, *Ber.* **64,** 2289 (1931); J. C. Irvine and J. P. Scott, *J. Chem. Soc.* **103,** 575 (1913); H. Ohle and K. Spencker, *Ber.* **61,** 2387 (1928).

160. H. Hibbert and N. M. Carter, *J. Am. Chem. Soc.* **50,** 3376 (1928); A. T. Ness, R. M. Hann, and C. S. Hudson, *ibid.* **70,** 765 (1948); M. A. Oldham and J. Honeyman, *J. Chem. Soc.* p. 986 (1946).

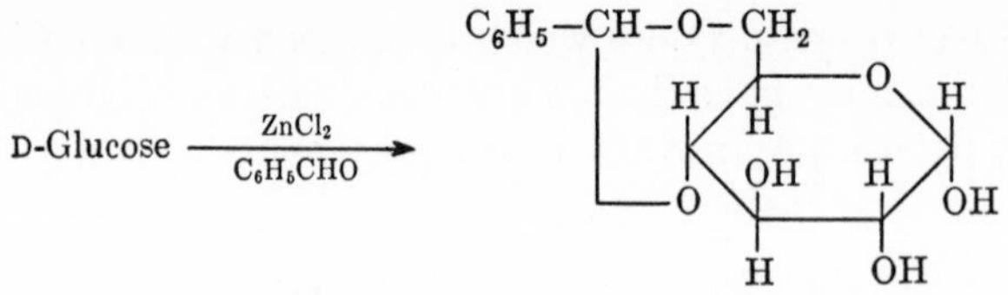

4,6-*O*-Benzylidene-α-D-glucopyranose

The mono-*O*-benzylidene-α-D-glucose, formed according to the reaction illustrated, reduces Fehling solution and forms a hydrazone and an osazone; therefore, it must have carbons 1 and 2 unsubstituted. The following sequence of reactions furnishes evidence to fix the structure of the substance as 4,6-*O*-benzylidene-α-D-glucose (*161*).

Mono-*O*-benzylidene-D-glucose $\xrightarrow[\text{(one mole)}]{(CH_3)_2SO_4,\ NaOH}$

methyl *O*-benzylidene-D-glucoside (I) $\xrightarrow[\text{(excess)}]{(CH_3)_2SO_4}$

methyl *O*-benzylidene-di-*O*-methyl-α-D-glucoside (II); 3-*O*-methyl-D-glucose $\xrightarrow[CH_3OH]{HCl}$

methyl 3-*O*-methyl-α-D-glucoside $\xrightarrow{C_6H_5CHO}$

methyl *O*-benzylidene-3-*O*-methyl-α-D-glucoside $\xrightarrow[NaOH]{(CH_3)_2SO_4}$

methyl *O*-benzylidene-di-*O*-methyl-α-D-glucoside (II)

The latter compound (II) is the same as that (II) synthesized above. From this evidence, the original *O*-benzylidene-D-glucose must have been unsubstituted at carbons 1, 2, and 3. Inasmuch as the *O*-benzylidene group may be removed from methyl *O*-benzylidene-D-glucoside (I) (by catalytic reduction) with the formation of methyl β-D-glucopyranoside, the ring must be of the pyranose type. The benzylidene group must occupy positions 4 and 6, and the original compounds is 4,6-*O*-benzylidene-α-D-glucopyranose.

The condensation of benzaldehyde (and probably other aldehydes) with sugars ordinarily does not produce furanose derivatives as so frequently happens in acetone-condensation reactions, discussed later. When the furanose ring is already present in the sugar derivative undergoing condensation, as in 1,2-*O*-isopropylidene-D-glucofuranose, the acetal ring formed is still of the six-membered type. For the example given, 3,5-*O*-benzylidene-1,2-*O*-isopropylidene-D-glucofuranose is formed (*162*). However, a second isomer with a five-membered ring is formed in substantial quantities (5,6-*O*-benzylidene-1,2-*O*-isopropylidene-D-glucofuranose) (*163*).

161. K. Freudenberg, H. Toepffer, and C. C. Andersen, *Ber*. **61**, 1750 (1928).
162. P. Brigl and H. Grüner, *Ber*. **65**, 1428 (1932).
163. P. A. Levene and A. L. Raymond, *Ber*. **66**, 384 (1933).

C. Condensation with Acetaldehyde and 2-Furaldehyde

Acetaldehyde condenses with D-glucose, in a manner analogous to that for benzaldehyde, to give 4,6-*O*-ethylidene-α-D-glucopyranose (I) (*164*). With alditols, *O*-ethylidene derivatives are formed. The action of sulfuric acid on paraldehyde is a convenient source of acetaldehyde, but with methyl α-D-glucopyranoside a product (II) is formed (methyl 4,6-*O*-ethylidene-2,3-*O*-oxidodiethylidene-α-D-glucopyranoside) which is unique in having a seven-membered ring formed from *trans* hydroxyl groups (*165*).

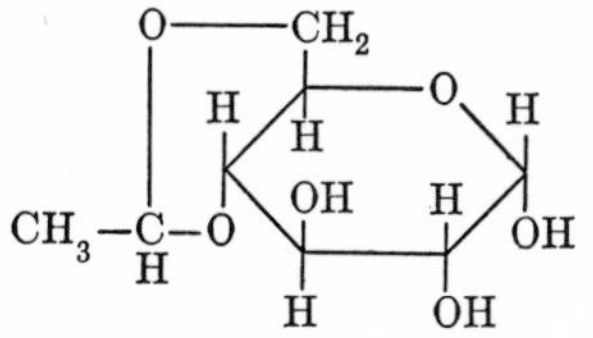

(I)

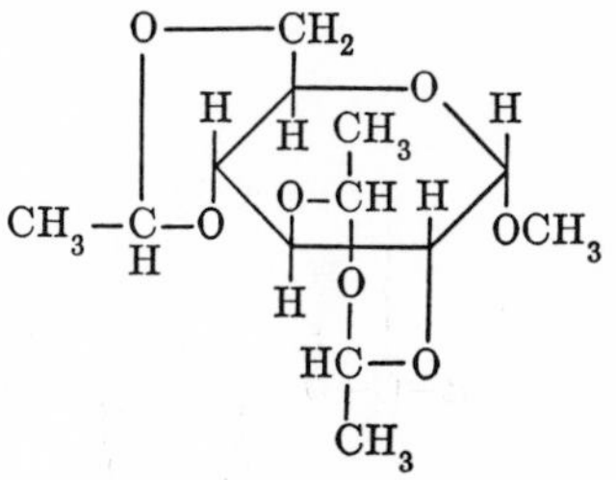

(II)

O-Ethylidene derivatives of alditols have been made by treatment of an alditol with acetylene in the presence of sulfuric acid and mercuric sulfate (*166*). Apparently the intermediate vinyl hydroxyethyl ether is formed which then condenses with a second hydroxyl group.

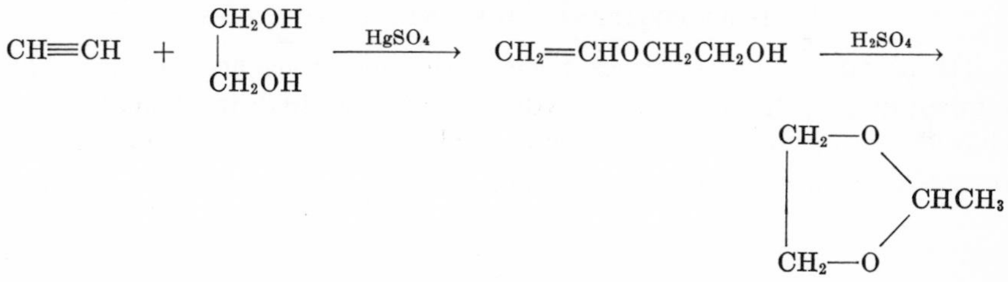

Proof for the mechanism is given by the ease with which the second reaction occurs when the vinyl ether, made by other methods, is allowed to react (*167*).

2-Furaldehyde ("furfural") reacts with methyl α-D-mannopyranoside yielding mono- and di-*O*-furylidene derivatives (*168*) which have both

164. B. Helferich and H. Appel, *Ber.* **64**, 1841 (1931); R. Sutra, *Bull. soc. chim. France* [5] **9**, 794 (1942).

165. H. Appel and W. N. Haworth, *J. Chem. Soc.* p. 793 (1938).

166. Chem. Fabrik Griesheim-Elektron, *German Patent* 271,381 (1912); *Chem. Abstr.* **9**, 356 (1915); J. S. Reichert, J. H. Bailey, and J. A. Nieuwland, *J. Am. Chem. Soc.* **45**, 1552 (1923); H. S. Hill and H. Hibbert, *ibid.* **45**, 3108 (1923).

167. H. S. Hill and L. M. Pidgeon, *J. Am. Chem. Soc.* **50**, 2718 (1928).

168. H. Bredereck, *Ber.* **68**, 777 (1935).

five- and six-membered rings as illustrated in the following formulas. With methyl α-D-glucopyranoside a 4,6-mono derivative was obtained. The furylidene groups cannot be removed by catalytic hydrogenation as is the case for benzylidene groups.

Cyclic acetals made by the reaction of 2-furaldehyde and glycol or glycerol have been suggested as plasticizers for lacquers. In the preparation

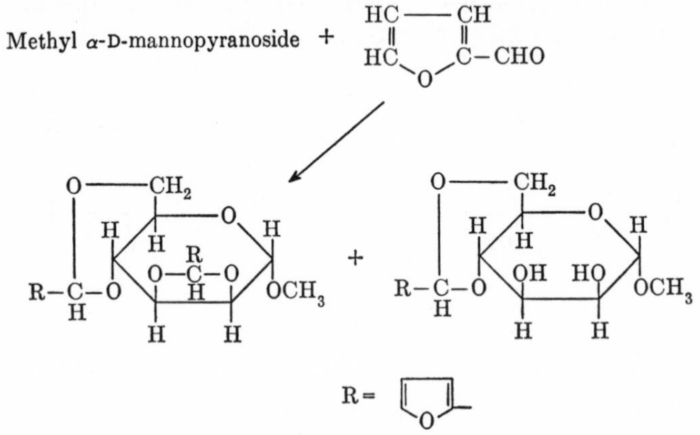
Methyl α-D-mannopyranoside +
R=

of these compounds, no catalyst is added, and the water is removed by azeotropic distillation with benzene (*169*).

D. Isopropylidene (Acetone) Derivatives

The sugars and derivatives react with anhydrous acetone at room temperature in the presence of hydrogen chloride, hydrogen sulfate, zinc chloride, cupric sulfate, or phosphoric anhydride, and di- or mono-*O*-isopropylidene derivatives are formed (*2a*, *170–172*).

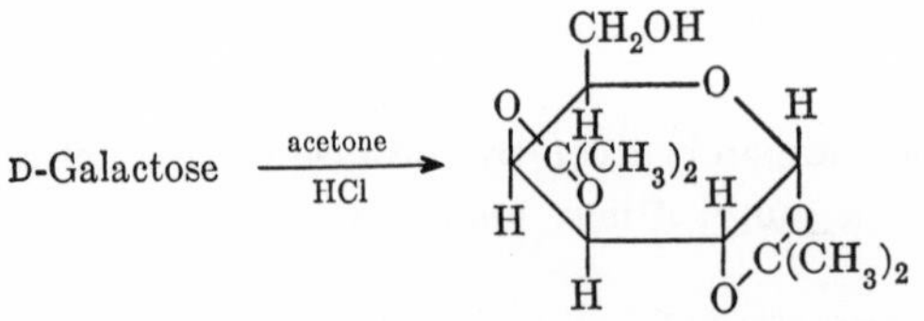
D-Galactose
acetone
HCl

1,2:3,4-Di-*O*-isopropylidene-D-galactopyranose

In most instances, condensation takes place between the acetone and

169. K. H. Hoover, *U. S. Patent* 1,934,309 (1934); *Chem. Abstr.* **28,** 485 (1934).

170. E. Fischer and C. Rund, *Ber.* **49,** 93 (1916).

171. H. Ohle and I. Koller, *Ber.* **57,** 1566 (1924).

172. H. O. L. Fischer and C. Taube, *ibid.* **60,** 485 (1927); L. Smith and J. Lindberg, *Ber.* **64,** 505 (1931); J. W. Pette, *ibid.* **64,** 1567; D. J. Bell, *J. Chem. Soc.* p. 1874 (1935); H. V. Grunenberg, C. Bredt, and W. Freudenberg, *J. Am. Chem. Soc.* **60,** 1507 (1938).

cis hydroxyl groups on contiguous carbon atoms in such a manner as to favor the introduction of two *O*-isopropylidene residues into the molecule (*170, 173*). For α-D-galactopyranose, the hydroxyl groups in positions 1 and 2 are on the same side of the ring (*cis*), and those in positions 3 and 4 also have a *cis* relation although the latter pair is on the opposite side of the ring from that at carbons 1 and 2. One acetone molecule reacts with one of these *cis* pairs and a second with the other pair. However, α-D-glucopyranose has only one pair of *cis* hydroxyls (those at positions 1 and 2) and, in order to make a second pair available, the furanose isomer reacts and forms 1,2:5,6-di-*O*-isopropylidene-D-glucofuranose.

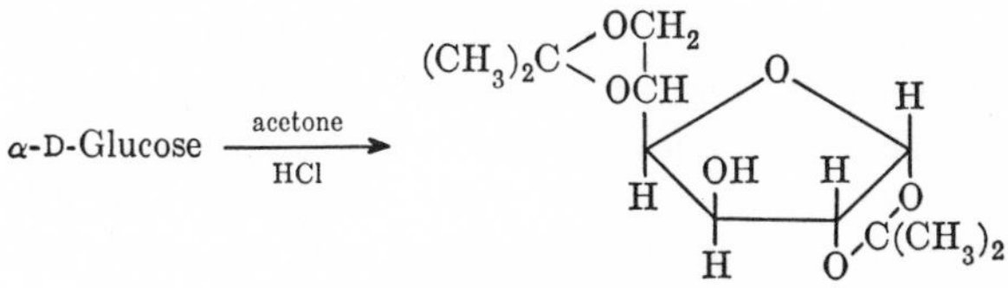
α-D-Glucose
acetone
HCl
$(CH_3)_2C$
OCH_2
OCH
O
H
OH
H
H
O
$C(CH_3)_2$
H
O

1,2:5,6-Di-*O*-isopropylidene-D-glucofuranose

D-Mannose also can provide two pairs of *cis* hydroxyls only in the furanose ring form, and the 2,3:5,6-di-*O*-isopropylidene-D-mannofuranose is formed (*174*). When a ring change is not possible, as with the glycosides under nonhydrolytic conditions, or when a ring change will not provide two free hydroxyls, as with the pentoses, the second acetone molecule may condense with hydroxyl groups which are not on contiguous carbon atoms. Thus, methyl α-D-mannopyranoside reacts with acetone (free of methyl alcohol) containing hydrogen chloride to produce methyl 2,3:4,6-di-*O*-isopropylidene-D-mannopyranoside (*175*).

The *O*-isopropylidene groups are easily removed by dilute acids. In most instances, one of the groups is much more readily removed than the other; by selection of the proper conditions, one group is hydrolyzed and the mono-*O*-isopropylidene sugar obtained. For di-*O*-isopropylidene-D-glucose, the group in the 5,6-position is hydrolyzed more than forty times as rapidly as that in the 1,2-position (*73*). Hence, treatment with acetic acid, or nitric acid and ethyl acetate, produces 1,2-*O*-isopropylidene-D-glucose from the di-*O*-isopropylidene derivative (*176*). The remaining group is hydrolyzed

173. C. G. Anderson, W. Charlton, and W. N. Haworth, *J. Chem. Soc.* p. 1329 (1929).

174. K. Freudenberg and A. Wolf, *Ber.* **58,** 300 (1925); E. H. Goodyear and W. N. Haworth, *J. Chem. Soc.* p. 3136 (1927).

175. R. G. Ault, W. N. Haworth, and E. L. Hirst, *J. Chem. Soc.* p. 1012 (1935).

176. H. W. Coles, L. D. Goodhue, and R. M. Hixon, *J. Am. Chem. Soc.* **51,** 523 (1929).

more than 500 times as rapidly as the alkyl glycosides and disaccharides (*73*).

The 1,2-*O*-isopropylidene sugars have a linkage formed from two acetal hydroxyls, as in sucrose. Hence, it would be expected that the group would be removed easily by acids. It is of interest that the 5,6-*O*-isopropylidene group is even more easily removed.

The structures of the *O*-isopropylidene sugars have been extensively investigated particularly by application of the methylation procedure (*177*).

Di-*O*-isopropylidene-D-glucose yields, upon methylation and subsequent acid hydrolysis, crystalline 3-*O*-methyl-D-glucose. The mono-*O*-isopropylidene-D-glucose obtained by the removal of one acetone group is substituted on the reducing carbon since it has no action on Fehling solution. Methylation produces mono-*O*-isopropylidene-tri-*O*-methyl-D-glucose which must have a furanose structure since, after acid hydrolysis and further methylation, methyl tetra-*O*-methyl-D-glucofuranoside is formed. This evidence fixes the structure of the di-*O*-isopropylidene-D-glucose as having only the hydroxyl on carbon 3 free and as having a furanose ring; the acetone groups must then be in positions 1,2 and 5,6 (*173*). For the mono-*O*-isopropylidene-D-glucose, the single acetone group is located at positions 1 and 2. A structural isomer, 1,2:3,5-di-*O*-isopropylidene-D-glucose (*178*), results for the condensation of acetone with 6-substituted D-glucoses.

Haworth, Hirst, and Chamberlain, (*179*) have isolated a tri-*O*-isopropylidene-D-gluconic acid which is readily hydrolyzed to a di-*O*-isopropylidene derivative, and this produces 2-*O*-methyl-D-gluconic acid upon methylation and subsequent hydrolysis. Positions 1 and 2 are thus substituted in the tri-*O*-isopropylidene derivative, and the carboxyl group is involved in the isopropylidene linkage.

D-Fructose condenses with acetone (*2a, 171*) to form two isomeric di-*O*-isopropylidene-D-fructoses. The first derivative upon methylation yields a monomethyl derivative which on partial hydrolysis gives a mono-*O*-isopropylidene-mono-*O*-methyl-D-fructose and on complete hydrolysis a mono-*O*-methyl-D-fructose which is convertible to the same osazone as 3-*O*-methyl-D-glucose. The methoxyl group is therefore at carbon 3. The mono-*O*-isopropylidene-3-*O*-methyl-D-fructose, after methylation and acid hydrolysis of the *O*-isopropylidene and glycosidic methoxyl group yields a tri-*O*-methyl-D-fructopyranose; the ring structure is demonstrated by further methylation to tetra-*O*-methyl-D-fructopyranose of known struc-

177. W. N. Haworth, "The Constitution of the Sugars." Edward Arnold, London, 1929.

178. H. Ohle and L. von Vargha, *Ber.* **62,** 2425 (1929).

179. W. N. Haworth, E. L. Hirst, and K. A. Chamberlain, *J. Chem. Soc.* p. 795 (1937).

ture. This evidence places the free hydroxyl of the di-*O*-isopropylidene-D-fructose at position 3 and the oxygen ring between carbons 2 and 6. This derivative is then 1,2:4,5-di-*O*-isopropylidene-D-fructose (I), and the corresponding mono-*O*-isopropylidene-D-fructose is 1,2-*O*-isopropylidene-D-fructopyranose (*180*).

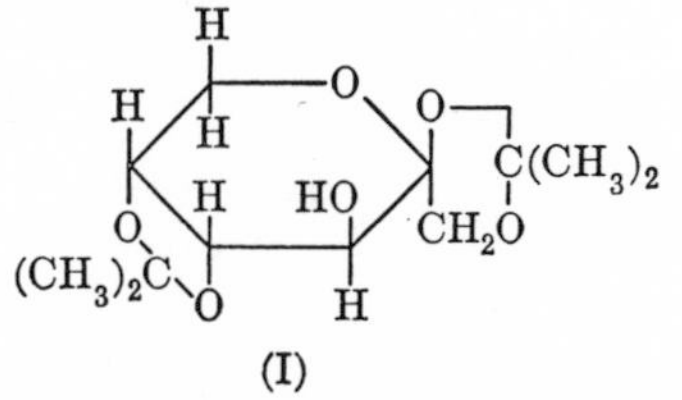

(I)

1,2:4,5-Di-*O*-isopropylidene-D-fructose

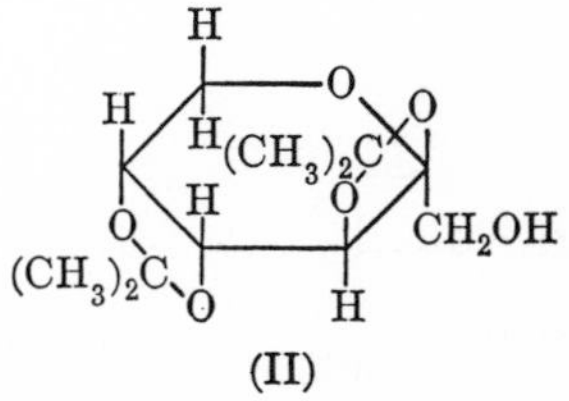

(II)

2,3:4,5-Di-*O*-isopropylidene-D-fructose

The structure of the second di-*O*-isopropylidene-D-fructose has been defined (*181*). It is known that carbon 1 in this isomer is open since, on oxidation with alkaline permanganate, an acid was obtained, without acetone removal, which on acid hydrolysis yielded 1-*C*-carboxy-D-arabinose (2-keto-D-gluconic acid) (*182*). Acid hydrolysis yielded a mono-*O*-isopropylidene-D-fructose characterized as a crystalline triacetate. Deacetylation of this nonreducing compound yielded a product consuming one mole of periodate per mole of substance. Only two possible nonreducing mono-*O*-isopropylidene derivatives are compatible with this analysis: 1,2-*O*-isopropylidene-D-fructofuranose and 2,3-*O*-isopropylidene-D-fructopyranose. The former is eliminated by the formation of a carboxyl group at carbon 1. Since hydrolysis by aqueous acid will not shift the position of an attached isopropylidene group, the structure of this mono-*O*-isopropylidene-D-fructose is therefore established as 2,3-*O*-isopropylidene-D-fructopyranose and the second diisopropylidene derivative is established as 2,3:4,5-di-*O*-isopropylidene-D-fructose (II).

Mono- and di-*O*-isopropylidene-D-glucoses, when injected into animals, are mainly eliminated in the urine, but an appreciable quantity of acetone is exhaled, particularly in the case of the latter derivative (*183*). The di-*O*-isopropylidene derivative is toxic to rabbits and rats although the mono derivative is nontoxic.

180. K. Freudenberg and A. Doser, *Ber.* **56,** 1243 (1923); H. Ohle, *ibid.* **60,** 1168 (1927); C. G. Anderson, W. Charlton, W. N. Haworth, and V. S. Nicholson, *J. Chem. Soc.* p. 1337 (1929).

181. M. L. Wolfrom, W. L. Shilling, and W. W. Binkley, *J. Am. Chem. Soc.* **72,** 4544 (1950).

182. H. Ohle, *Ber.* **58,** 2577 (1925); H. Ohle and G. Berend, *ibid.* **60,** 1159 (1927).

183. E. Dingemanse and E. Laqueur, *Enzymologia* **4,** 57 (1937).

E. Acetoacetic Ester Derivatives

D-Glucose condenses with ethyl acetoacetate and other β-keto esters and with β-diketones, in the presence of anhydrous zinc chloride, to give derivatives of furan (*184*). The constitution of some of the compounds has been verified by oxidation with lead tetraacetate (*185*) and with periodate ion (*186*). The aldose would appear to react in the form of its 1,2-enediol.

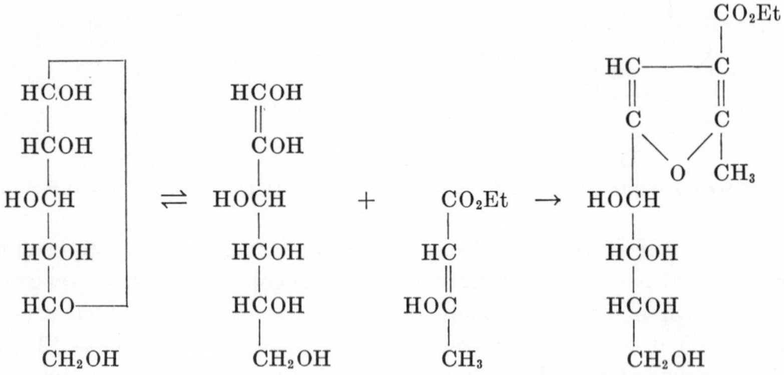

CO_2Et
HC
C
C
C
O
CH_3
HCOH
HCOH
HOCH
HCOH
HCO
CH_2OH
HCOH
COH
HOCH
HCOH
HCOH
CH_2OH
+
CO_2Et
HC
HOC
CH_3
HOCH
HCOH
HCOH
CH_2OH

α-D-Glucopyranose

The reaction of ethyl acetoacetate has been extended to glycolaldehyde and other aldoses under suitable selection of experimental conditions; it is probably applicable to aldoses in general. D-Fructose gives a lower yield of a crystalline product which has the D-*arabino*-tetrahydroxybutyl chain at the β-position of the furan ring. The reaction has been applied successfully to other ketoses and to the simple α-hydroxy ketones. 2-Amino-2-deoxy-D-glucose (D-glucosamine) reacts in aqueous acetone to give a pyrrole derivative.

Compounds of this type have considerable biochemical interest because they may explain the antiketogenic action of D-glucose in preventing the formation of ketone bodies during animal metabolism. *In vitro* studies have shown that the oxidation of the ester of acetoacetic acid by hydrogen peroxide proceeds much more rapidly in the presence of D-glucose than in its absence (*187*).

184. E. S. West, *J. Biol. Chem.* **66,** 63 (1925); **74,** 561 (1927); C. V. Moore, R. S. Erlanger, and E. S. West, *ibid.* **113,** 43 (1936); F. García Gonzáles, *Anales fís. y quím. (Madrid)* **32,** 815 (1934); *Advances in Carbohydrate Chem.* **11,** 97 (1956).

185. A. Müller and I. Varga, *Ber.* **72,** 1993 (1939).

186. J. K. N. Jones, *J. Chem. Soc.* p. 116 (1945).

187. P. A. Shaffer, *J. Biol. Chem.* **47,** 433, 449 (1921).

V. THE POLYOLS

Part I

Acyclic Polyols (Alditols or Glycitols)

R. L. Lohmar*

The designation "polyol" used here is synonymous with the longer customary term, polyhydric alcohol. The polyols may conveniently be divided into two classes, the acyclic polyols (alditols, glycitols, or "sugar alcohols"), which will be considered in Part I, and the alicyclic polyols (or cyclitols), which will compose Part II. Examples of each class are sorbitol and *myo*-inositol.

As a group the alditols are crystalline substances covering a wide range in melting point and varying in taste from faintly sweet to very sweet. The distribution in nature apparently is limited to plants of higher and lower orders. The alditols found in mannas and exudates are sometimes of secondary origin as a result of the action of bacteria on carbohydrates in the exudates. Polyols are found both in the free and combined form; glycosides in which polyols supply the aglycon groups occur in plants and an ester of a hexitol occurs in algae.

Alditols, particularly glycerol (*1*), ethylene glycol, sorbitol, and D-mannitol, have widespread commercial applications, frequently as a result of their hygroscopic properties. The organic monoesters, particularly of long-chain fatty acids, may have surface-active properties which make them of interest as emulsifiers, but the usual conditions of commercial esterification produce anhydro derivatives simultaneously (Chapter VII). Nitrate esters are important as explosives and as pharmaceuticals. The acetal derivatives (Chapter IV) have been extensively prepared and studied, but as yet have found no practical application.

* This chapter in the first edition was prepared by Dr. Sol Soltzberg, partially from notes made by R. Max Goepp, Jr.

1. Although ethylene glycol and glycerol (diol and triol, respectively) may be properly classified as sugar alcohols, they will not be considered here as they have been suitably covered in several monographs. See G. O. Curme, Jr., and F. Johnston, "Glycols," American Chemical Society Monograph 114, Reinhold, New York, 1952; C. S. Miner and N. N. Dalton, "Glycerol," American Chemical Society Monograph 117, Reinhold, New York, 1953.

Cheap methods for the synthesis of various deoxy alditols and ketoses with three to six carbon atoms have been developed, with acetylene as the starting material (*1a*). Propargyl alcohol (1-propyn-3-ol) and 3-butyn-2-ol are important intermediates. Formaldehyde or acetaldehyde react with hydrogen atoms adjacent to a triple bond, in the presence of copper acetylide catalyst.

$$HC{\equiv}CH \xrightarrow{HCHO} CH_2OH{-}C{\equiv}CH \rightarrow CH_2OH{-}C{\equiv}C{-}CH_2OH$$

1. CONFIGURATIONS, OCCURRENCE, AND PREPARATION

A. Tetritols

All of the theoretically possible tetritols are known.

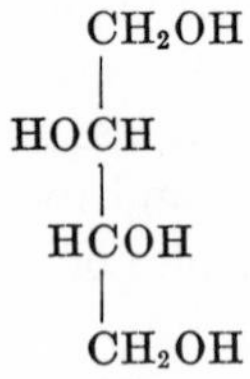

(I)
D-Threitol
("*l*-Erythritol")

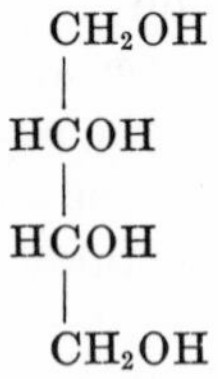

(II)
Erythritol
("*meso*-Erythritol")

D-Threitol (I), m.p. 88°, $[\alpha]_D$ +4.3° (H_2O); dibenzylidene derivative, m.p. 231°; is not found in nature. It was synthesized by Maquenne (*2*) from D-xylose by way of the Wohl degradation and sodium amalgam reduction.

L-Threitol, like its enantiomorph, is purely synthetic. It was obtained by Bertrand (*3*) from erythritol by bacterial oxidation to L-erythrulose followed by reduction with sodium amalgam.

DL-Threitol, tetraacetate m.p. 54–55°; dibenzylidene derivative m.p. 217–219°; was synthesized by novel means starting from 3,4-epoxy-1-butene (*4*). The steps required are given as follows:

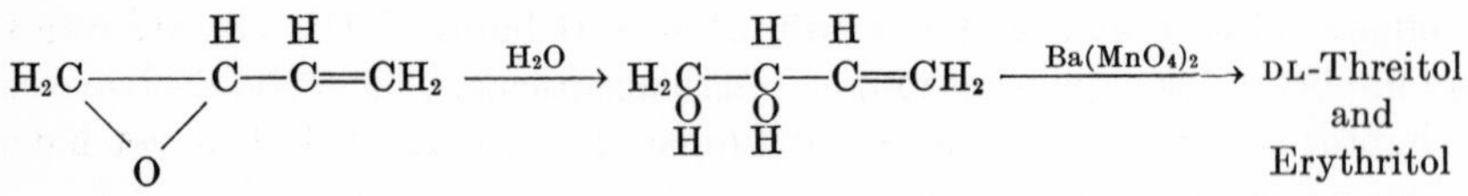

Erythrol

A somewhat different synthesis is based on the *cis* and *trans* forms of

1a. J. W. Reppe, "Acetylene Chemistry." Meyer, New York, 1949.
2. L. Maquenne, *Compt. rend.* **130,** 1402 (1900).
3. G. Bertrand, *Compt. rend.* **130,** 1472 (1900).
4. H. Pariselle, *Compt. rend.* **150,** 1343 (1910).

2-butene-1,4-diol diacetate (*5*). In this synthesis the separation of the *cis* and *trans* forms of the ethylenic precursor makes fractionation of the tetritols unnecessary.

Erythritol (II), m.p. 120°; tetraacetate, m.p. 85°; dibenzylidene derivative, m.p. 201°; occurs in nature in certain algae (*6*), lichens (*7*), and grasses (*8*).

In addition to the classical methods (reduction of appropriate aldose or ketose (*2*, *9*)), erythritol was obtained synthetically from 3,4-epoxy-1-butene (*4*) and from epichlorohydrin through the following series of steps (*10*):

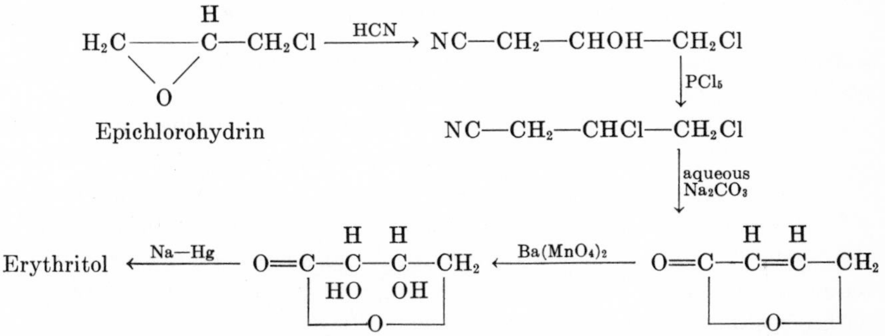
H
H_2C—C—CH_2Cl
HCN
NC—CH_2—CHOH—CH_2Cl
O
PCl_5
Epichlorohydrin
NC—CH_2—CHCl—CH_2Cl
aqueous Na_2CO_3
Erythritol
Na—Hg
H H
O=C—C—C—CH_2
HO OH
O
$Ba(MnO_4)_2$
H H
O=C—C=C—CH_2
O

Griner (*11*) also describes a very interesting synthesis from butadiene. More recently Glattfeld and Stack (*12*) obtained erythritol by the high-pressure reduction of butyl erythronate.

B. Pentitols

All of the pentitols predicted by theory are known. As in the case of the tetritols, only the D-configurations of the optically active polyols will be indicated.

D-Arabitol (III), m.p. 102°, $[\alpha]_D$ +7.82° (borax); pentaacetate, m.p. 76°; has been found in many lichens (*13*), both in the free form and as umbilicin,

5. R. A. Raphael, *J. Chem. Soc.* p. 401 (1952).

6. M. Bamberger and A. Landsiedl, *Monatsh.* **21,** 571 (1900); J. Tischer, *Z. physiol. Chem.* **243,** 103 (1936).

7. O. Hesse, *Ann.* **117,** 297 (1861); *J. prakt. Chem.* [2] **92,** 425 (1915); A. Goris and P. Ronceray, *Chem. Zentr.* **78,** I, 111 (1907).

8. A. W. Hofmann, *Ber.* **7,** 508 (1874).

9. O. Ruff, *Ber.* **32,** 3677 (1899).

10. R. Lespieau, *Bull. soc. chim. France* [4] **1,** 1112 (1907).

11. G. Griner, *Bull. soc. chim. France* [3] **9,** 218 (1893).

12. J. W. E. Glattfeld and A. M. Stack, *J. Am. Chem. Soc.* **59,** 753 (1937).

13. B. Lindberg, A. Misiorny, and C. A. Wachtmeister, *Acta Chem. Scand.* **7,** 591 (1953).

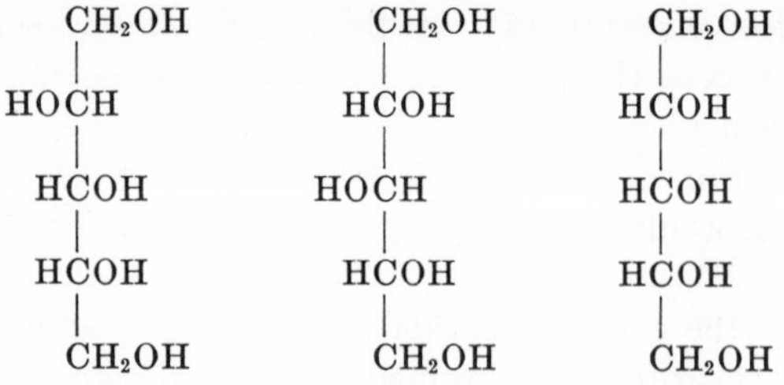

(III) D-Arabitol (D-Lyxitol) — (IV) Xylitol (*meso*) — (V) Ribitol (Adonitol) (*meso*)

a galactoside of D-arabitol. It is also found in the mushroom *Fistulina hepatica* to the extent of 9.5% on the dry weight (*14*).

Synthetically, D-arabitol has been obtained by the reduction of either D-arabinose (*15*) or D-lyxose (*16*) by means of sodium amalgam.

The reported physical constants of L-arabitol agree with those of the D-form except that the rotation in borax solution is somewhat smaller ($[\alpha]_D$ $-5.4°$ (*17*). It does not occur naturally and has been prepared by the reduction of L-arabinose (*18*) and by employing the Cannizzaro reaction with L-arabinose in the presence of nickel (*19*).

DL-Arabitol, m.p. 105°; pentaacetate, m.p. 95°; is not found in nature and can be prepared from an equimolar mixture of the enantiomorphs. It has been obtained synthetically along with ribitol by Lespieau (*20*). The synthetic approach used by Lespieau is of general application and is equivalent to a total synthesis. The steps taken are as follows:

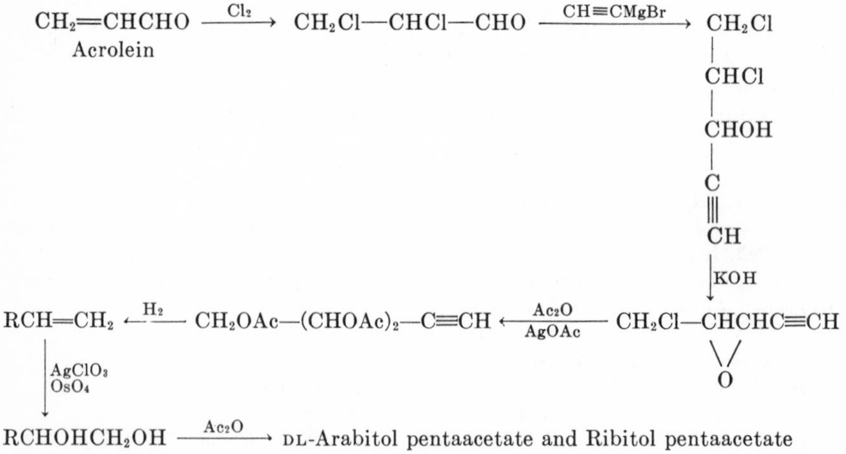
CH₂=CHCHO
Acrolein
Cl₂
CH₂Cl—CHCl—CHO
CH≡CMgBr
KOH
Ac₂O
AgOAc
H₂
RCH=CH₂
CH₂OAc—(CHOAc)₂—C≡CH
AgClO₃
OsO₄
RCHOHCH₂OH
DL-Arabitol pentaacetate and Ribitol pentaacetate

14. M. Frèrejacque, *Compt. rend.* **208,** 1123 (1939).
15. O. Ruff, *Ber.* **32,** 550 (1899).
16. O. Ruff and G. Ollendorf, *Ber.* **33,** 1798 (1900).

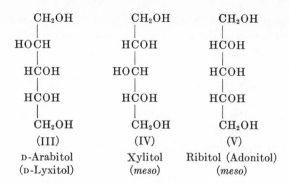

A more convenient method for synthesizing these pentitols from an acetylenic precursor is that of Raphael (*21*). The essential improvement over Lespieau's method is the use of aqueous *N*-bromosuccinimide in the hydroxylation of the terminal double bond.

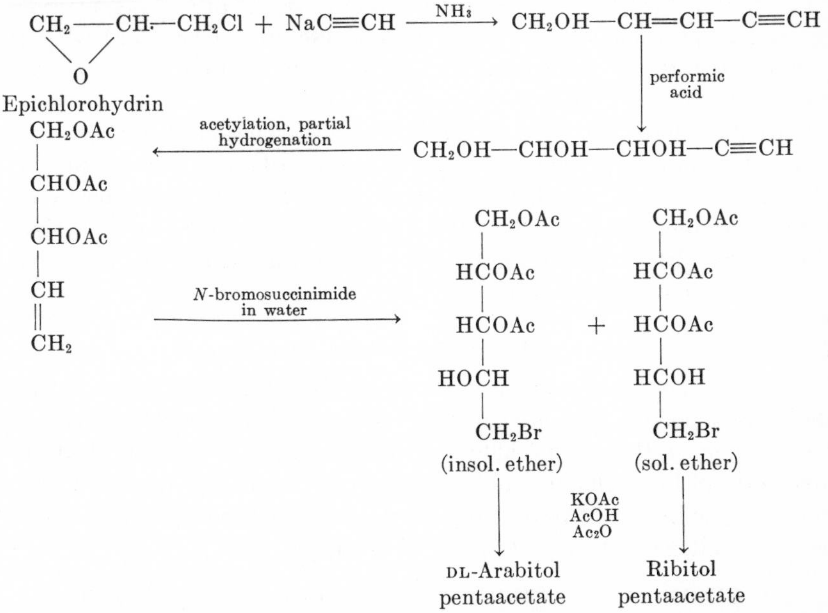
CH2—CH—CH2Cl + NaC≡CH
NH3
CH2OH—CH=CH—C≡CH
O
Epichlorohydrin
performic acid
CH2OAc
CHOAc
CHOAc
CH
CH2
acetylation, partial hydrogenation
CH2OH—CHOH—CHOH—C≡CH
N-bromosuccinimide in water
CH2OAc
HCOAc
HCOAc
HOCH
CH2Br
(insol. ether)
+
CH2OAc
HCOAc
HCOAc
HCOH
CH2Br
(sol. ether)
KOAc
AcOH
Ac2O
DL-Arabitol pentaacetate
Ribitol pentaacetate

Xylitol (IV), m.p. 61–61.5° (metastable modification), 93–94.5° (stable modification); tetraacetate, m.p. 62°; is not found in nature despite the abundance of its parent aldose, D-xylose (wood sugar). Although xylitol has been known for over fifty years (*17*, *22*), it had never been obtained crystalline until Wolfrom and Kohn (*23*) obtained the metastable form in 1942. Shortly thereafter the stable modification was reported by Carson, Waisbrot, and Jones (*24*), who were able to go from one form to the other at will. In the more recent work, D-xylose was reduced over nickel under pressure, whereas Fischer employed sodium amalgam. As pointed out by

17. E. Fischer and R. Stahel, *Ber.* **24,** 538 (1891).

18. H. Kiliani, *Ber.* **20,** 1234 (1887).

19. M. Delépine and A. Horeau, *Bull. soc. chim. France* [5] **4,** 1524 (1937).

20. R. Lespieau, *Advances in Carbohydrate Chem.* **2,** 107 (1946); *Compt. rend.* **203,** 145 (1936).

21. R. A. Raphael, *J. Chem. Soc.* p. S 44 (1949).

22. E. Fischer, *Ber.* **27,** 2487 (1894).

23. M. L. Wolfrom and E. J. Kohn, *J. Am. Chem. Soc.* **64,** 1739 (1942).

24. J. F. Carson, S. W. Waisbrot, and F. T. Jones, *J. Am. Chem. Soc.* **65,** 1777 (1943).

Hudson (*25*), pressure hydrogenation in general will yield a purer produc than that obtained by the sodium amalgam reduction of sugars.

Xylitol is one of the sweetest polyols known.

Ribitol (adonitol) (V), m.p. 102°; dibenzylidene derivative, m.p. 164–165°; has thus far been found in nature in only two plants, *Adonis vernalis* (*26*) and *Bupleurum falactum* root (the Chinese drug, Chei-Hou) (*27*). In a combined form it is a constituent of riboflavin (vitamin B_2) (see also Chapter VIII).

Synthetic ribitol has been prepared by the reduction of L-ribose with sodium amalgam (*28*). Oddly enough, whereas L-ribose is a synthetic pentose, ribitol does not appear to have been prepared from the naturally occurring D-ribose. Lespieau (*20, 29*) and Raphael (*21*) have each obtained ribitol along with DL-arabitol in their syntheses from noncarbohydrate precursors, mentioned previously.

C. Hexitols (*30*)

There are ten stereoisomeric hexitols possible and all are known. Like other acyclic polyols, they are named by adding the suffix "-itol" to the root of the name of the parent aldose. However, usage has established the name sorbitol for D-glucitol, and galactitol is often called dulcitol. Galactitol is a *meso* form, but D- (or L-)galactitol is necessary when the molecule has been rendered optically active by substitution.

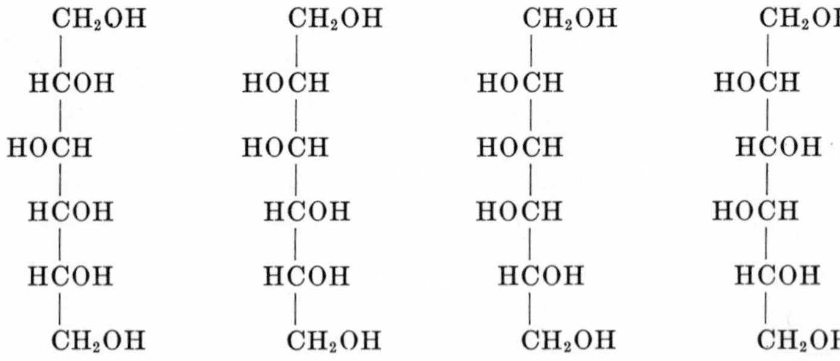

(VI) Sorbitol (D-Glucitol) — (VII) D-Mannitol — (VIII) D-Talitol — (IX) D-Iditol

25. C. S. Hudson, *Advances in Carbohydrate Chem.* **1,** 21 (1945).

26. W. V. Podwykssozki, *Arch. Pharm.* **227,** 141 (1889); E. Merck, *ibid.* **231,** 129 (1893).

27. F. Wessely and S. Wang, *Monatsh.* **72,** 168 (1938).

28. E. Fischer, *Ber.* **26,** 633 (1893).

29. R. Lespieau, *Bull. soc. chim. France* [5] **5,** 1638 (1938).

30. R. L. Lohmar and R. M. Goepp, Jr., *Advances in Carbohydrate Chem.* **4,** 211 (1949)

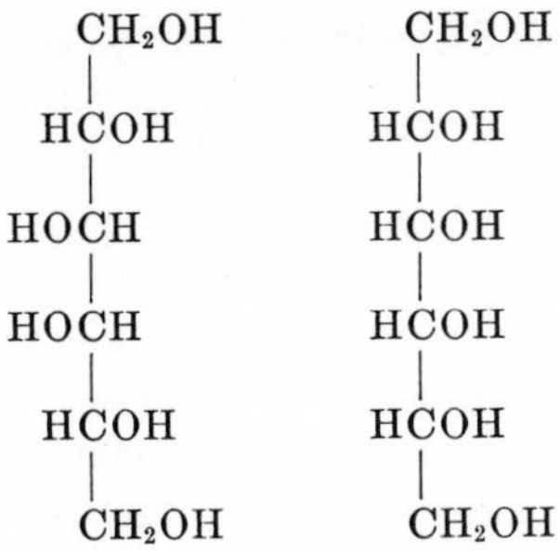

(X) Galactitol (Dulcitol) (*meso*)   (XI) Allitol (*meso*)

The physical properties of the hexitols and their most accessible derivatives, the hexaacetates, are given in Table I. Since the properties of the L-forms are recognizable from those of their enantiomorphs, the L-forms are not listed.

Sorbitol (D-glucitol, "D-sorbitol," "sorbite") (VI) is one of the most widespread of all the naturally occurring polyols. It is found exclusively in plants, apparently ranging from algae (seaweed) to the higher orders, especially in the fruit and berries, but not in grapes or only to an insignificant

TABLE I

PHYSICAL PROPERTIES OF THE HEXITOLS (*30*)

Hexitol	M.p. (°C.)	$[\alpha]_D$ in water	Hexaacetate M.p. (°C.)	Hexaacetate $[\alpha]_D$ in chloroform
Sorbitol				
stable form	97	−1.9°[a]	99	+10.0°
labile form	92			
D-Mannitol	166	−2.1°[b]	126	+25.0°
D-Iditol	73.5	+3.5°	121–2	+25.3°
D-Talitol	87–8	+3.2°	—	—
Galactitol	188.5	*meso*	168–9	*meso*
Allitol	150–1	*meso*	61	*meso*
DL-Glucitol	136–8	DL	117–19	DL
DL-Mannitol	170	DL	—	
DL-Iditol	—		165–6	DL
DL-Talitol	95–6	DL	—	

[a] $[\alpha]_D$ + 108° in acidified ammonium molybdate.
[b] $[\alpha]_D$ + 141° in acidified ammonium molybdate.

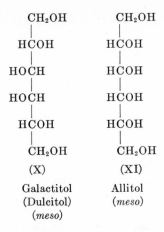

extent. It was discovered in the fresh juice of the berries of the mountain ash (*Sorbus aucuparia* L.) by Boussingault in 1872; sorbose had been found earlier in the fermented juice by Pelouze (1852). In the red seaweed *Bostrychia scorpoides*, sorbitol is found to the extent of 13.6% (*31*) and in *Sorbus commixta* Nedlund, to the amount of 10% (*32*). Strain (*33*) has examined a large number of plants and determined their sorbitol contents. Fruit of the plant family Rosaceae, such as pears, apples, cherries, prunes, peaches, and apricots, contain appreciable amounts of sorbitol (*34*).

Sorbitol has been obtained synthetically from D-glucose by reduction with sodium amalgam and by pressure hydrogenation using platinum, Raney nickel, or Adkins-type nickel catalyst. It has also been obtained by the electrolytic reduction of glucose and by the pressure hydrogenation of gluconic lactones.

Of the various processes, pressure hydrogenation and electrolytic reduction of D-glucose have been the industrially preferred operations (*35*). As a result of these two processes and the advent of cheap crystalline glucose of high purity, sorbitol is no longer a chemical curiosity but an established cheap article of commerce generally sold in aqueous solution.

By use of drastic conditions, hydrogenolysis results and glycerol, glycols, and other polyhydric alcohols are formed. Under certain conditions (*36*) yields of glycerol as high as 80% may be obtained. Although this is thought to make glycerol from sugars competitive with that from petroleum derivatives, the process has not found commercial use in this country. However, a similar process was used in Germany during World War II to make "glycerogen," a mixture of various polyhydric alcohols useful as a humectant.

An interesting variation of the hydrogenation process involves the use of a special cobalt sulfide catalyst to produce 1-deoxy-1-mercaptosorbitol (*37*) (thiosorbitol) from glucose.

The electrolytic process, which is a refinement of the original Creighton process (*35*), has been superceded by continuous pressure hydrogenation with a nickel catalyst.

L-Glucitol (D-gulitol) is not found in nature. It has been synthesized by

31. P. Hass and T. G. Hill, *Biochem. J.* **26**, 987 (1932).

32. Y. Asahina and H. Shimoda, *J. Pharm. Soc. Japan* **50**, 1 (1930).

33. H. H. Strain, *J. Am. Chem. Soc.* **59**, 2264 (1937); **56**, 1756 (1934).

34. C. Vincent and Delachanal, *Compt. rend.* **109**, 676 (1889).

35. R. M. Goepp, Jr., M. T. Sanders, and S. Soltzberg, *in* "Encyclopedia of Chemical Technology" (R. E. Kirk and D. F. Othmer, eds.), Vol. 1, p. 321. Interscience, New York, 1947.

36. R. R. Bottoms, *U. S. Patent*, 2,335,731 (1943).

37. M. W. Farlow, M. Hunt, C. M. Langkammerer, W. A. Lazier, W. J. Peppel, and F. K. Signaigo, *J. Am. Chem. Soc.* **70**, 1392 (1948); W. A. Lazier and F. K. Signaigo, *U. S. Patent* 2,402,640 (1946).

the reduction of D-gulose by sodium amalgam and by catalytic high-pressure hydrogenation (*17*, *38*), and from D-sorbose by means of sodium amalgam (*39*).

DL-Glucitol (DL-gulitol) has been made by mixing equimolar quantities of the two components and has also been isolated in small yield from a commercial sorbitol prepared by the electrolytic reduction of D-glucose under alkaline conditions (*38*).

D-Mannitol (VII), like sorbitol, is widespread among plants. However, unlike sorbitol, it is frequently found in exudates of plants. It is probably for this reason and because D-mannitol is a highly crystalline and only moderately soluble polyol that it was the first crystalline polyol discovered (*40*). It was isolated from the manna of the flowering or manna ash, *Fraxinus ornus*. It is also found in the exudates of the olive and plane trees, constituting 80 to 90 % of the latter's exudate (*41*). For a time D-mannitol was obtained commercially in Sicily from the sap of *Fraxinus rotundifolis*. Of all the natural sources, marine algae offer the greatest potential source of D-mannitol; it is found in all brown seaweeds. It is apparently a primary product of photosynthesis in the fronds which contain, at certain times of the year, over 20 % of D-mannitol (*42*). D-Mannitol is also found in grasses (*42a*).

There have been few reports of the occurrence of D-mannitol in the combined form. A monoacetate and mono- and diglucosides of D-mannitol have been found in algae (*42b*), and mannitol may be a terminal unit in the polysaccharide laminarin (*42c*).

D-Mannitol has been synthesized by several methods. The commercial methods have been the electroreduction and more recently catalytic reduction of D-glucose, under more or less alkaline conditions; sorbitol is formed simultaneously. Depending on the alkalinity, over 20 % of the glucose can be converted to D-mannitol in this manner. Catalytic hydrogenation of invert sugar to give a similar mixture of D-mannitol and sorbitol would appear to be a method capable of commercial exploitation.

For the best laboratory preparation, D-mannitol is obtained by the

38. M. L. Wolfrom, B. W. Lew, R. A. Hales, and R. M. Goepp, Jr., *J. Am. Chem. Soc.*, **68**, 2342 (1946).

39. C. A. Lobry de Bruyn and W. Alberda van Ekenstein, *Rec. trav. chim.* **19**, 7 (1900).

40. Proust, *Ann. chim. phys.* [1] **57**, 144 (1806).

41. E. Jandrier, *Compt. rend.* **117**, 498 (1893).

42. See: W. A. P. Black, *J. Soc. Chem. Ind.* **67**, 165 (1948).

42a. V. D. Harwood, *J. Sci. Food Agr.* **5**, 453 (1954).

42b. B. Lindberg, *Acta Chem. Scand.* **7**, 1119, 1218 (1953); B. Lindberg and J. McPherson, *ibid.* **8**, 1547 (1954).

42c. S. Peat, W. J. Whelan, and H. G. Lawley, *Chemistry & Industry* p. 35 (1955).

catalytic reduction of D-mannose obtained from the vegetable ivory nut (see Chapter II), or by the reduction of D-fructose or invert sugar.

Among other syntheses are the catalytic reduction of D-mannonic δ-lactone (*43*) and the microbiological conversion of D-glucose or sucrose. A species of *Aspergillus* is capable of producing a 50% yield of D-mannitol from D-glucose (*44*), whereas, based on fructose content, *Escherichia coli*, *Escherichia freundi* and *Salmonella paratyphi* are reported to give over 90% conversion of sugar-beet diffusion juice, carob beans, or grape juice (*45*).

L-Mannitol does not occur in nature. It has been obtained by the reduction of L-mannose with sodium amalgam (*46*) or the catalytic reduction of L-mannonic lactone with the aid of a platinum catalyst containing a little iron and under a pressure of 80 atmospheres (*47*).

DL-Mannitol (α-acritol) has been obtained by the reduction of α-acrose (see p. 104). Divinylglycol from acrolein was the starting point of Lespieau and Wiemann (*48*). The glycol was obtained from acrolein by reduction with the zinc–copper couple and was then oxidized with silver chlorate and osmium tetroxide to DL-mannitol. Allitol was obtained simultaneously. It is apparent, therefore, that this divinylglycol must be a mixture of diols in which the hydroxyls are *cis* and *trans*.

Another interesting synthetic approach which also constitutes a total synthesis was accomplished by Pace (*49*). Sodium acetoacetic ester was oxidized with iodine, the product saponified, and carbon dioxide eliminated to give 2,5-hexanedione. The diketone was reduced to the diol, which was transformed to the dibromide. The hexadiene was formed and converted to the tetrabromide and subsequently to the hexabromide, which upon treatment with alcoholic potassium hydroxide gave DL-mannitol.

D-Talitol (D-altritol) (VIII) does not occur in nature. It has been obtained by the sodium amalgam reduction of D-talonolactone (*50*) or D-talose (*51*). It is obtained in higher yield by the catalytic hydrogenation of D-altrose (*52*).

43. J. W. E. Glattfeld and G. W. Schimpff, *J. Am. Chem. Soc.*, **57**, 2204 (1935).

44. J. H. Birkinshaw, J. H. V. Charles, A. Hetherington, and H. Raistrick, *Trans. Roy. Soc.* (*London*) **B220**, 153 (1931).

45. V. Bolcato and G. Pasquini, *Indstria saccar. ital.* **32**, 408 (1939).

46. E. Fischer, *Ber.* **23**, 375 (1890).

47. E. Baer and H. O. L. Fischer, *J. Am. Chem. Soc.* **61**, 761 (1939).

48. R. Lespieau and J. Wiemann, *Compt. rend.* **194**, 1946 (1932); *Bull. soc. chim. France* [4] **53**, 1107 (1933).

49. E. Pace, *Arch. farmacol. sper.* **42**, 167 (1926).

50. E. Fischer, *Ber.* **27**, 1524 (1894).

51. G. Bertrand and P. Bruneau, *Compt. rend.* **146**, 482 (1908): *Bull. soc. chim. France* [4] **3**, 495 (1908).

52. R. M. Hann, W. T. Haskins, and C. S. Hudson, *J. Am. Chem. Soc.* **69**, 624 (1947).

L-Talitol (L-altritol) was the last of the hexitols to be synthesized. It was obtained by the reduction of L-altrose with a supported nickel catalyst at 2000 pounds pressure and 100°C (*53*).

DL-Talitol is a purely synthetic product that was obtained by mixing the enantiomorphs in equimolecular amounts (*53*). As pointed out by these investigators, the melting point (95–96°) does not agree with that (66–67°) reported by E. Fischer (*50*), who oxidized dulcitol with lead peroxide and reduced the product to the polyol, which was converted to the tribenzylidene derivative, m.p. 205–206°; the hexitol was recovered from the latter derivative. It was suggested that Fischer's product was either impure or a lower-melting polymorph. The preparation of the tribenzylidene derivative of the synthetic mixture would provide a second comparison of the two products.

D-Iditol (IX) is a synthetic product which has been prepared by the reduction of D-idose (*54*) and D-sorbose (*39*), the latter also producing L-glucitol.

L-Iditol ("sorbiérite") appears to be the rarest of the naturally occurring hexitols. It has been isolated only from the mother liquor after removing sorbitol by fermenting the juice of the mountain-ash berry (*Sorbus aucuparia*). It was at first thought to be an octitol, but Bertrand definitely established it as a hexitol (*55*). It has been synthesized by the reduction of L-sorbose to sorbitol and L-iditol; the sorbitol was removed by fermentation with sorbose bacteria and the nonfermentable L-iditol was isolated as the tribenzylidene derivative.

Although reduction of L-sorbose appears to yield equimolar amounts of the two hexitols, reduction of penta-*O*-acetyl-*keto*-L-sorbose appears to favor the formation of L-iditol. A 60% yield of L-iditol hexaacetate was obtained when penta-*O*-acetyl-*keto*-L-sorbose was hydrogenated over platinum catalyst in absolute ether at 4 atmospheres pressure. The hydrogenated product was further acetylated to the hexaacetate and fractionally crystallized (*56*). A 90% yield is claimed when the reduction is carried out in alcohol using Raney nickel and atmospheric pressure at room temperature (*57*).

Galactitol (dulcitol) (X) has a widespread distribution and is found in plants ranging from red seaweed and pentose-fermenting yeast (*Torula utilis*) to the mannas of higher plant life. Madagascar manna appears to be

53. F. L. Humoller, M. L. Wolfrom, B. W. Lew and R. M. Goepp, Jr., *J. Am. Chem. Soc.* **67**, 1226 (1945).

54. G. Bertrand and A. Lanzenberg, *Compt. rend.* **143**, 291 (1906); E. Fischer and I. W. Fay, *Ber.* **28**, 1975 (1895).

55. G. Bertrand, *Bull. soc. chim. France* [3] **33**, 166, 264 (1905).

56. F. B. Cramer and E. Pacsu, *J. Am. Chem. Soc.* **59**, 1467 (1937).

57. Y. Khouvine and G. Arragon, *Bull. soc. chim. France* [5] **5**, 1404 (1938).

relatively pure galactitol (*58*). At one time galactitol was called "melampyrum" or "melampyrite" after *Melampyrum nemorosum*, from which source it was first isolated (*59*). It was found to the extent of about 2 % in the common American shrub the burning bush (*60*) (*Euonymus atropurpureus* Jacquin).

Galactitol has been synthesized from D-galactose by direct reduction and by the Cannizzaro process of Delépine and Horeau (*19*). The equivalent of a total synthesis was achieved in the following manner (*61*):

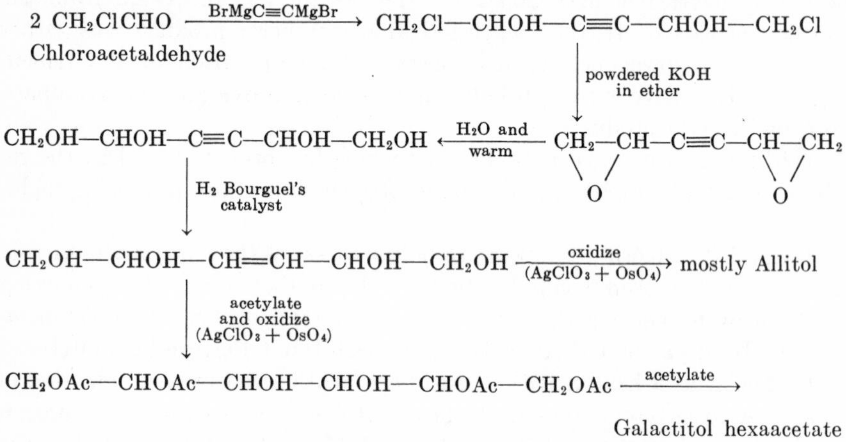
2 CH₂ClCHO
BrMgC≡CMgBr
CH₂Cl—CHOH—C≡C—CHOH—CH₂Cl
Chloroacetaldehyde
powdered KOH in ether
CH₂OH—CHOH—C≡C—CHOH—CH₂OH
H₂O and warm
CH₂—CH—C≡C—CH—CH₂
O
O
H₂ Bourguel's catalyst
CH₂OH—CHOH—CH═CH—CHOH—CH₂OH
oxidize (AgClO₃ + OsO₄)
mostly Allitol
acetylate and oxidize (AgClO₃ + OsO₄)
CH₂OAc—CHOAc—CHOH—CHOH—CHOAc—CH₂OAc
acetylate
Galactitol hexaacetate

The diolization of the double bond in this series of reactions appears to be analogous to the diolization of the double bond of conduritol, a cyclohexenetetrol (see Cyclitol section). When the hexenetetrol above was oxidized directly, the hydroxyls entered *cis* to the hydroxyls already present and allitol was the chief product; similarly, *allo*-inositol was obtained on oxidation of *o*-isopropylideneconduritol diacetate with potassium permanganate. On the other hand, for the two fully acetylated tetrols (acyclic and cyclic), the hydroxyls entered *trans* to those already present, giving galactitol and *muco*-inositol tetraacetate, respectively (p. 284).

Allitol (allodulcitol) (XI) does not occur in nature. It has been obtained along with DL-mannitol by the oxidation of Griner's divinylglycol (*48*). Wiemann (*62*) modified this synthesis by brominating Griner's divinylglycol instead of oxidizing it. He isolated a tetrabromide in which the hydroxyls were *cis*. Then, on debromination, the divinylglycol with exclusively

58. G. Bouchardat, *Ann. chim. phys.* [4] **27,** 68 (1872).
59. Hünefeld, *Ann.* **24,** 241 (1837).
60. See H. Rogerson, *J. Chem. Soc.* **101,** 1040 (1912).
61. R. Lespieau and J. Wiemann, *Compt. rend.* **198,** 183 (1934); R. Lespieau, *Bull. soc. chim. France* [5] **1,** 1374 (1934).
62. J. Wiemann, *Ann. chim.* [11] **5,** 267 (1936).

cis hydroxyls was obtained, which on oxidation with the silver chlorate–osmic acid reagent gave allitol with but a trace of galactitol.

An unequivocal synthesis of allitol was the reduction of D-allose with hydrogen and nickel catalyst (*63*). The resulting hexitol agreed in its constants with the product made by Lespieau and Wiemann.

D. Heptitols (*64*)

Thirteen of the sixteen theoretically possible heptitols are described in the literature. Several methods have been used for naming the heptitols and higher polyols. Although the nomenclature introduced and used by Hudson (*64*) has been popular in the past, the method used here is based on that now used for the corresponding heptoses, which is explained in Chapter I, page 48. The two heptitols known to occur in nature have also been given trivial names. Perseitol (D-*glycero*-D-*gala*-heptitol) (XIV) has been isolated from avocado (*Laurus persea* L.) (*65*). Volemitol (D-*glycero*-D-*talo*-heptitol) (XV) has been found in a mushroom, *Lactarius volemus* (*66*), in the roots of a number of plants of the primrose family (*67*), in lichens (*13*), and in an alga (*67a*) (free and glycosidically bound). The other known heptitols have been prepared by reduction of aldoheptoses or ketoheptoses, some of which are naturally occurring.

The relationships between the naturally occurring heptoses and the corresponding heptitols and hexoses are shown below:

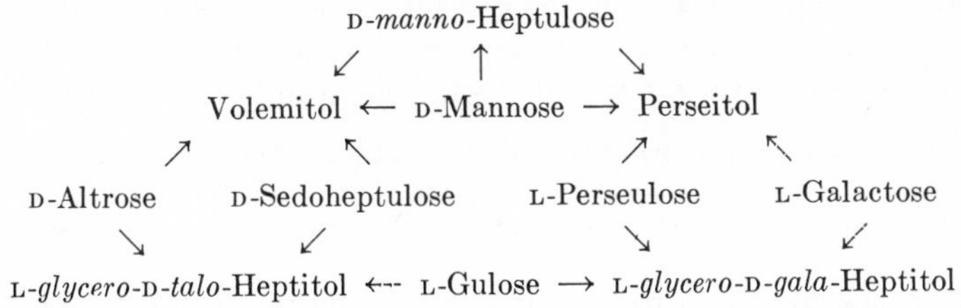
D-*manno*-Heptulose
Volemitol
D-Mannose
Perseitol
D-Altrose
D-Sedoheptulose
L-Perseulose
L-Galactose
L-*glycero*-D-*talo*-Heptitol
L-Gulose
L-*glycero*-D-*gala*-Heptitol

The full arrows represent demonstrated conversions. For galactose and gulose, the arrows with dotted lines represent conversions carried out with the enantiomorphic modifications.

The configurations of the D-series of some optically active heptitols and the *meso* forms are illustrated on p. 255. The physical constants of the known heptitols and their acetates, as well as references to their synthesis, are given in Table II.

63. M. Steiger and T. Reichstein, *Helv. Chim. Acta* **19**, 184 (1936).

64. For a review of the occurrence of these materials and their configuration, see C. S. Hudson, *Advances in Carbohydrate Chem.* **1**, 1 (1945).

65. L. Maquenne, *Compt. rend.* **107**, 583 (1888); *Ann. chim. phys.* [6] **19**, 5 (1890).

66. E. Bourquelot, *J. pharm. chim.* [6] **2**, 285 (1895).

67. J. Bougault and G. Allard, *Compt. rend.* **135**, 796 (1902).

67a. B. Lindberg and J. Paju, *Acta Chem. Scand.* **8**, 817 (1954).

TABLE II
PHYSICAL PROPERTIES OF THE HEPTITOLS

Heptitol	M.p. (°C.)	$[\alpha]_D$ in water	Heptaacetate M.p. (C.)	Heptaacetate $[\alpha]_D$ in chloroform	Ref. to prepn.
glycero-gulo-	129	*meso*	118	*meso*	*68*
D-*glycero*-D-*ido-*	129	+0.7°	118[a]	+25.3°[a]	*68, 69*
enantiomorph					*70*
D-*glycero*-D-*gala-*	187	−1.1°	119.5	−13.3°	*71, 72*
enantiomorph					*73*
D-*glycero*-D-*manno-*	153	+2.1°	63	+36.1°	*71, 74*
D-*glycero*-D-*gluco-*	128–9	−0.75°			*75, 76*
enantiomorph					*76*
D-*glycero*-L-*gluco-*	141.5	+2.4°	118	+11.4°	*68, 77*
enantiomorph					*78, 79*
glycero-ido-	110–12	*meso*	175–6	*meso*	*69*
glycero-allo-	145–146	*meso*	—	—	*79a*
D-*glycero*-D-*altro-*	125–128	−0.3°	—	—	*79a*

[a] These constants are for the heptabenzoate.

Bertrand and Nitzberg (*80*) reduced L-*gluco*-heptulose with sodium amalgam and obtained, along with the expected *glycero-gulo*-heptitol (XII), a product, "α-glucoheptulitol," of unknown structure, m.p. 144°, $[\alpha]_D$ −2.24° (H_2O). These constants show that "α-glucoheptulitol" is not the expected

68. E. Fischer, *Ann.* **270,** 64 (1892); L. H. Philippe, *Ann. chim. phys.* [8] **26,** 289 (1912).

69. J. W. Pratt, N. K. Richtmyer, and C. S. Hudson, *J. Am. Chem. Soc.* **74,** 2210 (1952).

70. W. D. Maclay, R. M. Hann, and C. S. Hudson, *J. Am. Chem. Soc.* **64,** 1606 (1942).

71. G. Pierce, *J. Biol. Chem.* **23,** 327 (1915).

72. G. Bertrand, *Compt. rend.* **149,** 226 (1909).

73. W. S. Smith, *Ann.* **272,** 182 (1893).

74. F. B. LaForge, *J. Biol. Chem.* **42,** 375 (1920).

75. L. Ettel, *Collection Czechoslov. Chem. Communs.* **4,** 513 (1932).

76. A. T. Merrill, W. T. Haskins, R. M. Hann, and C. S. Hudson, *J. Am. Chem. Soc.* **69,** 70 (1947).

77. F. B. LaForge, *J. Biol. Chem.* **41,** 251 (1920).

78. R. M. Hann and C. S. Hudson, *J. Am. Chem. Soc.* **61,** 336 (1939); G. Bertrand, *Compt. rend.* **149,** 225 (1909).

79. L. C. Stewart, N. K. Richtmyer, and C. S. Hudson, *J. Am. Chem. Soc.* **74,** 2206 (1952).

79a. J. W. Pratt and N. K. Richtmyer, *J. Am. Chem. Soc.* **77,** 6326 (1955).

80. G. Bertrand and G. Nitzberg, *Compt. rend.* **186,** 1172, 1773 (1928); Y. Khouvine and G. Nitzberg, *ibid.* **196,** 218 (1933).

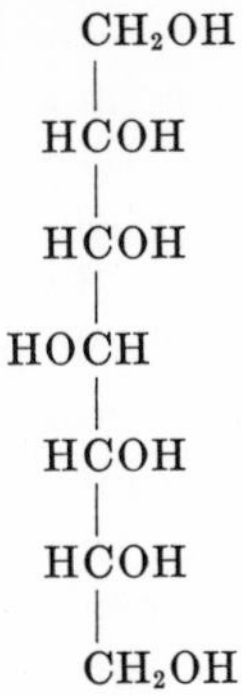

(XII)

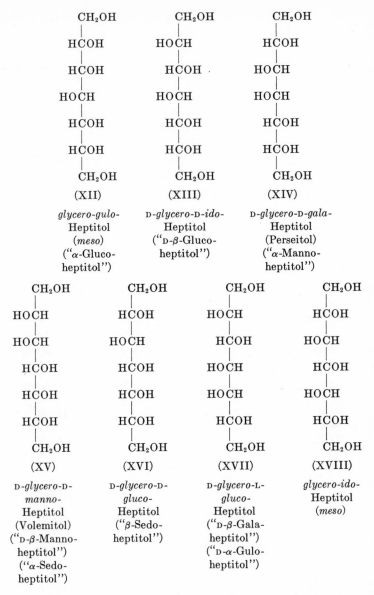

glycero-gulo-Heptitol (*meso*) ("α-Glucoheptitol")

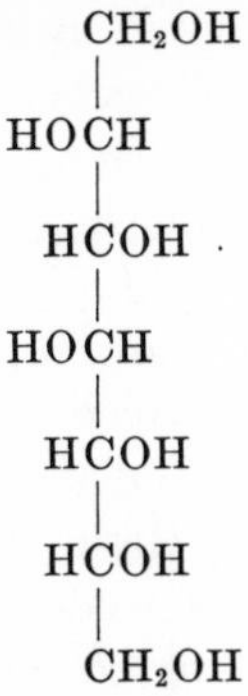

(XIII)

D-*glycero*-D-*ido*-Heptitol ("D-β-Glucoheptitol")

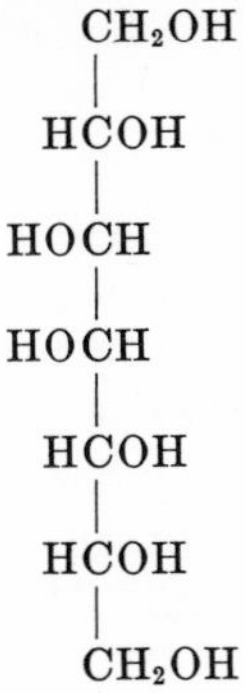

(XIV)

D-*glycero*-D-*gala*-Heptitol (Perseitol) ("α-Mannoheptitol")

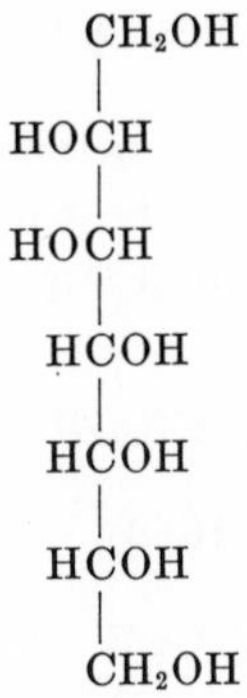

(XV)

D-*glycero*-D-*manno*-Heptitol (Volemitol) ("D-β-Mannoheptitol") ("α-Sedoheptitol")

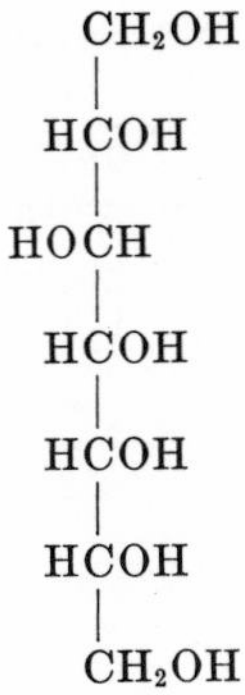

(XVI)

D-*glycero*-D-*gluco*-Heptitol ("β-Sedoheptitol")

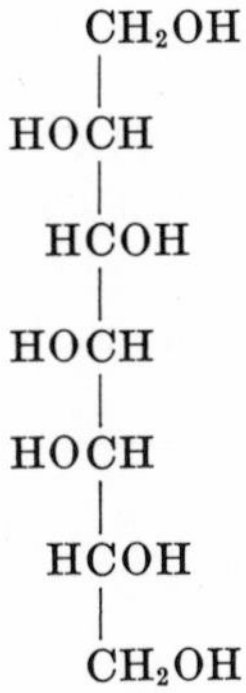

(XVII)

D-*glycero*-L-*gluco*-Heptitol ("D-β-Galaheptitol") ("D-α-Guloheptitol")

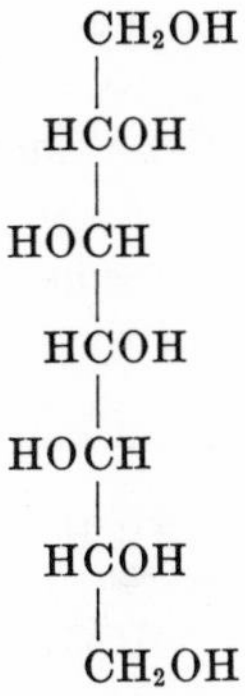

(XVIII)

glycero-ido-Heptitol (*meso*)

L-*glycero*-L-*ido*-heptitol (enantiomorph of (XIII)) and, although they agree with those of L-*glycero*-D-*gluco*-heptitol (enantiomorph of (XVII)), there is no ready explanation for the formation of the latter heptitol. The preparation of "α-glucoheptulitol" has been repeated by other workers (*81*) and its

81. F. L. Humoller, S. J. Kuman, and F. H. Snyder, *J. Am. Chem. Soc.* **61,** 3370 (1939).

enantiomorph (*82*) has been prepared by similar methods. The compound originally described as its hepta-*O*-acetyl derivative (m.p. 116–117°) has been shown to be that of *glycero-gulo*-heptitol (*81*). Likewise, tritylation leads to the ditrityl ether of the same heptitol (*81*). When "α-glucoheptuil-tol" is treated with 10% sulfuric acid, *glycero-gulo*-heptitol can be isolated (*81*). It has been concluded (*81*) that "α-glucoheptulitol" is a mixture of *glycero-gulo*-heptitol and an unidentified compound. The formation of this mixture is probably due to some peculiarity of the sodium amalgam reduction; catalytic hydrogenation over Raney nickel leads only to the two predicted heptitols (*83*). More work is needed on this unexplained anomaly in sugar chemistry. It could no doubt be solved by chromatography of the reduction products of L-*gluco*-heptulose.

E. Octitols, Nonitols, and Decitols

Four octitols, one nonitol, one decitol, and one dodecitol have been de-described. Of these only the configurations of the octitols are completely known. None occurs naturally.

The configurations, as far as are known, are represented in formulas (XIX) to (XXIV).

D-*erythro*-L-*gala*-Octitol (XIX), m.p. 153°, $[\alpha]_D$ +2.4° (H_2O); octaacetate, m.p. 88–89°, $[\alpha]_D$ +20.7° ($CHCl_3$); has been synthesized by the reduction of the corresponding octoses obtained from D-glucose and from D-galactose by way of the cyanohydrin synthesis (*84*).

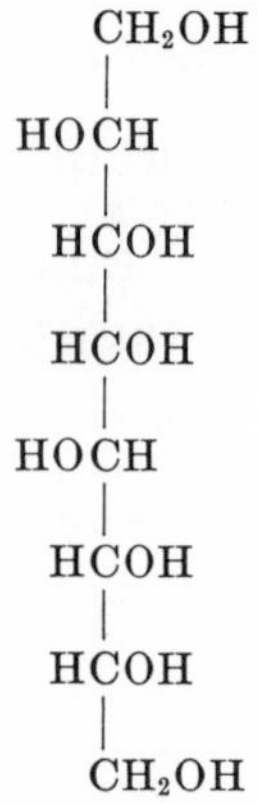

(XIX)
D-*erythro*-L-*gala*-Octitol

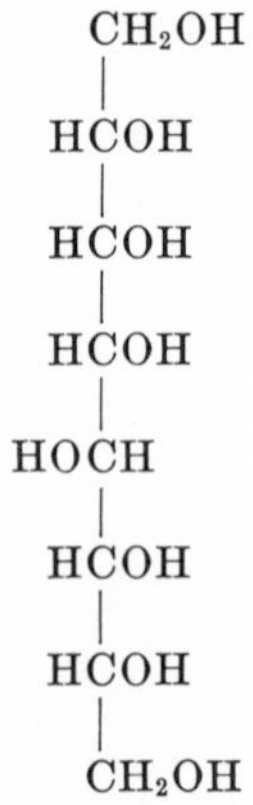

(XX)
D-*erythro*-L-*talo*-Octitol

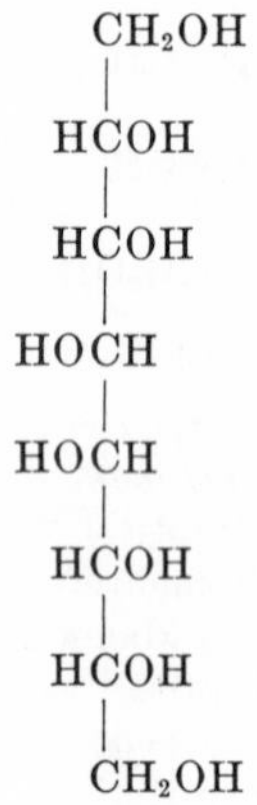

(XXI)
erythro-*manno*-Octitol

82. Y. Khouvine and G. Nitzberg, *Compt. rend.* **198,** 985 (1934).

83. Y. Khouvine, *Compt. rend.* **204,** 983 (1937).

84. R. M. Hann, A. T. Merrill, and C. S. Hudson, *J. Am. Chem. Soc.*, **66,** 1912 (1944).

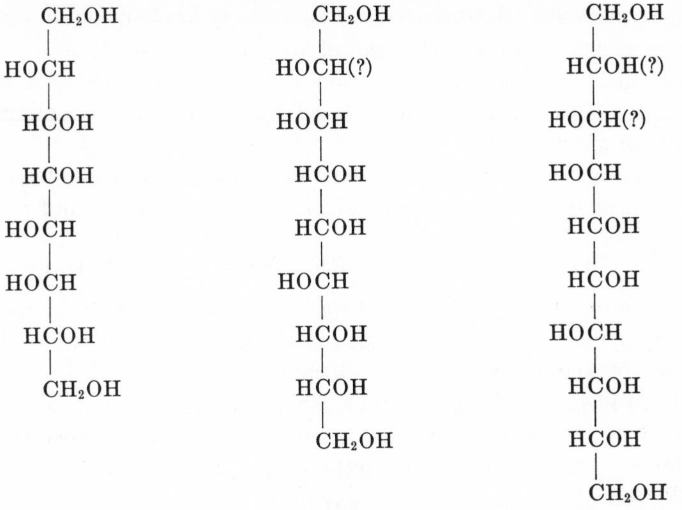

(XXII)	(XXIII)	(XXIV)
D-*threo*-L-*gala*-Octitol	"α,α,α-D-Gluco-nonitol"	"α,α,α,α-D-Gluco-decitol"

D-*erythro*-L-*talo*-Octitol (XX), m.p. 161–162°, $[\alpha]_D$ −0.8° (H_2O); octaacetate, m.p. 101–102°, $[\alpha]_D$ +17.4° ($CHCl_3$); was obtained by the reduction of the corresponding octose (*84*).

erythro-*manno*-Octitol (XXI), m.p. 262°, optically inactive; octaacetate, m.p. 166°; was likewise obtained by reduction of the corresponding octose, obtained from D-mannose by use of the cyanohydrin synthesis (*85*).

D-*threo*-L-*gala*-Octitol (XXII), m.p. 230°, $[\alpha]_D$ 0.0° (H_2O), −0.5° (borax); octaacetate, m.p. 141°, $[\alpha]_D$ +40.4° ($CHCl_3$); was obtained by reduction of the corresponding octose obtained from D-galactose by way of the cyanohydrin synthesis (*86*).

α,α,α-D-Glucononitol (XXIII), m.p. 198°, $[\alpha]_D$ +1.5° (H_2O), is a compound whose structure is not entirely known. The designation "α" indicates that this nonitol was obtained (*68*) by reduction of the most accessible nonose from D-glucose by way of the cyanohydrin synthesis.

α,α,α,α-D-Glucodecitol (XXIV), m.p. 222°, $[\alpha]_D$ +1.2° (H_2O); decaacetate, m.p. 149–150°, $[\alpha]_D$ +16° ($CHCl_3$); was synthesized by Philippe (*68*) in his extension of the cyanohydrin synthesis. Inasmuch as the configuration of

85. R. M. Hann, W. D. Maclay, A. E. Knauf, and C. S. Hudson, *J. Am. Chem. Soc.* **61**, 1268 (1939).

86. W. D. Maclay, R. M. Hann, and C. S. Hudson, *J. Am. Chem. Soc.* **60**, 1035 (1938).

the nonose preceding the decose is not completely known, the configurations of carbon atoms 2 and 3 of the decitol are not established.

A dodecitol has been isolated from the mother liquors of a mannitol preparation. Apparently it was formed by a reductive coupling of two molecules of glucose (*86a*).

The deoxypolyols are not considered here; the student is referred to the first edition of this text for an exposition of their synthesis and properties.

2. PROOFS OF STRUCTURE AND CONFIGURATION

In the main, the proof of structure and of configuration of the stereoisomeric polyols has been dependent on the proof of structure and of configuration of the parent sugar, determined as described in Chapter I. There have been occasions, however, when the configuration of the parent sugar and of the polyol derivable therefrom were simultaneously established by conversion of the sugar to the polyol. This has been true when the configuration of the carbohydrate has been known in part and the polyol resulting from the reduction of the carbohydrate was found to be optically inactive (*meso* structure). This type of proof has been of particular usefulness in the determination of the structures of the aldoses obtained by way of the cyanohydrin synthesis. Inasmuch as this synthesis invariably produces derivatives epimeric at carbon 2, the configuration of the 2-epimer likewise becomes known.

E. Fischer (*87*) used this type of proof in the establishment of the structures of the heptoses and heptitols derived from D-glucose. Thus, D-glucose on application of the cyanohydrin synthesis yielded two heptoses, D-*glycero*-D-*gulo*-heptose and D-*glycero*-D-*ido*-heptose. The glycitol obtained by reduction of the first of these was found to be optically inactive and, hence, must have a *meso* configuration. Of the two possible formulas (XII and XIII) only (XII) has a *meso* configuration and it must represent *glycero*-*gulo*-heptitol. The alcohol produced from the second product of the cyanohydrin synthesis can differ only in the configuration at carbon 2, and must be D-*glycero*-D-*ido*-heptitol (XIII). Hence, the configurations of the two heptitols and the two heptoses are established by this process.

Although the alcohols are superior to the glycaric (aldaric) acids as derivatives of aldoses for this type of structural proof because of their ease of crystallization, they have one marked deficiency, the low optical rotations. Hence, it is possible to assign erroneously a *meso* configuration to a substance that is actually optically active (*88*). Thus, "β-sedoheptitol"

86a. M. L. Wolfrom, W. W. Binkley, C. C. Spencer, and B. W. Lew, *J. Am. Chem. Soc.* **73,** 3357 (1951).

87. E. Fischer, *Ann.* **270,** 64 (1892). In this case, the proof was actually based on the corresponding saccharic acids.

88. F. B. LaForge, *J. Biol. Chem.* **42,** 367, 375 (1920).

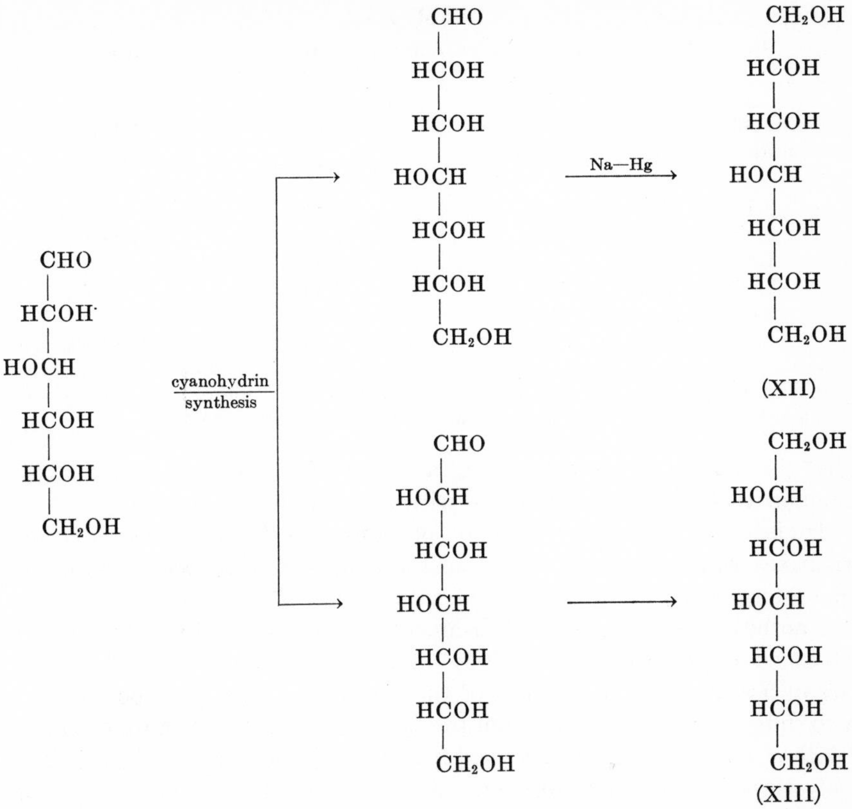
cyanohydrin synthesis
Na—Hg
(XII)
(XIII)

(XVI) obtained by reduction of natural sedoheptulose (D-*altro*-heptulose) was believed to be optically inactive; hence, incorrect configurations were assigned to it and to the 2-epimer, "α-sedoheptitol," the natural volemitol (XV). More recently it has been shown that (XVI) possesses a slight optical activity in water and a somewhat greater activity in borax (*76*).

Borax enhances the rotation of alditols (see Chapter IV), but even the use of borax may not be a sufficiently dependable indication, e.g., for D-*threo*-L-*gala*-octitol (XXII) (*85*). The observed rotation of this alditol in water using sodium light was 0.0° and in borax it was only −0.5°.

The use of ammonium molybdate solutions may also be of value for the purpose. The rotations of polyols are nearly constant over a wide range of concentrations when acidified molybdate is used (*89a, b*). Some values reported by Frèrejacque (*89a*) for D-mannitol are given in Table III.

The rotations in Table III are reported for $[\alpha]_{5461}$; the value for $[\alpha]_D$ is +141° (*89b*). Such values are very high for an alditol. It should be noted

89a. M. Frèrejacque, *Compt. rend.* **200,** 1410 (1935); **208,** 1123 (1939).
89b. N. K. Richtmyer and C. S. Hudson, *J. Am. Chem. Soc.* **73,** 2249 (1951).

TABLE III

ROTATIONS OF D-MANNITOL IN AMMONIUM MOLYBDATE SOLUTION[a]

(1) Mannitol (millimoles)	(2) MoO_3 (millimoles)	Ratio $\frac{(2)}{(1)}$	$[\alpha]^{20}_{5461}$
0.747	9.6	12.85	+168.8°
0.861	4.8	5.57	+169.1°
1.689	4.8	2.84	+168.8°
2.298	4.8	2.10	+167.8°
2.479	4.8	1.94	+164.4°
2.716	4.8	1.76	+148.8°

[a] Weighed amounts of D-mannitol were added to a solution of 5 ml. of N H_2SO_4 and 5 or 10 ml. of 0.1 N ammonium paramolybdate and diluted to 50 ml.

that the rotation is practically constant for ratios between 2.84 and 12.85. Similar results have been obtained with other alditols.

Hudson has suggested conversion of alditols to the fully acetylated derivatives which in every known instance have pronounced rotations in chloroform when the configurations are not *meso* (*64*).

Another method for the establishment of the configuration of an alditol obtained synthetically is especially valuable when both of the 2-epimers are optically active. It consists of the synthesis of the same polyol from two different aldoses. Thus, from the fact that D-mannose and L-galactose by the cyanohydrin synthesis yield four heptoses, which on reduction give only three different heptitols, one of which (perseitol) is produced from both D-mannose and L-galactose, the configuration of the four heptoses and three heptitols could be deduced. (For a discussion of these methods and detailed references, see Hudson (*64*).)

The configurations of the known octitols have been established by means of the methods mentioned above.

3. SYNTHESIS

The classical method for the synthesis of polyols is based on the reduction of the corresponding aldoses or ketoses. Aldoses give one product and ketoses two products, epimeric at carbon 2. Sodium amalgam, electrolytic reductions, and catalytic hydrogenations have been employed, direct hydrogenation and electrolytic reduction being the commercially preferred methods (see under Sorbitol). Several methods of reduction that do not require pressure vessels are available. Sufficient hydrogen is sorbed on Raney nickel to effect direct reduction of aldoses and ketoses without added hydrogen (*90*). Sugar acids, lactones, and anhydrides may be reduced

90. J. V. Karabinos and A. T. Ballun, *J. Am. Chem. Soc.* **75**, 4501 (1953); see also M. L. Wolfrom and J. N. Schumacher, *ibid.* **77**, 3318 (1955).

to glycitols with metallic hydrides (*91*). Thiol esters of aldonic acids are converted to alditols with Raney nickel (*92*).

The cyanohydrin synthesis (p. 106) frequently is used as an intermediate step in the preparation of the higher-carbon alditols. The lactones and esters of the aldonic acids or other derivatives may be reduced directly to the corresponding alditols. The reaction of diazomethane with aldonyl chlorides (p. 111) may be used for the same purpose, particularly in instances when the desired product is a minor product of the cyanohydrin synthesis. These and other methods of increasing the length of the carbon chain are discussed in Chapter II.

Amino alditols, derived from nitro alditols and from glycosylamines (Chapter VIII), may be converted to polyols by treatment with nitrous acid, but anhydro rings may be formed (p. 378).

The methods of total synthesis used in the preparation of pentitols and hexitols are of interest because of the departure from the methods of classical carbohydrate chemistry. Illustrations are given above under the pentitols and hexitols. The synthesis of glycitols from acetylene is commercially practical (see p. 242).

4. REACTIONS

A. Esterification

The esterification methods used for the sugars (Chapter III) are applicable to the polyols. The preparation and properties of organic and inorganic esters of polyol anhydrides are considered in Chapter VII. Fully esterified derivatives are generally unobtainable by direct esterification with organic acids because internal anhydrides are formed. Partial esters, especially diesters, may be obtained by the use of amounts of benzoyl or *p*-toluenesulfonyl chlorides insufficient for complete esterification (*93*).

A number of inorganic esters are known. The nitrates are explosive and also may be used as vasodilators just as glycerol trinitrate is used.

Dichlorohydrins, as a rule, are readily obtained by direct reaction although some are easily converted to anhydro polyols. Higher halohydrins can only be obtained by indirect means. Thus, erythritol tetraacetate was converted to a tetrabromohydrin, m.p. 118°, by hydrobromic acid in glacial acetic acid at 150°C., whereas mannitol hexaacetate could not be carried beyond the pentabromo stage at 130–140° (*94*). Mannitol was converted

91. M. L. Wolfrom and H. B. Wood, *J. Am. Chem. Soc.* **73**, 2933 (1951); R. K. Ness, H. G. Fletcher, Jr., and C. S. Hudson, *ibid.* **73**, 4759.

92. O. Jeger, J. Norymberski, S. Szpilfogel, and V. Prelog, *Helv. Chim. Acta* **29**, 684 (1946).

93. See Reference 30 for lists of many hexitol derivatives.

94. W. H. Perkin, Jr., and J. L. Simonsen, *J. Chem. Soc.* **87**, 855 (1905).

indirectly to a hexachlorohydrin by treatment of isomannide dichlorohydrin with fuming hydrochloric acid (see Chapter VII).

Thionyl chloride, as well as other inorganic acid chlorides, reacts with polyols to form mixed esters (see under Sulfate esters, Chapter III). In the presence of pyridine, partial chlorohydrin formation may occur (*95*).

Selenium oxychloride forms a selenite ester upon reaction with mannitol (*96*). Phosphorus pentachloride yields unsaturated chlorohydrins of mannitol and galactitol which have the composition $C_6H_6Cl_4$ (*97*).

Extremely interesting are the so-called complexes of alditols with various inorganic polybasic acids, their salts, or anhydrides in aqueous solutions. "Complexes" with boric, molybdic, tungstic, and other acids, as well as the oxides of antimony and arsenic, have been reported. It is believed that these complexes are true esters with one or more moles of alditol, a chelate type of structure being involved at some point. For the hexitols a compound with boric acid such as the following is postulated (*98*).

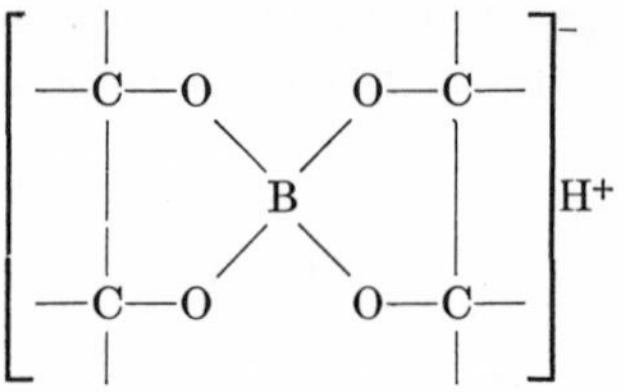

These compounds usually are known only in solution although some salts appear to have been obtained by precipitation of concentrated solutions with alcohol (*99*) (see also Chapter III).

Some of the effects produced by adding such acids or salts to solutions of polyhydroxy compounds are increased conductivity and acidity of the solution, exaltation of the rotation of optically active substances, and marked changes of volume. For an example, see Table III, above.

Böeseken and his students have studied extensively the conductivity of solutions containing polyhydroxy compounds and boric acid and have been able to apply the information thus obtained to the interpretation of the configuration of a number of compounds (see also Chapter I). The behavior of polyhydroxy compounds is explained on the basis of a tendency for the repulsion of adjacent hydroxyl groups (*100*). For open-chain α-glycols, the mutual repulsion of the hydroxyl groups with free rotation of

95. Z. Kitasato and C. Sone, *Ber.* **64,** 1142 (1931); R. Majima and H. Simanuki, *Proc. Imp. Acad.* (*Tokyo*) **2,** 544 (1926).

96. C. Chabrié and A. Bouchonnet, *Compt. rend.* **136,** 376 (1903).

97. J. C. Bell, *Ber.* **12,** 1271 (1879).

98. H. Diehl, *Chem. Revs.* **21,** 52 (1937).

99. A. Grün and H. Nossowitch, *Monatsh.* **37,** 409 (1916).

100. See J. Böeseken, *Advances in Carbohydrate Chem.* **4,** 189 (1949).

the carbon atoms does not permit complex formation, and, hence, very little change in conductivity is noted. When the hydroxyls are in a ring compound, free rotation is not possible and *cis* α-hydroxyls have a greater tendency than *trans* to form complexes. The increase in conductivity obtained for acylic polyols, from diols to hexitols, is explained on the basis of decreased symmetry with respect to the hydroxyls and, therefore, a decrease in their repulsive action; consequently, there will be a greater opportunity for complex formation and, as a result, greater conductivity.

Isbell (*101*) has used optical rotation to study the behavior of sorbitol and D-mannitol in aqueous borax solutions over a wide range of concentrations. He concluded that sorbitol forms three complex borates. In contrast, D-mannitol (and several hexoses) forms two borate compounds.

The various structures suggested for polyol borate complexes all postulate the formation of cyclic systems. It is probable, therefore, that conformational analysis (p. 40) can be used to elucidate the patterns followed by the various polyols in their reactions with borax. Such analysis has not been made, although some progress has been made in the analogous case of the cyclic acetals (*102*).

The effect of mannitol on the acidity of boric acid is sufficiently great that the latter behaves like a strong monobasic acid and can be titrated directly; this observation is the basis of common methods for the determination of boric acid.

Two crystalline monoborate esters of mannitol and one dimetaborate ester are described. All have been obtained by reaction under practically anhydrous conditions. They are as follows:

Monoborate, m.p. 88.5–89.5°, $[\alpha]_D^{20}$ +15.1° (pyridine) (*103*, *104*). This product was obtained by reaction of the components in ethanol solution.

Monoborate, m.p. 79–80°, $[\alpha]_D^{20}$ +5.73° (pyridine) (*104*). This substance was obtained by heating a concentrated aqueous solution of the reactants at 120°C. until approximately two moles of water of reaction were driven off and crystallizing the resulting melt from water.

The first substance appears to be a mannitol 1-monoborate, whereas the second is a mannitol 2-monoborate (*104*).

Mannitol dimetaborate (*105*), according to its analysis, appears to be an addition compound of two moles of metaboric acid and one mole of mannitol. However, on benzoylation only mannitol 1,6-dibenzoate is obtained;

101. H. S. Isbell, J. F. Brewster, N. B. Holt, and H. L. Frush, *J. Research Natl. Bur. Standards* **40,** 129 (1948).

102. J. A. Mills, *Advances in Carbohydrate Chem.* **2,** 1 (1955).

103. J. J. Fox and A. J. H. Gauge, *J. Chem. Soc.* **99,** 1075 (1911).

104. W. H. Holst, Paper presented before the Division of Sugar Chemistry and Technology, American Chemical Society, April (1939).

105. P. Brigl and H. Grüner, *Ann.* **495,** 70, 72 (1932).

hence, it is indicated that an ester-type linkage exists between the borate fragment and the mannitol. This borate was obtained by reaction of the components in anhydrous acetone. (Other products are described under boric acid esters in Chapter III.) It has not yet been determined whether esterification occurs when mannitol and boric acid are dissolved together in water.

B. Oxidation (*106*)

With nitric acid, the polyols may be oxidized to the corresponding dibasic acids. This procedure provides a qualitative identification of galactitol by converting it to insoluble mucic acid, but galactose and galacturonic acid give the same product. See (*106*).

With other oxidizing agents, it is possible to obtain reducing sugars. Bromine water produces a mixture of the corresponding aldoses and 2-ketoses. Before the bacterial process was perfected, oxidation of sorbitol by bromine to sorbose was widely used in the laboratory. (See (*106*).)

Hydrogen peroxide in the presence of ferrous ions likewise forms reducing sugars from polyols (*107*). Erythritol, mannitol, galactitol, and sorbitol were oxidized in this manner, and either the free sugars or the osazones were isolated.

Platinum, apparently acting as a carrier for oxygen, oxidizes polyhydric alcohols to reducing sugars and sugar acids (*108*). In the presence of a hydrogen acceptor such as quinone, sunlight causes the dehydrogenation of polyols to the corresponding aldoses (*109*). Potassium ferricyanide in a modified Hagedorn-Jensen procedure is capable of oxidizing polyols. However, the nature of the oxidation products was not ascertained (*110*).

When polyols were oxidized electrolytically at platinum electrodes in the absence of an electrolyte (*111*), aldoses and ketoses were formed and isolated as osazones or hydrazones. Acids also were formed, and, with erythritol, a keto acid was produced. When the oxidation was carried out in the presence of sodium bromide using carbon electrodes, ketoses were obtained free of degradation products (*112*).

106. See Chapter VI of this volume for additional details.

107. H. J. H. Fenton and H. Jackson, *J. Chem. Soc.* **75**, 1 (1899).

108. J. W. E. Glattfeld and S. Gershon, *J. Am. Chem. Soc.* **60**, 2013 (1938); E. von Gorup-Besanez, *Ann.* **118**, 257 (1861).

109. G. Ciamician and P. Silber, *Atti accad. nazl. Lincei Mem. classe sci. fis. mat. e nat. Sez I* [5] **10**, 92 (1901).

110. W. R. Todd, J. Vreeland, J. Myers, and E. S. West, *J. Biol. Chem.* **127**, 269 (1939).

111. C. Neuberg, *Biochem. Z.* **17**, 270 (1909).

112. J. E. Hunter, *Iowa State Coll. J. Sci.* **15**, 78 (1940).

Sodium chlorite appears to attack polyols rather slowly in comparison to aldoses, at least in the case of mannitol (*113*).

Oxidation of polyols by microorganisms is usually the best method for their conversion to ketoses. The yields are high, and the process is the preferred commercial one for the conversion of sorbitol to L-sorbose, an intermediate in the production of vitamin C. Additional information is given elsewhere in this text (Chapter II, Synthesis of ketoses).

C. Reduction

Reduction in the alditol series results in conversion to deoxy derivatives or hydrocarbons, for the only groups present are alcoholic hydroxyls. The reduction of alditols to secondary alkyl iodides by treatment with hydriodic acid according to the method of Erlenmeyer and Wanklyn (*114*) is mainly of historical interest.

Deoxyalditols are discussed in some detail in the first edition of this book.

Degradative reduction of polyols has not been investigated for very many substances. Sorbitol and glucose, which gives sorbitol under reducing conditions, have been converted to lower polyhydric alcohols by subjection to high temperatures and pressures and the action of oxides of copper and aluminum (*115*). Propylene glycol, glycerol, and polyols of higher molecular weights were obtained. It would be expected that all the higher polyols are capable of this type of degradative reduction.

D. Etherification

Etherification procedures for alditols are the same as those for the other carbohydrates (Chapter VII). Sometimes, however, the attainment of fully etherified products may be difficult. Mannitol, for example, could not be converted to the hexamethyl ether despite repeated treatment with methyl iodide and silver oxide (*116*) or with methyl sulfate and alkali (*117*).

E. Qualitative and Quantitative Determination

Chromatography, in its various modifications, is the best method to separate polyols from one another or from closely related compounds (*117a*). Polyols may also be separated as their borate complexes by ion-exchange

113. A. Jeanes and H. S. Isbell, *J. Research Natl. Bur. Standards* **27**, 125 (1941).

114. E. Erlenmeyer and J. A. Wanklyn, *Ann.* **135**, 129 (1865).

115. C. W. Lenth and R. N. DuPuis, *Ind. Eng. Chem.* **37**, 152 (1945).

116. J. C. Irvine and B. M. Paterson, *J. Chem. Soc.* **105**, 915 (1914).

117. W. N. Haworth, *J. Chem. Soc.* **107**, 10 (1915).

117a. B. W. Lew, M. L. Wolfrom, and R. M. Goepp, Jr., *J. Am. Chem. Soc.* **68**, 1449 (1946).

on strongly basic resins (*118*). Fractional crystallization of acetyl derivatives is very useful for the same purpose.

There are also certain specific reactions that serve to identify or quantitatively to determine some of the polyols. Among these are the oxidation of galactitol to insoluble mucic acid. Sorbitol forms a relatively insoluble pyridine complex, useful in the isolation of sorbitol from complex mixtures (*33*). As far as is known, only 2-deoxy-D-*arabo*-hexitol (2-deoxysorbitol) forms an analogous complex (*119*). The sorbitol–pyridine complex is decomposed at ordinary humidities to leave crystalline sorbitol.

Quantitative analysis is best effected by oxidation with periodate (see Chapter VI). Either macro or semimicro techniques may be used to determine the moles of oxidant consumed and the moles of formaldehyde and formic acid produced. When the structure of the polyol is known, any of these values gives a quantitative measure of the polyol present. If not, the ratio of the last two values can also give information as to the structure or composition of the polyol.

In the absence of interfering substances, quantitative determinations can sometimes be made by enhancing the low optical rotations of the polyols with borax. This method is not suited to sorbitol because the observed rotation changes sign with increased amounts of sorbitol at constant tetraborate concentration (*101*). The observed rotations are also low. The case of mannitol is more favorable. However, as the observed rotation does not vary linearly with mannitol concentration, a table of values or a curve must be constructed.

Adulteration of grape wine by the addition of fruit wines may be detected because of the presence of sorbitol in the latter. Litterscheid's *o*-chlorobenzaldehyde method appears to be the best of the various tests proposed. However, mannitol may interfere if present in excessive amounts (*120*, *120a*).

F. Biochemistry (*121*)

None of the polyols appears to have any specific fundamental physiological significance except glycerol and ribitol (adonitol), which is a component of vitamin B_2, riboflavin (see Chapter VIII). If fed in sufficiently large amounts to rats, polyols may have some narcotic effect (*122*). The amount required increases in general with the number of hydroxyls, ranging

118. L. P. Zill, J. X. Khym, and G. M. Cheniae, *J. Am. Chem. Soc.* **75,** 1339 (1953).

119. M. L. Wolfrom, M. Konigsberg, F. B. Moody, and R. M. Goepp, Jr., *J. Am. Chem. Soc.* **68,** 122 (1946).

120. J. Jeanprêtre, *Mitt. Gebiete Lebensm. u. Hyg.* **28,** 87 (1937).

120a. D. W. Steuart, *J. Sci. Food Agric.* **6,** 387 (1955).

121 . C. J. Carr and J. C. Krantz, Jr., *Advances in Carbohydrate Chem.* **1,** 175 (1945).

122. D. I. Macht and G. C. Ting, *Am. J. Physiol.* **60,** 496 (1922).

from 80 mg. of ethanol, per 100 g. of body weight, to over 380 mg. of perseitol and volemitol. The minimal dosage of dulcitol is 120 mg. and of mannitol is 320 mg.

As a class, the polyols appear to be capable of behaving as nutritive substrates for a large variety of microorganisms, but no single organism appears capable of utilizing every polyol. D-Mannitol seems to be more generally utilizable than sorbitol, whereas for the related sugars D-glucose is attacked more readily than D-mannose.

In the higher plants and particularly the fruits, the polyols appear to function as reserve carbohydrate, the amount present being seasonal and becoming less as the sugars increase during the ripening process.

In taste the polyols range from faintly sweet to extremely sweet, the threshold value for erythritol being considerably less than for sucrose (*123*).

Further data on the nutritional aspects of the alditols are given in Chapter XIV.

G. Anhydro Formation

Numerous anhydro derivatives have been prepared. These are discussed in Chapter VII.

H. Acetals

The alditols form acetals readily with aldehydes and ketones. These are discussed in Chapter IV.

123. C. J. Carr, F. Frances, and J. C. Krantz, Jr., *J. Am. Chem. Soc.* **58,** 1394 (1936).

Part II

The Inositols and Related Compounds (1, 2)

In view of the wide distribution of the cyclohexanehexols (called inositols or cyclitols) and the importance of one in particular (*myo*-inositol) to certain bacteria, plants, and perhaps even to warm-blooded animals, the naturally occurring and synthetic compounds of this carbocyclic class have received considerable study. Naturally occurring members include four inositols, monomethyl ethers, a dimethyl ether, monodeoxy derivatives, one dideoxy derivative, a methyl homolog, and deoxy carboxylic acids. Five inositols and many other synthetic members, including ketones (cycloses or inososes), are known.

The inositols themselves are typically crystalline, water-soluble, high-melting compounds having a sweet taste. As alcohols, their reactions are similar to those of the acyclic polyols, but because of their ring structure they are inherently more stable.

1. REPRESENTATION OF CONFIGURATION AND NOMENCLATURE

The inositols and related compounds are represented graphically by planar perspective formulas similar to the Haworth formulas (p. 38) for the ring forms of the sugars. Such planar representations (I–IX) are not "pictures" of the inositol molecule, which may assume nonplanar conformations— the "chair" and "boat" forms— in which the hydroxyl groups bear a somewhat different relationship to one another than simple *cis* or *trans* (Chapter I). The planar representations, however, do allow a more ready understanding of the relationships of the cyclitols to the acyclic sugar derivatives and are used here. It is customary to omit the hydrogen atoms in the planar formulas and to represent the hydroxyl groups as vertical lines. Certain biochemical reactions are best understood if a strainless, nonplanar form is assumed (see below).

Trivial names serve to identify the inositols and the related naturally occurring compounds. It is also possible to identify the inositols by a numerical system, wherein the orientation of hydroxyl groups above and below the ring is represented by a fraction. *neo*-Inositol (IV), for example, may be designated as 123/456-inositol and *allo*-inositol (III) as 1234/56-inositol. Formerly the common inositol, *myo*-inositol (V), was often called *meso*-inositol, but use of the latter term is discouraged because all but two

1. G. Dangschat, *in* "Modern Methods of Plant Analysis," (K. Paech and M. V. Tracey, eds.), p. 64. Springer, Berlin, 1955.

2. H. G. Fletcher, Jr., *Advances in Carbohydrate Chem.* **3,** 45 (1948).

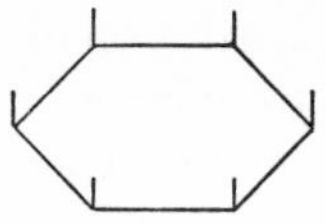

(I)
cis-Inositol

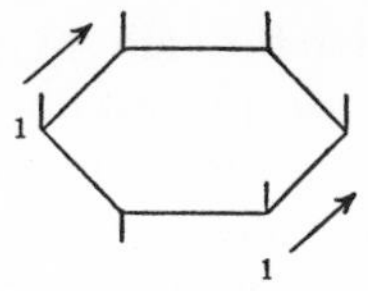

(II)
epi-Inositol

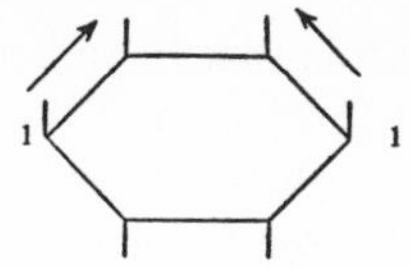

(III)
allo-Inositol

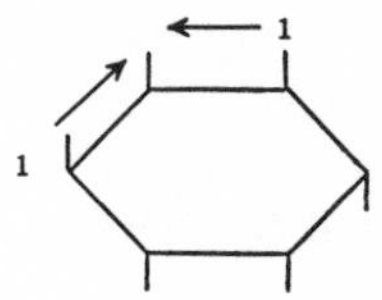

(IV)
neo-Inositol

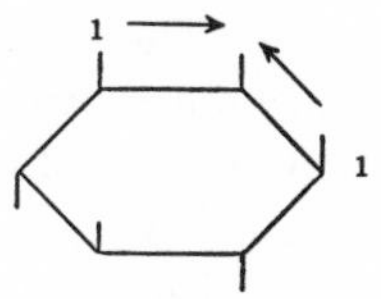

(V)
myo-Inositol

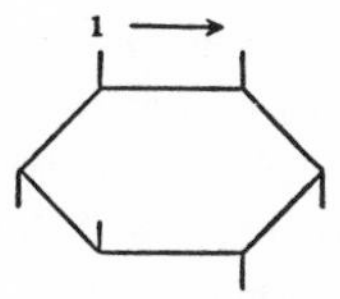

(VI)
D-Inositol

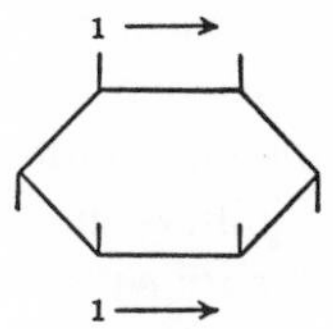

(VII)
muco-Inositol

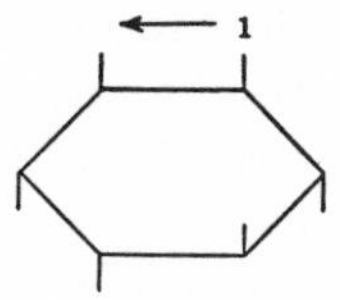

(VIII)
L-Inositol

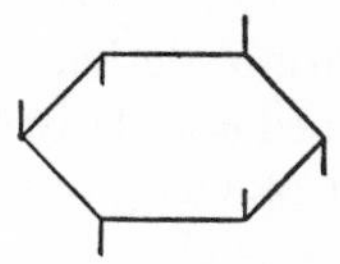

(IX)
scyllo-Inositol

of the inositols, D- and L-inositol, are optically inactive. The name *myo*-inositol was suggested (*3*) because this inositol was first found in muscle (*4*).

Because the cyclitols have no terminal carbon atom, there is no simple method of numbering the carbon atoms. It has been customary for workers to employ perspective formulas extensively to avoid confusion. Several attempts to arrive (*3*, *5–7*) at a rational and unequivocal system have been made within the past few years. It appears that the system of Fletcher, Anderson, and Lardy (*3*) will find widest acceptance. Their system is unique in that an alternating numbering sequence is used. Positions that are stereochemically equivalent are numbered 1, with numbering proceeding clockwise and counterclockwise as indicated in formulas (I–IX). The desirability of such a system becomes apparent when one considers

3. H. G. Fletcher, Jr., L. Anderson, and H. A. Lardy, *J. Org. Chem.* **16,** 1238 (1951).

4. J. Scherer, *Ann.* **73,** 322 (1850).

5. See Report of the Advisory Committee on Configurational Nomenclature, pamphlet available from Chemical Abstracts, Columbus, Ohio (1954). Examples of this nomenclature are found, *inter alia*, in G. E. McCasland and E. C. Horswill, *J. Am. Chem. Soc.* **75,** 4020 (1953).

6. B. Magasanik and E. Chargaff, *J. Biol. Chem.* **174,** 173 (1948).

7. S. J. Angyal and C. G. Macdonald, *J. Chem. Soc.* p. 686 (1952).

inositols that have become active through asymmetric substitution or other transformation. If names of optical enantiomorphs are to differ only by a configurational prefix (D or L), a single numbering convention cannot be used. (See for example the deoxyinositols below.) It is to be noted that all positions are equivalent in *scyllo*-inositol (IX) and in *cis*-inositol (I) so that no numbering convention is necessary. D-Inositol and L-inositol do not require an alternating numbering convention. (For a full exposition of the system, see the original article.) The following additional conventions serve to name the derivatives of known structure that are considered here.

All optically active derivatives are called D or L, based on the configuration of carbon 6. The configuration of carbon 6 is found by viewing the Fischer-type projection (p. 9) with carbons 5 and 1 away from the viewer and C-5 at the top. When an optically inactive cyclitol has been made asymmetric by substitution, the D or L is put at the beginning of the name, e.g., D-1-*O*-methyl-*muco*-inositol, but 3-*O*-methyl-D-inositol. When an inositol derivative contains less than six asymmetric carbon atoms, it is named as a derivative of the related inositol that has the maximum number of *cis* OH groups. If this leads to more than one possibility, the parent inositol is chosen that has the lowest possible number for its substituents *cis* to the OH on carbon 1.

Examples:

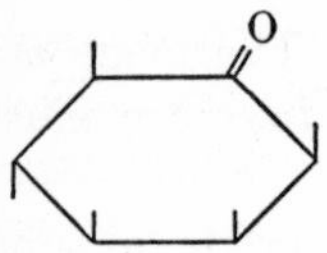
O

D-*epi*-Inosose-2
(D-2-Keto-*epi*-inositol)

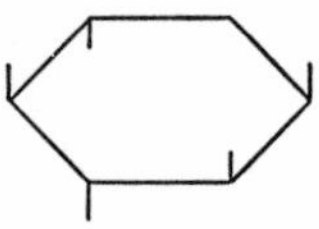

D-1-Deoxy-*myo*-inositol
(*l*-Viburnitol)

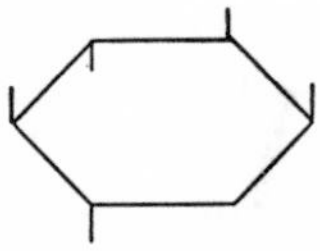

L-1-Deoxy-*myo*-inositol

2. OCCURRENCE AND SYNTHESIS

D-Inositol (*d*-inositol, *β*-inositol, matezodambose), m.p. 247–248°, $[\alpha]_D$ + 65° (H_2O), occurs as a monomethyl ether, pinitol, m.p. 186°, $[\alpha]_D$ + 65.5° (H_2O), in many plants, particularly conifers (*8*). The heartwood of the sugar pine, *Pinus lambertiana* Dougl., averages 4% by weight (range, 1.3–9.5%) of pinitol (*9*). Other sources are the red spruce (*Picea rubra*) (*10*), redwood (*Sequoia sempervirens*) (*11*), and the loco weed (*12*). Pinitol is sweet, very soluble in water, and stable in dilute acids and

8. See, for example V. Plouvier, *Compt. rend.* **234,** 362 (1952).
9. A. B. Anderson, *Tappi* **35,** 198 (1952); *Ind. Eng. Chem.* **45,** 593 (1953).
10. S. Gottlieb and F. E. Brauns, *J. Am. Chem. Soc.* **73,** 5880 (1951).
11. E. C. Sherrard and E. F. Kurth, *Ind. Eng. Chem.* **20,** 722 (1928).
12. D. C. Pease, M. J. Reider, and R. C. Elderfield, *J. Org. Chem.* **5,** 198 (1940).

alkalies, but, like other methyl ethers of cyclitols, it is demethylated quantitatively to the parent inositol by boiling hydriodic acid. It has recently been shown to be 5-*O*-methyl-D-inositol (*13a, b*). D-Inositol occurs free in trace amounts in sugar-pine heartwood (*14*).

L-Inositol is found in the free state in the drug *Euphorbia pilulifera* L. (*15*), but it is found principally as quebrachitol, 1-*O*-methyl-L-inositol (*7, 16*). This methyl ether is named for the quebracho tree, from which it was first isolated (*17*). It occurs in many other plants (*2, 18*), but its most ready source is the latex of the rubber tree (*Hevea brasiliensis*) (*19*).

Conversion of one of the active inositols into the other requires inversion of the configuration of carbon atoms 4 and 5 only.

DL-Inositol, m.p. 253°, is found in the free state in mistletoe berries (*20*). It is accompanied by *myo*-inositol, but it is readily separated since its hexaacetate has a greater solubility in alcohol than that of *myo*-inositol.

myo-Inositol (*meso*-inositol, *i*-inositol, dambose, phaseomannite), more often termed simply inositol, m.p. 225–227°, is the most common of the group, being found in microorganisms, plants, and animals. In plants it is generally present as phytin, a calcium-magnesium salt of phytic acid (*21*), the hexaphosphate ester of *myo*-inositol. Lower phosphates are likewise encountered (*22*) whose formation may be due to the action of a phosphatase, phytase (*23*), but mono- and diphosphates appear to be constituents of plant, animal, and bacterial phosphatides. *myo*-Inositol apparently is of widespread distribution in phosphatides of higher plants; it is found in seeds of corn (*24*), soy-bean (*25*), and peanut (*26*), among

13a. A. B. Anderson, D. L. MacDonald, and H. O. L. Fischer, *J. Am. Chem Soc.* **74,** 1479 (1952).

13b. S. J. Angyal, C. G. Macdonald, and N. K. Matheson, *J. Chem. Soc.* p. 3321 (1953).

14. C. E. Ballou and A. B. Anderson, *J. Am. Chem. Soc.* **75,** 648 (1953).

15. F. P. Hallett and L. M. Parks, *J. Am. Pharm. Assoc.* **40,** 474 (1951).

16. T. Posternak, *Helv. Chim. Acta* **35,** 50 (1952).

17. C. Tanret, *Compt. rend.* **109,** 908 (1889).

18. V. Plouvier, *Compt. rend.* **224,** 1842 (1947); **227,** 85, 225 (1948); **232,** 1239 (1951).

19. See J. van Alphen, *Ind. Eng. Chem.* **43,** 141 (1951).

20. G. Tanret, *Compt. rend.* **145,** 1196 (1907).

21. S. Posternak, *Compt. rend.* **169,** 138 (1919); *Helv. Chim. Acta* **4,** 150 (1921).

22. R. J. Anderson, *J. Biol. Chem.* **18,** 441 (1914); **20,** 463, 493 (1915).

23. R. J. Anderson, *J. Biol. Chem.* **20,** 475, 483 (1915).

24. C. R. Scholfield, T. A. McGuire, and H. J. Dutton, *J. Am. Oil Chem. Soc.* **27,** 352 (1950).

25. E. Klenk and R. Sakai, *Z. physiol. Chem.* **258,** 33 (1939); D. W. Woolley, *J. Biol. Chem.* **147,** 581 (1943); J. W. Hawthorne and E. Chargaff, *ibid.* **206,** 27 (1954).

26. H. H. Hutt, T. Malkin, A. G. Poole, and P. R. Watt, *Nature* **165,** 314 (1950); T. Malkin and A. G. Poole, *J. Chem. Soc.* p. 3470 (1953).

others. *myo*-Inositol occurs both free and combined in muscle and in the heart, lungs, liver, and other parts of the animal body, and in body fluids. It is present to the extent of 6.8 to 8.6% in the phosphatide of brain cephalin, or about 0.4% of the net weight of the brain (*27*). In certain bacterial phosphatides it is built into a polysaccharide, "manninositose" (*28*).

Corn-steep liquor (from industrial starch preparation) provides a good source of phytin, precipitated as the calcium salt (*29*). *myo*-Inositol is prepared industrially from phytic acid by autocatalytic hydrolysis at elevated temperature and pressure. Complete agreement on the structure of phytic acid and its salts has not been reached (*30*).

myo-Inositol has been synthesized by the hydrogenation of hexahydroxybenzene over palladium catalyst (*31a, b*). Attempts to repeat this synthesis failed (*32*), but this was shown to be due to the strength of the catalyst (*31b*); too active a catalyst favors hydrogenolysis over hydrogenation. With Raney nickel catalysis (*32*), equal amounts (*6%*) of *myo*-inositol and *scyllo*-inositol and a small amount of an unidentified inositol were isolated. It has been shown (*32a*) that this is the long-sought inositol having all hydroxyl groups *cis*. It is aptly named *cis*-inositol, m.p. *ca.* 390°.

A more definitive synthesis of *myo*-inositol is based on D-glucose. The relationship of the configurations of these two compounds is evident when the formula of D-glucose is represented in the following manner:

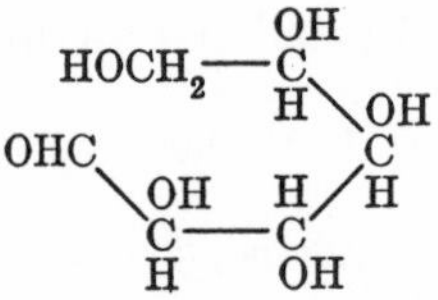
OH
HOCH2—C
H OH
OHC
C
OH H H
C—C
H OH

D-Glucose

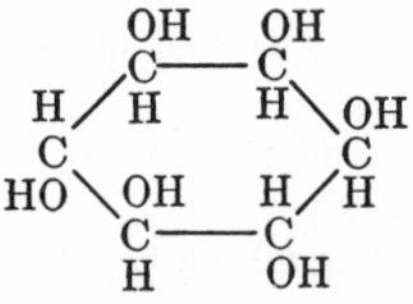
OH OH
C—C
H H H OH
C C
HO OH H H
C—C
H OH

myo-Inositol

This relationship and the widespread occurrence of the two compounds have been the cause of speculation on the biogenetic origin of *myo*-inositol from

27. J. Folch and D. W. Woolley, *J. Biol. Chem.* **142,** 963 (1942).

28. R. J. Anderson, W. C. Lothrop, and M. M. Creighton, *J. Biol. Chem.* **125,** 299 (1938).

29. See E. Bartow and W. W. Walker, *Ind. Eng. Chem.* **30,** 300 (1938); *U. S. Patent* 2,112,553 (March 29, 1938); F. A. Hoglan and E. Bartow, *Ind. Eng. Chem.* **31,** 749 (1939); G. Graefe, *Stärke* **4,** 275 (1952).

30. See, for example R. J. Anderson, *J. Biol. Chem.* **17,** 171 (1914); C. Neuberg, *Biochem. Z.* **9,** 557 (1908); S. Posternak, *Compt. rend.* **169,** 37 (1919); *J. Biol. Chem.* **46,** 453 (1921).

31a. H. Wieland and R. S. Wishart, *Ber.* **47,** 2082 (1914).

31b. R. Kuhn, G. Quadbeck, and E. Röhm, *Ann.* **565,** 1 (1949).

32. R. C. Anderson and E. S. Wallis, *J. Am. Chem. Soc.* **70,** 2931 (1948).

32a. S. J. Angyal and D. J. McHugh, *Chemistry & Industry* p. 947 (1955).

D-glucose. This transformation has recently been demonstrated (*32b*). Synthesis *in vitro* is based on the work of Grosheintz and Fischer (*33*). They found that 6-deoxy-6-nitro-D-glucose (or, likewise, 6-deoxy-6-nitro-L-idose) condensed in slightly alkaline solution to form two monodeoxymononitroinositols. These were converted to the corresponding amines, one of which can also be obtained by reduction of the phenylhydrazone or oxime of *myo*-inosose-2 (*scyllo-myo*-inosose) (*34a, b*). The final and crucial step, replacement of the amino group by hydroxyl, is difficult, since there is a tendency to form reducing compounds (*35*), later shown to be deoxyinososes (*36*), when the amino deoxyinositols are treated with nitrous acid. Posternak (*36*), however, was able to convert one of the amines to *myo*-inositol by nitrous acid deamination. The epimeric amine yielded *scyllo*-inositol. Walden inversions occurred in each case. This synthesis defines the configurations of three atoms only (carbon atoms corresponding to carbons 2, 3, and 4 of D-glucose). Equilibrium rearrangements apparently occur between the deoxynitroinositols and the 6-deoxy-6-nitrohexoses.

The path of synthesis shown below is for the isomers leading to *myo*-inositol only.

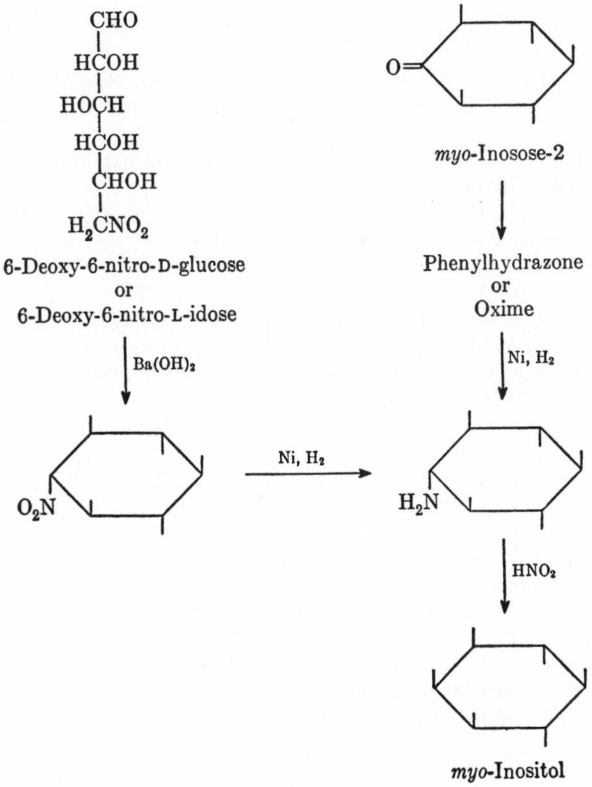
CHO
HCOH
HOCH
HCOH
CHOH
H2CNO2
6-Deoxy-6-nitro-D-glucose
or
6-Deoxy-6-nitro-L-idose
Ba(OH)2
O2N
Ni, H2
O=
myo-Inosose-2
Phenylhydrazone
or
Oxime
Ni, H2
H2N
HNO2
myo-Inositol

Two monomethyl ethers of *myo*-inositol are known: bornesitol (*37*), m.p. 199°, from Borneo rubber and opepe (*Sacrocephalus diderrichii*) wood (*37a*), and sequoyitol (*11*, *38*), m.p. 234–235°, from California redwood. Sequoyitol, a *meso* compound, is 5-*O*-methyl-*myo*-inositol (*39*). Bornesitol is optically active. A dimethyl ether, dambonitol, m.p. 195°, is found in the latex of Gabon (*40*) and other rubbers and in the latex of the Dyera tree (*41*). It has been shown to be 1,3-di-*O*-methyl-*myo*-inositol (*41a*).

The juice of the sugar beet (*Beta vulgaris*) contains galactinol (*42*), a galactoside of *myo*-inositol. The D-galactose is united to the *myo*-inositol in position 1 by an α-linkage (*43*).

scyllo-Inositol (scyllitol, cocositol, quercin), m.p. 352°, the fourth known naturally occurring inositol, though not abundant, is widely distributed, being found in the elasmobranch fishes (sharks, rays, dogfish) (*44*), in the dogwood (*45*), in the leaves of the cocos palm (*46*), in the acorn (*47*), and in mammalian urine (*48*). It can be obtained synthetically by reduction of *myo*-inosose-2 (bioinosose) (*49*) (see Fig. 1 and below).

d-Quercitol, m.p. 235–237°, $[\alpha]_D$ +25.6°, often called simply quercitol, is the most common of the deoxyinositols and it occurs in all parts of the

32b. W. H. Daughaday, J. Larner, and C. Hartnett, *J. Biol. Chem.* **212,** 869 (1955); J. W. Halliday and L. Anderson, *ibid.* **217,** 797 (1955).

33. J. M. Grosheintz and H. O. L. Fischer, *J. Am. Chem. Soc.* **70,** 1476, 1479 (1948).

34a. H. E. Carter, R. K. Clark, Jr., B. Lytle, and G. E. McCasland, *J. Biol. Chem.* **175,** 683 (1948).

34b. L. Anderson and H. A. Lardy, *J. Am. Chem. Soc.* **72,** 3141 (1950); G. E. McCasland, *ibid.* **73,** 2295 (1951).

35. B. Iselin and H. O. L. Fischer, *J. Am. Chem. Soc.* **70,** 3946 (1948).

36. T. Posternak, *Helv. Chim. Acta* **33,** 1597 (1950).

37. A. Girard, *Compt. rend.* **73,** 426 (1871).

37a. F. E. King and L. Jurd, *J. Chem. Soc.* p. 1192 (1953).

38. E. C. Sherrard and E. F. Kurth, *J. Am. Chem. Soc.* **51,** 3139 (1929).

39. L. Anderson, A. M. Landel, and E. B. Swan, paper presented at the meeting of the American Chemical Society, New York, September 1954.

40. A. Girard, *Compt. rend.* **67,** 820 (1828).

41. A. J. Comollo and A. K. Kiang, *J. Chem. Soc.* p. 3319 (1953).

41a. A. K. Kiang and K. H. Loke, *J. Chem. Soc.* p. 480 (1956).

42. R. J. Brown and R. F. Serro, *J. Am. Chem. Soc.* **75,** 1040 (1953).

43. E. A. Kabat, D. L. MacDonald, C. E. Ballou, and H. O. L. Fischer, *J. Am. Chem. Soc.* **75,** 4507 (1953).

44. G. Staedeler and J. J. Frerichs, *J. prakt. Chem.* [1] **73,** 48 (1858).

45. R. M. Hann and C. E. Sando, *J. Biol. Chem.* **68,** 399 (1926).

46. H. Müller, *J. Chem. Soc.* **91,** 1767 (1907); **101,** 2383 (1912).

47. C. Vincent and Delachanal, *Compt. rend.* **104,** 1855 (1887).

48. P. F. Fleury, J. W. Courtois, and A. L. Jouannet, *Bull. soc. chim. biol.* **33,** 1885 (1951); *Chem. Abstr.* **46,** 7634 (1952).

49. T. Posternak, *Helv. Chim. Acta* **25,** 746 (1942).

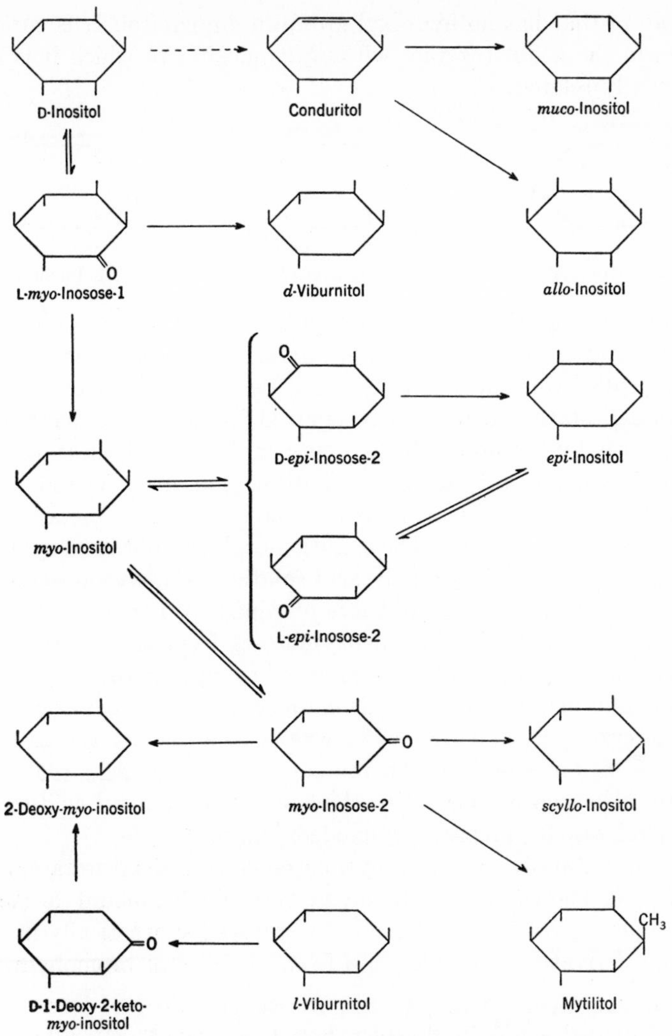
D-Inositol
Conduritol
muco-Inositol
L-myo-Inosose-1
d-Viburnitol
allo-Inositol
D-epi-Inosose-2
epi-Inositol
myo-Inositol
L-epi-Inosose-2
2-Deoxy-myo-inositol
myo-Inosose-2
scyllo-Inositol
D-1-Deoxy-2-keto-myo-inositol
l-Viburnitol
Mytilitol

FIG. 1. Some interrelationships of the inositols.*
* The conversion of D-(or L-) inositol to conduritol has not been demonstrated.

oak, particularly in the acorn (*50*), and in the leaves of the European palm (*51*), *Chaemerops humilis*. The systematic name for *d*-quercitol is D-1-deoxy-*muco*-inositol. Configurationally, it is related to both *muco*-inositol and D-inositol, since these two inositols differ only in the configuration of the

50. L. Prunier, *Ann. chim. phys.* [5] **15,** 1 (1878).
51. H. Müller, *J. Chem. Soc.* **91,** 1766 (1907).

carbon atom that has no hydroxyl group in *d*-quercitol. It is curious that it occurs in the acorn together with *scyllo*-inositol to which it is not configurationally related.

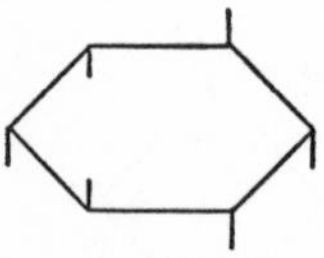

muco-Inositol

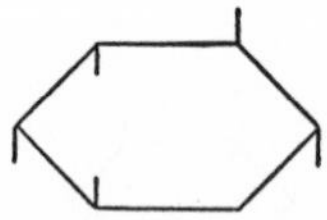

d-Quercitol

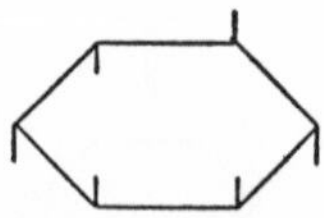

D-Inositol

l-Viburnitol (Fig. 1), an isomer of *d*-quercitol, m.p. 180–181°, $[\alpha]_D$ −49.5°, was first found in the leaves of *Gymnema sylvestre*, a milkweed (*52*). It was originally called (improperly) *l*-quercitol. Because of an error in the report of its optical rotation, it was not recognized for some time that it is identical (*53*) with *l*-viburnitol, which occurs in *Viburnum tinus* L. (*54*). Its systematic name is D-1-deoxy-*myo*-inositol, and it is related configurationally to both L-inositol and *myo*-inositol. It occurs along with *myo*-inositol in *Viburnum* tissues. The enantiomorph was obtained synthetically by the hydrogenation, in strongly acid solution, of L-*myo*-inosose-1 (*d*-inosose) (*55*) (Fig. 1). *dl*-Viburnitol was obtained by Posternak (*36*) by hydrogenation of the by-product deoxyinososes from the treatment of the same deoxynitroinositol that was converted to *scyllo*-inositol.

An optically inactive isomer, 2-deoxy-*myo*-inositol (deoxy-*scyllo*-inositol) (*scyllo*quercitol (*7*)), m.p. 233–235°, was synthesized by the catalytic reduction of *myo*-inosose-2 in the presence of mineral acid (*56*) (Fig. 1). Catalytic reduction of inososes or their oximes in mineral acid appears to be a general way for preparing monodeoxyinositols (*57a*, *b*).

Only one naturally occurring cyclohexanetetrol, dextrorotatory betitol, m.p. 224°, is known. It was found in very small amount in sugar-beet process liquors (*58*). Isomers have been prepared synthetically from cyclohexadiene derivatives (*59–61a*) and from an inositol bromohydrin (*61b*).

52. F. B. Power and F. Tutin, *J. Chem. Soc.* **85,** 624 (1904).

53. T. Posternak and W. H. Schopfer, *Helv. Chim. Acta* **33,** 343, 350 (1950).

54. H. Hérissey and G. Poirot, *Compt. rend.* **203,** 466 (1936); *J. pharm. chim.* **26,** 385 (1937).

55. T. Posternak, *Helv. Chim. Acta* **33,** 1594 (1950).

56. T. Posternak, *Helv. Chim. Acta* **24,** 1045 (1941).

57a. E. L. May and E. Mosettig, *J. Org. Chem.* **14,** 1137 (1949).

57b. B. Magasanik, R. E. Franzl, and E. Chargaff, *J. Am. Chem. Soc.* **74,** 2618 (1952).

58. E. O. von Lippmann, *Ber.* **34,** 1159 (1901).

59. P. Bedos and A. Ruyer, *Compt. rend.* **196,** 625 (1933).

60. T. Posternak and H. Friedli, *Helv. Chim. Acta* **36,** 251 (1953).

61a. G. E. McCasland and E. C. Horswill, *J. Am. Chem. Soc.* **76,** 1654 (1954).

61b. G. E. McCasland and E. C. Horswill, *J. Am. Chem. Soc.* **76,** 2373 (1954).

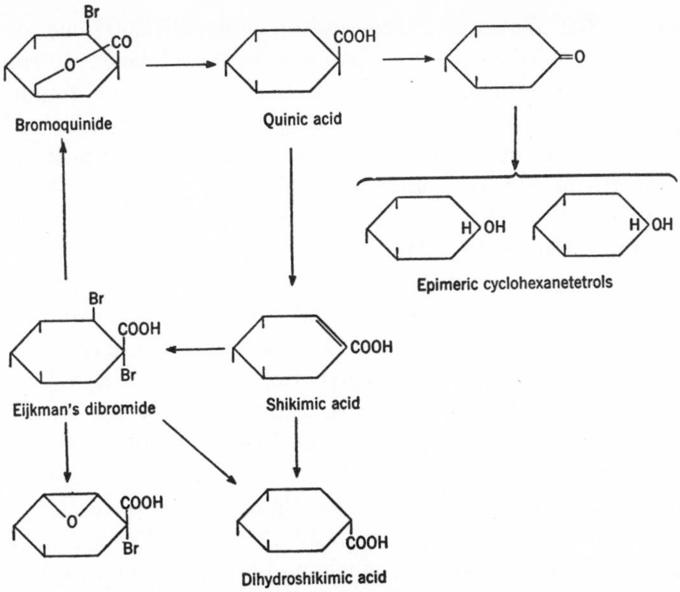
Br
CO
O
COOH
O
Bromoquinide
Quinic acid
H OH
H OH
Epimeric cyclohexanetetrols
Br
COOH
Br
COOH
Eijkman's dibromide
Shikimic acid
COOH
O
Br
COOH
Dihydroshikimic acid

FIG. 2. The quinic–shikimic acid group.

Two epimeric dideoxyinositols were obtained from quinic acid by way of the corresponding trihydroxycyclohexanone (*62*) (Fig. 2). Micheel cyclized the 1,6-diiodohydrin of di-*O*-methylene-D-mannitol by heating it with "molecular" silver in toluene or xylene at 165–170° to obtain a dimethylene derivative of a dideoxyinositol (*63*). Removal of the acetal groups gave

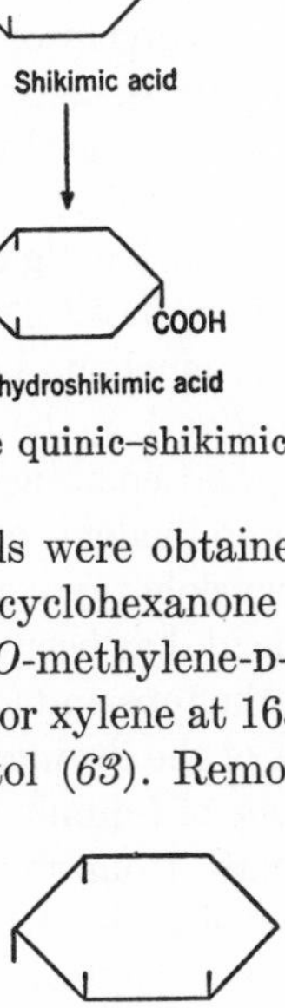

"tetrahydroxymannocyclitol." Inversion was unlikely because of the presence of the rather stable methylene groups; the final product is optically active. The elucidation of the structure and configuration of the cyclohexanetetrols is one of the more difficult aspects of inositol chemistry, but it is presently being accomplished (*61b*, *63a*). The structure and configuration of another isomer, dihydroconduritol (*62*), follows readily from its synthesis by hydrogenation of conduritol.

Conduritol (Fig. 1), m.p. 142–143°, a cyclohexenetetrol, occurs in the bark of the condurango tree (*64*). Two of the synthetic inositols, *allo*-

62. G. Dangschat and H. O. L. Fischer, *Naturwissenschaften* **27**, 756 (1939).
63. F. Micheel, *Ann.* **496**, 77 (1932).
63a. T. Posternak and D. Reymond, *Helv. Chim. Acta* **38**, 195 (1955).
64. K. Kubler, *Arch. pharm.* **246**, 620 (1908).

inositol, m.p. 270–275°, and *muco*-inositol, m.p. 285–290° dec., were obtained by oxidation of conduritol. Two synthetic cyclohexenetetrols, "conduritol-B" and "conduritol-C," have been obtained by debromination of bromohydrins of, respectively, *myo*-inositol and *epi*-inositol (*65*). They are racemates of optical (not structural) isomers of natural conduritol.

Mytilitol (*C*-methyl-*scyllo*-inositol) (*66*) (Fig. 1), m.p. 266–268°, is found in the muscle of *Mytilus edulis*, a mussel (*67*), and in a marine tunicate, *Cionia intestinalis* (*68*). The epimeric isomytilitol obtained synthetically through *myo*-inosose-2 (bioinosose) is 2-*C*-methyl-*myo*-inositol. Both pentaacetates and hexaacetates can be prepared from mytilitol; presumably the tertiary hydroxyl resists acetylation. Posternak (*66*) has also succeeded in synthesizing hydroxymytilitol, m.p. 247°, and hydroxyisomytilitol, m.p. 233°, from *myo*-inosose-2 by means of the Arndt-Eistert synthesis. These are the first-known heptahydric homologs of an inositol.

An optically active isomer of mytilitol, laminitol, m.p. 266–269°, $[\alpha]_D$ −3°, has been isolated from the marine alga *Laminaria cloustoni* (*68a*).

l-Quinic acid (D-1,3-dideoxy-*epi*-inositol-2-carboxylic acid) (Fig. 2), m.p. 162°, $[\alpha]_D$ −44°, is found in cinchona bark, meadow hay, the tops of whortle berries (*Vaccinum myrtillus* L.), the leaves of the mountain cranberry (*Vaccinum vitisidaea* L.), and combined with caffeic acid as chlorogenic acid in plants (*69*). The equivalent of a total synthesis has been effected, starting with 4-chlorocyclohexanone (*70*).

The enantiomorph, *d*-quinic acid, has been found only in the form of the racemate. Lippmann (*58*) dried the tops and leaves of sugar beets and found the racemate in the cooler parts of the drying apparatus. Eijkman (*71*) had previously shown that the lactone of *l*-quinic acid, quinide, is racemized by heat. Hence Lippmann's racemate from sugar beets may be an artifact. The dextrorotatory form may be obtained from the racemate by resolution or by the action of microorganisms, the levorotatory form being destroyed (*58*).

A related unsaturated compound, shikimic acid (Fig. 2), was found in the star anise (*Illicium verum* and *I. religiosum*) (*72*). Its presence has

65. G. E. McCasland and E. C. Horswill, *J. Am. Chem. Soc.* **75,** 4020 (1953); G. E. McCasland and J. M. Reeves, *ibid.* **77,** 1812 (1955). The synthesis of deoxy-*scyllo*-inositol and DL-viburnitol is also described in the first paper.

66. T. Posternak, *Helv. Chim. Acta* **27,** 457 (1944).

67. D. Ackermann, *Ber.* **54,** 1938 (1921); R. I. Daniel and W. Doran, *Biochem. J.* **20,** 676 (1926).

68. D. Ackermann and R. Janka, *Z. physiol. Chem.* **296,** 283 (1954).

68a. B. Lindberg and J. McPherson, *Acta Chem. Scand.* **8,** 1875 (1954).

69. H. O. L. Fischer and G. Dangschat, *Ber.* **65,** 1037 (1932).

70. R. Grewe, W. Lorenzen, and L. Vining, *Ber.* **87,** 793 (1954).

71. J. F. Eijkman, *Ber.* **24,** 1278 (1891); see also Ref. 70.

72. J. F. Eijkman, *Rec. trav. chim.* **4,** 32 (1885); **5,** 299 (1886).

been demonstrated in 30 of 34 gymnosperms investigated (*73*). *l*-Quinic acid has been converted to shikimic acid by degradation of the amide (*74*). The conversion of shikimic acid to *l*-quinic acid was effected (*75*) via a dibromide (*71*) of shikimic acid (Fig. 2).

epi-Inositol, m.p. 285°, results from the reduction of DL-*epi*-inosose-2 (*epi-meso*-inosose) (*76*) (Fig. 1).

Angyal and Matheson (*76a*) synthesized *neo*-inositol (IV), m.p. 315°, by applying the alkaline detosylation reaction (p. 165), which has found so much use in the acyclic field.

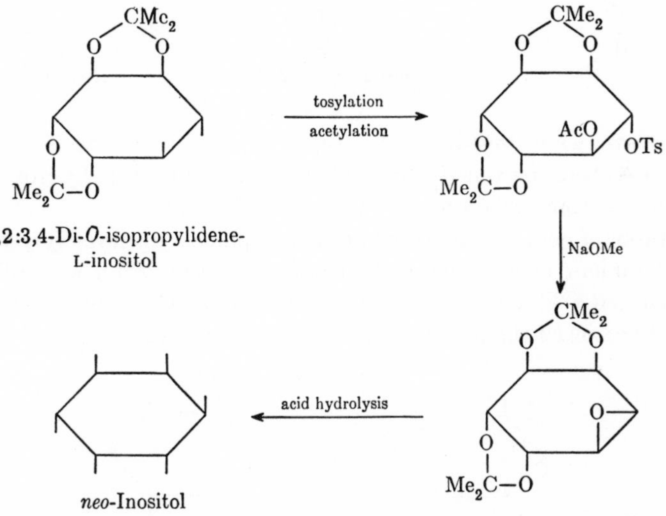
CMe₂
O
O
O
Me₂C—O
1,2:3,4-Di-O-isopropylidene-L-inositol
tosylation
acetylation
CMe₂
AcO
OTs
Me₂C—O
NaOMe
CMe₂
O—
Me₂C—O
acid hydrolysis
neo-Inositol

3. PROOFS OF STRUCTURE AND CONFIGURATION

A. *MYO*-INOSITOL

The characterization of *myo*-inositol as a cyclohexanehexol was made by Maquenne (*77*) in 1887 on the basis of the presence of six esterifiable hydroxyl groups, the indifference toward the usual reducing sugar reagents, the conversion to triiodophenol and benzene by hydriodic acid, and the conversion to tetrahydroxybenzoquinone and rhodizonic acid by strong nitric acid oxidation. This oxidation is general for the inositols and is the

73. S. Hattori, S. Yoshida, and M. Hasegawa, *Physiol. Plantarum* **7,** 283 (1954).

74. G. Dangschat and H. O. L. Fischer, *Naturwissenschaften* **26,** 562 (1938); *Biochim. et Biophys. Acta* **4,** 199 (1950).

75. R. Grewe and W. Lorenzen, *Ber.* **86,** 928 (1953).

76. T. Posternak, *Helv. Chim. Acta* **19,** 1333 (1936).

76a. S. J. Angyal and N. K. Matheson, *J. Am. Chem. Soc.* **77,** 4343 (1955).

77. L. Maquenne, *Compt. rend.* **104,** 225, 297, 1719 (1887).

basis for the classical Scherer (*78*) test for inositols, a red coloration being produced by heating the substance with nitric acid followed by the addition of ammonia and calcium chloride.

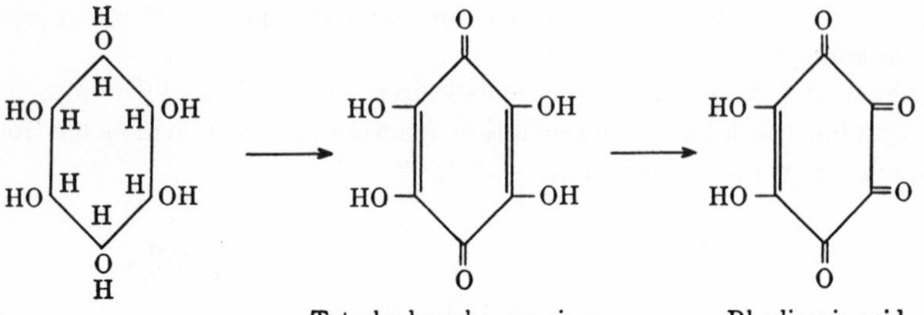

Tetrahydroxybenzoquinone
Rhodizonic acid

The syntheses of *myo*-inositol (*31a, b, 32*) and *scyllo*-inositol (*32*) from hexahydroxybenzene constitute total syntheses, since hexahydroxybenzene can be made from carbon monoxide or from glyoxal.

The proof of configuration was not accomplished until many years later. By independent means, the configuration of *myo*-inositol was established by Dangschat (*79*) and by Posternak (*49*). Previously, S. and T. Posternak (*80*) had narrowed the possibilities for *myo*-inositol to

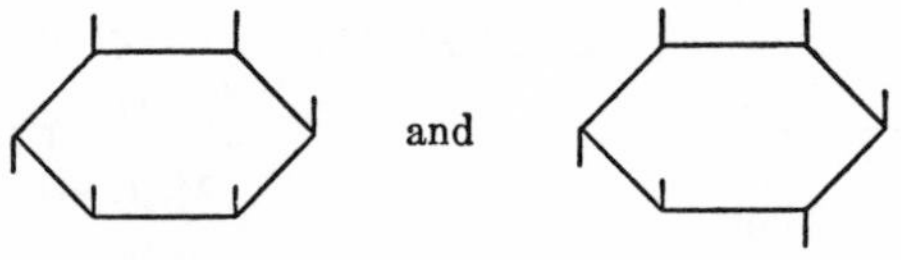

(II) (V)

by isolating both DL-talaric and DL-glucaric acids from the products obtained by the oxidation of *myo*-inositol with cold alkaline permanganate. Dangschat, making use of the acetonation technique of H. O. L. Fischer (see sections under conduritol, quinic, and shikimic acids), acetonated and acetylated *myo*-inositol to a monoisopropylidene tetraacetate. Hydrolysis of the isopropylidene radical followed by lead tetraacetate oxidation and then perpropionic oxidation led to the isolation of DL-idaric acid. From a consideration of formulas (II) and (V) it is evident that only (V) is consistent with the evidence. Hence, the course of the reactions must have

78. J. Scherer, *Ann.* **81,** 375 (1852).

79. G. Dangschat and H. O. L. Fischer, *Naturwissenschaften* **30,** 146 (1942).

80. S. Posternak and T. Posternak, *Helv. Chim. Acta* **12,** 1165 (1929); T. Posternak, *ibid.* **18,** 1283 (1935).

been as follows:

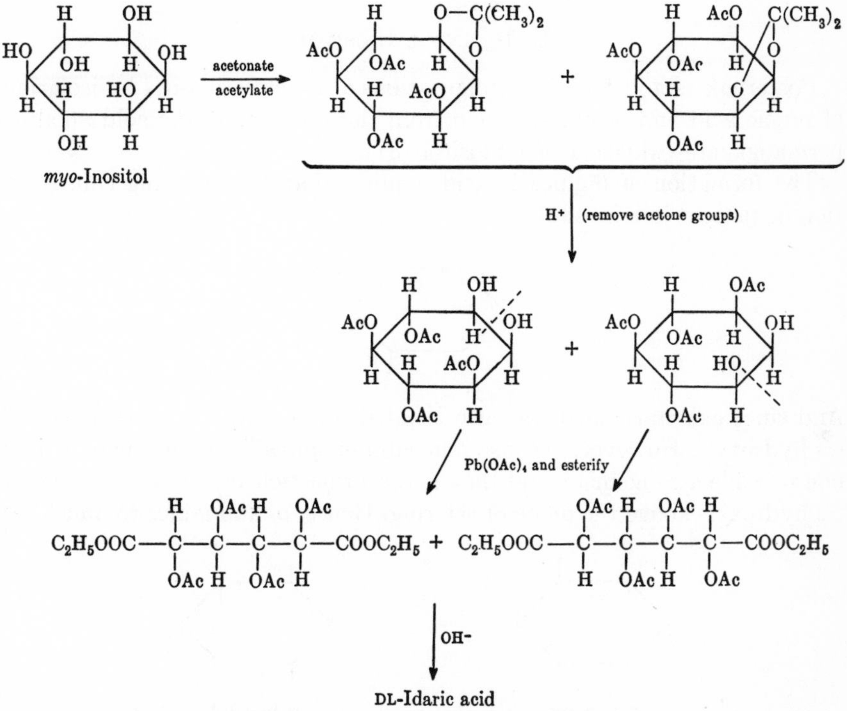
myo-Inositol
acetonate
acetylate
H+
(remove acetone groups)
Pb(OAc)4 and esterify
OH-
DL-Idaric acid

Posternak, on the other hand, applied the alkaline permanganate oxidation to *scyllo-myo*-inosose (bioinosose) and obtained DL-idaric acid (*49*). This evidence simultaneously establishes the configurations of the inosose, *myo*-inositol, and *scyllo*-inositol. The only configuration compatible with the recovery of DL-idaric acid from the inosose is:

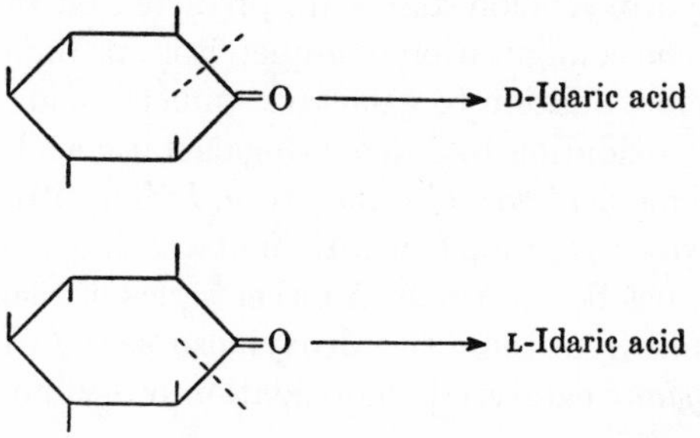
D-Idaric acid
L-Idaric acid

Since *myo*-inositol had previously been limited to configurations (II) and (V) (p. 280), it must have configuration (V); *scyllo*-inositol, an epimer of *myo*-inositol, obtained by reduction of this inosose, must have configuration (IX) (p. 269).

B. D- AND L-INOSITOL

Posternak established the configurations of D- and L-inositol by isolation of mucic acid and of glucaric acid from the products of the cold alkaline permanganate oxidation of L-inositol (*81*).

The formation of D-glucaric acid requires that the following configuration be present in L-inositol:

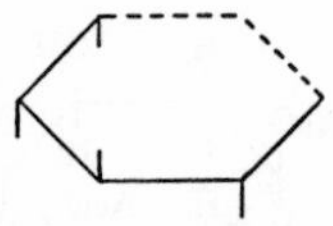

And since galactaric acid was also isolated, there must be another pair of *cis* hydroxyls. However, because L-inositol is optically active, there is only one possible arrangement and that is the projection of the second pair of *cis* hydroxyls above the plane of the ring. Hence, D- and L-inositol must be:

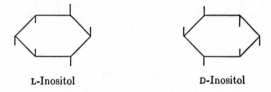

L-Inositol D-Inositol

C. *d*-QUERCITOL AND *l*-VIBURNITOL

The proofs of structure of these two deoxyinositols are considered together since they afford a good illustration of the interrelationships of inositols.

Sixteen pentahydroxycyclohexanes are predicted on the basis of stereochemical theory. The configuration of *d*-quercitol was limited to that shown below by nitric acid oxidation to galactaric (mucic) acid (*82*) and by alkaline permanganate oxidation to 3-deoxy-D-galactaric acid (metasaccharinic acid) (*83*). This same acid was obtained from *l*-viburnitol (*53*). Hence, the arrangement of hydroxyl groups on carbon atoms 2, 5, and 6 of *d*-quercitol and *l*-viburnitol must be the same. Another series of reactions also led to identical compounds from these two deoxyinositols (*53*). It was found that *Acetobacter suboxydans* catalyzed the oxidation of *l*-viburnitol to a deoxy-

81. T. Posternak, *Helv. Chim. Acta* **19,** 1007 (1932).
82. H. Kiliani and C. Scheibler, *Ber.* **22,** 517 (1889).
83. T. Posternak, *Helv. Chim. Acta* **15,** 948 (1932).

cyclose, which was converted to the osazone of a deoxyinosose. This same osazone could also be obtained by a similar series of reactions from *d*-quercitol. This showed that the configurations on carbon atoms 4, 5, and 6 of *l*-viburnitol are identical with those on carbon atoms 4, 3, and 2 of *d*-quercitol. Since the two are not identical, *l*-viburnitol must have the configuration shown. This was confirmed by its reduction to 2-deoxy-*myo*-inositol.

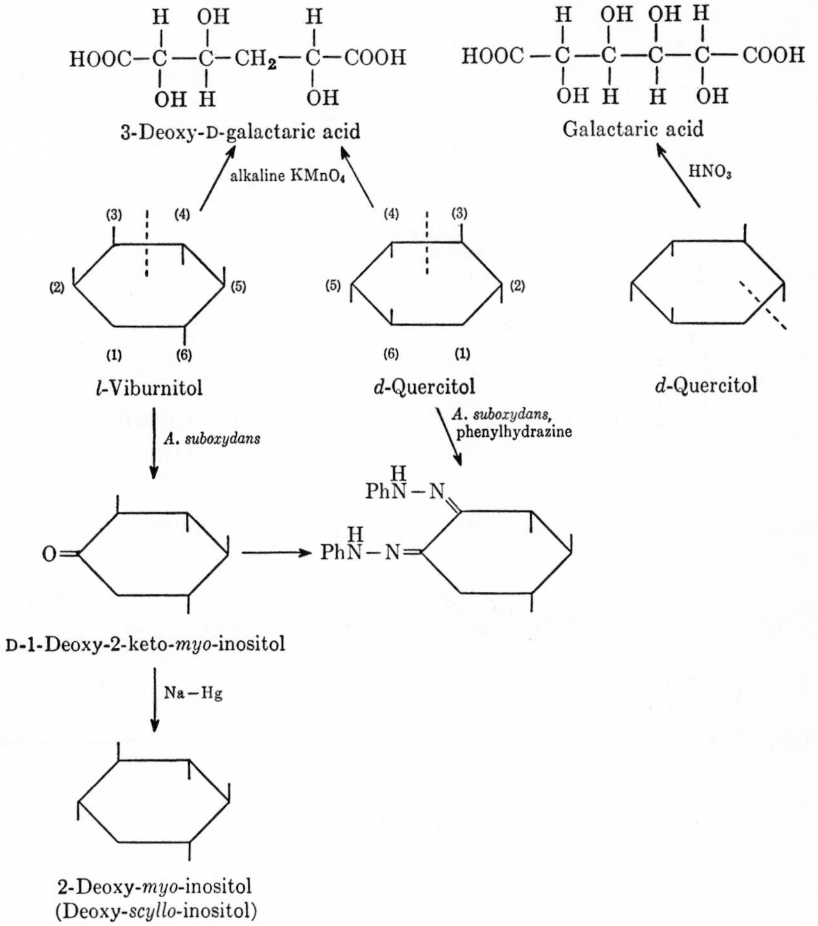
3-Deoxy-D-galactaric acid
Galactaric acid
alkaline KMnO4
HNO3
l-Viburnitol
d-Quercitol
d-Quercitol
A. suboxydans
A. suboxydans, phenylhydrazine
D-1-Deoxy-2-keto-myo-inositol
Na–Hg
2-Deoxy-myo-inositol
(Deoxy-scyllo-inositol)

D. Conduritol

The configuration of conduritol, and incidentally those of *allo*-inositol, *muco*-inositol, and dihydroconduritol, was elucidated in 1939 by Dangschat and Fischer (*62*), who applied the acetonation-oxidation technique previously used so successfully on quinic and shikimic acids. The steps utilized were as follows:

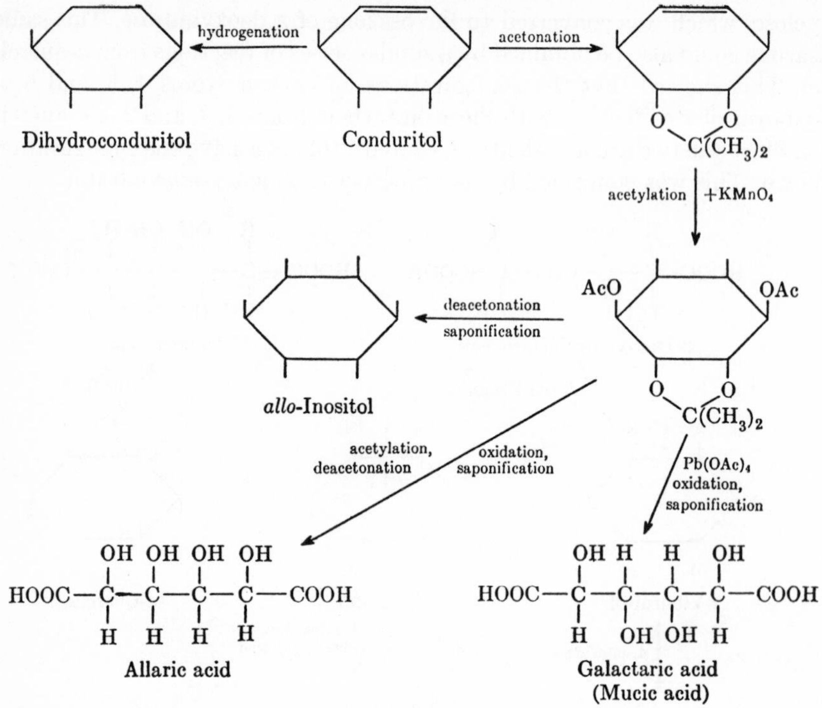
hydrogenation
acetonation
Dihydroconduritol
Conduritol
$C(CH_3)_2$
acetylation
$+KMnO_4$
AcO
OAc
deacetonation
saponification
allo-Inositol
acetylation,
deacetonation
oxidation,
saponification
$Pb(OAc)_4$
oxidation,
saponification
Allaric acid
Galactaric acid
(Mucic acid)

If, however, conduritol was first acetylated then the following results were obtained:

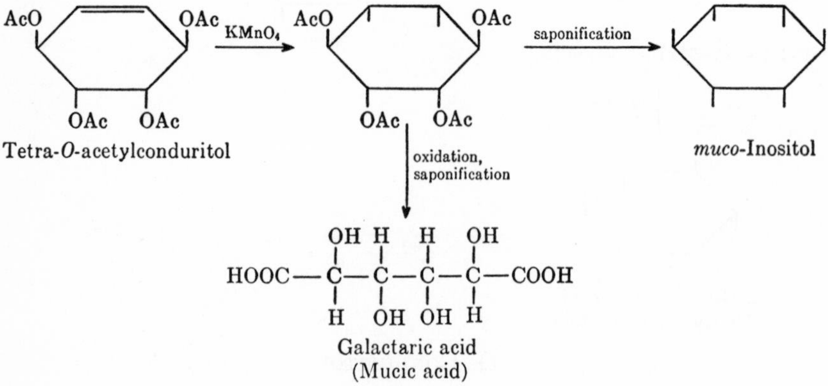
$KMnO_4$
saponification
Tetra-*O*-acetylconduritol
muco-Inositol
oxidation,
saponification
Galactaric acid
(Mucic acid)

E. Mytilitol

With the establishment of the configuration of *myo*-inosose-2 (see p. 281), Posternak (*66*) was able to proceed with the configuration of mytilitol, and a number of synthetic products, isomytilitol, hydroxymytilitol, and hydroxyisomytilitol, through the following series of reactions:

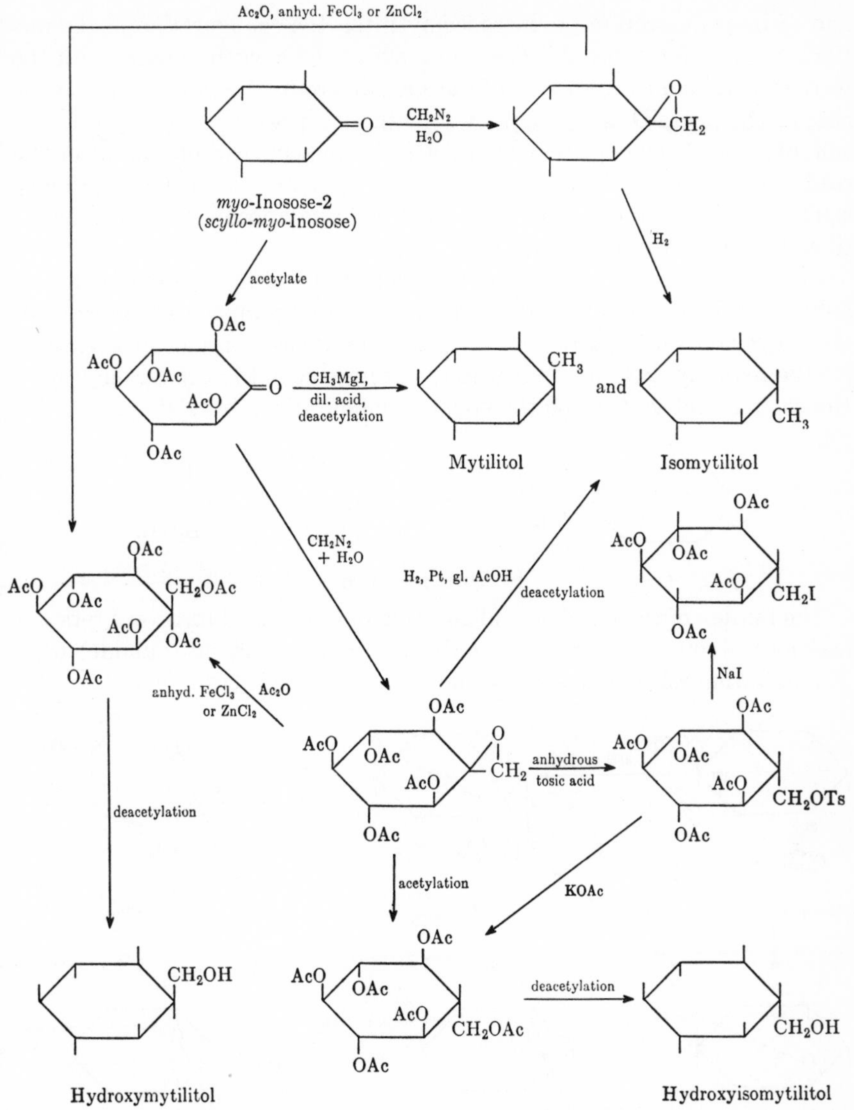
Ac₂O, anhyd. FeCl₃ or ZnCl₂
CH₂N₂
H₂O
myo-Inosose-2
(scyllo-myo-Inosose)
H₂
acetylate
CH₃MgI,
dil. acid,
deacetylation
and
Mytilitol
Isomytilitol
CH₂N₂
+ H₂O
H₂, Pt, gl. AcOH
deacetylation
NaI
anhyd. FeCl₃
or ZnCl₂
Ac₂O
anhydrous
tosic acid
deacetylation
acetylation
KOAc
deacetylation
Hydroxymytilitol
Hydroxyisomytilitol

In the Grignard reaction, mytilitol and isomytilitol are formed from the penta-*O*-acetylinosose. The configuration with three adjacent *cis* hydroxyl groups was assigned to isomytilitol and the other to mytilitol by analogy to the periodic acid oxidation of *scyllo*-inositol and *myo*-inositol. *scyllo*-Inositol has a completely *trans* configuration and is oxidized more slowly than *myo*-inositol. Similarly mytilitol is attacked less rapidly than isomytilitol.

Since hydrogenation of both the epoxide derivative of *myo*-inosose-2 and of its pentaacetate produces isomytilitol, the configuration of the tertiary carbon atom is established inasmuch as the oxygen remains with the tertiary carbon during scission of the epoxide group. Scission of the epoxide ring in the penta-*O*-acetyl derivative with either acetic acid or *p*-toluenesulfonic acid, likewise, does not involve the tertiary carbon atom, for the ready replacement of the tosyloxy group by iodine indicates a primary ester linkage. Therefore, the hydroxy derivative appears to be configurationally related to isomytilitol.

On the other hand, acetylation with acetic anhydride in the presence of anhydrous ferric chloride or zinc chloride apparently involves an opening of the ethylene oxide ring at the tertiary carbon with consequent inversion, for the hydroxy derivative ultimately obtained is not hydroxyisomytilitol. Hence, it would seem to be the epimer configurationally related to mytilitol.

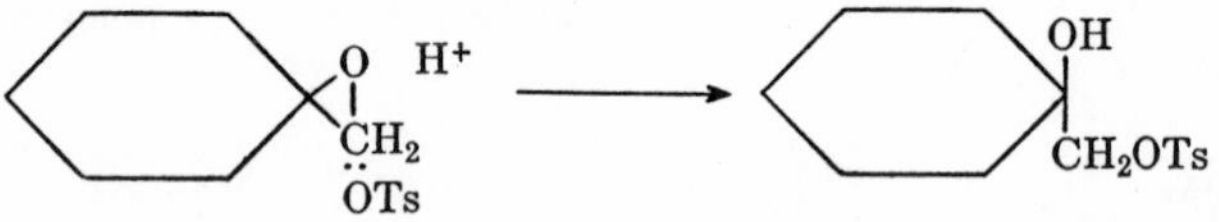
O H+
CH2
OTs
OH
CH2OTs

F. Quinic Acid

The burden of the proof of configuration of quinic acid rests on a series of reactions involving the acetone derivative and its lactone (quinide) (*84*). The following scheme illustrates the reactions involved:

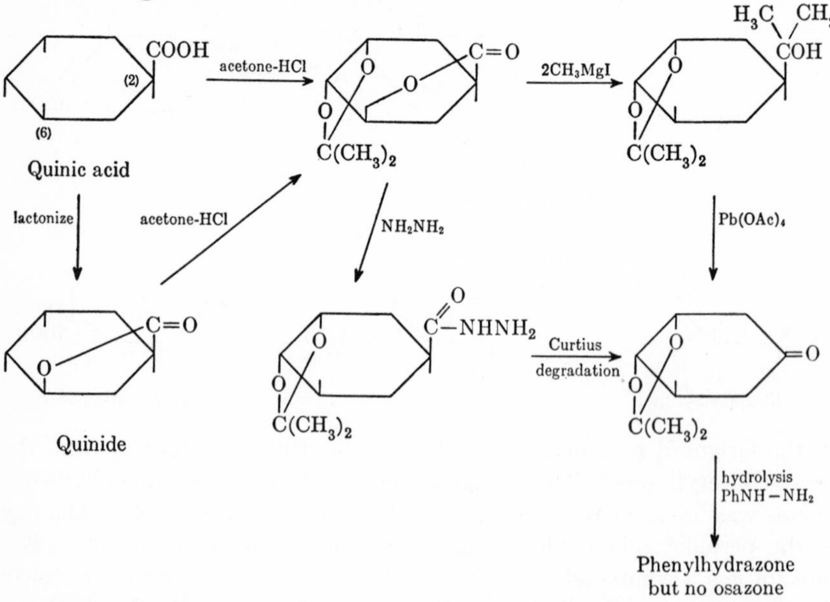
COOH
(2)
(6)
Quinic acid
acetone-HCl
C=O
O
O
O
C(CH3)2
2CH3MgI
H3C CH3
COH
C(CH3)2
lactonize
acetone-HCl
NH2NH2
Pb(OAc)4
C=O
O
Quinide
O
C—NHNH2
C(CH3)2
Curtius
degradation
=O
C(CH3)2
hydrolysis
PhNH—NH2
Phenylhydrazone
but no osazone

84. H. O. L. Fischer, *Ber.* **54,** 775 (1921); H. O. L. Fischer and G. Dangschat, *ibid.* **65,** 1009 (1932).

It had been previously established that quinic acid readily forms a lactone, called quinide. Quinide was shown to have a γ-lactone structure by conversion of the trimethyl ether to 3-hydroxy-4-methoxybenzoic acid (isovanillic acid). At the same time, this reaction established that the hydroxyl at carbon 6 and the carboxyl must be on the same side of the ring. Since the hydroxyl derivative obtained through the Grignard reaction consumes one mole of lead tetraacetate and from the results of the Curtius degradation, it follows that carbon 2 must have both a carboxyl and hydroxyl attached. Furthermore, since the resultant ketone cannot form an osazone, carbons 1 and 3 must be free of hydroxyl groups. By elimination, therefore, the remaining two hydroxyls must be at carbons 4 and 5. Finally, these must

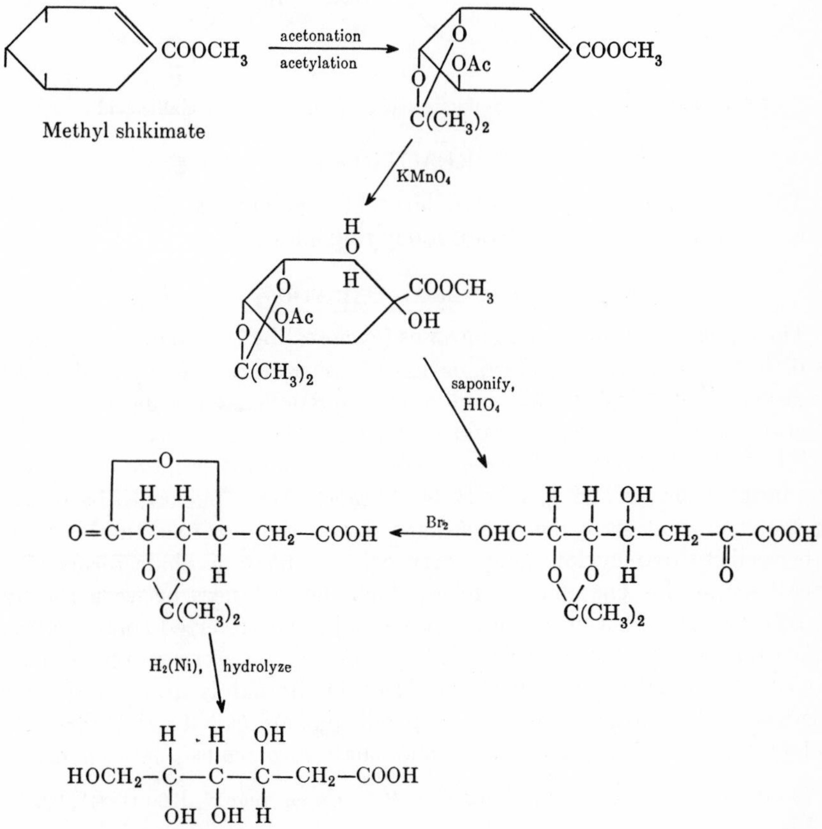
COOCH3
Methyl shikimate
acetonation
acetylation
OAc
C(CH3)2
KMnO4
OH
saponify,
HIO4
Br2
O=C–C–C–C–CH2–COOH
OHC–C–C–C–CH2–C–COOH
H2(Ni),
hydrolyze
HOCH2–C—C—C–CH2–COOH

2-Deoxy-D-*arabo*-hexonic acid
(2-Deoxygluconic acid)

be *cis* in order to form an acetone derivative and be *trans* to the hydroxyl at carbon 6 because quinic acid is optically active.

G. Shikimic Acid

The configuration of shikimic acid was established by H. O. L. Fischer and G. Dangschat (*85*) through the series of reactions shown on p. 287. These steps leave no question regarding the configuration of shikimic acid and the position of the double bond.

The structural similarities among quinic, shikimic, and gallic acids are striking and their possible relationship in the plant are discussed by Fischer and Dangschat.

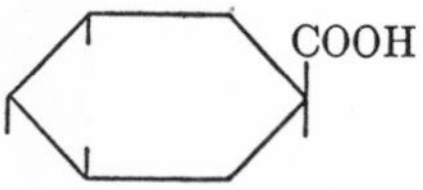
COOH

l-Quinic acid

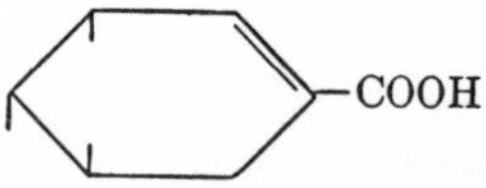
COOH

Shikimic acid

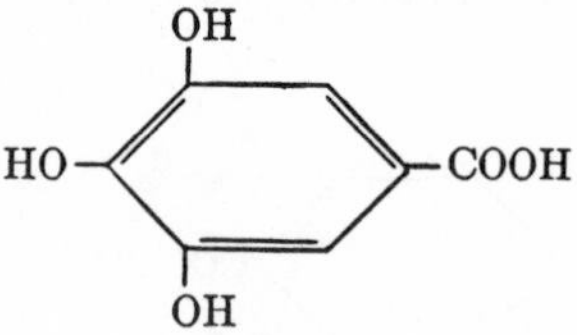
OH
HO
COOH
OH

Gallic acid

4. REACTIONS

The reactions of the cyclitols are those of the polyhydric alcohols, but the ring structure exerts an important modifying influence.

A. Bacterial Oxidation

The oxidation of inositols to inososes (cycloses) by *Acetobacter suboxydans* is of importance in the determination of configuration (e.g., Posternak's work on *myo*-inositol, p. 275) and in the interconversion of inositols by reduction of the inosose. Bertrand's rule (p. 133) accurately predicts the point of attack in the acyclic series, but the situation is more complex in the inositol series. The specificity of *A. suboxydans* appears to be related to the conformation of the cyclohexane ring of the inositols. Inositols, like other substituted cyclohexanes, may exist in boat or chair forms (*86*). (See Chapter I.) The chair form in which the distances between the hydroxyl groups is at a maximum appears to be the preferred conformation. Substituents that are oriented nearly parallel to the average plane of the puckered ring are called equatorial. They lie alternately above and below the plane. Substituents that are perpendicular are called axial (formerly, polar) (*87*). Conversion to the second chair form causes interchange of

85. H. O. L. Fischer and G. Dangschat, *Helv. Chim. Acta* **17,** 1200 (1934); **20,** 705 (1937).

86. For a comprehensive review, see H. D. Orloff, *Chem. Revs.* **54,** 347 (1954).

87. D. H. R. Barton, O. Hassel, K. S. Pitzer, and V. Prelog, *Nature* **172,** 1096 (1953); *Science* **119,** 49 (1954).

orientation. The use of molecular models is almost essential for an understanding of these concepts, but perspective representations of the two chair forms of *myo*-inositol are given below (X and XI). The equatorial substituents are indicated by dotted bonds. Note that the favored conformation (X) has only one axial hydroxyl group, that on carbon 2.

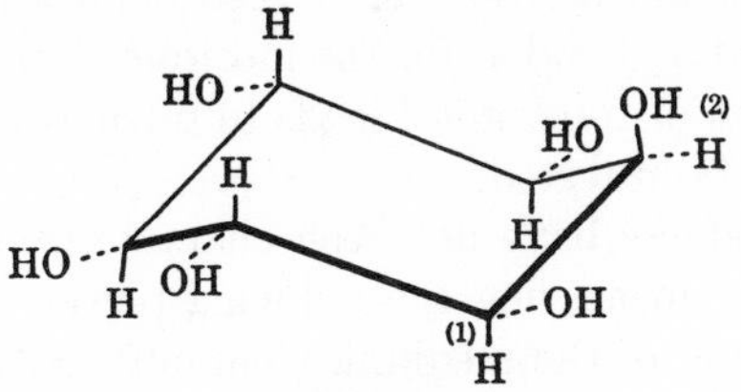

(X)

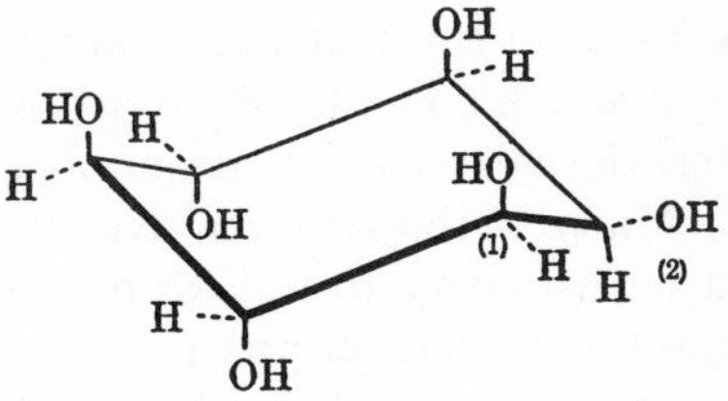

(XI)

With an understanding of the above concepts, it becomes possible to assign conformational requirements (which are determined by configuration) for the biochemical oxidation of inositols. Magasanik, Franzl, and Chargaff (*57b*) have shown these requirements to be: (1) Only axial hydroxyl groups are oxidized, and (2) the carbon atom in *meta*-position to the one carrying the axial hydroxyl group (in counterclockwise direction if north axial; clockwise, if south axial) must carry an equatorial hydroxyl group. South axial hydroxyl groups project downward and north axial, upward. These rules have been confirmed as minimal requirements (*88*) for the oxidation of inositols, monodeoxyinositols, and aminodeoxyinositols.

Several inososes have already been mentioned. Historically, *myo*-inosose-2 (2-keto-*myo*-inositol, *scyllo*-inosose, *scyllo-meso*-inosose, bioinosose) (Fig. 1), the product from *myo*-inositol (*49*, *89*, *90*), is best known. This same inosose is obtained when *myo*-inositol is oxidized with oxygen in the presence of platinum oxide in weakly acid solution (*91*). The yield is about half that obtained in the bacterial oxidation (85%) (*90*), but it is striking that both chemical (platinum) and biochemical (enzymes of *A. suboxydans*) catalysis cause oxygen to attack the substrate in the same position.

Oxidation of *epi*-inositol by *A. suboxydans* leads to D-*epi*-inosose-2 (Fig. 1) (*57b*, *92*).

Optically active forms can also be oxidized. L-*myo*-Inosose (*d*-inosose) is obtained from D-inositol (*93*) (Fig. 1). Likewise, L-inositol is converted to D-

88. T. Posternak and D. Reymond, *Helv. Chim. Acta* **36,** 260 (1953); L. Anderson, K. Tomita, P. Kussi, and S. Kirkwood, *J. Biol. Chem.* **204,** 769 (1953).

89. A. J. Kluyver and A. G. J. Boezaardt, *Rec. trav. chim.* **58,** 956 (1939).

90. T. Posternak, *Biochem. Prep.* **2,** 57 (1952).

91. K. Heyns and H. Paulsen, *Ber.* **86,** 833 (1953).

92. T. Posternak, *Helv. Chim. Acta* **29,** 1991 (1946).

93. B. Magasanik and E. Chargaff, *J. Biol. Chem.* **175,** 929 (1948).

myo-inosose. Reduction of these inososes leads to *myo*-inositol (Fig. 1). Thus, one is able to pass from the active to the *meso* state. This conversion has not been demonstrated *in vivo*. It is interesting that both the D- and L-forms are oxidized in the presence of *A. suboxydans*. The active inositols have a similarity to D- and L-mannitol of the acyclic series in that they contain the *manno*-configuration and in that certain positions are stereochemically equivalent (for mannitol: 1 and 6, 2 and 5, 3 and 4; for the inositols: 1 and 4, 2 and 3, 5 and 6). Bacterial oxidation of D-mannitol leads to D-fructose, but the behavior of L-mannitol has not been tested.

Many of the bacterial oxidation products have not been characterized; it is customary to test for oxidation by measuring the reducing power or (better) by measuring the oxygen uptake of the medium. Chargaff's rules allow prediction of the structures of the products. Deoxyinososes of known structure have been obtained by oxidation of deoxyinositols (Fig. 1) (*36*, *53*, *55*, *94*).

Oxidation of *myo*-inositol has been reported to yield a diketoinositol (*95a*), but others have been unable to confirm this (*95b*, *96*). On the other hand, there is evidence of the formation of several diketones from other substrates (*94*, *97*), and oxidation of D-inositol, if prolonged, yields an α-diketo compound, L-1,2-diketo-*myo*-inositol (*93*). L-Inositol gives the enantiomorph.

Inososes, like hexoses, form osazones when treated with phenylhydrazine, so that the isolation of osazones from the oxidation products is not, in itself, evidence of the formation of α-diketoinositols.

B. Behavior with Oxidizing Agents

a. Nitric Acid

The cyclitols are resistant to oxidation with dilute nitric acid, but with concentrated acid, depending on the conditions, a variety of products may be obtained ranging from carbon dioxide to cyclic ketones. Reference will be made here, as well as in subsequent sections, to those instances in which the ring has remained intact or in which it has been opened and compounds retaining all the original carbons have been isolated.

The Scherer test (*78*) for *myo*-inositol is dependent on the formation of rhodizonic acid (p. 280), whose calcium salt has a red color. This test is

94. B. Magasanik and E. Chargaff, *J. Biol. Chem.* **175,** 939 (1948).

95a. J. W. Dunning, E. I. Fulmer, J. F. Guymon, and L. A. Unterkofler, *Science* **87,** 72 (1938).

95b. E. I. Fulmer and L. A. Unterkofler, *Iowa State Coll. J. Sci.* **21,** 251 (1947).

96. H. E. Carter, C. Belinsky, R. K. Clark, Jr., E. H. Flynn, B. Lytle, G. E. McCasland, and M. Robbins, *J. Biol. Chem.* **174,** 415 (1948).

97. B. Magasanik and E. Chargaff, *J. Biol. Chem.* **174,** 173 (1948).

general for the inositols, but not for their methyl ethers. Salkowski (*98*) has modified the Scherer test so that as little as 0.1 mg. inositol may be detected. The test is carried out as follows: A little inositol is dissolved in 1–2 drops of nitric acid (sp. gr. 1.2), a drop each of 10% $CaCl_2$ and 1–2% H_2PtCl_6 solutions are added, and the mixture is cautiously concentrated on a porcelain crucible cover. A rose to brick-red color appears. Hoglan and Bartow, and Preisler and Berger (*99*) give detailed directions for the preparation of rhodizonic acid and tetrahydroxybenzoquinone in quantity from *myo*-inositol.

Posternak moderated the nitric acid oxidation and obtained about a 10% yield of pure DL-*epi*-inosose-2 (*90*). This is the racemate of the active form obtained by bacterial oxidation of *epi*-inositol, which was obtained by reduction of DL-*epi*-inosose-2 (Fig. 1) (*34a, 76*). The oxidation of *d*-quercitol to galactaric acid has already been mentioned.

b. *Alkaline Permanganate*

This oxidation, as employed by Posternak, was very useful in elucidating the configuration of the inositols (see above). From *myo*-inositol, S. and T. Posternak obtained DL-talaric and DL-glucaric acids. From *myo*-inosose-2, T. Posternak obtained DL-idaric acid. In these instances, the ring was opened to form dibasic acids. *d*-Quercitol was oxidized by Posternak (*53*) to 3-deoxy-D-galactaric acid. In all these oxidations, it was necessary to maintain low temperatures.

d-Quercitol was oxidized to benzoquinone by Prunier (*100*) with manganese dioxide in sulfuric acid.

l-Quinic acid was oxidized to benzoquinone by Wöhler (*101*). Derivatives of conduritol and shikimic acid were hydroxylated at the double bond by Fischer and Dangschat (*62, 85*).

c. *Hypobromite and Bromine*

d-Quercitol was oxidized by Kiliani and Schäfer, who used bromine on an aqueous solution of the cyclitol. They obtained a cyclohexanetrioldione characterized as the bis(phenylhydrazone), m.p. 180° (dec.) (*102*).

l-Quercitol was oxidized by Power and Tutin (*52*) to a cyclohexanetri-

98. E. Salkowski, *Z. physiol. Chem.* **69**, 466 (1910).

99. F. A. Hoglan and E. Bartow, *J. Am. Chem. Soc.* **62**, 2397 (1940); P. W. Preisler and L. Berger, *ibid.* **64**, 67 (1942); rhodizonic acid and tetrahydroxybenzoquinone are used as indicators in the volumetric determination of sulfate; a red color is formed in the presence of excess barium (cf. Scherer test).

100. L. Prunier, *Ann. chim. phys.* [5] **15**, 54 (1878).

101. F. Wöhler, *Ann.* **51**, 148 (1844).

102. H. Kiliani and J. Schäfer, *Ber.* **29**, 1765 (1896).

oldione using sodium hypobromite. They characterized the compound as the bis(phenylhydrazone), m.p. 209° (dec.).

d. Glycol-Splitting Reagents

Lead tetraacetate was employed for the oxidation of *muco*- and *allo*-inositol derivatives obtained by hydroxylation of the corresponding conduritol compounds (see above). Ultimately, the dibasic acids corresponding to the dialdehydes obtained by breaking the cyclitol ring were isolated and identified. Lead tetraacetate was also used to cleave 1,2:5,6-di-*O*-isopropylidene-D-(or L-)inositol to the corresponding *manno*-hexodialdose (*103*). The dialdoses were reduced to mannitol derivatives. In the L-series, this was accomplished by the use of the Meerwein-Pondorff reaction, which has had little application in the carbohydrate field.

Periodic acid does not oxidize *myo*-inositol according to the classical pattern. The consumption of 6 moles of oxidant with the formation of 6 moles of formic acid would be expected. Instead, a complex reaction ensues in which there is an overconsumption of oxidant and only about 4 moles of acid are produced (*104*). A mechanism has been advanced to account for these results (*104*). Similar results have been obtained with D-inositol and pinitol (*105*). Structural studies with periodic acid are of less application here than in other branches of carbohydrate chemistry, although useful results have been obtained (*61b*, *105a*) by taking into account the overoxidation caused by the β-dicarbonyl anomaly. Certain substituted derivatives, 1,3-di-*O*-methyl-*myo*-inositol (dambonitol) (*41a*) and isopropylideneinositols (*7*), for example, appear to be oxidized in the classical manner.

C. Reaction with Halogen Acids

The reactions of the cyclitols with halogen acids may be divided into two groups, halohydrin formation and aromatization.

a. Halohydrin Formation

There appears to be only one example of halohydrins obtained by direct action of halogen acids on the cyclitols; *d*-quercitol was heated at 100° with a solution of HCl (saturated at 10°), and a very small amount of substance, m.p. 198–200°, was obtained which had an analysis corresponding to a monochlorohydrin (*100*) and also one, m.p. 155°, that appeared to be a trichlorohydrin, $C_6H_7Cl_3(OH)_2$.

103. D-Isomer: C. E. Ballou and H. O. L. Fischer, *J. Am. Chem. Soc.* **75,** 3673 (1953); L-isomer: Reference 13b.

104. P. Fleury, G. Poirot, and J. Fievet, *Compt. rend.* **220,** 664 (1945).

105. A. M. Stephen, *J. Chem. Soc.* p. 738 (1952).

105a. P. Fleury, J. Courtois, W. C. Hamman, and L. L. Dizet, *Bull. soc. chim.* p. 1307 (1955).

A number of such derivatives have been obtained from cyclitol esters through the action of HCl or HBr on the ester (*46*) or by reacting an acyl halide (*106a, b*) with a cyclitol. Considerable isomerization occurs, since the same dibromohydrin tetraacetates are obtained from *myo*-inositol, *scyllo*-inositol, and pinitol (*61b*). Debromination to known cyclohexanepentols and -tetrols has enabled McCasland (*61b, 65*) to assign tentative structures, and, in some cases, configurations to the mono- and dibromohydrins.

In addition to the conversion of the three cyclitols to the same bromohydrins, Müller (*46*) found further evidence for isomerization. When the reaction mixture from *myo*-inositol or *scyllo*-inositol was treated with $Ba(OH)_2$, he was able to isolate "iso-inositol," which has since been shown to be DL-inositol (*107*). It is to be noted that inversion of any two adjacent carbon atoms of *scyllo*-inositol would give DL-inositol, while inversion of any one carbon atom would give *myo*-inositol. Inversion of the stereochemically equivalent carbon atoms (number 1) of *myo*-inositol would give DL-inositol. Müller also isolated an ill-characterized "pseudo-inositol."

b. Aromatization

The halogen acids acting directly on the cyclitols generally produce substances of a benzenoid nature. This behavior is especially characteristic of hydriodic acid, although instances where hydrochloric and hydrobromic acids have acted similarly are reported. Thus, Maquenne reported the isolation of 2,4,6-triiodophenol, phenol, and other aromatic substances (*77, 108*) by the action of fuming HI at 150–170° on D- and *myo*-inositol. Lautemann (*109*) reported benzoic acid from *l*-quinic acid using HI. Prunier (*100*) obtained benzene, phenol, hydroquinone, and benzoquinone from *d*-quercitol. Oswald (*110*) obtained benzoic acid by heating an aqueous solution of shikimic acid with PI_3.

Hydrochloric acid has been used for the aromatization of shikimic acid to *p*-hydroxybenzoic acid (*71*), and of *l*-quinic acid to hydroquinone and *p*-hydroxybenzoic acid (*111*). Conduritol was transformed in part to catechol by 12.5 to 25% HCl (*66*). Fuming hydrobromic acid converted *l*-quinic acid to hydroquinone, 3,4-dihydroxybenzoic, and benzoic acids (*112*). Müller (*46*)

106a. E. G. Griffin and J. M. Nelson, *J. Am. Chem. Soc.* **37,** 1552 (1915).

106b. A. E. O. Menzel, M. Moore, and O. Wintersteiner, *J. Am. Chem. Soc.* **71,** 1268 (1949).

107. H. G. Fletcher, Jr., and G. R. Findlay, *J. Am. Chem. Soc.* **70,** 4050 (1948); T. Posternak, *Helv. Chim. Acta* **31,** 2242 (1948).

108. L. Maquenne, *Compt. rend.* **109,** 968 (1889).

109. E. Lautemann, *Ann.* **125,** 9 (1863).

110. F. Oswald, *Arch. Pharm.* **229,** 84 (1891).

111. O. Hesse, *Ann.* **200,** 232 (1880).

112. R. Fittig and W. F. Hillebrand, *Ann.* **193,** 194 (1878).

reported the isolation of a small amount of bromobenzene as a result of the treatment of inositol hexaacetate with a glacial acetic acid solution of HBr.

Such aromatization is not peculiar to the halogen acids, for sulfuric acid or alkali at high temperatures or even heat alone will cause the dehydration of certain of the cyclitols to aromatics (*113*).

D. Esterification

Esterification of the cyclitols may be carried out using the free acid, acid anhydride, or acid chloride with or without catalysts in the usual manner (see Chapter IV). However, partial esters have in some instances been recovered from reactions in which full esterification was desired. The distribution of the acyl groups in these compounds is not known.

An interesting case of partial esterification is the acylation of *l*-quinic acid. If the acid and acetic anhydride are refluxed briefly, one obtains tri-*O*-acetylquinide (the lactone of quinic acid). If zinc chloride is present, tetra-*O*-acetylquinic acid is formed (*114*). However, if quinic acid and benzoyl chloride are heated at 130 to 140°, the main product is tetra-*O*-benzoylquinic acid. If the reaction is carried out in the presence of pyridine, tri-*O*-benzoylquinide is the chief product (*115*).

Some phosphate esters of *myo*-inositol have been prepared by the action of phytase on phytic acid (*80*, *116*), in order to arrive at a better understanding of the structure of the biologically important phytic acid. The structures of these esters are not known. Iselin (*117*) has prepared *myo*-inositol 2-phosphate and *scyllo*-inositol monophosphate via the penta-acetates derived from the reduction of penta-*O*-acetyl-*myo*-inosose-2. The *myo*-inositol derivative does not have the biological activity toward microorganisms that the free inositol has.

Esterification of *myo*-inositol with linseed oil fatty acids leads to a hexaester having excellent drying oil properties (*118*). However, the potential availability of *myo*-inositol from corn-steep liquor would not appear to be high enough to justify the industrial exploitation of this ester in paints. It has been pointed out that six million pounds annually of pinitol are potentially available from sugar-pine mill waste produced in California (*9*). If an inexpensive means of isolating the pinitol and demethylating it to D-inositol were found, it would be likely that similar esters of D-inositol

113. "Beilsteins Handbuch der Organischen Chemie," Vol. 6, p. 1186. Springer, Berlin, 1923; Vol. 10, p. 458, 536 1927.

114. E. Erwig and W. Koenigs, *Ber.* **22,** 1457 (1889).

115. P. Echtermeier, *Arch. Pharm.* **244,** 37 (1906).

116. R. J. Anderson, *J. Biol. Chem.* **12,** 97 (1912); **18,** 441 (1914); M. H. McCormik and H. E. Carter, *Biochem. Prep.* **2,** 65 (1952).

117. B. M. Iselin, *J. Am. Chem. Soc.* **71,** 3822 (1949).

118. J. P. Gibbons and K. M. Gordon, *Ind. Eng. Chem.* **42,** 1591 (1950).

could find industrial use. Large amounts of quebrachitol are available from the natural rubber industry (*19*).

E. Alkylidene Formation

Cyclitols do not form alkylidene derivatives with the same ease as acyclic carbohydrates. However, the technique of Dangschat and Fischer, wherein zinc chloride catalysis is used, enables the formation of isopropylidene derivatives. They made brilliant use of this reaction in their elucidation of the structures of shikimic acid, quinic acid, conduritol, and *myo*-inositol (see above). The structures of the naturally occurring methyl ethers, pinitol and quebrachitol, were determined with the aid of this reaction (*7*, *13a, b*). L-Inositol and *epi*-inositol can be converted to triisopropylidene derivatives (*7*). This requires acetonation of *trans* hydroxyl groups. A chair conformation of the ring does allow vicinal *trans* hydroxyl groups in the equatorial plane to approach one another closely (*7*).

F. Miscellaneous Reactions

Griffin and Nelson (*106a*) prepared a mono- and a dimethyl ether of *myo*-inositol by the action of dimethyl sulfate and alkali. These were characterized as their crystalline acetates. Partial ethyl ethers were prepared similarly. Griffin and Nelson's monomethyl ether is apparently DL-bornesitol (*119*) (p. 274), which was also obtained by methylation of 1,3,4,5,6-penta-*O*-acetyl-*myo*-inositol (*119*). Because an acyl migration occurred during this methylation, the structure of the methyl ether is not established. McGowan (*120*) obtained the completely methylated compound by use of the methylation technique of West and Holden (*121*). A by-product of the reaction was a pentamethyl ether, which was later crystallized (*122*).

There is only one instance in the literature of the preparation of a dicyclitol ether. This was obtained by Prunier (*100*) by heating *d*-quercitol at 235–250°. A compound, m.p. 228–230°, and having the composition $C_{12}H_{22}O_9$, sublimed. The residual sirup contained a small amount of substance (quercitan) which may be an internal ether.

The cyclitols can form complexes with metals similar to those of the glycitols. The formation of an insoluble reaction product with basic lead acetate is a means of removing *myo*-inositol almost quantitatively from solution (*123*).

119. L. Anderson and A. M. Landel, *J. Am. Chem. Soc.* **76,** 6130 (1954).

120. J. C. McGowan, *J. Soc. Chem. Ind.* **66,** 446 (1947).

121. E. S. West and R. F. Holden, *Org. Syntheses* **20,** 97 (1940).

122. G. E. McCasland and S. Boutsicaris, *J. Am. Chem. Soc.* **75,** 3845 (1953).

123. G. Meillère and P. Fleury, *J. pharm. chim.* [7] **1,** 384 (1911); J. Needham, *Biochem. J.* **17,** 422 (1923).

Inososes apparently exist in the enediol form in alkaline solution (*91*, *124*); they readily reduce 2,6-dichlorophenol-indophenol (the ascorbic acid reagent). Inososes cannot be acetylated under alkaline conditions, such as obtain with the conventional pyridine – acetic anhydride reagent, because aromatization occurs. Esters of inososes are likewise aromatized when heated with pyridine or sodium acetate (*56*). The deoxynitroinositols of Grosheintz and Fischer are converted to diacetyl-5-nitroresorcinol by pyridine and acetic anhydride (*33*). Attempts to convert cyclitols to cyclohexenetetrols (e.g., conduritol) by ordinary procedures of dehydration also result in the introduction of three double bonds.

The proportions of the two epimeric inositols obtained by reduction of inososes is dependent on the conditions used.

5. BIOCHEMISTRY (*1*, *125*)

Because of the widespread occurrence of *myo*-inositol in animals, plants, yeasts, molds, and bacteria, many attempts have been made at its synthesis. The chemical syntheses have been considered earlier in this chapter. Biochemical synthesis of inositol from D-glucose or D-glucose phosphate by action of a plant cyclase has been reported (*126*). The evidence for this transformation is a positive Scherer test; there has been no definitive evidence in the form of isolation of *myo*-inositol. Evidence for synthesis in the animal body is based on the isolation of C^{14}-labeled *myo*-inositol after the administration of C^{14}-labeled D-glucose (*32b*).

myo-Inositol was shown to be present in Bios I, a growth factor for yeast, by Eastcott (*127*) in 1928. This led eventually to the recognition of *myo*-inositol as a growth factor for other microorganisms and for warm-blooded animals (*128*). It is noteworthy also as an early use of microbiological assay as a research technique.

myo-Inositol has a curative action on dietary alopecia of the mouse (*128*) and also on a condition known as "spectacle eye" (*129*). It has been recognized that *myo*-inositol, along with other members of the B-complex vitamins, can prevent or decrease excessive deposits of fat in the liver (lipotropic action) (*125*). Although it appears that *myo*-inositol may have a lipotropic action for humans, no dietary requirement has been set. The

124. D. H. Couch and W. W. Pigman, *Anal. Chem.* **24,** 1364 (1952).

125. E. R. Weidlein, Jr., "The Biochemistry of Inositol," Bibliographic Series Bulletin No. 6. Mellon Institute, Pittsburgh, 1951.

126. O. Fernández, G. Izquierdo, and E. Martínez, *Farm. nueva (Madrid)* **9,** 563 (1944); *Chem. Abstr.* **40,** 4115 (1946); O. Fernández, M. de Mingo, and E. Martínez, *ibid.* **10,** 541 (1945); *Chem. Abstr.* **43,** 4229 (1949).

127. E. V. Eastcott, *J. Phys. Chem.* **32,** 1094 (1928).

128. D. W. Woolley, *J. Nutrition* **28,** 305 (1944).

129. P. L. Pavcek and H. M. Braun, *Science* **93,** 502 (1941).

occurrence of inositol is so ubiquitous that it is extremely difficult to prepare a diet in which it is deficient.

myo-Inositol appears to be converted to glucose in the animal body (*130*). However, this conversion is probably indirect. When *myo*-inositol labeled with deuterium in (mainly) position 2 was fed to phlorizinized rats, part of it was recovered as deuterated D-glucose (*131*). Since the glucose was labeled in the 6-position, a simple decyclization of inositol to hexose is not indicated (see formulas, p. 272).

Although complete accord has not been reached, lindane appears to be a metabolic antagonist for microorganisms that require inositol (*132*). Lindane is a hexachlorocyclohexane insecticide that is thought to have the same conformation as *myo*-inositol.

The presence of a cyclitol derivative in the antibiotic streptomycin is very interesting. (For more details, see Chapter X.) This derivative, streptamine, has been shown to be a diaminodideoxy-*scyllo*-inositol of the following structure (*133*):

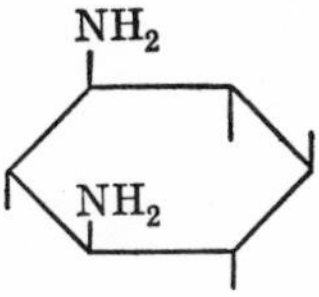
NH2
NH2

It has been synthesized by Wolfrom and associates from natural glucosamine (*133*) and by Heyns and Paulsen from *myo*-inositol (*133a*). Another antibiotic, neomycin, contains a related diaminotrideoxyinositol:

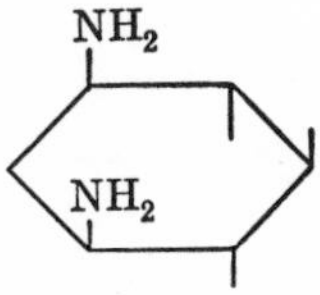
NH2
NH2

It is known that the amino groups are *cis*, but the configurations of the

130. M. R. Stetten and D. Stetten, Jr., *J. Biol. Chem.* **164,** 85 (1946); V. D. Wiebelhaus, J. J. Betheil, and H. A. Lardy, *Arch. Biochem.* **13,** 379 (1947).

131. T. Posternak, W. H. Schopfer, and D. Reymond, *Helv. Chim. Acta* **38,** 1283 (1955).

132. S. Kirkwood and P. H. Phillips, *J. Biol. Chem.* **163,** 251 (1946); R. C. Fuller, R. W. Barrett, and E. L. Tatum, *ibid.* **186,** 823 (1950).

133. M. L. Wolfrom, S. M. Olin, and W. J. Polglase, *J. Am. Chem. Soc.* **72,** 1724 (1950); H. Straube-Rieke, H. A. Lardy, and L. Anderson, *ibid.* **75,** 694 (1953).

133a. K. Heyns and H. Paulsen, *Ber.* **89,** 1152 (1956).

hydroxyl groups were assigned by analogy with streptamine (*134*). 2-Amino-2-deoxy-*neo*-inositol has been obtained by degradation of another antibiotic (*135*).

134. F. A. Kuehl, Jr., M. N. Bishop, and K. Folkers, *J. Am. Chem. Soc.* **73,** 881 (1951).

135. J. B. Patrick, R. P. Williams, C. W. Waller, and B. L. Hutchings, *J. Am. Chem. Soc.* **78,** 2652 (1956).

VI. ACIDS AND OXIDATION PRODUCTS

John W. Green

Aldonic acids, saccharic acids, ascorbic acids and analogs, and uronic acids are the most important classes of acidic carbohydrates. Some of these acids have achieved commercial importance, particularly ascorbic acid and gluconic acid, and the others have interesting potentialities. Slightly oxidized polysaccharides, particularly starch and cellulose (discussed under these substances in Chapter XII), provide commercially valuable modifications of these materials, although the nature of the oxidation has not received much scientific investigation. Naturally occurring acids include ascorbic acid, tartaric acid, and the uronic acids. Other acids are produced as a result of the action of microorganisms on carbohydrates and are found in natural products.

The characteristic oxidizable groupings in the carbohydrate series are:

$$-CHO \quad \text{or} \quad HO\overline{CH\ O}, \quad H\overset{|}{C}OH, \quad \overset{|}{C}H_2OH \quad \text{and} \quad -\overset{|}{\underset{|}{C}}-\overset{|}{\underset{|}{C}}-$$

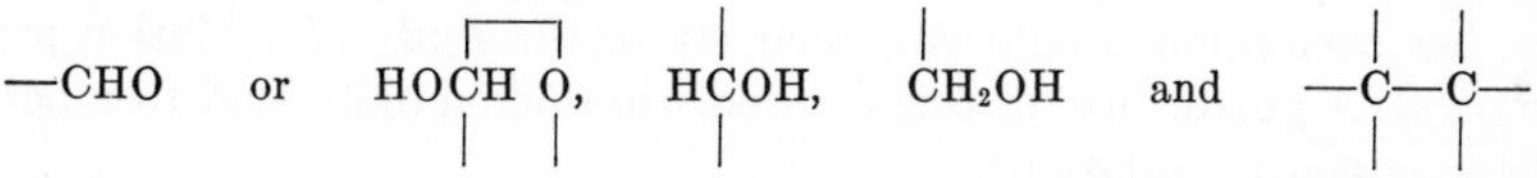

Some typical examples of oxidation reactions and products are given below.

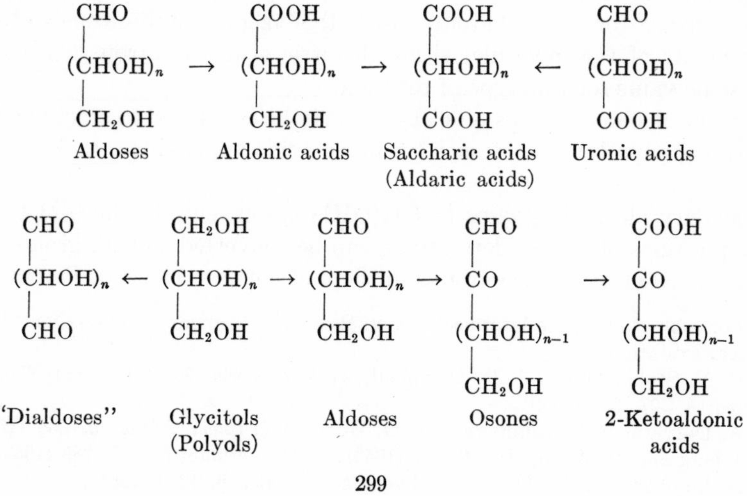

$$
\begin{array}{ccccc}
CHO & COOH & COOH & CHO \\
| & | & | & | \\
(CHOH)_n & \rightarrow & (CHOH)_n & \rightarrow & (CHOH)_n & \leftarrow & (CHOH)_n \\
| & | & | & | \\
CH_2OH & CH_2OH & COOH & COOH \\
\text{Aldoses} & \text{Aldonic acids} & \text{Saccharic acids} & \text{Uronic acids} \\
& & \text{(Aldaric acids)}
\end{array}
$$

$$
\begin{array}{ccccc}
CHO & CH_2OH & CHO & CHO & COOH \\
| & | & | & | & | \\
(CHOH)_n & \leftarrow & (CHOH)_n & \rightarrow & (CHOH)_n & \rightarrow & CO & \rightarrow & CO \\
| & | & | & | & | \\
CHO & CH_2OH & CH_2OH & (CHOH)_{n-1} & (CHOH)_{n-1} \\
& & & | & | \\
& & & CH_2OH & CH_2OH \\
\text{"Dialdoses"} & \text{Glycitols} & \text{Aldoses} & \text{Osones} & \text{2-Ketoaldonic} \\
& \text{(Polyols)} & & & \text{acids}
\end{array}
$$

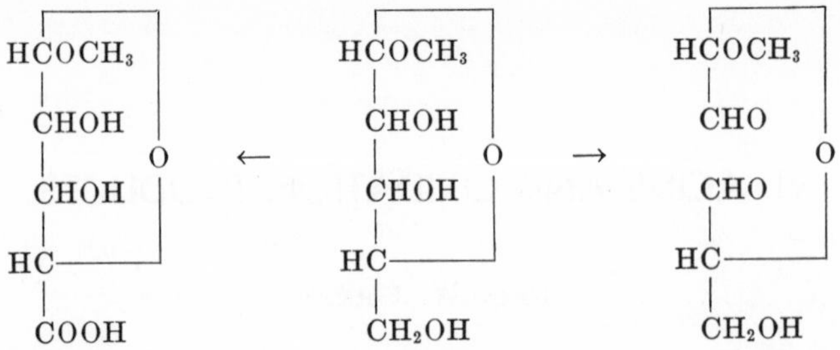

"Uronides" Glycosides Dialdehydes

The most commonly employed oxidative agents are halogens and oxyhalogen acids, nitric acid, and hydrogen peroxide. The general field of oxidants has not been explored systematically, and the oxidative mechanisms have received but little study (*1*). Relatively few oxidation reactions follow a single course or give high yields of single products. Probably the bromine or hypoiodite oxidation of aldoses to aldonic acids, the nitric acid oxidation of galactose to mucic acid, and the periodic acid oxidation of glycol-containing compounds represent reactions with highest yields. Ordinarily, the primary oxidation product may be further oxidized ("overoxidation"), or several groups may be attacked simultaneously.

The technique of paper-partition chromatography, which has been used so successfully in the analysis of reducing sugars and methylated derivatives, has been applied only very sparsely to the study of oxidation products (*2–4*). A greater use of this method will undoubtedly lead to a better understanding of oxidations.

The aldehyde (or hemiacetal) group is the most easily oxidized common group found in carbohydrates. Bromine and hypoiodite convert it readily to the carboxyl (or lactone) group. Most other agents simultaneously attack other points of the molecule, although nitric acid (or nitrous acid) may have some value for this type of reaction.

Primary alcoholic groups (—CH_2OH) may be converted to aldehyde and carboxyl groups by agents such as nitric acid, hypoiodites, and platinic oxide.

Secondary alcoholic groups [—CH(OH)—], particularly those in the 2- and 5-positions of hexose derivatives, can be converted to keto groups, especially if other oxidizable groups in the molecule are blocked. Permanga-

1. For such studies, see later sections on Hydrogen peroxide, Bromine, and Periodic acid oxidation.

2. F. N. Stokes and J. J. R. Campbell, *Arch. Biochem.* **30,** 121 (1951); *Can. J. J. Research* **C27,** 253 (1949).

3. A. Dyfverman, B. Lindberg, and D. Wood, *Acta Chem. Scand.* **5,** 253 (1951); B. Lindberg and D. Wood, *ibid.* **6,** 791 (1952); A. Dyfverman, *ibid.* **7,** 280 (1953).

4. B. Lindberg and O. Theander, *Acta. Chem. Scand.* **8,** 1870 (1954).

nate and oxyhalogen salts, the latter in the presence of catalysts, have been used for the purpose, but the yields are poor.

Most oxidative reagents will bring about cleavage of carbon–carbon bonds under sufficiently drastic conditions. Permanganates, chromates, and cerates may cause quantitative decomposition into carbon dioxide, formic acid, and formaldehyde. On the other hand, hydrogen peroxide (with ferric salts as catalyst) and oxygen in alkaline solution produce cleavage between carbons 1 and 2 of aldonic acids and sugars, respectively; the reactions are sufficiently specific to be of value for preparatory purposes. The cleavage of vicinal glycol groups (—CHOH—CHOH—) by periodic acid or lead tetraacetate, usually to dialdehydes, is extremely specific and important.

The remainder of this chapter will be devoted, first, to a discussion of the preparation and chemistry of carbohydrate acids and oxidation products and, finally, to the effect of specific oxidants.

1. PREPARATION AND REACTIONS

A. Aldonic Acids

The aldonic acids are the initial oxidation products produced from aldoses by most oxidants and are usually isolated as the metallic salts or the lactones. As a result of the ease with which the crystalline lactones, salts, amides, hydrazides, and other derivatives can be formed, aldonic acids are

$$R\text{—}(CHOH)_n\text{—}CHO \xrightarrow{O_2} R\text{—}(CHOH)_n\text{—}COOH$$

valuable for characterization of the sugars. The preparation of an aldonic acid of the same number of carbon atoms has often been used as proof of aldehyde structure; the ketoses in contrast undergo chain splitting and form lower aldonic acids. The aldonic acids can also be reduced by HI to the corresponding aliphatic acids. A reducing disaccharide containing two dissimilar sugar units can be converted to the aldobionic acid; subsequent hydrolysis will give an aldonic acid of one monosaccharide and an aldose, and show the position of the reducing group in the original disaccharide.

The aldonic acids, especially gluconic acid in the form of soluble salts, are important as cation sequestering agents for the purpose of introducing appropriate metallic ions such as iron, bismuth, and particularly calcium into the body in a neutral and easily assimilable form. Calcium lactobionate·$CaBr_2$ may have value as a sedative.

These acids are important precursors in the preparation of sugars with fewer carbon atoms. Oxidative degradation with H_2O_2 and iron salts (see p. 118) produces an aldose of one less carbon atom; thus, D-gluconic acid is converted to D-arabinose, and D-galactonic acid to D-lyxose. Nitriles and amides can also be degraded (see p. 119).

Methods for lengthening the carbon chains of sugars may involve the formation of aldonic acids as intermediates. The Kiliani cyanohydrin synthesis (see p. 106) creates two new aldonic acids with one more carbon atom than in the original aldose. The configuration of the new asymmetric atom can be assigned by use of the lactone rule discussed below.

Finally, an aldonic acid can be converted to its 2-epimer by the action of alkaline agents (see below).

Apparently, gluconic acid and its salts are not metabolized but are excreted in the urine (*5*). When the acid or salts is administered orally, only a small portion is absorbed as such, because of decomposition by microorganisms in the intestine. In proper amounts, gluconic acid and salts produce a decrease in the acidity of the urine.

a. Preparation

The synthesis of aldonic acids can be carried out in various ways. The methods involve not only the formation of a carboxyl group but frequently the creation or destruction of asymmetric carbon atoms. The methods given below are presented in a simplified manner, for side reactions and "overoxidation" often occur.

Oxidation of an Aldose to the Corresponding Aldonic Acid. Bromine or nitric acid are the main oxidants, the latter under mild conditions. The best yields are obtained by the use of bromine in a slightly acid buffered solution (pH 5–6) (see p. 340). The products are generally isolated as the metallic salts by direct crystallization from the reaction solution or by precipitation into ethanol. Yields as high as 95% have been reported in the case of glucose. Commercially the indirect use of bromine as an oxidant is employed in the electrolytic oxidation process with calcium bromide as a "catalyst"; the constant regeneration of free bromine in the solution allows a very economical operation. In the case of rhamnose, the oxidation product can be isolated directly as the lactone; this is one of the few cases for which recourse to metallic salts is not necessary.

Oxidative Degradation. In this type of synthesis one or more asymmetric carbon atoms is lost and several related sugars may give the same product. Fructose and glucose can be oxidized with oxygen in alkaline solution to give a 70% yield of sodium D-arabonate (*6*). L-Arabinose gives 40% of L-erythronic acid (*7*). In such alkaline solutions the formation of enols is

5. S. Hermann and associates, *Naunyn-Schmiedeberg's Arch. exptl. Pathol. Pharmakol.* **154,** 143 (1930); **190,** 309, 681 (1938); *Exptl. Med. Surg.* **3,** 35 (1945); M. B. Chenoweth, H. Civin, C. Salzman, M. Cohn, and H. Gold, *J. Lab. Clin. Med.* **26,** 1574 (1941).

6. O. Spengler and A. Pfannenstiel, *Z. Ver. deut. Zucker-Ind.* **85,** 546 (1933).

7. J. U. Nef, O. F. Hedenburg, and J. W. E. Glattfeld, *J. Am. Chem. Soc.* **39,** 1638 (1917).

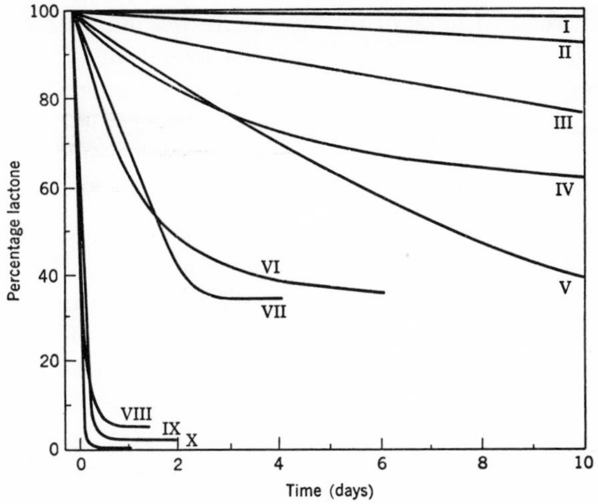
Percentage lactone
100
80
60
40
20
0
0
2
4
6
8
10
Time (days)
I
II
III
IV
V
VI
VII
VIII
IX
X

FIG. 1. Mutarotation of methylated lactones. (After Haworth.)

I. Tetra-*O*-methylmannonic γ-lactone
II. Tetra-*O*-methylgalactonic γ-lactone
III. Tri-*O*-methylxylonic γ-lactone
IV. Tetra-*O*-methylarabonic γ-lactone
V. Tetra-*O*-methylgluconic γ-lactone
VI. Tetra-*O*-methylmannonic δ-lactone
VII. Tri-*O*-methylxylonic δ-lactone
VIII. Tetra-*O*-methylgluconic δ-lactone
IX. Tetra-*O*-methylgalactonic δ-lactone
X. Tri-*O*-methylarabonic δ-lactone

undoubtedly important. Degradation of 2-ketohexonic acids with hydrogen peroxide and iron salts will give pentonic acids (*8*).

L-Ascorbic acid, an enediol, has been oxidized by sodium hypoiodite and by potassium permanganate to L-threonic acid (*9*). Such oxidation of double bonds does not occur in the enols alone, for D-arabinal is oxidized by H_2O_2 and OsO_4 in *tert*-butanol to D-erythronic acid in addition to D-arabinose (*10*). Periodic acid and lead tetraacetate are useful for the cleavage of hexitols and glycosides to glyceraldehyde and glycolaldehyde (see Chapter II).

Synthesis From Lower Aldoses. The Kiliani cyanohydrin synthesis has been discussed elsewhere (see p. 106). In this method a new asymmetric center is created, and two epimeric acids are formed in varying amounts (*10a*).

Change of Configuration Without Change in Number of Carbon Atoms. Epimerization of carbon 2 of an aldonic acid can be carried out in the presence of alkaline agents. This reaction is discussed later.

Synthesis of Acids from Noncarbohydrates. This reaction is a specialized

8. T. S. Gardner and E. Wenis, *J. Am. Chem. Soc.* **73,** 1855 (1951).

9. R. W. Herbert, E. L. Hirst, E. G. V. Percival, R. W. Reynolds, and F. Smith, *J. Chem. Soc. p.* 1270 (1933).

10. R. C. Hockett and S. R. Millman, *J. Am. Chem. Soc.* **63,** 2587 (1941).

10a. H. S. Isbell and R. Schaffer, *J. Am. Chem. Soc.* **78,** 1887 (1956).

one utilized in the synthesis of tetronic acids, because of the rarity of the tetroses: threose and erythrose. Thus, the oxidation of 3-chlorocrotonic acid with OsO_4 and $Ba(ClO_3)_2$ followed by the action of Ag_2O gives DL-threonic acid.

b. Equilibrium in Solution

The free aldonic acids seldom exist as such in aqueous solution; instead they readily form lactones (inner esters) by elimination of water as shown below. Either of the hydroxyls in the γ- and δ-positions can take part in this reaction. The δ-lactones usually hydrolyze easily and mutarotate rapidly in aqueous solution. In contrast, the γ-lactones are more stable and are converted only slowly in water to the equilibrium mixture of free acid and lactones. In Fig. 1 is shown the mutarotation of several methylated lactones (*11*). The distinction between the two types of lactones is very evident.

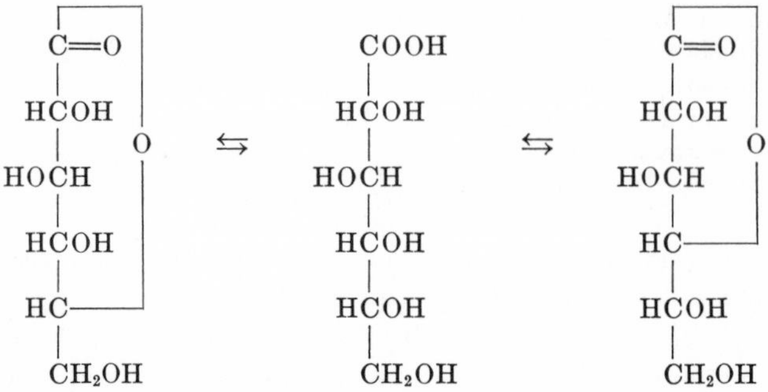

Solutions of aldonic acids or lactones equilibrate to mixtures of the free acids and the δ- and γ-lactones, the relative proportions of which depend upon the configuration of the asymmetric carbon atoms. The attainment of equilibrium conditions is reached only after many days at room temperature but is accelerated by the presence of strong acids. This equilibrium mixture of acid and lactone is often shown on a paper chromatogram; usually a slow-moving acid spot and a faster-moving lactone spot are obtained. For gluconic δ-lactone an initial rapid hydrolysis to a mixture consisting mainly of the free acid and δ-lactone occurs; subsequently a slow rise in rotation takes place until the value approaches that found for the other two forms. The changes in the rotation of gluconic acid and its lactones are given in Table I.

Equilibrium solutions of acids and lactones of the mannose series contain large proportions of γ-lactones, whereas those of the glucose series contain large proportions of the δ-lactones and free acids. The lactone of D-*glycero*-

11. W. N. Haworth, "The Constitution of Sugars," p. 24. Arnold, London, 1929.

TABLE I

OPTICAL ROTATIONS OF GLUCONIC ACID AND LACTONES (*12*)

Carbohydrate	Initial rotation $[\alpha]_D$	Final rotation $[\alpha]_D$	Time
D-Gluconic acid	−6.7°	+17.5°	10 days
D-Gluconic γ-lactone	+67.5°	+17.7°	14 days
D-Gluconic δ-lactone	+66°	+8.8°	24 hours
		+11.5°	95 hours
		+15.8°	25 days

D-*ido*-heptonic acid mutarotates without an increase in acidity, and apparently little or none of the free acid is formed.

A solution supersaturated with respect to both free acid and lactone can often be seeded with the appropriate crystals and the desired product obtained. Normally, the free aldonic acid is obtained by concentration of the aqueous solution at a low temperature *in vacuo*. The free acid can also be crystallized from a solution of the sodium salt in acetic acid. The lactones are formed by dehydration, often very easily. Water can be removed by distillation with butanol or dioxane or by heating *in vacuo*. The lactones are crystallized from an anhydrous solvent; in some cases, as with rhamnonic γ-lactone, they are formed very easily and crystallize readily from water.

Solvents have a definite effect on the equilibrium composition. Thus, mannonic acid dissolved in acetic acid with 16% of water shows a higher positive rotation than in water. The mutarotation is slower, but there is apparently a greater conversion to the δ-lactone than to the γ-lactone. The pH, temperature, and concentration also have an effect on the final equilibrium.

In addition to lactone formation, it is probable that extramolecular esterification may take place with the formation of aldonic esters of aldonic acids (e.g., gluconic acid gluconate) and chain polymerization also may occur. In such systems, the concentration of water present would be expected to exert a profound influence on the composition of the equilibrium solution. Lactic acid forms external esters (lactides), but this type of condensation through carboxyls and α-hydroxyls has not been observed for hexonic and pentonic acids.

c. *Epimerization*

The aldonic acids, in contrast to the reducing sugars, are relatively stable under alkaline conditions. The configuration of carbon 2 can be altered,

12. H. S. Isbell and H. L. Frush, *Bur. Standards J. Research* **11,** 649 (1933); J. U. Nef, *Ann.* **403,** 322 (1914); O. F. Hedenburg, *J. Am. Chem. Soc.* **37,** 345 (1915); H. S Isbell and C. S. Hudson, *Bur. Standards J. Research* **8,** 327 (1932).

however, by prolonged heating with various alkaline agents. Gluconic acid, heated with barium hydroxide at 100° for 115 hours, is converted (*13*) to the 2-epimer (mannonic acid) in a yield of 20%. As the reverse reaction under the same conditions provides only 12% conversion to gluconic acid, the attainment of equilibrium is very slow. This type of interconversion was first (*14*) carried out with quinoline at 140°. Aqueous pyridine (*15*) produces 25% conversion of galactonic acid to talonic acid in 115 hours at 100°. Dibasic acids behave similarly; mucic acid is transformed to DL-talomucic acid (*16*).

It is interesting that this epimerization can occur when the hydroxyl on carbon 2 is methylated. Both tetra-*O*-methylgluconic δ-lactone and tetra-*O*-methylgluconic γ-lactone can be converted to the corresponding mannose derivatives (*17*). The tri-*O*-methylxylonic lactones are transformed to those with the lyxose configuration.

The epimerization may take place through an intermediate enediol as for the sugars. The epimerization of methylated derivatives might occur

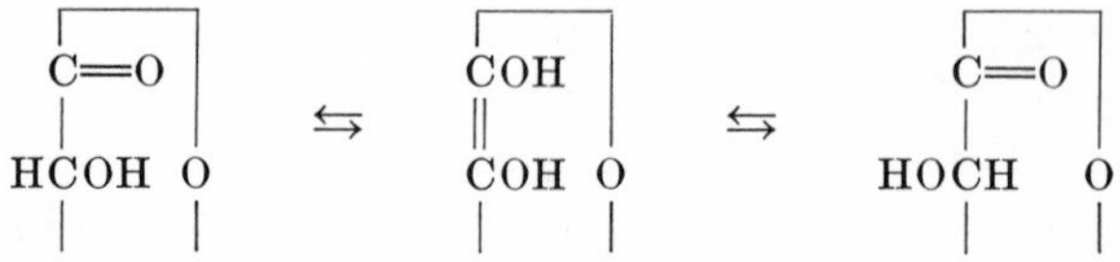
C=O
HCOH O
COH
COH O
C=O
HOCH O

since the methoxyl on carbon 2 is not involved. One possible objection to this concept is that the postulated enediol is also the enediol of an osone which should yield the same products and which might be formed from aldonic acids. No osones have been obtained from such reactions, but the compounds are very difficult to isolate.

d. Optical Rotatory Relationships

A number of empirical relationships between the optical rotations of acids, lactones, salts, and derivatives have been derived. The most important use of these relationships is for the determination of the configurations of the epimeric acids produced in the cyanohydrin synthesis.

The configurations of the hydroxyl groups on carbons 4 and 5 have a major influence on the rotations of lactones. The "lactone rule" in its qualitative form (*18*) stipulates that a lactone is more dextrorotatory than the free

13. H. T. Bonnett and F. W. Upson, *J. Am. Chem. Soc.* **55,** 1245 (1933).
14. E. Fischer, *Ber.* **23,** 799 (1890); **24,** 2136 (1891).
15. O. F. Hedenburg and L. H. Cretcher, *J. Am. Chem. Soc.* **49,** 478 (1927).
16. T. Posternak, *Naturwissenschaften* **23,** 287 (1935).
17. W. N. Haworth and C. W. Long, *J. Chem. Soc.* p. 345 (1929).
18. C. S. Hudson, *J. Am. Chem. Soc.* **32,** 338 (1910); F. J. Bates and associates, "Polarimetry, Saccharimetry and the Sugars," p. 434. Gov't Printing Office, Washington, D.C., 1942.

acid if the hydroxyl group involved in lactone formation lies on the right side in the Fischer projectional formula. The lactone will be more levorotatory than the acid if the hydroxyl group lies on the left side. Since most aldonic acids have only small rotations, and the lactones, because of ring formation, possess fairly strong rotations, the lactones can be divided into levorotatory and dextrorotatory groups. Both γ- and δ-lactones of gluconic and mannonic acid are dextrorotatory; gulonic and galactonic acids form levorotatory γ-lactones and dextrorotatory δ-lactones. D-Allonic γ-lactone provides an exception to the rule since it has a small negative rotation ($[\alpha]_D - 6.8°$) instead of the expected positive rotation.

The differences in rotation of pairs of γ-lactones epimeric at carbon 2 divide the lactones into two distinct classes (*19*): those with molecular epimeric differences in the range -3400 to -4000 (ribonic, arabonic, galactonic, talonic, and homomorphous lactones) and those with differences of another magnitude and positive sign ($+690$ for the xylonic and lyxonic lactone pair, and $+1460$ for the gluconic and mannonic lactone pair).

The configuration of carbon 2 exerts a major influence on the rotation of acyclic derivatives of the aldonic acids. The phenylhydrazides and amides are dextrorotatory when the hydroxyl group on carbon 2 lies to the right in the Fischer projectional formula (*20*). For these derivatives, gluconic and mannonic acid have rotations with different signs, whereas the derivatives of gluconic and galactonic acid have the same signs. The lactone and hydrazide rules are very valuable in the determination of configuration, especially of new aldonic acids formed by the cyanohydrin synthesis. These derivatives are generally used to characterize the acids and can also be employed for configurational identification. A similar rule also applies to the benzimidazole derivatives (*21*) and to the acetylated nitriles (*22*).

Normally the alkali salts of the aldonic acids are slightly more dextrorotatory than the free acids, when the hydroxyl of carbon 2 lies on the right (*23*). This correlation might be considered to be an extension of the hydrazide rule. The lead salts present an exception, apparently because a complex is formed between the lead ion and the hydroxyl on carbon 2 (*24*). The lead salts are acidic in contrast to the normal type. The rotatory displacement in relation to the calcium salts is levorotatory when the hydroxyl of carbon 2 is on the right.

19. C. S. Hudson, *J. Am. Chem. Soc.* **61,** 1525 (1939).

20. C. S. Hudson, *J. Am. Chem. Soc.* **39,** 462 (1917); **40,** 813 (1918).

21. N. K. Richtmyer and C. S. Hudson, *J. Am. Chem. Soc.* **64,** 1612 (1942).

22. V. Deulofeu, *Nature* **131,** 548 (1933).

23. P. A. Levene, *J. Biol. Chem.* **23,** 145 (1915); P. A. Levene and G. M. Meyer, *ibid.* **31,** 623 (1917).

24. H. S. Isbell, *J. Research Natl. Bur. Standards* **14,** 305 (1935).

e. Reactions of the Aldonic Acids

The aldonic acids show the reactions typical of aliphatic organic acids. Their aqueous solutions have a pH of 2 to 3. The free acids are soluble in water and slightly soluble in ethanol; they are more soluble in nonpolar solvents than the sugars, and less soluble than the lactones. Various salts can be formed and their utility depends upon the nature of the acid. Gluconic and galactonic acid, formed by the acidic oxidation of lactose, can be separated by the use of cadmium salts. Cadmium galactonate is less soluble in water than the gluconate; after removal of the former, the gluconic acid is isolated as the typical calcium salt. Some metallic salts are unstable; mercuric gluconate decomposes easily into free mercury, the mercurous salt, arabinose, and carbon dioxide. The use of lead salts for separating epimeric acids is described on page 108.

The nature of the cation may influence the reactivity of salts greatly (*25*). Thus, cadmium D-ribonate can be acetylated in 85% yield, but other salts give smaller yields: ammonium salt, 46%; potassium salt, 25%; calcium salt, 22%; and barium salt, 4%.

Esters of aldonic acids are prepared from δ-lactones, slowly from γ-lactones, by reaction with alcohols in the presence of hydrogen chloride or of the free aldonic acid (*26*). The acids may be recrystallized from boiling methanol without much esterification taking place (*27*). At the melting point, ethyl mannonate is converted to the γ-lactone with the loss of ethyl alcohol.

Lactones will give a positive "ester test," forming a hydroxamic acid when treated with alkaline hydroxylamine; this acid gives an intense color with ferric chloride. This test has been used as a means of detecting lactones on a paper chromatogram (*28*). Free acids do not give it, and the paper must be treated with diazomethane first in order to convert the acids present to the esters. This method has also been used for the quantitative determination of gluconic δ-lactone (*28a*).

Toward alkali, the lactones are less reactive than the acids. A solution of free acid can be neutralized with calcium carbonate or barium benzoate. Sodium carbonate reacts with the δ-lactones and an excess of sodium hydroxide with the γ-lactones.

The amides of the aldonic acids can be formed readily by the action of liquid ammonia on the lactones (*29*). These derivatives are often crystalline

25. K. Ladenburg, M. Tishler, J. W. Wellman, and R. D. Babson, *J. Am. Chem. Soc.* **66,** 1217 (1944).

26. See: O. F. Hedenburg, *J. Am. Chem. Soc.* **37,** 345 (1915).

27. K. Rehorst, *Ber.* **63,** 2279 (1930).

28. M. Abdel-Akher and F. Smith, *J. Am. Chem. Soc.* **73,** 5859 (1951).

28a. O. Cori and F. Lipmann, *J. Biol. Chem.* **194,** 417 (1952).

29. J. W. E. Glattfeld and D. Macmillan, *J. Am. Chem. Soc.* **56,** 2481 (1934).

and are useful for the characterization of the acids. The phenylhydrazides, prepared by reaction of acids or lactones with phenylhydrazine, can be converted to the free acids or lactones. Hydrolysis of hydrazides by alkalies is often slow or incomplete. Boiling copper sulfate solution gives a 90% yield of mannonic lactone, and the phenylhydrazine is oxidized to benzene and nitrogen (*30*). Nitrous acid has been used to convert hydrazides to the lactones (*31*).

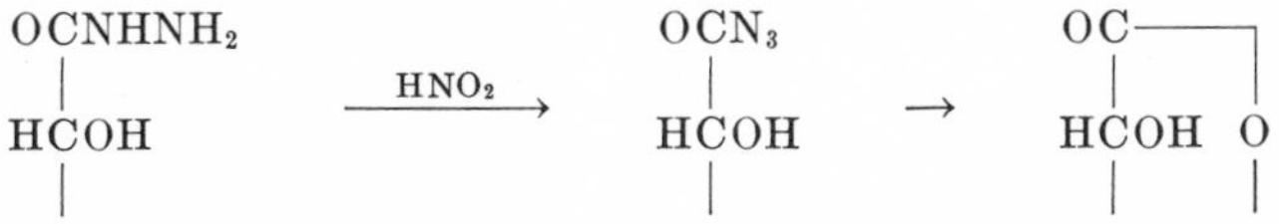

The aldonyl chlorides can be prepared (*32*) by treatment of acetylated aldonic acids with PCl_5. These chlorides are used for the preparation of open-chain derivatives of aldoses by catalytic reduction with hydrogen in xylene solution (*33*). Keto acetates with one carbon atom more than the aldonyl chloride are formed by the action of diazomethane. Acetic acid removes the diazo group. In this manner, L-fructose was made from L-arabonic acid (*34*).

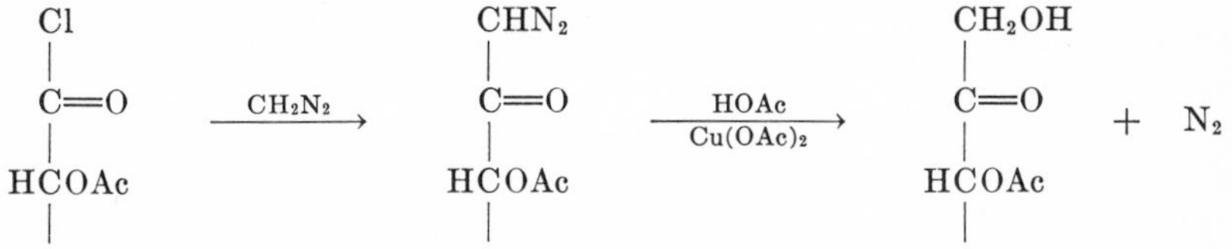

The action of HBr on the diazo compound is similar to that of acetic acid, and a 1-bromo keto acetate is formed. Silver oxide causes a rearrangement to a 2-deoxyaldonic acid (*35*).

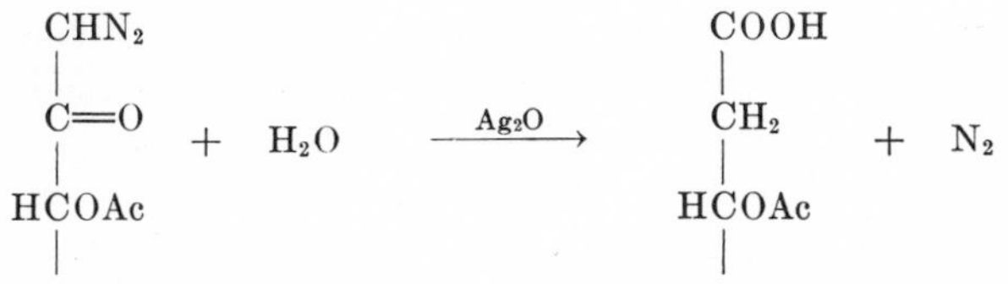

Reduction of thioesters to aldoses can be carried out by catalytic hydro-

30. R. M. Hann and C. S. Hudson, *J. Am. Chem. Soc.* **56,** 957 (1934).

31. A. Thompson and M. L. Wolfrom, *J. Am. Chem. Soc.* **68,** 1509 (1946).

32. R. T. Major and E. W. Cook, *J. Am. Chem. Soc.* **58,** 2477 (1936); M. L. Wolfrom, R. L. Brown, and E. F. Evans, *ibid.* **65,** 1021 (1943).

33. E. W. Cook and R. T. Major, *J. Am. Chem. Soc.* **58,** 2410 (1936).

34. M. L. Wolfrom and A. Thompson, *J. Am. Chem. Soc.* **68,** 791 (1946).

35. M. L. Wolfrom, S. W. Waisbrot, and R. L. Brown, *J. Am. Chem. Soc.* **64,** 1701, 2329 (1942).

genation methods. (See also p. 107.) Thus, ethyl thiol-D-ribonate tetraacetate gives *aldehydo*-D-ribose tetraacetate (*36*).

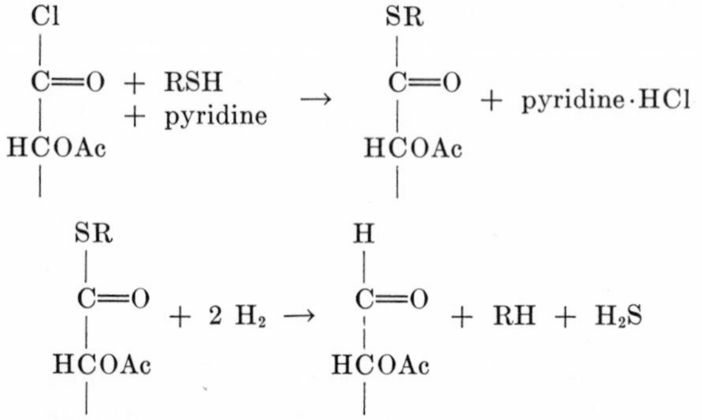

By catalytic hydrogenation, aldonic esters and lactones are reduced to glycitols (*37*). The reduction of lactones to sugars by sodium amalgam was introduced by Fischer and has been extensively employed for the purpose (see Chapter II). Esters, but not the free acids, are reducible. In order to obtain maximal yields, the acidity must be maintained in the range 3 to 3.5. The temperature should be kept below 15°, and a minimum of 2.5 equivalents of sodium are required (theory, 2) (*38*). Other methods are also available (see Chapter II).

B. Saccharic (or Aldaric) Acids (*39*)

The saccharic acids are polyhydroxy dicarboxylic acids, HOOC—$(CHOH)_n$—COOH, and are generally obtained from the sugars by the action of strong oxidizing agents. Several of these acids, tartronic, erythraric, xylaric, allaric, and galactaric, are optically inactive. The acid salts are often used for characterization, because of their low solubility in water. Mannaric and glucaric acids show abnormal behavior in alkaline solution, with rearrangement to enolic forms. Commercially, the acids, especially threaric and glucaric, have been utilized for the preparation of salts of therapeutical importance.

36. M. L. Wolfrom and J. V. Karabinos, *J. Am. Chem. Soc.* **68,** 1455 (1946).

37. J. W. E. Glattfeld and A. M. Stack, *J. Am. Chem. Soc.* **59,** 753 (1937).

38. N. Sperber, H. E. Zaugg, and W. M. Sandstrom, *J. Am. Chem. Soc.* **69,** 915 (1947); H. L. Frush and H. S. Isbell, *J. Research Bur. Standards* **54,** 267 (1955); R. Schaffer and H. S. Isbell, *ibid.* **56,** 191 (1956).

39. The term "aric" is used with the normal configurational prefix; the tartaric acids are threaric or erythraric acids, mucic acid is galactaric acid, and *gluco*-saccharic acid is glucaric acid. The name xylaric acid is much shorter than *xylo*-trihydroxyglutaric acid. For an additional discussion see below and Chapter I, particularly p. 28. In the present text both forms are used, but the new usage is preferred.

a. Tartronic and Malic Acid

Tartronic acid, HOOC—CH(OH)—COOH, or hydroxymalonic acid, may be considered as the simplest of the aldaric acids. It has been obtained by the oxidation of glucose or fructose with hydrogen peroxide and ferrous sulfate (*40*). It is also formed by the cyanohydrin synthesis from glyoxylic acid (*41*). The oxidation of glycerol gives only small amounts of this acid.

HOOC—CHO + HCN → HOOC—CH(OH)—CN → HOOC—CH(OH)—COOH

Malic acid, HOOC—CH_2—CH(OH)—COOH, may be considered as a deoxytetraric (tartaric) acid. It occurs widely in nature in fruits and berries. It is formed by the partial reduction of tartaric acids with HI or by the addition of the elements of water to fumaric or maleic acid. The natural acid is levorotatory in dilute solutions, but the rotation becomes positive with increasing concentration. This effect has also been noticed with L-tartaric (L-threaric) acid.

b. Tetraric Acids (Tartaric Acids) (42)

These acids exist in four forms:

L-Threaric acid (L-tartaric acid)
D-Threaric acid (D-tartaric acid)
DL-Threaric acid (DL-tartaric or racemic acid)
Erythraric acid (*meso*-tartaric acid).

L-Threaric acid occurs naturally as the monopotassium salt, especially in the juice of grapes. The sodium potassium salt ($NaKC_4H_4O_6 \cdot 4H_2O$) is known as Rochelle salt and the potassium antimonyl salt ($K(SbO)C_4H_4O_6 \cdot \frac{1}{2}H_2O$) as tartar emetic. The D-acid can be obtained from the racemic mixture by resolution of the cinchonine salts (*43*). The D-*glycero*-D-*gulo*-heptobenzimidazole forms a salt with L-threaric acid that allows of the resolution of the DL-form (*44*). Pasteur originally resolved this form by mechanical separation of crystals of the sodium ammonium salt.

The DL-racemate and the inactive isomer are formed from the L-acid by heating with water at 150 to 170°. Heating with alkali has the same effect, but the yields of the two products vary according to conditions (*45*). Separation is effected on the basis of the much greater solubility of the

40. C. F. Cross, E. J. Bevan, and C. Smith, *J. Chem. Soc.* p. 73, 469 (1898).

41. C. Böttinger, *Ber.* **14,** 729 (1881).

42. A common form of designation of these acids was to use *d* and *l* for the sign of rotation rather than L and D, respectively, for indications of configuration. For further discussion see p. 27.

43. W. Markwald, *Ber.* **29,** 42 (1897).

44. W. T. Haskins and C. S. Hudson, *J. Am. Chem. Soc.* **61,** 1266 (1939).

45. See "Organic Syntheses," Collective Vol. I, p. 484. 1932; "Beilsteins Handbuch der organischen Chemie," Vol. 3, p. 528. Springer, Berlin, 1921.

potassium hydrogen salt of the *meso*-acid (8% in water at 19°) compared with that of the racemic acid (0.5% in water at 19°). Oxidation of fumaric acid with chlorates and OsO_4 produces the DL-form, whereas the *meso*-isomer is obtained from maleic acid (*46*).

The optical rotation of L-threaric acid in water is positive at high concentrations but drops with dilution and finally becomes negative. Complex formation with salts, borates, and molybdates affects the optical rotation greatly. Rotational values in alcohols are very low.

The heating of L-threaric acid above 100° forms an anhydride; initially, gummy materials are formed as a result of external condensation, and finally at 170° an insoluble anhydride is produced.

The solubility of the monopotassium salt of the DL-racemic acid differs little from that of the L-acid, but the solubility of the calcium salts differs sufficiently to allow a separation (*47*).

The tartaric acids are formed by the oxidation of hexose sugars and of the keto acids. (See under Nitric acid and Alkaline oxygen oxidations, particularly.) The L-isomer has been recovered from grape residues by concentration on a basic ion-exchange resin (*48*).

c. Pentaric and Hexaric Acids

The four pentaric acids and ten hexaric acids are:

Pentaric (Hydroxyglutaric) Acids

Xylaric (*meso*)	= *xylo*-trihydroxyglutaric
Ribaric (*meso*)	= *ribo*-trihydroxyglutaric
D- and L-Arabaric	= D- and L-lyxaric
	= D- and L-*arabo*-trihydroxyglutaric

Hexaric Acids

D- and L-Mannaric	= D- and L-*manno*-saccharic
D- and L-Glucaric	= D- and L-*gluco*-saccharic
	= L- and D-gularic
D- and L-Idaric	= D- and L-*ido*-saccharic
D- and L-Talaric	= D- and L-talomucic
	= D- and L-altraric
Allaric (*meso*)	= allomucic
Galactaric (*meso*)	= mucic

The pentaric (hydroxyglutaric) acids are important primarily as reference compounds in structural proofs. They can be prepared by oxidation of the corresponding pentoses with nitric acid.

46. N. A. Milas and E. M. Terry, *J. Am. Chem. Soc.* **47,** 1412 (1925); G. Braun, *ibid.* **51,** 247 (1929).

47. A. Holleman, *Rec. trav. chim.* **17,** 69 (1898); J. M. Albahary, *Compt. rend.* **144,** 1232 (1907).

48. J. R. Matchett, *Ind. Eng. Chem.* **36,** 851 (1944).

Several of the hexaric acids are of especial interest. Galactaric (mucic) acid has a low solubility in water, and its formation by the nitric acid oxidation of galactose is used for the quantitative determination of galactose. Its formation by bromine oxidation is considered satisfactory evidence of the presence of galacturonic acid. The acid can be prepared on a large scale by the nitric acid oxidation of galactans prepared from certain woods (*49*). It is interesting that acetylation increases the solubility of galactaric acid in water. Ammonium galactarate (mucate) forms pyrrole when heated.

In contrast to galactaric acid, D-mannaric and D-glucaric acids are appreciably soluble in water. Glucaric acid is best prepared by the nitric acid oxidation of starch; yields as high as 65% are obtained in contrast to much lower yields from glucose or sucrose (*50*). This acid is generally characterized as the potassium acid salt or silver salt.

The saccharic acids do not reduce Fehling solution but will react with ammoniacal silver nitrate. However, the dilactones of mannaric and glucaric acids show an unexpected reducing action with Fehling solution (*51*). This same behavior is shown with the monoester monolactones of glucaric acid. The monolactones do not show this behavior. The alkali cleaves the lactone ring and the necessary hydrogen atom is provided from the neighboring carbon atom rather than from the solution. Uronic acid lac-

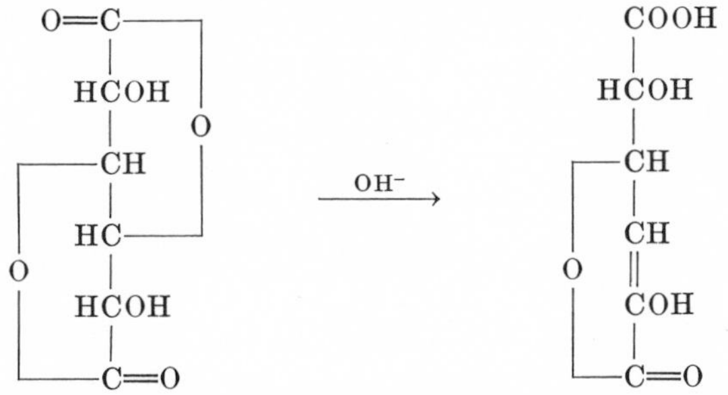
O=C
HCOH
O
CH
HC
O
HCOH
C=O
OH⁻
COOH
HCOH
CH
CH
O
COH
C=O

tones behave similarly. The resulting enol is the enolic lactone of a 4-deoxy 5-keto dibasic acid related to the ascorbic acids. These enols react with only a small amount of iodine, in contrast to the behavior of the ascorbic acids. However, four atoms of chlorine are taken up, whereas the ascorbic acids react with only half of this amount. In alkaline solution ozone attacks the double bond, forming oxalic acid and either erythruronic or threuronic acid.

2-Deoxy-D-galactaric acid forms a monolactone readily (*52*), whereas

49. A. W. Schorger, *U. S. Patent* 1,718,837 (June 25, 1929).

50. See H. Kiliani, *Ber.* **58,** 2344 (1925); O. T. Schmidt, H. Zeiser, and H. Dippold, *ibid.* **70,** 2402 (1937).

51. See F. Smith, *Advances in Carbohydrate Chem.* **2,** 101 (1946); see also J. W. W. Morgan and M. L. Wolfrom, *J. Am. Chem. Soc.* **78,** 1897 (1956).

52. W. G. Overend, F. Shafizadeh, and M. Stacey, *J. Chem. Soc.* p. 1487 (1951).

such a product is obtained only with difficulty from galactaric acid. The deoxylactone does not form an unsaturated acid with alkali, and behaves like the monolactone of glucaric acid.

The saccharic acids can be used as starting materials for other carbohydrate products. Epimerizations can be carried out with pyridine as with the aldonic acids. Galactaric acid is converted to DL-talaric acid. The two monolactones of D-glucaric acid are reduced by sodium amalgam to different products. The 3,6-lactone (IV) forms L-guluronic (V) and D-gluconic (VI) acids, and the 1,4-lactone (I) forms D-glucuronic (II) and L-gulonic (III) acids (*53*). The two lactones can be obtained from glucaric acid solutions by seeding with the proper nuclei.

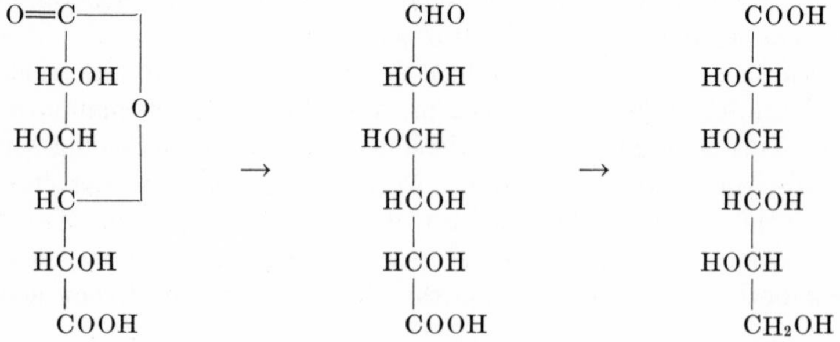

(I) (II) (III)

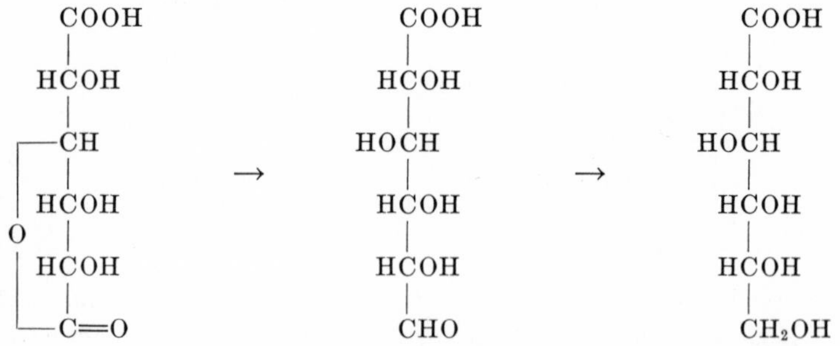

(IV) (V) (VI)

C. Uronic Acids (*54a, b, c*)

a. Preparation and Occurrence (See also Chapter XII)

The uronic acids may be defined as carbohydrate derivatives possessing both aldehyde (or hemiacetal) and carboxyl groups. The formulas for the three naturally occurring acids are given below.

53. M. Sutter and T. Reichstein, *Helv. Chim. Acta* **21,** 1210 (1938).
54a. See C. L. Mehltretter, *Advances in Carbohydrate Chem.* **8,** 231 (1953).

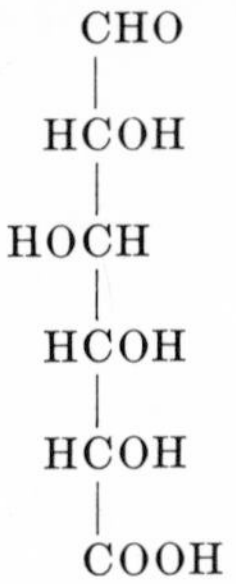

D-Glucuronic acid

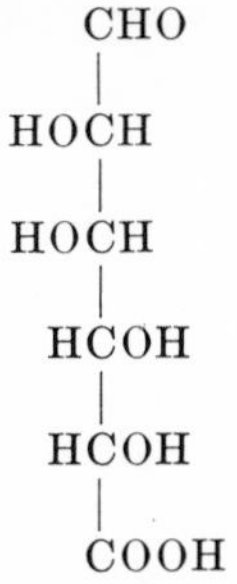

D-Mannuronic acid

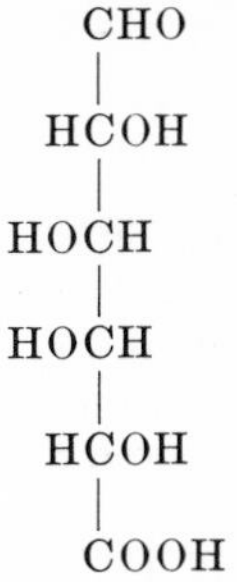

D-Galacturonic acid

The uronic acids biologically are very important. As shown in Table II, they occur as important building units in many polysaccharides, particularly pectins and alginic acid (Chapter XII). One, glucuronic acid, serves as a detoxifying agent in mammals, and some poisonous substances and metabolic products are eliminated in the urine as glucosiduronic acids (see Chapter X). The 4-*O*-methyl ether of D-glucuronic acid has been shown to be a building unit in mesquite gum (*55*) and other plant materials.

The isolation of uronic acids from polysaccharides is not easy. Some of the linkages are very resistant to acid hydrolysis. Sulfuric acid (4%) at 120° for 10 to 24 hours (*56*) is often required. This harsh treatment may decompose the products considerably, and the yields are generally low. Cold 80% sulfuric acid, 3% oxalic acid at 100°, boiling 98% formic acid 8 hours at 100° (for methylated alginic acid), and boiling 90% formic acid have been used for the hydrolysis of alginic acid (*57*). In the pectin field, enzymic hydrolysis has been used for the isolation of galacturonic acid; the procedure is very mild and excellent yields are obtained.

Two general methods for the synthesis of uronic acids have been developed: (1) the reduction of the monolactones of aldaric acids, and (2) the oxidation of primary alcoholic groups of sugars or derivatives. The monolactones of dibasic acids can be reduced by sodium amalgam in acid solution

---

54b. See N. E. Artz and E. M. Osman, "Biochemistry of Glucuronic Acid." Academic Press, New York, 1950; G. O. Aspinall, *Advances in Carbohydrate Chem.* **9,** 131 (1954).

54c. R. S. Teague, *Advances in Carbohydrate Chem.* **9,** 185 (1954); H. G. Bray, *ibid.* **8,** 251 (1953).

55. E. V. White, *J. Am. Chem. Soc.* **70,** 367 (1948).

56. E. Anderson, F. H. Russell, and L. W. Seigle, *J. Biol. Chem.* **113,** 683 (1936).

57. C. L. Butler and L. H. Cretcher, *J. Am. Chem. Soc.* **51,** 1914 (1929); W. A. G. Nelson and E. G. V. Percival, *J. Chem. Soc.* p. 58 (1942); S. K. Chanda, E. L. Hirst, E. G. V. Percival, and A. G. Ross, *ibid.* p. 1833 (1952); H. A. Spoehr, *Arch. Biochem.* **14,** 153 (1947).

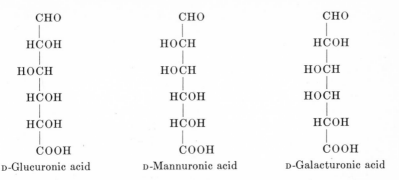

TABLE II

NATURAL OCCURRENCE OF URONIC ACIDS

D-Glucuronic Acid
1. Urine of animals (as conjugate).
2. Polysaccharides (see Chapter XII).
   Heparin (with D-glucosamine and sulfates).
   Chondroitin sulfate (with *N*-acetylchondrosamine and sulfates).
   Hyaluronic acid (with *N*-acetyl-D-glucosamine).
   Type II pneumococcus specific polysaccharide (with glucose and rhamnose).
   Type III pneumococcus specific polysaccharide (with glucose).
   Type VIII pneumococcus specific polysaccharide (with glucose).
   Azotobacter and *Rhizobia* capsular polysaccharides (with glucose).
   Friedländer's bacillus polysaccharides (with glucose).
   Cytophagae polysaccharide (with glucose).
3. Gum arabic and straws.
4. Saponins, glycosides, and oligosaccharides of certain types.
5. Various woods as monomethyl ethers.

D-Galacturonic Acid
1. Pectins and pectic acid.
2. Type I pneumococcus specific polysaccharide and limacoitin sulfate.
3. Mucilages.

D-Mannuronic Acid. Alginic acid from seaweeds, as the sole constituent.

(*58*). Glucaric acid was converted to glucuronic acid, but the maximal yield was 20%. This method was later applied to the reduction of mannaric acid to mannuronic acid, and of allaric acid to the corresponding uronic acid.

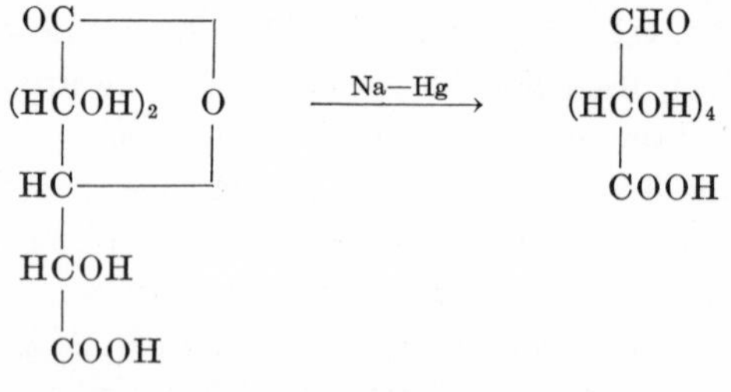
OC
(HCOH)₂ O
HC
HCOH
COOH
Na—Hg
CHO
(HCOH)₄
COOH

Unsubstituted primary alcoholic groups of derivatives of sugars have been oxidized to carboxyl groups; the reducing group must be protected. The use of gaseous oxygen and an activated-platinum carbon catalyst gives excellent yields (*59a*, *b*, *c*). Thus, 1,2-*O*-isopropylidene-D-glucose has been

58. E. Fischer and O. Piloty, *Ber.* **24,** 522 (1891); C. Niemann and K. P. Link, *J. Biol. Chem.* **100,** 407 (1933); C. Niemann, S. A. Karjala, and K. P. Link, *ibid.* **104,** 189 (1934).

59a. C. L. Mehltretter, B. H. Alexander, R. L. Mellies, and C. E. Rist, *J. Am. Chem. Soc.* **73,** 2424 (1951).

59b. C. A. Marsh, *J. Chem. Soc.* p. 1578 (1952).

59c. S. A. Barker, E. J. Bourne, and M. Stacey, *Chemistry & Industry* p. 970 (1951).

converted to 50 to 60% of the 1,2-*O*-isopropylidene-D-glucuronic acid at 50°. (−)-Menthyl α- and β-D-glucosiduronic acids have been prepared in good yields from the corresponding glucopyranosides; methyl α- and β-D-galactosiduronic acid and methyl α-D-mannosiduronic acid have been obtained similarly in 42, 22, and 44% yields, respectively. This method is a great advancement over earlier oxidations of acetylated or acetonated sugars with permanganate (*60*). Methyl α-D-mannopyranoside has also been oxidized with barium hypobromite at 3° for 16 to 20 days to yield 12% of "methyl α-mannuronide" (*61*). Treatment of 1,2-*O*-isopropylidene-D-xylopentosedialdehyde with $NaC^{14}N$ has given D-glucurone-6-C^{14}, a valuable tracer material (*62*).

Mehltretter (*54a*) has emphasized the importance of the hydrolytic step in the synthesis of glucuronic acid. High yields of a glucosiduronic acid may be offset by degradation of the glucuronic acid during acid hydrolysis (see p. 315). Thus, an 87% yield of the crude sodium salt of methyl α-glucopyranosiduronic acid was converted to only 16% glucurone (*59c*). In contrast, a 50 to 60% yield of 1,2-*O*-isopropylidene-D-glucuronic acid can be hydrolyzed to give 30% of lactone. Interest has been shown in the more easily hydrolyzed furanosiduronic acids, and in the naphthyl and phenyl glucopyranosiduronic acids (*62a*); the latter compounds can be hydrolyzed by the enzyme β-glucuronidase (Chapter X).

Much interest has been shown in the commercial production of glucuronic acid, because of the possible therapeutic effect in the treatment of rheumatic diseases (*62b*).

Uronic acids of the pentose series have been prepared by the oxidative degradation of amides. Mucic acid monoamide can be converted by the action of hydrogen peroxide and iron salts or by hypobromite to the corresponding lyxuronic acid (*63*). The acids were isolated as the phenylosazone-phenylhydrazides, or as the tetraacetates of the amide.

The biogenesis of glucuronic acid seems to be an oxidative process, involving phosphorylation of glucose, and occurring in the liver (*54c*, *64a*). Thus, a cell-free enzyme preparation, isolated from calf or guinea pig liver,

60. M. Stacey, *J. Chem. Soc.* p. 1529 (1939); H. Ohle and Gertrud Berend, *Ber.* **58,** 2585 (1925); R. G. Ault, W. N. Haworth, and E. L. Hirst, *J. Chem. Soc.* p. 517 (1935); M. Stacey and P. I. Wilson, *ibid.* p. 587 (1944).

61. E. L. Jackson and C. S. Hudson, *J. Am. Chem. Soc.* **59,** 994 (1937).

62. J. C. Sowden, *J. Am. Chem. Soc.* **74,** 4377 (1952).

62a. K-C. Tsou and A. M. Seligman, *J. Am. Chem. Soc.* **74,** 5605 (1952); *ibid.* **75,** 1042 (1953).

62b. E. A. Peterman, *J. Lancet* **67,** 451 (1947); E. A. Peterman *U. S. Patent* 2,520,255 (1950); C. L. Mehltretter, *U. S. Patent* 2,559,652 (1951); D. H. Couch and E. A. Cleveland, *U. S. Patent* 2,592,249 (1952); D. M. Gallagher, *U. S. Patent* 2,592,266 (1952).

63. M. Bergmann, *Ber.* **54,** 1362 (1921).

64a. A. Hemingway, J. Pryde, and R. T. Williams, *Biochem. J.* **28,** 136 (1934); W. L. Lipschitz and E. Bueding, *J. Biol. Chem.* **129,** 333 (1939).

has converted uridine diphosphate glucose to uridine diphosphate glucuronic acid (*64b*). The feeding of borneol and glucose labeled with C^{14} at carbon 1 or carbon 6 to animals has given bornyl glucosiduronic acid with most of the radioactivity at carbon 1 or carbon 6, respectively. Hence, the conversion probably goes through glucose or a C_6 intermediate, and not through C_3 fragments (*65*). Conversion of glucose labeled at carbon 6 to hyaluronic acid gave similar results (*66*). While glucose has been shown to be a definite precursor, labeled glucurone, when fed with borneol to animals, is converted only slightly to bornyl glucosiduronic acid; the resulting distribution of radioactivity can be explained only by the glucurone breaking down to C_3 fragments which are then recombined (*65*). (See also p. 597.)

Some work has been done on the formation of glucuronic acid from smaller fragments (*67*). Glycerol, labeled at carbon 1, when fed to rats gave a "glucuronide" with a distribution of radioactivity that would be predicted by a condensation of C_3 units. However, lactate labeled at carbon 3 gave a glucosiduronic acid with all the radioactivity at carbon 6.

The identification of the uronic acids is difficult (*68*). The alkaloidal salts frequently are used; cinchonine and brucine have value for glucuronic acid. Various hydrazines have been used to prepare derivatives, but often the products are complex, for hydrazides, hydrazones, and osazones are formed. A common method of identification is to convert the uronic acids by mild oxidation to the dibasic acids.

When hexuronic acids are boiled with strong acids and naphthoresorcinol, a blue color is formed. This reaction has been developed into a quantitative method (*69*). The coloring matter formed is extracted with benzene and determined photometrically. (See also Chapter XII, for identification and analysis.)

b. *Aldobiouronic Acids*

An aldobiouronic acid (I) may be defined as a disaccharide in which one of the sugar components is a uronic acid linked in glycosidic union to a

64b. J. L. Strominger, H. M. Kalckar, J. Axelrod, and E. S. Maxwell, *J. Am. Chem. Soc.* **76,** 6412 (1954).

65. J. F. Douglas and C. G. King, *J. Biol. Chem.* **202,** 865 (1953).

66. S. Roseman, J. Ludowieg, F. E. Moses, and A. Dorfman, *Arch. Biochem. and Biophys.* **42,** 472 (1953).

67. A. P. Doerschuk, *J. Biol. Chem.* **195,** 855 (1952); T. G. Bidder, *J. Am. Chem. Soc.* **74,** 161 (1952).

68. See E. Anderson and L. Sands, *Advances in Carbohydrate Chem.* **1,** 329 (1945); M. Stacey, *ibid.* **2,** 170 (1946).

69. See S. W. F. Hanson, C. T. Mills, and R. T. Williams, *Biochem. J.* **38,** 274 (1944); E. M. Knapp, *J. Biol. Chem.* **134,** 145 (1940).

hexose or pentose unit. Conceivably a disaccharide could exist which would contain a uronic acid unit with a glycosidic linkage at the hexose or pentose portion, as in (II) below, but compounds of this type are not known at present to occur naturally. A dihexuronic acid, probably 4-*O*-(α-D-galactopyranosyluronic acid)-D-galacturonic acid, has been isolated by the enzymic degradation of pectic acid (*70*), and a 4-*O*-(β-D-glucopyranosyluronic acid)-D-glucuronic acid has been synthesized by the oxidation of cyclohexyl β-maltoside pentaacetate (*71*). The last compound was made in a study of glycyrrhinic acid, which contains two glucopyranosyluronic acid units linked β,1 → 2′.

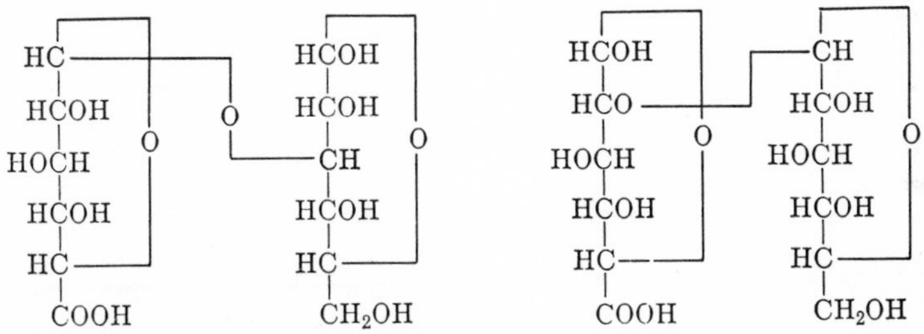
HC
HCOH
HOCH
HCOH
HC
COOH
O
O
HCOH
HCOH
CH
HCOH
HC
CH₂OH
O
HCOH
HCO
HOCH
HCOH
HC
COOH
O
CH
HCOH
HOCH
HCOH
HC
CH₂OH
O

(I) Aldobiouronic acid

(II) Pseudoaldobiouronic acid

Aldobiouronic acids are readily isolated because of the strong resistance of the biouronic linkage to acid hydrolysis. Whereas 4% acid at 100 to 120° is often used for the isolation of uronic acids, O'Dwyer (*72*) isolated an aldobiouronic acid from oakwood hemicellulose by the action of 1% sulfuric acid at 100°. This resistance to hydrolysis may explain the occurrence of uronides in soil. Some 10 to 15% of the organic carbon in surface soil appears to be combined uronic acids, and the amount increases with the depth of the soil (*73*) (see also p. 669, 717, 719).

In Table III the various known aldobiouronic acids are listed. Wood hemicelluloses, plant mucilages, gums, and bacterial polysaccharides provide the natural sources. In addition, several have been synthesized. Extreme interest has been evidenced in the bacterial products because of their relationship to immunological properties.

Hyalobiouronic acid, isolated from the mucopolysaccharide hyaluronic acid, contains a glucosamine unit, and has been identified as 3-*O*-(β-D-

70. J. K. N. Jones and W. W. Reid, *J. Chem. Soc.* p. 1361 (1954).
71. B. Lythgoe and S. Tripett, *J. Chem. Soc.* p. 1983 (1950).
72. M. H. O'Dwyer, *Biochem. J.* **28,** 2116 (1934)
73. A. G. Norman and W. V. Bartholomew, *Soil Sci.* **56,** 143 (1943).

TABLE III
SOURCES OF ALDOBIOURONIC ACIDS

Name	Source
A. Aldobiouronic Acids from Bacterial Polysaccharides	
O-(Glucosyluronic acid)-glucose	Type III pneumococcus specific polysaccharide (*74–76*) Type A Friedlander's bacillus
6-*O*-(Glucosyluronic acid)-glucuronic acid (gentiobiouronic acid)	Synthetic (*75*)
B. Aldobiouronic Acids from Plants	
2-*O*-(α-D-Glucopyranosyluronic acid)-D-xylose	Corn-cobs (*77*)
3-*O*-(α-D-Glucopyranosyluronic acid)-D-xylose	Wheat straw (*78*), pear wall xylan (*79*)
4-*O*-(α-D-Glucopyranosyluronic acid)-D-xylose	Corn-cobs (*77*)
(?)-*O*-(D-Glucopyranosyluronic acid)-D-xylose	Jute (*87*), cottonseed hulls (*88*), wheat straw (*89*)
2-*O*-(β-D-Glucopyranosyluronic acid)-D-mannose	Damson gum (*80*), cherry gum (*81*), tubers of *Asparagus fulcinus* (*82*)
6-*O*-(β-D-Glucopyranosyluronic acid)-D-galactose	Gum arabic (gum acacia) (*83–85*), black wattle gum (*86*), egg plum gum, almond tree gum, and peach tree gum
2-*O*-(4-*O*-Methyl-α-D-glucopyranosyluronic acid)-D-xylose	Aspen wood (*90*), corn-cobs (*91*), Western hemlock (*91a*)
4-*O*-(4-*O*-Methyl-α-D-glucopyranosyluronic acid)-L-arabinose	Lemon gum (*92*)
6-*O*-(4-*O*-Methyl-α-D-glucopyranosyluronic acid)-D-galactose	Mesquite gum (*93–95*)
2-*O*-(D-Galactopyranosyluronic acid)-L-rhamnose	Mucilage of slippery elm (*96, 97*) flaxseed mucilage (*98, 99*), okra mucilage (*100*) mucilage of *Plantago arenaria* (*101*)
Acid composed of D-xylose and an *O*-methyluronic acid	Oakwood (*102*)
O-α-D-Glucopyranosyluronic acid-(1 → 4)-*O*-β-D-xylopyranosyl-(1 → 4)-D-xylose	Corn-cob (*102a*)
Aldotriouronic acid composed of two xylose units and one *O*-methyluronic acid unit	Cottonwood (*103*)

74. M. Heidelberger and W. F. Goebel, *J. Biol. Chem.* **74,** 613 (1927).
75. R. D. Hotchkiss and W. F. Goebel, *J. Biol. Chem.* **115,** 285 (1936).
76. M. Heidelberger and W. F. Goebel, *J. Biol. Chem.* **74,** 619 (1927).
77. R. L. Whistler and L. Hough, *J. Am. Chem. Soc.* **75,** 4918 (1953).
78. G. A. Adams, *Can. J. Chem.* **30,** 698 (1952); C. T. Bishop, *ibid.* **31,** 134 (1953).
79. S. K. Chanda, E. L. Hirst, and E. G. V. Percival, *J. Chem. Soc.* p. 1240 (1951).

glucopyranosyluronic acid)-2-amino-2-deoxy-D-glucose (*104*). The tetrasaccharide, containing two glucosamine and two uronic acid units, has also been isolated. Chondrosine, a disaccharide from the polysaccharide chondroitin sulfate, is 3-*O*-(β-D-glucopyranosyluronic acid)-2-amino-2-deoxy-D-galactopyranose (*104a*). (See Chapter XII.)

Aldobiouronic acids represent the penultimate stage of hydrolysis of the polyuronides. The action can be stopped at earlier stages. From mesquite gum, acids representing several stages of hydrolysis were isolated (*93*). The aldobiouronic acid contained a galactose and an *O*-methylglucuronic acid unit, and the less-hydrolyzed acids two or three galactose units. Products of still lesser extent of hydrolysis contained four units of L-arabinose and three of galactose in addition to the uronic acid. An aldotriouronic

---

80. E. L. Hirst and J. K. N. Jones, *J. Chem. Soc.* p. 1174 (1938).

81. J. K. N. Jones, *J. Chem. Soc.* p. 558 (1939).

82. P. S. Rao, O. N. Rozdon, and R. P. Budhiraja, *Proc. Indian Acad. Sci.* **32A,** 264 (1950).

83. M. Heidelberger and F. E. Kendall, *J. Biol. Chem.* **84,** 639 (1929); W. F. Goebel and R. E. Reeves, *ibid.* **124,** 207 (1938); P. A. Levene and R. S. Tipson, *ibid.* **125,** 345 (1938); C. L. Butler and L. H. Cretcher, *J. Am. Chem. Soc.* **51,** 1519 (1929); S. W Challinor, W. N. Haworth, and E. L. Hirst, *J. Chem. Soc.* p. 258 (1931).

84. P. A. Levene, G. M. Meyer, and M. Kuna, *J. Biol. Chem.* **125,** 703 (1938).

85. S. N. Mukherjee and K. B. Ghosh, *J. Indian Chem. Soc.* **26,** 277 (1949).

86. A. M. Stephen, *J. Chem. Soc.* p. 646 (1951).

87. D. B. Das, P. K. R. Choudhury, and J. F. Wareham, *Science and Culture (India)*, **18,** 197 (1952).

88. M. H. O'Dwyer, *Biochem. J.* **20,** 664 (1926).

89. G. O. Aspinall and R. S. Mahomed, *J. Chem. Soc.* p. 1731 (1954).

90. J. K. N. Jones and L. E. Wise, *J. Chem. Soc.* p. 3389 (1952).

91. R. L. Whistler, H. E. Conrad, and L. Hough, *J. Am. Chem. Soc.* **76,** 1668 (1954).

91a. G. G. S. Dutton and F. Smith, *J. Am. Chem. Soc.* **78,** 2505 (1956).

92. P. Andrews and J. K. N. Jones, *J. Chem. Soc.* p. 1724 (1954).

93. E. Anderson and L. Otis, *J. Am. Chem. Soc.* **52,** 4461 (1930).

94. E. V. White, *J. Am. Chem. Soc.* **70,** 367 (1948).

95. M. Abdel-Akher, F. Smith, and D. Spriestersbach, *J. Chem. Soc.* p. 3637 (1952).

96. E. Anderson, *J. Biol. Chem.* **104,** 163 (1934).

97. R. E. Gill, E. L. Hirst, and J. K. N. Jones, *J. Chem. Soc.* p. 1469 (1939).

98. E. Anderson and J. A. Crowder, *J. Am. Chem. Soc.* **52,** 3711 (1930).

99. R. S. Tipson, C. C. Christman, and P. A. Levene, *J. Biol. Chem.* **128,** 609 (1939).

100. R. L. Whistler and H. E. Conrad, *J. Am. Chem. Soc.* **76,** 3544 (1954).

101. E. L. Hirst, E. G. V. Percival, and C. B. Wylam, *J. Chem. Soc.* p. 189 (1954).

102. M. H. O'Dwyer, *Biochem. J.* **28,** 2116 (1934).

102a. R. L. Whistler and D. I. McGilvray, *J. Am. Chem. Soc.* **77,** 2212 (1955).

103. E. Anderson, R. B. Kaster, and M. G. Seeley, *J. Biol. Chem.* **144,** 767 (1942)

104. B. Weissmann and K. Meyer, *J. Am. Chem. Soc.* **76,** 1753 (1954); B. Weissmann, K. Meyer, P. Sampson, and A. Linker, *J. Biol. Chem.* **208,** 417 (1954).

104a. E. A. Davidson and K. Meyer, *J. Am. Chem. Soc.* **76,** 5686 (1954); M. L. Wolfrom, R. K. Madison, and M. J. Cron, *ibid.* **74,** 1491 (1952).

acid, of proven structure, isolated from the hemicellulose B of corncob, is listed in Table III.

Oxidation of an aldobiouronic acid with bromine under nonhydrolytic conditions produces a dibasic acid in which the new carboxyl is formed from the original hexose or pentose unit. This is shown by the fact that such an acid (when the reducing portion of the original biouronic acid is a hexose) will form the same amount of furfural as the original acid under the action of 12% HCl. Evidently, the glycosidic linkage is formed from the hemiacetal group of the uronic acid. Oxidation with bromine under hydrolytic conditions produces a dibasic and an aldonic acid and allows identification of the two units.

c. Reactions of Uronic Acids

One of the most important reactions observed with uronic acids is the decarboxylation caused by heating with strong acids (usually about 12% hydrochloric acid). The quantitative evolution of one mole of carbon dioxide was first observed by Lefevre and Tollens (*105*) and has been developed as an analytical method by many workers. The formation of the carbon dioxide is quantitative according to the following equation:

$$C_6H_{10}O_7 \rightarrow C_5H_4O_2 + CO_2 + 3\ H_2O$$

The liberation of carbon dioxide has also been observed for nonuronic carbohydrates, but the evolution is generally very slow (*106*). Glucose will give 1.2% carbon dioxide by weight in 15 hours, when treated with 3.29 *N* HCl under a nitrogen atmosphere, but nonuronic acids, such as glucaric or gluconic acid, will give greater amounts, up to 8% carbon dioxide (*107*).

The mechanism of the decarboxylation is not well known. The above equation is not entirely correct, for the maximal yield of furfural ($C_5H_4O_2$) is only about 40%. It is unlikely that the reaction proceeds through the formation of a pentose. Pentoses have never been isolated from such a reaction, when the decarboxylation is conducted under mild conditions such that any added pentose could be recovered (*108*). Also, in the case of arabinose, the action of boiling 12% hydrochloric acid causes a 70 to 80% conversion to furfural, but in the case of galacturonic acid only 42% furfural is obtained.

Zweifel and Deuel (*108a*) have recently demonstrated the catalytic decarboxylation of uronic acids with heavy metal ions under slightly acidic

105. K. U. Lefevre and B. Tollens, *Ber.* **40,** 4513 (1907).

106. See R. L. Whistler, A. R. Martin, and M. Harris, *J. Research Natl. Bur. Standards* **24,** 13 (1940).

107. E. W. Taylor, W. F. Fowler, Jr., P. A. McGee, and W. O. Kenyon, *J. Am. Chem. Soc.* **69,** 342 (1947); S. Machida, *J. Chem. Soc.* (*Japan*) **64,** 1205 (1943).

108. C. M. Conrad, *J. Am. Chem. Soc.* **53,** 2282 (1931).

108a. G. Zweifel and H. Deuel, *Helv. Chim. Acta* **39,** 662 (1956).

conditions. D-Galacturonic acid is partially decarboxylated in water at 96°, the products being carbon dioxide and arabinose; no furfural is formed. The catalytic activity increases in the order: $Mg^{++} < Zn^{++} < Ni^{++} < Al^{+++} < Pb^{++}$. The reaction is more complete in pyridine at 80° with nickel acetate as the catalyst. Arabinose was isolated from the pyridine medium and identified; ribose and two unknown products were detected on the paper chromatogram. The methyl ester and methyl ethers of galacturonic acid, di-galacturonic acid and glucurone are also decarboxylated in pyridine. However there is practically no decomposition of methyl galactosiduronic acid, poly-galacturonic acid, glucaric or galactonic acids. The mechanism suggested is a coordinate linking of the metal ion at the C-1 hydroxyl; the displaced proton reacts with the nucleophilic C-5 atom to cause an electron pair between C-5 and C-6 to shift to C-5 and effect loss of carbon dioxide.

2-Keto and 5-keto aldonic acids also give carbon dioxide and furfural (see below) in yields similar to those for the uronic acids. However, ascorbic acid, as discussed later, gives a very high yield (above 80%) of furfural. "Reductic acid," an enolic substance similar in structure to the ascorbic

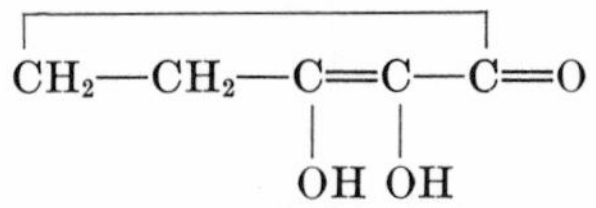
CH₂—CH₂—C=C—C=O
OH OH

acids, has been isolated (*109*) by the action of strong acid on pentoses and uronic acids. It is conceivable that decarboxylation and furfural formation proceed through an enolic intermediate of this type. The conversion of 2-keto acids to the ascorbic acid analogs is always accompanied by some furfural formation.

The aldobiouronic acids liberate carbon dioxide and form furfural in a manner similar to the uronic acids. With polysaccharide materials, the formation of carbon dioxide is considered very strong evidence for the presence of uronic acids. The evidence for a biological formation of pentosan material by the decarboxylation of uronic acid groupings is very weak, however, for some polyuronide materials contain both arabofuranose and galactopyranose units (see Chapter XII).

All uronic acids are thermally decarboxylated by heating 15 minutes at 255°; one mole of carbon dioxide is obtained, whether the starting material is the free acid, lactone, or salt. Nonuronide carboxyl-containing compounds give about 0.7 mole of carbon dioxide. The residues obtained from such treatment of hexuronic acids correspond in analysis to a five-carbon skeleton with 1.5 atoms of oxygen (*110*).

109. T. Reichstein and R. Oppenauer, *Helv. Chim. Acta,* **16,** 988 (1933); **17,** 390 (1934).

110. A. S. Perlin, *Can. J. Chem.* **30,** 278 (1952).

The presence of both aldehydic and acidic groups in uronic acids allows the formation of numerous types of derivatives. Phenylhydrazine will form hydrazides, hydrazones, and osazones. The action of acidic methanol leads to the formation of the ester of the "glycuronide". Rate studies have shown that the esterification reaction is 25 to 55 times as fast as glycoside formation, in the case of galacturonic acid (*111*). Reaction for 66 hours at 0° gave a good yield of the pure ester of methyl glucosiduronic acid. If the unesterified glycoside is desired, the ester grouping can be hydrolyzed with alkali and either the uronide or the uronide salt prepared.

In the preparation of the salts of glucuronic acid, titration with aqueous alkali causes extensive degradation. To avoid this effect, the lactone is added directly to alkali in aqueous alcohol, and the sodium, potassium, and ammonium salts crystallize directly in 80% or better yields (*112*).

The α-D-glucuronic acid 1-phosphate has been prepared by catalytic oxidation of glucose 1-phosphate, and the β-isomer from acetobromoglucuronic acid methyl ester and silver phosphate (*113*). Reaction of the bromoacetate with various blocked phenol amino acids in the presence of silver oxide and quinoline give the *O*-glucosiduronic acids (*114*).

All three natural uronic acids have been isolated as the free acids in crystalline form. Glucuronic acid is known only as the β-form, whereas the other two exist as α- and β-pyranoid forms. The crystalline γ-lactones of glucuronic and mannuronic acid have been prepared, and are known as glucurone and mannurone.

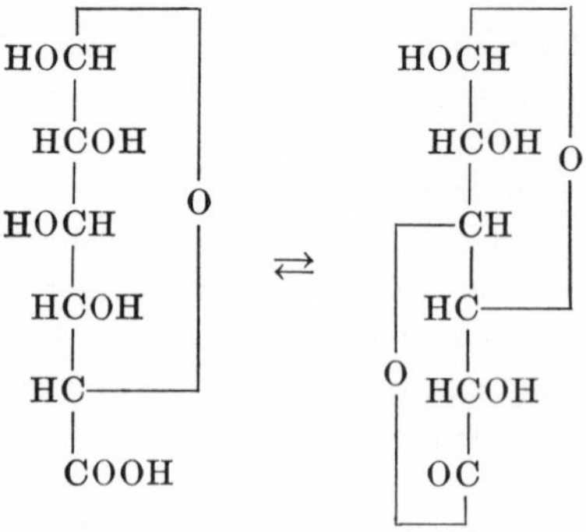
HOCH
HCOH
HOCH
HCOH
HC
COOH
O
⇄
HOCH
HCOH
CH
HC
HCOH
OC
O
O

β-Glucopyranuronic acid   Glucurone

The structure of D-glucurone has been shown to be a 3,6-lactone with a 1,4-hemiacetal or furanose ring. Methylation gives methyl 2,5-di-*O*-

111. E. F. Jansen and R. Jang, *J. Am. Chem. Soc.* **68,** 1475 (1946).
112. W. Hach and D. G. Benjamin, *J. Am. Chem. Soc.* **76,** 917 (1954).
113. O. Touster and V. H. Reynolds, *J. Biol. Chem.* **197,** 863 (1952).
114. A. Taurog, S. Abraham, and I. L. Chaikoff, *J. Am. Chem. Soc.* **75,** 3473 (1953).

methyl-α-D-glucofuranosidurono-3,6-lactone, originally called trimethylglucurone (*115*). The formation of high yields of crystalline methyl α- and β-glucofuranosiduronic acids (3 and 59%, respectively) from glucurone and methanolic HCl directly at room temperature is further evidence of the furanose ring. These furanosiduronic acids can then be reduced with sodium borohydride to the corresponding furanosides. A 72% yield of the 3,6-lactone of methyl β-D-glucofuranosiduronic acid has been obtained from glucurone, boiling methanol and the cation-exchange resin Nalcite HCR (*116*). This product can be changed by the action of hot methanol–HCl to the pyranosiduronate methyl ester. It is interesting that the furanosiduronic lactone reduces Fehling solution and has an abnormal absorption curve in alkali. These reactions have been attributed to the presence of two five-membered rings, one of which splits with the formation of enols as has been noted for the dilactones of aldaric acids (see p. 313).

Mannurone has been shown to have a 1,4-hemiacetal ring and a 3,6-lactone ring; with periodic acid, only the unblocked hydroxyls at carbons 1 and 2 are attacked, and D-araburonic acid is the product (*117*).

D-Glucuronolactone isonicotinylhydrazone has been reported to have a very high antitubercular activity *in vitro* and *in vivo* and comparatively low toxicity (*118*).

D. Keto Aldonic Acids

The keto aldonic acids of the hexose series are of the 2- and 5-keto types. The 2-keto acids have been called osonic acids because of their preparation by the oxidation of osones. The 5-keto acids have been termed keturonic

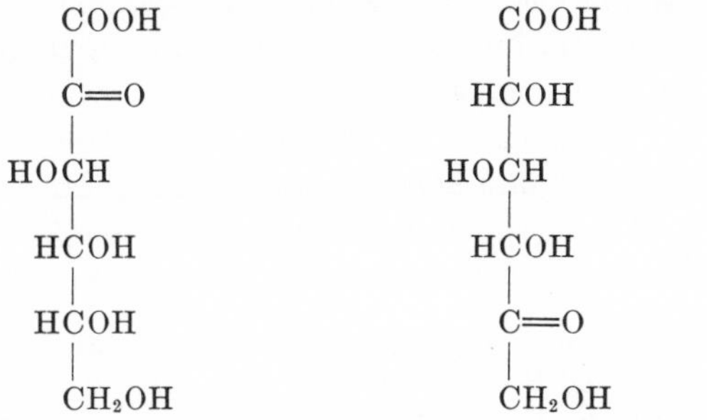

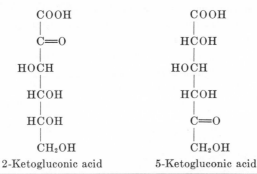

2-Ketogluconic acid   5-Ketogluconic acid

115. R. E. Reeves, *J. Am. Chem. Soc.* **62,** 1616 (1940); *ibid.* **76,** 934 (1954); F. Smith, *J. Chem. Soc.* p. 584 (1944); L. N. Owen, S. Peat, and W. J. G. Jones, *J. Chem. Soc.* p. 339 (1941).

116. Elizabeth M. Osman, K. C. Hobbs, and W. E. Walston, *J. Am. Chem. Soc.* **73,** 2726 (1951).

117. C. F. Huebner and K. P. Link, Abstracts American Chemical Society Meeting, Chicago (Sept. 1950).

118. P. P. T. Sah, *J. Am. Chem. Soc.* **75,** 2512 (1953).

acids, uronic acids related to ketoses, whereas the normal uronic acids are alduronic acids. Both types of keto acids show a great similarity to uronic acids in their color reactions and in the property of decarboxylation on heating with acids. The 2-keto acids, however, show a distinct difference in their ready enolization to ascorbic acid analogs (see p. 330). In this discussion, the term uronic acid will be reserved for the alduronic acids.

2-Ketogluconic acid has been isolated from a polysaccharide occurring in Irish moss (*119*), but no other similar product has been found in nature. Both 2-keto- and 5-ketogluconic acids have been prepared by the action of bacteria. Pyruvic acid and α-ketoglutaric acid (Chapter XIII) are also keto acids.

A number of methods are available for the synthesis of 2-keto acids. Gluconic acid methyl ester can be oxidized (*120*) with $NaClO_3$ and V_2O_5 (see also under Halic acid oxidations). Similar reactions produce the corresponding 2-keto acids of galactose, glucoheptose, and galaheptose. Galactosazone is oxidized by bromine to 2-ketogalactonic (or galactosonic) acid (*121*). Similarly, maltosazone is converted to the 2-ketomaltobionic acid. "Beta-diacetonefructose" is oxidized by potassium permanganate to di-*O*-isopropylidene-2-ketogluconic acid (*122*). Careful oxidation of unsubstituted ketoses with nitric acid has been partially successful. Bacterial action on glucose has given (*123*) yields as high as 80% of the 2-keto acid (see later in this chapter). Finally, direct synthesis of 2-keto-L-erythronic acid from 2-hydroxy-3-butenenitrile in a series of steps has been reported (*124*).

The 5-keto acids have been prepared by three general methods. Bacterial oxidation of glucose gives a 90% yield of 5-ketogluconic acid (*125*). 5-Keto-L-galactonic acid has been formed from D-galacturonic acid by the action of calcium and strontium hydroxides (*126*), but barium hydroxide gives different, strongly reducing products. Glucuronic acid appears to behave similarly. The permanganate oxidation of di-*O*-isopropylidenetagatose leads to the formation of 5-ketogalactonic acid (*127*).

The keto acids show some similarity to ketoses in their behavior toward oxidizing agents (*128*). 5-Ketogalactonic acid is not affected by bromine

119. E. G. Young and F. A. H. Rice, *J. Biol. Chem.* **164,** 35 (1946).

120. P. P. Regna and B. P. Caldwell, *J. Am. Chem. Soc.* **66,** 243 (1944).

121. T. Kitasato, *Biochem. Z.* **207,** 217 (1929).

122. H. Ohle and R. Wolter, *Ber.* **63,** 843 (1930).

123. J. J. Stubbs, L. B. Lockwood, E. I. Roe, B. Tabenkin, and G. E. Ward, *Ind. Eng. Chem.* **32,** 1626 (1940).

124. A. T. Küchlin, Jr., *Rec. trav. chim.* **49,** 705 (1930).

125. L. B. Lockwood, B. Tabenkin, and G. E. Ward, *J. Bacteriol.* **42,** 51 (1941).

126. F. Ehrlich and R. Guttmann, *Ber.* **67,** 573 (1934).

127. T. Reichstein and W. Bosshard, *Helv. Chim. Acta* **67,** 753 (1934).

128. H. Ohle, *Ber.* **17,** 155 (1934).

water at 15 to 20°. It reacts with sodium hypoiodite, but only one atom of iodine is consumed; 2-ketogluconic acid does not react with this agent in the cold. Highly purified salts of the acid reduce Fehling solution in the cold very slowly. A modified Benedict solution reacts readily with 5-ketogluconic acid; complete oxidation occurs at 25° in 7 to 14 minutes, whereas 2-ketogluconic acid, glucose, fructose, uronic acids, and simple aldehydes do not react appreciably under these conditions (*129*). Hence, a quantitative estimation is possible in the presence of these latter materials. Quantitative estimation of 2- and 5-keto acids has been carried out (*123*) by the Shaffer-Hartmann method; 2-ketogluconic acid has 87% of the reducing power of glucose and 5-ketogluconic acid, 80%.

The similarity of the keto aldonic acids and uronic acids has been mentioned earlier. 2-Ketogluconic acid gives a 33% yield of furfural in 4 hours and the 5-keto acid 42.5%, when heated with 12% hydrochloric acid (*130*). The evolution of carbon dioxide from the 5-keto acid is quantitative.

2-Keto-L-arabonic acid, prepared from the osone, loses carbon dioxide similarly, but the final product is not furfural but L-erythrose, isolated as the phenylosazone or as calcium L-erythronate after bromine oxidation (*131*).

The well-known naphthoresorcinol color is slowly developed by 2-ketogluconic acid in a manner resembling galacturonic acid.

2-Ketogluconic acid and its lactone exist only as sirups although hygroscopic crystals of the former have been reported (*124*). Esters can be easily prepared by the action of methanol and sulfuric acid on the sodium salt (*122*, *132*). The ester and salt mutarotate in the same direction as fructose. Ultraviolet absorption spectra (*133*) of solutions of the salts and acid indicate the absence of carbonyl or carboxyl groups, and, for alkaline solutions, the absorption is typical of an ethylenic or enolic linkage.

The keto aldonic acids have been investigated primarily as intermediates in the synthesis of ascorbic acids; 2-keto-L-gulonic acid is the most important of this series. The degradation of these acids to simpler acids has been utilized. Thus, 5-keto-D-gluconic acid can be oxidized by oxygen in alkaline solution with various catalysts or by nitric acid to tartaric and oxalic acids (*134*, *135*).

2-Keto aldonic acids can be converted by a Ruff degradation to aldonic

129. W. E. Militzer, *J. Biol. Chem.* **154,** 325 (1944).

130. E. G. Young and F. A. H. Rice, *J. Biol. Chem.* **164,** 35 (1946); F. Ehrlich and R. Guttmann, *Ber.* **67,** 573 (1934).

131. A. M. Gakhokidze, *J. Gen. Chem.* (*U.S.S.R.*) **11,** 109 (1941).

132. H. Ohle and G. Berend, *Ber.* **60,** 1159 (1927).

133. P. Niederhoff, *Z. physiol. Chem.* **181,** 83 (1929).

134. R. Pasternack and P. P. Regna, *U. S. Patent* 2,203,923 (June 11, 1940).

135. W. E. Barch, *J. Am. Chem. Soc.* **55,** 3653 (1933).

acids with one less carbon in the chain; thus L-xylonic acid is formed from 2-keto-L-gulonic acid (*8*).

5-Ketogluconic acid in sirupy form is unstable, turns black in a short time, and froths with the liberation of gas (*135*).

A 3-deoxy-2-ketogluconic acid 6-phosphate was isolated as an intermediate in the enzymic oxidation of gluconic acid 6-phosphate (*135a*). The formation of this acid by a dehydration mechanism is reminiscent of that of the saccharinic acids.

3-Keto derivatives are very rare compounds. Lindberg reported the formation of methyl 3-keto-D-glucopyranoside by chromic acid oxidation of the glucoside (*4*). 2-*O*-Methyl-L-*xylo*-3-hexulose has been prepared by reduction of a derivative of ascorbic acid (*135b*).

E. Ascorbic Acids (*136*)

a. General Properties and Reactions

Ascorbic acids, of which the best known is vitamin C or L-xyloascorbic acid, may be considered as reductones (I) or as represented by the general

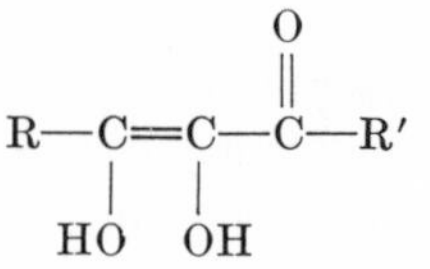
O
R—C═C—C—R′
HO OH

(I)

formulas (II) and (III). The compounds are characterized by an *enediolic* system. Varying degrees of antiscorbutic activity are shown by compounds of this group, but only the compounds of type (II), with the lactone ring on the right, are active in this respect.

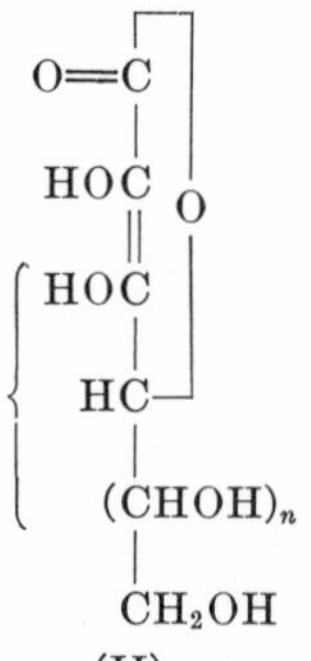
O═C
HOC
O
HOC
HC
(CHOH)$_n$
CH$_2$OH

(II)

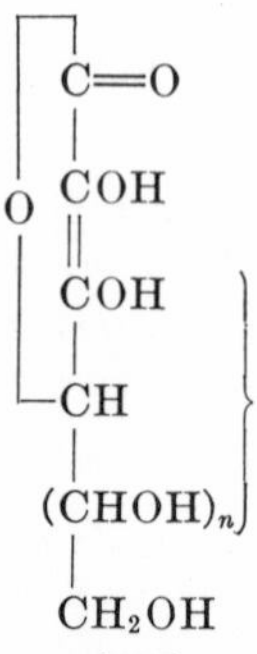
C═O
O
COH
COH
CH
(CHOH)$_n$
CH$_2$OH

(III)

135a. J. MacGee and M. Doudoroff, *J. Biol. Chem.* **210**, 617 (1954).
135b. J. K. N. Jones, *Abstr. Papers Am. Chem. Soc. Minneapolis*, 16D, 1955.
136. F. Smith, *Advances in Carbohydrate Chem.* **2**, 79 (1946).

The nomenclature of the ascorbic acids is based on the configuration of the osone actually or hypothetically used in its preparation (see below); the portion concerned is that shown in the bracket. Since carbon atom 3

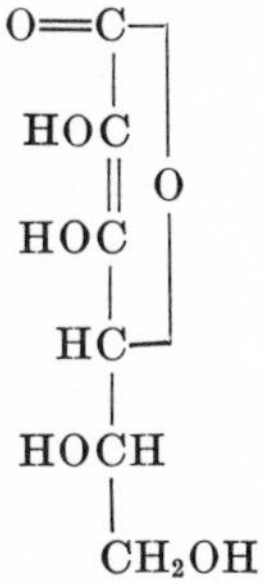
(IV)

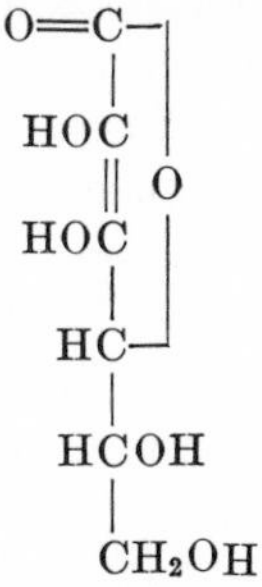
(V)

is not asymmetric, several names are possible. For vitamin C the names L-xylo- or L-lyxoascorbic acid (IV) have been used. Actually in these ascorbic acids there are only two asymmetric carbon atoms, and a better "nickname" for (IV) would be L-*threo*-hexoascorbic acid. A seven-carbon ascorbic acid would then be defined as D-*xylo*-heptoascorbic acid. There can be no confusion here, as both the configuration and the number of carbon atoms are given. A more definitive name, based on the carbohydrate rules, would be 2-keto-L-*threo*-hexono-γ-lactone 2,3-enediol (*137*).

The ascorbic acids can be considered as enolic lactones of the 2-keto and 3-keto aldonic acids. For vitamin C, there apparently exists an equilibrium between the ascorbic acid and the 3-keto acid. The latter has not been isolated, but hydrazone and "osazone" derivatives have been prepared

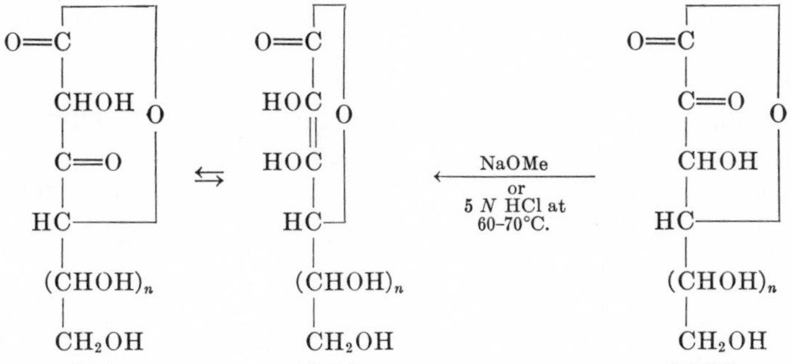
(VI) (VII) (VIII)

(*138*). Under normal conditions, the 2-keto acid apparently does not par-

137. Personal communication from M. L. Wolfrom and L. T. Capell.
138. E. G. Cox, E. L. Hirst, and R. J. W. Reynolds, *Nature* **130,** 888 (1932).

ticipate in the equilibrium. The kinetics of conversion of 2-keto acids to the ascorbic acids has been studied (*139*). The yields ranged from 70% for the 2-ketogulonic acid system to only 6% for 2-keto-D-galactoheptonic acid.

Four general methods are available for the preparation of ascorbic acids. The two most applicable involve the enolization of keto acids; the others involve condensations.

Enolization and Lactonization of 2-Keto Aldonic Acids (*140*). By the action of sodium methylate on the methyl esters, 2-keto acids are transformed into ascorbic acids (see (VII) and (VIII)). The reaction is almost quantitative. Lactonization and enolization take place simultaneously. Heat treatment of an aqueous solution of the free acid causes only a limited amount of conversion. Acids also act as catalysts (see above). From the acid hydrolyzate of the methyl glycoside of 3,4-*O*-isopropylidene-2-keto-L-ribonic acid, the 2-keto-L-ribonic acid could not be isolated, because L-erythroascorbic acid was formed very rapidly (*141*).

Cyanohydrin Synthesis from Osones (*142*). For this method, 3-keto aldonic acids are formed as intermediates which are not isolated. The first product, the nitrile, immediately enolizes with simultaneous ring formation to an *imino* analog (XI) of the ascorbic acid, and the latter is formed by

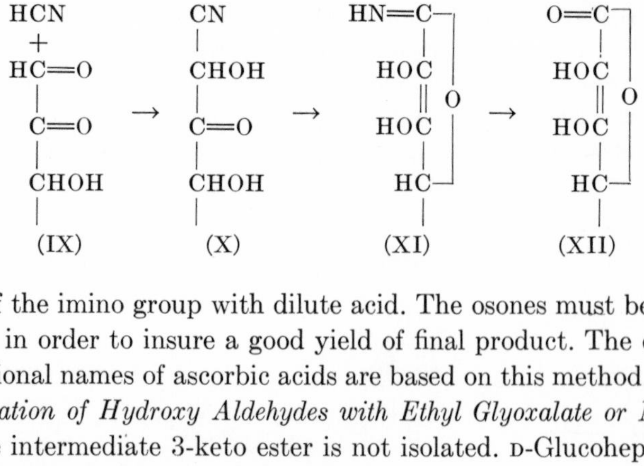

(IX) (X) (XI) (XII)

removal of the imino group with dilute acid. The osones must be in a very pure state in order to insure a good yield of final product. The customary configurational names of ascorbic acids are based on this method.

Condensation of Hydroxy Aldehydes with Ethyl Glyoxalate or Mesoxalate (*143*). The intermediate 3-keto ester is not isolated. D-Glucoheptoascorbic acid was prepared in this way from glucose.

139. P. P. Regna and B. P. Caldwell, *J. Am. Chem. Soc.* **66,** 246 (1944).

140. K. Maurer and B. Schiedt, *Ber.* **66,** 1054 (1933).

141. T. Reichstein, *Helv. Chim. Acta* **17,** 1003 (1934).

142. T. Reichstein, A. Grüssner, and R. Oppenauer, *Helv. Chim. Acta* **16,** 561 (1933); R. G. Ault, D. K. Baird, H. C. Carrington, W. N. Haworth, R. W. Herbert, E. L. Hirst, E. G. V. Percival, F. Smith, and M. Stacey, *J. Chem. Soc. p.* 1419 (1933).

143. B. Helferich and O. Peters, *Ber.* **70,** 465 (1937).

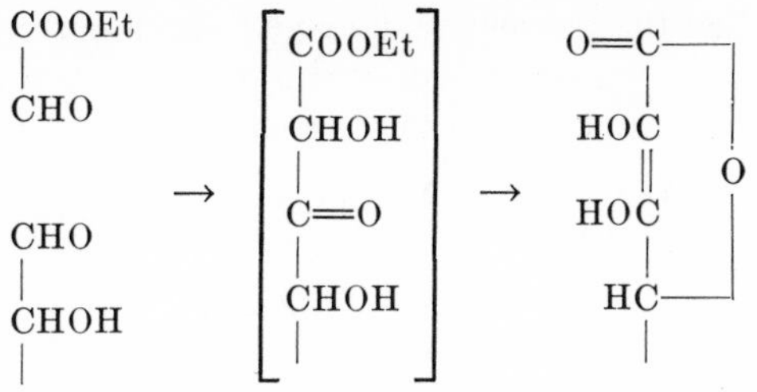

Condensation of Esters of Hydroxy Acids (*144*). This method is similar to the Claisen condensation.

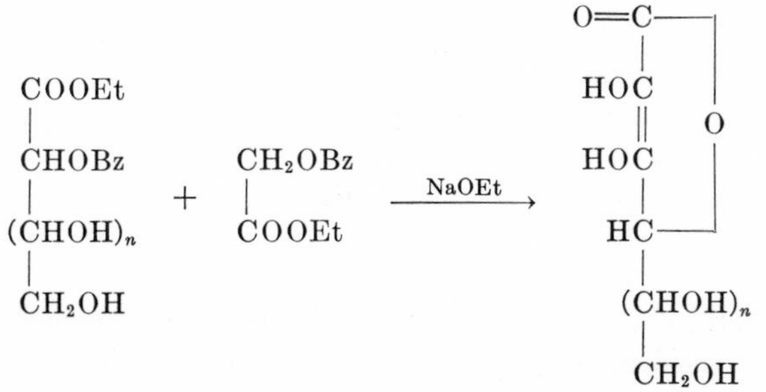

The ascorbic acids are weak acids as a result of the presence of the enolic groups rather than of the lactone ring (*138, 145*). They reduce Fehling solution, and the double bond is oxidized by acidic iodine solution. The reaction with iodine is used as a quantitative method to distinguish them from 2-keto acids. The action of boiling 12% HCl causes the formation of furfural in very high yields, above 80% (see above).

b. *Vitamin C* (L-*Xyloascorbic Acid*) (*146*)

Vitamin C is widely distributed in nature, especially in green vegetables and citrus fruits. It has been found in conifer needles, and its presence in the lowly potato provides an excellent dietary source for those unable to secure other foods. It is universally distributed in plant tissues, normally in the

144. F. Micheel and H. Haarkoff, *Ann.* **545,** 28 (1940).

145. R. W. Herbert, E. L. Hirst, E. G. V. Percival, R. J. W. Reynolds, and F. Smith, *J. Chem. Soc.* p. 1270 (1933).

146. H. R. Rosenberg, "Chemistry and Physiology of the Vitamins," p. 289. Interscience, New York, 1942; A. P. Meikeljohn, *Vitamins and Hormones* **11,** 61 (1953); Lind Bicententary Symposium *Proc. Nutrition Soc.* **12,** 202 (1953); B. B. Lloyd and H. M. Sinclair *in* "Biochemistry and Physiology of Nutrition" (G. H. Bourne and G. W. Kidder, eds.), Vol. I, p. 369. Academic Press, New York, 1953; W. H. Sebrell and R. S. Harris, eds., *in* "The Vitamins," Vol. I, Chapter 2, p. 177. Academic Press, New York, 1954.

reduced form. When the tissues are damaged, the ascorbic acid is oxidized as a result of various causes, including the presence of a specific ascorbic oxidase. The equilibrium between the ascorbic acid (IV) and the oxidation product, dehydroascorbic acid (XIII), is very important to plant and animal life (*147*). The ascorbic acid apparently functions as a hydrogen carrier.

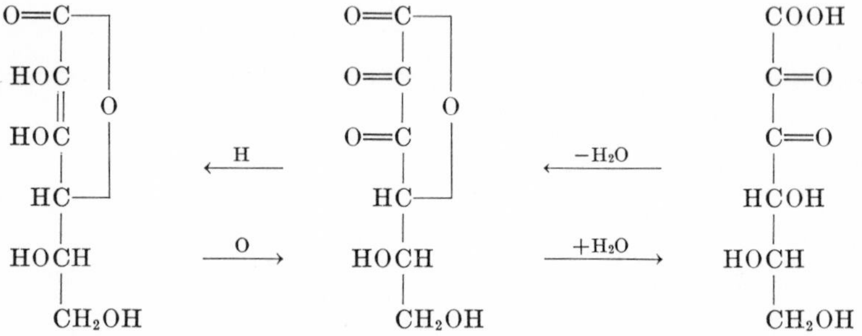

(IV) (XIII) (XIV)

The 2,3-diketo-L-gulonic acid (XIV) is formed spontaneously on dissolution of dehydroascorbic acid (*148*). Dehydroascorbic acid may be stored as a methanol complex, which is far more stable than the parent substance (*148a*).

Ascorbic acid is very sensitive to oxygen, especially in neutral solution, and to acidic iodine. The enolic grouping can be split by hypoiodite to form oxalic and L-threonic acids (*149*). Methylation with diazomethane at 0° forms a 3-methyl ether, which no longer reduces, but which is still acidic (*150*). Methylation at 20° forms a 2,3-dimethyl ether which does not react with hydrazines.

The stability of ascorbic acid in plant products is very important in the food industry. Oxidation in milk is accelerated by copper and sunlight. Low-temperature storage of foods (below 42°F.) is helpful in preventing loss.

In 1928 a strongly reducing "hexuronic acid" was isolated from adrenal cortex, oranges, and cabbages in a study of oxidation-reduction factors (*151*). This product was shown later to be identical with vitamin C, iso-

147. W. O. James and J. M. Cragg, *New Phytologist* **42,** 28 (1943); L. W. Mapson, *Vitamins and Hormones* **9,** 1 (1953).

148. J. R. Penney and S. S. Zilva, *Biochem. J.* **39,** 1 (1945).

148a. B. Pecherer, *J. Am. Chem. Soc.* **73,** 3827 (1951).

149. E. L. Hirst, *J. Soc. Chem. Ind.* **52,** 221 (1933).

150. T. Reichstein and R. Oppenauer, *Helv. Chim. Acta* **17,** 390 (1934).

151. A. Szent-Györgyi, *Biochem. J.* **22,** 1387 (1928).

lated from lemon juice (*152*). The constitution (*153*) was established in 1933, and the first successful synthesis was described in the same year (*142*).

The first synthesis was based on the addition of HCN to L-xylosone. D-Galacturonic acid was the starting material; reduction gave L-galactonic acid, and the amide was then degraded to L-lyxose, which was converted to L-xylosone. The most important commercial method utilizes sorbitol as the starting material (*154*). Bacterial oxidation produces L-sorbose, and the diacetone derivative (XV) is oxidized with permanganate to di-*O*-isopropylidene-2-keto-L-gulonic acid (XVI), which after hydrolysis of the acetone groups (XVII) can be converted to ascorbic acid (IV).

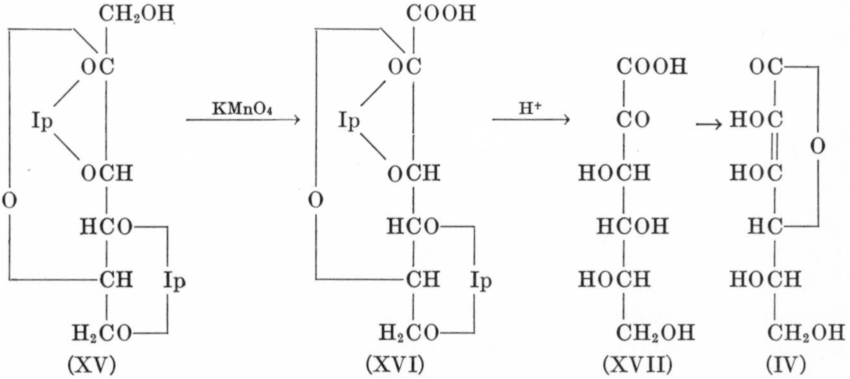

(Ip = $(CH_3)_2C=$)

The conversion of D-galacturonic acid to L-galactonic acid, and subsequent oxidation to 2-keto-L-galactonic acid, has been suggested as a method (*155*). Sorbose can be oxidized directly to the 2-keto-L-gulonic acid, but better yields are obtained with the diacetone derivatives.

F. Osones

The osones are known primarily in the form of their hydrazine derivatives, the osazones. These "dicarbonyl" sugars have achieved importance as intermediates in the synthesis of ascorbic acids. They also can be oxidized to 2-keto aldonic acids.

152. C. G. King and W. A. Waugh, *Science* **75,** 357 (1932); W. A. Waugh and C. G. King, *J. Biol. Chem.* **97,** 325 (1932).

153. R. W. Herbert, E. G. V. Percival, R. J. W. Reynolds, F. Smith, and E. L. Hirst, *J. Soc. Chem. Ind.* **52,** 221, 482 (1933); F. Micheel and K. Kraft, *Z. physiol. Chem.* **222,** 235 (1933).

154. T. Reichstein and A. Grüssner, *Helv. Chim. Acta* **17,** 311 (1934).

155. H. S. Isbell, *J. Research Natl. Bur. Standards* **33,** 45 (1944). P. P. Regna and B. P. Caldwell, *J. Am. Chem. Soc.* **66,** 243 (1944); R. Pasternack and P. P. Regna, *U. S. Patent* 2,207,991 (July 16, 1940); *U. S. Patent* 2,338,534 (Jan. 4, 1944).

The osones exist only as amorphous or sirupy materials. They are very labile and show the characteristics of enediols of the reductone type. For this reason the formula for D-glucosone, for example, might be represented best by (II) below, rather than (I). This formula is similar to a "reduced"

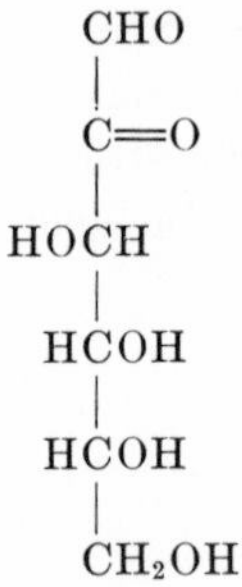

(I)

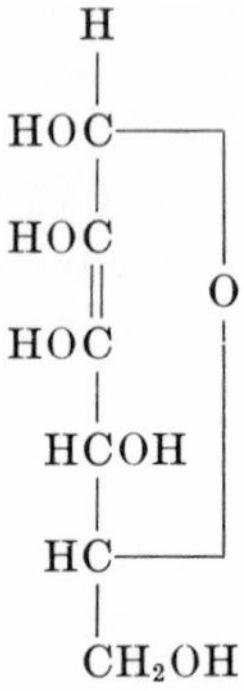

(II)

ascorbic acid. Reduction occurs with Fehling solution in the cold, and derivatives are obtained with hydrazines and diamines.

A hemiacetal ring structure, linked to carbon 5 or to carbon 6, has been suggested for D-glucosone, based on oxidation with lead tetraacetate. As no significant amount of formaldehyde was found (*156*), the —CHOH—CH_2OH grouping was apparently not present in the molecule. In contrast to this evidence, periodic acid oxidation gave formaldehyde and showed the structure to be a straight chain (*157*). Glucosone also condenses with acetone in the presence of concentrated sulfuric acid to give a crystalline 1,2:2,3:5,6-tri-*O*-isopropylideneglucosone hydrate (*158*), converted by partial hydrolysis to a 1,2:2,3-di-*O*-isopropylidene derivative. The constitution of the latter was shown by periodate oxidation, and also by methylation and hydrolysis to the known 5,6-di-*O*-methylglucosone. Evidently this derivative must have a furanoid structure. In contrast, 2,3,4,6-tetra-*O*-acetylglucosone has a pyranose structure, for this compound was prepared from acetobromoglucose which contains a pyranose ring. Glucosone shows a slight mutarotation in aqueous solution (*156*) and also reacts with Schiff's reagent. Until a crystalline form is obtained, the structure of glucosone in solution has little significance.

Several methods are available for the preparation of these compounds. Osazones can be hydrolyzed by acids or by carbonyl compounds. (See

156. C. E. Becker and C. E. May, *J. Am. Chem. Soc.* **71,** 1491 (1949).

157. P. Fleury and V. Vievet-Guinard, *Ann. pharm. franc.* **5,** 404 (1947).

158. S. Bayne, G. A. Collie, and J. A. Fewster, *J. Chem. Soc.* p. 2766 (1952); see also M. G. Blair, *Advances in Carbohydrate Chem.* **9,** 97 (1954).

under Osazones.) Alcohol-insoluble osazones are generally hydrolyzed with concentrated hydrochloric acid at a low temperature. Alcohol-soluble osazones can be split by the action of benzaldehyde. Pyruvic acid has also been used.

Catalytic oxidation of sugars and alcohols is a more direct method. Hydrogen peroxide and iron salts were used originally (see under Hydrogen peroxide oxidations). However, much better yields have been obtained by the direct oxidation with cupric salts (*159*). The action of a limited excess of cupric acetate for a short time on methanol solutions of L-sorbose or L-xylose has given a 60% yield of the osone.

The simplest osone, glycerosone or hydroxypyruvic aldehyde, has been prepared by the oxidation of dihydroxyacetone. This compound is enolic in character, reducing cold Fehling solution and forming acidic aqueous solutions (*160*). It exists normally as the trimer.

Glucose has been oxidized with *A. parasiticus* Speare and another unidentified mold (*161*). Yields of 8.6% of glucosone were obtained from glucose and 17% from maltose. Starch and sucrose gave 15 and 13.6% yields, respectively.

Substituted osones can be synthesized by the Grignard reaction. Di-*O*-isopropylidene-2-ketogluconic acid and phenyl magnesium bromide react to form 1-*C*-phenyl-2,3,4,5-di-*O*-isopropylideneglucosone (*162*). Some 1,1-*C*-diphenyl-2,3,4,5-di-*O*-isopropylidenefructose is also formed. Hydrolysis with boiling normal sulfuric acid in propanol forms the 1-*C*-phenylglucosone. This product is the first osone prepared in crystalline form.

A tetra-*O*-acetylglucosone hydrate is prepared by the treatment of tetra-*O*-acetyl-1,2-glucoseen with chlorine followed by silver carbonate (see under Glycoseens).

G. Dialdoses

Several compounds of the dialdose type (see formula, p. 299) have been prepared. Catalytic reduction of tetra-*O*-acetylgalactaric acid gave 2,3,4,5-tetra-*O*-acetyl-*galacto*-hexodialdose (*163*). Lead tetraacetate oxidation of tetra-*O*-acetyl-*myo*-inositol, tetra-*O*-acetyl-*allo*-inositol, and di-*O*-isopropylidene-D-inositol, respectively, gave the corresponding *ido*-hexodialdose,

159. J. K. Hamilton and F. Smith, *J. Am. Chem. Soc.* **74,** 5162 (1952).

160. W. E. Evans, Jr., C. J. Carr, and J. C. Krantz, Jr., *J. Am. Chem. Soc.* **60,** 1628 (1938); R. G. W. Norrish and J. G. A. Griffiths, *J. Chem. Soc.* p. 2829 (1928).

161. C. R. Bond, E. C. Knight, and T. K. Walker, *Biochem. J.* **31,** 1033 (1937); see also R. C. Bean and W. Z. Hassid, *Science* **124,** 171 (1956).

162. H. Ohle and I. Blell, *Ann.* **492,** 1 (1931).

163. F. Micheel, "Chemie der Zucker und Polysaccharide," pp. 176–177. Akademische Verlagsges., Leipzig, 1939.

allo-hexodialdose and D-*manno*-hexodialdose derivatives (*164*). Periodate oxidation of 1,2-*O*-isopropylidene-D-glucose cleaves the terminal carbon with the formation of the D-*xylo*-pentodialdose derivative (*165*); 2,3-*O*-isopropylidene-D-*threo*-tetrodialdose (*166*) was similarly prepared from 3,4-*O*-isopropylidene-D-mannitol.

None of these dialdoses is crystalline, but they give crystalline bis-hydrazones with phenyl- and *p*-nitrophenylhydrazine and also form tetra-ethyl thioacetals.

Methyl β-D-*gluco*-(5-formyl-pentopyranoside) has been prepared in amorphous condition by chromic acid oxidation of the methyl glucoside (*4*). This compound can be considered as the 1-methyl glucoside of D-*gluco*-hexodialdose.

2. OXIDATIVE AGENTS

A. Halogen Oxidations (*167*)

The halogens and their oxyacids probably are the most important oxidants used in the carbohydrate field. They are widely used as bleaching agents, but the mechanism of this action remains to be clarified. As reagents for preparatory purposes (particularly for aldonic acids and lactones) and for analytical procedures, they are very important. Periodic acid, discussed in a later section, has an important application for the elucidation of structures of carbohydrates. A number of valuable commercial products are made by treatment of polysaccharides with halogens, particularly chlorine or hypochlorous acid, but the nature of these actions, such as the modification of starch, has not been clarified.

Bromine and hypoiodite oxidations are particularly suitable for the preparation of aldonic acids from aldoses. Similarly, uronic acids are converted to saccharic acids. Of less value is the oxidation of primary alcoholic to aldehydic groups. In this manner, glycosides can be converted to uronides and polyols to aldoses and aldonic acids.

Secondary alcoholic groups are oxidized to keto groups, and the 2-keto and 5-keto acids are formed in this manner. More extended oxidation results in the cleavage of carbon–carbon bonds and the production of short-chain acids.

Periodic acid is of great value in that it usually produces quantitative

164. G. Dangschat, *Naturwissenschaften* **30,** 146 (1942); G. Dangschat and H. O. L. Fischer, *ibid.* **27,** 756 (1939); C. E. Ballou and H. O. L. Fischer, *J. Am. Chem. Soc.* **75,** 3673 (1953); *ibid.* **75,** 4695 (1953).

165. J. C. Sowden, *J. Am. Chem. Soc.* **73,** 5496 (1951); K. Iwadare, *Bull. Soc. Japan* **16,** 40 (1941).

166. H. O. L. Fischer and H. Appel, *Helv. Chim. Acta* **17,** 1574 (1934).

167. J. W. Green, *Advances in Carbohydrate Chem.* **3,** 129 (1947).

cleavage of pairs of vicinal hydroxyl groups and the formation of dialdehydes. Oxidations of this type are discussed in the next section.

The chemistry of bleaching and oxidizing agents, with emphasis on the variations of oxidation-reduction potentials with pH, has been reviewed (*168*). However, a quantitative examination of the oxidation products is not feasible with present techniques, and, until such methods are readily available, reaction mechanisms can be suggested only in a tentative manner.

It is particularly interesting that in spite of the cheapness and availability, chlorine and hypochlorite are not common oxidative agents for preparatory purposes.

a. Halogens and Hypohalites

The use of halogens and hypochlorites as oxidizing agents is complicated by the change in the nature of the oxidation as the conditions of temperature, acidity, and concentration vary. The halogens not only show considerable difference in the position of the various equilibria and the speed at which the equilibria are attained, but also in the maximal concentrations as expressed by the solubilities.

At 20°C. the solubility (*169*) of the halogens in water is: chlorine, 1.85 g./100 ml.; bromine, 3.58 g./100 ml.; and iodine, 0.28 g./100 ml. In aqueous solution, hydrolysis occurs as expressed by the following equation:

$$X_2 + H_2O \rightleftarrows HOX + HX$$

The equilibrium constants for the reaction are given (*170*) as:

$$\text{Chlorine, } K = 4.5 \times 10^{-4}$$

$$\text{Bromine, } K = 2.4 \times 10^{-8}$$

$$\text{Iodine, } K = 3.6 \times 10^{-13}$$

Evidently in acid solution, the equilibrium lies far to the left and the concentration of hypohalous acid is very small.

When alkali is added to the system, the concentration of hypohalite ion increases:

$$X_2 + 2\ NaOH \rightleftarrows NaOX + NaX + H_2O$$

Hence, the concentration of free halogen, halic acid, and hypohalite will vary greatly with the acidity. For 0.02 *M* chlorine solutions at room tem-

168. G. Holst, *Chem. Revs.* **54,** 169 (1954).

169. A. Seidell, "Solubilities of Inorganic and Metal Organic Compounds," Vol. 1. Von Nostrand, New York, 1940.

170. J. W. Mellor, "A Comprehensive Treatise on Inorganic and Theoretical Chemistry," Vol. 2. Longmans, Green, New York, 1927.

perature, for example, Ridge and Little (*171*) have shown that at pH 1, 82% of the total chlorine exists as free chlorine and 18% as hypochlorous acid. At pH 4, only 0.4% is free chlorine and 99.6% is hypochlorous acid. At pH 8, 21% exists as hypochlorous acid and 79% as hypochlorite. Obviously, the concentration of the oxidant and probably the nature of the oxidation will be influenced greatly by the acidity.

Hypohalites are converted to halates according to the equation:

$$2\ HOX + OX^- \rightleftarrows 2\ HX + XO_3^-$$

For hypochlorous acid, (*172*) the minimum stability exists at pH 6.7 and the maximum stability at pH 13. Various anions exert a catalytic effect. For hypobromite solutions, these positions of maximum and minimum stability are shifted to more alkaline conditions. The velocity of halate formation increases greatly in the order: $ClO_3 < BrO_3 < IO_3$.

Oxidation in Acid Solutions. In acid solutions the active oxidant is the free halogen or the hypohalous acid. As noted above, the proportions of these potential forms of the oxidant vary with the acidity of the solution and the nature of the halogen. However, unless a buffer or neutralizing substance is present, the solution will become strongly acid as a result of the formation of hydrohalic acid.

$$RCHO + Br_2 + H_2O \rightarrow RCOOH + 2\ HBr$$

$$RCHO + HOBr \rightarrow RCOOH + HBr$$

Hlasiwetz (*173*) first used halogens for the oxidation of sugars. Lactose was treated with bromine and glucose with chlorine. Gluconic acid was formed from glucose and isolated as the calcium salt. Kiliani (*174*) found that sugars were oxidized readily by bromine at room temperature and obtained yields of 50 to 70% of various aldonic acids.

The accumulation of HBr during the oxidation produces a definite inhibition of the rate of oxidation. The effect is more than one of an increasing acidity, for, although other strong acids also inhibit the rate, the effect is largest for HBr and HCl (*175*). To minimize this inhibiting influence, the reaction may be carried out in the presence of a buffer such as barium carbonate or barium benzoate (*176*). In general, the presence of buffers in-

171. B. P. Ridge and A. H. Little, *J. Textile Inst.* **33,** T33 (1942).
172. R. M. Chapin, *J. Am. Chem. Soc.* **56,** 2211 (1934).
173. H. Hlasiwetz, *Ann.* **119,** 281 (1861); H. Hlasiwetz and J. Habermann, *ibid.* **155,** 120 (1870).
174. H. Kiliani and S. Kleeman, *Ber.* **17,** 1296 (1884).
175. H. H. Bunzel and A. P. Mathews, *J. Am. Chem. Soc.* **31,** 464 (1909).
176. H. A. Clowes and B. Tollens, *Ann.* **310,** 164 (1899); C. S. Hudson and H. S. Isbell, *J. Am. Chem. Soc.* **51,** 2225 (1929); *Bur. Standards J. Research* **3,** 57 (1929).

creases the yields of aldonic acids, and, in addition, hydrolysis of disaccharides is prevented. Yields of 96% of gluconic acid and of 90% of xylonic acid (as salts) have been obtained when buffered solutions were employed.

When the oxidation period is extended, particularly under unbuffered conditions, keto acids may be formed in small yields. Rhamnose gives 5-ketorhamnonic lactone (*177*) and hexose sugars the 5-keto acids (*178*). Under more drastic conditions, carbon–carbon bonds are cleaved with the production of short-chain acids.

A variation of the bromine oxidation process which seems to be particularly feasible for the commercial production of aldonic acids involves the electrolysis between carbon electrodes of solutions containing sugars, small amounts of bromides, and a buffer such as calcium carbonate (*179*). Presumably the reaction takes place by the formation of free bromine at the anode; the bromine oxidizes the aldose to the aldonic acid and is reduced to bromide. Yields are almost theoretical in many cases. If the electrolytic method is not well controlled, saccharic acids and 2-keto and 5-keto aldonic acids may be produced (*180*). Whereas the normal electrolytic oxidation is conducted with direct current, a yield of 55% of gluconic acid has been obtained with alternating current (*181*) and platinum electrodes; a very low efficiency was observed with graphite electrodes.

The ketoses are resistant to the action of bromine (*182*); bromine oxidation is used sometimes to remove aldoses from mixtures such as invert sugar. By extending the period of oxidation and employing high temperatures, Kiliani obtained oxalic acid, bromoform, and glycolic acid (*183*). Milder conditions give keto acids such as 5-keto-L-gulonic acid from fructose and 5-keto-L-gluconic acid from sorbose (*184*). Calcium 2-keto-D-gluconate has yielded 65% of calcium arabonate by an electrolytic bromine oxidation (*185*).

For polyols, more drastic conditions for bromine oxidations are required

177. E. Votoček and S. Malachata, *Anales soc. españ. fís. y quím.* **27,** 494 (1929).

178. J. P. Hart and M. R. Everett, *J. Am. Chem. Soc.* **61,** 1822 (1939).

179. H. S. Isbell and H. L. Frush, *Bur. Standards J. Research* **6,** 1145 (1931); H. S Isbell, *U. S. Patent* 1,976,731 (Oct. 16, 1934); E. L. Helwig, *U. S. Patent* 1,895,414 (Jan. 24, 1933).

180. R. Pasternack and P. P. Regna, *U. S. Patent* 2,222,155 (Nov. 19, 1940); E. W. Cook and R. T. Major, *J. Am. Chem. Soc.* **57,** 773 (1935).

181. A. N. Kappanna and K. M. Joshi, *J. Indian Chem. Soc.* **29,** 69 (1952).

182. H. Kiliani and C. Scheibler, *Ber.* **21,** 3276 (1888).

183. H. Kiliani, *Ann.* **205,** 182 (1880).

184. M. R. Everett and F. Sheppard, "Oxidation of Carbohydrates; Keturonic Acids; Salt Catalysis," University of Oklahoma Medical School, Norman, 1944.

185. C. L. Mehltretter, W. Dvonch, and C. E. Rist, *J. Am. Chem. Soc.* **72,** 2294 (1950); C. L. Mehltretter and W. Dvonch, *U. S. Patent* 2,502,472 (1950).

than for aldoses. The oxidation product of sorbitol gives two osazones, glucosazone and gulosazone (*186*).

The mechanism of the oxidation of aldoses by bromine in the presence of barium carbonate and bromides (pH about 5.4) has been studied by Isbell and Pigman (*187*). Under these conditions the active oxidant is free bromine and not hypobromous acid. Molecular chlorine has been found to be the active oxidant in the oxidation of glucose by buffered chlorine water at pH 2.2 and 3.0 (*188*).

It is interesting that the ring forms of the sugars, rather than the free aldehyde, are oxidized directly under these conditions (*189*). Pyranoses yield δ-lactones and furanoses γ-lactones, directly.

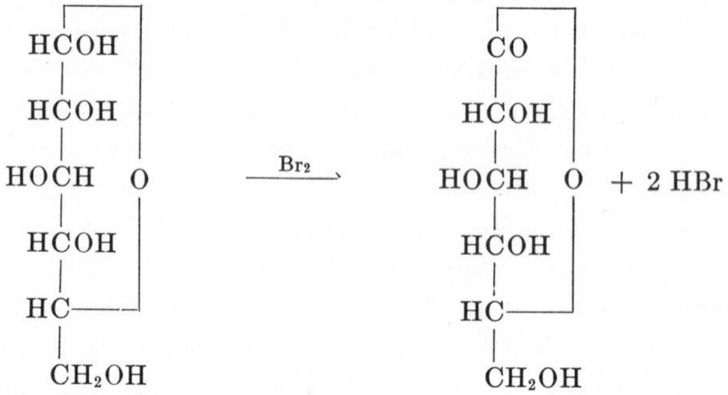

HCOH
HCOH
HOCH O
HCOH
HC
CH_2OH
Br_2
CO
HCOH
HOCH O
HCOH
HC
CH_2OH
+ 2 HBr

Glucopyranose Gluconic δ-lactone

The yields are high. The direct formation of δ-lactones from the sugars provides strong evidence that the crystalline sugars, in general, have pyranoid structures (see Chapter I).

In the hexose series as far as studied, the α-isomers are oxidized much more slowly than the β-isomers (*190*). β-Glucose, for example, oxidizes about 35 times more rapidly than the α-isomer. The anomeric forms of galactose show a similar difference as shown in Fig. 2. The data for a number of sugars are given in Table IV. When plotted on a semilogarithmic scale, the rate curves for the oxidation are approximately linear. Fig. 3 shows the data for several forms of mannose.

The effect of an adjacent grouping on the speed of oxidation of the carbonyl group has been shown in the case of 2-deoxy-D-galactose; this sugar

186. C. Vincent and Delachanal, *Compt. rend.* **111,** 51 (1890); E. Fischer, *Ber.* **23,** 3684 (1890); H. W. Talen, *Rec. trav. chim.* **44,** 891 (1925).

187. H. S. Isbell and W. W. Pigman, *Bur. Standards J. Research* **10,** 337 (1933).

188. N. N. Lichtin and M. H. Saxe, *J. Am. Chem. Soc.* **77,** 1875 (1955).

189. H. S. Isbell, *Bur. Standards J. Research* **8,** 615 (1932); H. S. Isbell and C. S. Hudson, *ibid.* **8,** 327 (1932).

190. H. S. Isbell and W. W. Pigman, *J. Research Natl. Bur. Standards* **18,** 141 (1937).

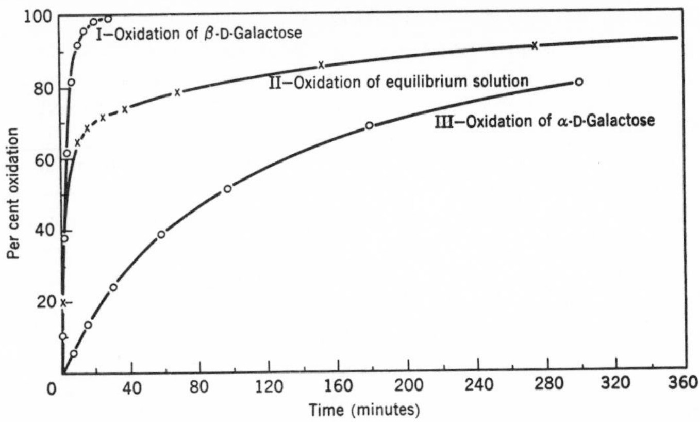
100
80
60
40
20
0
Per cent oxidation
I—Oxidation of β-D-Galactose
II—Oxidation of equilibrium solution
III—Oxidation of α-D-Galactose
40
80
120
160
200
240
280
320
360
Time (minutes)

FIG. 2. Rate of oxidation of D-galactose by bromine (*ca.* 0°C. pH = 5.4, buffered). (After Isbell and Pigman.)

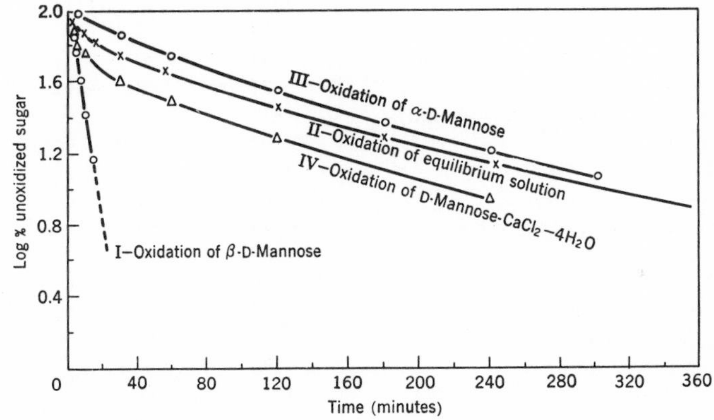
2.0
1.6
1.2
0.8
0.4
0
Log % unoxidized sugar
III—Oxidation of α-D-Mannose
II—Oxidation of equilibrium solution
IV—Oxidation of D-Mannose-CaCl2—4H2O
I—Oxidation of β-D-Mannose
40
80
120
160
200
240
280
320
360
Time (minutes)

FIG. 3. Rate of oxidation of D-mannose by bromine (*ca.* 0°C, pH = 5.4, buffered). (After Isbell and Pigman.)

is oxidized by unbuffered bromine water at about three times the rate for D-galactose (*191*).

The equilibrium solutions are oxidized at rates intermediate between those for the individual anomers (see Fig. 2 and 3), and the oxidation curve is composed of a rapid phase followed by a slow phase. Extrapolation of the slow portion (on a semilogarithmic plot) to zero time gives the amount of the two anomers in the equilibrium solution. The composition of equilibrium solutions of several sugars as determined in this manner agrees with that obtained by optical rotation studies (see Table III, Chapter I).

191. W. G. Overend, F. Shafizadeh, and M. Stacey, *J. Chem. Soc.* p. 2062 (1951).

TABLE IV

THE RATES OF OXIDATION OF THE ALPHA AND BETA SUGARS IN AQUEOUS SOLUTIONS CONTAINING 0.05 MOLE SUGAR AND 0.08 MOLE FREE BROMINE PER LITER AND BUFFERED WITH BARIUM CARBONATE AND CARBON DIOXIDE

Sugar	Oxidation with bromine water		
	Average value for velocity constant $k \times 10^2$	Relative reaction rates $\frac{k_{sugar}}{k_{\alpha\text{-D-glucose}}}$	Ratio of the rates for the α- and β-isomers k_β/k_α
α-D-Glucose	32	1	39.2
β-D-Glucose	1255	39	
α-D-Mannose	51	1.6	15.3
β-D-Mannose	781	24	
α-D-Galactose	42	1.3	37.9
β-D-Galactose	1590	50	
α-D-Talose	78	2.4	10.8
β-D-Talose (from equilibrium solution)	844	26	
α-D-Gulose·$CaCl_2$·H_2O	71	2.2	5.9
β-D-Gulose (from equilibrium solution)	418	13	
β-L-Arabinose	95	3.0	17.5[a]
α-L-Arabinose·$CaCl_2$·$4H_2O$	1658	52	
α-D-Xylose	90	2.8	18.6
β-D-Xylose (from equilibrium solution)	1673	52	
α-D-Lyxose	156	4.9	2.9
β-D-Lyxose	449	14	
D-Ribose (crystalline)	196	6.1	5.2
D-Ribose (from equilibrium solution)	1010	32	
L-Ribose (crystalline)	195	6.1	7.5
L-Ribose (from equilibrium solution)	1456	45.5	
α-L-Rhamnose, hydrate	90	2.8	8.6
β-L-Rhamnose (from equilibrium solution)	770	24	
α-Lactose, hydrate	29	0.9	32.8
β-Lactose	952	30	
α-Maltose (from equilibrium solution)	24	0.8	64.0
β-Maltose, hydrate	1528	48	

[a] k_α/k_β . For the nomenclature difficulties for arabinose, see p. 43.

One form of mannose (mannose·$CaCl_2$·$4H_2O$, Fig. 3) exhibits an oxidation curve intermediate between those for the α- and β-forms, and considerable mannonic γ-lactone is present in the solution. Consequently, it would appear that this modification is a mannofuranose.

The action of chlorine is much slower than that of bromine. Xylose has been converted to 30% of ammonium xylonate by the action of chlorine in the presence of ammonia (*192*). Methyl β-D-glucoside is converted first to gluconic acid, in 50% yields, by the action of chlorine water at room temperature for 14 days. Further oxidation for 25 days gives 5-ketogluconic acid; the products were identified by paper chromatography (*3*). The glucoside is apparently oxidized directly to gluconic acid, perhaps with an intermediate 1-*C*-chloro methyl glucoside being formed, but the possibility of glucose being formed as a hydrolytic product before oxidation is ruled out. Glucaric acid is a minor product. Galactosides give galactonic and galactaric acid, but not the 5-keto acid. Mannosides give only mannonic acid, and xylosides the xylonic acid and a small amount of the keto acid. All the β-glycosides (with the exception of the xylosides) react more rapidly than do the α-glycosides, in agreement with the oxidation of aldoses by bromine (*190*). Methyl β-cellobioside gives gluconic, 5-ketogluconic, glucaric, and cellobionic acids.

Oxidation with Hypohalites in Alkaline Solutions. In alkaline solution the halogens exist as hypohalous acid and hypohalite ions. The oxidation is likely to be more drastic than for the free halogens. Thus, whereas free iodine will not act as an oxidant, hypoiodite is a powerful oxidizing agent. Hypobromite and hypochlorite particularly are likely to produce oxidation of primary and secondary alcoholic groups and cause cleavage of carbon–carbon bonds. As noted above, the processes are complicated by the tendency of hypohalite to be converted to halate ions.

The oxidation of β-glucose by hypoiodous acid at pH 9.8 is initially at least 25 times as fast as that of the α-isomer (*193*). As the oxidation progresses, the simultaneous mutarotation tends to equalize the two rates. This difference in rates has been observed in the pH range of 7.6 to 11.8.

Alkaline hypoiodite has been proposed as a reagent for the quantitative determination of aldehyde groups (*194*). With careful control of conditions, aldoses are converted practically quantitatively to aldonic acids (Chapter XI). Measurement of the iodine consumed gives the amount of aldose originally present:

$$RCHO + I_2 + 3\ NaOH \rightarrow RCOONa + 2\ NaI + 2\ H_2O$$

In the reaction, the rate of iodate formation should be slower than the oxidation of the aldose. The reaction is slowed down by the presence of buffers such as borax (*195*).

Hypoiodites are used for preparatory as well as analytical purposes.

192. H. C. Fang, *Iowa State Coll. J. Sci.* **6,** 423 (1932).

193. K. D. Reeve, *J. Chem. Soc.* p. 172 (1951).

194. G. Romijn, *Z. anal. Chem.* **36,** 349 (1897); see also discussion in Chapters III and XII.

195. See K. Myrbäck and E. Gyllensvard, *Svensk Kem. Tidskr.* **54,** 17 (1942).

Goebel used barium hypobromite for the preparation of calcium gluconate and maltobionate (*196*). In methanol solution, high yields of the aldonic acids are obtained (*197*).

Ketoses are essentially inert to the action of hypoiodites under the conditions used for the determination of aldoses, although for accurate work small corrections may be necessary. With excessive amounts of alkali and slightly elevated temperatures, oxalic acid is produced (*198*).

More drastic oxidation of aldoses with hypoiodite leads to keto acids and finally to cleavage of carbon–carbon bonds. Hönig and Tempus (*199*) claimed to have oxidized glucose stepwise to gluconic acid, 2-ketogluconic acid, and D-arabonic acid. However, other workers claim that the main product is 5-ketogluconic acid (*200*).

Glycosides are converted by hypoiodite or hypobromite to uronides in rather low yields (*201*). Jackson and Hudson (*202*) obtained a yield of 12%

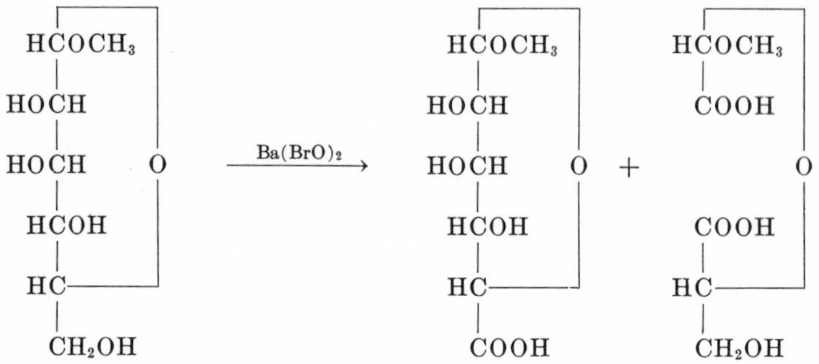
HCOCH₃
HOCH
HOCH
O
HCOH
HC
CH₂OH
Ba(BrO)₂
HCOCH₃
HOCH
HOCH
O
HCOH
HC
COOH
+
HCOCH₃
COOH
O
COOH
HC
CH₂OH

of the brucine salt of methyl α-mannosiduronic acid but showed that cleavage of carbon–carbon bonds also occurs.

Polyols are oxidized by alkaline solutions of halogens. Fischer and Tafel (*203*) obtained 20% yields of glycerosazone by the action of bromine and sodium carbonate on glycerol and subsequent treatment with phenylhydrazine. Galactitol gave an osazone which appeared to be galactosazone. Presumably, the oxidation takes place mainly at the primary alcoholic group.

196. W. F. Goebel, *J. Biol. Chem.* **72,** 809 (1927).

197. S. Moore and K. P. Link, *J. Biol. Chem.* **133,** 293 (1940).

198. K. Bailey and R. H. Hopkins, *Biochem. J.* **27,** 1965 (1933).

199. M. Hönig and F. Tempus, *Ber.* **57,** 787 (1924).

200. T. Reichstein and O. Neracher, *Helv. Chim. Acta* **18,** 892 (1935); W. Ruzicka *Z. Zuckerind. Böhmen-Mähren* **64,** 219 (1941).

201. M. Bergmann and W. W. Wolff, *Ber.* **56,** 1060 (1923); K. Smolenski, *Roczniki Chem.* **3,** 153 (1924).

202. E. L. Jackson and C. S. Hudson, *J. Am. Chem. Soc.* **59,** 994 (1937).

203. E. Fischer and J. Tafel, *Ber.* **20,** 3384 (1887); **22,** 106 (1889).

Amides with free hydroxyl groups at carbon 2 are degraded to sugars with one less carbon atom by treatment with hypochlorites. This is the basis of the Weerman method of degrading sugars, discussed elsewhere (Chapter II).

b. Halic Acids (HXO_3)

Chloric acid in conjunction with catalysts, particularly vanadium pentoxide (*204*), has as its principal use the oxidation of aldonic acids or lactones to the 2-keto acids, intermediates in the preparation of ascorbic acid and analogs, as discussed in a preceding section.

D-Gluconic γ-lactone and potassium D-galactonate in methanol solution in the presence of phosphoric acid and V_2O_5 are oxidized by chloric acid to methyl 2-keto-D-gluconate and methyl 2-keto-D-galactonate, respectively (*205*).

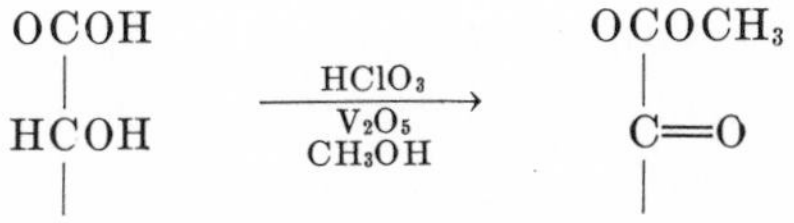

Iodic acid in strong sulfuric acid at 100°C. is reported to show a rather remarkable specificity; ketoses, sucrose, and pentoses are oxidized, but aldohexoses and lactose are not attacked (*206*). At still higher temperatures, hexoses are oxidized quantitatively to carbon dioxide and water (*207*).

Under mild conditions of temperature and in the absence of a catalyst, aldoses, ketoses, and sucrose are inert to the action of chloric acid over several weeks time (*208*). Bromates in alkaline solution also exert no oxidative action (*209*).

c. Chlorous Acid ($HClO_2$)

Chlorous acid is of particular interest because of its use for the removal of lignin and other noncarbohydrates from woody tissue without appreciable action on the carbohydrates. (See Chapter XII, under Holocellulose.) It also is reported to be an effective bleaching agent.

Jeanes and Isbell (*208*) found that under mild conditions aldoses are oxidized to the aldonic acids but that nonreducing carbohydrates and ke-

204. R. Pasternack and P. P. Regna, *U. S. Patent* 2,203,923 (June 11, 1940); *U. S. Patent* 2,207,991 (July 16, 1940); *U. S. Patent* 2,188,777 (Jan. 30, 1940).

205. P. P. Regna and B. P. Caldwell, *J. Am. Chem. Soc.* **66,** 243 (1944); H. S. Isbell, *J. Research Natl. Bur. Standards* **33,** 45 (1944).

206. R. J. Williams and M. Woods, *J. Am. Chem. Soc.* **59,** 1408 (1937).

207. W. Hurka, *Mikrochemie ver. Mikrochim. Acta* **30,** 259 (1942).

208. A. Jeanes and H. S. Isbell, *J. Research Natl. Bur. Standards* **27,** 125 (1941).

209. P. Van Fossen and E. Pacsu, *Textile Research J.* **16,** 163 (1946).

toses are only slowly attacked. The rapidity of oxidation is in the order: pentoses > hexoses > disaccharides; α-hexoses > β-hexoses. The yields of aldonic acids, however, are less than for bromine oxidations (*210*). The equation for the oxidation in acidic solution was expressed as:

$$RCHO + 3\ HClO_2 \rightarrow RCOOH + HCl + 2\ ClO_2 + H_2O$$

The quantitative stoichiometry of the glucose – chlorous acid reaction has been studied in detail (*211*); the reagent used was sodium chlorite in a phosphoric acid – phosphate buffer at pH 2.4–3.4. The molar ratio of oxidant consumed to glucose consumed was 3:1, without overoxidation over extended time periods. The decomposition of the reagent throughout the oxidation was determined; the rate was proportional to the geometric mean of the chlorite concentration. The method is recommended for the determination of aldehyde groups in carbohydrates, especially alkali-sensitive ones.

Glucose in a mixture with fructose can be determined quantitatively by oxidation with sodium chlorite at pH 4.0; the chlorine dioxide evolved in the reaction is measured (*211a*).

B. Reagents Cleaving Glycols

A number of reagents exhibit relatively sharp specificity for the cleavage of bonds between adjacent carbon atoms carrying hydroxyl groups. The most important of these are periodic acid and lead tetraacetate. The requisite properties of an oxidant of this type have been defined (*212*) as follows:

1. "The central atom of the oxidant must have a diameter, about 2.5 to 3.0×10^{-8} cm., which is large enough to bridge the space between hydroxyl groups in a 1,2-glycol.

2. "The central atom of the oxidant must be able to coordinate at least two hydroxyl groups in addition to groups already attached to it.

3. "The valence of the central atom must exceed by two units, rather than by one or three, the valence of the next lowest stable state.

4. "The oxidant must have an E_0 oxidation potential in the neighborhood of about -1.7 volts with respect to the next lowest stable valence state."

In general such oxidants are pictured (*213*) as operating by the formation

210. See comments by J. W. Green, reference 167, p. 180.

211. H. F. Launer and Y. Tomimatsu, *Anal. Chem.* **26,** 383 (1954); *J. Am. Chem. Soc.* **76,** 2591 (1954).

211a. F. Stitt, S. Friedlander, H. J. Lewis, and F. E. Young, *Anal. Chem.* **26,** 1478 (1954).

212. L. J. Heidt, E. K. Gladding, and C. B. Purves, *Paper Trade J.* **121,** 81 (1945).

213. R. Criegee, L. Kraft, and B. Rank, *Ann.* **507,** 159 (1933).

of an ester with the glycol, the ester being decomposed with the oxidant liberated in its lower state of valence, and the remaining free radical rearranging to the dialdehyde. (See below under Periodic acid.)

For periodate and lead tetraacetate, the intermediate complexes are too unstable to enable isolation, but with similar materials crystalline esters have been obtained (thallic esters of fatty acids and potassium osmate).

An alternative mechanism for this type of oxidation is based on a free radical mechanism (*214*). Lead tetraacetate, for example, decomposes in hot solution according to the following equation:

$$Pb(OCOCH_3)_4 \rightarrow Pb(OCOCH_3)_2 + 2\cdot OCOCH_3$$

The neutral acetate radicals may dehydrogenate 1,2-glycols as follows:

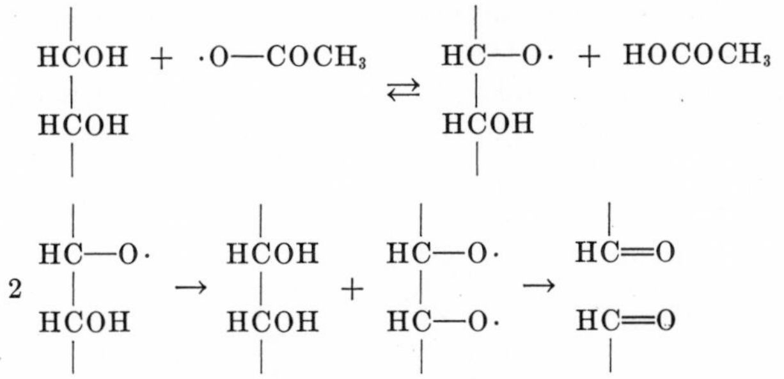

Periodic acid and lead tetraacetate are the most important agents of this type, but sodium perbismuthate ($NaBiO_3$) and hydrated trivalent silver ion (Ag^{+++}) also possess the necessary properties and oxidize glycols in a similar manner (*212*).

Periodic acid has its principal value for analytical and structural determinations. Lead tetraacetate is used for structural determinations (Chapter IV) and preparatory purposes (Chapter II). For the latter purpose, sodium perbismuthate shows considerable promise because the original material and its reduction products are difficultly soluble in water and may be easily separated from reaction products of the glycol.

Cis 1,2-glycols are oxidized more rapidly than *trans* glycols by both lead tetraacetate and periodic acid, but the former reagent manifests such a marked difference in rate for *cis* and *trans* groups that it has been used for their estimation (pp. 217 and 396). Lead tetraacetate, because of its ease of hydrolysis, is usually employed in organic solvents, whereas aqueous solutions of periodic acid usually are used. Toward oxalic acid and α-hydroxy acids, the two reagents exhibit a marked difference. Oxalic acid is not attacked by periodic acid, and glycolic acid is attacked only slowly at room

214. W. A. Waters, *Trans. Faraday Soc.* **42,** 184 (1946).

temperature ($214a$). In contrast, lead tetraacetate attacks oxalic acids and α-hydroxy acids readily (215).

Periodic acid is an extremely valuable reagent. When hydroxyl groups, or an amino and a hydroxyl group, are located on neighboring carbon atoms, cleavage of the intermediate carbon–carbon bond occurs upon treatment with periodic acid:

$$R'CHOH—CHOH—R + HIO_4 \rightarrow R'CHO + RCHO + HIO_3 + H_2O$$

$$R'CHNH_2—CHOH—R + HIO_4 \rightarrow R'CHO + RCHO + HIO_3 + NH_3$$

In many cases, the reactions are practically quantitative.

The use of periodic acid as a reagent for glycols was first applied by Malaprade. In the glycol series, Fleury and associates (216) showed that it is specific for 1,2-diols. The general application of the reagent has been reviewed by Jackson and by Dyer (217).

The oxidation appears to take place through the intermediate formation of an unstable ester. Criegee (213) postulated the reaction as:

$$H^+ + IO_4^- + \begin{array}{c} | \\ HCOH \\ | \\ HCOH \\ | \end{array} \rightarrow \begin{array}{c} | \\ —CO \\ \diagdown \\ \diagup \\ —CO \\ | \end{array} IO_4^{-3} \rightarrow$$

$$(IO_3^-) + \left[\begin{array}{c} | \\ HCO— \\ | \\ HCO— \\ | \end{array} \right] \rightarrow \begin{array}{c} | \\ HCO \\ \\ HCO \\ | \end{array} \quad \text{(dialdehyde)}$$

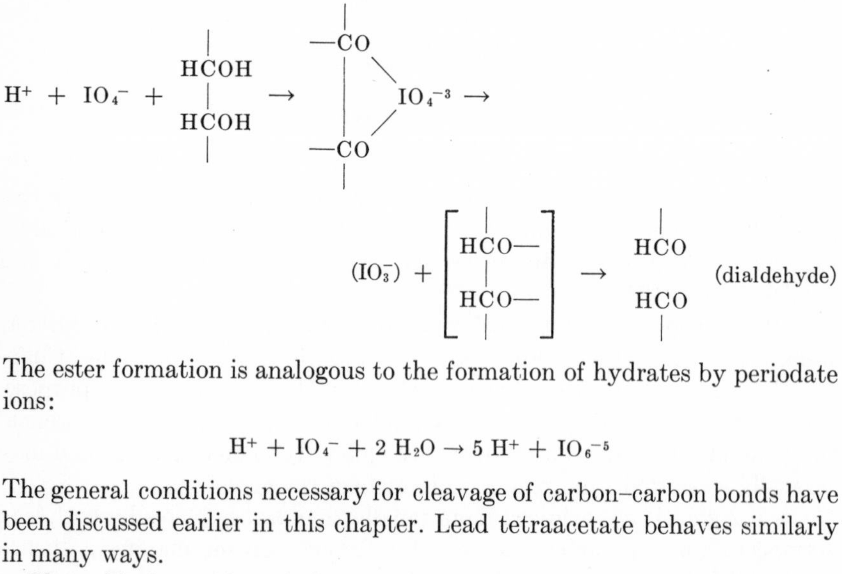

The ester formation is analogous to the formation of hydrates by periodate ions:

$$H^+ + IO_4^- + 2 H_2O \rightarrow 5 H^+ + IO_6^{-5}$$

The general conditions necessary for cleavage of carbon–carbon bonds have been discussed earlier in this chapter. Lead tetraacetate behaves similarly in many ways.

The oxidation with periodate is second-order with respect to polyol and

$214a$. C. F. Huebner, S. R. Ames, and E. C. Bubl, *J. Am. Chem. Soc.* **68**, 1621 (1946).

215. R. Criegee, *Sitzber. Ges. Beförder. ges. Naturw. Marburg* **69**, 25 (1934); *Chem. Abstr.* **29**, 6820 (1935).

216. P. Fleury and J. Lange, *Compt. rend.* **195**, 1395 (1932).

217. E. L. Jackson, *in* "Organic Reactions," Vol. 2, p. 341. Wiley, New York, 1944; J. R. Dyer, *in* "Methods of Biochemical Analysis," (D. Glick, ed.), Vol. 3. Interscience, New York, 1956; J. M. Bobbitt, *Advances in Carbohydrate Chem.* **11**, 1 (1956).

periodate (*218*). It proceeds more rapidly in acid solution than in alkaline solution. *Cis* pairs of hydroxyls react more rapidly than *trans* groups. The effective oxidation potential in acid solution is about −0.8 volts (*212*).

When more than two vicinal hydroxyl groups are available, the oxidation continues through this portion of the molecule with the formation of formic acid from secondary alcoholic groups and formaldehyde from primary alcoholic groups:

$$CH_2OH—(CHOH)_n—CH_2OH \xrightarrow{HIO_4} n\ HCOOH + 2\ HCHO$$

Compounds containing carbonyl and hydroxyl groups are oxidized.

$$RCO—CH_2OH \rightarrow RCOOH + HCHO$$

$$RCO—CHO \rightarrow RCOOH + HCOOH$$

$$RCH(OH)—COOH \rightarrow CO_2 + RCHO \text{ (slow)}$$

Aldonic and saccharic acids yield glyoxylic acid (*216*, *219*).

$$CH_2OH—(CHOH)_4—COOH + 4\ HIO_4 \rightarrow$$
$$CHO—COOH + HCHO + 3\ HCOOH + H_2O + 4\ HIO_3$$

$$COOH—(CHOH)_4—COOH + 3\ HIO_4 \rightarrow$$
$$2\ CHO—COOH + 2\ HCOOH + H_2O + 3\ HIO_3$$

Glucose consumes five atoms of oxygen producing one mole of formaldehyde and five moles of formic acid. Inositol (a hexahydroxycyclohexane) is oxidized to formic acid and glycolic acid, 4 moles of oxidant being consumed rapidly and 6.7 moles at the end of several days (Chapter V).

In a carbon chain, the reaction stops when a carbon atom is reached which does not carry an unsubstituted hydroxyl, a carbonyl, or an amino group. Glycosides, for example, give dialdehydes:

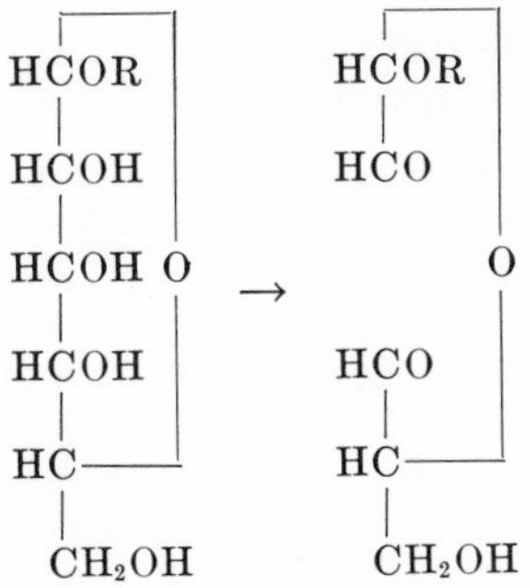

218. C. C. Price and H. Kroll, *J. Am. Chem. Soc.* **60,** 2726 (1938); C. C. Price and M. Knell, *ibid.* **64,** 552 (1942).

219. P. Fleury and J. Lange, *J. pharm. chim.* (8) **17,** 313 (1933); P. Fleury, G Poirot, and J. Fievet, *Compt. rend.* **220,** 664 (1945).

The amount of oxidant consumed as well as the nature of the reaction products provide proof for the structure of the glycoside. (For further discussion, see under Structure of glycosides, Chapter IV.) Periodic acid oxidation also provides information of great value for the determination of the structures of glycosans, ether derivatives, oligo- and polysaccharides (Chapters VII, IX, and XII). It is also an important method of correlating the configuration of the anomeric carbon atoms, particularly in glycosides (p. 36 and p. 218).

In several instances, 1,2-glycols have been found to be resistant to the action of periodic acid (*220*). These include 1,6-anhydroglucofuranose, tetra-*O*-acetylinositol, and 1,6-anhydro-α-D-galactofuranose. The 2,3,6-tri-*O*-methylglucose and 3,4-di-*O*-methylglucose resist attack by periodate at carbon 5 and the adjacent free OH group. Hence, lack of oxidation by periodic acid cannot be taken as conclusive evidence of the absence of 1,2-glycol groups.

The formaldehyde formed in a periodate reaction is determined gravimetrically with Dimedon, or colorimetrically with chromotropic acid, after the excess oxidant is destroyed with ethylene glycol, stannous chloride, sodium arsenite, or sodium bisulfite (*221*). The formic acid is generally titrated directly. Titration to pH 6.0 will measure all the formic acid present. Titration to higher alkalinities will usually measure any formic acid bound as an ester (*222*) but also other acidic products; the end-point may be indefinite. Sucrose will give 80 to 90% of the theoretical formic acid, and maltose and lactose similarly low values. Both formaldehyde and formic acid are attacked only extremely slowly by periodate, but light apparently accelerates an oxidation to carbon dioxide and water (*223*).

The possibility of a formyl ester being formed during periodate oxidation has been considered by many workers (*224*). Thus, 2- and 3-mono-*O*-methyl-L-rhamnose and 2,3- and 3,4-di-*O*-methyl-L-rhamnose are incompletely oxidized by sodium periodate. The 3,4-di-*O*-methyl-L-rhamnose consumed only 70% of the expected amount of oxidant and gave only 10%

220. R. J. Dimler, H. A. Davis, and G. E. Hilbert, *J. Am. Chem. Soc.* **68,** 1377 (1948); G. Dangschat and H. O. L. Fischer, *Naturwissenschaften* **30,** 146 (1942); B. H. Alexander, R. J. Dimler, and C. L. Mehltretter, *J. Am. Chem. Soc.* **73,** 4658 (1951); G. D. Greville and D. H. Northcote, *J. Chem. Soc.* p. 1945 (1952).

221. A. C. Corcoran and I. H. Page, *J. Biol. Chem.* **170,** 165 (1947); M. Lambert and A. C. Neish, *Can. J. Research* **B28,** 83 (1950); W. E. Mitchell and E. E. Percival, *J. Chem. Soc.* p. 1423 (1954); R. E. Reeves, *J. Am. Chem. Soc.* **63,** 1476 (1941).

222. M. Morrison, A. C. Kuyper, and J. M. Orten, *J. Am. Chem. Soc.* **75,** 1502 (1953).

223. F. S. H. Head and G. Hughes, *J. Chem. Soc.* p. 2046 (1952); p. 603 (1954).

224. F. Brown, L. Hough, and J. K. N. Jones, *J. Chem. Soc.* p. 1125 (1950); G. R. Barker and D. C. C. Smith, *Chemistry & Industry* p. 1035 (1952); F. S. Head and G. Hughes, *J. Chem. Soc.* p. 603 (1954).

of the theoretical amount of formic acid. The remainder of the acid was considered to be bound as a formyl ester. Such an ester has been isolated after the oxidation of 3-*O*-mesyl-D-glucose, the product being a crystalline 2-*O*-mesyl-4-formyl-D-arabinose; the presence of the formate group was confirmed by elementary analysis and by infrared absorption analysis. The oxidation course for cellobiose consists of a fast reaction to an intermediate compound, presumably a formic ester, and a slow reaction whose rate is determined by the rate of hydrolysis of the ester. Carbon dioxide was also produced in this last oxidation.

Anomalies have also been shown in the oxidation behavior of lead tetraacetate (*225*). Oxidant is consumed in the case of derivatives of D-arabinose thioacetal; this consumption is affected by the position of the glycol groups in the various compounds relevant to the thioacetal group.

The steric requirements for tetraacetate oxidations are higher than for periodate oxidations. As the common C-1 ring conformation (Chapter I) of glycosides does not allow for true *cis* relationships, many of the glycosides are not oxidized by lead tetraacetate (*225a*).

Periodate and lead tetraacetate can also act as oxidizing agents toward other easily oxidizable groups. Cleavage may occur in deoxysugars after oxidation of methylene groups which are suitably activated by the production of adjacent carbonyl groups during the initial stages of the reaction. Thus, although ribose consumes four moles, 2-deoxyribose consumes five moles of periodate (*225b*). Oxidation and further cleavage also occur sometimes at the position of ring closure (*225c*). The bornyl β-D-glucosiduronic acid and the methyl α-D-galactosiduronic acid methyl ester consume five moles of periodate each. Ethyl β-D-galactofuranoside consumes one mole more than the expected amount of lead tetraacetate.

Huebner, Ames, and Bubl (*214a*) examined the reaction of periodate with many compounds containing active methylene and potentially active methylene groups. They concluded that oxidation occurs at a hydrogen when the following set of requirements is fulfilled: There is present a three-carbon system consisting of a free carboxyl or aldehyde group, an α-carbon bearing one hydrogen, and a β-carbonyl which may be aldehydo, keto, carboxyl, or carbalkoxy. Certain other groups, for example, the benzimidazole nucleus, may also cause activation (*225c*). Cyclic β-diketones may also be oxidized (Chapter IV).

The variation in behavior of disaccharides has been used as a structural

225. S. B. Baker, *J. Am. Chem. Soc.* **64,** 827 (1952); A. S. Perlin, Abstracts American Chemical Society Meeting, New York (Sept. 12–17, 1954).

225a. R. E. Reeves, *J. Am. Chem. Soc.* **72,** 1499 (1950).

225b. L. A. Manson and J. O. Lampen, *J. Biol. Chem.* **191,** 87 (1951).

225c. See C. F. Huebner, R. Lohmar, R. J. Dimler, S. Moore, and K. P. Link, *J. Biol. Chem.* **159,** 503 (1945).

guide. Thus, 1,6-linked disaccharides consume the most oxidant and give the highest yield of formic acid, whereas 1,4-disaccharides give the least amount of formic acid, and a tetrose is obtained from the hydrolyzed oxidation product. The oxidized 1,3-disaccharide can be hydrolyzed to a pentose (1 mole). Similar behavior is shown by the 2-, 4-, and 6-*O*-methyl-D-galactoses, the first alone giving formaldehyde.

As a preparatory method, oxidation with periodic acid is of particular importance for the preparation of short-chain sugars. For example, 2,3-*O*-benzylidene-D-arabitol (I) consumes one mole of periodic acid and yields 2,3-*O*-benzylidine-D-threose (II) which can be converted to a crystalline isopropylidene derivative (*226*). The oxidation of aldoses by one mole of lead tetraacetate in acetic acid will cause degradation to aldoses containing one less carbon; thus, D-arabinose and D-lyxose have been prepared in yields of more than 35% from D-glucose and D-galactose, respectively (*227*). The

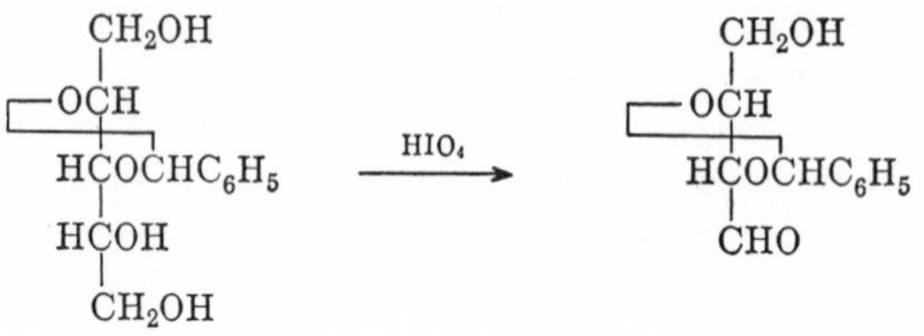

CH_2OH
OCH
$HCOCHC_6H_5$
HCOH
CH_2OH
HIO_4
CH_2OH
OCH
$HCOCHC_6H_5$
CHO

(I) (II)

reaction seems to be controlled by the formation of a stable formyl ester at carbon 5. Use of two moles of oxidant leads to the formation of D-erythrose and L-glyceraldehyde from D-glucose and L-arabinose, respectively.

Limited periodate oxidation of 3-*O*-methyl hexoses has led to the formation of 2-*O*-methyl pentoses, thus allowing the preparation of valuable reference compounds (*227a*). The success of this reaction has been attributed to the stability of the intermediate formyl ester formed by cleavage of the glycol grouping at C-1 and C-2.

Greater utilization of periodate as an oxidant has been suggested in the development of an electrolytic method (*228*); starch is oxidized in 2% sulfuric acid containing iodic acid. This method is similar in concept to the electrolytic bromine method of Isbell and Frush (*179*).

226. W. T. Haskins, R. M. Hann, and C. S. Hudson, *J. Am. Chem. Soc.* **65,** 1663 (1943).

227. A. S. Perlin, *J. Am. Chem. Soc.* **76,** 2595 (1954); A. S. Perlin and C. Brice, *Can. J. Chem.* **33,** 1216 (1955).

227a. G. W. Huffman, B. A. Lewis, F. Smith, and D. R. Spriestersbach, *J. Am. Chem. Soc.* **77,** 4346 (1955).

228. W. Dvonch and C. L. Mehltretter, *J. Am. Chem. Soc.* **74,** 5522 (1952).

C. Nitric Acid and Nitrogen Oxides

Oxidations with nitric acid under the best conditions convert primary alcoholic and aldehydic groups to carboxylic groups. Frequently, however, cleavage of carbon–carbon bonds occurs. For galactose the conversion to insoluble mucic acid, COOH—$(CHOH)_4$—COOH, takes place to an extent greater than 70 %, and the reaction is used for the quantitative determination of this sugar (*229*, *230*). This oxidation has been halted before completion and a 10 % yield of the L-galacturonic acid obtained (*231*). Smaller

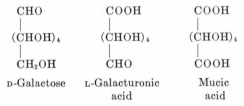

CHO	COOH	COOH
|	|	|
$(CHOH)_4$	$(CHOH)_4$	$(CHOH)_4$
|	|	|
CH_2OH	CHO	COOH
D-Galactose	L-Galacturonic acid	Mucic acid

yields of glucaric acid are obtained from glucose, and considerable quantities of oxalic acid and some tartaric acid are obtained (*232*). Among the products of the oxidation of fructose are formic acid, oxalic acid, *meso*-tartaric acid, and glycolic acid, but the reaction seems to require more severe conditions than for glucose, and with dilute acid (32 %) and low temperatures the ketoses are not attacked.

Oxidation of methylated sugars with nitric acid has been used extensively for the purpose of demonstrating the position of unsubstituted hydroxyl groups. (See under Structure of glycosides and sugars such as maltose, sucrose, etc.)

Cleavage of carbon–carbon bonds appears to be facilitated by the presence of catalysts such as vanadium salts, and tartaric and oxalic acids are formed in good yields at the expense of saccharic acids (*233*). Since hot nitric acid acts as a hydrolyzing agent as well as an oxidizing agent, oligo- and polysaccharides may be used.

Kiliani (*234*) has made an extensive study of the nitric acid oxidations of

229. See C. A. Browne and F. W. Zerban, "Sugar Analysis," pp. 691, 728. Wiley, New York, 1941; A. W. van der Haar, "Monosaccharide and Aldehydsäuren," Borntraeger, Berlin, 1920.

230. W. W. Pigman, B. L. Browning, W. H. McPherson, C. R. Calkins, and R. L. Leaf, Jr., *J. Am. Chem. Soc.* **71,** 2200 (1949).

231. W. E. Militzer and R. Angier, *Arch. Biochem.* **10,** 291 (1946).

232. H. Kiliani, *Ann.* **205,** 163, 172 (1880); *Ber.* **54,** 463 (1921); W. E. Stokes and W. E. Barch, *U. S. Patent* 2,257,284 (Sept. 30, 1941).

233. J. K. Dale and W. F. Rice, Jr., *J. Am. Chem. Soc.* **55,** 4984 (1933); S. Soltzberg, *U. S. Patent* 2,380,196 (July 10, 1945); A. F. Odell, *U. S. Patent* 1,425,605 (Aug. 15, 1922).

234. H. Kiliani, *Ber.* **54,** 456 (1921); **55,** 75, 2817 (1922); **56,** 2016 (1923); **58,** 2344 (1925).

carbohydrates. He found that aldoses are oxidized to aldonic and saccharic acids or their lactones. Glucose, for example, gives gluconic acid and glucaric acid. Polyols can be oxidized to aldonic acids; glycerol gives glyceric acid. Aldonic acids are oxidized to 2-keto acids, saccharic acids, and uronic acids (*235*). The formation of these products indicates that the oxidation of aldoses without cleavage of carbon–carbon bonds probably proceeds through the following series of reactions:

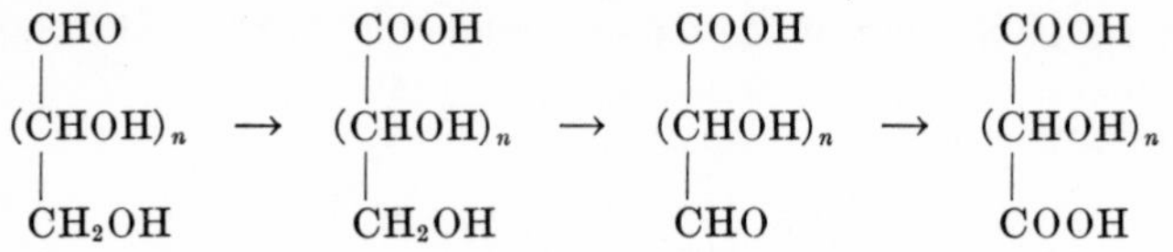
CHO
(CHOH)n
CH2OH
COOH
(CHOH)n
CH2OH
COOH
(CHOH)n
CHO
COOH
(CHOH)n
COOH

Alternatively, the reaction may proceed via the ring forms of the sugars and the lactones, but this refinement of the mechanism has not been clarified. Under the strongly acidic conditions of these oxidations, equilibria between the various ring and open-chain forms should be established quickly. In this connection, it should be noted that whereas galactose gives mucic acid (the open-chain form), mannonic acid gives a dilactone.

The formation of 2-keto or 5-keto aldonic acids indicates that cleavage of carbon–carbon bonds may result from further oxidation of such intermediates. Vanadium salts appear to promote this reaction.

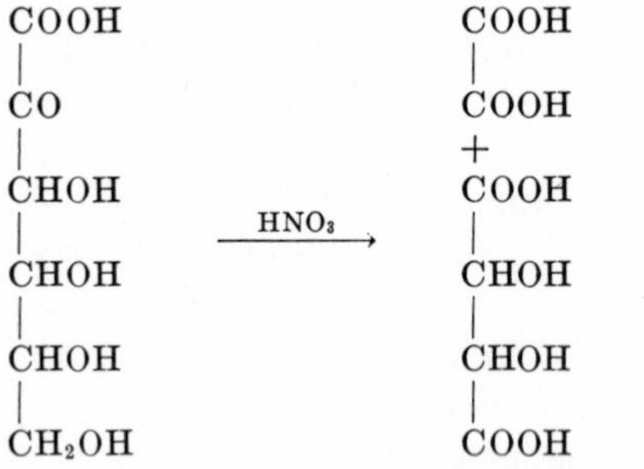
COOH
CO
CHOH
CHOH
CHOH
CH2OH
HNO3
COOH
COOH
+
COOH
CHOH
CHOH
COOH

2-Keto aldonic acid — Oxalic acid and Tartaric acid

The specificity of the oxidation may be increased by the use of nitrogen dioxide (NO_2) rather than nitric acid (*236*). With this reagent in gaseous form or in nonaqueous solution, a marked specificity for the oxidation of primary alcoholic groups (in the absence of aldehyde groups) has been

235. H. Kiliani, *Ber*. **54,** 456 (1921); **55,** 75 (1922); W. Militzer and R. Angier, *Arch. Biochem*. **10,** 291 (1946).

236. K. Maurer and G. Drefahl, *Ber*. **75,** 1489 (1942); K. Maurer and G. Reiff, *J. makromol. Chem*. **1,** 27 (1943); E. C. Yackel and W. O. Kenyon, *J. Am. Chem. Soc*. **64,** 121 (1942); C. C. Unruh and W. O. Kenyon, *ibid*. **64,** 127 (1942).

shown. Glycosides are oxidized to uronic acids, cellulose to a polyglucuronic acid, and diethyl acetal to glyoxylic acid.

$$\begin{array}{c} R \\ | \\ CH_2OH \end{array} \xrightarrow{NO_2} \begin{array}{c} R \\ | \\ COOH \end{array}$$

The nature of the oxidant in such systems has received some study (*230*). Concentrated nitric acid exhibits an initial period of inhibition when used as an oxidizing agent and will not exert an oxidizing action in the presence of urea which removes nitrous acid. This period may be eliminated by the addition of fuming nitric acid, oxides of nitrogen, nitrous acid, or other materials (*230, 237*). Nitrogen dioxide appears to require the presence of water for its reaction. These facts indicate that nitric acid is not the true oxidant, but instead the effective agent is nitrous acid which in the presence of NO establishes an equilibrium (*238*) with nitric acid according to the equation:

$$HNO_3 + 2\ NO + H_2O \rightleftarrows 3\ HNO_2$$

The catalytic effect of oxides of nitrogen and of sodium nitrite appears to operate by the establishment of the above equilibrium. The action of nitrogen dioxide may be similar, for in the presence of water, a similar equilibrium condition is reached:

$$2\ NO_2 + H_2O \rightleftarrows HNO_3 + HNO_2$$

By the employment of conditions favorable for the establishment of these equilibria and unfavorable for carbon–carbon bond cleavage, the specificity of the reaction is increased greatly. For example, mucic acid is produced in 90% yield (*230*), whereas with hot nitric acid the usual yield is about 75%.

Oxidation of primary alcoholic groups appears to take place through the intermediate formation of an ester of nitric (or nitrous) acid (*239*). In the initial stages of oxidation, cellulose contains combined nitrogen which increases and then slowly decreases. Nitric acid appears to act as a catalyst for the deesterification.

D. Oxygen in Alkaline or Neutral Solution

The study of the action of molecular oxygen on sugars is of considerable interest from the standpoint of the mechanism of the *in vivo* oxidations of

237. H. Kiliani, *Ber.* **54,** 456 (1921); G. D. Hiatt, *U. S. Patent* 2,256,391 (Sept. 16, 1941); J. G. M. Bremner, R. H. Stanley, D. G. Jones, and A. W. C. Taylor, *U. S. Patent* 2,389,950 (Nov. 27, 1945).

238. V. H. Veley, *Trans. Roy. Soc.* **52,** 27 (1893); *J. Chem. Soc.* (*Abstracts*) **64,** 413 (1893).

239. P. A. McGee, W. F. Fowler, Jr., E. W. Taylor, C. C. Unruh, and W. O. Kenyon, *J. Am. Chem. Soc.* **69,** 355 (1947).

sugars. The reaction also has considerable value for the degradations of sugars to acids having shorter chains (see Chapter II).

In alkaline solution, oxygen degrades the sugars to aldonic acids having one carbon atom less than the sugar. Air or oxygen may be used and relatively high yields of acids are obtained (*240*). For example, potassium D-arabonate has been obtained from D-glucose in a yield of 60 to 75%. Ketoses act similarly, and in the case of L-sorbose, 2-keto-L-gulonic acid and L-xylonic acid are produced in good yield (*241*). The formation of 2-ketogulonic acid indicates that the reaction proceeds through the osone, probably formed from the enediol:

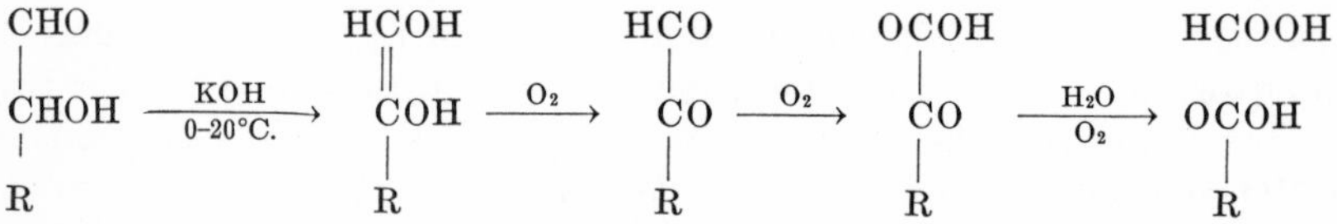
CHO
CHOH
R
KOH
0–20°C.
HCOH
COH
R
O₂
HCO
CO
R
O₂
OCOH
CO
R
H₂O
O₂
HCOOH
OCOH
R

3-(α-D-Glucopyranosyl)-D-arabonic acid is obtained from maltose, and the β-isomer from cellobiose (*242*). 3-(β-D-Galactopyranosyl)-D-arabonic acid is formed similarly from lactose. A quantitative experiment on the effect of oxygen on glucose in aqueous potassium hydroxide shows the main products to be D-arabonic acid and formic acid, with lactic, oxalic, and carbonic acids formed in minor amounts (*243*).

In neutral solution in the presence of platinum catalyst, the process is mainly one of dehydrogenation, and the oxidation of mannose is postulated (*244*) as follows:

D-Mannose → D-mannonic acid → L-mannuronic acid → mannaric acid

For fructose, the reaction seems to proceed differently:

Fructose → glucosone → 2-ketomannonic acid → D-arabinose

The platinum oxide catalyst converts the hexitols to the corresponding aldoses and ketoses which are carried through the above series of reactions by the oxygen. Mannitol is oxidized by PtO_2 to D-mannose, isolated as methyl α-mannoside in a yield of 20%. Fructose is formed simultaneously. With a platinum-activated carbon catalyst, L-sorbose has been converted to 2-keto-L-gulonic acid, 2,3-*O*-isopropylidene-L-sorbose to 2,3-*O*-isopropyl-

240. J. U. Nef, *Ann.* **403,** 204 (1914); O. Spengler and A. Pfannenstiel, *Z. Wirtschaftsgruppe Zuckerind.* **85,** 546 (1935).

241. O. Dalmers and K. Heyns, *U. S. Patent* 2,190,377 (Feb. 13, 1939); H. S. Isbell, *J. Research Natl. Bur. Standards* **29,** 227 (1942).

242. E. Hardegger, K. Kreis, and H. El Khadem, *Helv. Chim. Acta* **35,** 618 (1952).

243. B. Warshowsky and W. M. Sandstrom, *Arch. Biochem. and Biophys.* **37,** 46 (1952).

244. J. W. Glattfeld and S. Gershon, *J. Am. Chem. Soc.* **60,** 2013 (1938).

idene-2,5-anhydro-L-gularic acid, and D-glucose to 54% of D-glucaric acid (*245*). Preparations of uronic acid derivatives have been discussed earlier (*61*).

Under conditions simulating biological processes (neutrality and a temperature of 37.5°C.), oxygen attacks glucose, glyceraldehyde, glycerol, and related products (*246*). One mole of carbon dioxide is formed per mole of D-glucose. Sodium ferropyrophosphate is used as catalyst. With phosphate and arsenate as catalysts, fructose is much more sensitive than glucose, and the rate of oxidation is dependent upon the concentration of salt present and not on the pH (*247*).

In the absence of catalyst, alkaline solutions of aldonic acids and glycitols are relatively stable to oxygen. However, in the presence of salts of iron, nickel, cobalt, and copper, oxygen is consumed (*248*). Carbon dioxide and formic acid are among the oxidation products.

From the standpoint of the conditions encountered during the manufacture of sucrose, the action of oxygen on sucrose solutions in the presence and absence of lime is important. Carbon dioxide is liberated from hot neutral solutions, and acids are formed. The increase in acidity results in inversion of the sucrose and decomposition of the resulting hexoses. The presence of lime or an increase in alkalinity speeds up the decomposition (*249*).

E. Hydrogen Peroxide

The principal value of oxidations with hydrogen peroxide is for the degradation of aldonic acids to sugars with one less carbon atom; ferric sulfate is used as a catalyst (see p. 118). It is noteworthy that although ferric salts catalyze this reaction, ferrous salts are used for sugars and ferric salts are not effective.

With sugars, the products depend upon the conditions and the presence and nature of the catalyst. In any case, the products are usually mixtures. At low temperatures and in the presence of ferrous sulfate, glucose and fructose are converted to glucosone and on further oxidation to glycolic acid, glyoxylic acid, and trihydroxybutyric acid (*250*). At low temperatures in

245. K. Heyns, *Ann.* **558,** 177 (1948); N. R. Trenner, *U. S. Patent* 2,428,438 (Oct. 7, 1947); C. L. Mehltretter, C. E. Rist, and B. H. Alexander, *U. S. Patent* 2,472,168 (June 7, 1949).

246. H. A. Spoehr and H. W. Milner, *J. Am. Chem. Soc.* **56,** 2068 (1934).

247. M. Clinton, Jr., and R. Hubbard, *J. Biol. Chem.* **119,** 467 (1937).

248. See W. Traube and F. Kuhbier, *Ber.* **69,** 2664 (1936).

249. See M. Garino, M. Parodi, and V. Vignolo, *Gazz. chim. ital.* **65,** 132 (1935); *Chem. Abstr.* **29,** 5419 (1935).

250. C. F. Cross, E. J. Bevan, and C. Smith, *J. Chem. Soc.* **73,** 463 (1898); R. S. Morrell and J. M. Crofts, *ibid.* **75,** 786 (1899); **83,** 1284 (1903); H. A. Spoehr, *Am. Chem. J.* **43,** 227 (1910).

the absence of catalysts, oxidation is very slow, but at high temperatures (*251*) the main product is carbon dioxide with some formic acid.

The nature of the products formed under various conditions and the mechanism of the reaction have been investigated by Küchlin (*252*). At low temperatures and for dilute solutions in the presence of ferrous sulfate, the following products were formed from glucose and identified as derivatives: glucosone, 2-ketogluconic acid, and 2,3-diketogluconic acid; in concentrated solutions, formaldehyde also was found. The formation of these products at low temperatures was ascribed to the following series of reactions:

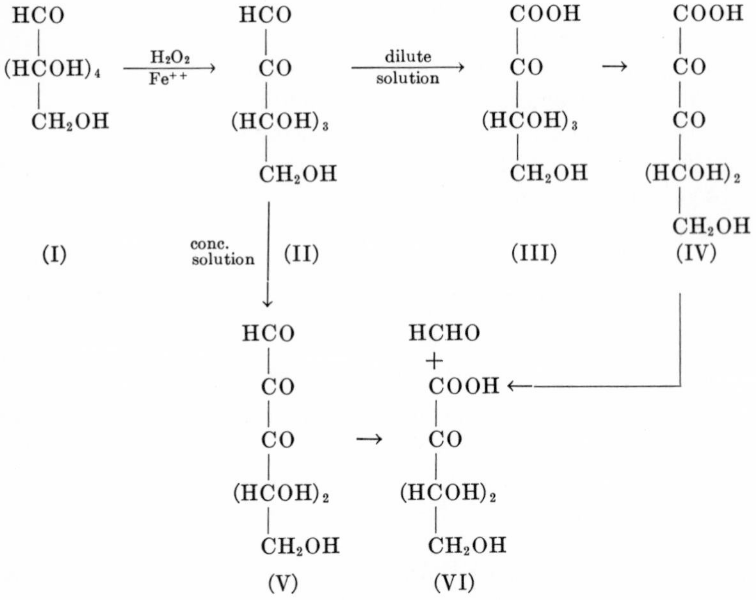
HCO
(HCOH)4
CH2OH
H2O2
Fe++
(I)
HCO
CO
(HCOH)3
CH2OH
(II)
dilute
solution
COOH
CO
(HCOH)3
CH2OH
(III)
COOH
CO
CO
(HCOH)2
CH2OH
(IV)
conc.
solution
HCO
CO
CO
(HCOH)2
CH2OH
(V)
HCHO
+
COOH
CO
(HCOH)2
CH2OH
(VI)

At higher temperatures, carbon dioxide, formic acid, oxalic acid, glycolic acid, tartronic acid, glyceric acid, and other acids were shown to be formed. The formation of carbon dioxide is ascribed to decarboxylation of the 2,3-diketo acid (IV), and oxalic acid and trihydroxybutyric acid arise from cleavage of the C_2–C_3 bond. Compound (V) cleaves to glyoxylic acid and trihydroxybutyric acid. Compound (VI) is oxidized further to 2,3-diketoarabonic acid, which on cleavage gives oxalic acid and glyceric acid.

The catalytic effect of ferrous salts is ascribed by Küchlin to the formation of a complex between ferrous ions and the carbonyl group and its

251. J. H. Payne and L. Foster, *J. Am. Chem. Soc.* **67,** 1654 (1945); A. A. Kultyugin and L. H. Sokolova, *Arch. sci. biol.* (*U.S.S.R.*) **41,** 145 (1936).

252. A. T. Küchlin, Jr., *Rec. trav. chim.* **51,** 887 (1932); and earlier papers.

neighboring hydroxyl group. This complex is oxidized, and the ferrous ion is converted to the ferric ion. Dissociation takes place, and the ferric ion is reduced to the ferrous state by further oxidation of the osones thus formed. Ferric ions will not catalyze the oxidation of sugars by hydrogen peroxide. Since ferric ions are used in the Ruff degradation of aldonic acids to sugars having one less carbon atom, ferrous ions if formed must be rapidly reoxidized by the hydrogen peroxide to ferric ions.

According to Haber and Weiss (*253*), ferrous salts bring about the decomposition of hydrogen peroxide into free radicals:

$$Fe^{++} + HO—OH \rightarrow Fe^{+++} + HO\cdot + (:O—H)^-$$

Waters (*253*) suggests that the neutral hydroxyl radicals are the catalysts in ferrous ion – catalyzed oxidations of α-hydroxy acids to 2-keto acids:

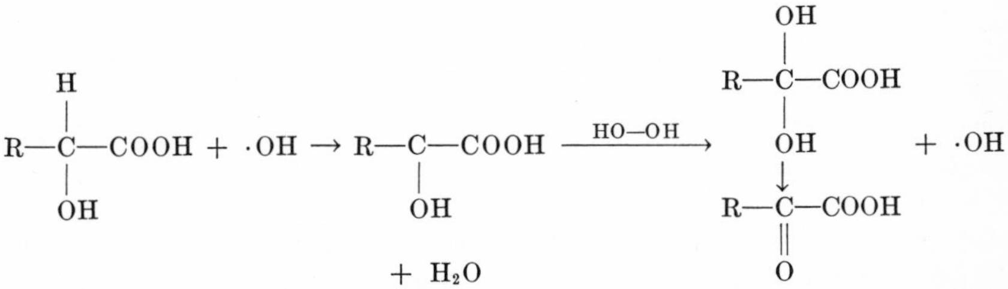

HO—OH
+ H₂O
+ ·OH

In the absence of catalysts, the oxidation may proceed by quite a different mechanism. Glucuronic acid has been prepared (*254*) in small yield by the oxidation of glucose with hydrogen peroxide without catalyst at 37°C. Küchlin (*252*) provided evidence that the main products at moderately high temperatures are formic acid and tartronic acid. He explains this type of oxidation as proceeding through the steps of uronic acid formation, oxidative splitting-out of formic acid, and repetition of the process:

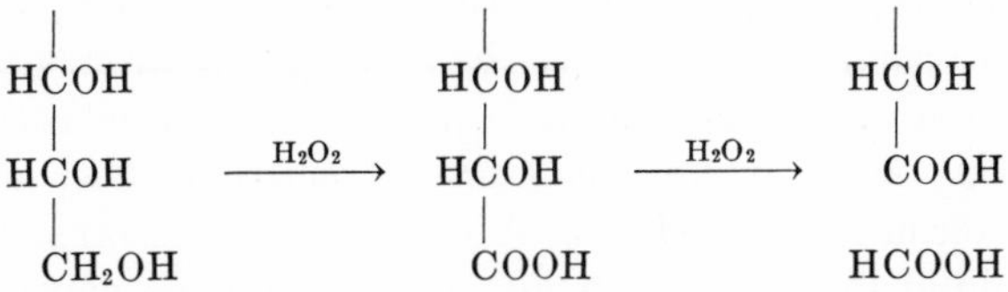

H₂O₂
H₂O₂

The formation of carbon dioxide is believed to be a secondary reaction. In the absence of catalysts, other carbohydrates probably are also oxidized initially at the primary alcoholic group.

The use of hydrogen peroxide with a platinum catalyst has been reported briefly (*60*). The action is similar to that of oxygen, and about 40% of

253. See W. A. Waters, *Ann. Repts. Progr. Chem.* (*Chem. Soc. London*) **42,** 145 (1945).

254. A. Jolles, *Biochem. Z.* **34,** 242 (1911).

crude methyl α-D-galactosiduronic acid was obtained at 20° from the corresponding galactoside.

The effect of variations in the conditions of the reaction have also been studied by Küchlin (*255*). For fructose with ferrous sulfate as a catalyst, the maximum velocity of reaction is between pH 3.2 and 5.4. The effect of an increase of temperature on the reaction is small in strongly acid solution but increases as the solution becomes more alkaline. The initial reaction velocity is proportional to the concentration of catalyst and is independent of the quantity of *ferric* salts. It is proportional to the hydrogen peroxide concentration.

Primary alcoholic groups are oxidized to aldehydes by peroxide and ferrous ions. Mannose (as the hydrazone) has been synthesized (*256*) from

$$R—CH_2OH \xrightarrow[H_2O_2]{Fe^{++}} R—CHO$$

mannitol in yields of about 40%. In the absence of ferrous ions, even with ferric ions present, no reaction occurs. Presumably, the quantity of ferrous ions present is critical, for it would be expected that with sufficient catalyst the reaction would proceed further as indicated above.

Everett and Sheppard (*184*) have studied the formation of reducing substances by the action of two molar equivalents of hydrogen peroxide on dilute solutions of gluconic δ-lactone at room temperature for a short time (30 minutes). Salts of K, Na, Li, Fe, Cu, and Ni (carbonates, sulfates, and acetates) catalyze the formation of reducing material. Of a number of anions tested, only bicarbonate, bismuthate, cyanate, and tungstate ions exhibited catalytic action. Some of the observed effect may be due to changes in the hydrogen-ion concentration.

Lactones and polyols showed increasing reducing power when treated with hydrogen peroxide in the presence of potassium bicarbonate. Sugars were not affected greatly, and uronic acids lost in reducing power. For the polyols, copper sulfate is more effective than potassium bicarbonate. For gluconic δ-lactone and copper sulfate or potassium bicarbonate as catalysts, acetate, fluoride, and arsenate ions exert a synergistic effect manifested in an increased formation of reducing substances. On the other hand, many substances inhibit the reaction; iodides and *p*-aminobenzoates are example of such inhibitors.

F. Organic Per-Acids

Various sugar mercaptals have been converted to the disulfones by the action of organic per-acids (*257*). Thus, D-glucose diethyl mercaptal pentaacetate is oxidized by perphthalic acid to D-*arabo*-3,4,5,6-tetraacetoxy-

255. A. Th. Küchlin, *Biochem. Z.* **261,** 411 (1933).
256. H. J. H. Fenton and H. Jackson, *J. Chem. Soc.* **75,** 1 (1899).
257. D. L. MacDonald and H. O. L. Fischer, *J. Am. Chem. Soc.* **74,** 2087 (1952);

1,1-bis(ethanesulfonyl)-1-hexene, and this unsaturated disulfone is split at the double bond by hydrazine to give D-arabinose. D-Lyxose is similarly prepared. The unacetylated mercaptals can be converted to the unsaturated disulfones with aqueous perpropionic acid, and the disulfones are degraded easily in aqueous ammonia to the corresponding aldose with one less carbon. Thus, D-erythrose and D-threose are obtained in high yields from the arabinose and xylose derivatives, and arabinose from the mannose mercaptal. The ring in *scyllo-myo*-inosose has been broken, by conversion to the mercaptal, and *xylo*-dialdose obtained. Fructose diethyl mercaptal in dioxane with perpropionic acid gives D-erythrose directly, instead of the disulfone.

G. Relatively Unspecific Oxidants

Most of the oxidants considered in previous sections will under some conditions produce general carbon–carbon cleavage and general oxidation of the various possible products. However, under carefully controlled conditions, it is possible to direct the reactions so that desirable products are obtained in appreciable yield. With other oxidants, the necessary conditions have not been established, except in special instances, and the products are carbon dioxide and a complex mixture of short-chain compounds. This condition is particularly true for oxidations of reducing sugars. Among such oxidants are chromates, permanganates, silver oxide, copper sulfate, and cuprammonium, usually in alkaline solution. Interestingly enough, some of these oxidants are used for precise analytical work, under empirical but highly standardized conditions. (See also discussion of analytical methods in Chapter XI.)

a. Chromic Acid and Ceric Sulfate (Acid Conditions)

Wet Combustions. Hot acid solutions of chromic acid and of ceric sulfate oxidize carbohydrate materials to carbon dioxide, formic acid, and formaldehyde. The quantity of oxidant consumed constitutes a fairly precise measure of the amount of carbohydrate present (*258*).

The equations for the oxidation of several sugars by ceric sulfate are:

$$2\ C_6H_{12}O_6\ \text{(glucose)} + 13\ O \rightarrow H_2O + CO_2 + 11\ HCOOH$$

$$2\ C_6H_{12}O_6\ \text{(fructose)} + 13\ O \rightarrow 3\ H_2O + 3\ CO_2 + 7\ HCOOH + 2\ HCHO$$

$$C_{12}H_{22}O_{11}\ \text{(sucrose)} + 13\ O \rightarrow 2\ CO_2 + 9\ HCOOH + HCHO + H_2O$$

For sucrose, an accuracy of $\pm 0.3\%$ is claimed.

Biochem. et Biophys. Acta **12,** 203 (1953); L. Hough and T. J. Taylor, *Chemistry & Industry* p. 575 (1954); D. L. MacDonald and H. O. L. Fischer, *J. Am. Chem. Soc.* **77,** 4348 (1955).

258. G. Birstein and M. Blumental, *Bull. soc. chim.* (5) **11,** 573 (1944); *Chem. Abstr.* **40,** 2437 (1946).

TABLE V

THE OXIDATION OF VARIOUS ORGANIC COMPOUNDS USING ALKALINE PERMANGANATE, PERIODIC, SULFATO CERIC, AND CHROMIC ACIDS (*260*)

Compound	Formula	Alkaline $KMnO_4$	Periodic acid	Sulfato-ceric acid	chromic acid
Acetic acid	CH_3COOH	X	X	X	X
Oxalic acid	$COOH \cdot COOH$	...	...	2	...
Formic acid	$H \cdot COOH$	2	X	X	...
Glycolic acid	$CH_2OH \cdot COOH$	6	X	3.95	...
Malonic acid	$COOH \cdot CH_2 \cdot COOH$	...	...	6.66	...
Tartaric acid	$COOH \cdot CHOH \cdot CHOH \cdot COOH$	10	2	7.20	...
Succinic acid	$COOH \cdot CH_2 \cdot CH_2 \cdot COOH$	...	...	X	...
Malic acid	$COOH \cdot CHOH \cdot CH_2 \cdot COOH$	12	X	9.25	...
Citric acid	$(CH_2COOH)_2 \cdot COH \cdot COOH$	18	X	15.85	...
Pyruvic acid	$CH_3 \cdot CO \cdot COOH$	...	...	2	...
Ethylene glycol	$CH_2OH \cdot CH_2OH$	(10)	2	...	...
Glycerol	$CH_2OH \cdot CHOH \cdot CH_2OH$	(14)	4	8	14
Erythritol	$CH_2OH \cdot (CHOH)_2 \cdot CH_2OH$	(18)	6	...	...
Arabitol	$CH_2OH \cdot (CHOH)_3 \cdot CH_2OH$	...	8	...	...
Mannitol	$CH_2OH \cdot (CHOH)_4 \cdot CH_2OH$	(26)	10	...	...
Phenol	C_6H_5OH	(28)	...	...	...
Salicylic acid	$C_6H_4 \cdot OH \cdot COOH$	(28)	...	...	...
Gallic acid	$C_6H_2(OH)_3 \cdot COOH$	24	...	...	...
Formaldehyde	$H \cdot CHO$	(4)	X	...	...
Glucose	$CH_2OH \cdot (CHOH)_4 \cdot CHO$	(24)	10	...	...
Fructose	$CH_2OH \cdot (CHOH)_3 \cdot CO \cdot CH_2OH$	(24)	8	...	...
Sucrose	$C_{12}H_{22}O_{11}$	(48)	...	...	...
Ethyl alcohol	C_2H_5OH	...	X	...	...

Chromic acid acts similarly and has been used for the volumetric determination of cellulose materials (*259*). Acid permanganate under the same conditions presumably would exhibit similar reactions.

$$C_6H_{10}O_5 + 4\ Cr_2O_7^{--} + 32\ H^+ \rightarrow 6\ CO_2 + 21\ H_2O + 8\ Cr^{+++}$$

A summary (*260*) of the effect of four oxidants on a number of organic materials is given in Table V. In the table, X indicates no reaction. The figures given are the number of equivalents of oxidant consumed. Whole numbers represent stoichiometrical reactions, and nonintegers, empirical reactions. Parentheses indicate results obtained by the improved permanganate method of Stamm (*261*). Ceric sulfate oxidations were carried out

259. See H. F. Launer, *J. Research Natl. Bur. Standards* **20,** 87 (1938); **18,** 333 (1937).

260. G. F. Smith, "Cerate Oxidimetry," G. F. Smith Chemical Co., Columbus, Ohio, 1942.

261. H. Stamm, *Angew. Chem.* **47,** 791 (1934).

by the procedure of Willard and Young (*262*) and perchlorate – ceric acid ($H_2Ce(ClO_4)_6$) by that of Smith and Duke (*263*).

Mild chromic acid oxidation of methyl β-D-glucoside has given both the 3-keto and the 6-aldehydo derivatives (*4*). The yields were very low, as the reaction was carried out for only a limited time, and 90% of the glucoside was recovered unaltered.

b. Neutral and Alkaline Permanganate

When relatively few functional groups are free, it is sometimes possible to use alkaline permanganate for the oxidation of specific groupings. 1,2:3,4-Di-*O*-isopropylidenegalactose can be oxidized (*264*) to the corresponding uronic acid. 3-*O*-Methyl-L-xylonic acid is obtained from 1,2-*O*-isopropylidene-3-*O*-methyl-D-glucofuranose by permanganate oxidation and subsequent reduction of the xyluronic acid (*265*).

Glucose can be oxidized completely to carbon dioxide and water by hot alkaline solutions of potassium permanganate (*266*). As the alkalinity increases above 0.03 *N*, oxalic acid is produced, and, in 1.8 *N* KOH, yields of 42% of oxalic acid are obtained (*267*). Similar results are obtained from other hexoses, pentoses, and glyceraldehyde (*268*). The ratio of carbon dioxide to oxalic acid differs for various sugars, but at high temperatures the differences become small. The polyols are oxidized to the same products as the sugars, and the effect of alkalinity is the same as for the corresponding sugars (*269*). Hence, it would appear that the sugars are intermediate products in the oxidation. The equivalents of oxidant required for several carbohydrates are given in Table V.

Alkaline permanganate at 0° acting on glucaric acid gives small yields of tartaric acid (*270*).

In neutral or slightly acid solution, at room temperature, the ease of reactivity (*271*) of a number of sugars to permanganate is:

Maltose > fructose > arabinose > galactose>
mannose > glucose > lactose; β-glucose > α-glucose

For fructose, the maximal rate of oxidation takes place at pH 3.5 to 4.5.

262. H. H. Willard and P. Young, *J. Am. Chem. Soc.* **50,** 1322 (1928).
263. G. F. Smith and F. R. Duke, *Ind. Eng. Chem. Anal. Ed.* **13,** 558 (1941).
264. C. Niemann and K. P. Link, *J. Biol. Chem.* **104,** 195, 743 (1934).
265. W. Bosshard, *Helv. Chim. Acta* **18,** 956 (1935). See also examples under Keto acids and Ascorbic acids, earlier in this chapter and also p. 291.
266. A. Smolka, *Monatsh.* **8,** 1 (1887).
267. E. J. Witzemann, *J. Am. Chem. Soc.* **38,** 159 (1916).
268. W. L. Evans and associates, *J. Am. Chem. Soc.* **47,** 3085 (1925); **47,** 3098 (1925).
269. W. L. Evans and C. W. Holl, *J. Am. Chem. Soc.* **47,** 3102 (1925).
270. E. Fischer and A. W. Crossley, *Ber.* **27,** 394 (1894).
271. R. Kuhn and T. Wagner-Jauregg, *Ber.* **58,** 1441 (1925).

c. *Silver Oxide*

Aldohexoses, fructose, arabinose, erythritol, glyceraldehyde, glucaric acid, and galactonic lactone are oxidized by silver oxide at 50°C. (in water or *N* KOH) to carbon dioxide, oxalic acid, formic acid, and glycolic acid (*272*).

d. *Copper Salts in Alkaline Solution*

The most important methods for the quantitative determination of reducing sugars are based on oxidation with hot alkaline solutions of copper salts (see Chapter XI). The composition of the oxidation products has been investigated; in general, monobasic acids with one to six carbon atoms are formed accompanied by oxalic acid, carbon dioxide, and lactic acid.

Copper sulfate in sodium carbonate solution (Soldaini's reagent) oxidized glucose (at 100°C. for 8 hours) to a mixture of acids, more than 60% of which are nonvolatile. In the nonvolatile fraction, the following acids were identified: gluconic, mannonic, D-arabonic, erythronic, threonic, glyceric, and glycolic acids (*273*). The same products are formed by the action of Fehling solution on glucose (*274*), although the Fehling solution has a higher alkali concentration. From 199 g. of fructose, Nef reported the isolation of carbon dioxide (2.4 g.), formic acid (13.8 g.), and nonvolatile acids (106 g.) composed of: glycolic acid (22 g.), glyceric acid (18 g.), trihydroxybutyric acids (35 g.), and aldohexonic acids (30 g.). According to Nef (*275*), the oxidation with copper acetate in neutral solution proceeds differently; much more oxygen is consumed, greater amounts of carbon dioxide are produced, and erythronic acid seems to be the main oxidation product.

In ammoniacal solutions of copper salts, the oxidation products are likely to contain nitrogen atoms (*276*). Glucose, fructose, and mannose give oxalic acid, imidazoles, HCN, and urea.

H. Microbial Oxidations (*277*)

Fermentative processes are of considerable value for the production of carbohydrate materials or closely related substances from carbohydrates.

272. H. Kiliani, *Ann.* **205,** 191 (1880); K. Dreyer, *ibid.* **416,** 203 (1918); W. L. Evans and associates, *J. Org. Chem.* **1,** 1 (1936).

273. F. W. Jensen and F. W. Upson, *J. Am. Chem. Soc.* **47,** 3019 (1925).

274. E. Anderson, *Am. Chem. J.* **42,** 40 (1909); J. U. Nef, *Ann.* **357,** 214 (1907); see also J. Habermann and M. Hönig, *Monatsh.* **3,** 651 (1882); **5,** 208 (1884).

275. J. U. Nef, *Ann.* **335,** 332 (1904); **357,** 259 (1907).

276. J. Parrod and associates, *Compt. rend.* **190,** 328 (1930); **192,** 1136 (1931); **200,** 1884 (1935); **212,** 610 (1941).

277. For a general summary of the subject see J. R. Porter, "Bacterial Chemistry and Physiology," pp. 896–1030. Wiley, New York, 1946.

Large amounts of acetone, butyl alcohol, ethyl alcohol, acetic acid, lactic acid, citric acid, L-sorbose, and gluconic acid are made industrially by fermentative methods. In fermentative processes, oxidizing as well as reducing conditions may be employed. Laboratory and industrial preparations of many other substances such as glycols have been carried out. The oxidation of polyols to ketoses is considered elsewhere as a preparatory method for ketoses. Microorganisms exhibit a marked specificity in their choice of substrates and in the reaction products. This property is useful for the qualitative and quantitative determination of sugars as well as for the identification of microorganisms. The formation of uronic acids and osones has been mentioned earlier. The present discussion will be limited to fermentative methods for the preparation of aldonic and keto aldonic acids.

Gluconic acid is produced by the action of many species of bacteria and molds on glucose (*278*). Enzymes, glucose dehydrogenases, from molds, bacteria, and liver, bring about this reaction (*279*). Boutroux found gluconic acid to be a metabolic product of acetic acid bacteria. Numerous bacteria and fungi oxidize glucose to gluconic acid, and the process is used for the commercial production of gluconic acid and its lactones and salts. Molds of species of *Aspergillus* and *Penicillium* are particularly suitable for large-scale production. Using *Aspergillus niger* and fermentations under air pressure in rotating drums, yields of 90 to 99% of gluconic acid are obtained (*280*). When calcium carbonate is present, calcium gluconate will crystallize directly.

Some strains of *A. niger* will oxidize D-mannose to mannonic acid and D-galactose to D-galactonic acid (*281*). Many species of *Pseudomonas* and also *Acetobacter xylinum* will oxidize pentoses to the corresponding pentonic acids (*282*). The yields are not always high but probably can be increased by improvements in the strains and in the cultural conditions.

Acetobacter suboxydans may oxidize glucose to 5-ketogluconic acid (*283*). Gluconic acid is formed initially and only subsequently is converted to the

278. L. Boutroux, *Compt. rend.* **91,** 236 (1880); A. J. Brown, *J. Chem. Soc.* **49,** 172' 435 (1886).

279. See W. Franke and F. Lorenz, *Ann.* **532,** 1 (1937).

280. A. J. Moyer, P. A. Wells, J. J. Stubbs, H. T. Herrick, and O. E. May, *Ind. Eng. Chem.* **29,** 777 (1937); E. A. Gastrock, N. Porges, P. A. Wells, and A. J. Moyer, *ibid.* **30,** 782 (1938); N. Porges, T. F. Clark, and S. I. Aronovsky, *ibid.* **33,** 1065 (1941).

281. H. Knobloch and H. Mayer, *Biochem. Z.* **307,** 285 (1941).

282. L. B. Lockwood and G. E. N. Nelson, *J. Bacteriol.* **52,** 581 (1946); G. Bertrand *Compt. rend.* **127,** 124, 728 (1898).

283. J. J. Stubbs, L. B. Lockwood, E. T. Roe, B. Tabenkin, and G. E. Ward, *Ind. Eng. Chem.* **32,** 1626 (1940); A. J. Kluyver and A. G. J. Boezaardt, *Rec. trav. chim.* **57,** 609 (1938); K. R. Butlin and W. H. D. Wince, *J. Soc. Chem. Ind.* **58,** 363 (1939).

5-keto acid. 2-Ketogluconic acid is formed by some *Acetobacter* species, but *Pseudomonas* species give yields of over 80% after 25 hours when the solutions are strongly aerated in rotating drums (*284*). (See also under Keto acids.)

I. Enzymic Oxidations

Numerous enzymes exist in living tissues which *in vivo* or *in vitro* catalyze the oxidation (and reduction) of carbohydrates, and are important in their metabolism. Usually these are dehydrogenations (or hydrogenations). These enzymes are discussed in detail in Chapter XIII.

An enzyme, originally called "glucose oxidase," and now notatin or penicillin B, catalyzes the oxidation of glucose by molecular oxygen to gluconic acid. It has been isolated from various molds, especially *Aspergillus niger* and *Penicillium glaucum* (*285*). The enzyme is very specific for β-D-glucose (*286*). Since the initial reaction product is gluconic δ-lactone, the glucopyranose ring is unbroken. Hydrogen peroxide is also formed. As indicated earlier, bromine oxidation also proceeds similarly.

This enzyme has been called an oxidase, but experiments with ordinary molecular oxygen and water enriched with O^{18} have shown that the action is that of a dehydrogenase; the enzyme catalyzes the transfer of two hydrogen atoms from glucose to gaseous oxygen (*287*).

A purified glucose dehydrogenase, isolated from animal liver, will also catalyze the oxidation of glucose to gluconic acid (*288*). A coenzyme (either TPN or DPN) is necessary in this type of reaction, to provide the phosphorylated intermediates. The reaction is reversible and specific for β-D-glucose; it will not proceed with α-D-glucose and only slowly with D-xylose. In this type of reaction the pyranose ring in the glucose 6-phosphate is unbroken, the δ-lactone of gluconic acid 6-phosphate being formed (*289*).

284. L. B. Lockwood, B. Tabenkin, and G. E. Ward, *J. Bacteriol.* **42,** 51 (1941).

285. D. Muller, *Biochem. Z.* **199,** 136 (1928); *Enzymologia* **10,** 40 (1941).

286. D. Keilin and E. F. Hartree, *Biochem. J.* **50,** 331 (1952).

287. R. Bentley and A. Neuberger, *Biochem. J.* **45,** 584 (1949).

288. H. J. Strecker and S. Korkes, *Nature* **168,** 913 (1951); *J. Biol. Chem.* **196,** 769 (1952).

289. B. L. Horecker, P. Z. Smyrniotis, and J. E. Seegmiller, *J. Biol. Chem.* **193,** 383 (1951); J. E. Seegmiller and B. L. Horecker, *ibid.* **194,** 261 (1952).

VII. ETHERS, ANHYDRO SUGARS, AND UNSATURATED DERIVATIVES

JOHN C. SOWDEN

External and internal ether derivatives are known. The former, particularly the methyl ethers, find important applications in the determination of ring structures of the sugars and of the positions of linkage of the monosaccharide units comprising the oligo- and polysaccharides. (See Chapters IX and XII.) Internal ethers (anhydro sugars), especially of the epoxide type, are useful intermediates for sugar interconversions since their formation as well as their cleavage with substitution by a wide variety of reagents is accompanied by Walden inversion on one or other of the carbon atoms involved. Both internal and external ethers occur occasionally in natural products. Methyl ethers are represented by 3-*O*-methyl-D-galactose in slippery elm mucilage (*1*), 4-*O*-methyl-D-glucuronic acid in several plant polysaccharides (*2*), and the various 3-*O*-methyldeoxyaldohexoses of the cardiac glycosides (*3*). Both 3,6-anhydro-D- and 3,6-anhydro-L-galactose have been identified in natural polysaccharides (*4*), whereas styracitol (1,5-anhydro-D-mannitol) and polygalitol (1,5-anhydro-D-glucitol) occur in several plant species.

Glycals, glycoseens, and alditoleens are sugar derivatives containing olefinic unsaturation, resulting from the formal removal either of two hydroxyl groups or of a molecule of water from adjacent carbon atoms of the parent sugar structure. Unsaturated derivatives such as furfural and ascorbic acid are discussed elsewhere.

1. ETHER DERIVATIVES (EXTERNAL)

The application of the usual alkylating procedures of organic chemistry to the sugars and derivatives gives sugar ethers. Except for the glycosidic

1. L. Hough, J. K. N. Jones, and E. L. Hirst, *Nature* **165,** 34 (1950).

2. E. V. White, *J. Am. Chem. Soc.* **70,** 367 (1948); L. Hough, J. K. N. Jones, and W. H. Wadman, *J. Chem. Soc.* p. 796 (1952), C. M. Stewart and D. H. Foster, *Nature* **171,** 792 (1953).

3. See R. C. Elderfield, *Advances in Carbohydrate Chem.* **1,** 147 (1945).

4. C. Araki, *J. Chem. Soc. Japan* **61,** 775 (1940); C. Araki and S. Hirase, *Bull. Chem. Soc. Japan* **26,** 463 (1953); E. E. Percival, *Chemistry & Industry* p. 1487 (1954); A. N. O'Neill, *J. Am. Chem. Soc.* **77,** 2837 (1955).

alkoxyl group which is easily removed by acids, all the simple aliphatic alkoxyl linkages are of the true ether type, and the groups are very resistant to removal. This property has made the sugar ethers, and in particular the methyl ethers, of great importance for the structural determination of the mono-, di-, and polysaccharides. Although the more recently developed periodic acid oxidation (Chapter VI) is simpler to apply for structural determinations, methylation methods retain their importance in this application, particularly in view of the discovery of periodate-resistant glycol groupings and of still other structures that "overoxidize" with periodic acid.

Many fully and partially methylated sugars have been characterized to serve as reference compounds for structural determinations (*5*).

Although a 2-*O*-methyl group is lost readily during osazone formation (*6*), ordinarily the ethers are extremely resistant to hydrolysis. Most are cleaved only by drastic treatment with hydrogen iodide or with hydrogen bromide – acetic anhydride (*7*), reagents that are prone to cause further and often undesirable changes in the sugar residue. When it is desirable to employ the ether linkage as a temporary blocking group, the benzyl ethers may be used to advantage since they possess the usual stability to hydrolysis but may be cleaved under very mild conditions by catalytic hydrogenolysis (*8*) or, alternatively, by acetolysis (*9*). Trityl (triphenylmethyl) ethers, in contrast to the simpler ethers, are easily hydrolyzed by acid and are widely used for the preparation of partially substituted derivatives of carbohydrates.

Numerous ethers of cellulose, starch, and bacterial dextran are of established or potential industrial importance. (See also Chapter XII.) Treatment of the polysaccharides with alkali and methyl chloride, ethyl chloride, benzyl chloride, ethylene oxide (or ethylene chlorohydrin), sodium chloroacetate, and allyl bromide gives, respectively, the methyl, ethyl, benzyl, hydroxyethyl, carboxymethyl, and allyl ethers. The cellulose derivatives

5. For compilations of known methyl ethers, see E. J. Bourne and S. Peat (D-glucose), *Advances in Carbohydrate Chem.* **5,** 145 (1950); D. J. Bell (D-galactose), *ibid.* **6,** 1 (1951); see also G. G. Maher, *ibid.* **10,** 273 (1955); R. A. Laidlaw and E. G. V. Percival (aldopentoses, rhamnose, fucose), *ibid.* **7,** 1 (1952); see also G. G. Maher, *ibid.* **10,** 257 (1955); G. O. Aspinall (D-mannose); *ibid.* **8,** 217 (1953); G. O. Aspinall (hexuronic acids), *ibid.* **9,** 131 (1954).

6. P. Brigl and R. Schinle, *Ber.* **62,** 1716 (1929); E. G. V. Percival and J. C. Somerville, *J. Chem. Soc.* p. 1615 (1937); G. R. Barker, *J. Chem. Soc.* p. 2035 (1948).

7. J. C. Irvine and A. Hynd, *J. Chem. Soc.* **101,** 1145 (1912); K. Hess and F. Neumann, *Ber.* **68,** 1371 (1935).

8. K. Freudenberg, H. Toepffer, and C. C. Andersen, *Ber.* **61,** 1750 (1928).

9. R. Allerton and H. G. Fletcher, Jr., *J. Am. Chem. Soc.* **76,** 1757 (1954).

are the most widely used (*10*). Methylated cellulose attains cold water solubility at approximately 50% methylation. This solubility presumably is due to hydrate formation since the derivative precipitates when the solution is heated. Fully methylated cellulose, like the parent polysaccharide, is insoluble in water.

Of considerable interest are the ω-(*p*-aminoacetophenone) ethers of cellulose containing about one ether group for each three glucose units (*10a*). These may be diazotized and coupled to provide cellulose-azo dyes, and the latter may be rendered water-soluble by carboxymethylation.

The allyl ethers of sugars and glycosides polymerize in the presence of oxygen. They are prepared best by treatment of glycosides with allyl bromide and alkali (*11*).

A. Alkylation Methods

a. Dimethyl Sulfate and Alkali (*Haworth*)

The most widely used procedure for alkylation depends on the action of dimethyl sulfate and 30% sodium hydroxide. Applied first by Denham and Woodhouse to the methylation of cellulose, it was shown by Haworth to be applicable to the simple sugars and glycosides (*12*). This method was utilized by Haworth, Hirst, and associates in their extensive structural investigations. The procedure has the advantage of cheapness, of the solubility of the sugars in the reagents, and of direct application not only to the glycosides but also to the sugars and to their acetyl derivatives. Acetyl groups are saponified under the conditions of the reaction and replaced by methyl groups. This modified procedure is of particular importance for the polysaccharides, since the acetates are more soluble in organic solvents than are the unsubstituted substances. Some improvements in the original procedure have been described (*13*).

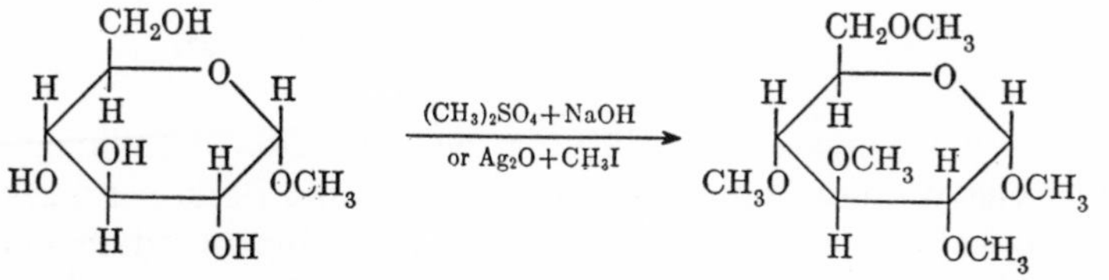
CH2OH
H
O
H
H
OH
H
HO
OCH3
H
OH
(CH3)2SO4+NaOH
or Ag2O+CH3I
CH2OCH3
OCH3
CH3O
OCH3
OCH3

Methyl α-D-glucopyranoside   Methyl tetra-*O*-methyl-α-D-glucopyranoside

---

10. See J. F. Haskins, *Advances in Carbohydrate Chem.* **2,** 279 (1946); J. V. Karabinos and M. Hindert, *ibid.* **9,** 285 (1954).

10a. R. R. McLaughlin and D. B. Mutton, *Can. J. Chem.* **33,** 646 (1955).

11. See A. N. Wrigley and E. Yanovsky, *J. Am. Chem. Soc.* **70,** 2194 (1948).

12. W. S. Denham and H. Woodhouse, *J. Chem. Soc.* **103,** 1735 (1913); W. N. Haworth, *ibid.* **107,** 13 (1915).

13. E. S. West and R. F. Holden, *J. Am. Chem. Soc.* **56,** 930 (1934); J. Y. Macdonald, *ibid.* **57,** 771 (1935); E. S. West and R. F. Holden, *Org. Syntheses* **20,** 97 (1940).

b. Alkyl Iodide and Silver Oxide (Purdie)

The well-known reagent of Purdie (alkyl iodide and silver oxide) also may be applied to the alkylation of sugar derivatives (*14*). Sugars with a free reducing group must be converted first to glycosides because of the oxidizing action of the silver oxide. Other limitations are the cost of the reagents, the insolubility of many sugar derivatives in the methyl iodide, and the number of treatments with the reagent, often six or more, necessary for complete methylation. By the addition of methyl alcohol or dioxane, dissolution may be aided. The number of treatments required may be reduced by a preliminary application of the Haworth procedure.

In the above methods, particularly for sluggishly reacting compounds like penta-*O*-methylmannitol or partially methylated polysaccharides, much of the reagent is expended in forming methanol and methyl ether as a result of the reaction of the alkylating agent with solvent or with byproducts of the reaction (water). Often the methylation becomes very inefficient or fails to reach completion.

c. Alkyl Iodide and Sugar Alkoxide

Modifications of the Williamson ether synthesis are applicable to the sugars, but the synthesis is difficult to apply because of the low solubility of many carbohydrates in solvents inert to sodium.

$$2\ \mathrm{ROH} + 2\ \mathrm{Na} \rightarrow 2\ \mathrm{RONa} + \mathrm{H_2}$$

$$\mathrm{RONa} + \mathrm{CH_3I} \rightarrow \mathrm{ROCH_3} + \mathrm{NaI}$$

Freudenberg and Hixon (*15*) applied the Williamson synthesis to di-*O*-isopropylidene-D-fructose and prepared the sodium derivative by reaction with sodium in benzene solution. The sodium derivative reacted with methyl iodide to give 3-*O*-methyl-di-*O*-isopropylidene-D-fructose:

$$\mathrm{HCOH} \xrightarrow{\mathrm{Na}} \mathrm{HCONa} \xrightarrow{\mathrm{CH_3I}} \mathrm{HCOCH_3}$$

A solvent of much greater versatility for the preparation of sodium derivatives of carbohydrates is liquid ammonia. Schmid and Becker (*16*) showed that the liquid ammonia technique could be used to prepare sodium derivatives of carbohydrates. Muskat prepared the sodium derivatives of sugars; after removal of the liquid ammonia, the products were resuspended in an inert solvent and alkylated with methyl iodide. Potassium and lithium derivatives also were made by Muskat (*17*).

14. T. Purdie and J. C. Irvine, *J. Chem. Soc.* **83,** 1021 (1903); R. Kuhn *et al.*, *Angew. Chem.* **67,** 32 (1955); *Ber.* **88,** 1537 (1955).

15. K. Freudenberg and R. Hixon, *Ber.* **56,** 2125 (1923).

16. L. Schmid and B. Becker, *Ber.* **58,** 1966 (1925).

17. I. E. Muskat, *J. Am. Chem. Soc.* **56,** 2449 (1934); S. Soltzberg, *U. S. Patent* 2,234,200 (1938).

The liquid ammonia method makes possible the completion of the methylation process often in three or four operations. With polyols, the mono- and disodium derivatives are so insoluble that it is preferable to commence with the Haworth procedure and then change to the liquid ammonia method.

The method has been refined for use with 5- to 10-mg. samples, and in conjunction with the use of C^{14}-methyl iodide the estimation of the methylated sugars in methylated polysaccharides has been facilitated (*17a*).

Thallium salts of glycosides, made by treatment of glycosides with aqueous thallous hydroxide, react with methyl iodide to give methyl ethers (*18*).

Alkoxides are readily formed from partially substituted polyols and sugars by treatment with sodium naphthalenide (*19*) in 1,2-dimethoxyethane solution and subsequent reaction with alkyl halides then produces ethers (*20*). The reaction sequence is simple to apply, and the method deserves further investigation.

Diazomethane partially methylates starch, lichenin, inulin, cellulose, and simple sugars (*21*).

d. General Discussion

The hemiacetal hydroxyl is more readily alkylated than the true alcoholic hydroxyls and can be methylated selectively by treatment of the sugar with one equivalent of the Haworth reagent (see Chapter IV). When the hemiacetal hydroxyl of an aldohexose is blocked, some selective methylation of the hydroxyls at carbons 2 and/or 6 may be achieved with alkali and methyl iodide (*22*). With starch and cellulose, it has been reported (*23*) that alkali and methyl iodide lead preponderantly to the 2-*O*-methyl derivative, the hydroxyl group at carbon 6 presumably being rendered less

17a. H. S. Isbell and H. L. Frush, Abstracts American Chemical Society Meeting, Minneapolis, p. 6D. (Sept. 1955).

18. C. M. Fear and R. C. Menzies, *J. Chem. Soc.* p. 937 (1926); for summary, see R. C. Menzies, *ibid.* p. 1378 (1947).

19. N. D. Scott, J. F. Walker, and V. L. Hansley, *J. Am. Chem. Soc.* **58,** 2442 (1936).

20. E. Baer and H. O. L. Fischer, *J. Biol. Chem.* **140,** 397 (1941); J. C. Sowden and H. O. L. Fischer, *J. Am. Chem. Soc.* **63,** 3244 (1941); J. C. Sowden and D. J. Kuenne, *ibid.* **74,** 686 (1952).

21. L. Schmid, *Ber.* **58,** 1963 (1925); R. E. Reeves and H. J. Thompson, *Contribs. Boyce Thompson Inst.* **11,** 55 (1939); R. E. Reeves, *Ind. Eng. Chem.* **35,** 1281 (1943); F. S. H. Head, *Shirley Inst. Mem.* **25,** 209 (1951); *J. Textile Inst.* **43,** T1 (1952); L. Hough and J. K. N. Jones, *Chemistry & Industry* p. 380 (1952); R. Kuhn and H. H. Baer, *Chem. Ber.* **86,** 724 (1953).

22. See J. M. Sugihara, *Advances in Carbohydrate Chem.* **8,** 1 (1953).

23. T. Lieser, *Ann.* **470,** 104 (1929); K. M. Gaver, *U. S. Patent* 2,397,732 (1946); J. M. Sugihara and M. L. Wolfrom, *J. Am. Chem. Soc.* **71,** 3509 (1949).

reactive by hydrogen bonding. However, subsequent work (*23a*) has indicated that the methylation of cellulose with these reagents is random in nature.

The usual method of preparing partially methylated sugars consists in blocking all of the groups which are to be free in the final product, then methylating the compound and finally removing the blocking groups. Blocking groups must be able to withstand the methylating conditions without hydrolysis; for the Haworth procedure, the isopropylidene and benzylidene derivatives, stable to alkaline conditions and removed by acids, are often of value. The 3-*O*-methyl-D-glucose (III) is synthesized by the methylation of 1,2:5,6-di-*O*-isopropylidene-D-glucofuranose (diacetone glucose) (I); as the only free hydroxyl is at carbon 3, the 3-*O*-methyl derivative (II) is formed. Acid hydrolysis then removes the isopropylidene groups.

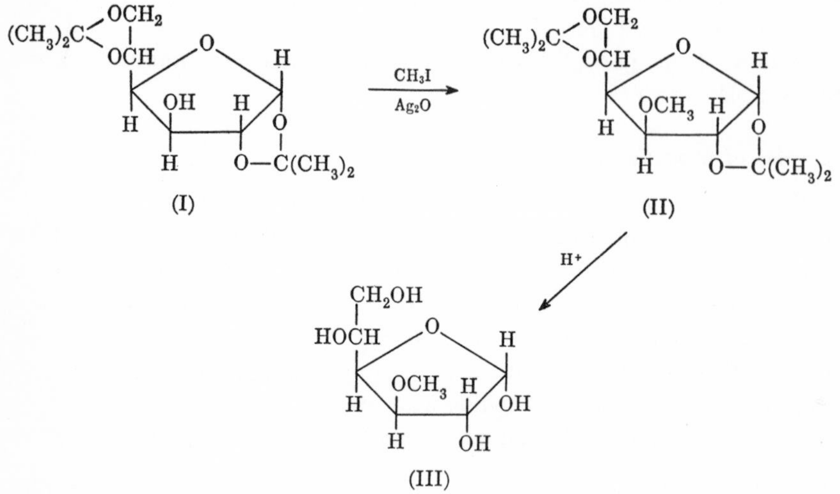
(I)
(II)
(III)

Monomethyl ethers also may be prepared by the ring scission, with accompanying monomethylation, of epoxy-type anhydro sugars by sodium methoxide (see p. 390).

B. Trityl Derivatives

Triphenylmethyl chloride, $(C_6H_5)_3C—Cl$, was shown by Helferich and associates (*24*) to react with sugars, glycosides, and derivatives to form the triphenylmethyl ethers, commonly called trityl derivatives. The reagent exhibits a marked difference in the rate of reactivity for the primary

23a. K. Hess, K. E. Heumann, and R. Leipold, *Ann.* **594,** 119 (1955).
24. See B. Helferich, *Advances in Carbohydrate Chem.* **3,** 79 (1948).

TABLE I

RATE OF REACTION OF SUGAR DERIVATIVES WITH TRITYL CHLORIDE

Substance	Excess of trityl chloride	*k*
1,2:3,4-Di-*O*-isopropylidene-D-galactopyranose	4-fold	0.014
	8-fold	0.036
2,3:4,6-Di-*O*-isopropylidene-L-sorbofuranose	4-fold	0.0052
	8-fold	0.0055
1,2:5,6-Di-*O*-isopropylidene-D-glucofuranose	4-fold	0.00012
	8-fold	0.00016

and secondary alcoholic hydroxyls of the sugar molecule, and conditions often may be selected for bringing about reactions with the primary groups alone. For the hexose sugars, the 6-*O*-trityl derivatives are produced by reaction with trityl chloride or bromide in pyridine solution.

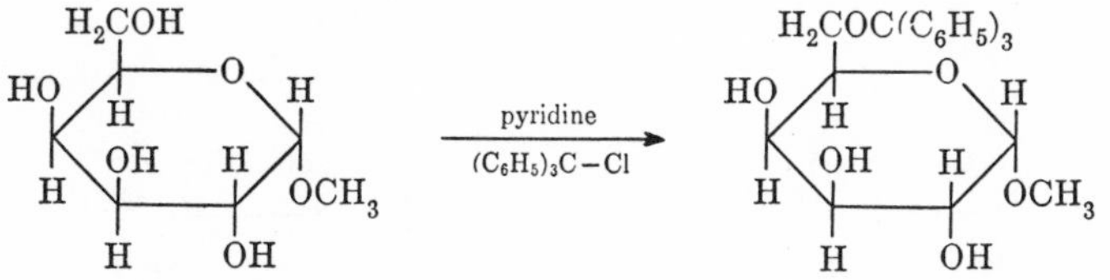
pyridine
$(C_6H_5)_3C-Cl$

Methyl α-D-galactopyranoside   Methyl 6-*O*-trityl-α-D-galactopyranoside

Under more prolonged treatment, or at elevated temperatures, secondary alcoholic groups also react: certain of the methyl pentopyranosides and 6-deoxyhexosides, which contain no primary hydroxyls, have been found to give mono- and ditrityl derivatives (*25*); D-ribose, when tritylated at 100°, gives a tritrityl derivative (*26*).

The rates of reaction of triphenylmethyl chloride with several characteristic compounds are given (*27*) in Table I, which also illustrates the effect of the trityl chloride concentration. For the 8-fold excess, the *primary* alcoholic group of the galactose derivative reacts 226 times as rapidly as the *secondary* alcoholic group of the glucose derivative. However, the difference between the *primary* alcoholic group of the sorbose derivative and the *secondary* hydroxyl of the glucose derivative is only 34 times.

This kinetic comparison is made between primary hydroxyl groups and

25. R. C. Hockètt and C. S. Hudson, *J. Am. Chem. Soc.* **56,** 945 (1934); E. L. Jackson, R. C. Hockett, and C. S. Hudson, *ibid.* **56,** 947 (1934).

26. H. Bredereck and W. Greiner, *Ber.* **86,** 717 (1953).

27. R. C. Hockett, H. G. Fletcher, Jr., and J. Ames, *J. Am. Chem. Soc.* **63,** 2516 (1941).

ring secondary groups. Since a considerable portion of the difference may arise from steric factors of different ring conformations (Chapter I), the difference between acyclic primary and secondary hydroxyl groups may not be as great.

The reagent reacts with both primary hydroxyls of fructose, but by use of the proper proportions, mono- or di-*O*-tritylfructose is formed (*28*). All of the primary hydroxyls of di- and trisaccharides react easily, and the reaction is sometimes used to determine the number of such groups in the molecule (*29*).

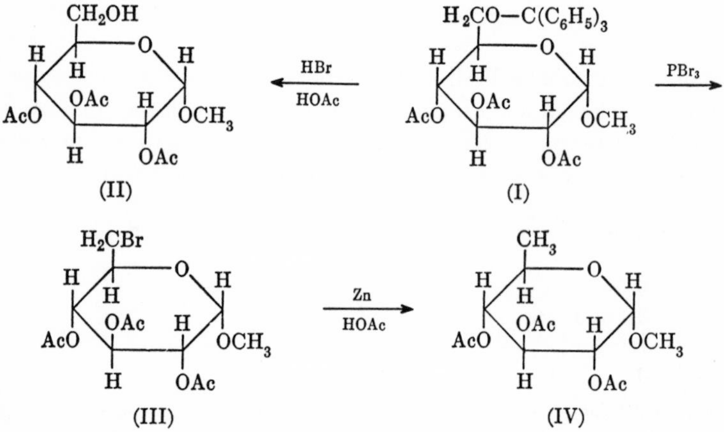
HBr
HOAc
PBr₃
Zn
HOAc

(II) (I) (III) (IV)

The trityl derivatives have their greatest value for the preparation of acetylated sugars in which the primary hydroxyl groups are unsubstituted (II) and for the corresponding halogen derivatives (III). The acetylaldohexoses with unsubstituted primary hydroxyls are important intermediates in the preparation of disaccharides of the gentiobiose type (see Chapter IX) and of 6-*O*-methyl sugars.

The action of hydrogen bromide in acetic acid, which normally is used to cleave the acetylated trityl ethers (I → II), leads in some instances to the bromodeoxy sugar derivative (*30*). 5-*O*-Trityl-D-ribofuranose triacetate also behaves abnormally with HBr – HOAc, yielding a dimolecular anhydride, probably 1,5′:5,1′-di-D-ribofuranose anhydride (*31*).

The trityl ethers are readily hydrolyzed by aqueous acids with the libera-

28. B. Helferich, *J. prakt. Chem.* [2] **147,** 60 (1936).

29. K. Josephson, *Ann.* **472,** 230 (1929).

30. M. L. Wolfrom, J. L. Quinn, and C. C. Christman, *J. Am. Chem. Soc.* **56,** 2789 (1934); **57,** 713 (1935); **58,** 39 (1936); M. L. Wolfrom, W. J. Burke, and S. W. Waisbrot, *ibid.* **61,** 1827 (1939).

31. G. R. Barker and M. V. Lock, *J. Chem. Soc.* p. 23 (1950); H. Bredereck, M. Köthnig, and E. Berger, *Ber.* **73,** 956 (1940).

tion of the sugar hydroxyl and triphenylcarbinol. Catalytic hydrogenolysis, with hydrogen and platinum or palladium, also cleaves the *primary* trityl ethers, regenerating the sugar hydroxyl with the formation of triphenylmethane (*26*, *32*).

2. ANHYDRO DERIVATIVES

The anhydro sugars and their derivatives (*33a, b*) are inner ethers formed by the intramolecular elimination of the elements of water from two alcoholic hydroxyl groups with the formation of a heterocyclic anhydro ring. Sugars with anhydro rings whose formation involved the hemiacetal hydroxyl group are inner glycosides (glycosans, sugar anhydrides), rather than inner ethers, and are discussed in Chapter IV.

Anhydro sugars or sugar alcohols are known in which the ring oxygen atom bridges 2, 3, 4, or 5 carbon atoms. Of these, compounds with the 3-membered (ethylene oxide or epoxy type) and 5-membered (tetramethylene oxide or hydrofuran type) heterocyclic rings are the most common and useful. Anhydro sugars of the epoxy class are especially valuable for the preparation of deoxy, aminodeoxy, and *O*-methyl derivatives as well as for interconversions of sugars through Walden inversions of configuration.

The rare 4-membered (trimethylene oxide) anhydro ring is represented in 3,5-anhydro-1,2-*O*-isopropylidene-D-xylose (*34*) and 1,3-anhydro-2,4-*O*-methylenexylitol (*35*).

The 6-membered (pentamethylene oxide) anhydro ring is present in methyl 2,6-anhydro-α-D-altroside (*36*) and in the naturally occurring 1,5-anhydrohexitols, styracitol and polygalitol.

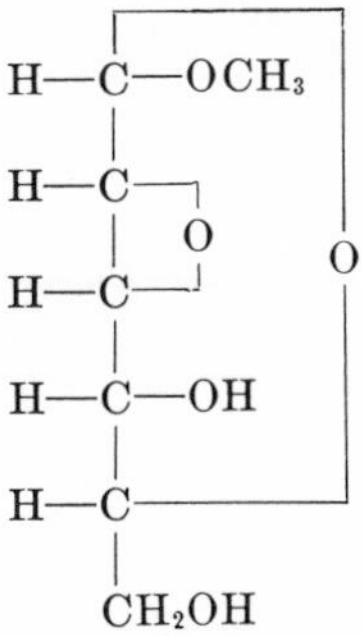

H—C—OCH₃
H—C
O
O
H—C
H—C—OH
H—C
CH₂OH

Methyl 2,3-anhydro-α-D-allopyranoside

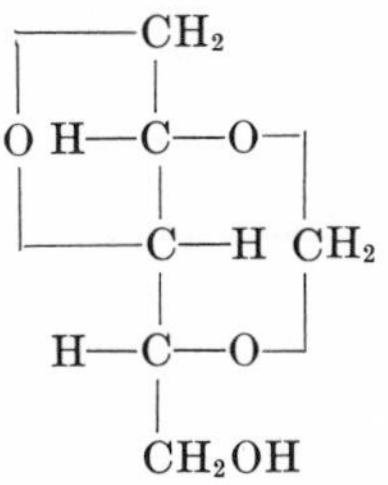

CH₂
O H—C—O
C—H CH₂
H—C—O
CH₂OH

1,3-Anhydro-2,4-*O*-methylenexylitol

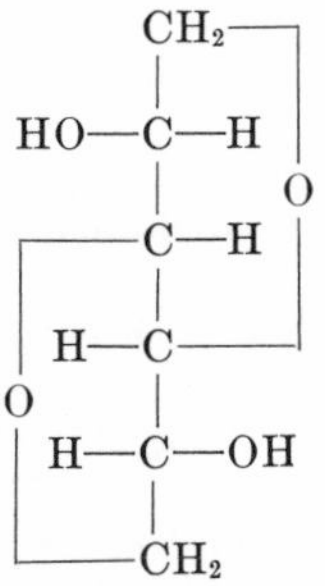

CH₂
HO—C—H
O
C—H
H—C
O
H—C—OH
CH₂

1,4:3,6-Dianhydro-D-mannitol

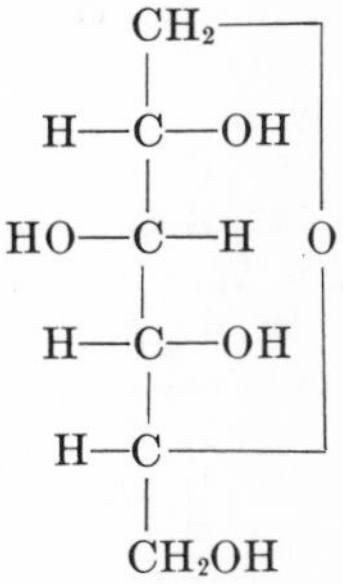

CH₂
H—C—OH
HO—C—H
O
H—C—OH
H—C
CH₂OH

1,5-Anhydro-D-glucitol (Polygalitol)

---

32. F. Micheel, *Ber.* **65,** 262 (1932); P. E. Verkade, W. D. Cohen, and A. K. Vroege, *Rec. trav. chim.* **59,** 1123 (1940); P. E. Verkade, F. D. Tollenaar, and T. A. P. Posthumus, *ibid.* **61,** 373 (1942).

33a. See S. Peat (anhydro sugars), *Advances in Carbohydrate Chem.* **2,** 37 (1946).

A. Methods of Preparation

a. Alkaline Elimination of Halogen or Sulfonic Ester Groups

On attempting to remove the bromine from methyl 6-bromo-6-deoxy-β-D-glucopyranoside triacetate by treatment with barium hydroxide, Fischer and Zach (*37*) found that simple hydrolysis did not occur and that the product was an anhydro sugar, methyl 3,6-anhydro-β-D-glucopyranoside. Ohle and co-workers (*38*) later observed that the 3,6-anhydro ring also was formed when a derivative of D-glucose 6-*p*-toluenesulfonate, with an unsubstituted hydroxyl group at carbon 3, was treated with alkali. This displacement behavior of the tosyloxy moiety is in contrast to the normal hydrolytic behavior of the carboxylic esters, wherein no cleavage of the oxygen–alkyl bond occurs.

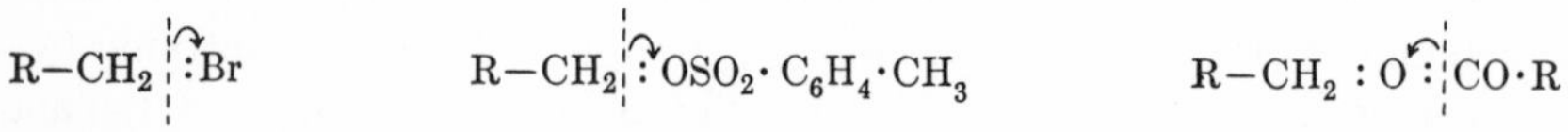

Displacement of halogen ester — Displacement of tosyl ester — Hydrolysis of carboxylic ester

Other sugar esters that readily undergo displacement, rather than hydrolysis, under alkaline conditions are the methanesulfonates, sulfates (*39*), and, to some extent, the nitrates (*40*). No clear-cut example of displacement under alkaline conditions of a sugar phosphate ester has been recorded (*41*). (See Chapter III.)

From a large accumulation of data concerning the action of alkali on halogen and sulfonic esters of the sugars, the conditions necessary for the formation of anhydro rings by this method have been clarified. The pre-

33b. L. F. Wiggins (anhydro alditols), *Advances in Carbohydrate Chem.* **5,** 191 (1950).

34. P. A. Levene and A. L. Raymond, *J. Biol. Chem.* **102,** 331 (1933).

35. R. M. Hann, N. K. Richtmyer, H. W. Diehl, and C. S. Hudson, *J. Am. Chem. Soc.* **72,** 561 (1950).

36. D. A. Rosenfeld, N. K. Richtmyer, and C. S. Hudson, *J. Am. Chem. Soc.* **70,** 2201 (1948).

37. E. Fischer and K. Zach, *Ber.* **45,** 456 (1912).

38. H. Ohle, L. von Vargha, and H. Erlbach, *Ber.* **61,** 1211 (1928).

39. E. G. V. Percival and T. H. Soutar, *J. Chem. Soc.* p. 1475 (1940); R. B. Duff and E. G. V. Percival, *ibid.* p. 830 (1941); E. G. V. Percival, *ibid.* p. 119 (1945); E. G. V. Percival and R. B. Duff, *Nature* **158,** 29 (1946); R. B. Duff and E. G. V. Percival, *J. Chem. Soc.* p. 1675 (1947); R. B. Duff, *ibid.* p. 1597 (1949).

40. E. K. Gladding and C. B. Purves, *J. Am. Chem. Soc.* **66,** 76, 153 (1944); E. G. Ansell and J. Honeyman, *J. Chem. Soc.* p. 2778 (1952).

41. See P. A. Levene, A. L. Raymond, and A. Walti, *J. Biol. Chem.* **82,** 191 (1929); A. L. Raymond and P. A. Levene, *ibid.* **83,** 619 (1929); E. E. Percival and E. G. V. Percival, *J. Chem. Soc.* p. 874 (1945).

requisite is the presence, either actual or potential, in the molecule of a free hydroxyl group, so situated sterically that the oxygen anion produced from it by the alkali can perform a rearward-approach, nucleophilic attack on the alkyl carbon of the ester function. The result is the displacement of the ester function with concomitant closure of the anhydro ring. If the alkyl carbon of the ester function was asymmetric in the original ester, Walden configurational inversion of this carbon invariably accompanies the ester elimination process. In essentially all instances, the attacking oxygen anion must be so situated in the molecule that the resulting anhydro ring is either of the epoxy or hydrofuran type. If a choice exists in the molecule between epoxy and hydrofuran ring closure, the former is produced preferentially. The following model structures (I, II, III, IV) illustrate steric relationships between hydroxyl and tosyl ester functions that result in anhydro ring formation. (See also p.166.)

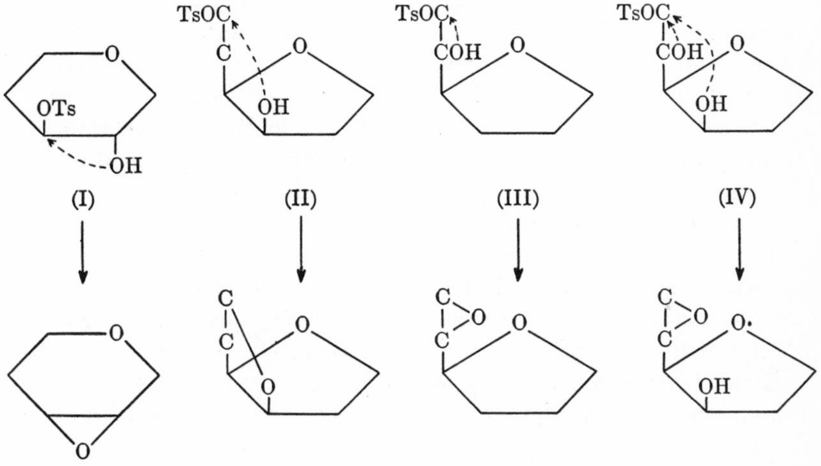
TsOC
C
O
OTs
OH
COH
(I)
(II)
(III)
(IV)

In structures (V), (VI), and (VII), the oxygen anion of the hydroxyl group is sterically unable to attack the rear of the ester alkyl carbon. In these instances, anhydro ring formation does not occur, and the esters are extremely stable to alkali. A few examples of such structures are known in which a slow, normal hydrolysis of the ester may be induced by drastic treatment with base.

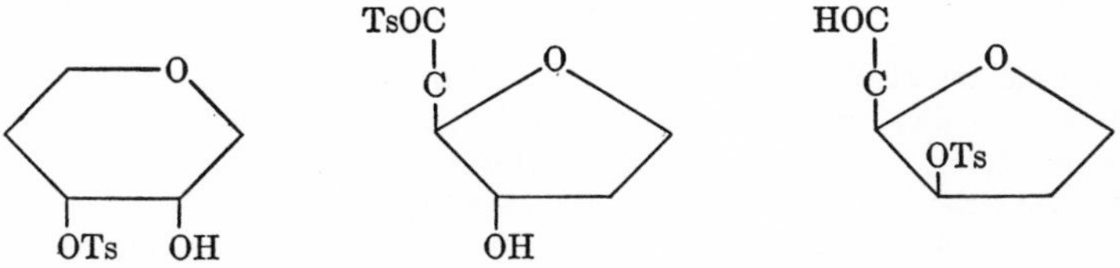
TsOC
HOC
C
O
OTs
OH

(V) (VI) (VII)

Although the epoxy ring is more readily formed than the hydrofuran ring, the latter is more stable to further anionic attack. Consequently, an epoxy anhydro sugar may be the *initial* product of alkaline elimination of a halogen or sulfonic ester, but it may in turn be subjected to intramolecular rearrangment to a hydrofuran anhydro sugar (VIII → IX) (*42*).

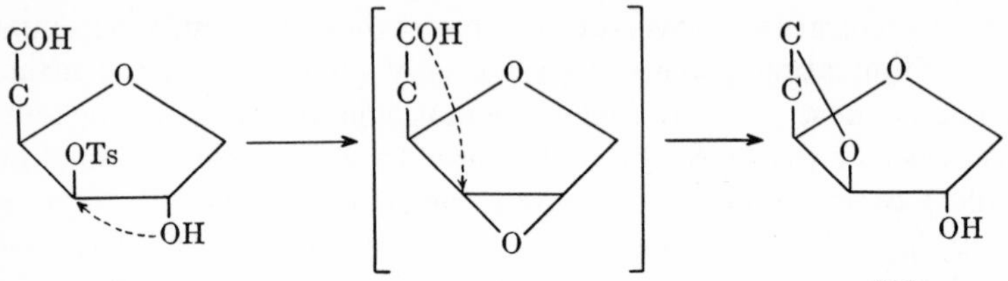

(VIII) (IX)

The most commonly used reagent for the conversion of sugar halogen or sulfonic esters into anhydro sugars is sodium methoxide in methanol solution. The alkali-sensitive hemiacetal group may be protected as a glycoside during the reaction. The alkali-stable isopropylidene or benzylidene acetals also are employed frequently to protect the hemiacetal function or to block alcoholic hydroxyls in the sugar structure that would interfere with the desired course of anhydro ring formation.

A wide variety of epoxy and hydrofuran anhydro sugars and anhydro alditols has been prepared by the alkaline elimination of halogen, tosyl, or mesyl ester functions. In the alditol series, the reaction also has been utilized to introduce a second anhydro ring into the monoanhydro alditols. Thus, 1,5:3,6-dianhydro-D-galactitol ("D-neogalactide") was prepared from 2,3,4-tri-*O*-benzoyl-6-*O*-tosyl-1,5-anhydro-D-galactitol by treatment with sodium methoxide (*43*), and, in an analogous manner, 1,5-anhydro-D-glucitol (polygalitol) was converted to 1,5:3,6-dianhydro-D-glucitol ("neosorbide") (*44*).

b. Deamination of Aminodeoxy Sugars and Aminodeoxy Alditols

Application of nitrous acid deamination to the naturally occurring chitosamine (*45*) (2-amino-2-deoxy-D-glucose) provided Fischer and Tiemann (*46*) with the first recorded example of a hydrofuran anhydro sugar. The sirupy product, chitose, could be oxidized to give, successively, an

42. H. Ohle and H. Wilcke, *Ber.* **71,** 2316 (1938).

43. H. G. Fletcher, Jr., and C. S. Hudson, *J. Am. Chem. Soc.* **72,** 886 (1950).

44. S. B. Baker, *Can. J. Chem.* **32,** 628 (1954).

45. G. Ledderhose, *Z. physiol. Chem.* **2,** 213 (1878).

46. F. Tiemann, *Ber.* **17,** 241 (1884); E. Fischer and F. Tiemann, *ibid.* **27,** 138 (1894).

anhydro hexonic acid (chitonic acid) and an anhydro aric acid ("isosaccharic acid"); the latter also is produced by the direct action of nitric acid on chitosamine. (See summary below.) If, however, chitosamine first was oxidized by bromine to the corresponding aldonic acid (chitosaminic acid) and then deaminated with nitrous acid, the resulting anhydro aldonic acid (chitaric acid) and the anhydro aric acid produced from it by oxidation ("epiisosaccharic acid") were found to be isomeric with the corresponding acids obtained from chitose. Thus, an odd number of inversions of configuration must be involved in one of the processes.

The hydrofuran ring in chitose and the anhydro sugar acids derived from it involves carbons 2 and 5, since "isosaccharic acid" when heated in hydrogen chloride gas produces furan-α,α'-dicarboxylic acid (*47*) and the acetylation-dehydration of chitonic acid yields 5-acetoxymethylfuroic acid (*48*).

Levene and La Forge (*49*) established the configuration of "epiisosaccharic acid" as 2,5-anhydro-D-glucaric acid by comparing it with the synthetic enantiomorph, prepared from D-xylose by the cyanohydrin synthesis.

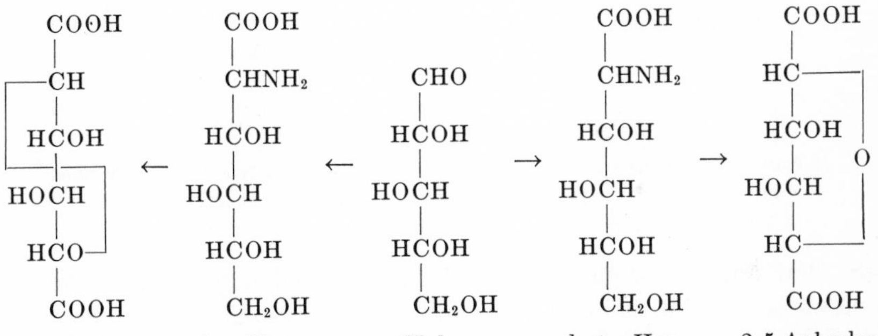

2,5-Anhydro-D-idaric acid — *levo*-Hexosaminic acid — D-Xylose — *dextro*-Hexosaminic acid — 2,5-Anhydro-D-gularic (2,5-Anhydro-L-glucaric) acid

The product of this synthesis can have either the D-*gulo* (L-*gluco*) or D-*ido* configuration, whereas "isosaccharic" and "epiisosaccharic" acids can have only the D-*manno* or D-*gluco* (L-*gulo*) configuration. Hence, regardless of the configuration of any of the intermediate products, if the dibasic end-product is the enantiomorph of either "isosaccharic" or "epiisosaccharic" acid, it must have the L-*gluco* (D-*gulo*) structure. In actual fact,

47. F. Tiemann and R. Haarmann, *Ber.* **19,** 1257 (1886).

48. E. Fischer and E. Andreae, *Ber.* **36,** 2587 (1903).

49. P. A. Levene and F. B. LaForge, *J. Biol. Chem.* **21,** 345, 351 (1915); P. A. Levene, *ibid.* **36,** 89 (1918); *Biochem. Z.* **124,** 37 (1921).

Levene and La Forge found the following:

	"Epiisosaccharic acid"	2,5-Anhydro-L-glucaric acid
Free acid	Monohydrate from acetone, m.p. 160°C., water-free $[\alpha]^{20}_{D}$ +39.7° (water)	Crystals from acetone, m.p. 163°C. $[\alpha]^{20}_{D}$ −38.8° (water)
Acid potassium salt	$[\alpha]_{D}$ +38.5° (water)	Monohydrate, $[\alpha]^{20}_{D}$ −38.1° (water)

"Isosaccharic acid" melts at 185°C., and has $[\alpha]^{20}_{D}$ +46.1°

From this, "epiisosaccharic acid" is accorded the 2,5-anhydro-D-*gluco* configuration, "isosaccharic acid" is the 2,5-anhydro-D-*manno* isomer, and chitose is 2,5-anhydro-D-mannose.

The various transformations of chitosamine may be summarized as follows:

2,5-Anhydro-D-mannose (Chitose) —Br_2→ 2,5-Anhydro-D-mannonic acid (Chitonic acid)

2-Amino-2-deoxy-D-glucose (Chitosamine) —HNO_2→ 2,5-Anhydro-D-mannose (Chitose)

2,5-Anhydro-D-mannonic acid (Chitonic acid) —HNO_3→ 2,5-Anhydro-D-mannaric acid ("Isosaccharic acid")

2-Amino-2-deoxy-D-glucose (Chitosamine) —Br_2→ 2-Amino-2-deoxy-D-gluconic acid (Chitosaminic acid)

2-Amino-2-deoxy-D-gluconic acid (Chitosaminic acid) —HNO_2→ 2,5-Anhydro-D-gluconic acid (Chitaric acid)

2,5-Anhydro-D-gluconic acid (Chitaric acid) —HNO_3→ 2,5-Anhydro-D-glucaric acid ("Epiisosaccharic acid")

Similar reaction sequences have been observed with 2-amino-2-deoxy-D-mannose (epichitosamine) and 2-amino-2-deoxy-D-galactose (chondrosamine) and their derived aminodeoxy aldonic acids.

It has been suggested (*33a*) that formation of the hydrofuran ring in the deamination of the 2-amino-2-deoxyaldohexoses (I → II) results from attack on the diazotized amino group by the *ring* oxygen, rather than by one of the sugar hydroxyls. Thus, inversion would occur regardless of the configuration at carbon 2.

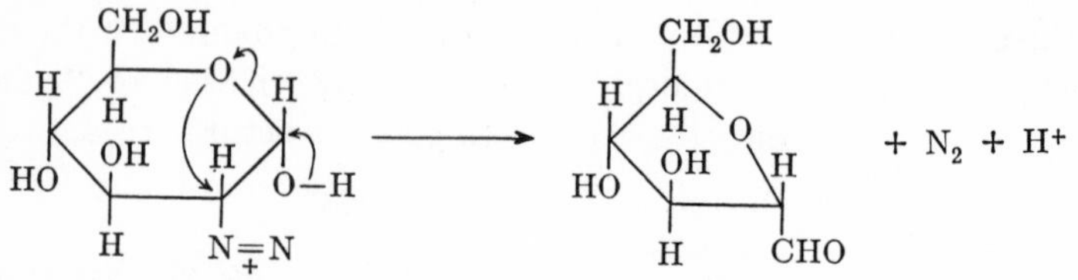
CH₂OH
H
H
O
H
OH
H
HO
O—H
H
N≡N
+
CH₂OH
H
H
O
OH
H
HO
H
CHO
+ N₂ + H⁺

(I) (II)

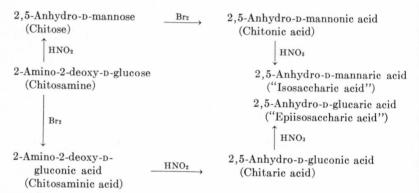

The retention of configuration at carbon 2 in the deamination of the

2-amino-2-deoxyaldonic acids has been explained (*50*) as resulting from a double inversion at this carbon, with the intermediate participation of the carboxyl group (III → IV).

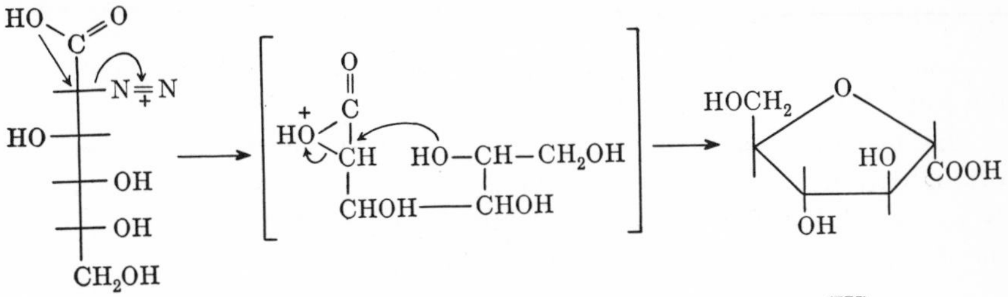

(III) (IV)

The elimination of diazotized amino groups by simple intramolecular interaction with hydroxyl groups, to produce epoxy and hydrofuran anhydro rings, may also proceed smoothly in the nitrous acid deamination of appropriate amino sugar structures, with configurational inversion occurring only in those instances where the original amino group was situated on an asymmetric carbon (*51*).

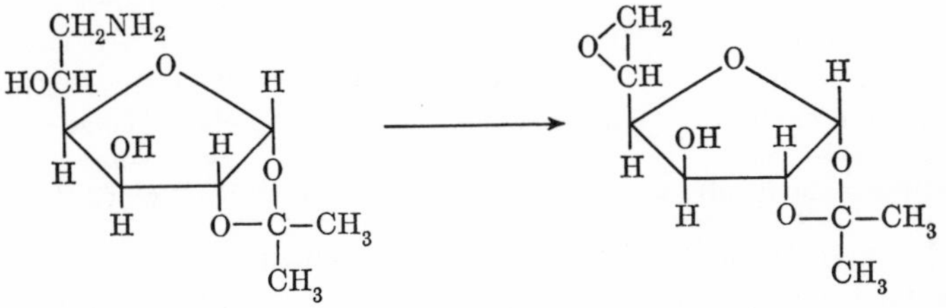

(V) (VI)

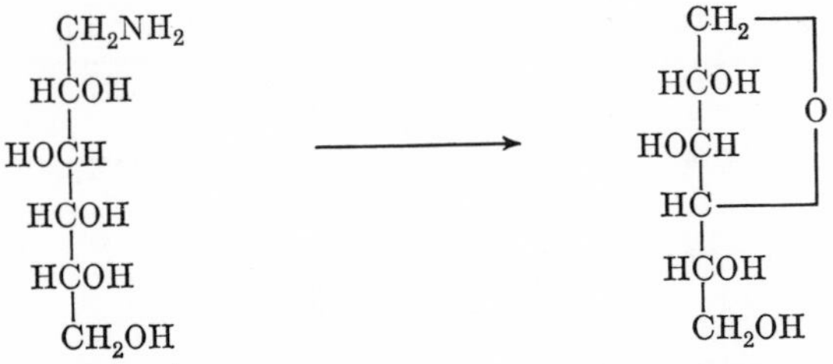

(VII) (VIII)

Deamination of 6-amino-6-deoxy-1,2-*O*-isopropylidene-D-glucofuranose (V → VI), wherein a choice of 3- or 5-membered ring formation exists,

50. A. B. Foster, *Chemistry & Industry* p. 627 (1955).

51. P. A. Levene and H. Sobotka, *J. Biol. Chem.* **71,** 181 (1926); H. Ohle and R. Lichtenstein, *Ber.* **63,** 2905 (1930); L. F. Wiggins, *Nature* **157,** 299 (1946); V. G. Bashford and L. F. Wiggins, *J. Chem. Soc.* p. 299 (1948); *Nature* **165,** 566 (1950).

yields the epoxy anhydro product rather than the alternative product with two fused hydrofuran rings. In contrast, 1-amino-1-deoxy-D-glucitol yields 1,4-anhydro-D-glucitol upon deamination (VII → VIII).

c. Reduction of Sugar Derivatives to Anhydro Alditols

Catalytic reduction of various sugar derivatives, with the retention of the sugar ring, may be employed to prepare anhydro alditols.

The naturally occurring styracitol was synthesized by Zervas (*52*) through catalytic hydrogenation of tetra-*O*-acetyl-1,2-D-glucopyranoseen (see p. 403). The other predicted 2-epimer, polygalitol, later was found in the mother liquors in much smaller amount (*53*).

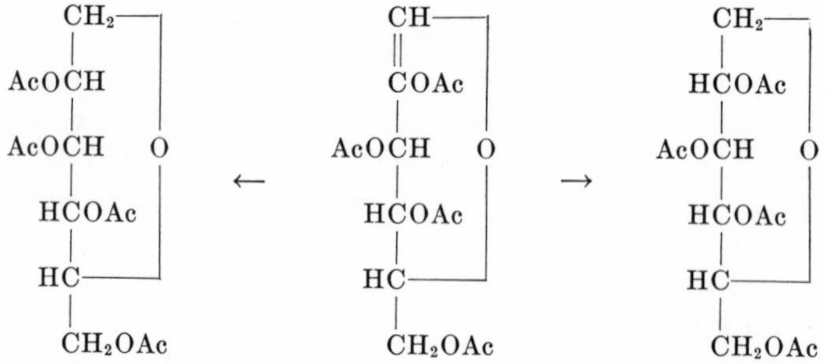

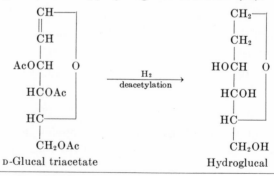

Styracitol tetraacetate (Tetra-*O*-acetyl-1,5-anhydro-D-mannitol) — Tetra-*O*-acetyl-1,2-D-glucopyranoseen — Polygalitol tetraacetate (Tetra-*O*-acetyl-1,5-anhydro-D-glucitol)

The 1,2-glycoseens related to cellobiose, gentiobiose, D-galactose, and D-xylose have been reduced in a similar manner to anhydro alditols (*54*).

Crystalline 1,5-anhydro-2-deoxy-D-*arabo*-hexitol (hydroglucal) is obtained by the hydrogenation of D-glucal triacetate (see p. 400) and subsequent hydrolysis of the sirupy hydroglucal triacetate (*55*).

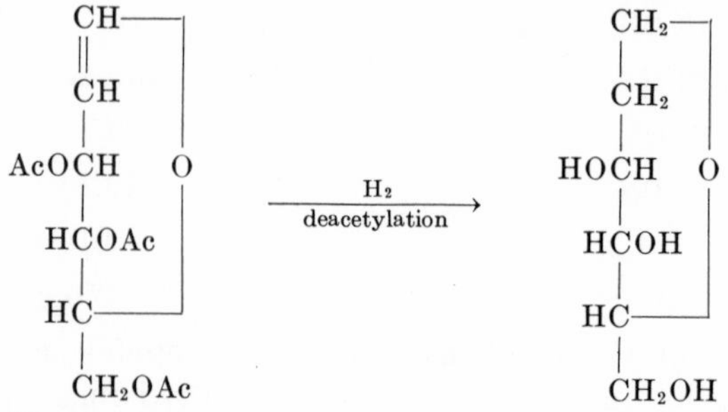

D-Glucal triacetate — Hydroglucal

52. L. Zervas, *Ber.* **63**, 1689 (1930).

53. N. K. Richtmyer, C. J. Carr, and C. S. Hudson, *J. Am. Chem. Soc.* **65**, 1477 (1943).

The reduction of the 1,2-glycoseens leads to a pair of 2-epimeric products, since carbon 2 becomes asymmetric in the process. Accordingly, the configurations of the two products must be determined independently. This difficulty is avoided when certain 1-thio sugar derivatives are reductively desulfurized to anhydro alditols. A single product then is obtained whose configuration is defined by that of the starting thio sugar. Richtmyer, Carr, and Hudson (*53*) applied Raney nickel desulfurization to octa-*O*-acetyl-β,β-di-D-glucopyranosyl disulfide (I) and to tetra-*O*-acetyl-1-thio-β-D-glucopyranose (II). The product in each case was polygalitol (1,5-anhydro-D-glucitol) tetraacetate.

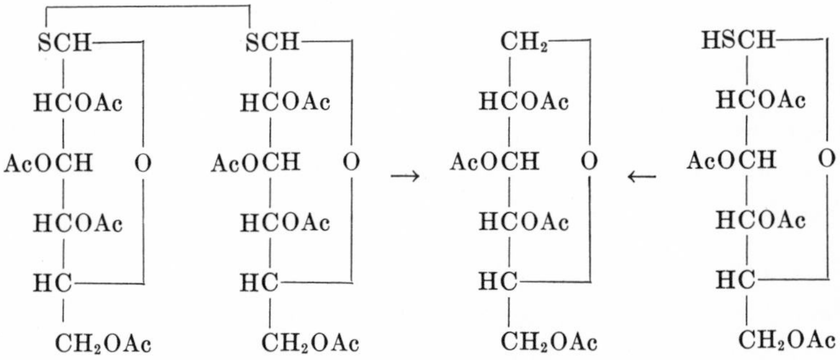

(I) Polygalitol tetraacetate (II)

Reductive desulfurization has been extended to the appropriate ethyl 1-xanthate or ethyl, phenyl, and naphthyl 1-thioglycosides to prepare the 1,5-anhydro derivatives of D-glucitol, D-mannitol, galactitol, cellobiitol, gentiobiitol, maltitol, lactitol, D-arabitol, ribitol, and xylitol (*56*). When a 1-thioaldofuranoside is reductively desulfurized, the product is the corresponding 1,4-anhydro alditol (*57*).

The most convenient reductive method for preparing anhydro alditols involves the reaction of the acetylated or benzoylated glycosyl halides with lithium aluminum hydride. The aldopyranosyl halides (III) yield 1,5-anhydro alditols in good yield, whereas the furanosyl derivatives (IV) provide

54. K. Maurer and K. Plötner, *Ber.* **64,** 281 (1931); W. Freudenberg and E. F. Rogers, *J. Am. Chem. Soc.* **59,** 1602 (1937); H. G. Fletcher, Jr., and C. S. Hudson, *ibid.* **69,** 921 (1947).

55. E. Fischer, *Ber.* **47,** 196 (1914); M. Bergmann and W. Freudenberg, *ibid.* **62,** 2783 (1929).

56. See H. G. Fletcher, Jr., and N. K. Richtmyer, *Advances in Carbohydrate Chem.* **5,** 1 (1950).

57. C. F. Huebner and K. P. Link, *J. Biol. Chem.* **186,** 387 (1950).

anhydro alcohols with the hydrofuran ring (*58*). The ester functions are reductively cleaved in the reaction.

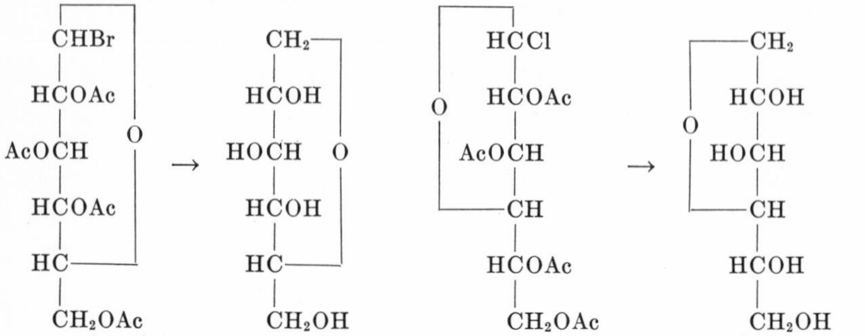

(III) Polygalitol (IV) 1,4-Anhydro-D-galactitol

When the halogen function is at a nonterminal carbon, as in tetra-*O*-benzoyl-D-fructopyranosyl bromide, two epimeric 2,6-anhydro alditols result (*59*).

d. Direct Dehydration of Alditols

The reducing aldohexose and 2-ketoheptose sugars dehydrate to varying extents under comparatively mild conditions, such as boiling with aqueous mineral acids, to form sugar anhydrides (inner glycosides) in which the hemiacetal group is involved in forming the anhydro ring (see Chapter IV). Considerably more drastic conditions of dehydration usually are necessary to convert the alditols to anhydro alditols. Consequently, the preferred ring size formed in the latter dehydrations is of the stable hydrofuran type.

Erythritol gives a sirupy 1,4-anhydroerythritol (1,4-erythritan) on heating with dilute sulfuric acid or with phosphoric acid and subsequent saponification of the monophosphate ester (*60*). Dehydration of L-threitol by heating with 50% sulfuric acid yields the crystalline 1,4-anhydro-L-threitol (1,4-L-threitan) (*61*).

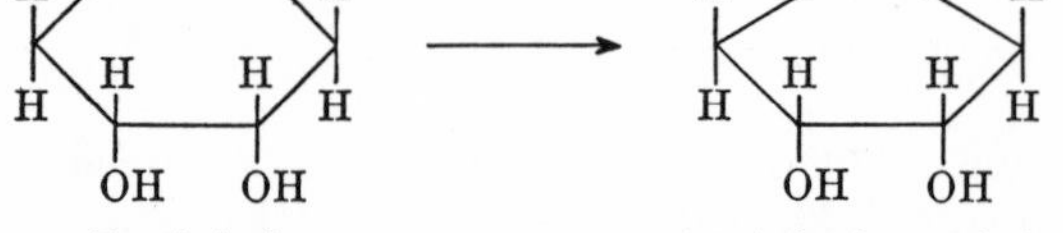

Erythritol 1,4-Anhydroerythritol

58. R. K. Ness, H. G. Fletcher, Jr., and C. S. Hudson, *J. Am. Chem. Soc.* **72,** 4547 (1950); **73,** 3742 (1951).

59. R. K. Ness and H. G. Fletcher, Jr., *J. Am. Chem. Soc.* **75,** 2619 (1953).

In the pentitol series, xylitol on being heated with acids or with zinc chloride gives crystalline 1,4-anhydroxylitol and a sirupy dianhydro derivative, presumably with the 1,4:2,5-ring structure (*62*).

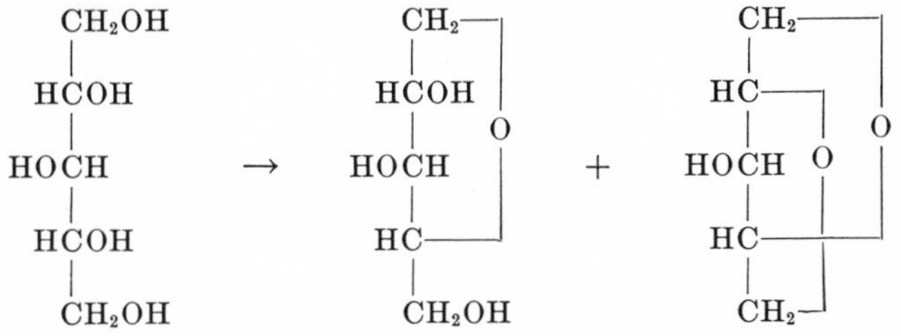

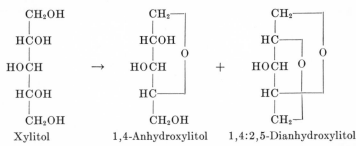

Xylitol 1,4-Anhydroxylitol 1,4:2,5-Dianhydroxylitol

1,4-Anhydro-D-mannitol, prepared by Bouchardat (*63*) by heating D-mannitol under pressure with hydrochloric acid, was the first authentic anhydro alditol to be described. Subsequently, acid-catalyzed dehydration was employed to prepare the 1,4-anhydro derivative of D-glucitol (*64*). Application of more drastic conditions of acid-catalyzed dehydration to D-mannitol, D-glucitol, and, also, L-iditol (*65*) leads to the 1,4:3,6-dianhydro compounds ("isohexides") containing two fused, *cis*-oriented hydrofuran rings (p. 386). The yield (35–40%) from D-mannitol and hydrochloric acid is lower than from the other two hexitols and the presence in the product of at least three additional dianhydrohexitols has been reported (*66*). One of these is 1,5:3,6-dianhydro-D-mannitol ("neomannide"). Some substitution of secondary hydroxyl groups by chlorine also occurs in the reaction.

The formation of 1,4:3,6-dianhydrohexitols in the galactitol, allitol, and altritol (talitol) series may be predicted to take place much less readily, if at all, since the second ring closure necessarily would involve hydroxyl groups on opposite sides of the initial hydrofuran ring (see formula, p. 386).

Since the involvement of a secondary hydroxyl group of an alditol in anhydro ring formation could lead to inversion of the asymmetric carbon, the configurations of such anhydro products must be established by inde-

60. A. Henninger, *Ann. chim. phys.* [6] **7,** 224 (1886); P. Carré, *ibid.* [8] **5,** 345 (1905).

61. H. Klosterman and F. Smith, *J. Am. Chem. Soc.* **74,** 5336 (1952).

62. J. F. Carson and W. D. Maclay, *J. Am. Chem. Soc.* **67,** 1808 (1945); F. Grandel, *U. S. Patent* 2,375,915 (1945).

63. G. Bouchardat, *Ann. chim. phys.* [5] **6,** 100 (1875).

64. S. Soltzberg, R. M. Goepp, Jr., and W. Freudenberg, *J. Am. Chem. Soc.* **68,** 919 (1946).

65. A. Fauconnier, *Bull. soc. chim. France* [2] **41,** 119 (1884); R. Montgomery and L. F. Wiggins, *J. Chem. Soc.* p. 390 (1946); H. G. Fletcher, Jr., and R. M. Goepp, Jr., *J. Am. Chem. Soc.* **68,** 939 (1946).

66. R. Montgomery and L. F. Wiggins, *J. Chem. Soc.* p. 2204 (1948).

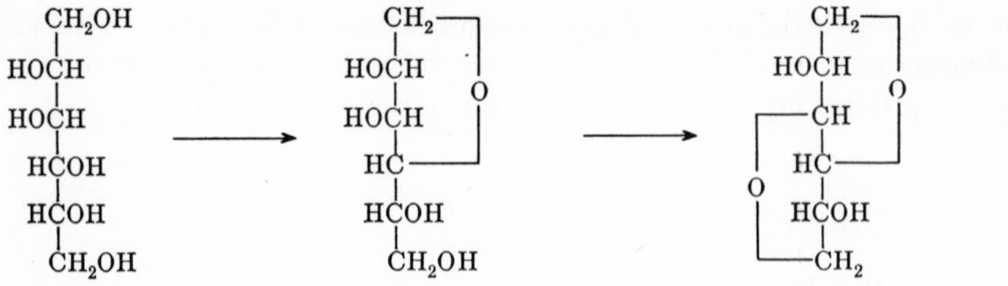

D-Mannitol — 1,4-Anhydro-D-mannitol — 1,4:3,6-Dianhydro-D-mannitol

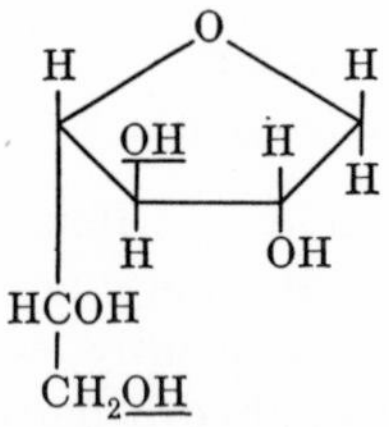

1,4-Anhydro-D-galactitol

pendent means (*33b*). For example, the 1,4-anhydrohexitol ("arlitan") formed by the acid-catalyzed dehydration of D-glucitol could conceivably have the galactitol configuration due to inversion on carbon 4. However, methylation of the anhydro alditol (I) gave the same product (II) as that obtained by reduction, followed by anhydro ring closure, of 2,3,5,6-tetra-*O*-methyl-D-glucofuranose (III) (*64*). Moreover, the anhydro alditol was found not to be the enantiomorph of synthetic 1,4-anhydro-L-galactitol, and thus it must have the D-glucitol configuration (*67*).

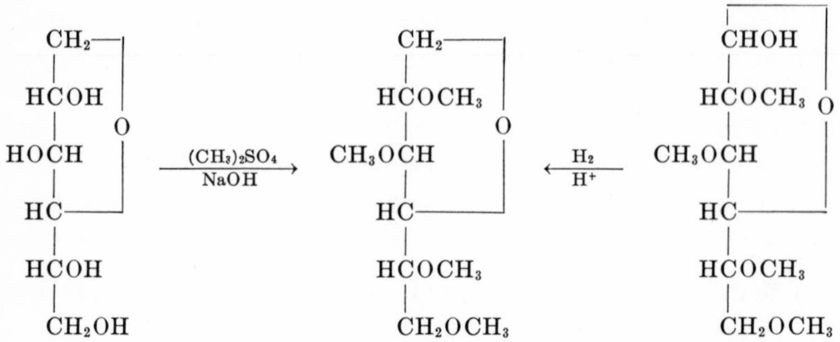

(I) (II) (III)

When the primary hydroxyl groups of mannitol are blocked, as in 1,6-di-*O*-benzoyl-D-mannitol, acid-catalyzed dehydration gives several

67. R. C. Hockett, M. Conley, M. Yusem, and R. I. Mason, *J. Am. Chem. Soc.* **68**, 922 (1946).

anhydro products, including 1,6-di-*O*-benzoyl-2,5-anhydro-D-glucitol through inversion at carbon 2 (*68*).

The sugar osazones are particularly prone to acid-catalyzed dehydration, and form monoanhydro derivatives when their alcoholic solutions are boiled with a trace of acid (*69*). (See also Chapter VIII.) With the hexose phenylosazones, there is produced a mixture of the epimeric 3,6-anhydrohexose phenylosazones resulting from dehydration with and without

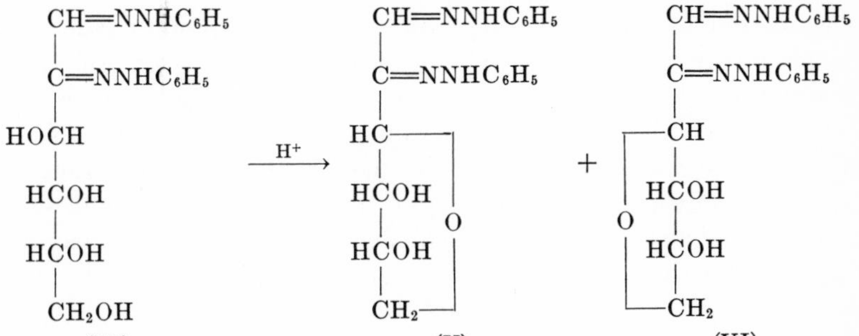
CH=NNHC6H5
C=NNHC6H5
HOCH
HCOH
HCOH
CH2OH
H+
HC
O
CH2
+
CH

(IV) (V) (VI)

inversion at carbon 3 (*70*). Thus, D-*arabo*-hexose phenylosazone (D-glucosazone (IV)) gives a mixture of 3,6-anhydro-D-*ribo*- (V) and 3,6-anhydro-D-*arabo*-hexose phenylosazone (VI).

The sugar benzimidazoles (VII), obtained from the condensation of aldonic acids with *o*-phenylenediamine, also readily undergo acid-catalyzed

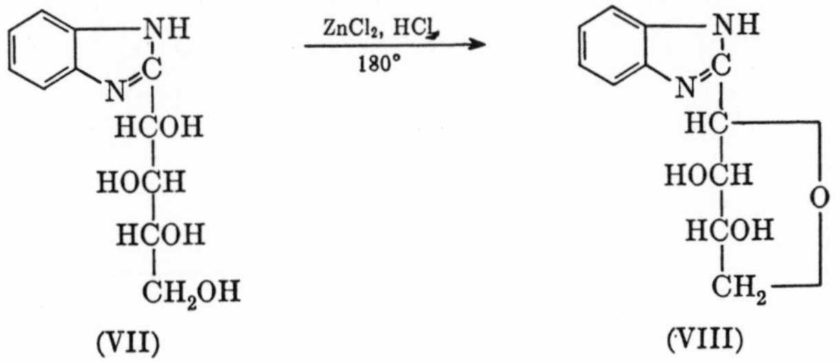
NH
N
C
HCOH
HOCH
HCOH
CH2OH
ZnCl2, HCl
180°
HC
O
CH2

(VII) (VIII)

dehydration to the corresponding hydrofuran anhydro derivatives (VIII) (*71*).

68. P. Brigl and H. Grüner, *Ber.* **66,** 1945 (1933); **67,** 1582 (1934); R. C. Hockett, M. Zief, and R. M. Goepp, Jr., *J. Am. Chem. Soc.* **68,** 935 (1946).

69. O. Diehls and R. Meyer, *Ann.* **519,** 157 (1935).

70. E. Hardegger and E. Schreier, *Helv. Chim. Acta* **35,** 232, 993 (1952); E. Schreier, G. Stöhr, and E. Hardegger, *ibid.* **37,** 35, 574 (1954); see also L. Mester and A. Major, *J. Am. Chem. Soc.* **77,** 4305 (1955).

71. C. F. Huebner, R. Lohmar, R. J. Dimler, S. Moore, and K. P. Link, *J. Biol. Chem.* **159,** 503 (1945).

B. REACTIONS OF ANHYDRO SUGARS

a. *Effect of the Hydrofuran Anhydro Ring on Sugar Reactivities*

Introduction of the planar hydrofuran anhydro ring into a sugar structure may result in elements of strain that have a profound effect on the reactivities of the sugar lactol ring. Haworth, Owen, and Smith (*72*) concluded that the anhydro ring assumes the character of the principal ring while the pyranose or furanose lactol rings play a subsidiary role.

The methyl D-glucopyranosides are considerably more stable to acid hydrolysis than are the methyl D-glucofuranosides. With the methyl 3,6-anhydro-D-glucosides, however, this order of stability is reversed. Moreover, when the anhydropyranoside is treated with methanolic hydrogen chloride, a smooth conversion to the more stable anhydrofuranoside occurs. This conversion does not require the presence of methanol since it is accomplished also with ethereal hydrogen chloride. Methyl 3,6-anhydro-α-D-glucopyranoside also is converted to the corresponding α-furanoside by dilute aqueous sulfuric acid under conditions that are sufficiently mild to preclude any substantial hydrolysis of the glycoside. Thus, the methoxyl group remains attached to carbon 1 throughout the isomerization, which presumably is effected by interaction of the proton and the oxygen of the sugar lactol ring (*33a*).

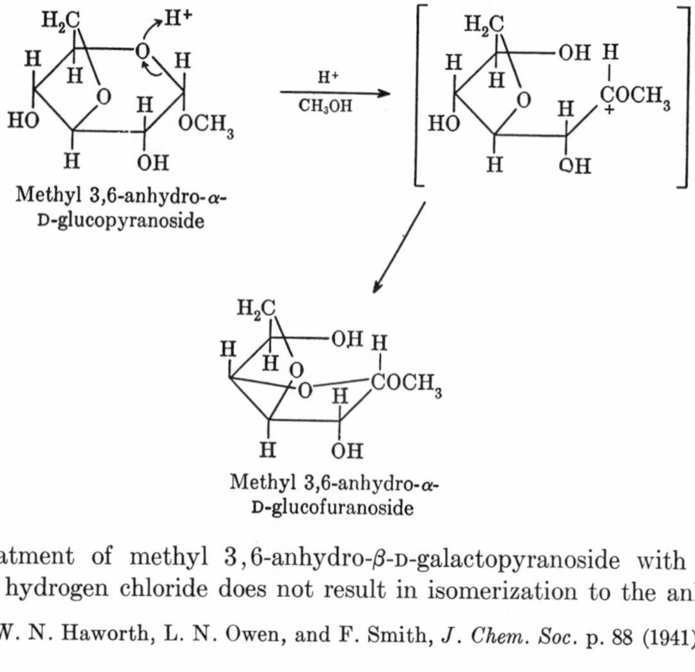
H+
CH3OH
Methyl 3,6-anhydro-α-D-glucopyranoside
Methyl 3,6-anhydro-α-D-glucofuranoside

Treatment of methyl 3,6-anhydro-β-D-galactopyranoside with methanolic hydrogen chloride does not result in isomerization to the anhydro-

72. W. N. Haworth, L. N. Owen, and F. Smith, *J. Chem. Soc.* p. 88 (1941).

furanoside due to the juxtaposition of the anhydro ring and the hydroxyl group at carbon 4; instead, the strainless 3,6-anhydro-D-galactose dimethyl

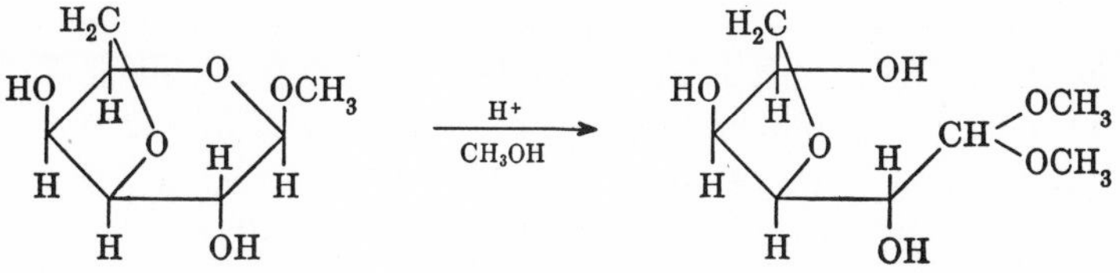
H+
CH_3OH

Methyl 3,6-anhydro-β-D-galactopyranoside   3,6-Anhydro-D-galactose dimethyl acetal

acetal is formed (*73*). The anhydropyranoside is hydrolyzed very readily by aqueous acids.

The methyl 3,6-anhydroaldohexopyranosides (II) cannot be formed by the application of glycosidation conditions to the parent 3,6-anhydro sugars, the furanosides being formed exclusively. They can be prepared, however, by introducing the 3,6-anhydro ring through standard procedures into the normal methyl aldohexopyranoside structures (I).

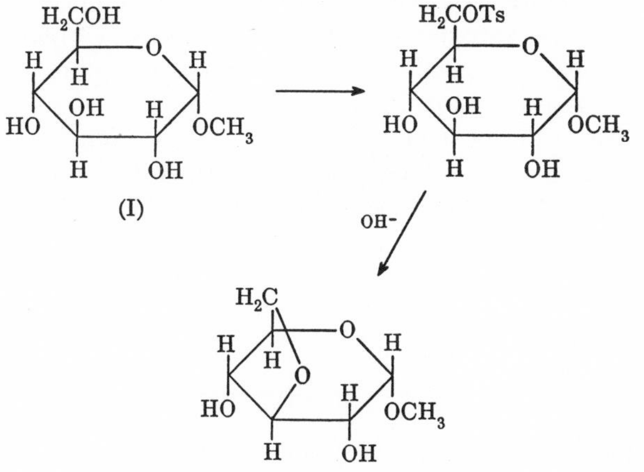
OH-

(I)   (II)

An extreme case of glycoside lability, promoted by the presence of the hydrofuran anhydro ring, is found in methyl or ethyl 2,5-anhydro-L-arabofuranoside (*74*). These glycosides hydrolyze to *aldehydo*-2,5-anhydro-L-arabinose when dissolved in distilled water at room temperature.

The reactivities shown by the hydrofuran anhydro glycosides lead to the

73. W. N. Haworth, J. Jackson, and F. Smith, *J. Chem. Soc.* p. 620 (1940).

74. M. Cifonelli, J. A. Cifonelli, R. Montgomery, and F. Smith, *J. Am. Chem. Soc.* **77**, 121 (1955).

conclusion that the unsubstituted hydrofuran anhydro sugars exist in solution only as the furanose and/or *aldehydo* modifications.

The presence of the hydrofuran ring also may alter drastically the stability of acetal substituents. For example, the benzylidene acetal moiety, normally stable to alkali, is removed from 3,5-*O*-benzylidene-6-chloro-6-deoxy-1,4-anhydro-D-glucitol when the compound is heated in alkaline or neutral solution (*75*). Similarly, 1,4:3,6-dianhydro-2,5-*O*-methylene-D-mannitol loses its methylene group upon heating in aqueous solution (*76*).

b. Ring Scission

The epoxy anhydro sugars are in general the most reactive, and their anhydro ring can be opened readily with a variety of reagents.

The epoxide ring, as noted previously in this chapter and Chapter III, is readily formed through the displacement of a suitable ester function by a neighboring *trans* hydroxyl group under the influence of sodium methoxide in methanol solution. If the conditions of treatment with the alkali are made somewhat more strenuous, the epoxide ring is attacked in turn by the methoxide ion. Nucleophilic displacement occurs with ring opening and, since either carbon of the anhydro ring may be attacked, a mixture of monomethyl ethers normally results. Configurational inversion occurs on the carbon accepting the methoxyl group, and the two possible products each have a *trans* disposition of the hydroxyl and methoxyl functions. Compared to the configuration of the original ester from which the anhydro sugar was prepared, that of the two products is, respectively, identical and doubly in-

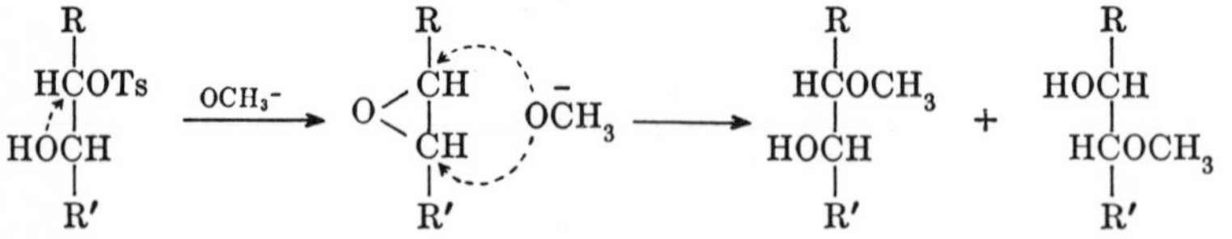
R
HCOTs
HOCH
R′
OCH₃⁻
O
CH
CH
OCH₃
HCOCH₃
HOCH
+
HOCH
HCOCH₃

verted. The product with a configuration identical to that of the ester now has a methoxyl group replacing the original ester function, whereas the product of doubly inverted configuration now has methoxyl replacing the hydroxyl of the starting ester.

The epoxide ring also may be opened hydrolytically, through the action of either alkali or acid in aqueous solution. The configurational course of the hydrolytic scission is the same as that depicted above with sodium methoxide. Thus, 3,4-anhydro-1,2-*O*-isopropylidene-D-psicose is hydrolyzed by aqueous sodium hydroxide to a mixture of products containing

75. R. Montgomery and L. F. Wiggins, *J. Chem. Soc.* p. 237 (1948).
76. S. B. Baker, *Can. J. Chem.* **31,** 821 (1953).

1,2-*O*-isopropylidene-D-fructose (*77*). With aqueous sulfuric acid, methyl 3,4-anhydro-β-D-galactoside (see formulas) gives a mixture of D-glucose and D-gulose (*78*). If aqueous halogen acids are employed, however, sub-

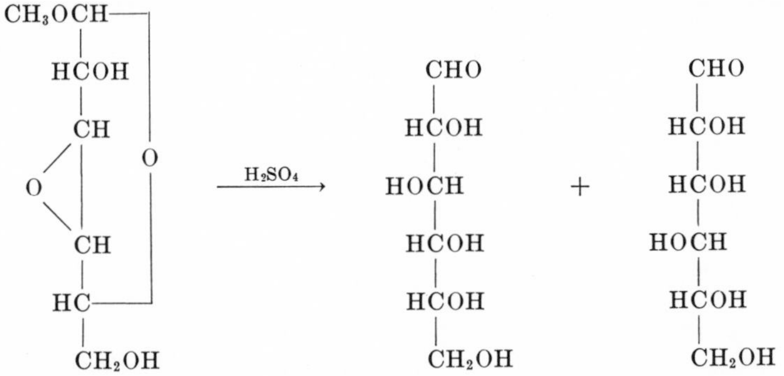

Methyl 3,4-anhydro-β-D-galactopyranoside   D-Glucose   D-Gulose

stitution by halogen accompanies ring scission and a mixture of halodeoxy sugars results (*79*).

The action of ammonia or amines on the epoxy sugars results in ring opening with the formation of aminodeoxy sugars or their derivatives. An interesting example is found in the conversion of D-xylose to 3-amino-3-deoxy-D-ribose, a structural component of the antibiotic puromycin (*80*). The transformation (see formulas on p. 392) is remarkable in that derivatives of all four D-aldopentoses are involved.

Other reagents that open the epoxide ring with substitution, to give the useful derivatives indicated in parentheses, include phenols (phenyl ethers) (*81*), carboxylic acids (esters) (*82*), hydrogen sulfide in the presence of barium hydroxide (thiols) (*82*), sodium methyl mercaptide (methyl thioethers) (*83*), dipotassium hydrogen phosphate or dibenzylphosphoric acid (phosphate esters) (*84*), alkyl or aryl magnesium halides (halodeoxysugars)

77. H. Ohle and L. von Vargha, *Ber.* **62,** 2435 (1929).
78. A. Müller, *Ber.* **68,** 1094 (1935).
79. A. Müller, *Ber.* **67,** 421 (1934).
80. B. R. Baker, R. E. Schaub, J. P. Joseph, and J. H. Williams, *J. Am. Chem. Soc.* **76,** 4044 (1954).
81. H. Ohle, E. Euler, and R. Voullième, *Ber.* **71,** 2250 (1938).
82. H. Ohle and W. Mertens, *Ber.* **68,** 2176 (1935).
83. R. Jeanloz, D. A. Prins, and T. Reichstein, *Experientia* **1,** 336 (1945), *Helv. Chim. Acta* **29,** 371 (1946).
84. O. Bailly, *Ann. Chim.* **6,** 96 (1916); G. P. Lampson and H. A. Lardy, *J. Biol. Chem.* **181,** 693 (1949); W. E. Harvey, J. J. Michalski, and A. R. Todd, *J. Chem. Soc.* p. 2271 (1951).

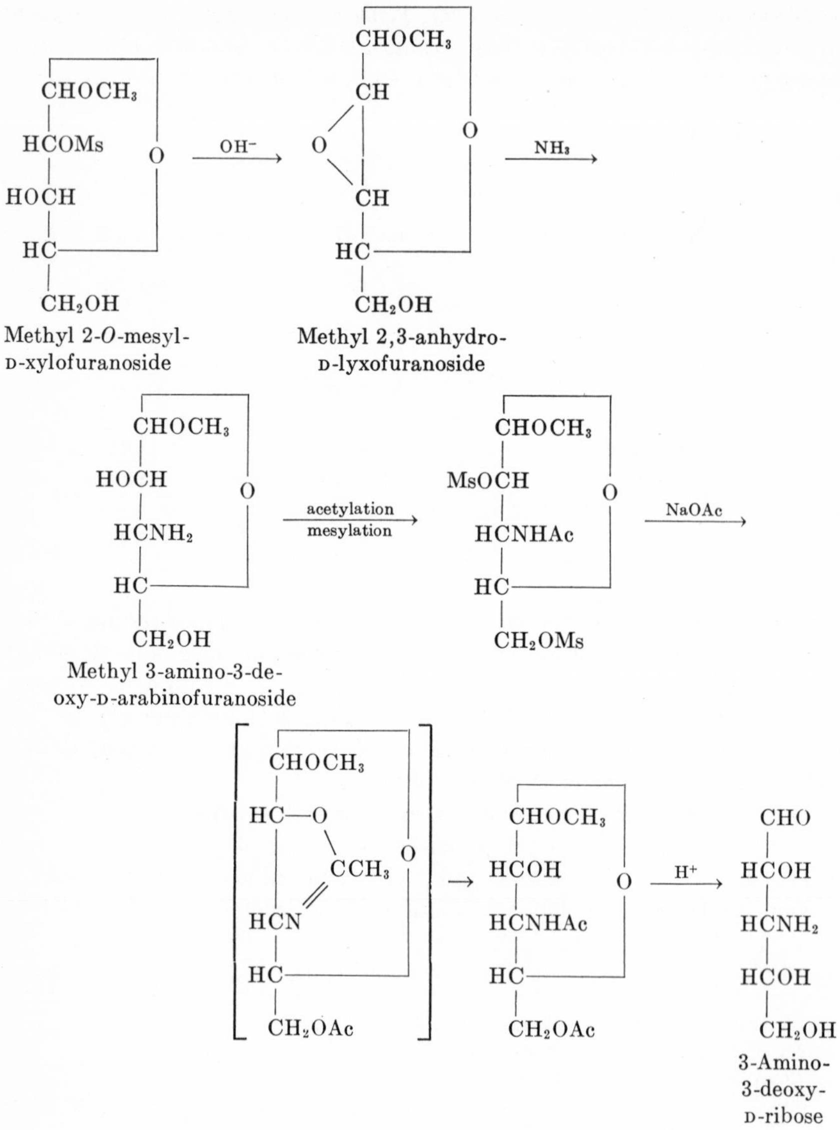
Methyl 2-O-mesyl-D-xylofuranoside
Methyl 2,3-anhydro-D-lyxofuranoside
Methyl 3-amino-3-deoxy-D-arabinofuranoside
acetylation
mesylation
NaOAc
3-Amino-3-deoxy-D-ribose

(*85*), and dialkyl or diaryl magnesium (*C*-alkyl or *C*-aryl derivatives) (*86*).

85. L. F. Wiggins and D. J. C. Wood, *J. Chem. Soc.* p. 1566 (1950); F. H. Newth, G. N. Richards, and L. F. Wiggins, *ibid.* p. 2356 (1950); G. N. Richards and L. F. Wiggins, *ibid.* p. 2442 (1953).

86. A. B. Foster, W. G. Overend, M. Stacey, and G. Vaughn, *J. Chem. Soc.* p. 3308 (1953); G. N. Richards, *J. Chem. Soc.* p. 2013 (1955).

Reductive scission of the epoxide ring to produce deoxysugars may be accomplished by catalytic hydrogenation or with lithium aluminum hydride (*87*):

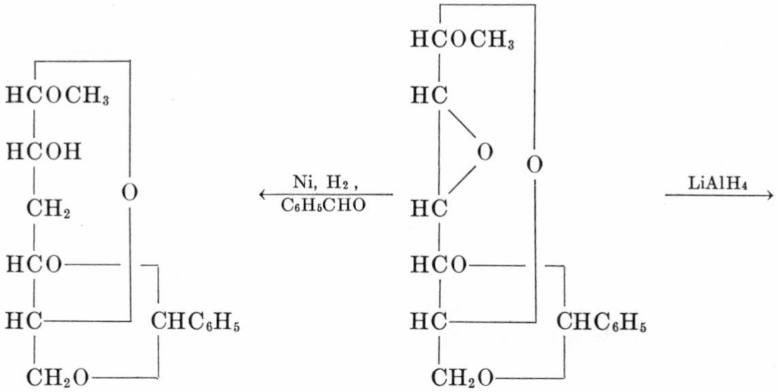
HCOCH3
HCOH
CH2
HCO
HC
CH2O
O
CHC6H5
Ni, H2,
C6H5CHO
HC
LiAlH4

(59%)

Methyl 2,3-anhydro-4,6-*O*-benzylidene-α-D-allopyranoside

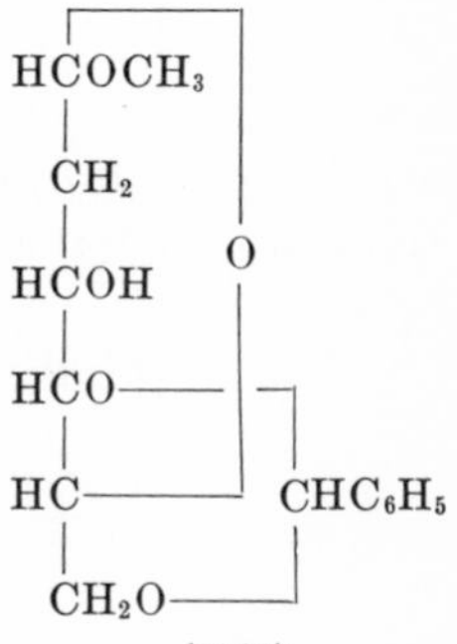
HCOCH3
CH2
HCOH
HCO
HC
CH2O
O
CHC6H5

(56%)

When the epoxide ring occupies a terminal position in the sugar chain, ring opening occurs almost exclusively through scission of the *primary* carbon-to-oxygen bond to give products with the same configuration as the anhydro sugar. For example, 5,6-anhydro-1,2-*O*-isopropylidene-D-glucofuranose (see formulas) provides only derivatives of D-glucose when the epoxide ring is opened by intermolecular reaction with a wide variety of nucleophilic reagents (*77*, *81*, *82*). No satisfactory generalization has been developed that predicts the preponderant direction of ring opening for an epoxy function that occupies a nonterminal position. The ratio of the yields of the two possible isomers that are formed in such ring openings

87. K. Freudenberg, H. Eich, C. Knoevenagel, and W. Westphal, *Ber.* **73,** 441 (1940); T. Posternak, *Helv. Chim. Acta* **27,** 457 (1944); E. Vischer and T. Reichstein, *ibid.* **27,** 1332 (1944); D. A. Prins, *ibid.* **29,** 1 (1946); *J. Am. Chem. Soc.* **70,** 3955 (1948).

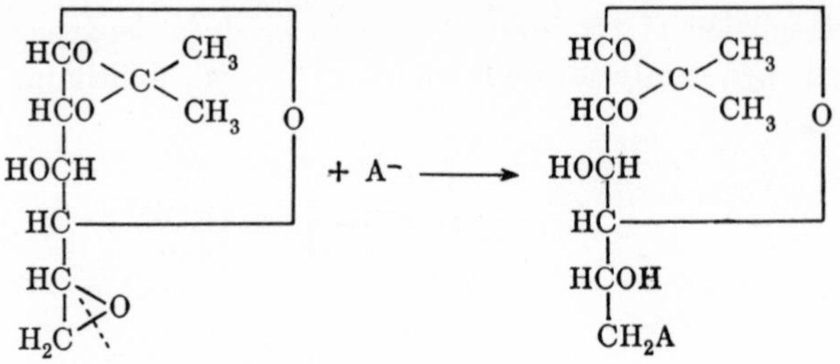

5,6-Anhydro-1,2-*O*-isoproplidene-D-glucofuranose

may be quite different under only slight variations in the scission reaction. For example, the action of methyl and ethyl magnesium halides, respectively, give very different ratios of the two alternative halodeoxy products (*85*).

Although ring opening of an epoxy function on two asymmetric carbons normally involves configurational inversion, an apparent exception is found in the treatment of methyl 2-*O*-acetyl-3,4-anhydro-6-*O*-trityl-α-D-galactopyranoside in acetone solution with hydrogen chloride (*88*). D-Galactose and D-gulose, but no D-glucose, are found in the product after deacetylation and hydrolysis (see formulas). The D-galactose presumably arises through an intermediate acetonated derivative (*89*). Whether or not this

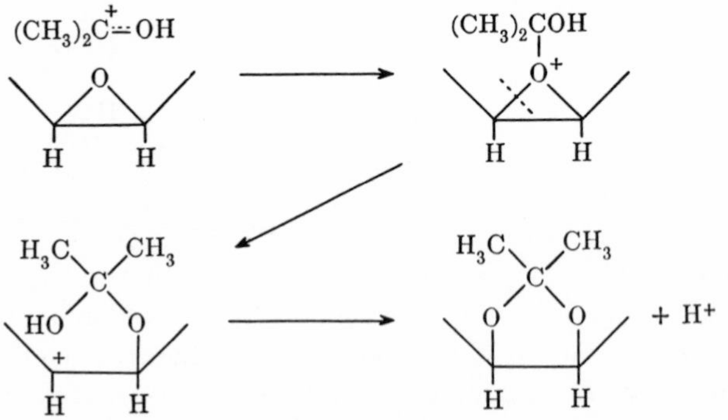

reaction is a general one for the *cis* opening of epoxide rings remains to be established.

Most reagents that readily open the epoxide ring are without effect on the much more stable hydrofuran anhydro ring. The latter may be opened, however, by acetolysis under vigorous conditions (*90*). Halogen acids or

88. J. W. H. Oldham and G. J. Robertson, *J. Chem. Soc.* p. 685 (1935).
89. V. Y. Labaton and F. H. Newth, *J. Chem. Soc.* p. 992 (1953).
90. T. L. Cottrell and E. G. V. Percival, *J. Chem. Soc.* p. 749 (1942).

phosphorus tribromide also open the hydrofuran ring, producing halodeoxy derivatives (*91*). In analogy to the ready loss of a 2-*O*-methyl group during osazone formation, 2,5-anhydro-L-arabinose gives L-arabinose phenylosazone when treated with phenylhydrazine (*74*).

c. *Oxidation and Reduction Products of Anhydro Alditols*

Oxidation of either polygalitol or styracitol with hydrogen peroxide and ferrous sulfate leads to a product, presumably D-*arabo*-hexopyranosone, from which D-glucose phenylosazone results on treatment with phenylhydrazine. With hypobromite, however, oxidation apparently leads to 1,5-anhydro-D-*erythro*-2,3-hexosone since subsequent treatment with

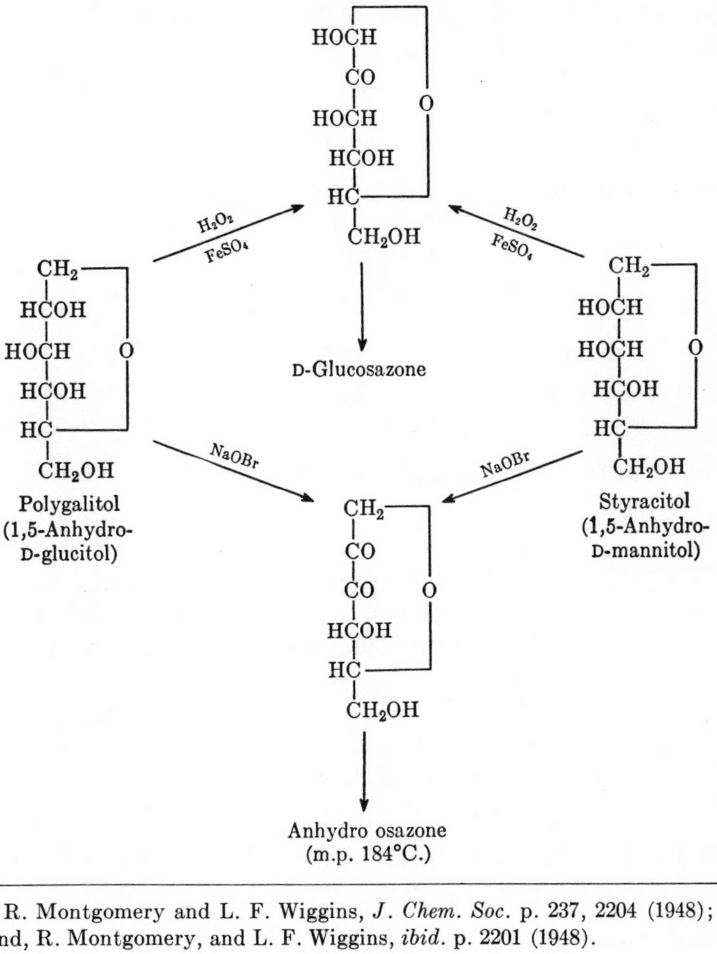
HOCH
CO
O
HOCH
HCOH
HC
CH₂OH
H₂O₂
FeSO₄
H₂O₂
FeSO₄
D-Glucosazone
CH₂
HCOH
HOCH
HCOH
HC
CH₂OH
Polygalitol
(1,5-Anhydro-
D-glucitol)
CH₂
HOCH
HOCH
HCOH
HC
CH₂OH
Styracitol
(1,5-Anhydro-
D-mannitol)
NaOBr
NaOBr
CH₂
CO
CO
HCOH
HC
CH₂OH
Anhydro osazone
(m.p. 184°C.)

91. R. Montgomery and L. F. Wiggins, *J. Chem. Soc.* p. 237, 2204 (1948); W. G. Overend, R. Montgomery, and L. F. Wiggins, *ibid.* p. 2201 (1948).

phenylhydrazine yields the same anhydro osazone as that obtainable directly from 2-hydroxy-D-glucal (p. 403) (*92*).

Cleavage of glycol groups in the anhydro alditols by lead tetraacetate proceeds normally. The all *trans* ring glycol array in polygalitol is oxidized more slowly than is the *cis-trans* structure in styracitol (*93*). The single *trans* glycol grouping in 2,5-anhydro-D-glucitol is attacked only very slowly by the oxidant.

Anhydro alditols containing pairs of vicinal hydroxyl groups may be converted reductively to unsaturated derivatives by heating with formic acid. Thus 1,4-anhydroerthritol yields *sym*-dihydrofuran (*94*). Similarly, 1,4-anhydro-D-mannitol (or D-mannitol itself) provides the strongly levorotatory 2-vinyl-2,5-dihydrofuran, b.p. 107–109°, $[\alpha]_D$ −168° (*95*). The structure of the latter compound was established by catalytic hydrogenation to 2-ethyltetrahydrofuran.

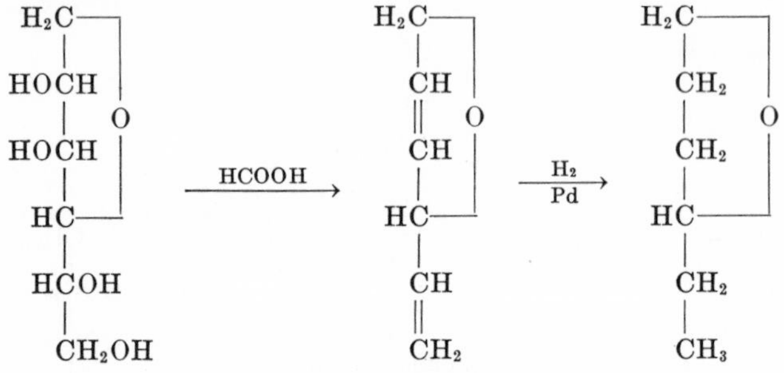
HCOOH
H2
Pd

1,4-Anhydro-D-mannitol — 2-Vinyl-2,5-dihydrofuran — 2-Ethyltetrahydrofuran

d. Substitution Products of Anhydro Alditols

The free hydroxyl groups of the anhydro alditols may be replaced by chlorine through treatment with phosphorus pentachloride, or thionyl chloride and pyridine. In this manner, 1,4:3,6-dianhydro-D-mannitol ("isomannide") yields an exceptionally stable dichlorodideoxy derivative which is unaffected by fused potassium hydroxide, phosphorus pentachloride at 125°, sodium amalgam, or zinc and dilute sulfuric acid (*96*). Fuming

92. Y. Asahina, *Ber.* **45,** 2363 (1912); M. Bergmann and L. Zervas, *ibid.* **64,** 2032 (1931); J. Shinoda, S. Sato, and D. Sato, *ibid.* **65,** 1219 (1932).

93. R. C. Hockett, M. T. Dienes, and H. E. Ramsden, *J. Am. Chem. Soc.* **65,** 1474 (1943).

94. A. Henninger, *Ann. chim. phys.* [6] **7,** 211, 217 (1886).

95. A. Henninger, *Ber.* **7,** 264 (1874); A. Fauconnier, *Compt. rend.* **100,** 914 (1885); P. van Romburgh and J. H. N. van der Burg, *Proc. Acad. Sci. Amsterdam* **25,** 335 (1922); C. D. Hurd and E. M. Filachione, *J. Am. Chem. Soc.* **61,** 1156 (1939).

96. L. F. Wiggins, *J. Chem. Soc.* p. 4 (1945).

hydrochloric acid, however, opens the rings to form a crystalline 1,2,5,6-tetrachlorohydrin. The chlorinated products obtained from 1,4:3,6-dianhydro-D-mannitol are believed to have the L-*ido* configuration since the replacement of hydroxyl by chlorine probably occurs by nucleophilic displacement with configurational inversion (*96a*).

When 2,5-di-*O*-tosyl-1,4:3,6-dianhydro-D-mannitol is heated in acetone solution with sodium iodide, both tosyloxy functions are replaced by iodine. Similar treatment of the analogous dianhydro-D-glucitol derivative results in replacement of only one of the tosyloxy groups (*97*). When either of the above di-*O*-tosyldianhydrohexitols is treated with methanolic ammonia, both tosyloxy groups are replaced by amino groups. These displacements of the tosyloxy function by iodine or the amino group presumably occur with configurational inversion (*96a*). 2,5-Di-*O*-tosyl-1,4:3,6-dianhydro-L-iditol and methanolic ammonia yield a 2,5-imino-1,4:3,6-dianhydrohexitol (*98*). From steric considerations, the latter is presumed to have the D-mannitol configuration.

With a cold mixture of nitric and sulfuric acids, styracitol gives a crystalline, explosive tetranitrate (*99*). With the same reagent, 1,4:3,6-dianhydro-D-glucitol and 1,4:3,6-dianhydro-D-mannitol give crystalline dinitrates, whereas 1,4-anhydro-D-glucitol and 1,4-anhydro-D-mannitol yield sirupy products. These anhydride nitrates show depressor action, similar to that of glycerol trinitrate and D-mannitol hexanitrate (*100*).

Partial esterification of the hexitol anhydrides with long-chain fatty acids provides products of considerable industrial importance (*101*). In early work, Bloor (*102*) treated D-mannitol with lauric and stearic acids in concentrated sulfuric acid at 38°. Among the crystalline products isolated were monoanhydro- and dianhydro-D-mannitol dilaurates and distearates. In modern industrial practice, D-mannitol or D-glucitol is heated with one or more equivalents of the fatty acids derived from hard fats, drying oils, or semidrying oils. Acid or alkaline catalysts are used, with vigorous agitation and, usually, a current of carbon dioxide. Little is known about the actual composition of the resulting esterification products except that they are mixtures of esterified hexitol anhydrides. Their use-

96a. A. C. Cope and T. Y. Shen, *J. Am. Chem. Soc.*, **78,** 3177 (1956).

97. R. C. Hockett, H. G. Fletcher, Jr., E. L. Sheffield, R. M. Goepp, Jr., and S. Soltzberg, *J. Am. Chem. Soc.* **68,** 930 (1946).

98. R. Montgomery and L. F. Wiggins, *J. Chem. Soc.* p. 393 (1946); V. G. Bashford and L. F. Wiggins, *ibid.* p. 371 (1950).

99. Y. Asahina, *Arch. Pharm.* **247,** 157 (1909).

100. For a review of the biochemistry of the alditols and their derivatives, see C. J. Carr and J. C. Krantz, Jr., *Advances in Carbohydrate Chem.* **1,** 175 (1945).

101. See H. A. Goldsmith, *Chem. Revs.* **33,** 257 (1943).

102. W. R. Bloor, *J. Biol. Chem.* **7,** 427 (1910); **11,** 141, 429 (1912).

fulness apparently depends in part on their mixed character, since the relatively pure ester synthesized from 1,4-anhydro-D-glucitol and one equivalent of lauroyl chloride is much inferior in solubility characteristics and emulsifying power to the technical product from D-glucitol and commercial lauric acid (containing minor amounts of C_{10}, C_{14}, and C_{16} acids) and shows somewhat less than the required hydroxyl content for a monoanhydrohexitol monoester.

The partial esters have valuable surface-active properties (*103*), and their comparatively bland taste and practical freedom from toxicity (*100*) gives them a wide field of usefulness as emulsifiers or solubilizing and blending agents. Esters with the approximate compositions of D-glucitan monolaurate, palmitate, stearate, and oleate carry the trade names Span 20, 40, 60, and 80, respectively. These products are dispersible, but not soluble, in water. An equally useful series of water-soluble, surface-active products, the Tweens, are obtained from the Spans by reaction with ethylene oxide to give polyglycol ethers. From ten to thirty moles of ethylene oxide per mole of fatty acid are required to give satisfactory water solubility, depending on the chain length of the acid. Since the water solubility is conferred by the accumulation of neutral nonionic oxyethylene groups, $—OC_2H_4—OC_2H_4—OC_2H_4OH$, the products are not electrolytes in the ordinary sense, like the anionic or cationic soaps, and do not lose their effectiveness in solutions containing strong electrolytes.

Synthetic drying oils from D-glucitol and D-mannitol, and drying oil acids have been described (*104*). Dianhydrohexitols completely esterified with saturated, medium-length fatty acids are useful as plasticizers (*105*). Analogous esterification products have been obtained from the reaction of hexitols with rosin drying oil acids, phthalic anhydride, and succinic and citric acids. The diacrylate and dimethacrylate esters of the dianhydrohexitols polymerize readily on being heated (*106*).

The methyl, ethyl, and butyl ethers of the monoanhydro and dianhydro hexitols may be used as plasticizers (*107*). The diallyl and dimethallyl ethers of 1,4:3,6-dianhydro-D-glucitol slowly polymerize when in contact with oxygen (*108*).

103. First recognized, for products from D-mannitol, by G. Izar and P. Ferro, *Biochem. Z.* **59,** 234 (1914).

104. A. A. Blagonravova and A. Y. Drinberg, *J. Appl. Chem.* (*U.S.S.R.*) **11,** 1642 (1938); J. D. Brandner, R. H. Hunter, M. D. Brewster, and R. E. Bonner, *Ind. Eng. Chem.* **37,** 809 (1945).

105. R. M. Goepp, Jr., *U. S. Patent* 2,394,439 (1946).

106. H. Gregory, W. N. Haworth, and L. F. Wiggins, *J. Chem. Soc.* p. 488 (1946); *British Patent* 586,141 (1947).

107. K. R. Brown, *U. S. Patent* 2,420,519 (1947).

108. H. Gregory and L. F. Wiggins, *J. Chem. Soc.* p. 1405 (1947).

3. UNSATURATED DERIVATIVES

Unsaturated sugar derivatives, containing ethylenic double bonds, include the glycals, glycoseens, and alditoleens. The glycal structure results from the formal removal of two adjacent hydroxyl groups, one of which is the hemiacetal hydroxyl, from the lactol form of the sugar. The glycoseens are derived from the sugar lactol structure by the formal removal of a molecule of water from adjacent carbon atoms, or by abstraction of two neighboring hydroxyls which do not include the hemiacetal hydroxyl. The alditoleens result from the formal removal of two adjacent hydroxyls from the alditol structure. With the exception of the glycals, which frequently

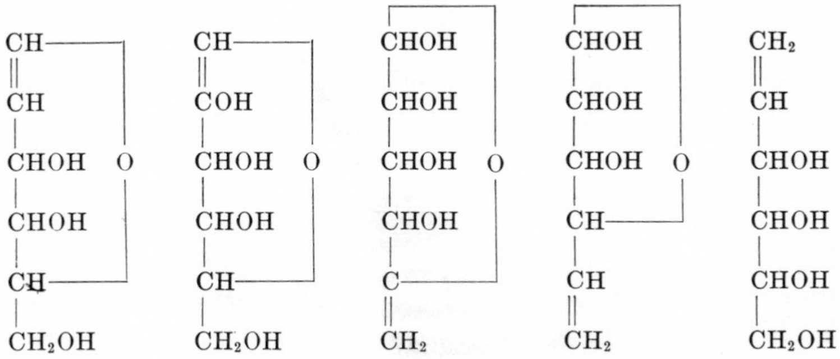

Glycal | 1,2-Hexopyranoseen (2-Hydroxyglycal) | 5,6-Hexopyranoseen | 5,6-Hexofuranoseen | 1,2-Alditoleen

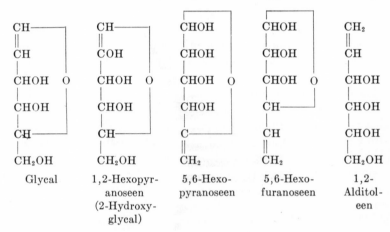

crystallize with ease, most of the unsaturated sugars are known only in the form of derivatives.

Products of still higher degrees of dehydration are the furan derivatives that result from the action of mineral acids on the reducing sugars (p. 57). Under alkaline conditions, enediols are in equilibrium with reducing sugars. Among natural products, ascorbic acid represents a sugar derivative containing a stable enediol system.

A. GLYCALS (*109*)

The glycals, first reported by Fischer and Zach, were extensively investigated by Bergmann and Schotte. They are important intermediates for the interconversion of epimeric sugars and for the preparation of 2-deoxyaldoses (Chapter II).

The acetylated glycals result from the reductive removal of halogen and the neighboring acetate group from the acetylated glycosyl halides through

109. For a review of the chemistry of the glycals, see B. Helferich, *Advances in Carbohydrate Chem.* **7**, 210 (1952).

the action of zinc and acetic acid. The reaction is catalyzed by platinic chloride (*110*) or copper salts (*111*). Deacetylation with methanolic ammonia, alcoholic alkali, or sodium alkoxides then gives the free glycals.

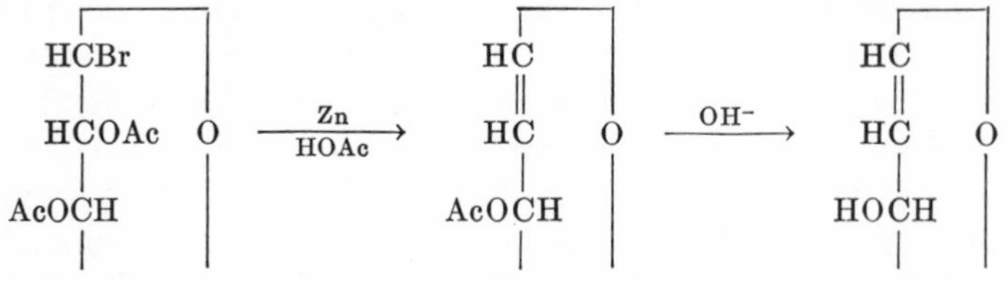
HCBr
HCOAc
AcOCH
O
Zn
HOAc
HC
HC
AcOCH
O
OH⁻
HC
HC
HOCH
O

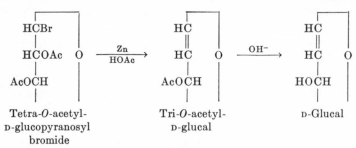

Tetra-*O*-acetyl-D-glucopyranosyl bromide — Tri-*O*-acetyl-D-glucal — D-Glucal

The class name of the glycals was originated by Fischer in consequence of the aldehyde reactions shown by the initial, crude preparations. The actual structure of D-glucal soon was established, however, by the following evidence (*112*): The pure substance is nonreducing toward Fehling solution. It readily decolorizes alkaline permanganate and adds bromine or chlorine to form saturated dihalides. Catalytic hydrogenation leads to dihydro-D-glucal (1,5-anhydro-2-deoxy-D-*arabo*-hexitol). Oxidation of D-glucal triacetate with ozone leads to a mixture of D-arabinose triacetate and D-arabonic acid triacetate.

Hydroxylation of the double bond of a glycal or its derivatives with perbenzoic acid yields mixtures of the two epimeric sugars related to the glycal. Thus, D-glucal provides D-glucose and D-mannose. The steric course of the reaction may be largely controlled by the choice of starting material and reaction conditions. For example, D-glucal and perbenzoic acid in aqueous ethyl acetate produce mainly D-mannose (*113*), whereas 3-*O*-methyl-D-glucal under comparable conditions yields predominantly 3-*O*-methyl-D-glucose (*114*). The hydroxylation also may be accomplished, although in lower yields, with hydrogen peroxide and osmium tetroxide in *t*-butanol solution (*115*). With these latter reagents, the D-glucose configuration is formed preferentially from D-glucal and its triacetate.

Addition of the elements of water to the double bond of the glycals, by treatment with dilute sulfuric acid at low temperature, yields 2-deoxy-

110. R. E. Deriaz, W. G. Overend, M. Stacey, E. G. Teece, and L. F. Wiggins, *J. Chem. Soc.* p. 1879 (1949).

111. B. Iselin and T. Reichstein, *Helv. Chim. Acta* **27,** 1146, 1200 (1944).

112. E. Fischer, *Ber.* **47,** 196 (1914); E. Fischer, M. Bergmann, and H. Schotte, *ibid.* **53,** 509 (1920).

113. M. Bergmann and H. Schotte, *Ber.* **54,** 440 (1921).

114. P. A. Levene and A. L. Raymond, *J. Biol. Chem.* **88,** 513 (1930).

115. R. C. Hockett, A. C. Sapp, and S. R. Millman, *J. Am. Chem. Soc.* **63,** 2051 (1941).

aldoses (Chapter II). Alternatively, alcohols may be added to the double bond, under the influence of dry hydrogen chloride, to provide the alkyl 2-deoxyglycosides (*116*).

Hydrogen halides add readily to the glycals (*112*), with the halogen attaching at carbon 1 to yield the corresponding 2-deoxyglycosyl halides (*117*). The addition of chlorine or bromine to the glycal double bond gives mixtures of very reactive stereoisomeric dihalides. The halogen group at carbon 1 is readily replaced by hydroxyl, alkoxyl, or acetoxyl, and the halogen at carbon 2 then can be reductively removed to provide derivatives of 2-deoxyaldoses. The dihalides (I), on treatment with lead oxide, lose their halogen and disproportionate to 2-deoxyglyconic acids (II) (*118*). The latter have been called "orthosaccharinic acids" since they are isomeric

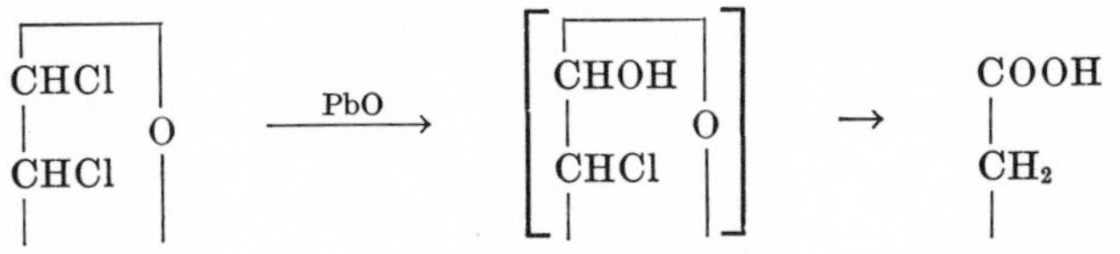
CHCl
O
CHCl
PbO
CHOH
O
CHCl
COOH
CH₂

(I) (II)

with the saccharinic acids obtained by the action of alkali on reducing sugars (p. 66).

It is noteworthy that the 2-halo-2-deoxyaldoses, obtainable from the glycal dihalides by treatment with moist silver oxide, yield the normal osazones with phenylhydrazine (*112*). This elimination of halogen at carbon 2 by phenylhydrazine is reminiscent of the similar elimination of methoxyl (p. 458) and of the hydrofuran anhydro ring (p. 395).

The glycals condense with phenanthraquinone, under the influence of light, to give substituted dioxene derivatives (*119*). Ozonization of the product thus obtained from D-glucal, followed by hydrolysis of the resulting cyclic diester of diphenic acid, gives D-glucose in high yield.

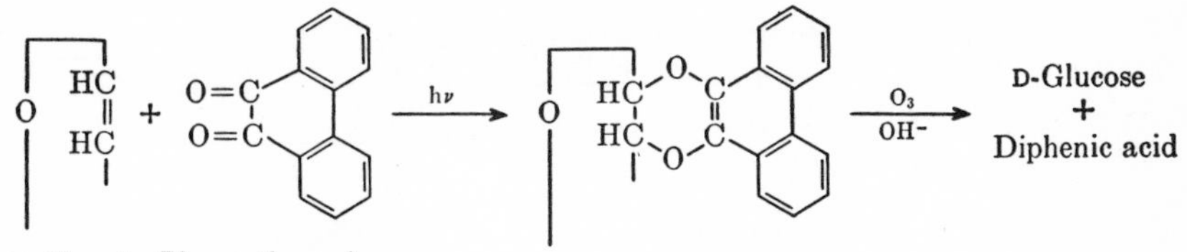
HC
O
HC
+
O=C
O=C
hν
HC
HC
O
O
C
C
O₃
OH⁻
D-Glucose
+
Diphenic acid

D-Glucal Phenanthraquinone

The glycals undergo intramolecular rearrangement with extreme ease. The heating of an aqueous solution of tri-*O*-acetyl-D-glucal causes the mi-

116. W. G. Overend, F. Shafizadeh, and M. Stacey, *J. Chem. Soc.* p. 992 (1951).
117. J. Davoll and B. Lythgoe, *J. Chem. Soc.* p. 2526 (1949).
118. S. N. Danilov and A. M. Gakhokidze, *J. Gen. Chem. U.S.S.R.* **6**, 704 (1936).
119. B. Helferich and E. von Gross, *Chem. Ber.* **85**, 531 (1952); B. Helferich, E. N. Mulcahy, and H. Ziegler, *ibid.* **87**, 233 (1954).

gration of the double bond to the 2,3-position, with accompanying loss of the acetate group at carbon 3 (*120*). The product, di-*O*-acetyl-D-pseudo-glucal, on deacetylation with dilute barium hydroxide undergoes further rearrangment to a mixture of D-isoglucal and D-protoglucal (*121*). The latter substance retains asymmetry only at carbon 5 and, consequently, is obtained also from D-galactal (*122*). The products of glycal preparation and rearrangement from D-mannose are identical with those from D-glucose.

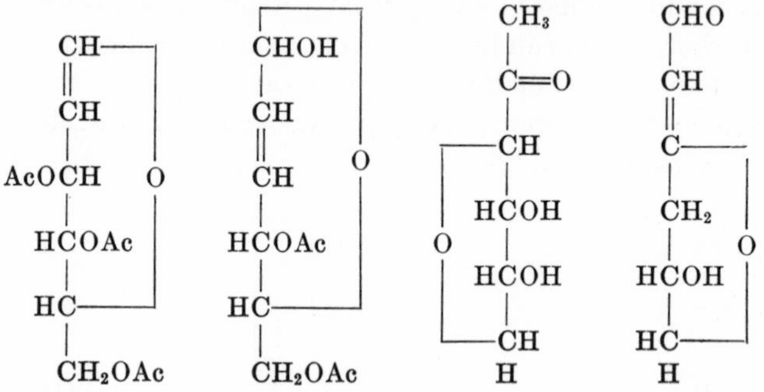

D-Glucal triacetate — D-Pseudoglucal diacetate — D-Isoglucal — D-Proto-glucal

The evidence for the structures of D-pseudo-, D-iso-, and D-protoglucal has been reviewed by Helferich (*109*).

B. Glycoseens and Alditoleens

The 1,2-glycoseens (*123*) (2-hydroxyglycals) are prepared (*124*) by warming the acetylated, benzoylated, or methylated (*125*) glycosyl halides in an inert solvent with a secondary amine, usually diethylamine, or other bases. The elements of hydrogen bromide, thus, are eliminated between carbons 1 and 2 with the formation of the substituted 1,2-glycoseen. The

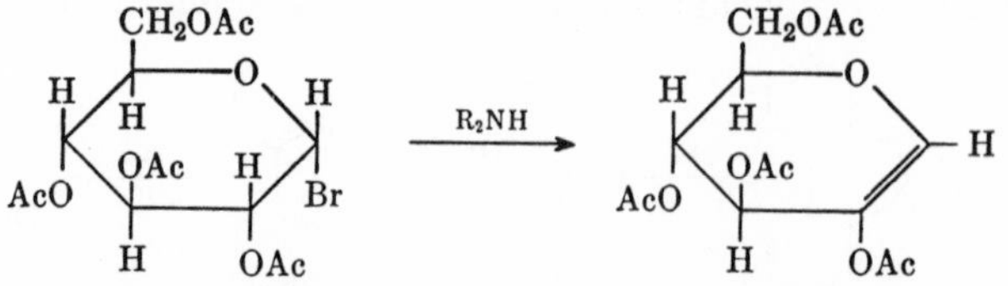

D-Glucosyl bromide tetraacetate — 1,2-D-Glucoseen tetraacetate

120. M. Bergmann and W. Freudenberg, *Ber.* **64,** 158 (1931).

121. M. Bergmann, L. Zervas, and J. Engler, *Ann.* **508,** 25 (1934).

122. H. Lohaus and O. Widmaier, *Ann.* **520,** 301 (1935).

123. For a review of the 1,2-glycoseens, see M. G. Blair, *Advances in Carbohydrate Chem.* **9,** 97 (1954).

124. K. Maurer, *Ber.* **62,** 332 (1929); K. Maurer and W. Petsch, *ibid.* **66,** 995 (1933).

125. M. L. Wolfrom and D. R. Husted, *J. Am. Chem. Soc.* **59,** 2559 (1937); M. L. Wolfrom, E. G. Wallace, and E. A. Metcalf, *ibid.* **64,** 265 (1942).

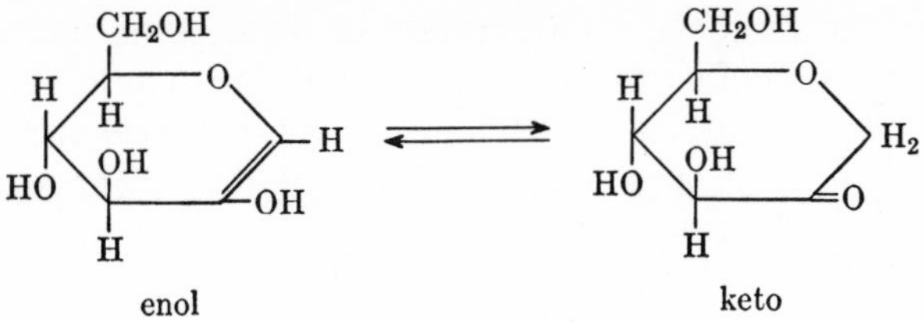
enol
keto

1,2-D-Glucoseen

free 1,2-glycoseens probably form an equilibrium mixture of the enol and keto modifications. However, only derivatives of the enol form have been prepared in a pure state. Deacetylation of 1,2-D-glucoseen tetraacetate leads to an amorphous product which cannot be converted to the original, crystalline tetraacetate by reacetylation. Cautious deacetylation of the tetraacetate, followed by treatment with phenylhydrazine, leads to an osazone that is presumably derived from the keto modification. This osazone is identical with that obtained from 1,5-anhydro-D-glucitol (polygalitol) or 1,5-anhydro-D-mannitol (styracitol) by oxidation with hypobromite and subsequent treatment with phenylhydrazine (p. 395).

The structure of 1,2-D-glucoseen tetraacetate was established by its catalytic hydrogenation to a mixture of polygalitol and styracitol tetraacetates (p. 382). The position of the double bond also was confirmed through isolation of D-arabonic acid triacetate after oxidation of 1,2-D-glucoseen tetraacetate with permanganate (*124*).

Hydroxylation of the double bond of 1,2-D-glucoseen tetraacetate is accomplished either with perbenzoic acid (*126*) or, indirectly, through the addition of chlorine and its replacement with hydroxyl provided by moist

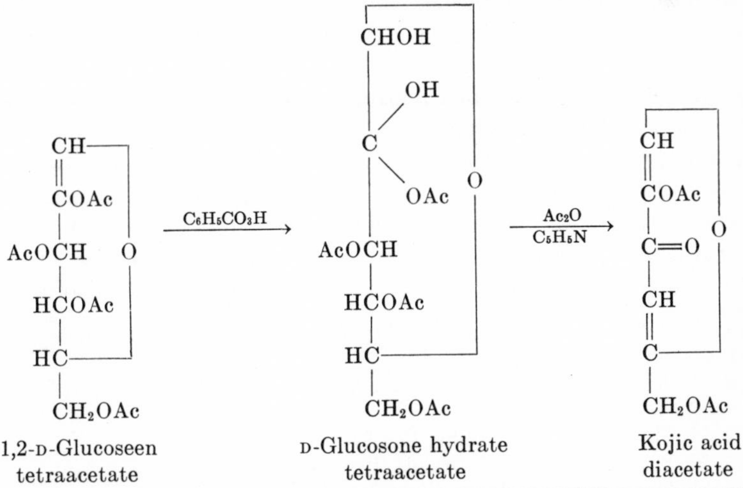
1,2-D-Glucoseen tetraacetate
D-Glucosone hydrate tetraacetate
Kojic acid diacetate

126. M. Stacey and L. M. Turton, *J. Chem. Soc.* p. 661 (1946).

ether (*124*). The product, a tetraacetate of D-glucosone hydrate, is converted by the action of acetic anhydride in pyridine to kojic acid diacetate. Kojic acid, which contains no asymmetric centers, also is a product of microbial action on a large variety of polyhydroxy compounds (sugars, inulin, galactitol, glycerol, etc.).

The substituted 5,6-hexoseens may be prepared by treatment of appropriate 6-bromo or 6-iodo glycoside derivatives in pyridine or acetonitrile solution with silver fluoride or sulfate or, alternatively, with sodium methoxide in methanol solution (*127*). When the sugar lactol ring is labilized in these compounds by removal of the protecting groups, isomerization to the keto isomer occurs (*128*).

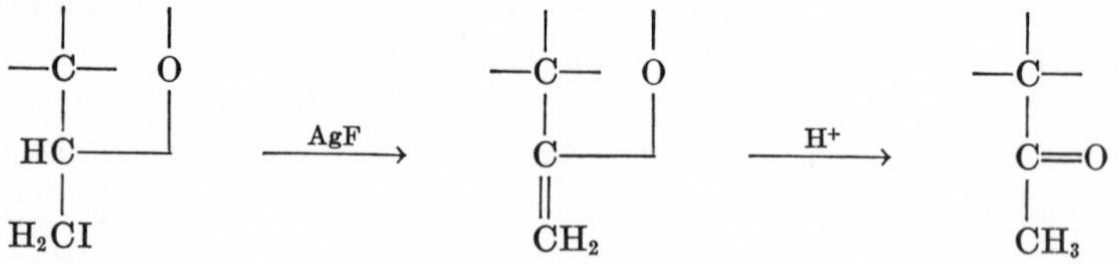
AgF
H^+

6-Deoxy-6-iodohexose — 5,6-Hexoseen — "1,5-Dicarbonyl-6-deoxyhexose"

Treatment of 1,2:3,5-di-*O*-isopropylidene-6-*O*-tosyl-D-glucofuranose with ammonia or sodium methoxide also leads to the unsaturated derivative, 1,2:3,5-di-*O*-isopropylidene-5,6-D-glucofuranoseen (*129*).

A glycoseen containing a nonterminal double bond is obtained when 1,2:5,6-di-*O*-isopropylidene-3-*O*-tosyl-D-glucofuranose is heated with hydrazine (*130*). Partial replacement of the tosyloxy function by hydrazine occurs and a by-product is the acetonated 3,4-glucoseen. The position of the double bond was established through identification of the products of ozonolysis and through hydrogenation to a derivative of D-*xylo*-3-deoxyhexose (3-deoxy-D-galactose) (*131*).

In the glycoseens described above, the double bond may be construed as having been formed by removal of the equivalent of a molecule of water from the normal sugar structure. Glycoseens may also result by removal of the equivalent of two adjacent hydroxyl groups from certain sugar structures. For example, 1,2-*O*-isopropylidene-6-*O*-tosyl-D-glucofuranose, on treatment with sodium iodide in acetone solution, provides an unsaturated compound, presumably 1,2-*O*-isopropylidene-5,6-glucofuranoseen

127. B. Helferich and E. Himmen, *Ber.* **61,** 1825 (1928); K. Freudenberg and K. Raschig, *ibid.* **62,** 373 (1929).

128. B. Helferich and E. Himmen, *Ber.* **62,** 2136 (1929); H. Ohle and R. Deplanque, *ibid.* **66,** 12 (1933).

129. H. Ohle and L. von Vargha, *Ber.* **62,** 2425 (1929).

130. K. Freudenberg and F. Brauns, *Ber.* **55,** 3233 (1922).

131. F. Weygand and H. Wolz, *Chem. Ber.* **85,** 256 (1952).

(*132*). This formation of a double bond through reaction of an appropriate tosyl or mesyl ester with sodium iodide has been studied more extensively in the alditol series. The prerequisite structure for the formation of an unsaturated compound is the presence, on the carbon atom adjacent to the tosyl or mesyl ester function, of another easily displaced ester group, such as tosyl or mesyl, or of a free hydroxyl group (*133*). Thus, tri-*O*-tosylglycerol and tetra-*O*-tosylerythritol are completely detosylated by sodium iodide in acetone solution, with the formation of unsaturated products (*134*). A number of crystalline, substituted alditoleens have been obtained from D-glucitol and D-mannitol (*135*).

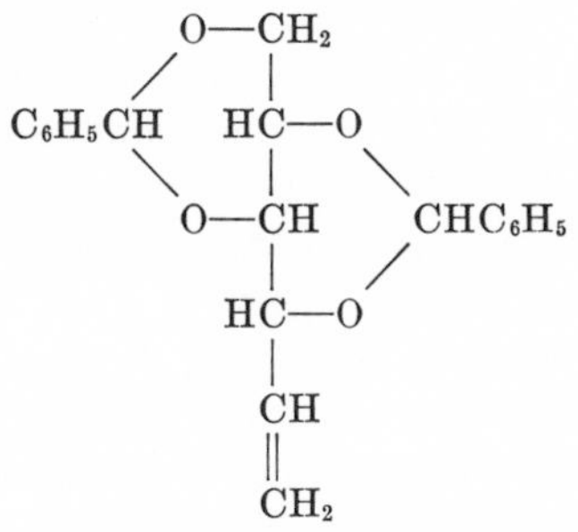

1,3:2,4-Di-O-benzylidene-D-glucitoleen

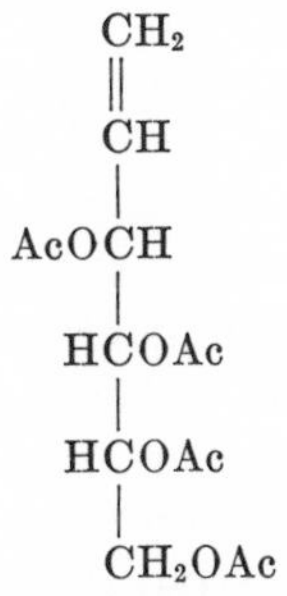

1,2-D-Mannitoleen tetraacetate

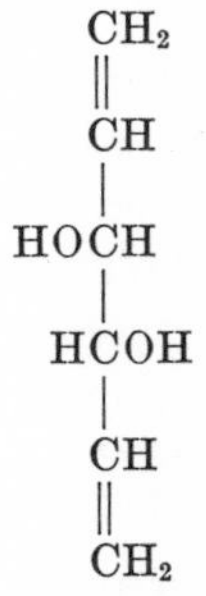

D-Divinylglycol

The addition of hypobromous acid to the double bond of the alditoleens, followed by treatment with acetic anhydride and sodium acetate to replace bromine by acetate in the resulting bromohydrin, provides a method for the interconversion of alditols (*136*).

The unsaturated derivatives of the sugars are highly reactive and versatile substances and the present status of their chemistry is an open invitation to further research.

132. D. J. Bell, E. Friedmann, and S. Williamson, *J. Chem. Soc.* p. 252 (1937).

133. For a discussion of the mechanism involved, see P. Bladon and L. N. Owen, *J. Chem. Soc.* p. 598 (1950); A. B. Foster and W. G. Overend, *ibid.* p. 3452 (1951); F. H. Newth, *ibid.* p. 471 (1956).

134. P. A. Levene and C. L. Mehltretter, *Enzymologia* **4,** (2), 232 (1937); R. S. Tipson and L. H. Cretcher, *J. Org. Chem.* **8,** 95 (1943).

135. R. M. Hann, A. T. Ness, and C. S. Hudson, *J. Am. Chem. Soc.* **66,** 73 (1944); P. Karrer and P. C. Davis, *Helv. Chim. Acta* **31,** 1611 (1948).

136. P. Bladon and L. N. Owen, *J. Chem. Soc.* p. 598 (1950).

VIII. NITROGENOUS DERIVATIVES

Glycosylamines, Nucleic Acids and Hydrolysis Products, Hydrazones, Osazones, Oximes, Amino Sugars, Etc.

WARD PIGMAN*

Nitrogenous carbohydrate derivatives such as the nucleic acids, nucleoproteins, some viruses, several vitamins of the B-complex, and some coenzymes are undoubtedly to be considered among the most important of the carbohydrate derivatives. Many of the polysaccharides which exhibit highly specific and characteristic immunological reactions yield amino sugars after hydrolysis. Other sugar derivatives containing nitrogen have considerable importance for purposes of identification and synthesis. The ease with which the sugars react with amines, amino acids, and proteins makes it probable that the resulting derivatives are of greater biological importance than has been generally realized. These derivatives may have an important role in the changes of solubility and of color that take place during the drying of foods (melanoidin reaction).

The most common type of nitrogenous derivatives is that which is formed by the reaction of the aldehyde (or hemiacetal) group of the sugars with compounds containing amino groups:

$$R\text{—}CHO + R'NH_2 \rightarrow R\text{—}CH\text{=}NR' + H_2O$$

If this equation represents the reaction, the products are Schiff bases, but it is probable that the ring form of the sugar reacts:

$$\left.\begin{array}{l} HCOH \\ | \\ HCOH \\ | \end{array}\right| O + R'NH_2 \rightarrow \left.\begin{array}{l} HCNHR' \\ | \\ HCOH \\ | \end{array}\right| O + H_2O$$

The compounds represented by $R'NH_2$ include alkyl- and arylamines, hydrazines, oximes, ammonia, and amino acids. Usually amide groups will not condense readily in this fashion, but urea derivatives are known.

* The sections on Glycosylamines and Hydrazones and Osazones were revised by Lawrence Rosen; the section on Nucleic acids and related materials by Elliot Volkin and David Doherty; the section on Glycosamines by Jane Reid Patton and the section on combinations with proteins by David Platt.

Hydrocyanic acid adds readily to sugars. As this reaction has its primary use in the synthesis of the higher sugars, it is discussed in another chapter (Chapter II).

An important additional group of nitrogenous derivatives is the amino sugars, among which are the glycosamines. These compounds represent sugars in which the hydroxyl of a primary or secondary alcohol group has been replaced by an amino group.

Although many derivatives have been made by condensing sugars with substances containing NH_2 groups, the chemistry of the compounds is still in a very incomplete state. Many of the compounds in which the hemiacetal hydroxyl group of the sugar is substituted by a N—R or a similar group mutarotate when dissolved in solution. Evidently, these compounds are much less stable than the corresponding glycosides. The mutarotations appear to arise from numerous causes which include (1) dissociation into the sugar and nitrogenous base, (2) isomerization between the various ring and open-chain forms, and (3) structural changes such as the rearrangement of aldose to ketose derivatives. Many of these compounds are known to exist in both the ring and acyclic forms. Very little is known concerning the relationship of the strength of the base to the stability and the properties of its condensation products with the sugars.

The glycosylamines have been of considerable interest because the nucleosides, hydrolytic products of the nucleic acids, are members of the group. The discovery that several biologically important coenzymes are glycosylamines or their derivatives has greatly stimulated research in the field.

Glycosylamines from long-chain aliphatic amines such as dodecyl- and octadecylamine have been suggested as wetting agents and as textile softeners. Those made by condensing D-glucose with aromatic amines are said to be useful antioxidants for rubber. Since many important pharmaceuticals contain amino groups, it is possible to condense them with sugars and, thus, modify their biochemical action and solubility characteristics.

A number of glycosylamines have been tested as inhibitors of the growth of tubercle bacilli, and the influenza and mumps viruses. Because of the ease of dissociation of most glycosylamines into their components, it might be expected that the action would be similar to that of the free amine, except that the effective concentration might be greater. In general, the inhibitory activity of these glycosylamines parallels that of the free bases.

1. GLYCOSYLAMINES (*1*)*

A. Unsubstituted Glycosylamines

The treatment of sugars in alcoholic solution (or suspension) with ammonia produces glycosylamines (glycosimines or glycose ammonias) by

* Revised by Lawrence Rosen.

the replacement of one hydrogen of ammonia by a glycosyl group (*2*). The same reaction takes place readily in liquid ammonia solution. This class of substances comprises the lowest homologs of the glycosylamine series.

With ammonium chloride as a catalyst, Frush and Isbell (*3*) obtained two D-galactosylamines, one as a complex with one mole of ammonia; these apparently represent α- and β-pyranoid isomers. Diglycosylamines may also form in this type of preparation, since two isomeric di-D-glucosylamines were prepared under very similar conditions (*4*).

The preferred nomenclature is to refer to the parent structure as a glycosylamine. Thus, D-glucose condensed with ammonia yields D-glucosylamine. When an alkylamine is condensed, such as *n*-butylamine, the resultant compound is *N*-*n*-butyl-D-glucosylamine. This type of compound has been referred to as *N*-glycosides because the cyclic structures are analogous to those of the ordinary or *O*-glycosides. For the *N*-glycosides, the linkage is through a nitrogen atom instead of an oxygen atom; hence, names like *n*-butylamine *N*-glycoside have been used. The preferred nomenclature is based on the original suggestion of Votoček and Valentin (*5*) that the compounds be named as substituted amines, as for example, D-glucosyl-*n*-butylamine, or in current practice, *N*-*n*-butyl-D-glucosylamine.

The hexosimines form pentaacetyl derivatives in which one acetyl group is connected to the nitrogen atom; the *O*-acetyl groups of the glucose derivative may be removed with the formation of *N*-acetylglucosylamine. This procedure is probably the best method for preparing the acetamide derivatives of the sugars, for direct combination has not yielded crystalline products.

An isomeric acetamide derivative has been prepared by the action of ammonia on *aldehydo*-glucose pentaacetate (*6*, *7*); lead tetraacetate oxidation shows that it has a furanose structure. Evidently, the ammonia combines with the aldehyde group and an acetyl group migrates to the amino group from the 4-position.

Diacetamide derivatives may result (*6*) from the action of ammonia on the acetylated nitriles (Wohl degradation), a process in which a carbon atom is lost. These substances probably have open-chain structures.

---

1. G. P. Ellis and J. Honeyman, *Advances in Carbohydrate Chem.* **10,** 95 (1955).

2. C. A. Lobry de Bruyn and A. P. N. Franchimont, *Rec. trav. chim.*, **12,** 286 (1893); E. J. Lorand, *U. S. Patent* 2,235,938 (Mar. 25, 1941); I. E. Muskat, *J. Am. Chem. Soc.* **56,** 693 (1934).

3. H. L. Frush and H. S. Isbell, *J. Research Natl. Bur. Standards* **47,** 239 (1951).

4. P. Brigl and H. Keppler, *Z. physiol. Chem.* **180,** 38 (1929).

5. E. Votoček and F. Valentin, *Collection Czechoslov. Chem. Communs.* **6,** 77 (1934).

6. R. C. Hockett and L. B. Chandler, *J. Am. Chem. Soc.* **66,** 957 (1944).

7. C. Niemann and J. T. Hays, *J. Am. Chem. Soc.* **67,** 1302 (1945).

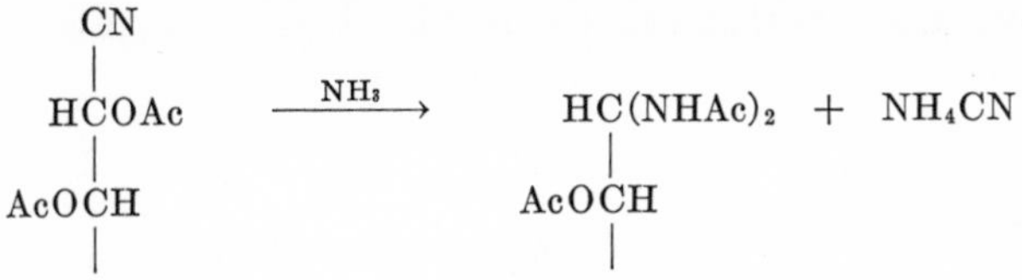

The simple glycosylamines are hydrolyzed by dilute acids (*8*, *9a*, *b*), and are reduced to 1-amino alcohols (*8*). Evidence to be presented below indicates that the acyclic and ring forms probably exist in an equilibrated solution; hence, the ring and open-chain structures will be used interchangeably in the present discussion.

B. *N*-Substituted Glycosylamines

Schiff, in studying the reactions of amines with aldehydes, found that condensation products, the so-called Schiff bases, are formed:

$$R—CHO + R'—NH_2 \rightarrow R—CH{=}N—R' \text{ (Schiff base)}$$

When the reaction was first applied to the sugars, amorphous products were obtained which were considered to have the Schiff base structure. By heating glucose or fructose in an alcoholic solution of aniline, Sorokin (*10*) was able to prepare crystalline products, although the crystallinity of *N*-phenyl-D-glucosylamine is in doubt (*10*, *11*). Many other crystalline glycosylamines are known at present in the aliphatic (*5*, *12*) and aromatic (*13*, *14*) series of amines.

In certain of their reactions, the substances behave as Schiff bases. However, since methylation by the use of methyl iodide and silver oxide and subsequent hydrolysis of the glucosylaniline (glucose anilide) (I) lead to tetra-*O*-methylglucopyranose (III) (*15*) the compound probably has a pyranose ring (*16*). The identical tetra-*O*-methyl pyranose ether (II) was obtained by methylation of *N*-phenyl-D-glucosylamine (I) by the use of dimethyl sulfate and sodium hydroxide, though only in 25% yield (*17a*, *b*).

8. A. R. Ling and D. R. Nanji, *J. Chem. Soc.* **121**, 1682 (1922); W. Wayne and H. Adkins, *J. Am. Chem. Soc.* **62**, 3314 (1940).

9a. H. S. Isbell and H. L. Frush, *J. Research Natl. Bur. Standards* **46**, 132 (1951).

9b. H. L. Frush and H. S. Isbell, *J. Research Natl. Bur. Standards* **47**, 239 (1951).

10. B. Sorokin, *J. prakt. Chem.* [2] **37**, 291 (1888).

11. J. Honeyman and A. R. Tatchell, *J. Chem. Soc.* p. 967 (1950).

12. E. Mitts and R. M. Hixon, *J. Am. Chem. Soc.* **66**, 483 (1944).

13. B. Helferich and A. Mitrowsky, *Chem. Ber.* **85**, 1 (1952).

14. F. Weygand, *Ber.* **72**, 1663 (1939).

15. Called 2,3,5,6-tetramethylglucose at the time.

16. J. C. Irvine and R. Gilmour, *J. Chem. Soc.* **93**, 1429 (1908).

17a. G. P. Ellis and J. Honeyman, *J. Chem. Soc.* p. 2053 (1952).

17b. J. G. Douglas and J. Honeyman, *J. Chem. Soc.* p. 3674 (1955).

This low yield suggests that ring forms other than the pyranose may be in solution.

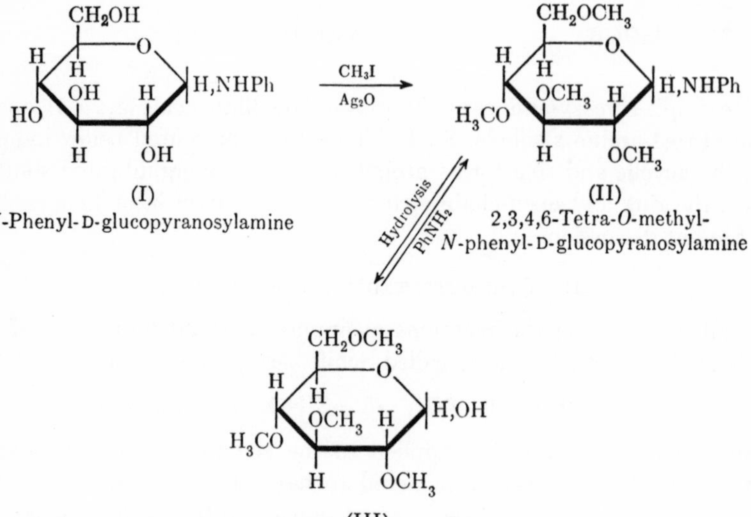
CH₂OH
H
H
OH
H
H,NHPh
HO
H
OH
CH₃I
Ag₂O
CH₂OCH₃
OCH₃
H₃CO
H,NHPh
Hydrolysis
PhNH₂
H,OH

(I) *N*-Phenyl-D-glucopyranosylamine

(II) 2,3,4,6-Tetra-*O*-methyl-*N*-phenyl-D-glucopyranosylamine

(III) 2,3,4,6-Tetra-*O*-methyl-D-glucopyranose

Certain *o*-nitroaniline derivatives of L-arabinose and D-ribose (IV) have been shown to have ring structures (*18*). They form triacetates, and all of the acetyl groups are removed by treatment with alcoholic ammonia, which does not hydrolyze *N*-acetyl groups. Two reaction products of ribose with aniline have been isolated (*19*). Both compounds form amorphous triacetates (*19*, *20*). Removal of the aniline residue from these amorphous triacetates followed by acetylation of the resulting triacetates gave, in both cases, 1,2,3,4-tetra-*O*-acetylribopyranose (*20*). Structural changes may have occurred during acetylation (*20*); anomerization of *N*-phenyl-D-

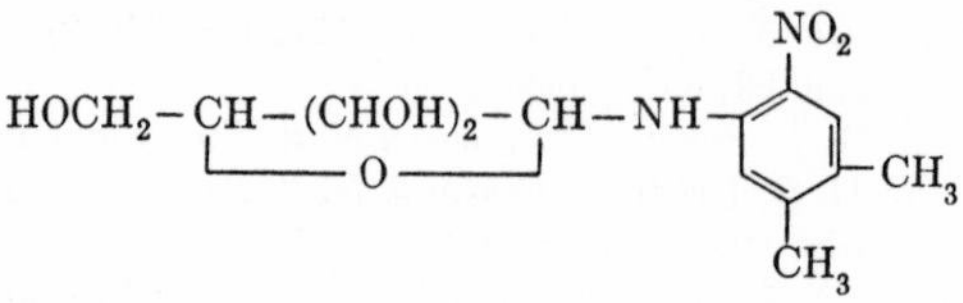
NO₂
HOCH₂–CH–(CHOH)₂–CH–NH
O
CH₃
CH₃

(IV)

ribosylamine also may have occurred prior to acetylation. For certain

18. R. Kuhn and R. Ströbele, *Ber.* **70,** 773 (1937).

19. L. Berger and J. Lee, *J. Org. Chem.* **11,** 75 (1946).

20. G. A. Howard, G. W. Kenner, B. Lythgoe, and A. R. Todd, *J. Chem. Soc.* p. 855 (1946).

N-arylglycosylamines, one isomer may be formed in anhydrous ethanol, whereas another isomer appears to be formed in aqueous ethanol (*21*).

Acetylation techniques have been very valuable in showing that pyranoid ring forms usually exist in solution for compounds such as *N*-phenyl- (*11*, *22*) and *N*-*p*-tolyl-D-glucosylamine (*17a*), *N*-phenyl- and *N*-*p*-tolyl-D-fructosylamine (*23*) and *N*-phenyl-D-galactosylamine (*24*). The α- and β-anomers have been separated by direct fractional crystallization (*11*, *22*, *25*) or by utilization of the complex which is formed between the β-isomer and carbon tetrachloride (*22*, *26a,b*). Similar evidence was obtained by benzoylation (*17a,b*) and by methylation (*17a*). Periodate oxidation studies also indicate that the *N*-acetyl derivatives of L-arabinosylamine, D-galactosylamine, and D-glucosylamine have pyranoid structures (*9a,b* *27*).

Infrared spectroscopic data (*28*) for solid *N*-*o*-tolyl- and *N*-β-naphthyl-D-glucosylamine shows peaks at 6.05 μ. Such peaks are usually due to a —C=N— grouping, indicative of a Schiff base. The compounds *p*-tolyl- and *p*-nitrophenyl-D-glucosylamine, however, do not show such a peak. In the reaction between 2,3,4,5-tetra-*O*-acetyl-*aldehydo*-D-ribose and aniline in ethanol or methanol, crystalline compounds corresponding to the Schiff base type (V) were isolated; these contained one molecule of ethanol or methanol. The infrared absorption spectra of these compounds, however, showed that they did not have the Schiff base structure (V), but were of

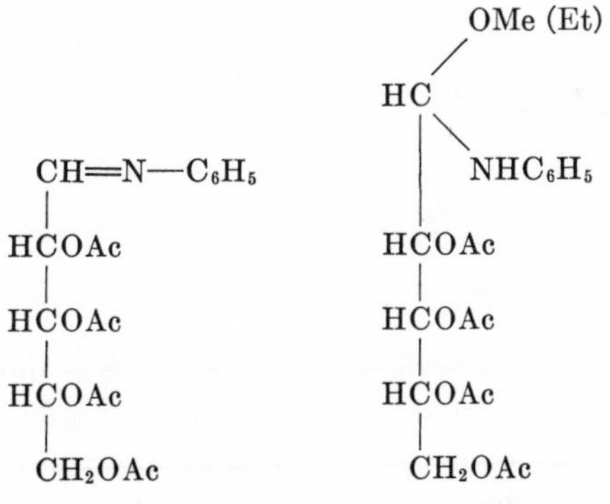
CH=N—C6H5
HCOAc
HCOAc
HCOAc
CH2OAc
OMe (Et)
HC
NHC6H5
HCOAc
HCOAc
HCOAc
CH2OAc

(V) (VI)

21. G. P. Ellis and J. Honeyman, *J. Chem. Soc.* p. 1490 (1952).
22. W. Pigman and K. C. Johnson, *J. Am. Chem. Soc.* **75**, 3464 (1953).
23. C. P. Barry and J. Honeyman, *J. Chem. Soc.* p. 4147 (1952).
24. K. Butler, F. Smith, and M. Stacey, *J. Chem. Soc.* p. 3371 (1949).
25. R. Bognár and P. Nánási, *J. Chem. Soc.* p. 185 (1955).
26a. M. Frèrejacque, *Compt. rend.* **202**, 1190 (1936).
26b. M. Frèrejacque, *Compt. rend.* **207**, 638 (1938).
27. C. Niemann and J. T. Hays, *J. Am. Chem. Soc.* **62**, 2960 (1940).
28. F. Legay, *Compt. rend.* **234**, 1612 (1952).

the aldehyde-ammonia addition type (VI) (*29*). Maltosylalkylamines may also have a structure similar to the aldehyde ammonias (*30*). The existence of the Schiff base form in solution is supported by the observation that HCN adds to certain glycosylamines to form nitriles (*31*):

$$R—N{=}CH—(CHOH)_4—CH_2OH + HCN \rightarrow$$

$$\overset{\displaystyle CN}{\underset{\displaystyle |}{R—NH—CH}}—(CHOH)_4—CH_2OH$$

a. Preparation

N-Substituted glycosylamines having aliphatic amines and substituted anilines as aglycons are prepared simply by reaction of the amine and aldose, or acetylated aldose, in aqueous or alcoholic solution (*5, 10, 14, 26a, 32*). The preparation of *N-p*-tolyl- or *N*-phenyl-D-fructosylamine requires acid catalysis, better results being obtained by the use of the amine hydrochloride as the catalyst than of ammonium chloride (*23*). Acid catalysis may also be necessary for ketoses and to condense certain weak amines and urea with aldoses (*33*) but often may be unnecessary and even undesirable (*34*).

$$\text{Glucose} \xrightarrow[\text{H}_2\text{O, alcohol 20°C.}]{\text{aniline}} (HO)H_2C—CH—(CHOH)_3—\overset{\displaystyle H}{C}—NH—C_6H_5$$
$$\underset{\text{——O——}}{\rule{0pt}{0pt}}$$

$$\text{Penta-}O\text{-acetylglucose} \xrightarrow[\text{HOAc, 20°C}]{\text{toluidine}}$$

$$(AcO)H_2C—CH—(CHOAc)_3—\overset{\displaystyle H}{C}—NH—C_6H_4CH_3$$
$$\underset{\text{——O——}}{\rule{0pt}{0pt}}$$

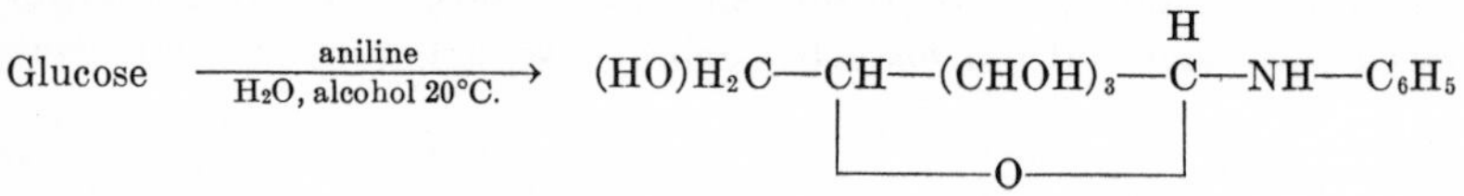

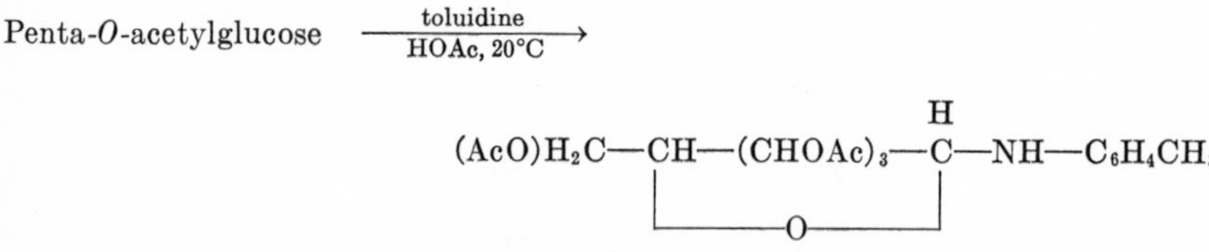

The mechanism of glycosylamine formation has not been established experimentally. However, a glycosylamine is probably formed by nucleophilic substitution of the hemiacetal hydroxyl group by an amine. The reaction may also occur through the open-chain form, with subsequent ring closure. Quite weak amines and amides require acid catalysis; the function of the acid catalyst is probably to convert the sugar to its conjugate acid form, which is sufficiently reactive for the weak amine to effect condensa-

29. M. Stacey, quoted by G. P. Ellis and J. Honeyman, see reference *1*, page 100

30. J. H. Werntz, *U. S. Patent* 2,181,929 (Dec. 5, 1939).

31. W. von Miller and J. Plöchl, *Ber.* **27**, 1284 (1894); E. Votoček and O. Wichterle, *Collection Czechloslov. Chem. Communs.* **9**, 109 (1937).

32. K. Hanaoka, *J. Biochem. (Japan)* **31**, 95 (1940).

33. F. Weygand, W. Perkow, and P. Kuhner, *Ber.* **84**, 594 (1951).

34. R. Kuhn and L. Birkofer, *Ber.*, **71**, 621 (1938).

tion. This mechanism is suggested by the work of Conant and Bartlett (*35*), who studied the condensation of acetone with semicarbazide.

From D-ribose, pyranosylamines were believed to be formed at room temperature, whereas furanosylamines (the stable isomer) were formed when the solutions were refluxed (*19*). However, observations on a number of *N*-arylglycosylamines indicate that the presence of water may affect the type of isomer produced (*21*).

Of particular interest are the glycosylamines of diamines. Such substances are intermediates in the synthesis of isoalloxazine derivatives similar to riboflavin, a component of a hydrogen-transporting coenzyme. The glycosyl derivatives of *o*-nitroaniline, prepared by the reaction of *o*-nitroaniline and sugars, are reduced by hydrogen in the presence of alkyl amines to the glycosyl derivatives of *o*-phenylenediamine (*36*). An alternative procedure involved coupling glycosyl derivatives of substituted *o*-phenylenediamines with diazonium salts and reducing the resulting azo dyes with hydrogen and nickel, or zinc and acetic acid (*37*). The glycosyl derivatives of 1,2-diamino-4,5-dimethylbenzene react with alloxan to form flavin glycosides (see Riboflavin synthesis, p. 439).

o-Phenylenediamine reacts with two moles of glucose to form the diglucosyl derivative or with one mole to give a cyclic derivative involving both amino groups (*38*). Under oxidizing conditions, a benzimidazole structure is produced. Griess and Harrow report that at least four compounds are formed from glucose and *o*-phenylenediamine. The structures of these

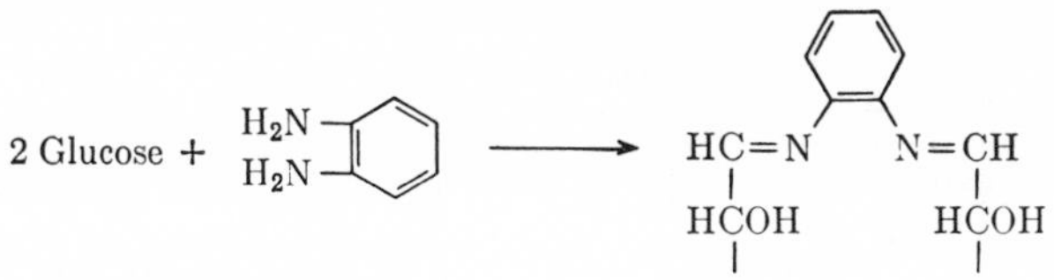
2 Glucose +
H₂N
H₂N
HC=N
N=CH
HCOH
HCOH

compounds need study particularly in light of the present knowledge of the Amadori rearrangement (p. 422).

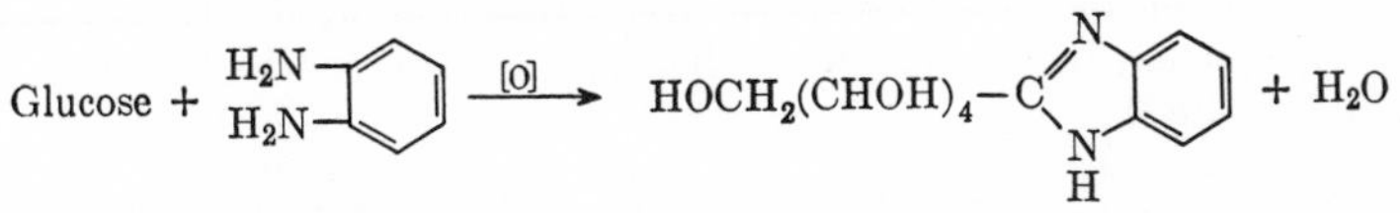
Glucose +
H₂N
H₂N
[O]
HOCH₂(CHOH)₄–C
N
N
H
+ H₂O

A better method for the preparation (*39*) of these derivatives involves the

35. J. B. Conant and P. D. Bartlett, *J. Am. Chem. Soc.* **54,** 2881 (1932).

36. *British Patent* 461,245 (Feb. 8, 1937).

37. P. Karrer, *U. S. Patent* 2,237,074 (Apr. 1, 1941).

38. P. Griess and G. Harrow, *Ber.* **20,** 281, 2205, 3111 (1887); B. Schilling, *ibid.* **34,** 902 (1901).

39. S. Moore and K. P. Link, *J. Biol. Chem.* **133,** 293 (1940); See also N. K. Richtmyer, *Advances in Carbohydrate Chem.* **6,** 175 (1951).

reaction of the aldonic and saccharic acids with *o*-phenylenediamine:

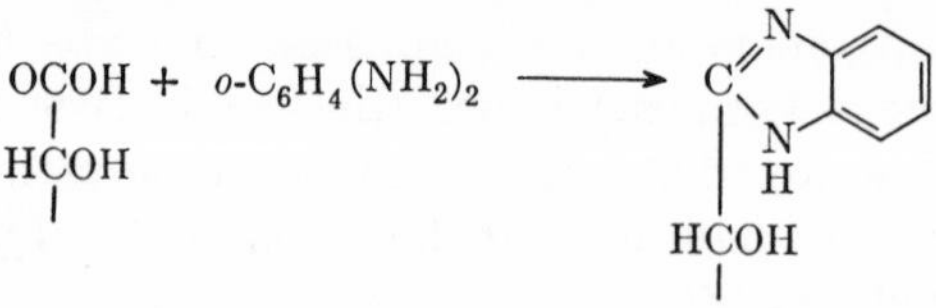
OCOH + o-C6H4(NH2)2
HCOH
N
C
N
H
HCOH

Xylobenzimidazole forms the 2,5-anhydro derivative when heated with zinc chloride (*40*). The benzimidazoles are useful for the characterization of the sugars and of the aldonic, saccharic, saccharinic, and uronic acids (*39*, *39a*).

Syntheses of pentosyl and glucosyl derivatives of benzimidazole and substituted benzimidazoles have been reported (*41*). A crystalline phosphate of 1-α-D-ribofuranosyl-5,6-dimethylbenzimidazole (α-ribazole) has been isolated as a degradation product of vitamin B_{12} (*42*) and has been tentatively identified as the α-ribazole 3′-phosphate (*43*).

Ribofuranosyl derivatives of substituted benzimidazoles have been found to have virus inhibitory activity (*44*).

From glucosone, compounds with quinoxaline structures may be produced (*45*). In the presence of hydrazine and *o*-phenylenediamine, 1-deoxy-1-*p*-toluino-D-fructose or -D-tagatose is converted to a quinoxaline compound in the pH range 6 to 8 by a mechanism similar to osazone formation (*46*).

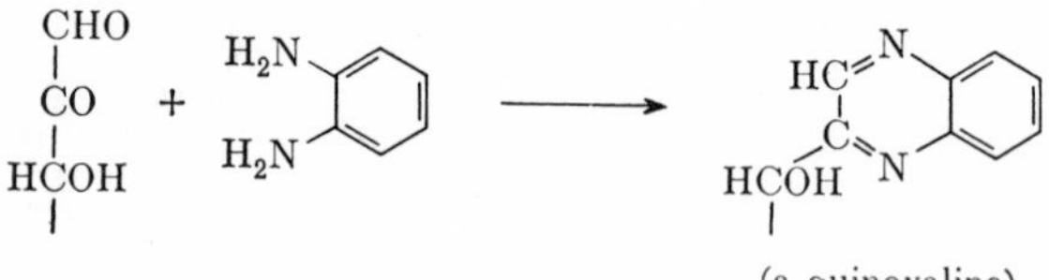
CHO
CO
HCOH
H2N
H2N
HC
N
C
N
HCOH
(a quinoxaline)

Urea, substituted ureas, thiourea, and guanidine condense directly with

39a. J. C. Sowden and D. J. Kuenne, *J. Am. Chem. Soc.* **75,** 2788 (1953).

40. C. F. Huebner, R. Lohmar, R. J. Dimler, S. Moore, and K. P. Link, *J. Biol. Chem.* **159,** 503 (1945).

41. J. Davoll and G. B. Brown, *J. Am. Chem. Soc.* **73,** 5781 (1951); P. Mammalis, V. Petrow, and B. Sturgeon, *J. Pharm. and Pharmacol.* **2,** 503, 512 (1950). D. Heyl, E. C. Chase, C. H. Shunk, M. U. Moore, G. A. Emerson, and K. Folkers, *J. Am. Chem. Soc.* **76,** 1355 (1954).

42. E. A. Kaczka, D. Heyl, W. H. Jones, and K. Folkers, *J. Am. Chem. Soc.* **74,** 5549 (1952).

43. E. A. Kaczka and K. Folkers, *J. Am. Chem. Soc.* **75,** 6317 (1953).

44. I. Tamm, *Science* **120,** 847 (1954).

45. H. Ohle, *Ber.* **67,** 155 (1934).

46. F. Weygand and A. Bergmann, *Ber.* **80,** 255 (1947).

glucose under conditions similar to those used for the amines (*47*), but acid catalysts are necessary. The urea derivative forms a pentaacetate upon acetylation with acetic anhydride and zinc chloride. Since one acetyl group is bound to a nitrogen atom, the compound probably has a ring structure; otherwise, a hexaacetate would be expected. The *N*-glucosylurea reduces Fehling solution much more slowly than D-glucose. The Barfoed reagent is not affected in thirty seconds at 100°C. Upon treatment with phenylhydrazine, the compound is converted to the osazone but more slowly than for glucose.

The salts and lactones of the aldonic and saccharic acids react readily with phenylhydrazine to form the hydrazides (*48*). The low solubility and ease of crystallization of the hydrazides have led to their use for the characterization and isolation of the acids. Aniline reacts in a manner similar to phenylhydrazine.

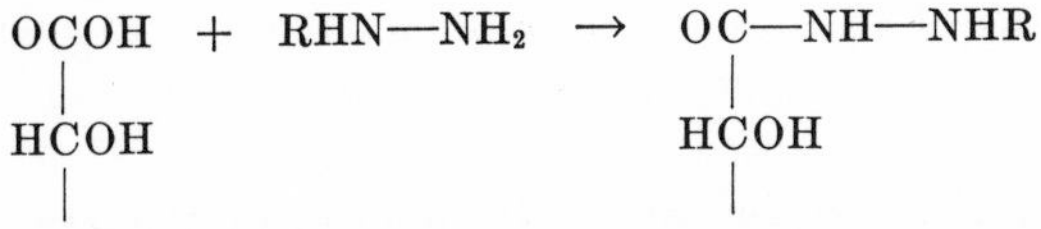
OCOH
HCOH
+ RHN—NH₂ →
OC—NH—NHR
HCOH

Many aminopyrimidines do not condense directly with sugars. The lack of reactivity may be due to tautomerism of the amidine type:

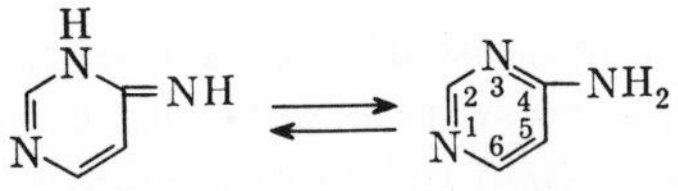
H
N
NH
N
N
NH₂
N
1 2 3 4 5 6

However, 4,6-diamino-2-methylpyrimidine in alcoholic solution reacts with xylose to give 6-amino-4-D-xylosylamino-2-methylpyrimidine (*49*). The reaction of glucose and fructose with 2,4,5-triamino-6-hydroxypyrimidine yields pteridine compounds (*50*) which, when subjected to a folic acid-forming reaction, do not give biologically active compounds (*50*).

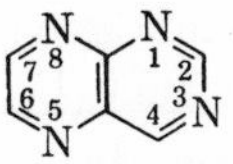
N N
N N
1 2 3 4 5 6 7 8

Pteridine

Glucosylamines formed from sulfanilamides are of interest because of

47. N. Schoorl, *Rec. trav. chim.* **22,** 31 (1903); R. S. Morrell and A. E. Bellars, *J. Chem. Soc.* **91,** 1010 (1907); B. Helferich and W. Kosche, *Ber.* **59,** 69 (1926); K. Quehl, *U. S. Patent* 2,116,640 (May 10, 1938); J. G. Erickson and J. S. Keps, *J. Am. Chem. Soc.* **75,** 4339 (1953).

48. L. Maquenne, *Bull. soc. chim. France* [3] **48,** 719 (1887); E. Fischer and F. Passmore, *Ber.* **22,** 2728 (1889).

49. J. Baddiley, B. Lythgoe, and A. R. Todd, *J. Chem. Soc.* p. 571 (1943).

50. P. Karrer and R. Schwyzer, *Helv. Chim. Acta* **31,** 782 (1948).

the pharmacological importance of the aglycon (*51*). They may be prepared by the reaction of the sulfanilamide with glucose and are split, *in vivo*, with the liberation of sulfanilamide. Glucosylamines, reported for sulfapyridine, sulfamethylthiazole, and sulfaguanidine, contain two moles of sugar (*52*). The biological action of the products is similar to that of the aglycon, except that for the sulfapyridine derivative activity against cholera organisms was shown.

An important method of synthesis is based on the reaction of the acetylglycosyl halides with nitrogenous compounds or their metallic salts.

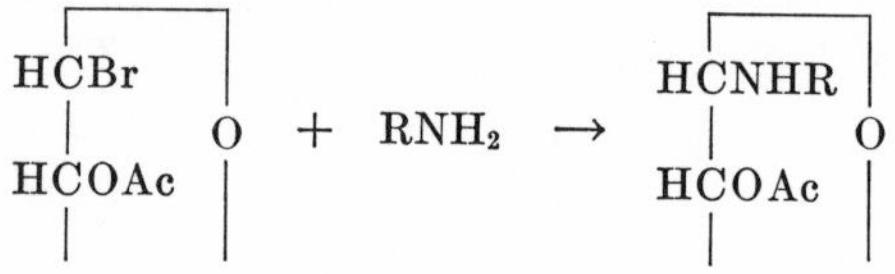
HCBr
O
HCOAc
+ RNH₂ →
HCNHR
O
HCOAc

The silver salts of purines and pyrimidines react in this way (*53*). These compounds are synthetic nucleosides. (Naturally occurring nucleosides are discussed later in this chapter.)

The acetylglycosyl halides react with silver cyanate or thiocyanate when refluxed in xylene solution to give derivatives with —NCO or —NCS groups in place of the halogen atom (*54*). The products generally are amorphous but are valuable intermediates for the preparation of glycosylamines of the urea and hydantoin series. The sugar isocyanates react with ammonia to produce *N*-glycosylureas and with alcohols to give urethans. The sugar isothiocyanates yield the corresponding thio derivatives.

$$(\text{Ac—Gl})\text{—NCO} + NH_3 \rightarrow (\text{Ac—Gl})\text{—NH—CO—}NH_2$$

$$(\text{Ac—Gl})\text{—NCS} + C_2H_5OH \rightarrow (\text{Ac—Gl})\text{—NH—CS—O}C_2H_5$$

(Ac—Gl is the acetylated glycosyl group)

Tetra-*O*-acetylglucosylisothiocyanate (I) reacts with glycine ethyl ester hydrochloride to give tetra-*O*-acetylglucosyl ethyl thiohydantoate (II), which on desulfuration and saponification is converted to glucosylhydantoin (III) or to glucosylhydantoic acid (IV) (*55*).

By condensation of acetylglycosyl bromides with *potassium* thiocyanate

51. Many references to the preparation and properties of these compounds are given by E. L. Jackson, *J. Am. Chem. Soc.* **64**, 1371 (1942).

52. S. I. Lur'e and M. M. Shemyakin, *J. Gen. Chem.* (*U.S.S.R.*) **14**, 935 (1944); *Chem. Abstr.* **39**, 4597 (1945).

53. E. Fischer and B. Helferich, *Ber.* **47**, 210 (1914); P. A. Levene and J. Compton, *J. Biol. Chem.* **114**, 9 (1936); **117**, 37 (1937).

54. E. Fischer, *Ber.* **47**, 1377 (1914); T. B. Johnson and W. Bergmann, *J. Am. Chem. Soc.* **60**, 1916 (1938).

55. K. Haring and T. B. Johnson, *J. Am. Chem. Soc.* **55**, 395 (1933).

$$(Ac—Gl)—N{=}C{=}S + H_2NCH_2COOR \xrightarrow{HCl}$$
(I)

$$(Ac—Gl)—NH—CS—NH—CH_2COOR \xrightarrow[ROH]{AgNO_3}$$
(II)

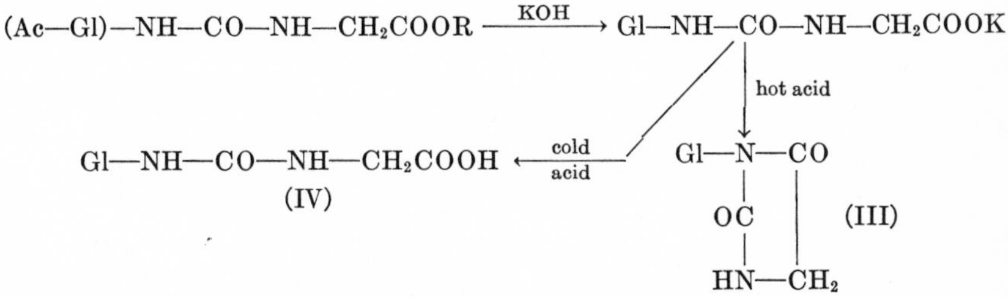

(IV) (III)

(instead of *silver* thiocyanate), the glycosyl thiocyanates are produced (instead of the isothiocyanates):

$$(Ac—Gl)—Br + KCNS \rightarrow (Ac—Gl)—SCN$$

At higher temperatures, rearrangement of the thiocyanate may take place with the formation of the isothiocyanate (*56*).

Potassium thiocyanate and strong hydrochloric acid react with aldose sugars to give compounds which appear to have a μ-thiolglucoxazoline structure (*57*) (V or VI). The products are oxidized by H_2O_2 to the corresponding μ-hydroxyglucoxazolines.

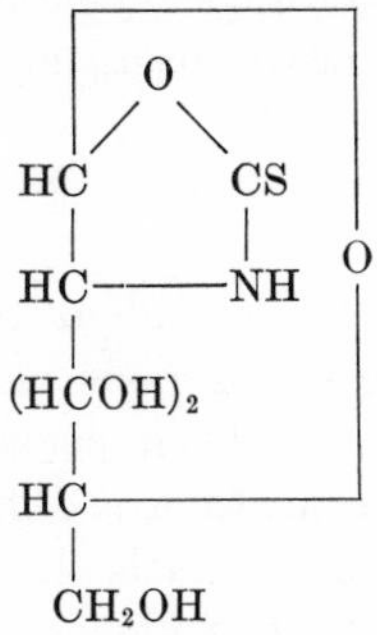

(V)

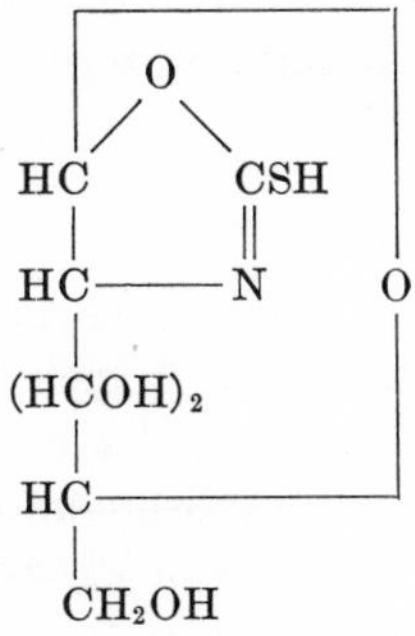

(VI)

Nitrogenous bases may react directly with acetylglycosyl bromides. In this manner 1-glucosylcytosine (VII) has been prepared (*58*). With more

56. A. Müller and A. Wilhelms, *Ber.* **74,** 698 (1941).

57. G. Zemplén, A. Gerecs, and M. Rados, *Ber.* **69,** 748 (1936); W. H. Bromund and R. M. Herbst, *J. Org. Chem.* **10,** 267 (1945).

58. G. E. Hilbert and E. F. Jansen, *J. Am. Chem. Soc.* **58,** 60 (1936).

basic nitrogenous substances the reaction is likely to lead to the production of 1,2-glycoseens (see under Glycoseens). The action of diethylamine on tetra-*O*-acetylglucosyl bromide leads to tetra-*O*-acetyl-1,2-glucoseen (*59*)

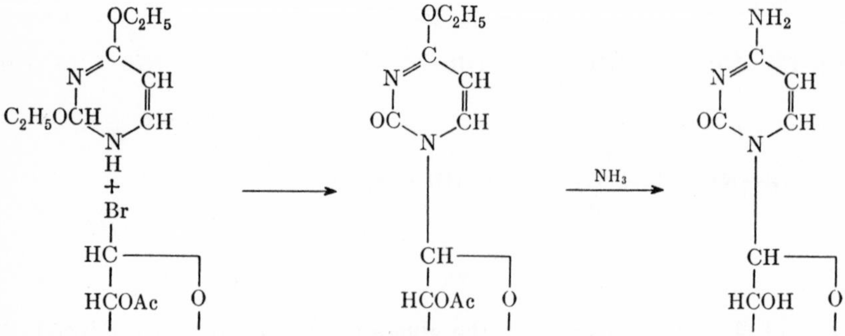
OC_2H_5
C
N
CH
C_2H_5OCH
CH
N
H
+
Br
HC
HCOAc
O
OC_2H_5
C
N
CH
OC
CH
N
CH
HCOAc
O
NH_3
NH_2
C
N
CH
OC
CH
N
CH
HCOH
O

(VII)

or, depending on the conditions, to tetra-*O*-acetyl-*N*-glucosyldiethylamine (*60*). (See Chapter VII.)

Nicotinamide (3-pyridinecarboxamide) condenses with tetra-*O*-acetylglucosyl bromide to give tetra-*O*-acetyl-*N*-glucosylnicotinamide hydrobromide, which is readily reduced in the aromatic nucleus by $Na_2S_2O_4$ (sodium dithionite) to 1,2- or 1,6-dihydro derivatives (*61*). The reduced and deacetylated glycosylamine has absorption bands identical with those of reduced DPN, a hydrogen-transporting coenzyme of many biological systems (p. 745), and it is oxidized by the flavin coenzyme in the presence of air. The corresponding glycosylpyridines have absorption curves different from those of DPN.

b. Reactions of Glycosylamines

The reactions of the glycosylamines are dependent to a considerable extent on the nature and basicity of the nitrogenous base involved. Unfortunately, the reactions have usually not been considered from this standpoint, and the establishment of generalizations is difficult.

The ease of hydrolysis of glycosylamines parallels the base strength of the corresponding amine, with the exception of glucosylamine itself (*12*, *62*). Normal acetic acid was found to be a more effective hydrolyzing agent than 0.5 *N* hydrochloric acid, whereas the effect of dilute sodium hydroxide

59. K. Maurer, *Ber.* **62,** 332 (1929).

60. J. W. Baker, *J. Chem. Soc.* p. 1205 (1929).

61. P. Karrer, B. H. Ringier, J. Büchi, H. Fritzsche, and U. V. Solmssen, *Helv. Chim. Acta* **20,** 55 (1937).

62. W. Pigman, E. A. Cleveland, D. H. Couch, and J. H. Cleveland, *J. Am. Chem. Soc.*, **73,** 1976 (1951).

TABLE I (*12*, *62*)

EQUILIBRIUM DATA FOR SOLUTIONS OF GLUCOSYLAMINES

5% SOLUTIONS AT 30°

Compound	Hydrolysis at equilibrium (%)			
	N HOAc	0.5 *N* HCl	H_2O	0.01 *N* NaOH
Glucosylamine (glucose ammonia)	100	100	0	..
Glucosyl-*n*-butylamine	100	13[a]	55	62
Glucosyl-*n*-hexylamine	100	4[a]	73	..
Glucosyl-*n*-octylamine	96	9[a]	..	..
Glucosyl-*n*-decylamine	100	22[a]	..	..
Glucosyl-*n*-dodecylamine	100	100	..	..
Glucosylphenylamine	80	90	44	0
Maltosyl-*n*-dodecylamine	*ca.* 100	0	0	..
Ba salt of glucosylglycine	100	...	75	..

[a] Forty-eight hour values; probably not equilibrium values.

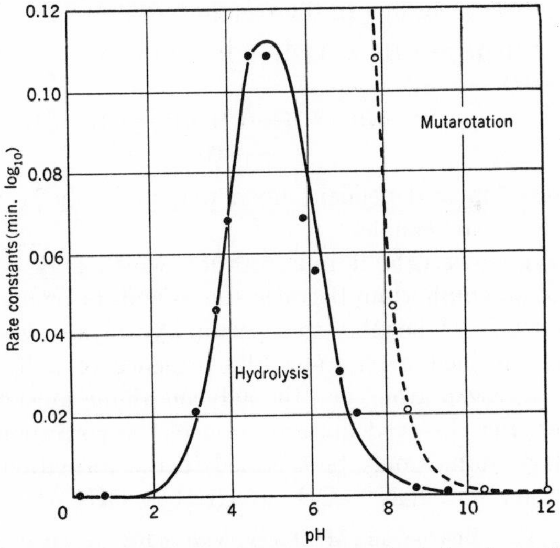

0.12
0.10
0.08
0.06
0.04
0.02
Rate constants (min. log10)
0
2
4
6
8
10
12
pH
Mutarotation
Hydrolysis

FIG. 1. Rate constants for mutarotation and hydrolysis of L-arabinosylamine.

was most markedly dependent upon the nature of the amine moiety (see Table I). Isbell and Frush (*9a*) have found that the rates of hydrolysis of some glycosylamines have an optimal pH around pH 3 to 4 (Fig. 1).

When an excess of acid is added rapidly to L-arabinosylamine, the optical rotation drops to a lower point than when the acid is added slowly (*9a*). The lower rotation may arise from the formation of a diarabinosylamine.

During slow addition of acid, hydrolysis of the L-arabinosylamine occurs without the complication of the diarabinosylamine being formed.

Some developing solvents used in paper chromatography of sugars contain ammonia. With such solvents the formation of glycosylamines may occur. Such products may be identified by their reactions with ninhydrin (*63*).

Mild acid hydrolysis removes the amine group from acetylated or benzoylated glycosylamines; this procedure provides a method for the preparation of partially acetylated or benzoylated sugars in which the reducing group is free (*17a,b 64*).

The natural *N*-ribosyl derivatives of purines and pyrimidines are fairly stable in the presence of alkali and do not reduce Fehling solution, but many synthetic glycosylamines exhibit a considerable reducing action. Acidic substances may bring about the isomerization of the glycosylamines to ketose derivatives (Amadori rearrangement); the isomerization of ketosylamines to aldose derivatives without catalysis has also been reported (*65*). The glycosylamines may undergo decomposition upon storage (*66*) or in solution (*67*). Transglycosylation of aromatic glycosylamines occurs readily and proceeds according to the reaction (*68*):

$$\mathrm{R{-}NH{-}\underbrace{CH{-}(CHOH)_3{-}CH}_{O}{-}CH_2OH + R'{-}NH_2 \rightarrow}$$

$$\mathrm{R'{-}NH{-}\underbrace{CH{-}(CHOH)_3{-}CH}_{O}{-}CH_2OH + R{-}NH_2}$$

This type of reaction is dependent upon pH, probably is catalyzed by protons, and is often reversible.

Many glycosylamines exhibit mutarotation which may be due to the establishment of an equilibrium between the α- and β-isomers and the corresponding Schiff base or possibly to a partial hydrolysis (*16*, *62*, *69*, *9a,b*). The mechanism outlined necessitates the presence of a hydrogen atom attached to the nitrogen atom, i.e., the aglycon amine must be a primary amine. However, the observed mutarotation of the corresponding derivatives of secondary amines may be ascribed to the formation of an intermediate quaternary ion: $R_2N^+{=}CH{-}(CHOH)_4{-}CH_2OH$.

63. R. J. Bayly, E. J. Bourne, and M. Stacey, *Nature* **168,** 510 (1951); I. D. Raacke-Fels, *Arch. Biochem. and Biophys.* **43,** 289 (1953).

64. J. Lee and L. Berger, *U. S. Patent* 2,384,104 (Sept. 4, 1945).

65. J. F. Carson, *J. Am. Chem. Soc.* **77,** 1881, 5957 (1955). See also: K. Heyns and K. H. Meinecke, *Ber.* **86,** 1453 (1953).

66. J. E. Hodge and C. E. Rist, *J. Am. Chem. Soc.* **75,** 316 (1953).

67. S. Bayne and W. H. Holms, *J. Chem. Soc.* p. 3247 (1952); L. Rosen, K. C. Johnson, and W. Pigman, *J. Am. Chem. Soc.* **75,** 3460 (1953).

68. R. Bognár, P. Nánási, and E. Nemes-Nánási, *J. Chem. Soc.* **189,** 193 (1955).

69. J. C. Irvine and R. Gilmour, *J. Chem. Soc.* **95,** 1545 (1909); R. Kuhn and L. Birkofer, *Ber.* **71,** 1535 (1938); J. W. Baker, *J. Chem. Soc.* p. 1205 (1929).

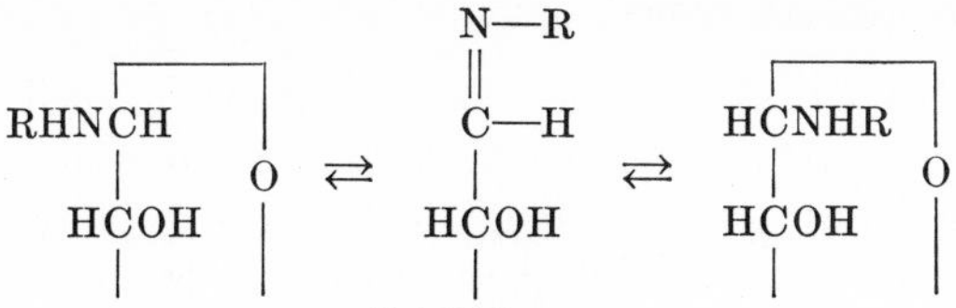

Schiff base

Hodge and Rist (*70*) found that the D-glucosyl derivatives of piperidine and diethanolamine do not mutarotate in dry pyridine, whereas the D-galactosyl and D-mannosyl derivatives of piperidine do mutarotate.

Isbell and Frush (*9a*) have proposed a mechanism for the mutarotation of the glycosylamines:

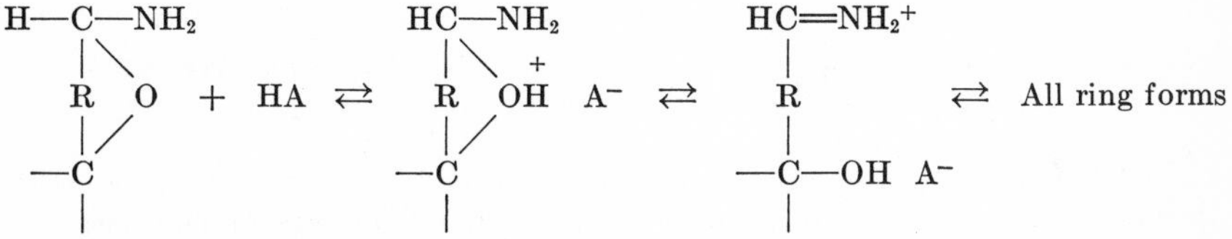

(I) R=(CHOH)$_n$ (II) (III)

After addition of a proton to the ring form of the glycosylamine (I), the resulting conjugate acid (II) is cleaved to form the intermediate imonium ion (III). The imonium ion may react reversibly to produce the various ring isomers. This mechanism accounts for the much greater catalytic effect of acid catalysts upon the mutarotation of glycosylamines than upon the corresponding free sugars; the formation of the imonium ion (III) from the conjugate acid (II) should be much more easily effected than the corresponding step in the sugar series.

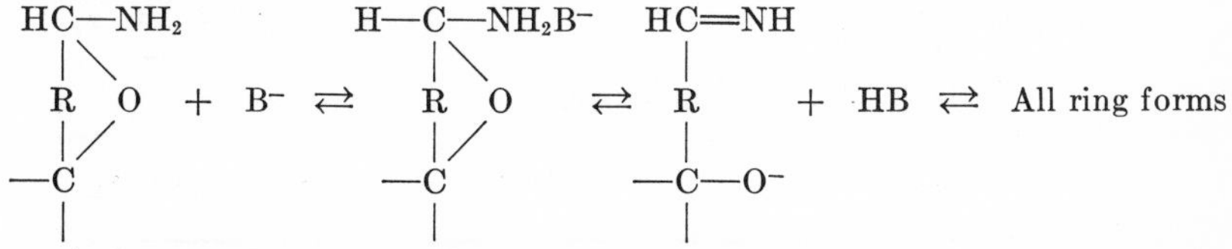

(IV) R=(CHOH)$_n$ (V) (VI)

In comparison with the sugars, the mechanism for basic catalysis accounts for the lessened catalytic effect of the hydroxyl ion on the mutarotation of the glycosylamines. The amino nitrogen will have less tendency to donate a proton (V → VI) than will the hemiacetal hydroxyl of the sugars. Other mechanisms for mutarotation may also be operative simultaneously.

The imonium ion intermediate (III) is used by Isbell and Frush (*9a*) to account for the limitation of the hydrolysis of glycosylamines to a narrowly restricted pH range.

70. J. E. Hodge and C. E. Rist, *J. Am. Chem. Soc.* **74,** 1494 (1952).

c. Amadori Rearrangement (71)

Amadori (*72*) reported that the product initially formed from D-glucose and *p*-toluidine was very labile and isomerized in the presence of acids into a "stable" form. The "labile" isomer was thought to be the glycosylamine and the "stable" isomer the Schiff base. However, the "stable" isomer gives positive color reactions for ketoses; it is reduced to *N*-*p*-tolylmannamine (III) and it forms a hydroxylamine derivative (*73*). From this evidence, it is clear that an isomerization from a D-glucose (I) to a D-fructose (II) derivative has taken place. This is called the Amadori rearrangement.

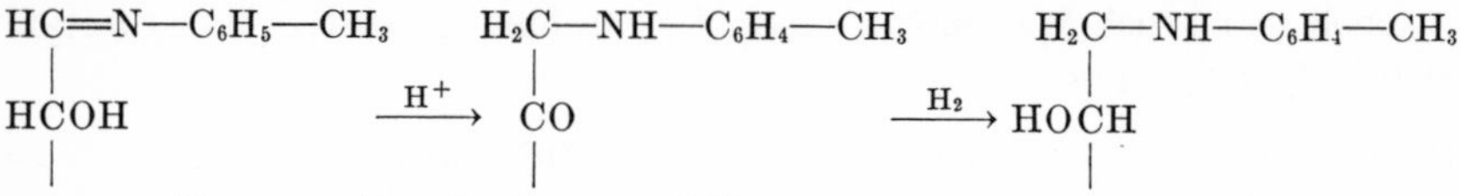

(I) (Amadori rearrangement) (II) (III)

Hydrogenation of the ketose derivative (II) produces 1-deoxy-1-(arylamino) sugar alcohols. Since a new asymmetric center is produced, two isomeric alcohols may be formed, but the yield of the two possible isomers is influenced greatly by the acidity of the medium employed for the hydrogenation (*74*). In acid solution, catalytic reduction of 1-deoxy-1-*p*-toluinofructose (IV) takes place only in the aromatic ring (V); but in alkaline or neutral solution, it takes place with the formation of 1-deoxy-1-*p*-toluinomannitol (*p*-tolyl-D-mannamine) (VI):

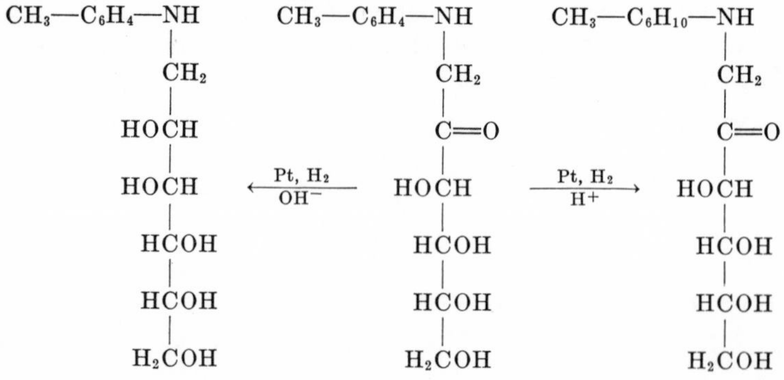

(VI) (IV) (V)

However, for 1-deoxy-1-*p*-toluino-L-ribulose, acid reduction yields 1-deoxy-

71. J. E. Hodge, *Advances in Carbohydrate Chem.* **10,** 169 (1955).

72. M. Amadori, *Atti accad. Lincei,* [6] **2,** 337 (1925); **13,** 72, 195 (1931); C. N. Cameron, *J. Am. Chem. Soc.* **48,** 2737 (1926).

73. R. Kuhn and F. Weygand, *Ber.* **70,** 769 (1937).

74. F. Weygand, *Ber.* **73,** 1259, 1278 (1940).

1-toluino-L-arabitol whereas alkaline reduction produces 1-deoxy-1-toluino-L-ribitol (*74*). These reactions provide a new method for the production, from the readily available arabinosylamines, of 1-(*N*-substituted)-ribitol derivatives of the type of riboflavin. The reactions are also of interest in providing a possible mechanism for the *in vivo* formation of riboflavin.

The work of Weygand and co-workers (*73, 74*) was most important in the early elucidation of the Amadori rearrangement. The rearrangement appeared to be general for aldosyl derivatives of primary arylamines, and acid catalysis was deemed necessary. On this basis, Weygand (*74*) and Smith and Anderson (*75*) proposed mechanisms for the Amadori rearrangement. One mechanism postulated by Weygand involves the following steps:

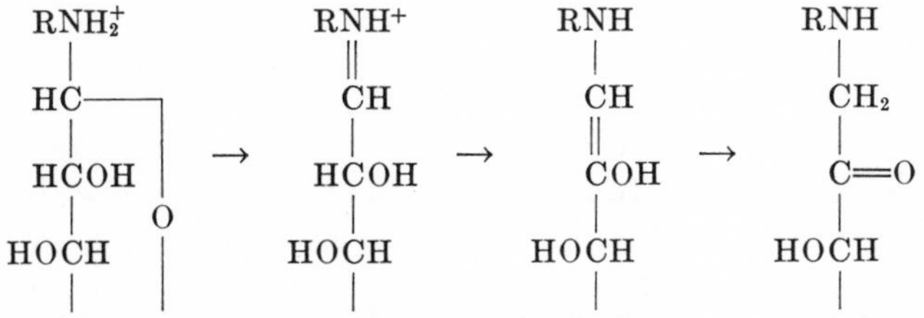

(VII) (VIII) (IX) (X)

The catalytic effect of hydrogen ions on the conversion makes it probable that the reaction takes place through the cation of the Schiff base (VIII) and the sugar enol (IX), which rearranges to give the 1-amino-1-deoxyketose (X).

The Amadori rearrangement also occurs for the glycosylamine derivatives of some secondary alkylamines and of primary and secondary aralkylamines; it occurs in alcoholic solution in the presence of compounds such as ethyl malonate and acetylacetone which contain active hydrogen atoms (*66*). The direct reaction product from D-glucose and dibenzylamine was actually 1-dibenzylamino-1-deoxy-D-fructose (XI) (*66*) and not *N,N*-dibenzyl-D-glucosylamine (XII) as indicated earlier by Kuhn and Birkofer (*76*). This rearrangement was effected without benefit of acid catalysis (*70*) or by the use of ethyl malonate (*66*). The true *N,N*-dibenzylglucosylamine (XII) could not be isolated.

Carson (*65*) induced a reverse Amadori rearrangement with the conversion of *N*-alkylfructosylamines to aldose derivatives. By the reaction of primary alkylamines with fructose under anhydrous conditions, crystalline monoamino condensation products were obtained. *N*-Ethylfructosylamine was the only fructosylamine isolated. Usually the products were 2-amino-2-deoxyaldoses, probably of glucose configuration. Presumably,

75. L. I. Smith and R. H. Anderson, *J. Org. Chem.* **16,** 963 (1951).
76. R. Kuhn and L. Birkofer, *Ber.* **71,** 621 (1938).

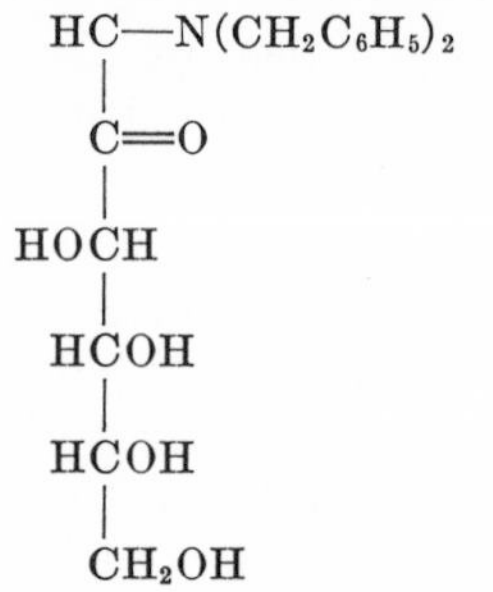

(XI)

1-Dibenzylamino-1-deoxy
D-fructose

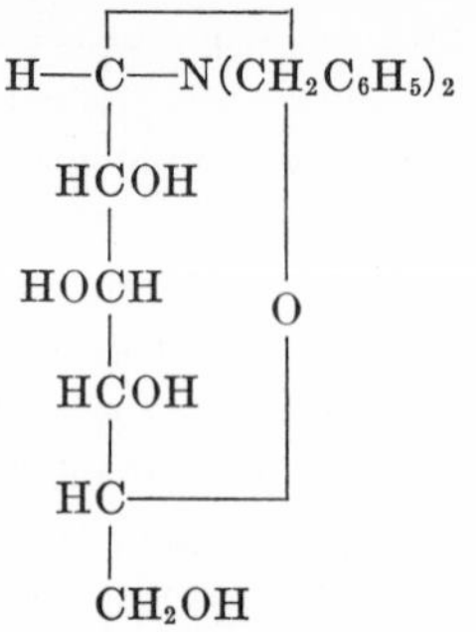

(XII)

N,N-Dibenzyl-D-
glucosylamine

by a continuation of this process, numerous amine groupings may be introduced into a hexose (*77*). In contrast to the ready rearrangement of fructosyl derivatives of alkylamines, it has not been possible to rearrange fructosyl derivatives of primary arylamines to the aldose derivative. These fructosyl derivatives are prepared (*23*) under the same conditions as are used in the rearrangement of aldosyl derivatives of the same primary arylamines. *N*-Benzylfructosylamine does undergo rearrangement (*77a*).

Aldosyl derivatives of *p*-nitroaniline, a very weak base, have not been observed to undergo the Amadori rearrangement, and their preparation (*33*) is based on methods which are used to rearrange the aldosyl derivatives of the stronger primary arylamines (*74*).

d. *Nucleosides**

This biologically important and growing class of compounds may be best defined, as proposed by Schlenk, as the *N*-glycosides (glycosylamines) of naturally occurring heterocyclic bases. They are tertiary amines usually composed of the D-ribosyl- and 2-deoxy-D-ribosylamine derivatives of purines and pyrimidines, obtained by the partial hydrolysis of the widely distributed nucleic acids. The structures of the purines and pyrimidines most commonly found in nucleosides are outlined in Fig. 2 and names of the corresponding nucleosides are given. Other nucleosides have been isolated from a wide variety of sources. An adenine derivative first isolated from yeast extracts in 1925 (*78a*) has had its structure established as 9′-(5-*S*-methyl-β-D-ribofuranosyl)adenine by both the degradative and

* Revised by David G. Doherty.

77. J. G. Erickson, *J. Am. Chem. Soc.* **77**, 2839 (1955).

77a. J. F. Carson, *J. Am. Chem. Soc.* **78**, 3728 (1956).

78a. U. Suzuki and T. Mori, *Biochem. Z.* **162**, 413 (1925).

FIG. 2. Skeleton structure for purines and pyrimidines

Aglycon type	Naturally occurring aglycons	Corresponding Nucleoside	Chemical Structure of Aglycon
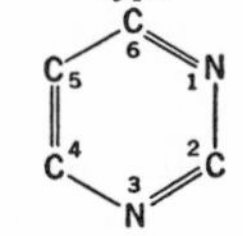	Cytosine	Cytidine	4-Amino-2-pyrimidone
	Uracil	Uridine	2,6-Pyrimidinedione
	Thymine	Thymidine	5-Methyl-2,6-pyrimidinedione (5-methyluracil)
Pyrimidine nucleus			
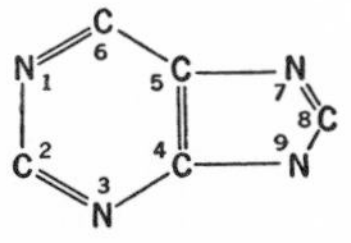	Adenine	Adenosine	6-Aminopurine
	Guanine	Guanosine	2-Amino-6-purinone
	Hypoxanthine	Inosine	6-Purinone
Purine nucleus			

synthetic approaches (*78b*). Nucleosides have also been isolated from sponges (spongothymidine (*79*)), mold products (puromycin (*80*)) and amicetin (*81a*), and mushrooms (nebularine (*81b*)). Vicine, isolated from vetch seed and formerly thought to be a glycosylamine, has been established as the 5-*O*-β-D-glucopyranosyl derivative of 2,4-diamino-5,6-dihydroxypyrimidine (*82*). Products of the partial degradation of the vitamin B_{12} complex have been shown to contain a base entirely different from those previously mentioned; it is 1-D-ribofuranosyl-5,6-dimethylbenzimidazole (*83a*). Finally, a compound closely related to a nucleoside containing L-lyxose, i.e., L-lyxoflavin, has been isolated from human heart muscle and identified by comparison with a synthetic sample (*83b*).

Preparation of Nucleosides. Levene and Jacobs (*83c*) treated ribonucleic acid with ammonia in an autoclave (175°) and isolated the crystalline purine and pyrimidine ribonucleosides, adenosine and guanosine (9-*N*-β-D ribofuranosyladenine and -guanine) and cytidine and uridine (9-*N*-β-D-ribofuranosylcytosine and -uracil) respectively. Improvements in the chemical hydrolysis have been made through the use of magnesium oxide

78b. F. Weygand, O. Trauth, and R. Lowenfeld, *Ber.* **83,** 563, (1950); J. Baddiley, *J. Chem. Soc.* p. 1348 (1951); K. Satoh and K. Makino, *Nature* **167,** 238 (1951).

79. W. Bergmann and R. J. Feeney, *J. Am. Chem. Soc.* **72,** 2809 (1950); *J. Org. Chem.* **16,** 981 (1951).

80. C. W. Waller, P. W. Fryth, B. L. Hutchings, and J. H. Williams, *J. Am. Chem. Soc.*, **75,** 2025 (1953).

81a. E. H. Flynn, J. W. Hinman, E. L. Caron, and D. O. Woolf, *J. Am. Chem. Soc.* **75,** 5867 (1953).

81b. G. B. Brown and V. S. Weliky, *J. Biol. Chem.* **204,** 1019 (1953).

82. A. Bendich and G. C. Clements, *Biochim. et Biophys. Acta* **12,** 462 (1953); U. Suzuki and T. Mori, *Biochem. Z.* **162,** 413 (1925); G. Wendt, *Z. physiol. Chem.* **272,** 152 (1942).

83a. N. G. Brink, F. W. Holly, C. H. Shunk, E. W. Peel, J. J. Cahill and K. Folkers, *J. Am. Chem. Soc.* **72,** 1866 (1950).

83b. E. Sodi Pallares and H. Martínez Garza, *Arch. Biochem.* **22,** 63 (1949).

83c. P. A. Levene and W. A. Jacobs, *Ber.* **43,** 3154 (1910).

(*84a*), lead hydroxide (*84b*), aqueous pyridine (*84c*), or lanthanum catalysis (*84d*), instead of aqueous ammonia. Chemical hydrolysis of deoxyribonucleic acid for the production of deoxyribonucleosides has been limited to the use of lead hydroxide (*85*). Milder, and in the case of deoxyribonucleic acid, more desirable enzymic hydrolytic procedures involve the use of almond emulsin (*84b*) and crude or purified intestinal enzymes (*86*). Purified nucleotidases have also been used to hydrolyze the phosphate group of pure nucleotides (*87*).

All the modern techniques, such as ion-exchange (*88a*), paper chromatography (*88b*), countercurrent liquid extraction (*85*), and electrophoretic separation (*88c*), have been applied to the difficult problem of the separation of nucleoside mixtures into pure components. The older chemical precipitation methods (*88d*) are still useful for the preparation of nucleosides on a larger scale.

Investigations on the reversal of nucleosidase activity established that purified nucleosidases from rat liver could synthesize inosine and guanosine from ribose 1-phosphate and the respective purines (*89a*). This procedure has been extended to the enzymic synthesis of *N*-ribosylnicotinamide (*89b*) and *N*-2-deoxyribosylhypoxanthine and -azaguanine (*89c*) from their respective bases and ribose 1-phosphate. Reactions such as these may play a role in the natural synthesis of nucleotides.

Structure of Nucleosides. The purine and pyrimidine bases associated with

84a. F. P. Phelps, *U. S. Patent* 2,152,662 (Apr. 4, 1939).

84b. K. Dimroth, L. Jaenicke, and D. Heinzel, *Ann.* **566,** 206 (1950).

84c. H. Bredereck, A. Martini and F. Richter, *Ber.* **74,** 694 (1941).

84d. F. A. Allen and J. E. Bacher, *J. Biol. Chem.* **188,** 59 (1951).

85. F. Weygand, A. Wacker, and H. Dellweg, *Z. Naturforsch.* **6b,** 140 (1951).

86. W. Klein and S. J. Thannhauser, *Z. physiol. Chem.* **231,** 96 (1935).

87. L. A. Heppel and R. J. Hilmoe, *J. Biol. Chem.* **188,** 665 (1951); L. Shuster and N. O. Kaplan, *ibid.* **201,** 535 (1953).

88a. W. E. Cohn *in* "The Nucleic Acids." (E. Chargaff and J. N. Davidson, eds., Vol. 1, p. 237. Academic Press, New York, 1955; L. Jaenicke and K. von Dahl, *Naturwissenschaften* **39,** 87 (1952); P. Reichard and B. Estborn, *Acta Chem. Scand.* **4,** 1047 (1950).

88b. R. D. Hotchkiss, *J. Biol. Chem.* **175,** 315 (1948); C. E. Carter, *J. Am. Chem. Soc.* **72,** 1466 (1950).

88c. K. Dimroth, L. Jaenicke, and I. Vollbrechtshausen, *Z. physiol. Chem.* **289,** 71 (1952).

88d. H. Bredereck, *Ber.* **71,** 1013 (1938).

89a. H. M. Kalckar, *J. Biol. Chem.* **158,** 723 (1945); *ibid.* **167,** 477 (1947).

89b. J. W. Rowen and A. Kornberg, *J. Biol. Chem.* **193,** 497 (1951).

89c. M. Friedkin, *J. Am. Chem. Soc.* **74,** 112 (1952); D. B. Strominger and M. Friedkin, *J. Biol. Chem.* **208,** 663 (1954).

the nucleosides were the first structural components to be identified. Mild acid hydrolysis (purines) or vigorous acid hydrolysis (pyrimidines) cleaved the glycosylamine linkage liberating the bases, which were readily separated and isolated as various pure salts. The identification of the carbohydrate components, and especially deoxyribose, was a far more difficult task. Hammarsten (*90a*), in 1894, was the first to recognize that one carbohydrate component was a pentose, and in the intervening period until 1909, it was variously claimed to be D-xylose, DL-arabinose, and D-lyxose, on the basis of derivatives of impure material. In that year, Levene and Jacobs succeeded in obtaining the sugar in a pure crystalline form and determined its physical properties, which differed markedly from the other three known pentoses (*90b*). They compared several osazone derivatives, oxidized the sugar to an aldonic acid comparable to the previously synthesized D-ribonic acid, and further to an optically inactive pentaric acid, and thus concluded correctly that the pentose was D-ribose. The identification of 2-deoxy-D-ribose was more difficult, since it is readily converted by strong acids to levulinic acid, forms soluble hydrazones, and does not form an osazone. Careful hydrolysis of a pure deoxyribonucleoside with 0.01 N HCl by warming for 10 minutes permitted the isolation of a crystalline deoxypentose. Comparison of its chemical tests and physical properties with a synthetic 2-deoxy-L-ribose revealed no differences except sign of rotation and established it as 2-deoxy-D-ribose (*90c*).

The structure of the sugar ring in the ribonucleosides was established originally as furanose by the laborious procedure of methylation, hydrolysis to the methylated sugar, and oxidation to the optically inactive di-*O*-methyl-*meso*-tartaric acid (*90d*). Further evidence was obtained by the formation of trityl derivatives that could be replaced by tosyl and, finally, by iodine groups (*90e*). Since trityl chloride reacts preferentially with primary alcohol groups, and only primary tosyl groups can be readily replaced by iodine, the furanose structure received additional support. The simple direct periodate titration of the nucleosides reveals 1 mole of periodate consumed and no formic acid liberated (*90f*). These results are correct for pentofuranosides since pentopyranosides with three adjacent hydroxyl groups require 2 moles of periodate and liberate 1 mole of formic acid. The furanose structure of the deoxyribonucleosides was established in an analogous way by the formation of trityl derivatives (*90e*) and the lack of con-

90a. O. Hammarsten, *Z. physiol. Chem.* **19,** 19 (1894).

90b. P. A. Levene and W. A. Jacobs, *Ber.* **42,** 1198, 3247 (1909).

90c. P. A. Levene, L. A. Mikeska, and T. Mori, *J. Biol. Chem.* **85,** 785 (1929–30).

90d. P. A. Levene and R. S. Tipson, *J. Biol. Chem.* **94,** 809 (1932); **97,** 491 (1932).

90e. P. A. Levene and R. S. Tipson, *J. Biol. Chem.* **105,** 419 (1934); **109,** 623 (1935); **121,** 131 (1937).

sumption of periodate (*91*), i.e., a 2-deoxypentofuranoside would not have the adjacent pair of hydroxyl groups required for reaction with periodate.

The configuration of the glycosylamine linkage of nucleosides can be obtained by the periodate method, since one of the two asymmetric centers of the dialdehyde formed in the reaction retains the configuration of the glycosidic carbon. Dialdehydes were formed from a series of synthetic *N*-glucosyl purines and pyrimidines whose structure was known from the route of synthesis; a comparison of these with the dialdehydes formed from the natural nucleosides showed that they were identical and established the β-configuration (*92a*). Confirmation of the β-configuration has been obtained with the 2′,3′-*O*-isopropylidine 5′-*O*-tosyl derivative of adenosine and cytidine. The derivatives of both bases easily form cyclonucleosides with the remaining basic ring nitrogen; steric considerations indicate that such a reaction can take place only for the β-glycosylamines (*92b*). Similar proof has also been offered (*92c*) for the β-configuration of the deoxyribonucleosides.

The point of attachment of the sugar to the bases was another difficult structural question to resolve. In the pyrimidine series, methylation and hydrolysis of uridine (*93a, b*) gave 1-methyluracil, and established the linkage at the nitrogen at position 3. In the purines, methylation of xanthosine gave a *N*-ribosyltheophylline and eliminated nitrogen atoms 1 and 3 from consideration (*93b*); a choice was left between nitrogen atoms 7 and 9. Position 9 was finally selected after a comparison of the absorption spectra of the nucleosides with the corresponding 7- and 9-methyl aglycons showed them to be identical with the 9-methyl compounds (*94a*). Similar reasoning was applied to the purine deoxyribonucleosides to fix their linkage with deoxyribose at the *N*-9 position (*94b*). In the pyrimidine nucleosides the linkage is at *N*-3, since thymidine has been methylated and hydrolyzed to yield 1-methylthymine (*93b*). Additional confirmation has been provided by the synthesis of the ribonucleosides in an unequivocal manner (Fig. 3).

90f. B. Lythgoe and A. R. Todd, *J. Chem. Soc.* p. 592 (1944).

91. D. M. Brown and B. Lythgoe, *J. Chem. Soc.* p. 1990 (1950); L. A. Manson and J. O. Lampen, *J. Biol. Chem.* **191,** 87 (1951).

92a. B. Lythgoe, H. Smith, and A. R. Todd, *J. Chem. Soc.* p. 355 (1947); J. Davoll, B. Lythgoe, and A. R. Todd, *ibid.* p. 833 (1944).

92b. V. M. Clark, A. R. Todd, and J. Zussman, *J. Chem. Soc.* p. 2952 (1951).

92c. W. Andersen, D. H. Hayes, A. M. Michelson, and A. R. Todd, *J. Chem. Soc.* p. 1882 (1954); A. M. Michelson and A. R. Todd, *ibid.* p. 816 (1955).

93a. P. A. Levene and R. S. Tipson, *J. Biol. Chem.* **104,** 385 (1934).

93b. H. Bredereck, G. Müller, and E. Berger, *Ber.* **73,** 1058 (1940).

94a. J. M. Gulland and E. R. Holiday, *J. Chem. Soc.* p. 765 (1936); J. M. Gulland and L. F. Story, *ibid.* p. 692 (1938).

94b. J. M. Gulland and L. F. Story, *J. Chem. Soc.* p. 259, 692 (1938).

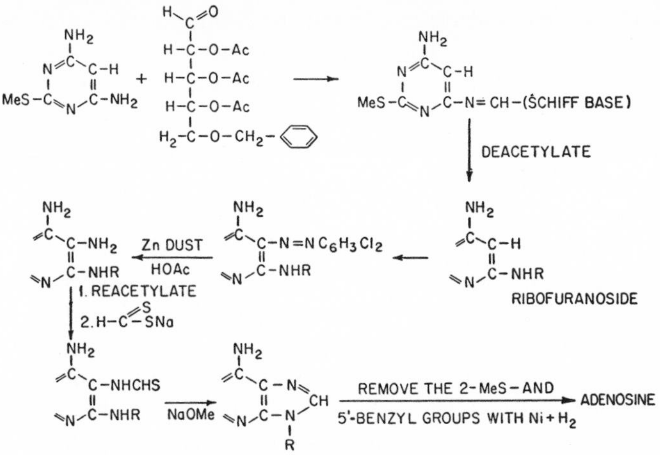
NH2
MeS
CH-(SCHIFF BASE)
DEACETYLATE
Zn DUST
HOAc
1. REACETYLATE
2.H-C-SNa
RIBOFURANOSIDE
NaOMe
REMOVE THE 2-MeS-AND
5'-BENZYL GROUPS WITH Ni+H2
ADENOSINE

FIG. 3

Synthesis of Nucleosides. The purine and pyrimidine ribonucleosides have been synthesized by Todd and co-workers by several methods that establish their structure. The pyrimidine nucleosides were synthesized by a method originally elaborated by Hilbert and co-workers (*94c*) for the preparation of *N*-glycosylpyrimidines. Tri-*O*-acetyl-D-ribofuranosyl bromide was coupled with 2,6-diethoxypyrimidine; the product was treated with either methanolic hydrogen chloride to produce uridine, or methanolic ammonia to produce cytidine (*94d*). A modification of this method utilizing the mercury salt of thymine was used to prepare a series of thymine nucleosides (*94e*). The purine nucleosides have been synthesized by three general routes. The first method involves coupling the acetohalogen sugar with 2,8-dichloroadenine (*95a*) or 2,8-diacetoaminoadenine (*95b*) followed by conversion to the corresponding *N*-glycosyladenine or -guanine. This established the β-configuration and the ring structure of the nucleosides but not rigidly the *N*-9 substitution. A second method is unambiguous in this respect. A 4,6-diaminopyrimidine is converted to the *N*-glycosylamine and aminated at position 5; this product is thioformylated at position 5, and then cyclyzed to the purine by treatment with sodium alkoxides (*96*) (Fig. 3). A third method, the coupling of an acetohalogen sugar to a substituted

94c. G. E. Hilbert and T. B. Johnson, *J. Am. Chem. Soc.* **52,** 4489 (1930); G. E. Hilbert and E. F. Jansen, *ibid.* **58,** 60 (1936).

94d. G. A. Howard, B. Lythgoe, and A. R. Todd, *J. Chem. Soc.* p. 1052 (1947).

94e. J. J. Fox, N. Yung, J. Davoll and G. B. Brown, *J. Am. Chem. Soc.* **78,** 2117 (1956).

95a. J. Davoll, B. Lythgoe, and A. R. Todd, *J. Chem. Soc.* p. 967, 1685 (1948).

95b. J. Davoll and B. A. Lowy, *J. Am. Chem. Soc.* **73,** 1650 (1951).

96. G. W. Kenner, C. W. Taylor, and A. R. Todd, *J. Chem. Soc.* p. 1620 (1949).

imidazole (*97a*), followed by conversion to a purine, has been limited to *N*-glycosylxanthines (*97b*). The deoxyribonucleosides have not been synthesized, chiefly because of the difficulty in obtaining 2-deoxy-D-ribose and of preparing from it an acetohalogenodeoxyribofuranose suitable for coupling it to the bases.

2. NUCLEOTIDES (*98*)*

A. Preparation and Structures

Two classes of nucleotides, named ribonucleotides and deoxyribonucleotides according to their sugar component, can be isolated by selective degradative techniques from their respective nucleic acids. Careful partial hydrolysis of ribonucleic acid (RNA) liberates nucleotides (phosphorylated nucleosides) composed of one mole each of ribose, phosphoric acid, and a purine or pyrimidine base. Hydrolytic conditions must be mild to avoid the formation of nucleosides through the loss of phosphoric acid. Mild alkaline hydrolysis of RNA yields two purine (adenine or guanine) and two pyrimidine (cytosine or uracil) nucleotides, whereas mild acid hydrolysis yields the two pyrimidine nucleotides with some degradation and extensively degrades the purine nucleotides (*99*). The increased acid stability of the pyrimidine nucleotides in comparison with the purine nucleotides permits their separation by acid treatment. Enzymic hydrolysis of RNA, especially in older work when pure enzyme preparations were not available, gave results which were difficult to interpret in terms of nucleotide structure. Deoxyribonucleic acid (DNA), however, is resistant to ordinary acid and alkaline hydrolysis and can be broken down to deoxynucleotides only by enzymic procedures to yield two purine (adenine and guanine) and two pyrimidine (cytosine and thymine) deoxynucleotides (*100*). In addition,

* Revised by Elliot Volkin and David G. Doherty under U.S.A.E.C. Contract No. W-7405-eng-26.

97a. R. A. Baxter and F. S. Spring, *J. Chem. Soc.* p. 378 (1947); R. A. Baxter, A. C. McLean, and F. S. Spring, *J. Chem. Soc.* p. 523 (1948).

97b. G. A. Howard, A. C. McLean, G. T. Newbold, F. S. Spring, and A. R. Todd, *J. Chem. Soc.* p. 232 (1949).

98. General references: P. A. Levene and L. W. Bass, "Nucleic Acids," American Chemical Society Monograph No. 56, Chemical Catalog Company, New York, 1931; E. Chargaff and J. N. Davidson, eds., "The Nucleic Acids." Academic Press, New York, 1955; G. W. Kenner, *Fortschr. Chem. org. Naturstoffe* **8,** 96 (1951).

99. H. S. Loring, P. M. Roll, and J. G. Pierce, *J. Biol. Chem.* **174,** 729 (1948); H. S. Loring and F. H. Carpenter, *ibid.* **150,** 381 (1943); H. S. Stundel, *Z. physiol. Chem.* **188,** 203 (1930); P. A. Levene, *J. Biol. Chem.* **40,** 415 (1919); **55,** 9 (1923).

100. E. Volkin, J. X. Khym, and W. E. Cohn, *J. Am. Chem. Soc.* **73,** 1533 (1951); W. Klein and S. J. Thannhauser, *Z. physiol. Chem.* **218,** 173 (1933); **224,** 252 (1934); **231,** 96 (1935); R. O. Hurst, J. A. Little, and G. C. Butler, *J. Biol. Chem.* **188,** 705 (1951).

small quantities of a fifth deoxynucleotide, deoxyribosyl-5-methylcytidylic acid, can be isolated by careful fractionation techniques (*101*).

The separation of nucleotides and deoxynucleotides, previously a formidable task involving the fractional crystallization of heavy metal and alkaloid salts (*102*), has been made much easier by developments in analytical techniques. Ion-exchange methods may be used for the purification, isolation, and identification of both classes of nucleotides from hydrolysis mixtures (*103*). Countercurrent distribution (*104*) and starch (*105*) and cellulose-column (*106*) as well as paper-strip chromatography (*107*) have also proved to be useful in separating nucleotides from natural sources. Spectrophotometric procedures based on the characteristic ultraviolet absorption spectra of the purines and pyrimidines have been the most convenient method to locate, estimate, and identify the fractions obtained in the previous separations. Since the nucleotides are acid in nature, they are often named as acids, e.g., adenylic acid, cytidylic acid. The general constitution of the purine nucleotides (and by analogy the pyrimidine nucleotides) is demonstrated by their hydrolysis by acids to a purine and ribose (or 2-deoxyribose) monophosphate and by alkalies to the nucleosides and phosphoric acid. The order of the constituents in a purine nucleotide must, therefore, be:

$$\text{purine} \overset{H^+}{\underset{\downarrow}{—}} \text{sugar} \overset{OH^-}{\underset{\downarrow}{—}} \text{phosphoric acid}$$

Structural proof has already been offered above, under the nucleosides, to establish the purine-sugar linkage as 9-D-ribofuranosyl [or 9-(2′-deoxy-D-ribofuranosyl)]. The location of the phosphate group on the ribose chain, especially with regard to the 2′- and 3′-positions, has proved to be a more

101. W. E. Cohn, *J. Am. Chem. Soc.* **73,** 1539 (1951); G. R. Wyatt, *Biochem. J.* **48,** 584 (1951).

102. J. X. Khym, D. G. Doherty, and W. E. Cohn, *J. Am. Chem. Soc.* **76,** 5523 (1954); P. Reichard, Y. Takenaka, and H. S. Loring, *J. Biol. Chem.* **198,** 599 (1952); H. Bredereck and G. Richter, *Ber.* **71,** 718 (1938); M. B. Buell, *J. Biol. Chem.* **150,** 389 (1943).

103. W. E. Cohn, *J. Am. Chem. Soc.* **71,** 2275 (1949); W. E. Cohn and C. E. Carter, *ibid.* **72,** 2606 (1950); **72,** 4273 (1950); W. E. Cohn, *ibid.* **72,** 1471 (1950).

104. G. H. Hogeboom and G. T. Barry, *J. Biol. Chem.* **176,** 935 (1948).

105. P. Reichard, *Nature* **162,** 662 (1948); *J. Biol. Chem.* **179,** 763 (1949).

106. J. G. Buchanan, A. W. Johnson, J. A. Mills, and A. R. Todd, *J. Chem. Soc.* p. 2845 (1950); C. A. Dekker and A. R. Todd, *Nature* **166,** 557 (1950).

107. C. E. Carter, *J. Am. Chem. Soc.* **72,** 1466 (1950); B. Magasanik, E. Vischer, R. Doniger, D. Elson, and E. Chargaff, *J. Biol. Chem.* **186,** 37 (1950); W. E. Cohn and C. E. Carter, *ibid.* **72,** 4273 (1950); J. Montveiul and P. Boulanger, *Compt. rend.* **231,** 247 (1950); P. Boulanger and J. Montveiul, *Bull. soc. chim. biol.* **33,** 784, 791 (1951).

difficult problem which has only recently been unambiguously resolved (*108*, *109*). The adenylic acid and its deaminated product inosinic acid (*110*), found free in yeast or tissue extracts, were the first to have the location of the phosphoric ester group definitely established. Acid hydrolysis of inosinic acid yielded an acid-stable ribose phosphate which could be oxidized by nitric acid to ribonic acid phosphate (*111*). Since no D-ribaric acid phosphate was produced, the 5-position of ribose must have been blocked by the phosphoric ester group. Confirmation of the 5-phospho ester position was obtained by the synthesis of inosinic acid, and later adenylic acid, by the phosphorylation of 2′,3′-mono-*O*-isopropylidineribofuranosylhypoxanthine and 2′,3′-mono-*O*-isopropylidineribofuranosyladenosine followed by the removal of the isopropylidine group yielding 5′-phosphate esters identical to the natural product (*112*). Other nucleotides with acid-stable phosphate groups were considered by analogy with adenosine 5′-phosphate to be 5′-phosphate esters, an assumption which has now been confirmed in an unequivocal manner (*113*) by the synthesis of all the 5′-ribonucleotides.

Hydrolysis of ribonucleic acid by mild alkaline treatment yields four mononucleotides containing acid-labile phosphoric ester groups. Early degradative studies on nucleotides were based on either the acid hydrolysis of inosinic acid (from yeast adenylic) and xanthylic acid (from guanylic) or on a glycosyl exchange reaction with the purine nucleotides. These led to the isolation of what was then thought to be a single ribose phosphate which could be reduced to an inactive ribitol phosphate (a *meso* compound). In addition, as this ribose phosphate could be converted to both *O*-phosphonoribopyranosides and -furanosides, unsubstituted positions at C-4 and C-5 were indicated (*114*). This evidence was regarded as proof that the phosphate residue occupied the 3-position on the ribose chain. However, improved analytical methods resulted in the discovery of an isomeric pair of adenylic acids (*107*), termed *a* and *b* in the order of their elution from an ion-exchange column; this reopened the question of the structure of nucleotides obtained by the alkaline hydrolysis of nucleic acids. Subsequently,

108. J. J. Fox, L. F. Cavalieri, and N. Chang, *J. Am. Chem. Soc.* **75**, 4315 (1953); J. M. Ploesser and H. S. Loring, *J. Biol. Chem.* **178**, 431 (1949); H. M. Kalckar, *ibid.* **167**, 445 (1947).

109. J. X. Khym, D. G. Doherty, E. Volkin, and W. E. Cohn, *J. Am. Chem. Soc.* **75**, 1262 (1953).

110. G. Embden and G. Schmidt, *Z. physiol. Chem.* **181**, 130 (1929); G. Schmidt, *ibid.* **179**, 243 (1928).

111. P. A. Levene and W. Jacobs, *Ber.* **44**, 746 (1911).

112. P. A. Levene and R. S. Tipson, *J. Biol. Chem.* **111**, 313 (1935); **121**, 131 (1937); H. Bredereck, E. Berger, and G. Ehrenberg, *Ber.* **73**, 269 (1940).

113. A. M. Michelson and A. R. Todd, *J. Chem. Soc.* p. 2476 (1949); J. Baddiley and A. R. Todd, *ibid.* p. 648 (1947).

14. P. A. Levene and S. A. Harris, *J. Biol. Chem.* **98**, 9 (1932); **101**, 419 (1933).

isomeric pairs of the other nucleotides, guanylic, uridylic, and cytidylic acids (*115*), were isolated and related to the isomeric adenylic acids (*103*). Extensive experiments established that the isomers were: (1) not 5′-phosphates (*103*), (2) easily interconvertible in acid media (*103, 116*), (3) stable to periodate, (4) obtained synthetically by the phosphorylation of 5-trityladenosine and subsequent removal of the trityl group (*113, 117*) and (5) obtained by the alkaline hydrolysis of the cyclic 2′,3′-phosphates of adenosine, cytosine, and uridine (*118*).

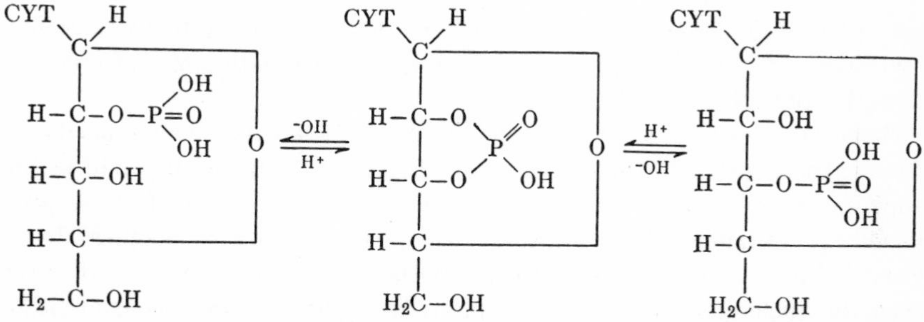

These considerations make it clear that the *a*- and *b*-isomers were 2′- and 3′-substituted phosphates. Measurements of the physical, chemical, and enzymic properties of the isomers supported the original suggestion that the *a*-isomers were 2′-phosphates and the *b*-isomers were 3′-phosphates (*119*). Initial identification by the synthetic approach was invalidated by the discovery that the synthetic 2′-isomers were actually 5′-isomers and that the key compound benzylidineadenosine was 2′,3′ instead of 3′,5′ (*120*). The final proof of the structure of the isomers was obtained by the hydrolysis of the pure *a*- and *b*-isomers with ion-exchange resin to the respective *a*- and *b*-ribose phosphates which were converted to their respective methyl ribopyranoside phosphates. The glycoside derived from *a* consumed 1 mole of periodate; these results indicated a vicinal hydroxyl grouping and located the phosphate at the 2-position. Position 4 was excluded by the furanoside structure of the original nucleotide. The glycoside from *b* consumed no periodate, and, hence, had the phosphate at the 3-position. Further confirmation was obtained by the reduction of ribose-*a* phosphate to an optically active ribitol 2-phosphate different from that from ribose-*b*

115. W. E. Cohn, *J. Am. Chem. Soc.* **72,** 1471 (1950); H. S. Loring, N. G. Luthy, H. W. Bortner, and L. W. Levy, *ibid.* **72,** 2811 (1950).

116. D. M. Brown, L. J. Haynes, and A. R. Todd, *J. Chem. Soc.* p. 3229 (1950).

117. H. Bredereck and E. Berger, *Ber.* **73,** 1124 (1940); J. M. Gulland and G. I. Hobday, *J. Chem. Soc.* p. 746 (1940).

118. D. M. Brown, D. I. Magrath, and A. R. Todd, *J. Chem. Soc.* p. 2708 (1952).

119. L. F. Cavalieri, *J. Am. Chem. Soc.* **75,** 5268 (1953).

120. D. M. Brown, L. J. Haynes, and A. R. Todd, *J. Chem. Soc.* p. 3299 (1950).

phosphate. Ribitol 3-phosphate was completely oxidized by periodate, consuming 6 moles and liberating inorganic phosphate (*102*). Acetylation of adenosine, separation and identification of a crystalline 3,5-di-*O*-acetyl derivative, phosphorylation, and deacetylation yielded a pure adenylic-*a* isomer (*121*). The structures of the pyrimidine nucleotide isomers *a* and *b* were established as 2′ and 3′ substituted phosphates respectively by both the degradative (*121a*) and synthetic approach (*121b*).

The lability of the 2′- and 3′- nucleotides to acids may be compared to the acid lability of glycerol 1-phosphate; the production of a mixture by the alkaline hydrolysis of nucleic acids is similar to the alkaline hydrolysis of glycerol monomethyl 1-phosphate to methanol and glycerol 1- and 2-phosphates (*122*).

Since DNA is resistant to chemical cleavage, less extensive studies have been carried out with deoxynucleotides. Enzymic degradation produces, in addition to the bases and deoxynucleosides, the five deoxynucleotides previously mentioned (*100*, *101*). Early separations involving chemical fractionation have been supplanted by ion-exchange techniques similar to those used for nucleotides. Since no phosphate isomerization can occur at position 2′ and the enzyme selectively breaks the phosphate ester linkage, only one deoxynucleoside phosphate is obtained. Comparison of the acid stability of the phosphate group with the known ribose nucleotides as well as the order of elution from the ion-exchange column suggests that the deoxynucleotides are 5′-phosphate esters (*123*). Additional confirmation is provided by their hydrolysis by a specific 5′-phosphatase to the deoxynucleoside and inorganic phosphate (*124*). Still further proof is provided by synthesis from the deoxynucleosides of deoxyadenylic, deoxyguanylic, deoxycytidylic, and deoxythymidylic acids identical with the natural products (*125*). In addition, studies by the synthetic route have established that the glycosyl linkage has the β-configuration similar to the ribose nucleotides (*126*).

121. D. M. Brown, G. D. Fasman, D. I. Magrath, and A. R. Todd, *J. Chem. Soc.* p. 1448 (1954).

121a. W. E. Cohn and D. G. Doherty, *J. Am. Chem. Soc.* **78,** 2863 (1956).

121b. D. M. Brown, A. R. Todd, and S. Varadarajan, *J. Chem. Soc.* p. 2388 (1956).

122. O. Bailly and J. Gaume, *Bull. soc. chim. France* **2,** 354 (1935); O. Bailly, *Compt. rend.* **206,** 1902 (1938); P. E. Verkade, J. C. Stoppelinburg, and W. D. Cohen, *Rec. trav. chim.* **59,** 886 (1940); E. Baer and M. Kates, *J. Biol. Chem.* **175,** 79 (1948).

123. E. Volkin, J. X. Khym, and W. E. Cohn, *J. Am. Chem. Soc.* **73,** 1535 (1951).

124. C. E. Carter, *J. Am. Chem. Soc.* **73,** 1573 (1951).

125. A. M. Michelson and A. R. Todd, *J. Chem. Soc.* p. 951 (1953); *ibid.* p. 34 (1954); D. H. Hayes, A. M. Michelson, and A. R. Todd, *ibid.* p. 808 (1955).

126. A. M. Michelson and A. R. Todd, *J. Chem. Soc.* p. 816 (1955); W. Andersen, D. H. Hayes, A. M. Michelson, and A. R. Todd, *ibid.* p. 1882 (1954).

B. Nucleoside Di- and Triphosphoric Acids

In 1928 Lohmann isolated a compound from muscle tissue extracts which consisted of adenosine esterified with 3 moles of phosphoric acid (*127*). Acid hydrolysis of the adenosine triphosphate (ATP) yielded 1 mole of adenine, 1 mole of ribose monophosphate, and 2 moles of phosphoric acid, whereas neutral hydrolysis gave adenosine 5′-phosphate (muscle adenylic

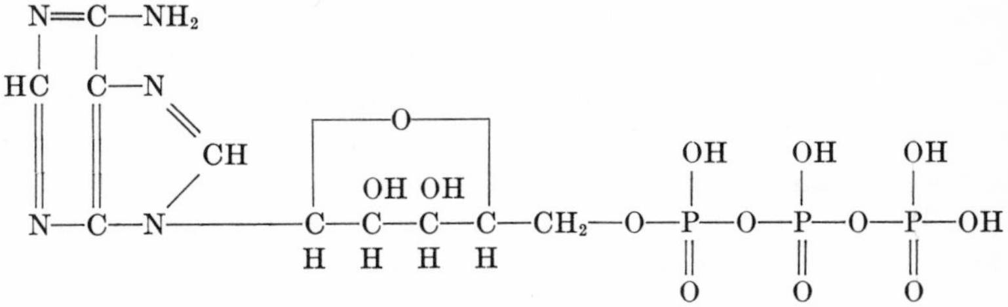

Adenosine triphosphoric acid
(Lohmann)

acid) and pyrophosphoric acid. The linear formula illustrated was initially proposed by Lohman, but definitive proof was lacking at that time. Although other formulations (*128*) have been suggested, most enzymic and chemical evidence supports the linear formula. Since ATP is one of the most important coenzymes in the transfer of energy from exergonic to endergonic processes through transphosphorylation reactions in animals, plants, and microorganisms, the proof of its structure will be briefly considered.

Selective enzymic procedures can degrade ATP stepwise to adenosine diphosphate (ADP) (*129*) and inorganic phosphate. ADP is converted to either adenosine 5′-phosphate or adenosine and pyrophosphate. The production of pyrophosphate could occur only by hydrolysis of the ribose phosphate ester linkage, thus establishing the linear nature of ADP. Additional proof for the structure of ADP may be found in the elegant synthetic approach of Baddiley and Todd (*130*), who found that mild acid hydrolysis of 2′,3′-*O*-isopropylideneadenosine 5′-(dibenzyl phosphate) removed the isopropylidine group as well as one benzyl group. The resultant adenosine 5′-(benzyl phosphate) was converted to the silver salt and condensed with

127. K. Lohmann, *Biochem. Z.* **203,** 164 (1928); *Naturwissenschaften* **17,** 624 (1929); C. H. Fiske and Y. SubbaRow, *Science* **70,** 381 (1929).

128. H. K. Barrenscheen and W. Filz, *Biochem. Z.* **250,** 281 (1932); T. Satoh, *J. Biochem.* (*Japan*) **21,** 19 (1935).

129. J. M. Gulland and E. Walsh, *J. Chem. Soc.* p. 169 (1945).

130. J. Baddiley and A. R. Todd, *J. Chem. Soc.* p. 648 (1947).

dibenzyl chlorophosphonate to yield adenosine 5′-(tribenzyl diphosphate). Hydrogenolysis of the benzyl groups yielded an ADP identical with the natural product. It was readily established that the third phosphate in ATP was not at the 2′- or 3′-hydroxyls of the ribose moiety but was indeed at the 5′-position. Extension of the monodebenzylation process to adenosine 5′-(tribenzyl diphosphate) followed by phosphorylation and hydrogenolysis gave an ATP identical with the natural product (*131*). In an effort to synthesize the isomeric ATP with a branched chain Michelson and Todd (*132*) coupled the disilver salt of adenosine 5′-phosphate with 2 moles of dibenzyl chlorophosphonate and after hydrogenolysis isolated an ATP again identical with the natural product. Electrometric titration revealed only one secondary phosphoryl dissociation in accord with the linear structure rather than the two secondary phosphoryl dissociations that would be present in the branched-chain isomer. Most likely, the isomeric forms of ATP are in equilibrium through a cyclic intermediate as shown in the accompanying formulas. Khorana (*133*) has devised a novel synthesis of ADP and ATP involving the treatment of adenosine 5′-phosphate with an

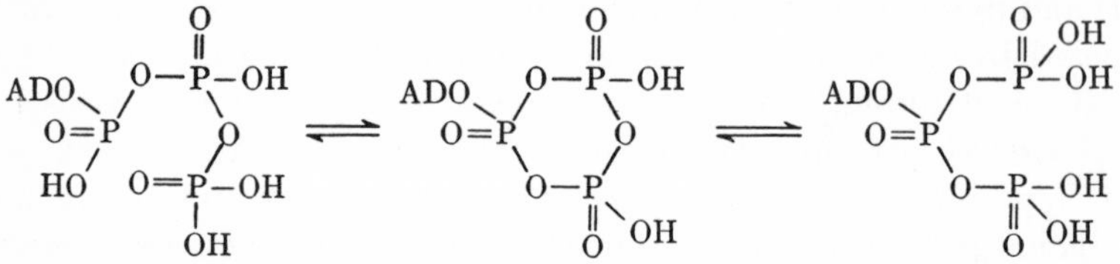
ADO
O=P
HO
O—P—OH
O
O=P—OH
OH
ADO
O=P
O—P—OH
O
O—P
OH
ADO
O=P
O—P—OH
OH
O—P—OH
OH

excess of phosphoric acid and dicyclohexyl carbodiimide, followed by an ion-exchange separation of the products. A potentially useful method for pyrophosphate synthesis via imidoyl phosphates prepared by the Beckmann rearrangement of cyclopentanoneoxime *p*-nitrobenzenesulfonate in the presence of a phosphodiester has been developed by Kenner, Todd and Webb (*133a*) and used for the syntheses of ATP in good yields (*133b*).

ATP has been shown to react with carboxylic acids (*133c*), amino acids (*133d*), and sulfate (*133e*) in the presence of the appropriate enzyme system to yield biologically active mixed anhydrides of AMP plus pyrophos-

131. J. Baddiley, A. M. Michelson, and A. R. Todd, *J. Chem. Soc.* p. 582 (1949).

132. A. M. Michelson and A. R. Todd, *J. Chem. Soc.* p. 2487 (1949).

133. H. G. Khorana, *J. Am. Chem. Soc.* **76,** 3517 (1954).

133a. G. W. Kenner, A. R. Todd, and R. F. Webb, *J. Chem. Soc.* p. 1231 (1956).

133b. B. H. Chase, G. W. Kenner, A. R. Todd, and R. F. Webb, *J. Chem. Soc.* p. 1370 (1956).

133c. P. Berg, *J. Am. Chem. Soc.* **77,** 1363 (1955).

133d. M. B. Hoagland, *Biochim. et Biophys. Acta* **16,** 288 (1955); M. B. Hoagland, E. B. Keller, and P. C. Zamecnik, *J. Biol. Chem.* **218,** 345 (1956); J. A. DeMoss, S. M. Genuth, and G. D. Novelli, *Proc. Natl. Acad. Sci. U. S.* **42,** 325 (1956).

133e. H. Hilz and F. Lipmann, *Proc. Natl. Acad. Sci. U. S.* **41,** 880 (1955); P. W. Robbins and F. Lipmann, *J. Am. Chem. Soc.* **78,** 2652 (1956).

phate. These anhydrides seem to be involved in the incorporation of acetate and sulfate into biological molecules and in addition may play an important role in the synthesis of proteins.

The elegant ion-exchange separation techniques evolved in the recent years have enabled investigators to isolate from yeast, bacteria, and animal tissues, uridine 5′-di- (UDP) and -triphosphates (UTP) (*134*), cytidine 5′-di- (CDP) and -triphosphates (CTP), and guanosine 5′-di- (GDP) and -triphosphates (GTP) (*135*). Application of the synthetic approaches developed for ADP and ATP has permitted the ready synthesis of uridine 5′-di- and -triphosphates (*136*) and could be applied to the other two pairs of nucleotides (CDP, CTP; GDP, GTP). Although the functions of these latter compounds have not been elucidated, it seems probable that they are involved as coenzymes in transphosphorylation reactions similar to ATP.

C. Biologically Important Substances Related to Nucleotides

As defined, the nucleotides are *N*-glycosylpurines or -pyrimidines esterified with phosphoric acid (*N*-base-sugar-phosphoric acid). Several vitamins of the B group and coenzymes have closely similar structures with different aglycons, with ribitol instead of ribose, or with a different sugar esterifying the end of the phosphate chain. The function of some of these compounds is discussed in Chapter XIII.

Coenzyme I. A heat-stable, dialyzable substance occurs in yeast and muscle tissue which is essential for the *in vitro* fermentation of sugars by yeast extract. Concurrent work in the laboratories of Warburg, Christian, and Griese, and Euler and Schlenk (*137*) established the following formula for coenzyme I (also known as cozymase, codehydrogenase I, or diphosphopyridine nucleotide (DPN):

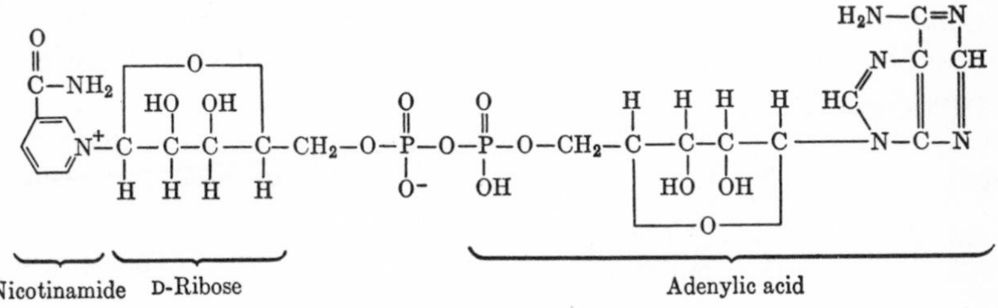
Nicotinamide
D-Ribose
Adenylic acid

Cozymase or Coenzyme I (DPN)

134. S. H. Lipton, S. A. Morrell, A. Frieden, and R. M. Bock, *J. Am. Chem. Soc.* **75,** 5449 (1953).

135. H. Schmitz, R. B. Hurlbert, and V. R. Potter, *J. Biol. Chem.* **209,** 41 (1954).

136. R. H. Hall and H. G. Khorana, *J. Am. Chem. Soc.* **76,** 5056 (1954); N. Anand, V. M. Clark, R. H. Hall, and A. R. Todd, *J. Chem. Soc.* p. 3665 (1952); G. W. Kenner, A. R. Todd, R. F. Webb, and F. J. Weymouth, *ibid.* p. 2288 (1954).

137. O. Warburg, W. Christian, and A. Griese, *Biochem. Z.* **282,** 157 (1935); H. von Euler and F. Schlenk, *Z. physiol. Chem.* **246,** 64 (1937).

Coenzyme I might be considered as a mixed dinucleotide consisting of adenylic acid and a second nucleotide compound which has one of the B-complex vitamins (nicotinamide) as the nitrogen base. Almond emulsin hydrolyzes coenzyme I and N'-ribosylnicotinamide may be separated from the hydrolyzate (*138*).

Coenzyme I functions as a hydrogen acceptor, or donor in the reduced form, only in the presence of a specific protein, as the coenzyme for many biological oxidation-reduction reactions. Although other positions in the nicotinamide ring (*139*) have been implicated as being involved in the take-up of hydrogen atoms, evidence obtained with deuterium (*140*) indicates that the reduction is probably at the double bond in the para position. More than 35 different enzymic reactions are known for which coenzyme I transports hydrogen from metabolites to the next highest carrier in oxidation-reduction potential. The reactions have been reviewed by Singer and Kearney (*141*). In reactions of this type the protein is now generally considered to be the apoenzyme and the protein-coenzyme complex, the enzyme or holoenzyme, thus: apoenzyme + coenzyme $\rightleftharpoons$ holoenzyme (enzyme).

Coenzyme II (*Triphosphopyridine Nucleotide* (*TPN*), *Codehydrogenase II*). Warburg and Christian (*142*) in 1931 discovered a dialyzable, heat-stable coenzyme associated with glucose 6-phosphate dehydrogenase which acted similarly to coenzyme I in the transport of hydrogen. In the following years, it was found in many plant and tissue extracts and obtained in a pure form. It was rapidly established that the structure was similar to coenzyme I, but the location of a third phosphate group was not known (*143*). The development of analytical techniques for nucleotides enabled Kornberg and Pricer (*144*) to isolate an adenosine diphosphate different from adenosine pyrophosphate; the diphosphate was isolated from an enzymic digest of coenzyme II and was further degraded by means of a potato phosphatase to adenylic acid-*a* which was later established as the 2′-phosphate. (See p. 439 for formula.)

Coenzyme III. A third thermostable, dialyzable factor, coenzyme III, capable of replacing DPN in a number of dehydrogenases, has been iso-

138. F. Schlenk, *Arch. Biochem.* **3,** 93 (1943).

139. P. Karrer, G. Schwarzenbach, and G. E. Utsinger, *Helv. Chim. Acta* **20,** 72 (1937).

140. M. E. Pullman, A. San Pietro, and S. P. Colowick, *J. Biol. Chem.* **206,** 129 (1954).

141. T. P. Singer and E. B. Kearney, *Advances in Enzymol.* **15,** 79 (1954); *in* "The Proteins" (H. Neurate and K. Bailey, eds.), Vol. II, Part A, p. 123. Academic Press, New York, 1954.

142. O. Warburg and W. Christian, *Biochem. Z.* **242,** 206 (1931).

143. H. von Euler and F. Schlenk, *Z. physiol. Chem.* **246,** 64 (1937); F. Schlenk, B. Hogberg, and S. Tingstam, *Arkiv Kemi Mineral. Geol.* **A13,** 11 (1939).

144. A. Kornberg and W. E. Pricer, Jr., *J. Biol. Chem.* **186,** 557 (1950).

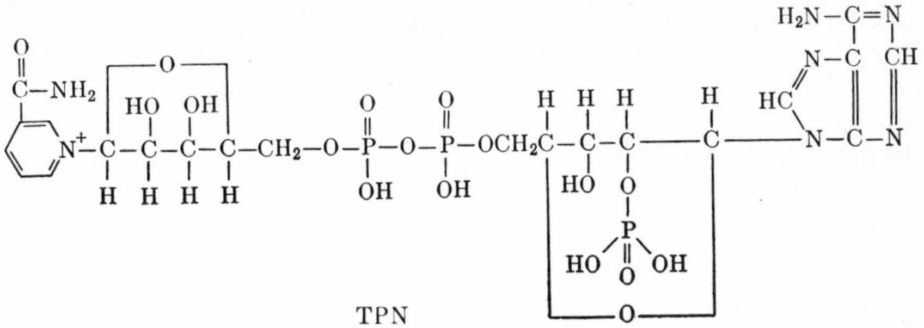
TPN

lated from baker's yeast by Singer and Kearney (*145*). Extensive investigations have established that coenzyme III consists of the complete DPN structure with an additional undetermined linkage which neutralizes one of the acid groups.

Flavin Coenzymes. Although many flavin derivatives have been suspected of functioning in oxidizing enzymic systems as prosthetic groups, only two—riboflavin 5-phosphate (flavin mononucleotide, FMN) and flavinadenine dinucleotide—have been definitely established in enzymic systems. Riboflavin 5′-phosphate (FMN) was identified by Warburg and Christian (*146*) as a constituent of the "old yellow enzyme" and its structure elucidated by several workers in different laboratories. Riboflavin, also known as vitamin B_2 or lactoflavin, has been synthesized by the following procedure which establishes its structure (*147*):

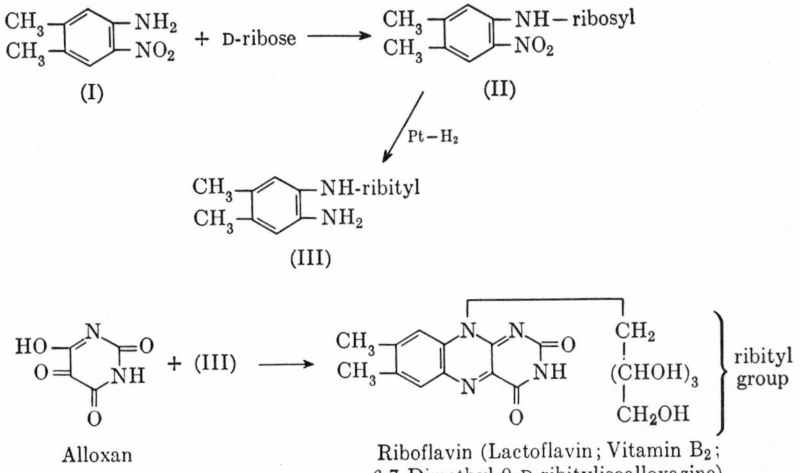
+ D-ribose
(I)
(II)
Pt–H₂
(III)
+ (III)
ribityl group
Alloxan

Riboflavin (Lactoflavin; Vitamin B_2; 6,7-Dimethyl-9-D-ribitylisoalloxazine)

145. T. P. Singer and E. B. Kearney, *Biochim. et Biophys. Acta* **8**, 700 (1952); **11**, 290 (1953).

146. O. Warburg and W. Christian, *Naturwissenschaften* **20**, 688, 980 (1932).

147. P. Karrer, K. Schöpp, and P. Benz, *Helv. Chim. Acta* **18**, 426 (1935); R. Kuhn,

Kuhn established the structure of FMN by synthesizing a triacetate (see formulas) identical with the triacetate from the natural product (*148*). Forest and Todd (*149*) phosphorylated a substituted riboflavin, and after removal of the protecting groups isolated a compound identical with the natural FMN material.

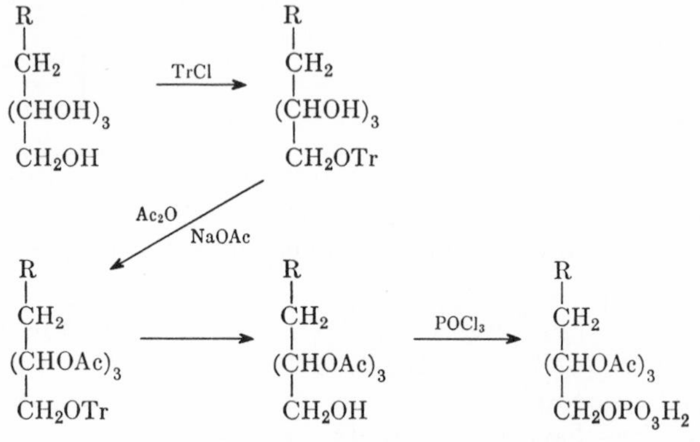
TrCl
Ac₂O
NaOAc
POCl₃

(R = substituted isoalloxazine radical)

Flavin adenine dinucleotide (FAD), discovered and characterized by Warburg and Christian (*150*), has also had its structure confirmed by the elegant synthetic approach of Christie and co-workers (*151*). It is interesting to note that both FMN and FAD are not strictly nucleotides since the bond is between the isoalloxazine ring and an alditol, ribitol, rather than a sugar.

Both FMN and FAD, in conjunction with their specific proteins, function as typical dehydrogenases catalyzing the transfer of hydrogen from the reduced forms of the pyridine nucleotides DPN and TPN, to oxygen, a dye such as methylene blue, or to the cytochrome system.

Additional Coenzymes. Cardini and associates (*152*) in 1950 discovered a coenzyme associated with "galactowaldenase" which was shown to be uridine 5′-diphosphate glucose (UDPG) both by degradation (*152*) and several years later by synthesis (*153*). This enzyme, galactowaldenase, effects the

K. Reinemund, and R. Ströbele, *Ber.* **68,** 1765 (1935); F. Bergel, A. Cohen, and J. W. Haworth, *J. Chem. Soc.* p. 165 (1945); M. Tishler, J. W. Wellman, and K. Ladenburg, *J. Am. Chem. Soc.* **67,** 2165 (1945).

148. R. Kuhn, H. Rudy, and F. Weygand, *Ber.* **69,** 1543 (1936).

149. H. S. Forest and A. R. Todd, *J. Chem. Soc.* p. 3295 (1950).

150. O. Warburg and W. Christian, *Biochem. Z.* **298,** 150 (1938).

151. S. M. H. Christie, G. W. Kenner, and A. R. Todd, *J. Chem. Soc.* p. 46 (1954).

152. C. E. Cardini, A. C. Paladini, R. Caputto, and L. F. Leloir, *Nature* **165,** 191 (1950); R. Caputto, L. F. Leloir, C. E. Cardini, and A. C. Paladini, *J. Biol. Chem.* **184,** 333 (1950).

153. G. W. Kenner, A. R. Todd, and R. F. Webb, *J. Chem. Soc.* p. 2843 (1954).

transformation of D-galactose 1-phosphate to D-glucose 1-phosphate. Leloir and Cardini (*154*) have also shown that the coenzyme can be implicated in the enzymic formation of sucrose from fructose and the glucose in the coenzyme. Since the original discovery of UDPG, a number of similar compounds, i.e., uridine diphosphate galactose, uridine diphosphate aminouronic peptide, uridine diphosphate glucuronic acid, uridine diphosphate acetylglucosamine, and guanosine diphosphate mannose, have been isolated from natural sources although their functions have not yet been resolved (*155*). The nomenclature of these compounds requires systemization. Additional information concerning some of these substances is given under Galactose (Chapter II), Sucrose (Chapter IX), and in Chapter XIII.

3. NUCLEIC ACIDS (*98*)*

The nucleic acids are polymers of a large number of appropriate mononucleotide residues (base-sugar-phosphate) joined by internucleotidic ribose phosphate esterifications; the polymeric linkage is the phosphate ester bond. Their biological importance is evident from the fact that two types, called RNA and DNA, are found in all cells and some viruses. Although DNA appears to exist exclusively within the cell nucleus, RNA (though more abundant in the cytoplasm) also occurs to some extent in the nucleus. RNA represents the sole nucleic acid type associated with the plant viruses (*156*), whereas the bacterial viruses, which are rich in DNA, apparently lack RNA (*157*). (For histochemical identification, see Chapter XI.)

The most acceptable methods of isolation of the nucleic acids avoid the use of hydrolytic agents (acid, alkali, prolonged heating) but depend on processes which are designed to denature and to precipitate the associated cell protein; agents for this purpose are detergents, guanidine hydrochloride, and chloroform (*158*). Nucleic acids prepared in this manner are of high molecular weight and, particularly for DNA, their solutions exhibit abnormally high viscosities.

The ultimate hydrolysis products of the nucleic acids (*98*) are approximately equimolar quantities of the nitrogenous bases (two purines and two pyrimidines), pentose (D-ribose from RNA and 2-deoxy-D-ribose from DNA), and phosphoric acid. The two purine bases, adenine and guanine,

* Revised by Elliot Volkin and David G. Doherty under U.S.A.E.C. Contract No. W-7405-eng-26.

154. L. F. Leloir and C. E. Cardini, *J. Am. Chem. Soc.* **75,** 6084 (1953).

155. L. F. Leloir, *Arch. Biochem. Biophys.* **33,** 186 (1951); J. T. Park, *J. Biol. Chem.* **194,** 877, 885, 897 (1952); G. J. Dalton and I. D. E. Storey, *Biochem. J.* **53,** xxxvii (1953); E. Cabib, L. F. Leloir, and C. E. Cardini, *J. Biol. Chem.* **203,** 1055 (1953); **206,** 779 (1954).

156. C. A. Knight, *J. Biol. Chem.* **197,** 241 (1952).

157. F. W. Putnam, *Advances in Protein Chem.* **8,** 177 (1954).

158. F. W. Allen, *Ann. Rev. Biochem.* **23,** 99 (1954).

are found in both RNA and DNA, but the only pyrimidine common to both types is cytosine; uracil is the other pyrimidine base of RNA, and the pyrimidine thymine is found in DNA. In addition, it should be noted that DNA from some sources contains significant quantities of 5-methylcytosine (*101*) as well as cytosine, whereas the DNA of some bacterial viruses contains 5-hydroxymethylcytosine (*159*) to the complete exclusion of cytosine.

Structure. The precise identification of the mode of linkage of the phosphate residues to adjacent ribose moieties in the nucleic acid chain has been established, primarily as a result of the development of ion-exchange (*103*) and paper (*107*) chromatographic methods. The basic structure for both types of nucleic acid is represented diagrammatically below (after Brown and Todd (*160*)) with the phosphorus atoms esterified at carbons

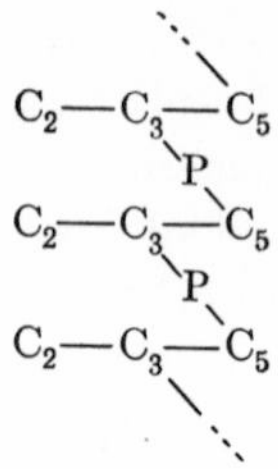

C2—C3—C5
P
C2—C3—C5
P
C2—C3—C5

3 and 5 of the pentose. The evidence supporting such a structure is presented in the following section.

Ribonucleic Acid. A major contribution to the formulation of RNA structure was the demonstration that alkaline hydrolysis of RNA quantitatively liberates about equal amounts of mononucleotide isomers of all four bases (*103*). Although it was readily established that none of these mononucleotides is the 5′-phosphate isomer, it was not until some years later that Cohn and associates (*102*) by controlled degradation experiments, and Brown and associates (*121*) by the synthetic route, established that the products were isomers involving phosphate attachment at positions 2 and 3 of the ribose. Of equal significance was the discovery (*161*) that hydrolysis of RNA by the enzyme phosphodiesterase (snake venom or intestinal) liberates mononucleotides exclusively of still another type, the 5′-mononucleotides. It was thus necessary to establish the mechanisms which could account for one phosphodiester structure in the RNA chain giving rise to three isomers of each mononucleotide.

Alkaline hydrolysis of the internucleotidic linkages was proposed (*160*, *162*) to take place by intermediate cyclization of the 3′-phosphoryl linkage,

159. G. R. Wyatt and S. S. Cohen, *Biochem. J.* **55,** 774 (1953).
160. D. M. Brown and A. R. Todd, *J. Chem. Soc.* p. 52 (1952).
161. W. E. Cohn and E. Volkin, *J. Biol. Chem.* **203,** 319 (1953).
162. D. Lipkin, P. T. Talbert, and M. Cohn, *J. Am. Chem. Soc.* **76,** 2871 (1954).

to the 2′-position with concomitant rupture of the 5′-linkage; the cyclic esters were than assumed to be hydrolyzed randomly to yield an approximately equal mixture of the 2′- and 3′-mononucleotides, as illustrated under Nucleotides. The mechanism is similar to that previously demonstrated for the acid or alkaline intramolecular phosphate shift in the hexose phosphates (Chapter III); the reaction results finally in a migration of about half the phosphate groups to another ribose carbon. In support of this postulate was the verification of the existence of the cyclic 2′,3′-intermediates in partial RNA hydrolyzates (*163*) as well as the synthesis of these latter compounds (*118*).

The action of the enzyme phosphodiesterase, on the other hand, takes place by a straightforward hydrolysis of the phosphorus linkage adjoining carbon 3 of ribose to yield 5′-mononucleotides (see formulas) (*161*). On this latter observation is based the conclusion that half the phosphoryl attach-

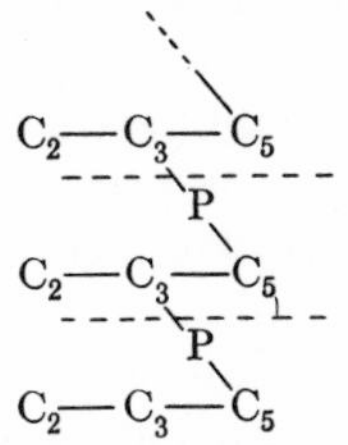
C_2—C_3—C_5
P
C_2—C_3—C_5
P
C_2—C_3—C_5

(- - - -) Point of hydrolysis
by phosphodiesterase

ments in RNA are to carbon 5 of the ribose units. This finding was additionally significant in so far as it indicated a more direct relation between nucleic acid and the variety of free 5′-nucleotides known to exist in biological systems.

Hydrolysis of RNA by crystalline pancreatic ribonuclease likewise proceeds through intermediate 2′,3′-cyclization (*164*), but in this case the action is specifically limited to phosphoryl linkages associated with the pyrimidine nucleotides; the cyclic intermediates subsequently are degraded by the enzyme only to the 3′-nucleotide type. Thus, the end-products are polynucleotides which terminate in 3′-pyrimidine nucleotide groups, and pyrimidine mononucleotides of the 3′-variety (*165*). The structural identification of many of the polynucleotides demonstrated that no simple alternating sequence of purines and pyrimidines exist in the intact RNA.

Since only the synthetic 3′-diesters of pyrimidine nucleotides are hydrolyzed by ribonuclease, the 3′-form (rather than 2′-) must preexist in at least

163. R. Markham and J. D. Smith, *Biochem. J.* **52,** 552 (1952).
164. R. Markham and J. D. Smith, *Biochem. J.* **52,** 558, 565 (1952).
165. E. Volkin and W. E. Cohn, *J. Biol. Chem.* **205,** 767 (1953).

the pyrimidine nucleotide linkages of the RNA chain (*166*). Finally, the 3′-linkage may be assigned to the purine as well as pyrimidine nucleotides in the RNA polymer by virtue of the observation that a purified enzyme from spleen yields exclusively 3′-purine and -pyrimidine mononucleotides, without concomitant cyclization as part of the mechanism (*167*).

The foregoing data permit only the 3′,5′-internucleotidic linkage in the RNA chain, to the exclusion of 2′,3′- or 2′,5′-structures.

Deoxyribonucleic Acid. Since only carbons 3 and 5 of the 2-deoxyribose are available for esterification in DNA, the linkages are all most probably of the 3′,5′-type. Purified phosphodiesterase quantitatively liberates 5′-mononucleotides from thymus DNA (*100*). On the other hand, no method has as yet been developed for degradation of these nucleic acid to 3′-deoxy-mononucleotides, although the pyrimidine 3′,5′-diphosphates have been isolated from acid hydrolyzates of DNA. Crystalline pancreatic deoxyribonuclease rapidly degrades DNA to very low molecular weight polynucleotides, but identification of many of these products reveals no certain route for the action of the enzyme (*168*).

DNA exhibits rather different properties from RNA in its susceptibility to acid and alkaline hydrolysis. The extreme acid lability of the *N*-glycosyl-purine linkages in DNA allows the quantitative liberation of free purines by very mild acid treatment, leaving a high molecular weight residue (called apurinic acid or thymic acid) complete in pyrimidine, deoxyribose, and phosphate composition (*169*). DNA, however, is quite stable to alkaline action since the absence of a hydroxyl group on carbon 2 of deoxyribose precludes the possibility of labilization through a cyclic 2′,3′-phosphate intermediate.

On the basis of X-ray scattering analysis, and chemical evidence which reveals a strict equimolar relation of adenine to thymine and guanine to cytosine (*170*), Watson and Crick (*171*) have formulated a macrostructure for DNA. The authors propose a helical coil involving two DNA chains, the two strands being held together by hydrogen bonds involving the aforementioned pairs of bases on opposite chains. In order more completely to account for some of the properties of DNA, the structure has been modified to include alternating "breaks" at regular places in the two chains (*172*).

166. D. M. Brown, C. A. Dekker, and A. R. Todd, *J. Chem. Soc.* p. 2715 (1952).

167. D. M. Brown, L. A. Heppel, and R. J. Hilmoe, *J. Chem. Soc.* p. 40 (1954).

168. R. L. Sinsheimer, *J. Biol. Chem.* **208,** 445 (1954).

169. C. Tamm, H. S. Shapiro, and E. Chargaff, *J. Biol. Chem.* **199,** 313 (1952).

170. G. R. Wyatt, *J. Gen. Physiol.* **36,** 201 (1952); S. Zamenhof, G. Brawerman, and E. Chargaff, *Biochim. et Biophys. Acta* **9,** 402 (1952).

171. J. D. Watson and F. H. C. Crick, *Nature* **171,** 737 (1953).

172. C. A. Dekker and H. K. Schachman, *Proc. Natl. Acad. Sci.* (*U. S.*) **40,** 894 (1954).

Evidence now indicates that DNA from a single source may be separated by certain fractionation procedures into a variety of DNA's of differing base composition (*173*).

Biological Significance of the Nucleic Acids. It has long been felt that DNA has some direct function in the transmission of heritable characteristics through cell generations. The most striking evidence in support of this concept comes from the work with the so-called transforming principle, whereby it can be demonstrated that highly purified DNA preparation (transforming principle) from one bacterial strain is capable of permanently conferring specific genetic characters to a related bacterial strain (*174*). In addition, it appears from various researches with isotopes that DNA remains as a quite stable chemical entity during the division of mammalian cells (*98*).

IN VITRO *Syntheses of RNA and DNA.* An outstanding development in the study of RNA synthesis has come about through the researches of Ochoa and his associates (*174a, b, c, d*). These workers partially purified an enzyme, polynucleotide phosphorylase, from *Azotobacter vinelandii* which effects the synthesis of highly polymerized ribopolynucleotides from 5′-nucleoside diphosphates with the release of orthophosphate. The diphosphates of adenosine, inosine, uridine, cytidine, and guanosine are individually reactive, and, more important, mixtures of the appropriate diphosphates will yield a mixed polynucleotide. Such biosynthetic polynucleotides may attain average molecular weights ranging from 50,000 to 350,000. Chemical and enzymatic degradation of the polymers show that the constituent nucleosides are linked through 3′,5′-ribose diphosphate bonds as in natural RNA, and, furthermore, mixed biosynthetic polynucleotides hydrolyzed with pancreatic ribonuclease yield products such as those obtained from natural RNA. The biosynthetic reaction is reversible and is catalyzed by Mg^{++}.

Kornberg and associates have demonstrated (*174e*) that extracts of *E. coli* B can polymerize the triphosphates of thymidine, deoxyguanosine, deoxycytidine, or deoxyadenine into a product whose properties are closely

173. C. F. Crompton, R. Lipschitz, and E. Chargaff, *J. Biol. Chem.* **211,** 125 (1954); G. L. Brown and M. Watson, *Nature* **172,** 339 (1953).

174. R. D. Hotchkiss, *in* "Dynamics of Virus and Rickettsial Infections" (F. W. Hartman *et al.*, eds.), p. 405. Blakiston, New York, 1954.

174a. M. Grunberg-Manago and S. Ochoa, *J. Am. Chem. Soc.* **77,** 3165 (1955).

174b. M. Grunberg-Manago, P. J. Ortiz, and S. Ochoa, *Science* **122,** 907 (1955).

174c. M. Grunberg-Manago, P. J. Ortiz, and S. Ochoa, *Biochim. et Biophys. Acta* **20,** 269 (1956).

174d. S. Ochoa, *Federation Proc.* **15,** 832 (1956).

174e. A. Kornberg, I. R. Lehman, M. J. Bessman, and E. S. Simms, *Biochim. et Biophys. Acta* **21,** 197 (1956).

similar to those of natural DNA. The reaction was revealed by using labeled substrates rather than by a demonstration of net synthesis of the product. The system requires ATP and a primer, the latter resembling a partial digest of DNA.

4. COMBINATIONS OF SUGARS WITH AMINO ACIDS AND PROTEINS (*175*)*

Colorimetric methods indicate that most proteins contain several per cent of carbohydrates (*176*). The carbohydrate portion, although small, is of considerable biological importance. Many such combinations act as antigens and induce the formation of antibodies in animals, and often the specificity is due mainly to the carbohydrate portion. It has been suggested that the enzymes which hydrolyze carbohydrates (glycosidases) may be proteins which contain carbohydrates and that the sugar portion may be responsible for the marked specificity shown by these enzymes (*177*).

Several C-1 amino acid derivatives of D-fructose apparently have been isolated from natural products such as liver extracts (*178*); possibly Amadori rearrangements (*179*) (p. 724) may be a method of establishing stable carbohydrate-protein linkages.

The combinations of amino acids with sugars may play an important part in the changes which take place during the dehydration and storage of natural products. As shown by the early researches cf Maillard and others (*180*) solutions of sugars and amino acids develop brown-to-black colors and pronounced odors when heated. The development of these changes may be detrimental in many foods such as in dried fruits and eggs. On the other hand, they may be beneficial as in malt, for the color, odor, and foaming properties impart desirable characteristics to beer (*181*).

A. Preparation

The relationship of condensation products of sugars and amino acids to labile complexes of carbohydrates and amino acids and to the melanoidin reaction has stimulated the study of the simplest systems. The amino acids

* Revised by David Platt.

175. For early history see S. Fränkel and C. Jellinek, *Biochem. Z.* **185,** 392 (1927).

176. M. Sørensen and G. Haugaard, *Biochem. Z.* **260,** 247 (1933); S. Gurin and D. B. Hood, *J. Biol. Chem.* **139,** 775 (1941).

177. B. Helferich, W. Richter, and S. Grunler, *Ber. Verhandl. sachs. Akad. Wiss. Leipzig Math. phys. Kl.* **89,** 385 (1938).

178. H. Borsook, A. Abrams, and P. Lowy, *J. Biol. Chem.* **215,** 111 (1955); A. Gottschalk, *Yale J. Biol. Med.* **26,** 352 (1954).

179. A. Abrams, P. H. Lowy, and H. Borsook, *J. Am. Chem. Soc.* **77,** 4794 (1955).

180. L. C. Maillard, *Ann. chim.* [11] **5,** 258 (1916); [11] **7,** 113 (1917).

181. See J. P. Danehy and W. Pigman, *Advances in Food Research* **3,** 241 (1951); J. E. Hodge, *J. Agr. Food Chem.* **1,** 928 (1953).

may condense with the aldehyde group of sugars in a manner similar to that of amines:

$$
\begin{array}{ccccc}
 & & & & \text{R} \\
 & & & & | \\
\text{HCO} & & \text{R—CH—COOR} & & \text{HC}{=}\text{N—CH} \\
| & + & | & \rightarrow & | \quad\quad | \\
\text{HCOH} & & \text{NH}_2 & & \text{HCOH} \quad \text{COOH} \\
| & & & & | \\
\end{array}
$$

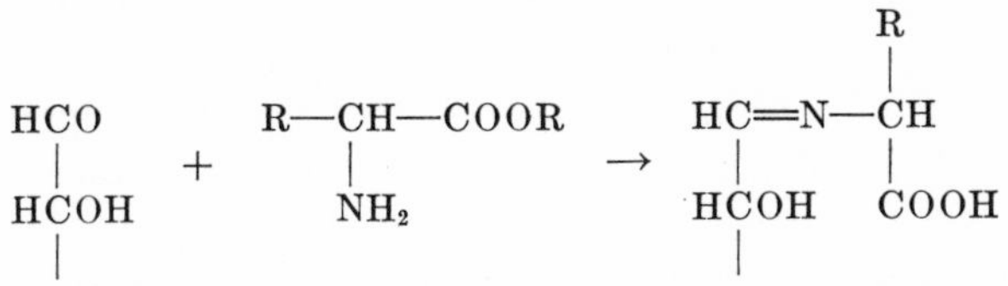

The reaction may take place by direct combination in aqueous or alcoholic solution or in the semisolid state, but usually it is difficult to isolate the reaction products. Alanine (CH_3—$CHNH_2$—$COOH$) and the ethyl ester of glycine (NH_2—CH_2—$COOC_2H_5$) condense with glucose to give the corresponding N-glucosylamino acids (182). Because of the similar conditions of this reaction to those occurring during the dehydration of foods, these syntheses have particular interest.

Cysteine reacts particularly readily with reducing sugars probably because a secondary thiazoline ring is formed (183):

$$
\begin{array}{ccccc}
 & & & & \text{CH}_2\text{—CH—COOH} \\
 & & & & \diagup \quad\quad\quad | \\
\text{HSCH}_2\text{—CH—COOH} & + & \text{glucose} & \rightarrow & \text{S} \\
| & & & & \diagdown \quad\quad\quad | \\
\text{NH}_2 & & & & \text{C}{=}\text{N}^+\text{H} \\
 & & & & | \\
 & & & & \text{HCOH} \\
 & & & & | \\
 & & & & \text{HCOH} \\
 & & & & | \\
\end{array}
$$

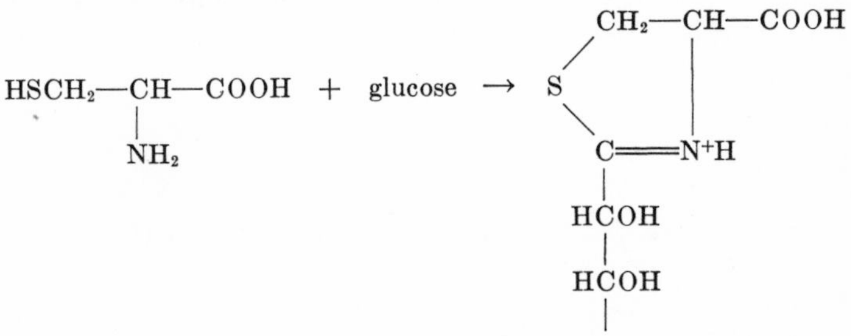

The main evidence for the thiazoline structure is the negative test for —SH groups given with the sodium nitroprusside reagent.

More certain results are obtained by the interaction of the esters or amides of amino acids and tetra-O-acetylglucosyl bromide (184). The

$$
\begin{array}{ccccc}
\overline{\text{HCBr}} \quad| & & & & \overline{\text{HC—N—CH}_2\text{—CONH}_2} \\
| \quad\quad\;| \; \text{O} & + & \text{CH}_3\text{NH—CH}_2\text{—CONH}_2 & \rightarrow & | \quad\; | \quad\quad\quad | \\
\text{HCOAc} \;| & & & & \text{CH}_3 \quad | \quad\quad\quad \text{(II)} \\
| & & \text{(I)} & & \quad\quad\;\; \text{O} \\
 & & & & \text{HCOAc} \quad| \\
 & & & & | \\
\end{array}
$$

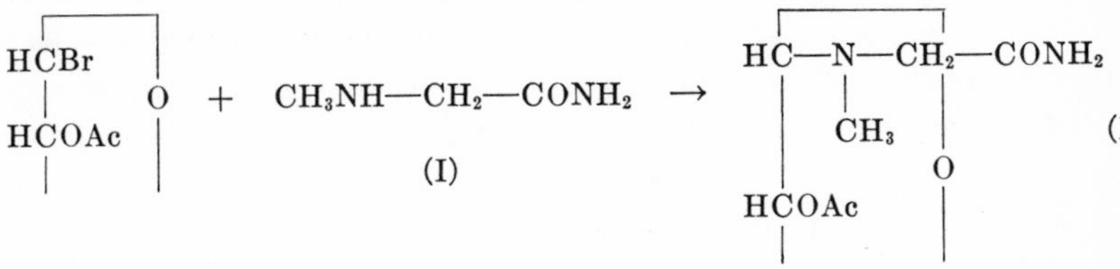

182. J. C. Irvine and A. Hynd, *J. Chem. Soc.* **99**, 161 (1911); H. von Euler and K. Zeile, *Ann.* **487**, 163 (1931).

183. M. P. Schubert, *J. Biol. Chem.* **130**, 601 (1939); G. Ågren, *Enzymologia* **9**, 321 (1941).

184. K. Maurer and B. Schiedt, *Z. physiol. Chem.* **206**, 125 (1932).

reaction of the compound sarcosine amide (I) with tetra-*O*-acetylglucosyl bromide is illustrated. The tetraacetate (II) yields *N*-glucosylsarcosine amide upon deacetylation. The *N*-glucosylglycylglycine and other similar compounds have been made by this method (*185*).

Some function of certain amino acids other than the amino group also may be utilized for condensations with sugars. Thus, the phenolic group of tyrosine (p-HO—C_6H_4—CH_2—$CH(NH_2)$—COOH) condenses with tetra-*O*-acetylglucosyl bromide to form an *O*-glucoside if the amino group is suitably blocked (as with a carbobenzoxy group) (*186*).

By using the carbobenzoxy method for peptide synthesis, acyl sugar derivatives are obtained in which the acyl group is an amino acid radical (*187*). Carbobenzoxyglycyl chloride reacts with the sodium salt of 4,6-*O*-benzylideneglucose to form 1-carbobenzoxyglycyl-4,6-*O*-benzylidene-D-glucopyranose, which on catalytic hydrogenation gives 1-*O*-glycylglucose.

The 5,6-anhydrohexoses react (p. 393) with amino acids with the formation of sugars having amino acids substituted on carbon 6. The 6-deoxy-6-(*N*-alanino)glucose (V) is prepared (*188*) from alanine (IV) and 1,2-*O*-isopropylidene-5,6-anhydroglucose (III). Other amino acids have also been used (*189*); both mono- and di-*N*-substituted amino acid derivatives are produced.

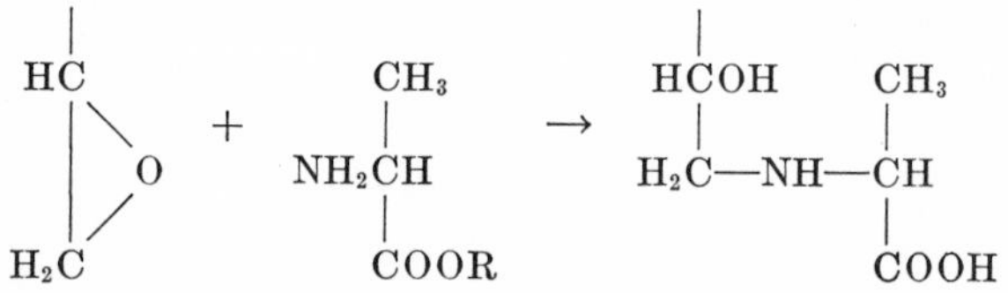

(III) (IV) (V)

Another procedure for obtaining combinations of sugars and amino acids depends on the acylation of the amino group of amino sugars. The *N*-glycyl-D-glucosamine or *N*-alanyl-D-glucosamine is obtained from the action of carbobenzoxyglycyl chloride or carbobenzoxy-L-alanyl chloride, respectively, on tetra-*O*-acetyl-β-D-glucosamine (*190*). Other derivatives have been made by similar reactions (*191*). An additional method utilizes the reduction of the tetra-*O*-acetyl-(*N*-α-azidopropionyl)glucosamine and simi-

185. H. von Euler and K. Zeile, *Ann.* **487,** 163 (1931).
186. R. F. Clutton, C. R. Harington, and T. H. Mead, *Biochem. J.* **31,** 764 (1937).
187. M. Bergmann, L. Zervas, and J. Overhoff, *Z. physiol. Chem.* **224,** 52 (1934).
188. B. Helferich and R. Mittag, *Ber.* **71,** 1585 (1930).
189. M. K. Gluzman and V. I. Kovalenko, *Chem. Abstr.* **48,** 138, 603, 3254 (1954).
190. M. Bergmann and L. Zervas, *Ber.* **65,** 1201 (1932).
191. D. G. Doherty, E. A. Popenoe, and K. P. Link, *J. Am. Chem. Soc.* **75,** 3466 (1953).

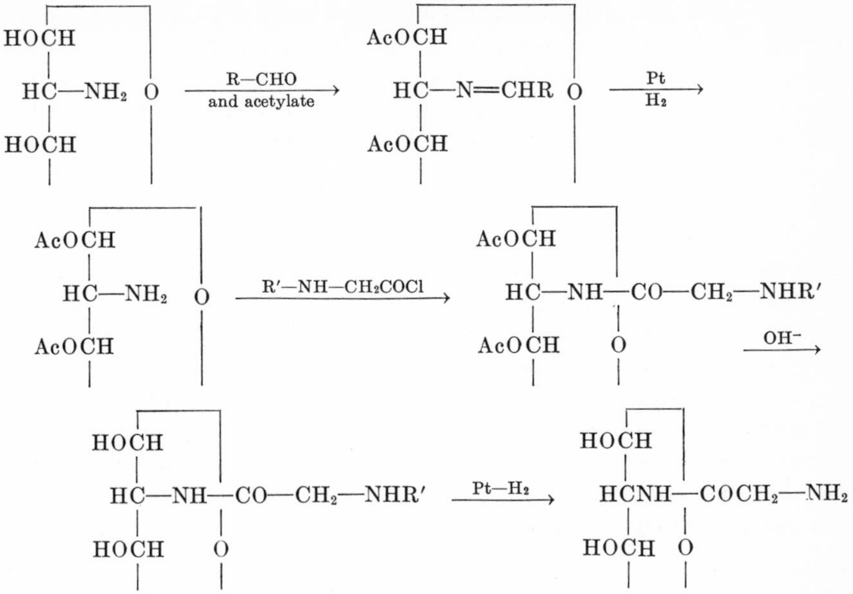

($R = p\text{-}CH_3O—C_6H_4—$; $R' = C_6H_5—CH_2—O—CO—$)

lar derivatives by hydrogen with platinum oxide as catalyst (*192*). (See formulas below.)

The action of some dipeptidase enzymes on such derivatives has been studied by Bergmann and associates (*193*) and an interesting correlation with the enzymic hydrolysis of dipeptides demonstrated. The dipeptides of naturally occurring α-amino acids (those belonging to the L-series) and

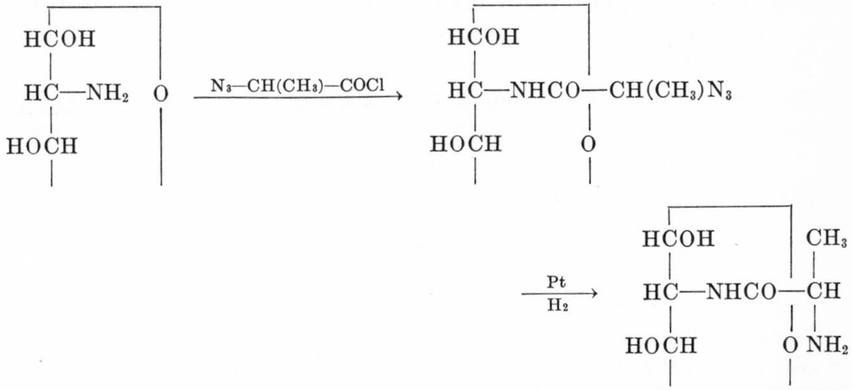

192. A. Bertho and J. Maier, *Ann.* **495,** 113 (1932); **498,** 50 (1932).

193. M. Bergmann, L. Zervas, H. Rinke, and H. Schleich, *Z. physiol. Chem.* **224,** 33 (1934).

the 2-deoxy-2-(glycylamino)mannonic acid have the same configuration for the asymmetric carbon carrying the substituted amino group; both are hydrolyzed by the dipeptidase. Similar derivatives of 2-amino-2-deoxy-gluconic acid (glucosaminic acid) which correspond to dipeptides of the D-amino acid series are unaffected by the dipeptidase.

Many derivatives of aldonic acids and amino acids have been made by the condensation of *O*-acetylaldonyl chlorides with amino acids or their esters. Deactylation gave the esters or amides and, in a few instances, the free *N*-aldonylamino acids (*194*).

Sugars may be brought into combination with proteins by coupling the proteins with diazonium salts of the glycosides. Goebel, Avery, and Heidelberger used this method in their work on the production of synthetic antigens in which the protein is combined with groups of known structure. The diazonium salt is made by the usual procedure of treating an amine with nitrous acid; the amine group in these experiments is in the aglycon group of an aminophenyl glycoside, prepared in turn by reduction of the corresponding nitrophenyl glycoside (*195*).

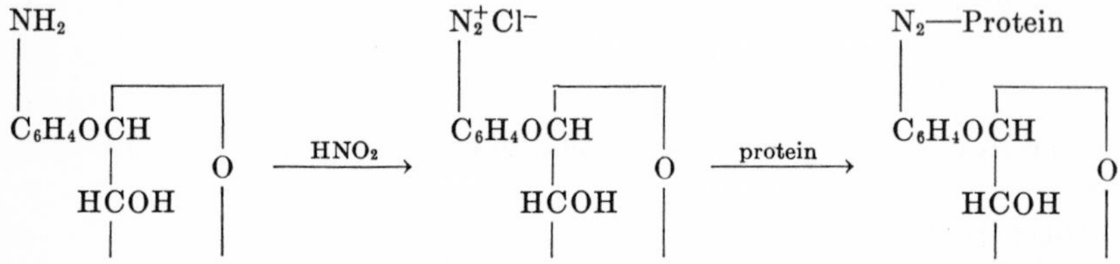
NH₂
C₆H₄OCH
HCOH
O
HNO₂
N₂⁺Cl⁻
C₆H₄OCH
HCOH
O
protein
N₂—Protein
C₆H₄OCH
HCOH
O

(Synthetic antigen)

Another process involves coupling the azide formed by the action of nitrous acid on *O*-β-glucosyl-*N*-carbobenzoxytyrosine hydrazide with proteins and removing the carbobenzoxy group with the aid of sodium in liquid ammonia (*186*).

Mixtures of proteins and sugars react in the semidry state or in concentrated solution (*181*). In some instances, a hexose unit will add to many of the amino groups in stable combination. For bovine serum albumin and D-glucose, as much as 17% of the product was acid-stable combined D-glucose.

B. Protein-Carbohydrate Compounds as Synthetic Antigens (*196*)

Certain substances called antigens induce the formation of antibodies in serum and other body fluids when they are introduced parenterally into

194. D. G. Doherty, *J. Biol. Chem.* **201**, 857 (1954).

195. See O. T. Avery, W. F. Goebel, and F. H. Babers, *J. Exptl. Med.* **55**, 769 (1932); a somewhat similar method is described by B. Woolf, *Proc. Roy. Soc.* **B130**, 60 (1941).

196. J. Marrack, *Ergeb. Enzymforsch.* **7**, 281 (1938).

animal tissue. The serum which contains the antibodies is known as an antiserum. It reacts specifically with certain antigens as is evidenced by the formation of a precipitate or by other reactions. Synthetic antigens, containing carbohydrates, have been prepared by Avery, Heidelberger, Goebel, and associates. These compounds are made as described above. Synthetic antigens of this type were prepared from several proteins and from the glycosides of a number of mono- and disaccharides. The antisera formed by the introduction of these antigens into animals were tested for their reaction against the original antigens. It was demonstrated that the principal specificity is related to the carbohydrate rather than to the protein component (*197*). For the four antigens

(Protein-I)-β-glucoside	(Protein-II)-β-glucoside
(Protein-I)-β-galactoside	(Protein-II)-β-galactoside

those formed from different proteins but having the same carbohydrate portion form precipitates with the antisera produced by the use of either as the antigen. Those with the same protein but with different carbohydrate components are serologically different, i.e., neither forms a precipitate with the antiserum produced by the use of the other as the antigen. This behavior is particularly striking since the two proteins alone are serologically different and since the carbohydrates alone do not act as antigens. Many synthetic antigens of this type have been prepared and exhibit similar specificity effects.

Microorganisms frequently form polysaccharides in culture media which, although usually not antigenic, are able to precipitate immune sera prepared against the true antigen, the protein-polysaccharide of the microorganism (*198*). The pneumococcus polysaccharides have received the most study and these are specific for the various types (strains) of pneumococci. These microorganisms have capsules which have been shown to consist of the type-specific polysaccharides. From the polysaccharide of the type III pneumococcus, a synthetic antigen was prepared by diazotization of the *p*-aminobenzyl ether of the polysaccharide and then coupling with serum globulin (*199*). This antigen evoked an antiserum exhibiting reactions similar to those of the antiserum produced by type III pneumococcus. The constitution of some of these polysaccharides is discussed later (Chapter XII). They usually contain uronic acids and/or amino sugars. It is then of considerable interest that synthetic antigens, prepared by the above procedure from the *p*-nitrobenzyl glycosides of glucuronic, gentiobiuronic, and cellobiuronic acids confer immunity against pneumococci. All of these pro-

197. W. F. Goebel, O. T. Avery, and F. H. Babers, *J. Exptl. Med.* **60,** 599 (1934).

198. M. Heidelberger and O. T. Avery, *J. Exptl. Med.* **40,** 301 (1924); W. T. J. Morgan, *Biochem. J.* **30,** 909 (1936).

199. W. F. Goebel and O. T. Avery, *J. Exptl. Med.* **54,** 431 (1931).

tein-azobenzyl uronides evoke antisera in rabbits which, when introduced into mice, protect them (passive immunity) against type II pneumococcal infection. Although the cellobiosiduronic acid antiserum from rabbits produces a temporary (passive) immunity to type III and VIII pneumococcal infections in mice, the gentiobiosiduronic acid antiserum is ineffective. The corresponding antisera prepared from the glycosides of galacturonic acid, cellobiose, and gentiobiose fail to protect mice against pneumococcal infection by these types (*200*).

5. REACTIONS OF THE SUGARS WITH SUBSTITUTED HYDRAZINES AND HYDROXYLAMINE*

Hydrazines (R—NH—NH_2), hydroxylamine (NH_2OH), semicarbazide (H_2N—$NHCONH_2$), and other nitrogenous bases react with sugars in a manner somewhat similar to that of the amines. Many of the products mutarotate in solution and exist as ring forms and as acyclic derivatives analogous to the Schiff base isomers of the *N*-glycosides or glycosylamines. The most important of these sugar derivatives are those prepared from phenylhydrazine and other hydrazines. The oximes are intermediates in the Wohl method of shortening the carbon chains of sugars, and both the oximes and semicarbazones have been utilized for the preparation of the acyclic *aldehydo*-sugars (p. 143).

A. Hydrazones and Osazones (*201a, b*)

The reaction of phenylhydrazine with the sugars was discovered by Fischer (*202*) and was extensively employed in the classical work which established the configuration of the sugars. The products obtained have been widely employed for characterization and identification although they are somewhat difficult to purify, and the melting points are often decomposition points (*203*).

Hydrazones. When one mole each of phenylhydrazine and sugar react, phenylhydrazones are formed. Most hydrazones are water soluble, but the mannose phenylhydrazone is so insoluble that it may be used for the quantitative estimation of mannose. The hydrazones are often of value for the separation of sugars, for they may be converted to the original sugars by

* Revised by Lawrence Rosen.

200. W. F. Goebel, *Science* **91,** 20 (1940); *J. Exptl. Med.* **72,** 33 (1940).

201a. A. W. van der Haar, "Anleitung zum Nachweis, zur Trennung und Bestimmung der Monosaccharide und Aldehydsäuren." Borntraeger, Berlin, 1920.

201b. E. G. V. Percival, *Advances in Carbohydrate Chem.* **3,** 23 (1948).

202. E. Fischer, *Ber.* **17,** 579 (1884).

203. E. Fischer, *Ber.* **41,** 73 (1908).

treatment with benzaldehyde or with concentrated hydrochloric acid. Sub-

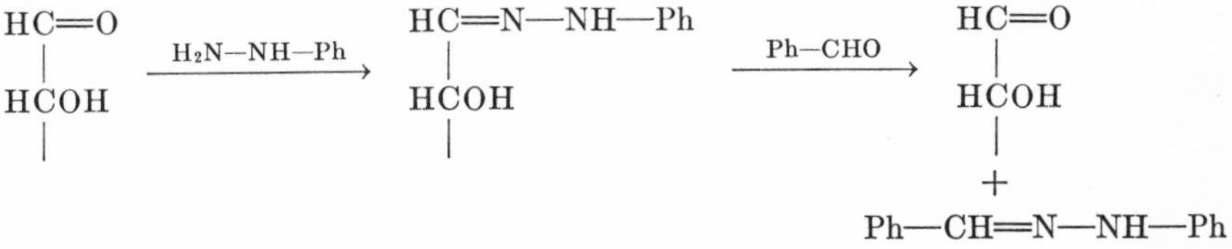
HC=O
H₂N—NH—Ph
HCOH
HC=N—NH—Ph
HCOH
Ph—CHO
HC=O
HCOH
+
Ph—CH=N—NH—Ph

stituted hydrazones less soluble than the phenylhydrazones are usually employed. Lloyd and Doherty (*204*) have prepared the 2,4-dinitrophenylhydrazones of hexoses and pentoses. A hydrazine which is reported (*205*) to show great specificity in reacting only with aldoses of certain configurations has the following formula: $H_2N—N(CH_3)\text{-}C_6H_4—CH_2—C_6H_4—N(CH_3)—NH_2$. Substituted hydrazines suitable for the identification of some important sugars are given under the individual sugars (Chapter II, Table I, and Chapter XI). *p*-Tolylsulfonylhydrazine is useful for ribose, arabinose, xylose, and fucose, but not for galactose, rhamnose, and fructose (*206*). The conditions best adapted for identification purposes are described in detail by van der Haar (*201a*). The formation of the hydrazones takes place most rapidly at pH 4 to 5 and in the presence of high concentrations of buffer. Phosphate ion is reported to have a greater catalytic effect than acetate ion (*207*), and hydrochloric acid catalyzes hydrazone but not osazone formation, particularly in the absence of air (*208*).

Ardagh and Rutherford (*207*) find the reaction to be of second-order, whereas Compton and Wolfrom (*209*) report it to be pseudo-monomolecular when a hydrazine hydrochloride solution buffered with acetate ions is used.

Information valuable for the interpretation of the structure of the hydrazones is provided (*209*) by the reaction of α-methylphenylhydrazine with tetra-*O*-acetylgalactopyranose (I), tetra-*O*-acetylgalactofuranose (II), and *aldehydo*-penta-*O*-acetylgalactose (III). As all the hydrazones formed are converted to the same penta-*O*-acetylgalactose methylphenylhydrazone (IV) when acetylated, it appears that these hydrazones have open-chain structures.

The rate of hydrazone formation for three types of galactose acetates is

204. E. A. Lloyd and D. G. Doherty, *J. Am. Chem. Soc.* **74**, 1214 (1952); see also L. M. White and G. E. Secor, *Anal. Chem.* **27**, 1016 (1955).

205. J. v. Braun and O. Bayer, *Ber.* **58**, 2215 (1925); F. L. Humoller, S. J. Kuman, and F. H. Snyder, *J. Am. Chem. Soc.* **61**, 3370 (1939).

206. D. G. Easterby, L. Hough, and J. K. N. Jones, *J. Chem. Soc.* p. 3416 (1951).

207. E. G. R. Ardagh and F. C. Rutherford, *J. Am. Chem. Soc.* **57**, 1085 (1935).

208. A. Orning and G. H. Stempel, Jr., *J. Org. Chem.* **4**, 410 (1939); G. H. Stempel, Jr., *J. Am. Chem. Soc.* **56**, 1351 (1934).

209. J. Compton and M. L. Wolfrom, *J. Am. Chem. Soc.* **56**, 1157 (1934).

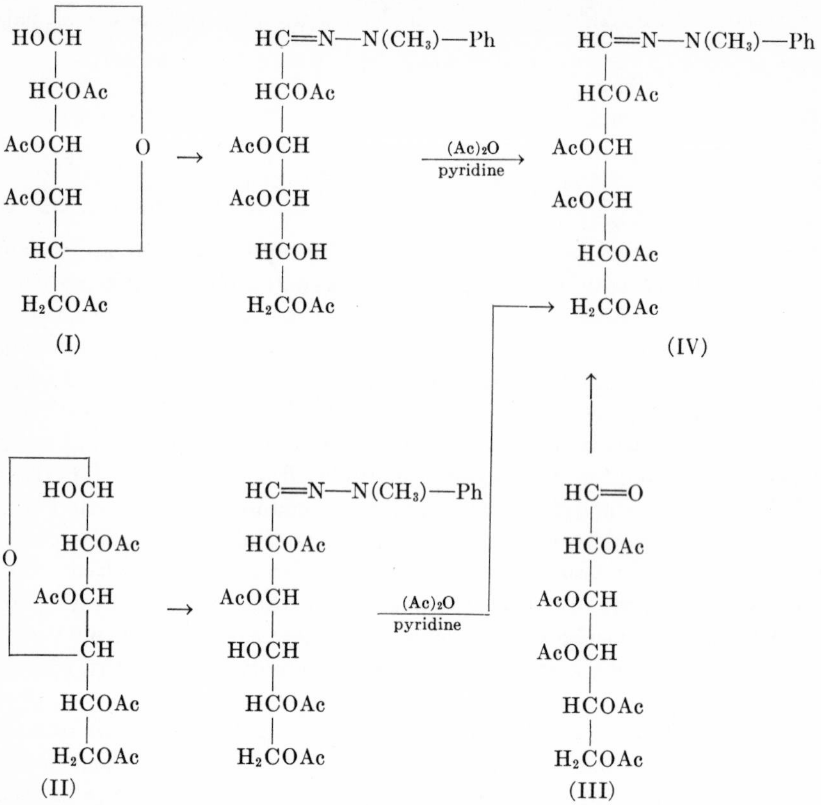

very different:

	k
Aldehydo-galactose pentaacetate	0.054
Tetra-*O*-acetylgalactofuranose	0.016
Tetra-*O*-acetylgalactopyranose	0.00052

This difference in the rate of hydrazone formation makes it probable that the rate-determining reaction is either the opening of the rings (for the cyclic acetates) to form the acyclic derivatives or the direct reaction of the original substances with the substituted hydrazine.

Although the acetylated galactose hydrazones probably have acyclic structures, the hydrazones with free hydroxyls may exist in the ring forms. In solution, the sugar hydrazones show complex mutarotations which pass through a maximum or minimum (*208*, *210*, *211*). The failure of the mutarotation equation to follow the first-order equation indicates that three or more substances take part in the equilibrium. Three isomeric glucose

210. H. Jacobi, *Ann.* **272,** 170 (1892).
211. C. L. Butler and L. H. Cretcher, *J. Am. Chem. Soc.* **53,** 4358 (1931).

phenylhydrazones exist (*212*), and their structures have been extensively investigated by Behrend and collaborators. The so-called "beta" isomer is usually obtained, and the labile "alpha" isomer is easily transformed into the "beta" form. Behrend and Reinsberg (*213*) showed that the crystalline pentaacetate of the "α"-glucose phenylhydrazone has one acetyl group attached to a nitrogen atom because removal of the phenylhydrazine group gives acetylphenylhydrazine. Since one hydroxyl escapes acetylation, it is probably involved in ring formation, and the "α"-glucose phenylhydrazone is a cyclic isomer. The acetylated "beta" isomer, however, gives phenylhydrazine. Two isomeric *p*-nitrophenylhydrazones of glucose and of mannose have been reported (*214*). The method of distinguishing between cyclic and acyclic acetyl derivatives has been improved by the development of methods for distinguishing between *N*-acetyl and *O*-acetyl groups (see below under Osazones).

Another method of establishing structures depends upon the well-defined reaction of benzenediazonium chloride with acyclic phenylhydrazones to form diphenylformazans (*215*); no well-defined product is obtained from cyclic isomers. This method has given the same results as the acetylation method, and, in addition, has shown that the third isomer of glucose phenylhydrazone is also cyclic.

Sugar Osazones. By treatment of sugars with an excess of phenylhydrazine at 100°C., two phenylhydrazine residues are introduced into the molecule, and sugar osazones, difficultly soluble in water, are formed (*216*). Optimal conditions for the preparation of glucosazone have been determined (*217*). The reaction proceeds most rapidly in the presence of acetate buffers at a pH of about 4 to 6; in more acid solution (particularly in the absence of air), and with the free base, only the hydrazone is formed (*208*, *218*). The presence of sodium bisulfite in the reaction mixture inhibits the formation of colored by-products (*219*).

Osazone formation is favored by the presence of electron-attracting groups attached to the hydrazine radical and is inhibited by the presence of alkyl groups. Nitrophenylosazones are formed with ease under mild conditions. Fructose reacts much more readily with phenylhydrazine and methylphenylhydrazine than does glucose to yield osazones (*220*).

212. Z. H. Skraup, *Monatsh.* **10**, 401 (1889); C. L. Butler and L. H. Cretcher, *J. Am. Chem. Soc.* **51**, 3161 (1929).

213. R. Behrend and W. Reinsberg, *Ann.* **377**, 189 (1910).

214. W. Alberda van Ekenstein and J. J. Blanksma, *Rec. trav. chim.* **22**, 434 (1903).

215. L. Mester and A. Major, *J. Am. Chem. Soc.* **77**, 4297 (1955).

216. E. Fischer, *Ber.* **17**, 579 (1884).

217. D. D. Garard and H. C. Sherman, *J. Am. Chem. Soc.* **40**, 955 (1918); G. J. Bloink and K. H. Pausacker, *J. Chem. Soc.* p. 622 (1951).

218. J. Kenner and E. C. Knight, *Ber.* **69**, 341 (1936).

219. R. H. Hamilton, Jr., *J. Am. Chem. Soc.* **56**, 487 (1934).

The formation of osazones requires 3 moles of phenylhydrazine per mole of sugar but 1 mole is reduced during the reaction to yield 1 mole each of aniline and ammonia (*221*). To explain the formation of the aniline and ammonia, the following mechanism has been proposed (*222*).

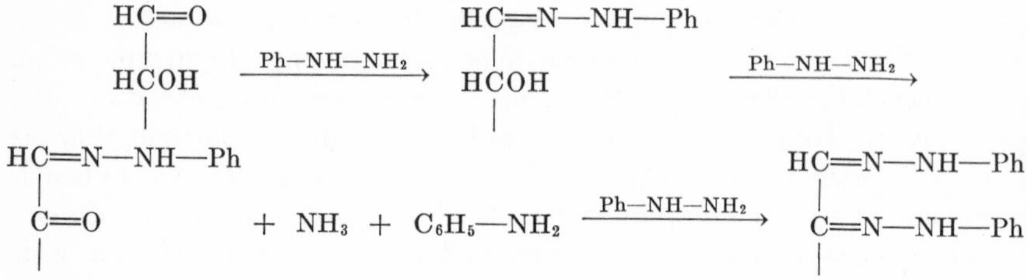

It seems unlikely that a reducing agent as mild as the secondary alcoholic group (at carbon 2) could reduce the phenylhydrazine especially since titanium trichloride does not. 1-Deoxy-1-arylaminofructoses react with phenylhydrazines under the conditions which favor osazone formation. The yields are often higher than in the usual procedure starting with a sugar, and the rate may be markedly increased (*223a*). Hydrazine and methylhydrazine are able to oxidize 1-deoxy-1-arylaminoketoses to the osone stage in approximately neutral solution (*46*). Weygand and Reckhaus (*223b*) have proposed a mechanism of osazone formation involving the Amadori rearrangement. This mechanism is illustrated for the formation of a phenylosazone (VII) from a hydrazone (I).

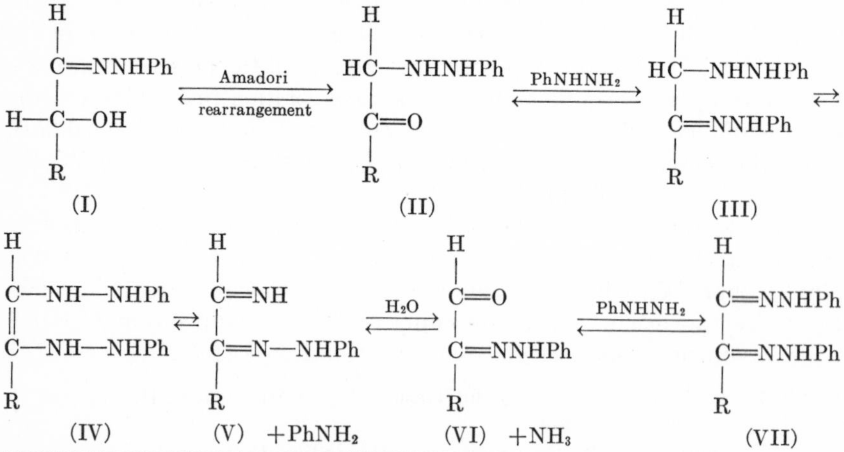

220. J. Ashmore and A. E. Renold, *J. Am. Chem. Soc.* **76,** 6189 (1954).

221. E. Knecht and F. P. Thompson, *J. Chem. Soc.* **125,** 222 (1924).

222. E. Fischer, *Ber.* **20,** 821 (1887).

223a. F. Weygand and M. Reckhaus, *Ber.* **82,** 442 (1949).

223b. F. Weygand, *Ber.* **73,** 1284 (1940); F. Weygand and M. Reckhaus, *ibid.* **82,** 438 (1949); F. Friedberg and L. Kaplan, *J. Am. Chem. Soc.* **79,** 2600 (1957) indicate that this mechanism is unlikely.

A mechanism of osazone formation utilizing the same intermediate (III) as the Weygand-Reckhaus mechanism (I–VII) has been proposed by Bloink and Pausacker (*224*). The key step may be the formation of a cyclic transition state (III′) between the intermediate (III) and a molecule of phenylhydrazine hydrochloride which is reductively cleaved to yield the osazone (VII′) directly as well as ammonia and aniline simultaneously.

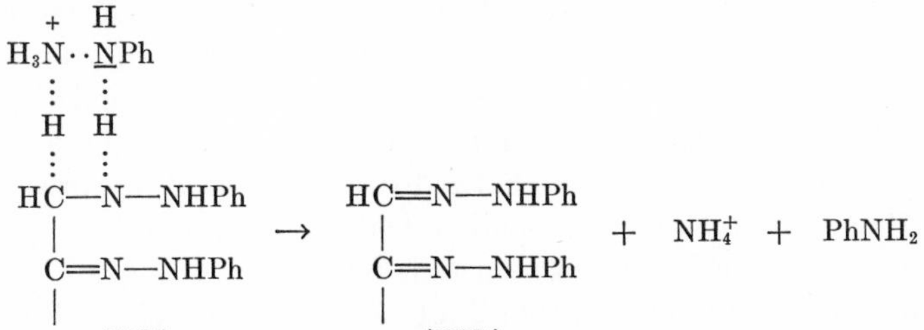
H
H_3N··NPh
H H
HC—N—NHPh
C═N—NHPh
HC═N—NHPh
C═N—NHPh
+ NH_4^+ + $PhNH_2$

(III′) (VII′)

In the Weygand and Reckhaus mechanism (*223b*), one of the *first two* molecules of phenylhydrazine is reductively cleaved to aniline and ammonia to yield the α-hydrazinocarbonyl intermediate (VI); this intermediate reacts with the third molecule of phenylhydrazine to give the osazone. In the mechanism of Bloink and Pausacker (*224*), the *third* reacting molecule of phenylhydrazine is reductively cleaved to aniline and ammonia.

On the basis of this difference, Bloink and Pausacker (*224*) attempted experimentally to distinguish between these mechanisms. The relative rates of ammonia production and phenylhydrazine consumption were measured in the reaction of phenylhydrazine with benzoin phenylhydrazone (II):

Comparison of Weygand-Reckhaus and Bloink-Pausacker Mechanisms

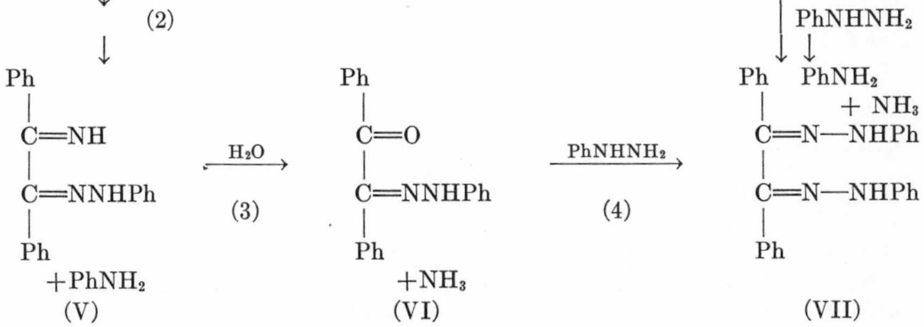
Ph
C═N—NHPh
HC—NHNHPh
Ph
(III)
$PhNHNH_2$
(1)
Ph
C═O
HC—NHNHPh
Ph
(II)
$PhNHNH_2$
Ph
C═N—NHPh
HC—NHNHPh
Ph
(III)
(2)
$PhNHNH_2$
$PhNH_2$
+ NH_3
Ph
C═NH
C═NNHPh
Ph
+$PhNH_2$
(V)
H_2O
(3)
Ph
C═O
C═NNHPh
Ph
+NH_3
(VI)
$PhNHNH_2$
(4)
Ph
C═N—NHPh
C═N—NHPh
Ph
(VII)

---

224. G. J. Bloink and K. H. Pausacker, *J. Chem. Soc.* p. 661 (1952).

The Bloink and Pausacker mechanism (II, III, VII) requires that for the conversion of benzoin hydrazone (II) to the osazone, the molar ratio of phenylhydrazine consumed to ammonia produced initially should be greater than two. The Weygand-Reckhaus mechanism (II, III, V, VI, VII) requires a molar ratio initially less than two. Since the molar ratio was found to be initially greater than two, the Bloink-Pausacker mechanism seemingly was supported. However, Bloink and Pausacker made two tacit assumptions. First, in the Weygand and Reckhaus mechanism, step (3), leading to the production of ammonia by hydrolysis of the imino compound (V), occurs much faster than the subsequent step (4) in which the second mole of phenylhydrazine would be consumed. Secondly, steps (2) and (3), proceed more rapidly than step (1), and compound (III) does not accumulate. Evidently, further investigation of the mechanism is required.

The formation of osazones from 2-methoxybutanone (*225*), 2-methoxy- (*226*) and 2-chlorocyclohexanone (*227*), and 2-*O*-methyl and 2-amino sugars indicates the ready lability of the functional group alpha to the carbonyl function. In these cases, osazone formation may proceed by direct replacement of the alpha functional group by a phenylhydrazine molecule to give (III) without prior hydrolysis to give an alpha hydroxy compound.

The phenylosazones of the sugars, because of their insolubility, are of considerable value for the identification of the sugars (p. 609). Since the asymmetry of carbon 2 is destroyed in their preparation, the osazones of three related sugars (the two epimers and the corresponding ketose) are identical:

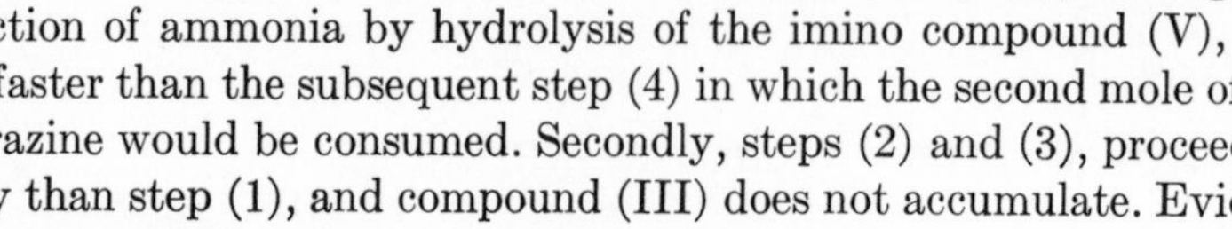
HCO
HCOH
and
HCO
HOCH
HC═N—NH—Ph
C═N—NH—Ph
H₂COH
C═O

There are but four D- and four (enantiomorphous) L-hexose phenylosazones and only two D- and two L-pentose derivatives. Thus, the preparation of the osazone of an unknown sugar may be utilized for the preliminary allocation of the unknown to a group of three possible sugars, and the final identification may be made on the basis of the preparation of difficultly soluble hydrazones which are characteristic of the individual sugars. (See above under Hydrazones.) Photomicrographs of many phenylosazones, of considerable value for identification purposes, are given by Hassid and McCready (*228*). The rotations of the hydrazones and osazones are utilized for distinguishing between D- and L-isomers, and for this purpose a mixture

225. J. G. Aston, J. T. Clarke, K. A. Burgess, and R. B. Greenburg, *J. Am. Chem. Soc.* **64,** 300 (1942).

226. H. Adkins and A. G. Rossow, *J. Am. Chem. Soc.* **71,** 3836 (1949).

227. G. J. Bloink and K. H. Pausacker, *J. Chem. Soc.* p. 1328 (1950).

228. W. Z. Hassid and R. M. McCready, *Ind. Eng. Chem. Anal. Ed.* **14,** 683 (1942).

of two volumes of alcohol and three volumes of pyridine frequently has been used as a solvent (*229*). Confirmation of the identity of the osazones is achieved by conversion to the corresponding osotriazoles (see below).

Although advantageous for the identification of the sugars, the phenyl osazones are not applicable to the isolation of sugars. The phenylhydrazine groups are removed by treatment with benzaldehyde, concentrated hydrochloric acid, or particularly well by pyruvic acid (*230*), but the resulting product, a sugar osone, is a mixed ketose-aldose.

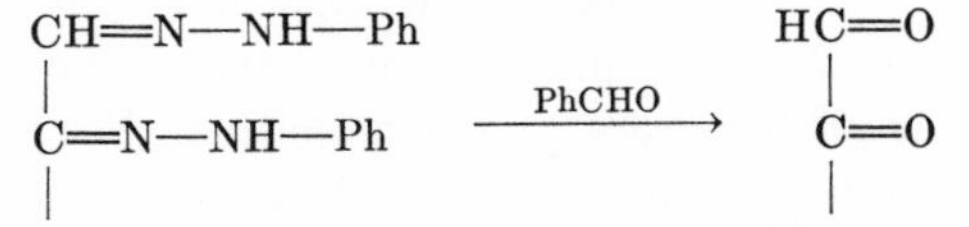

$$
\begin{array}{ccc}
\mathrm{CH{=}N{-}NH{-}Ph} & & \mathrm{HC{=}O} \\
| & \xrightarrow{\text{PhCHO}} & | \\
\mathrm{C{=}N{-}NH{-}Ph} & & \mathrm{C{=}O} \\
| & & | \\
\text{Glucose phenylosazone} & & \text{Glucosone}
\end{array}
$$

Since the sugar osazones mutarotate in alcoholic pyridine solution (*231*) the classical formula for these substances may be questioned, and there is much evidence that they exist in cyclic as well as acyclic forms. The mutarotation has been ascribed to a partial hydrolysis of the osazones, and appreciable quantities of the sugar and hydrazine exist in the equilibrium solution (*232*). This explanation is also supported by the ease with which the hydrazine radicals of the osazones are exchanged with hydrazine molecules in the solvent (*233*). When the second hydrazine is different from that used in making the osazone, mixed osazones are formed (*232, 234*).

$$
\begin{array}{c}
\mathrm{HC{=}N{-}NHR} \\
| \\
2 \quad \mathrm{C{=}N{-}NHR} \quad + \ 2\,\mathrm{NH_2{-}NHR'} \ \rightarrow \\
|
\end{array}
$$

$$
\begin{array}{ccccc}
\mathrm{HC{=}N{-}NHR'} & & \mathrm{HC{=}N{-}NHR} & & \\
| & & | & & \\
\mathrm{C{=}N{-}NHR} & + & \mathrm{C{=}N{-}NHR'} & + & 2\,\mathrm{RNH{-}NH_2} \\
| & & | & &
\end{array}
$$

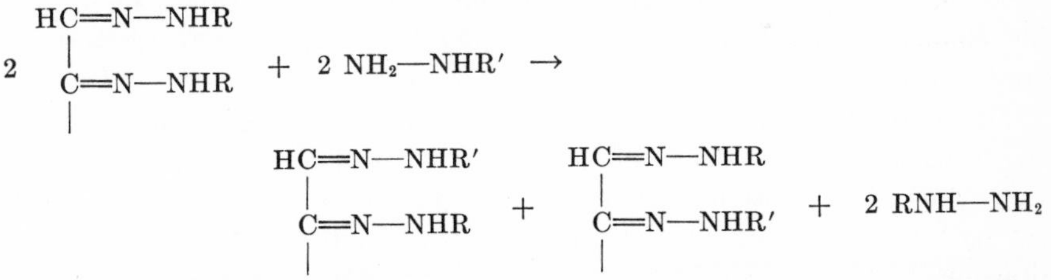

229. It should be noted that in early work in this field it was often the custom to report the observed rotation rather than the calculated specific rotation. Also, the rotations given by P. A. Levene and F. B. LaForge, *J. Biol. Chem.* **20,** 429 (1915), for a number of important osazones must be multiplied by 100 to give the correct values; cf. F. W. Zerban and L. Sattler, *Ind. Eng. Chem.* **34,** 1182 (1942).

230. E. Fischer and E. F. Armstrong, *Ber.* **35,** 3141 (1902); L. Brüll, *Ann. chim. appl.* **26,** 415 (1936).

231. E. Zerner and R. Waltuch, *Monatsh.* **35,** 1025 (1914).

232. L. L. Engel, *J. Am. Chem. Soc.* **57,** 2419 (1935); V. C. Barry, J. E. McCormick, and P. W. D. Mitchell, *J. Chem. Soc.* p. 222 (1955).

233. I. Mandl, *Arch. Biochem.* **25,** 109 (1950).

234. E. E. Percival and E. G. V. Percival, *J. Chem. Soc.* p. 750 (1941); E. Votoček and R. Vondráček, *Ber.* **37,** 3848 (1904); C. Neuberg, *ibid.* **32,** 3387 (1899).

Mild acetylation of the glucose and galactose phenylosazones leads to tetraacetates which are shown, by a method of distinguishing between *N*-acetyl and *O*-acetyl groups, to have all of the acetyl groups esterified with hydroxyls. The method depends upon the stability of *N*-acetyl groups to alkaline conditions under which *O*-acetyl groups are removed (*235*). Since all acetyl groups are esterified with hydroxyl groups, the tetra-*O*-acetylglucose and galactose phenylosazones must be open-chain compounds, for the presence of a ring would allow only a triacetate to be formed. It should be noted, however, that this method may not always be relied upon. For example, α,β-diacetylphenylhydrazine gives up one acetyl group under the conditions of the *O*-acetyl determination. (See also p. 463.)

A comparison of the absorption curves of the sugar osazones with those of simple substances (*232*) indicates that the sugar osazones are acyclic, but methylation studies (*236*) show the presence of a ring structure as illustrated in the following series of reactions:

$$\text{Glucosazone} \xrightarrow[\text{NaOH}]{(CH_3)_2SO_4} \text{tri-}O\text{-methylglucosazone} \xrightarrow{p\text{-nitrobenzaldehyde}}$$

$$\text{tri-}O\text{-methylglucosone} \xrightarrow[\text{HOAc}]{\text{Zn}} \text{3,4,5-tri-}O\text{-methylfructopyranose}$$

Since the hydroxyl of carbon 6 is not methylated, it is probably involved in ring formation. Inasmuch as the methylation of the osazones proceeds with difficulty and most of the products are amorphous, this evidence cannot be considered as final, although the analogous behavior of the osazones, hydrazones, and other nitrogenous derivatives makes a ring structure seem probable. Similar methylation evidence indicates a ring structure for galactosazone (*237*).

Further evidence for an acyclic structure for glucosazone is provided by the formation of a formazan after treatment with benzenediazonium chloride (*238*). The osazone may have a six-membered chelate ring formed by hydrogen bonding of the two hydrazine radicals. (See under Hydrazones.)

The osazones of the sugars are converted to osotriazoles when they are heated in aqueous copper sulfate solution (*239*). These derivatives offer considerable promise for the identification of the sugars and as confirmatory

235. M. L. Wolfrom, M. Konigsberg, and S. Soltzberg, *J. Am. Chem. Soc.* **58,** 490 (1936).

236. E. E. Percival and E. G. V. Percival, *J. Chem. Soc.* p. 1398 (1935).

237. J. R. Muir and E. G. V. Percival, *J. Chem. Soc.* p. 1479 (1940).

238. L. Mester, *J. Am. Chem. Soc.* **77,** 4301 (1955).

239. R. M. Hann and C. S. Hudson, *J. Am. Chem. Soc.* **66,** 735 (1944); W. T. Haskins, R. M. Hann, and C. S. Hudson, *J. Am. Chem. Soc.* **70,** 2288 (1948); E. Hardegger and H. El Khadem, *Helv. Chim. Acta* **30,** 900, 1478 (1947); E. Hardegger, H. El Khadem, and E. Schreier, *ibid.* **34,** 253 (1951).

tests for the presence of the parent osazones. The opportunity for isomerism is less than for the osazones; hence, the melting points and optical rotations are of greater value for identification purposes.

Osotriazoles of diketones previously had been described by von Pechmann (*240*) who obtained them by the oxidation of the corresponding dihydrazones. The corresponding osotriazoles of the sugars are formed directly by the action of copper sulfate. The formation of the phenyl-D-glucosotriazole (II) from glucose phenylosazone (I) is illustrated. Its structure is demonstrated by oxidation with periodic acid to the 2-phenyl-4-formylosotriazole (III) which is identical with the product obtained previously by von Pechmann from mono-*O*-acetyldinitrosoacetone phenylhydrazone (IV).

Reduction of glucose phenylosazone by zinc and acetic acid (*241*) or by catalytic hydrogenation (*242*) leads to the complete removal of one group,

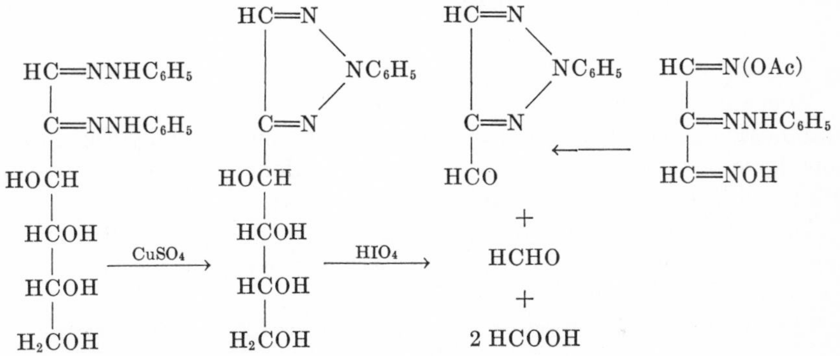
HC=NNHC6H5
C=NNHC6H5
HOCH
HCOH
HCOH
H2COH
CuSO4
HC=N
NC6H5
C=N
HOCH
HCOH
HCOH
H2COH
HIO4
HC=N
NC6H5
C=N
HCO
+
HCHO
+
2 HCOOH
HC=N(OAc)
C=NNHC6H5
HC=NOH

(I) (II) (III) (IV)

the splitting of the other, and the formation of 1-deoxy-1-aminofructose, often called isoglucosamine. The structure of the amine is shown by its reaction with nitrous acid to produce D-fructose (*243*). Similar derivatives, with a substituted amino group, result through the Amadori rearrangement of the corresponding glycosylamines as described earlier in this chapter.

When the acetyl groups of acetylated sugar osazones are removed by the use of sodium hydroxide, anhydro derivatives are formed. Percival (*244*) has shown that the phenylosazones of the tetraacetates of glucose, galactose, and gulose yield the same dianhydrohexose phenylosazone and, hence, that the anhydro rings must involve carbons 3 and 4. This conclusion must be correct, for the three sugars differ only in the configurations of these two

240. H. von Pechmann, *Ber.* **21,** 2751 (1888); *Ann.* **262,** 265 (1891).
241. E. Fischer, *Ber.* **19,** 1920 (1886).
242. K. Maurer and B. Schiedt, *Ber.* **68,** 2187 (1935).
243. E. Fischer and J. Tafel, *Ber.* **20,** 2566 (1887).
244. E. G. V. Percival, *J. Chem. Soc.* p. 1384 (1938).

carbons. Evidently, different numbers of Walden inversions must take place in the formation of the anhydro ring. The structure (V) is confirmed by the inability of the compound to yield a trityl derivative (no -CH_2OH group) and by the formation of a monotosyl derivative (one free hydroxyl). The configuration of the asymmetric carbon atoms has not been demonstrated.

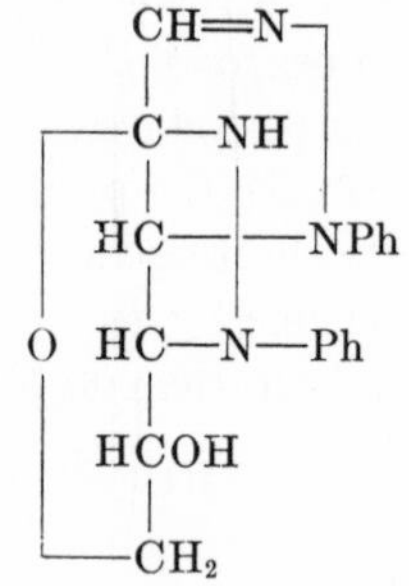
CH=N
C—NH
HC— —NPh
O HC—N—Ph
HCOH
CH2

(V)

Monoanhydro derivatives of glucosazone, galactosazone, xylosazone, arabinosazone, cellobiosazone, and lactosazone, and a dianhydromaltosazone have been made by boiling alcoholic solutions of the osazones with dilute sulfuric acid (*245*). (See also p. 387.)

An acetylated monoanhydro derivative of mannose phenylhydrazone serves for the confirmation of the identity of mannose, which is customarily isolated as the phenylhydrazone (see Chapter II).

The solubility characteristics of the reaction products of the sugars with unsubstituted *hydrazine* (NH_2—NH_2) are not favorable for identification purposes. The aldoses form aldazines, and the ketoses ketazines, in which 2 moles of the sugar are combined with 1 mole of the hydrazine (*246*). However, hydrazine reacts readily with sugar lactones to give characteristic derivatives useful for identification. The lactones may be regenerated from the hydrazides by treatment with nitrous anhydride (*247*).

B. Oximes

The sugars, probably in the free-aldehyde form (I), react (*248*) with hydroxylamine to give the sugar oximes (II or III):

245. O. Diehls and R. Meyer, *Ann.* **519,** 157 (1935); E. Fischer, *Ber.* **17,** 579 (1884); **20,** 821 (1887); E. G. V. Percival, *J. Chem. Soc.* p. 783 (1945); L. Mester and A. Major, *J. Am. Chem. Soc.* **77,** 4305 (1955); E. Schreier, G. Stöhr, and E. Hardegger, *Helv. Chim. Acta* **37,** 574 (1954).

246. E. Davidis, *Ber.* **29,** 2308 (1896).

247. A. Thompson and M. L. Wolfrom, *J. Am. Chem. Soc.* **68,** 1509 (1946).

248. P. Rischbieth, *Ber.* **20,** 2673 (1887); E. Fischer and J. Hirschberger, *ibid.* **22,** 1155 (1889).

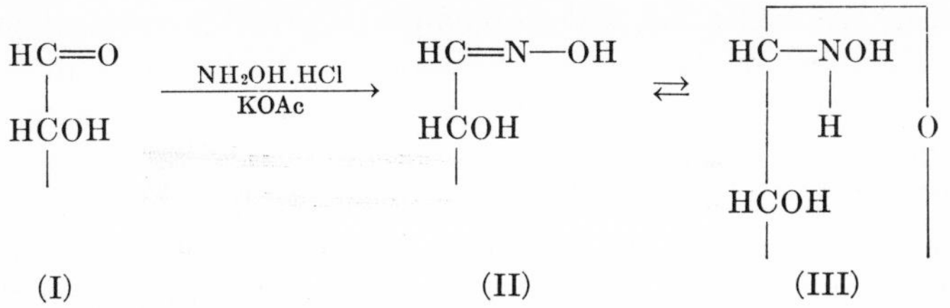

The oximes are too soluble in water and in alcohols to be of general value for the identification of the sugars, but they are very useful for preparing acyclic derivatives and for shortening the carbon chains of the sugars (Wohl degradation).

Since the oximes mutarotate (*249*), the simple structure (II) is not sufficient unless *syn* and *anti* isomers exist. By analogy with the sugars, the mutarotation may be the result of the establishment of an equilibrium between the open-chain (II) and cyclic isomers (III). Although only one crystalline glucose oxime is known, two crystalline hexaacetates have been isolated (*250*). One is obtained by the reaction of *aldehydo*-penta-*O*-acetylglucose with hydroxylamine followed by acetylation. Because it is prepared from the acyclic form of glucose, it must be the acyclic oxime. At low temperatures, acetylation of glucose oxime produces a second hexaacetate (*251*). This second isomer probably is a ring modification, because crystalline 2,3,4,6-tetra-*O*-methylglucose is produced after methylation and hydrolysis (*16*). Confirmation of these structures for the hexaacetates of the glucose oximes is given by a method which distinguishes between *N*-acetyl (or *N*-acetoxy) and *O*-acetyl groups. As would be expected, the cyclic modification has an *N*-acetoxy group, and the acyclic hexaacetate has only *O*-acetyl groups (*252*). This method depends upon the stability of the *N*-acetoxy group in alkaline solution. Thus, the acid-hydrolysis procedure of Freudenberg and Harder (*253*) removes all the acetyl groups of both hexaacetates of the glucose oximes, but alkaline hydrolysis removes only five *O*-acetyl groups from the cyclic form and all six from the open-chain form. This resistance of *N*-acetyl and *N*-acetoxy groups to alkaline hydrolysis also seems to exist for other nitrogenous derivatives of the sugars. (See, however, p. 460.)

In solution, as is evidenced by the mutarotation and other reactions of

249. H. Jacobi, *Ber*. **24,** 696 (1891).

250. M. L. Wolfrom and A. Thompson, *J. Am. Chem. Soc.* **53,** 622 (1931); A. Wohl, *Ber*. **26,** 730 (1893).

251. R. Behrend, *Ann*. **353,** 106 (1907).

252. M. L. Wolfrom, M. Konigsberg, and S. Soltzberg, *J. Am. Chem. Soc.* **58,** 490 (1936).

253. K. Freudenberg and M. Harder, *Ann*. **433,** 230 (1923).

the oximes, the cyclic and acyclic modifications of the sugar oximes seem to be in equilibrium. Deacetylation of the acyclic hexaacetate of glucose oxime leads to the known, cyclic, crystalline glucose oxime. This isomerization is additional proof for an equilibrium between the various forms. Studies of the acetylation of the sugar oximes furnish additional proof (*250, 251*). Low-temperature acetylation of glucose oxime (III) with acetic anhydride and pyridine produces the acetylated cyclic isomer (VII); at higher temperatures, the gluconpremature nitrile pentaacetate (IV) is the main product. Since at the higher temperatures the acyclic hexaacetate of glucose oxime (V) gives good yields of the glucononitrile pentaacetate (IV), the acyclic oxime (VI) is probably an intermediate in the preparation of the nitrile. Thus, both cyclic and acyclic acetates are formed in the acetylation reaction.

The products obtained upon acetylation of the sugar oximes depend not only on the temperature but also on the configuration of the sugar involved

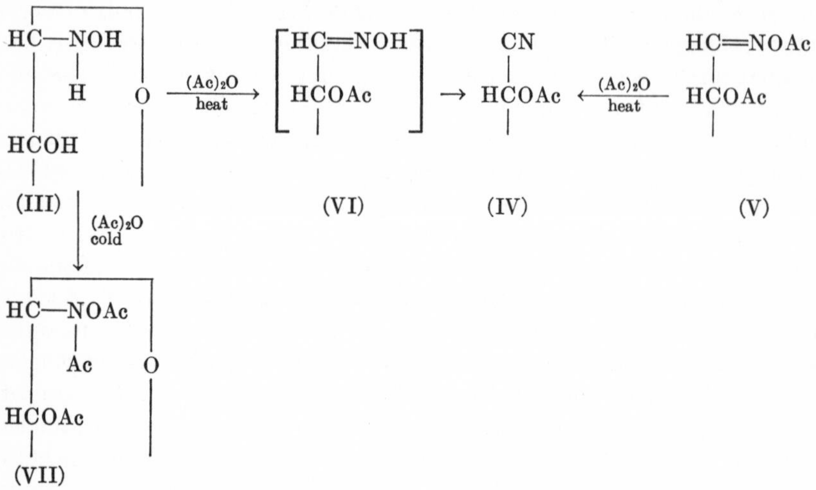
HC—NOH
H
O
HCOH
(III)
(Ac)₂O heat
HC=NOH
HCOAc
(VI)
CN
HCOAc
(IV)
(Ac)₂O heat
HC=NOAc
HCOAc
(V)
(Ac)₂O cold
HC—NOAc
Ac
O
HCOAc
(VII)

(*254*). The arabinose, rhamnose, xylose, and glucosamine oximes yield only the nitriles as a result of low-temperature acetylation; glucose gives the cyclic hexaacetate and mannose and fucose the acyclic hexaacetates; galactose yields a mixture of all three types. At higher temperatures, the proportion of the nitrile in the reaction mixture increases considerably.

The Wohl method for shortening the carbon chain of the sugars utilizes the acetylated nitrile prepared by the above procedure and is described in more detail elsewhere (Chapter II).

254. R. M. Hann and C. S. Hudson, *J. Am. Chem. Soc.* **59,** 1898 (1937); E. Restelli de Labriola and V. Deulofeu, *ibid.* **62,** 1611 (1940); V. Deulofeu, *Advances in Carbohydrate Chem.* **4,** 119 (1949).

6. DERIVATIVES IN WHICH AN AMINO GROUP REPLACES A PRIMARY OR SECONDARY HYDROXYL GROUP (*255*)*

A. Amino Sugars (Glycosamines) (*256*).

Occurrence. Sugar derivatives which have an amino group in place of one of the primary or secondary hydroxyls of the sugars comprise the amino sugars. The glycosylamines (osimines) have been considered separately on page 407 since their amino group is much more labile than that in the stable amino sugars. The amino sugars are of considerable interest because several are found among the hydrolytic products of many animal and bacterial polysaccharides and glycoproteins. Most natural members of this group are 2-amino-2-deoxyaldoses. Chitin, the principal polysaccharide of fungi, insects, and crustaceae, gives 2-amino-2-deoxyglucose (glucosamine or chitosamine) on hydrolysis (*257*). A second naturally occurring aminohexose is chondrosamine, which forms galactosazone on treatment with phenylhydrazine (*256*, *258*); it is 2-amino-2-deoxygalactose, also known as galactosamine (see below).

The *N*-methyl derivative of L-glucosamine (the enantiomorph of the common D-glucosamine) has been isolated from the degradation product of streptomycin (*259*). It is interesting to speculate that the antibiotic activity of the streptomycin may arise from the presence of the L-form of the glucosamine.

Several rare amino sugars have been found in antibiotics. From puromycin (Achromycin), 3-amino-3-deoxy-D-ribose has been isolated by Waller and co-workers (*260*). The configuration of the amino sugar was confirmed by its synthesis from L-arabinose, with methyl 2,3-anhydro-β-L-ribopyranoside (*261*) as an intermediate (p. 392). Among the hydrolysis products of erythromycin, obtained from *Streptomyces erythreus*, is an amino sugar with the empirical formula $C_8H_{17}NO_3$. Its structure has been partially determined as a 3-dimethylamino-3,4,6-trideoxyhexose (*262*). On hydrolysis

* Revised by Jane Reid Patton.

255. P. W. Kent and M. W. Whitehouse, "Biochemistry of the Aminosugars." Academic Press, New York, 1955.

256. P. A. Levene, *Biochem. Z.* **124,** 37 (1921); *J. Biol. Chem.* **63,** 95 (1925); "Hexosamines and Mucoproteins" Longmans, Green, New York, 1925.

257. G. Ledderhose, *Z. physiol. Chem.* **2,** 213 (1878); **4,** 139 (1880).

258. P. A. Levene and F. B. LaForge, *J. Biol. Chem.* **18,** 123 (1914).

259. F. A. Kuehl, Jr., E. H. Flynn, F. W. Holly, R. Mozingo, and K. Folkers, *J. Am. Chem. Soc.* **68,** 536 (1946).

260. C. W. Waller, P. W. Fryth, B. L. Hutchings, and J. H. Williams, *J. Am. Chem. Soc.* **75,** 2025 (1953).

261. B. R. Baker and R. E. Schaub, *J. Org. Chem.* **19,** 646 (1954).

262. R. K. Clark, Jr., *Antibiotics & Chemotherapy* **3,** 663 (1953).

pikromycin yields an isomeric substance, apparently an amino sugar (*263*). A dimethylamino-6-deoxyaldohexose whose empirical formula is represented by $C_8H_{17}NO_4$ (*264*) has been obtained from carbomycin.

The importance of D-glucosamine and D-galactosamine to the animal body has been demonstrated by the many sites in which they have been found. These include human blood group substances (*265*), stomach lining, uterus, inner layer of the aorta, lymph nodes, lung, brain, thyroid glands, adrenals, salivary glands (*266*), human bile (*267*), heparin, ovomucoid (*268*), human milk (*269*), hyaluronic acid, chondroitin sulfate, serum glycoproteins, heart, and cornea. (See Chapter XII.)

Except in glycogen, the hexosamines and glucuronic acid are the most common sugar components of animal polysaccharides and glycoproteins. The presence of an amino uronic acid, although readily conceivable, has not been established. But the synthesis of 2-amino-2-deoxy-D-glucuronic acid has been accomplished by the oxidation with platinum oxide of benzyl 2-carbobenzoxyamino-2-deoxy-α-D-glucopyranoside and the removal of the two substituent groups by catalytic hydrogenation to the free amino uronic acid (*271*).

Structure. The structure of glucosamine is shown by the following reactions. The reducing group is unsubstituted (*272*) since the compound reduces Fehling solution and is oxidized by bromine to a six-carbon acid (2-amino-2-deoxygluconic acid, glucosaminic acid). The reaction with phenylhydrazine takes place with the loss of the amino group and the formation of glucosazone (*273*). This evidence locates the amino group at position 2, but the compound might be related configurationally to either glucose or mannose. Since both glucose and mannose derivatives may be obtained from glucosamine, a Walden inversion must be involved in at least one of the reactions. The information obtained from the hydrolysis of the tosyl and the anhydro derivatives of the sugars, has made it possible to predict the occurrence of Walden inversions, and glucosamine has been shown to be a derivative of glucose and not of mannose.

263. H. Brockmann and R. Strufe, *Ber.* **86,** 876 (1953).
264. F. A. Hochstein and P. P. Regna, *J. Am. Chem. Soc.* **77,** 3353 (1955).
265. D. Aminoff and W. T. J. Morgan, *Nature* **162,** 579 (1948).
266. A. M. Kuzin and B. N. Gladyshev, *Biokhimiya* **15,** 316 (1950); *Chem. Abstr.* **45,** 197 (1951).
267. H. Tiba, *Tôhoku J. Exptl. Med.* **52,** 103 (1950).
268. P. W. Kent, *Research* **3,** 427 (1950).
269. H. W. Ruelius and M. M. Girard, *Arch. Biochem. and Biophys.* **50,** 512 (1954).
271. K. Heyns and H. Paulsen, *Ber.* **88,** 188 (1955).
272. E. Fischer and F. Tiemann, *Ber.* **27,** 138 (1894).
273. F. Tiemann, *Ber.* **19,** 49 (1886).

The final evidence (*274*) is provided by the synthesis of a glucosamine derivative (I) (accompanied by a derivative of 3-amino-3-deoxy-altrose) by the reaction of ammonia on methyl 2,3-anhydro-4,6-di-*O*-methyl-β-mannoside (II) (*275*). Inasmuch as ammonia reacts in the same manner with anhydro rings as does sodium methylate and inasmuch as the same anhydromannoside reacts with sodium methylate with the formation of glucose (III) and altrose derivatives, the glucosamine in all probability has the glucose configuration. Application of Hudson's isorotation principle also leads to a correlation with the glucose instead of the mannose configuration (*276*).

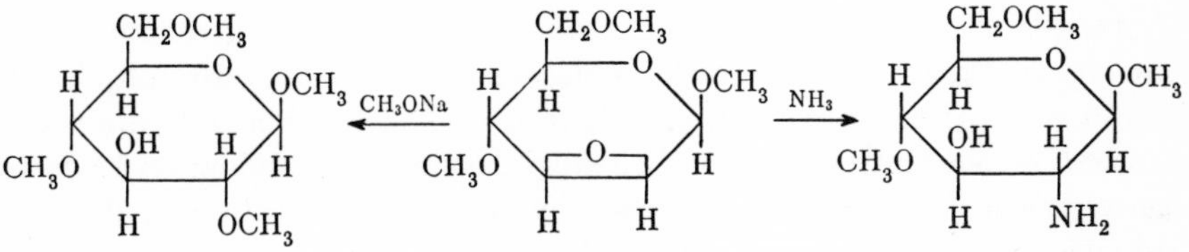
CH₃ONa
NH₃

(III) Methyl 2,4,6-tri-*O*-methyl-β-glucoside

(II) Methyl 2,3-anhydro-4,6-di-*O*-methyl-β-mannoside

(I) Methyl 2-amino-2-deoxy-4,6-di-*O*-methyl-β-glucoside (methyl 4,6-di-*O*-methyl-β-glucosaminide)

Chondrosamine has been synthesized by methods that fix its configuration as 2-amino-2-deoxygalactose (*277*). The synthesis has been accomplished by the ammonolysis of 1,6:2,3-dianhydrotalose (IV). The ammonia adds to the 2,3-anhydro ring, and subsequently the 1,6-anhydro ring is cleaved by acid hydrolysis. One of the two products obtained was shown to be identical with natural chondrosamine. Since the addition of

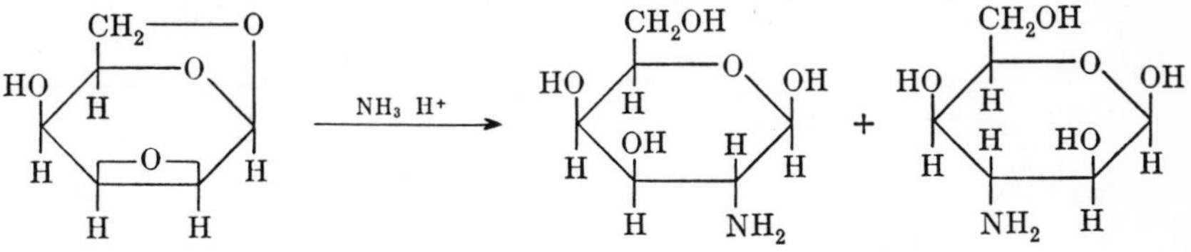
NH₃ H⁺

(IV) (V) (VI)

---

274. Most of the previous work has also shown that the substance has the glucose structure; the evidence has been reviewed by S. Peat, *Ann. Repts. Progr. Chem.* (*Chem. Soc. London*) **34,** 289 (1937).

275. W. N. Haworth, W. H. G. Lake, and S. Peat, *J. Chem. Soc.* p. 271 (1939).

276. A. Neuberger and R. V. P. Rivers, *J. Chem. Soc.* p. 122 (1939).

277. S. P. James, F. Smith, M. Stacey, and L. F. Wiggins, *Nature* **156,** 309 (1945).

ammonia to the anhydro ring very probably takes place with Walden inversion at the carbon atom to which the amino group becomes attached, the natural material (V) must be a galactose derivative and the other a 3-amino-3-deoxyidose derivative (VI).

Proof for the configuration of (VI) is given by its synthesis (along with 4-amino-4-deoxymannose) from 1,6:3,4-dianhydrotalose by ammonolysis and hydrolysis as above.

At least in alkaline solution, glucosamine may not exist in the pyranose form (*278*). The rate of oxidation of glucosamine by hypoiodous acid coincides closely with that of the galactose-arabinose homomorphous group of aldoses rather than that of the glucose-xylose group.

Anhydro Derivatives from Glucosamine. Treatment of glucosamine with nitrous acid does not lead to the replacement of an amino by a hydroxyl group; instead an anhydro ring is formed (*257*, *279*). The anhydro sugar formed, called chitose (I), is a 2,5-anhydro sugar, for oxidation leads to chitonic acid (II), which is converted by the action of acetic anhydride to 5-hydroxymethylfuroic acid (III) of known structure.

When the above order of operations is reversed, i.e., when the oxidation precedes the treatment with nitrous acid, chitaric acid is formed. This anhydroaldonic acid is isomeric with chitonic acid. (For additional details, see Chapter VII).

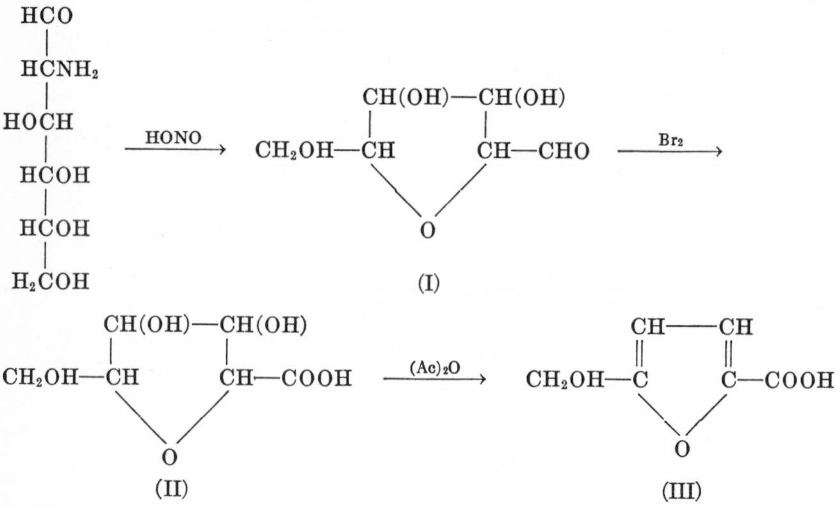
HCO
HCNH2
HOCH
HCOH
HCOH
H2COH
HONO
CH(OH)—CH(OH)
CH2OH—CH
CH—CHO
O
(I)
Br2
CH(OH)—CH(OH)
CH2OH—CH
CH—COOH
O
(II)
(Ac)2O
CH——CH
CH2OH—C
C—COOH
O
(III)

Preparation and Synthesis of Amino Sugars. Lobster and crab shells, which consist of calcium carbonate, chitin, and protein material, are hydrolyzed

278. O. G. Ingles, *Nature* **163,** 484 (1949).
279. E. Fischer and E. Andreae, *Ber.* **36,** 2587 (1903).

by concentrated hydrochloric acid to yield glucosamine (*257*, *280*). From 400 g. of crab shells, 50 g. of glucosamine hydrochloride, the usual form of the amino sugar, was obtained (*281*). The mycelium of various fungi has also been used as a source of this material.

Galactosamine (chondrosamine) is obtained by the hydrolysis of the chondroitin sulfuric acid of cartilage and nasal septa by hydrochloric acid or zinc chloride (*282*, *283*). A small amount of glucosamine usually is present in the hydrolyzate. Cation-exchange resins provide a simple method for the purification of the hexosamines and for the separation of glucosamine from galactosamine (*282*, *284*).

Two forms of glucosamine hydrochloride have been described, one the common α-D-isomer with $[\alpha]_D$ $+100° \rightarrow +72.5°$, and the other the β-D-isomer with $[\alpha]_D$ $+25.0° \rightarrow +72.6°$, in water (*285*). Salts of other acids have been prepared (*286*). By treatment with alkylamines, the α-D- and β-D-isomers of the free glucosamine have been prepared with rotations:

$$([\alpha]\ +100° \rightarrow +47.5° \leftarrow +14°, \text{ in water})$$ (*286*, *287*).

The difficultly soluble *N*-carbobenzoxyglucosamine, prepared by the action of carbobenzoxy chloride ($C_6H_5CH_2OCOCl$) on glucosamine, has been suggested (*288*) for the separation of the amino sugar from accompanying sugars. Schiff bases, particularly those from 2-hydroxy-1-naphthaldehyde, are of value for the isolation of both glucosamine and chondrosamine (*289*).

The classical method for the synthesis of 2-amino sugars of the natural type utilizes the osimines obtained by the action of ammonia on sugars (*283*, *290*). The process, which involves the addition of hydrogen cyanide to the osimines, results in the lengthening of the carbon chain; hence, D-arabinosimine must be used for obtaining glucosamine. The creation of a new asymmetric carbon results in the formation of two epimeric nitriles which are hydrolyzed to the corresponding acids and then reduced to the corresponding sugar amines. The glucosamine prepared in this fashion is identical with the natural product. The isomer obtained from the second nitrile, 2-mannosamine, is the true epiglucosamine. A second

280. C. S. Hudson and J. K. Dale, *J. Am. Chem. Soc.* **38,** 1434 (1916).
281. M. L. Wolfrom and M. J. Cron, *J. Am. Chem. Soc.* **74,** 1715 (1952).
282. S. Roseman and J. Ludowieg, *J. Am. Chem. Soc.* **76,** 301 (1954).
283. P. A. Levene, *J. Biol. Chem.* **26,** 147 (1916).
284. S. Gardell, *Acta Chem. Scand.* **7,** 207 (1953).
285. J. C. Irvine and J. C. Earl, *J. Chem. Soc.* **121,** 2370 (1922).
286. R. Breuer, *Ber.* **31,** 2193 (1898).
287. O. Westphal and H. Holzmann, *Ber.* **73,** 1274 (1942).
288. E. Chargaff and M. Bovarnick, *J. Biol. Chem.* **118,** 421 (1937).
289. Z. E. Jolles and W. T. J. Morgan, *Biochem. J.* **34,** 1183 (1940).
290. E. Fischer and H. Leuchs, *Ber.* **36,** 24 (1903).

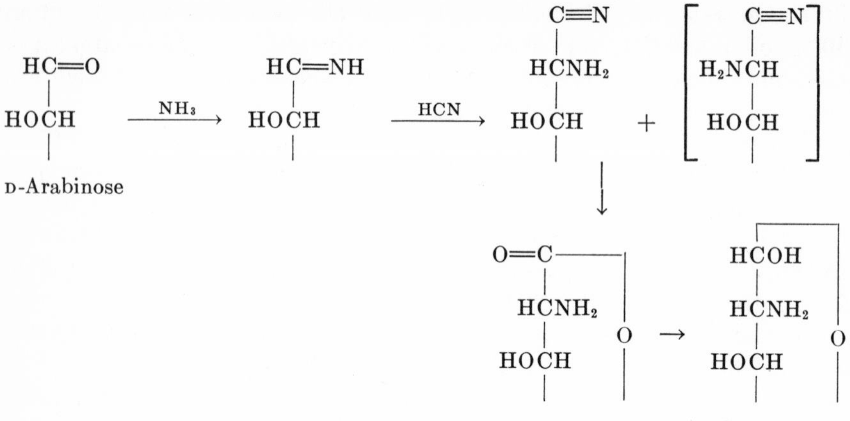

D-Arabinose

Glucosamine

so-called "epiglucosamine," prepared by the following sequence of reactions (*291*), has been shown to be 3-amino-3-deoxyaltrose (*292*).

Glucal $\xrightarrow{Br_2}$ 1,2-dibromoglucal $\xrightarrow[Ag_2CO_3]{CH_3OH}$

methyl 2-bromo-2-deoxyglucoside $\xrightarrow{NH_3}$

methyl 3-amino-3-deoxyaltroside ("methyl epiglucosaminide")

This transformation from a glucose to an altrose derivative probably takes place through the intermediate formation of a 2,3-anhydro derivative, as originally suggested by Fischer, Bergmann, and Schotte (*291*), and involves several Walden inversions. Evidence for this mechanism is supplied by the synthesis (considered above in connection with the discussion of the configuration of glucosamine) of 3-amino-3-deoxyaltrose and 2-amino-2-deoxyglucose derivatives from methyl 2,3-anhydro-β-mannoside and ammonia. The preparation of amino sugars from the glycals is of particular value when amino derivatives of the rarer sugars are desired, for Walden inversions take place during the formation of the anhydro rings and during the opening of the rings by ammonia.

The preparation of the 6-amino derivatives involves the action of ammonia on the 6-halogeno (*293*), the 6-tosyl, or the 5,6-anhydro derivatives (*294*) of the sugars. The 6-pyridinium derivative has also been prepared by the action of pyridine on 1,2,3,4-tetra-*O*-acetyl-6-methanesulfonyl-α-D-

291. E. Fischer, M. Bergmann, and H. Schotte, *Ber.* **53,** 509 (1920).
292. W. N. Haworth, W. H. G. Lake, and S. Peat, *J. Chem. Soc.* p. 271 (1939).
293. E. Fischer and K. Zach, *Ber.* **44,** 132 (1911).
294. H. Ohle and L. von Vargha, *Ber.* **61,** 1203 (1928); **69,** 1022, 1636, 2311 (1936).

glucose (*295*). Synthetic nucleosides have been prepared from methyl 2,3-*O*-isopropylidene-5-*O*-mesyl-D-ribofuranoside (*295a*).

As described previously, glucosazone may be reduced to 1-amino-1-deoxyfructose (isoglucosamine). The 1-(arylamino)fructoses also are formed by the action of dilute acids on the glycosylamines (see Amadori rearrangement).

The first known pentosamine, 2-amino-2-deoxy-D-xylose, was synthesized as the hydrochloride salt through periodate cleavage of ethyl 2-acetamido-2-deoxy-α-D-glucothiofuranoside at C5–C6 (*296*).

Although hexosamines are known to occur in biological material, their path of synthesis is uncertain. Both glucose and fructose, when incubated with either ammonia or ammonium chloride in the presence of phosphate ions at neutral pH, form small amounts of a hexosamine, probably glucosamine (*297*), possibly by a reverse Amadori rearrangement of fructosylamine. If such a system is operative in the animal body, the synthesis of hexosamines may not depend on an enzymic reaction. An indication that the synthesis of glucosamine may be due to an enzymically catalyzed process (*298*) was given by the preparation of an enzyme from *Neurospora crassa* which catalyzes the reaction:

$$\text{Hexose 6-phosphate} + \text{glutamine} \rightarrow \text{glucosamine 6-phosphate} + \text{glutamate}$$

Glucose and ammonia are the natural precursors of glucosamine (*299*, *300*). Radioisotopic studies using C^{14} indicate that glucosone may be on the path of biosynthesis (*300*). (See also Chapter XIV.)

Reactions of the Amino Sugars. The amino groups as well as the hydroxyl groups are acetylated when the usual methods for acetylation are employed, and α- and β-isomers are produced. The *N*-acetyl group is more stable than *O*-acetyl groups, and, by alkaline hydrolysis of the fully acetylated derivative, *N*-acetylglucosamine is obtained. The reaction of the sugar amines with aldehydes leads to Schiff bases. Those formed from 2-hydroxy-1-naphthaldehyde are valuable for the separation of small quantities of glucosamine and chrondosamine (*289*). That from *p*-methoxybenzaldehyde

295. B. M. Iselin and J. C. Sowden, *J. Am. Chem. Soc.* **73,** 4984 (1951).

295a. H. M. Kissman and R. B. Baker, paper presented at the 126th meeting of the American Chemical Society, Atlantic City, N. J., Sept. 16–21, 1956.

296. M. L. Wolfrom and K. Anno, *J. Am. Chem Soc.* **75,** 1038 (1953).

297. K. Heyns and W. Koch, *Z. Naturforsch.* **7b,** 486 (1952); K. Heyns *et al.* (*65*).

298. L. F. Leloir and C. E. Cardini, *Biochim. et Biophys. Acta* **12,** 15 (1953); S. Roseman, paper presented at the 126th meeting of the American Chemical Society, Atlantic City, N. J., Sept. 16–21, 1956.

299. A. J. Bollet, N. F. Boas, and J. J. Bunim, *Science* **120,** 348 (1954); S. Roseman, F. E. Moses, J. Ludowieg, and A. Dorfman, *J. Biol. Chem.* **203,** 213 (1953); S. V. Rieder, *Federation Proc.* **12,** 258 (1953).

300. C. E. Becker and H. G. Day, *J. Biol. Chem.* **201,** 795 (1953).

has value for obtaining the tetra-*O*-acetylglucosamine (*301*). Thus, the Schiff base (I) is acetylated; the aldehyde residue then is removed by acids to give 1,3,4,6-tetra-*O*-acetylglucosamine (II). Acyl derivatives of the amino sugars in which the acylating substance is an amino acid or polypeptide have been studied (see earlier section of this chapter).

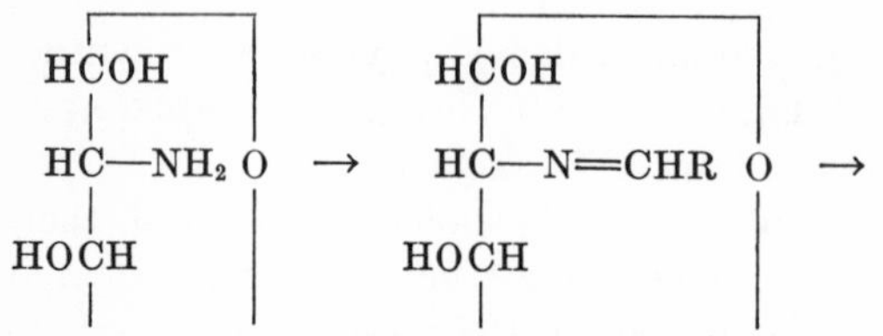

(R= *p*-$CH_3O—C_6H_4—$)
(I)

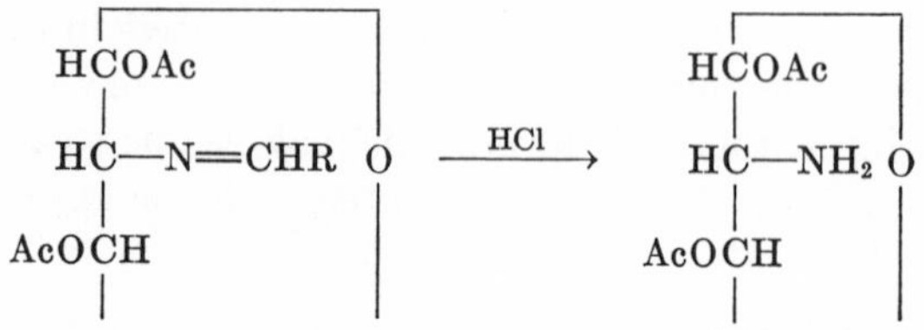

(II)

For the preparation of the 2-amino-2-deoxyaldonic acids, the common bromine oxidation does not give good yields, and mercuric oxide is the preferred oxidant. By the use of mercuric oxide, "glucosaminic acid" was obtained in yields of 62% (*302*). Lactone formation does not occur in solution, unless the amino group is substituted. Epimerization of the acid occurs in pyridine solution at 100°, and the corresponding mannose derivative is formed (*303*). Numerous degradative oxidations have been studied (*304*).

The amino sugars form hydrazones, oximes, glycosyl halides, glycosides, and benzylidene derivatives analogous to those of the sugars.

Glycoside formation does not take place directly, and prior acylation of the amino group is required (*305*). The methyl glycoside ("methyl glucosaminide") is very resistant to acid hydrolysis and was previously considered to have a betaine structure (*306*). The resistance to acid hydrolysis

301. M. Bergmann and L. Zervas, *Ber.* **64,** 975 (1931).
302. See M. L. Wolfrom and M. J. Cron, *J. Am. Chem. Soc.* **74,** 1715 (1952).
303. See P. W. Kent and M. W. Whitehouse, ref. 255.
304. Y. Matsushima, *Sci. Papers Osaka Univ.* **No. 31,** 1 (1951); **No. 32,** 7 (1951); **No. 33,** 9 (1951); **No. 34,** 11 (1951); **No. 35,** 13 (1951); K. Heyns and W. Koch, *Ber.* **86,** 110 (1953); Y. Sumiki and M. Yaita, *J. Agr. Chem. Soc. Japan* **19,** 723 (1943); *Chem. Abstr.* **43,** 578 (1949).
305. M. Viscontini and J. Meier, *Helv. Chim. Acta* **35,** 807 (1952).
306. J. C. Irvine and A. Hynd, *J. Chem. Soc.* **101,** 1128 (1912).

is probably due to the action of the positively charged amino group in repelling the hydrogen ion as it approaches the linkage undergoing hydrolysis (*307*). The value for the activation energy of the hydrolytic reaction agrees with this concept, for it is similar to that of the ordinary glycosides. The pyranose ring structure of the methyl 2-amino-2-deoxy-glucoside is shown by the following reactions (*306*, *308*):

$$\text{Methyl 2-amino-2-deoxyglucoside} \xrightarrow[\text{CH}_3\text{I}]{\text{Ag}_2\text{O}}$$

$$\text{methyl 2-deoxy-2-(dimethylamino)glucoside} \xrightarrow{\text{Ba(OH)}_2}$$

$$\text{methyl glucoside (not isolated)} \longrightarrow$$

$$\text{methyl tetra-}O\text{-methylglucoside} \xrightarrow{\text{H}^+} \text{2,3,4,6-tetra-}O\text{-methylglucose}$$

A number of the mono- and dimethyl derivatives of glucosamine and galactosamine have been prepared (*309*) as reference compounds for the determination of the linkage of the amino sugars in natural products.

D-Glucosamine is phosphorylated by brain extracts (*310*) and by crystalline yeast hexokinase (*311*). An enzyme found in rabbit muscle catalyzes the interconversion of the 6-phosphate and the labile 1-phosphate (*312*). *N*-Acetylation results from the action of an enzyme in extracts of pigeon liver (*313*).

Ledderhose (*257*) reported that ordinary yeasts do not ferment glucosamine (*314*). *Saccharomyces ellipsoideus* apparently deaminates it and forms pentoses (*315*). It is attacked by numerous bacteria with the formation of acids and sometimes with the liberation of carbon dioxide (*314*). *Strep. faecalis* ferments glucosamine slowly, whereas *Proteus vulgaris* acts more rapidly on galactosamine than on glucosamine. In neither case is carbon dioxide evolved (*255*). (See also p. 621.)

Foster and Stacey have compiled a comprehensive list of the properties of the known derivatives of glucosamine and galactosamine (*316*). The phenyl 2-acetylamino-2-deoxyglucosides are hydrolyzed by almond emulsin, but the enzyme (β-glucosaminidase) differs from the β-glucosidase which

307. R. C. G. Moggridge and A. Neuberger, *J. Chem. Soc.* p. 745 (1938).
308. A. Neuberger, *J. Chem. Soc.* p. 29 (1940).
309. R. W. Jeanloz, *J. Am. Chem. Soc.* **74,** 4597 (1952); *ibid.* **76,** 555 (1954); *ibid.* **76,** 558 (1954); P. Stoffyn and R. W. Jeanloz, *ibid.* **76,** 561 (1954); *ibid.* **76,** 563 (1954).
310. R. P. Harpur and J. H. Quastel, *Nature* **164,** 693 (1949).
311. D. H. Brown, *Biochim. et Biophys. Acta* **7,** 487 (1951).
312. D. H. Brown, *J. Biol. Chem.* **204,** 877 (1953).
313. T. C. Chou and M. Soodak, *J. Biol. Chem.* **196,** 105 (1952).
314. L. Sternfeld and F. Saunders, *J. Am. Chem. Soc.* **59,** 2653 (1937).
315. C. Antoniani *et al.*, *Chem. Abstr.* **48,** 12874 (1954).
316. A. B. Foster and M. Stacey, *Advances in Carbohydrate Chem.* **7,** 247 (1952).

hydrolyzes the β-glucosides (*317*). Snail emulsin from *Helix pomatia* has also been shown to have different enzymes for the hydrolysis of glucosides and 2-acetylamino-2-deoxyglucosides (*318*).

Analysis. Glucosamine may be estimated by the usual iodine titration or by copper-reduction methods. A procedure based on the production of a color by the reaction of alkali-treated *N*-acetylglucosamine with the Ehrlich reagent (*p*-dimethylaminobenzaldehyde in hydrochloric acid) has been devised for the determination of glucosamine (*319*). The reagent gives a red color with pyrroles, indicating that a heterocyclic ring may be formed by the action of alkali on *N*-acetylglucosamine. The structure of the product formed by the action of alkali on *N*-acetylglucosamine has been investigated by White (*320*) who concludes that a glucoxazoline is formed:

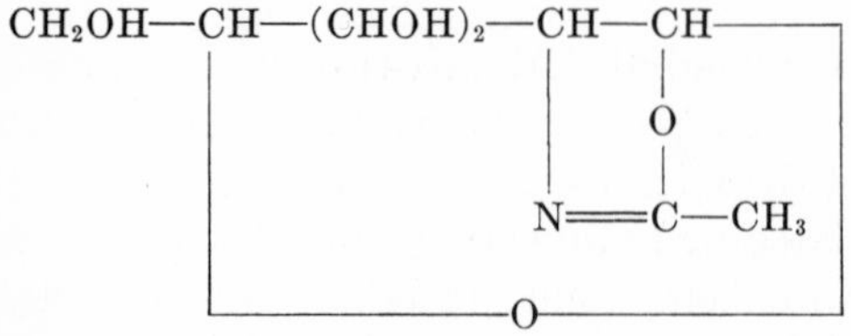

2-Methyl-4,5-glucopyrano-—Δ^2-oxazoline

Undoubtedly the reaction is more complex than was, at first, realized. The many modifications of the original technique, designed to give more reproducible results, confirm the complexity of the reaction (*321*). Schloss (*322*) has isolated three chromogenic materials formed by the action of alkaline acetylacetone on glucosamine, and found evidence for the presence of a fourth.

Because of the large number of substances which interfere (*321*) with the hexosamine color determination, a preliminary separation from contaminating substances, either by ion-exchange (*284*, *323*), or by paper chromatography (*324*), should be made.

Several substances, widely distributed in the animal body, have been

317. B. Helferich and A. Iloff, *Z. physiol. Chem.* **221**, 252 (1933).

318. A. Neuberger and R. V. P. Rivers, *Biochem. J.* **33**, 1580 (1939).

319. F. Zuckerkandl and L. Messiner-Klebermass, *Biochem. Z.* **236**, 19 (1931); W. T. J. Morgan and L. A. Elson, *Biochem. J.* **28**, 988 (1934).

320. T. White, *J. Chem. Soc.* p. 428 (1940); W. H. Bromund and R. M. Herbst, *J. Org. Chem.* **10**, 267 (1945).

321. D. Aminoff, W. T. J. Morgan, and W. M. Watkins, *Biochem. J.* **51**, 379 (1952); N. H. Horowitz, M. Ikawa, and M. Fling, *Arch. Biochem.* **25**, 226 (1950); Y. Hamasato and K. Akakura, *J. Biochem. (Japan)* **34**, 159 (1941).

322. B. Schloss, *Anal. Chem.* **23**, 1321 (1951).

323. S. M. Partridge, *Biochem. J.* **45**, 459 (1949); N. F. Boas, *J. Biol. Chem.* **204**, 553 (1953).

324. H. Masamune and M. Maki, *Tôhoku J. Exptl. Med.* **55**, 299 (1952); H. Masamune and Z. Yoshizawa, *Tôhoku. J. Exptl. Med.* **59**, 1 (1953).

found to give the hexosamine color with *p*-dimethylaminobenzaldehyde without prior treatment with alkali (the direct Ehrlich test). These substances include sialic acid, hemataminic acid, and neuraminic acid. The interference by these substances has not been taken into account in many hexosamine determinations in animal tissues (see Chapter XII, Sialic acid).

Because of the similarity between the paper-chromatographic R_f values of glucosamine and galactosamine, derivatives are frequently prepared to distinguish between the two amino sugars. They may be oxidized to arabinose and lyxose by ninhydrin and the two pentoses identified by paper chromatography (*325*). The dinitrophenyl derivatives of the two amino sugars may also be prepared and separated by paper chromatography in the presence of borate ions (*326*). The *N*-2,4-dinitrophenylaminohexitols may also be prepared and separated by paper chromatography (*327*). A developing solvent composed of pyridine–ethyl acetate–water–acetic acid (5:5:3:1 vol./vol.), however, enables separation of the individual hexosamines and uronic acids (*327a*).

A method to distinguish between glucosamine and galactosamine, which does not depend on the production of a colored product, has been devised (*328*). The electrical resistance of the effluent from an ion-exchange column is recorded automatically and continuously. This method gives more accurate results with galactosamine than with glucosamine.

B. Glycamines and Aminodeoxyalditols

Derivatives of sugar alcohols in which a CH_2OH group has been replaced by a CH_2NH_2 or CH_2NHR group are known as glycamines. The systematic name would be 1-amino-1-deoxyalditols. The first of these derivatives was prepared by Maquenne and Roux (*329*) by the reduction of oximes. Because vitamin B_2 (riboflavin) is a derivative of D-ribamine (1-amino-1-deoxyribitol), the group of glycamines holds considerable interest for the biochemist. Glucamine (1-amino-1-deoxy-D-glucitol) and *N*-methylglucamine (1-deoxy-1-methylamino-D-glucitol) appear to show some promise as intermediates for the preparation of wetting agents (*330*) and as solubil-

325. S. Gardell, F. Heijkenskjöld, and A. Rochnorlund, *Acta Chem. Scand.* **4,** 970 (1950).

326. E. F. Annison, A. F. James, and W. T. J. Morgan, *Biochem. J.* **48,** 477 (1951); P. W. Kent, G. Lawson, and A. Senior, *Science* **113,** 354 (1951).

327. S. Leskowitz and E. A. Kabat, *J. Am. Chem. Soc.* **76,** 5060 (1954).

327a. F. G. Fischer and H. J. Nebel, *Z. physiol. Chem.* **302,** 10 (1955).

328. B. Drake and S. Gardell, *Arkiv. Kemi* **4,** 469 (1952).

329. L. Maquenne and E. Roux, *Compt. rend.* **132,** 980 (1901); E. Roux, *Ann. chim. phys.* [8] **1,** 72 (1904).

330. See for example W. S. Calcott, *U. S. Patent* 2,060,850 (Nov. 17, 1936); *U. S. Patent* 2,016,956, (Oct. 8, 1935); H. A. Piggot, *U. S. Patent,* 1,985,424, (Dec. 25, 1934); *U. S. Patent* 2,091,105 (Aug. 24, 1937).

izing groups for pharmaceuticals such as theophylline (*331*), and *p*-amino-salicylic acid (*332*).

The lower homologs of this series include ethanolamine (NH_2CH_2-CH_2OH) and 2,3-dihydroxy-*n*-propylamine. Ethanolamine in particular has achieved considerable industrial importance.

As described earlier, the glycosylamines (I) may be reduced by catalytic hydrogenation to glycamines (II) (*333*).

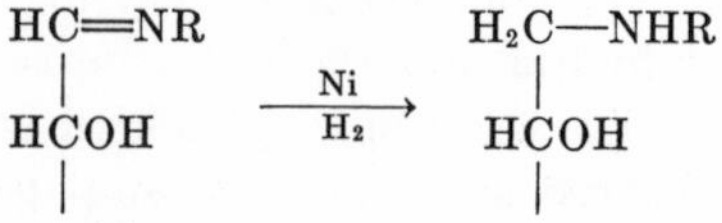

(I) (II)

The rearrangement of *N*-glucosylarylamines gives 1-arylamino-1-deoxy-fructoses, which may be reduced to glucamines and mannamines. (See under Amadori rearrangement.) Reduction of glucosazone with sodium amalgam gives fructosamine (1-amino-1-deoxyfructose) (*334*).

Closely related derivatives are produced by the reduction of glucosamine and derivatives to a product sometimes known as glucosaminol. A more systematic name is 2-amino-2-deoxy-D-glucitol. The *N*-acetyl derivative is obtained by the catalytic hydrogenation of *N*-acetylglucosamine and the unacetylated compound by reduction of the hydrochloride (*335*). Free glucosamine undergoes an interesting Cannizzaro reaction when reduced catalytically to give 2-amino-2-deoxygluconic acid (glucosaminic acid) and 2-amino-2-deoxy-D-glucitol (*336*).

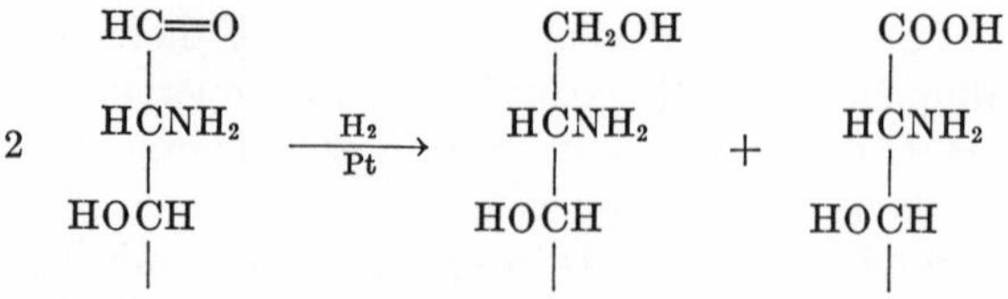

Nitro alcohols corresponding to the glycamines are obtained by treatment of sugars with nitromethane (*337*). The 2,4-*O*-benzylidene-L-xylopyranose

331. E. H. Volwiler and E. E. Moore, *U. S. Patent* 2,161,114 (June 6, 1939).

332. G. Auricchio, *Boll. soc. ital. biol. sper.* **25,** 1042 (1949); *Chem. Abstr.* **45,** 582 (1951).

333. See references previously given and R. B. Flint and P. L. Salzberg, *U. S. Patent* 2,016,962–3 (Oct. 8, 1935); P. L. Salzberg, *U. S. Patent* 2,193,433 (Mar. 12, 1940); H. Straube-Rieke, H. A. Lardy, and L. Anderson, *J. Am. Chem. Soc.* **75,** 694 (1953).

334. E. Fischer, *Ber.* **19,** 1920 (1886).

335. P. Karrer and J. Meyer, *Helv. Chim. Acta* **20,** 626 (1937).

336. P. A. Levene and C. C. Christman, *J. Biol. Chem.* **120,** 575 (1937).

337. J. C. Sowden and H. O. L. Fischer, *J. Am. Chem. Soc.* **67,** 1713 (1945); **68,** 1511 (1946).

in methanol solution adds nitromethane under the influence of sodium methylate to give 2,4-*O*-benzylidene-6-deoxy-6-nitro-D-glucitol from which the benzylidene group is removed by hydrolysis with acids. Catalytic reduction gives the corresponding amino alcohols.

The glycamines may serve as intermediates in the synthesis of 2-deoxy-sugars. 2-Deoxy-D-ribose was prepared by nitrous acid oxidation of 2-amino-2-deoxyribitol (*338*), obtained from D-arabinose and D-ribulose.

Glucamine may be converted to 1,4-anhydro-D-glucitol by the action of sodium nitrite in acetic acid (*339*).

338. Y. Matsushima and Y. Imanaga, *Nature* **171**, 475 (1953).
339. V. G. Bashford and L. F. Wiggins, *J. Chem. Soc.* p. 299 (1948).

IX. OLIGOSACCHARIDES

W. Z. HASSID AND C. E. BALLOU

The oligosaccharides (*1*) comprise a large group of polymeric carbohydrates consisting of relatively few monosaccharide units (Greek "oligos," a few), which, on complete acid hydrolysis, yield only simple sugars. They are composed of monosaccharide residues joined through glycosidic linkages with the loss of $n - 1$ molecules of water (n = number of monosaccharide residues). Thus,

$$C_6H_{12}O_6 + C_6H_{12}O_6 - H_2O = C_{12}H_{22}O_{11} \text{ (disaccharide)}$$

$$3\ C_6H_{12}O_6 - 2\ H_2O = C_{18}H_{32}O_{16} \text{ (trisaccharide)}$$

On the basis of the number of monosaccharide residues per mole, the oligosaccharides are classified as disaccharides, trisaccharides, tetrasaccharides, pentasaccharides, etc. No sharp distinction can be drawn between the oligosaccharides and the polysaccharides, for the structures are similar and only the molecular weights are different. In the present discussion the term will be limited to carbohydrates with less than ten monosaccharide residues in the molecule. Generally, the polysaccharides have a much greater degree of polymerization, in some cases several thousand.

Most common disaccharides are dihexoses, although a few natural members of the group such as primeverose are known in which a pentose and a hexose are united together. The monosaccharide units of an oligosaccharide may be alike, as in maltose, which on hydrolysis gives two molecules of D-glucose, or different, as in sucrose or raffinose, the former consisting of D-glucose and D-fructose, and the latter of D-glucose, D-fructose, and D-galactose residues. Aldobiouronic acids and disaccharides containing amino sugars are discussed elsewhere. (Chapters VI, XII.)

Besides the many known naturally occurring free oligosaccharides, a great variety of this class of compound can be obtained by enzymic degradation or controlled hydrolysis of a polysaccharide with acid. As an example, the treatment of starch with amylases produces maltose; under certain conditions of acid hydrolysis, isomaltose can be obtained from starch, and cellobiose from cellulose.

1. B. Helferich, E. Bohn, and S. Winkler, *Ber.* **63**, 989 (1930).

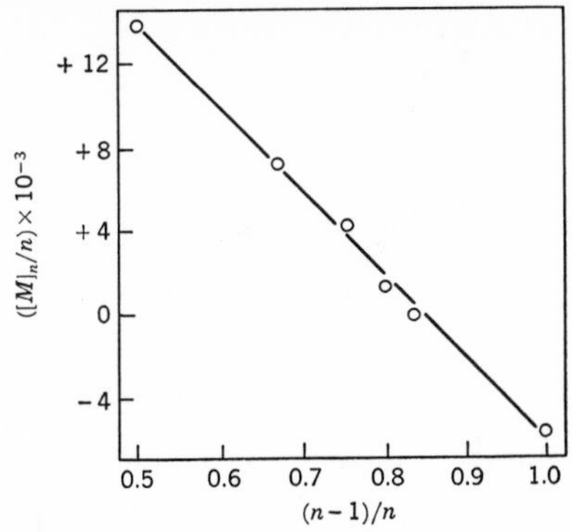
+ 12
+ 8
+ 4
0
- 4
$([M]_n/n) \times 10^{-3}$
0.5
0.6
0.7
0.8
0.9
1.0
$(n-1)/n$

FIG. 1. Relation between degree of polymerization (n) and molecular rotation (M)

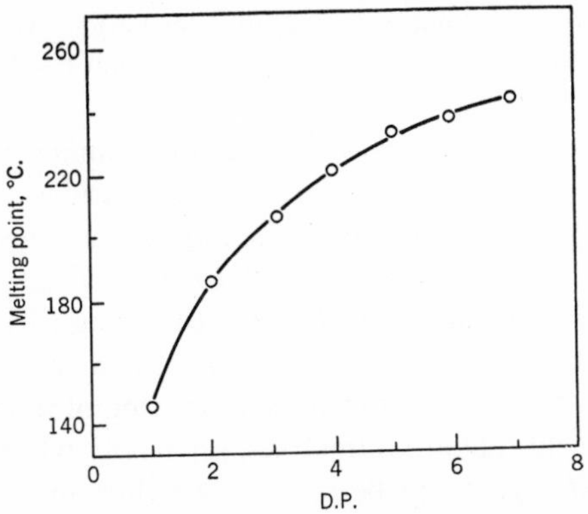
260
220
180
140
Melting point, °C.
0
2
4
6
8
D.P.

FIG. 2. Melting points of xylodextrins as a function of the degree of polymerization (D.P.).

The isolation of several series of polymeric homologous oligosaccharides from partially degraded polysaccharides has been facilitated by the development of adsorption techniques. As a result of the study of such homologs, certain linear relationships have been observed. These relationships, such as those between the degree of polymerization (D.P.) and the optical rotation (*2*), the D.P. and the melting point (*3*), and chromatographic properties (*4*) are illustrated in Figs. 1, 2, and 3. In general, the properties of the oligosaccharides regularly approach those of the high polymer (Chapter XII).

At least one of the monosaccharide residues in an oligosaccharide is combined through an oxygen bridge of the hemiacetal hydroxyl to a second

2. E. E. Dickey and M. L. Wolfrom, *J. Am. Chem. Soc.* **71,** 828 (1949).
3. R. L. Whistler and C. C. Tu, *J. Am. Chem. Soc.* **75,** 646 (1953).
4. D. French and G. M. Wild, *J. Am. Chem. Soc.* **75,** 2612 (1953).

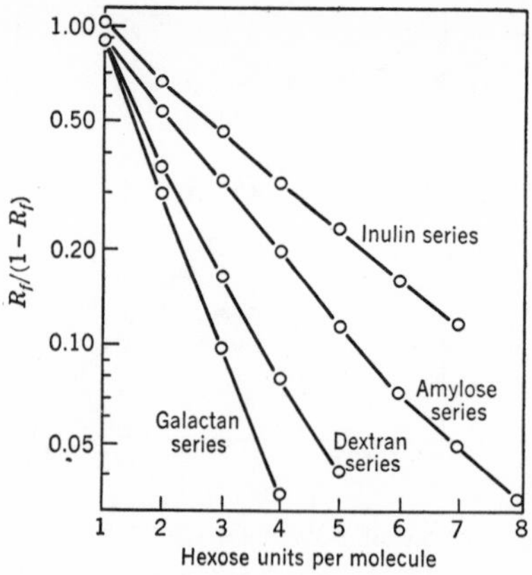
1.00
0.50
0.20
0.10
0.05
$R_f/(1-R_f)$
Inulin series
Amylose series
Galactan series
Dextran series
1 2 3 4 5 6 7 8
Hexose units per molecule

FIG. 3. Chromatographic mobilities of oligosaccharide series, where R_f is the fraction of the distance moved with respect to the solvent front.

hydroxyl of another residue, just as D-glucose is linked to methanol in the methyl glycosides. Hence, the natural oligosaccharides are true glycosides. The glycosides having an alcoholic or phenolic aglycon group are sometimes distinguished from those having a sugar or oligosaccharide radical as the nonglycosidic portion of the molecule by designating them as "heterosides" and "holosides," respectively. Inasmuch as there are five free hydroxyl groups in a hexose, the possibilities of combination of monosaccharide units to form an oligosaccharide are numerous, especially when it is remembered that the combining sugars can be joined by either an α- or β-linkage. The reducing oligosaccharides are named as glycosyl aldoses (or glycosyl ketoses), and the nonreducing oligosaccharides as glycosyl aldosides (glycosyl ketosides) (*5*).

According to the presence or absence of reducing groups in the molecule, the unsubstituted oligosaccharides are conveniently classified as reducing and nonreducing. This property is important, for it provides a test for the existence of a monosaccharide residue with an unsubstituted anomeric carbon. When such an unsubstituted group is present, the sugar reduces alkaline copper salt solutions, mutarotates, and forms glycosides and osazones, as do the monosaccharides. On the other hand, in a nonreducing oligosaccharide, which can neither form an osazone nor mutarotate, it is obvious

5. The terms "glycosido" and "glycosyl" have been used as synonyms in much of the older literature. In the present work, glycosyl will be used and will refer to the radical obtained by removal of the anomeric hydroxyl from a reducing sugar.

In the present text, the number referring to the position of attachment of the glycosyl radical to the reducing residue is placed before the glycosyl radical, e.g., 4-*O*-β-D-galactosyl-D-glucose. This is consistent with the usage such as D-glucose 6-benzoate, or 6-*O*-benzoyl-D-glucose.

that all the reducing groups of the constituent sugars are glycosidically linked to one another; examples of this type of structure are furnished by sucrose, trehalose, and raffinose.

1. SYNTHESIS OF OLIGOSACCHARIDES (*6*)

There are three general methods available for the synthesis of oligosaccharides. These methods are based on isomerizations or degradations of existing oligosaccharides, and on the condensation of monosaccharide units. To contribute to the knowledge of the structure of a particular disaccharide, the condensation method must be such that the reaction takes place between known positions, as otherwise several structural isomers are possible. The restriction of the reaction to predetermined positions is accomplished by blocking, with easily removable groups such as acetyls, all the hydroxyl groups except those between which the condensation is to occur. Additional complications are introduced when asymmetric centers are involved since it must be known whether inversions take place. Probably the most useful reaction is the Koenigs-Knorr synthesis (p. 194) which depends on the reaction of the acetylglycosyl halides with the unsubstituted hydroxyls of a second monosaccharide molecule. This method is seriously limited, however, by the difficulty in obtaining α-linkages.

A. Rearrangement and Degradation of Oligosaccharides

These methods are usually applicable only to the reducing oligosaccharides, i.e., those having an unsubstituted hemiacetal grouping, since most isomerizations involve the reducing group.

Alkaline Rearrangement. The reducing disaccharides isomerize in the presence of alkali to give a mixture of three sugars which consist of the two 2-epimeric aldoses and the corresponding ketose. This action of dilute alkali is the same as that on the monosaccharides (Chapter I). The method is particularly important for obtaining ketose disaccharides, but has been applied in only a few cases. Lactose yields (*7*) lactulose, 4-*O*-β-D-galactosyl-D-fructose, which is interesting because the crystalline sugar is apparently a furanose form. Melibiose gives epimelibiose by an ammonia-catalyzed isomerization (*8*). The pyridine rearrangement has been used to convert 3-*O*-β-D-glucopyranosyl glyceraldehyde to 3-*O*-β-D-glucopyranosyl dihydroxyacetone (*9*).

Glycal Synthesis. This method depends upon the preparation of a glycal (which has a double bond between carbons 1 and 2 of the reducing residue

6. For a recent review see W. L. Evans, D. D. Reynolds, and E. A. Talley, *Advances in Carbohydrate Chem.* **6**, 27 (1951).

7. E. M. Montgomery and C. S. Hudson, *J. Am. Chem. Soc.* **52**, 2101 (1930).

8. L. Hough, J. K. N. Jones, and E. L. Richards, *J. Chem. Soc.* p. 295 (1954).

9. H. W. Arnold and W. L. Evans, *J. Am. Chem. Soc.* **58**, 1890 (1936).

of the molecule) and the oxidation of the glycal with perbenzoic acid to give two 2-epimeric aldoses as described previously for the monosaccharides (Chapters II and VII). The epimers of lactose, maltose, and cellobiose have been obtained by this method (*10*).

Degradation Reactions. By use of the several methods described for shortening the carbon chain of the monosaccharides (Chapter II), the reducing carbon of the disaccharides also may be removed. Calcium lactobionate is oxidized by hydrogen peroxide with ferric salts as catalyst (Ruff degradation) to 3-*O*-β-D-galactosyl-D-arabinose (*11*) and acetylated gentiobionic acid nitrile gives 5-*O*-D-glucosyl-D-arabinose by the action of sodium methoxide (Wohl-Zemplén method). This sugar is of particular interest as it cannot form a pyranose ring. Under certain conditions, glycals may be cleaved by ozonolysis to give an aldose with one less carbon atom. This reaction has been applied to disaccharides with results similar to those obtained by the Ruff or Wohl-Zemplén methods (*12*).

Walden Inversions. Several reactions, not of general application, are of importance for obtaining special disaccharides. Cellobiose octaacetate, when subjected to the procedure which usually produces the acetylglycosyl fluorides, gives the expected product and the corresponding derivative of the 2-epimeric disaccharide, 4-*O*-β-D-glucosyl-D-mannose (*13*). In this instance, the action of anhydrous hydrogen fluoride inverts the configuration of the second carbon and also replaces the acetoxy group at carbon 1 by a fluorine atom. In a somewhat similar manner, lactose and cellobiose octaacetate under chlorinating conditions (aluminum chloride and phosphorus pentachloride in chloroform solution) yield, in addition to the expected hepta-*O*-acetylglycosyl chloride, isomeric compounds produced by Walden

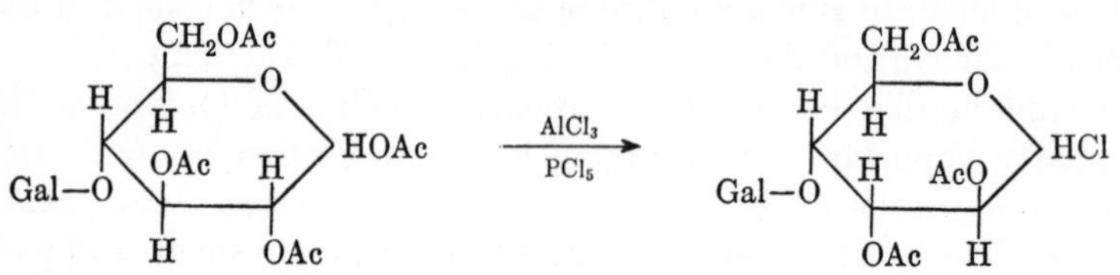
CH2OAc
O
H
H
OAc
H
HOAc
Gal—O
H
OAc
AlCl3
PCl5
CH2OAc
O
H
H
H
AcO
HCl
Gal—O
OAc
H

inversions at carbons 2 and 3 of the reducing part of the molecules. The new disaccharides are neolactose (4-*O*-β-D-galactosyl-D-altrose) from lactose and celtrobiose (4-*O*-β-D-glucosyl-D-altrose) from cellobiose (*14*). These

10. M. Bergmann and H. Schotte, *Ber.* **54**, 1564 (1921); W. N. Haworth, E. L. Hirst, *et al.*, *J. Chem. Soc.* pp. 2636, 2644 (1930).

11. G. Zemplén, *Ber.* **60**, 1309 (1927); O. Ruff and G. Ollendorff, *ibid.* **33**, 1798 (1900).

12. For a review, see reference *6*.

13. D. H. Brauns, *J. Am. Chem. Soc.* **48**, 2776 (1926).

14. A. Kunz and C. S. Hudson, *J. Am. Chem. Soc.* **48**, 1978, 2435 (1926); N. K. Richtmyer and C. S. Hudson, *ibid.* **57**, 1716 (1935); **58**, 2534 (1936).

disaccharides are of particular importance in providing new sources of D-altrose, a sugar difficult to obtain by older methods.

Anomeric Rearrangement. The transformation of certain glycosides from the β- to the α-configuration by the action of stannic chloride or titanium tetrachloride was observed by Pacsu (*15*). Recently this transformation has been applied to the oligosaccharides, effecting the synthesis of isomaltose from gentiobiose (see Isomaltose).

Dideoxy Disaccharides. The tosyl groups of 6,6′-di-*O*-tosylcellobiose are replaceable with iodine by the action of sodium iodide in acetone solution. The resulting 6,6′-dideoxy-diiodocellobiose may be reduced by catalytic hydrogenation to 6,6′-dideoxycellobiose (*16*). A similar compound with one 6-deoxy and one primary hydroxyl group is obtained by the addition of tetra-*O*-acetyl-D-glucosyl bromide to the anhydro ring of 5,6-anhydro-D-glucose (see below).

B. Condensation of Two Monosaccharide Units

Koenigs-Knorr Reaction. This reaction, described in Chapter IV for the preparation of the glycosides, is probably the most widely applicable and important of the methods. An acetylglycosyl halide, usually the bromide, reacts with the unsubstituted hydroxyl of a second monosaccharide molecule in the presence of silver carbonate or silver oxide with the formation of a glycosidic linkage between the two molecules. In most instances the glycosidic carbon has the β-configuration as is demonstrated by the formation of β-glycosides when an alcohol rather than a second monosaccharide molecule is employed in the reaction. The process involves a Walden inversion and usually proceeds smoothly in high yields when the halogen and the acetyl group on carbons 1 and 2, respectively, have a *cis* relation. If they are *trans*, however, orthoesters may be formed (Chapter III). Disaccharides with D-glucose, D-galactose, D-arabinose, and D-xylose constituting the glycosidic portion of the molecule are easily obtained in this manner. When it is desired to synthesize an α-glucosidic linkage, the use of mercuric acetate or pyridine as the catalyst rather than silver salts often gives the desired result. Melibiose (6-*O*-α-D-galactosyl-D-glucose) is synthesized by the action of tetra-*O*-acetyl-D-galactosyl bromide on 1,2,3,4-tetra-*O*-acetyl-D-glucose in the presence of quinoline. Condensation of tri-*O*-acetyl-D-xylosyl bromide and a D-glucose derivative having an unsubstituted hydroxyl group at carbon 6 may take place in the presence of mercuric acetate exclusively with inversion of configuration and the formation of a primeverose (6-*O*-β-D-xylosyl-D-glucose) derivative (*17*). If the amount of catalyst employed is small, an additional reaction without inversion takes place with the simul-

15. E. Pacsu, *Ber.* **61,** 137, 1508 (1928); *ibid.* **52,** 2563, 2568, 2571 (1930).
16. J. Compton, *J. Am. Chem. Soc.* **60,** 1203 (1938).
17. G. Zemplén and R. Bognár, *Ber.* **72,** 1160 (1939).

taneous formation of isoprimeverose (6-*O*-α-D-xylosyl-D-glucose) which has an α-glycosidic linkage. Disaccharides with linkages through primary alcoholic groups (gentiobiose type) are easily obtained by these methods since

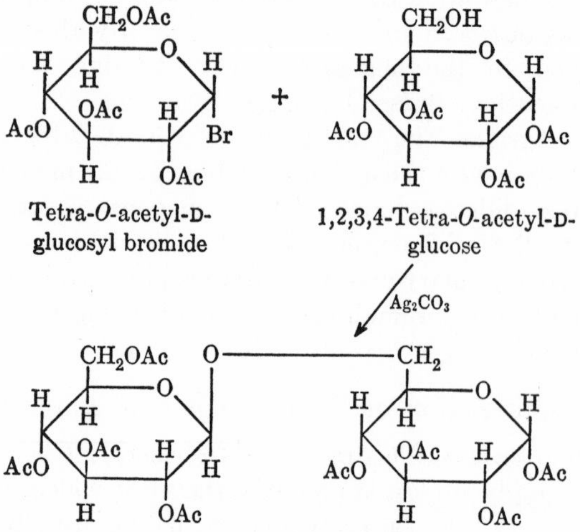

Octa-*O*-acetylgentiobiose

the necessary monosaccharide derivatives with free primary hydroxyl groups and with the other groups blocked are readily obtained from the corresponding trityl derivatives.

The method may be applied to the preparation of trisaccharides by utilizing a 1-halogeno acetylated disaccharide in place of tetra-*O*-acetyl-D-glucosyl bromide. The β-cellobiosyl-D-glucose and D-mannose and the 6-β-maltosyl-D-glucose are prepared in this manner (*18*). Dihydroxyacetone can be condensed with acetylglycosyl halides to form simple types of disaccharides (*19*). The D-ribosyldihydroxyacetone is particularly interesting in that the acetylated compound has an orthoester structure.

It is more difficult to obtain sugar derivatives with single free hydroxyls other than glycosidic or primary hydroxyls. However, valuable derivatives of this type are the isopropylidene sugars and the isopropylidene anhydro sugars. By condensation of 2,3-*O*-isopropylidene-1,6-anhydro-D-mannopyranose with tetra-*O*-acetyl-D-galactosyl bromide, subsequent hydrolysis of the isopropylidene and acetyl groups, and cleavage of the anhydro ring with acids, 4-*O*-β-D-galactosyl-D-mannose (epilactose) is obtained. The epilactose is then carried through the glycal synthesis to produce lactose. 4-*O*-β-D-Glucosyl-D-mannose (epicellobiose) and cellobiose are prepared by

18. B. Helferich and W. Schafer, *Ann.* **450,** 229 (1926); S. H. Nichols, Jr., W. L. Evans, and H. D. McDowell, *J. Am. Chem. Soc.* **62,** 1754 (1940).

19. C. W. Klingensmith and W. L. Evans, *J. Am. Chem. Soc.* **61,** 3012 (1939).

the same procedure from tetra-*O*-acetyl-D-glucosyl bromide and the 2,3-*O*-isopropylidene-1,6-anhydro-D-mannopyranose. More details of these methods are given under Cellobiose, Gentiobiose, Melibiose, and Lactose later in this chapter.

Ethylene Oxide Additions. When 1,2-*O*-isopropylidene-5,6-anhydro-D-glucofuranose reacts with tetra-*O*-acetyl-D-glucosyl bromide, condensation takes place with the simultaneous opening of the anhydro ring, addition of the glucosyl group to the oxygen attached to carbon 5, and addition of bromine to carbon 6. Catalytic reduction replaces the bromine by a hydrogen atom, and there is obtained an unusual disaccharide methylose derivative, 5-*O*-β-D-glucosyl-6-deoxy-D-glucose (*20*).

A second application of this reaction is of far greater significance, having resulted in the first chemical synthesis of sucrose. The reaction of 3,4,6-tri-*O*-acetyl-1,2-anhydro-D-glucopyranose with alcohols to give β-D-glucosides was first observed by Brigl (*21*). This reaction was later used by Haworth and Hickinbottom in a condensation of the anhydro compound with 2,3,4,6-tetra-*O*-acetyl-β-D-glucopyranose to give "neotrehalose" heptaacetate (*22*). Recently, Lemieux and Uber (*23*) have condensed the an-

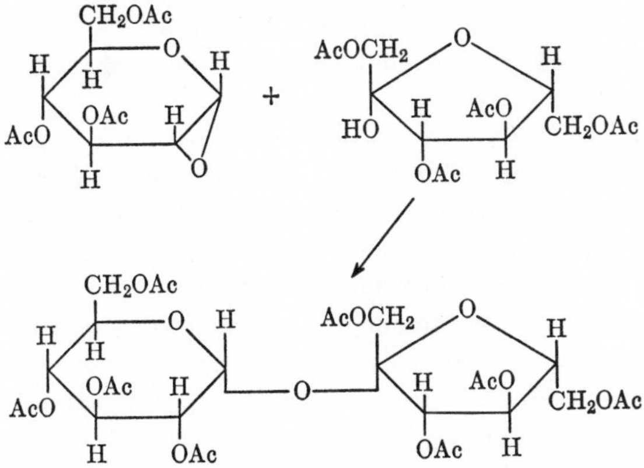
CH₂OAc
O
H
H
H
OAc
H
AcO
H
O
+
AcOCH₂
O
H
H
AcO
HO
CH₂OAc
OAc
H
CH₂OAc
O
H
H
H
OAc
H
AcO
O
AcOCH₂
O
H
H
AcO
CH₂OAc
H
OAc
OAc
H

hydride with 1,3,4,6-tetra-*O*-acetyl-D-fructose to give a 5% yield of sucrose isolated as the octaacetate (see Sucrose).

Thermal Condensations. Two moles of sugar may condense when heated *in vacuo*. Maltose is said to be produced in this manner from β-D-glucose and α-D-glucose and from β-D-glucose and 1,6-anhydro-β-D-glucose. The

20. K. Freudenberg, H. Eich, C. Knoevenagel, and W. Westphal, *Ber.* **73,** 441 (1940).

21. P. Brigl, *Z. physiol. Chem.* **122,** 245 (1922).

22. W. N. Haworth and W. J. Hickinbottom, *J. Chem. Soc.* p. 2847 (1931).

23. R. U. Lemieux and G. Huber, *J. Am. Chem. Soc.* **75,** 4118 (1953); *ibid.* **78,** 4117 (1956).

use of zinc chloride improves the yields. The maltose is separated as the acetate in yields of 5% to 10% (*24*). Lactose may have been obtained in this manner from β-D-glucose and either β-D-galactose or 1,6-anhydro-β-D-galactose (*25*). The synthesis by thermal condensation, however, does not provide any information as to the structures of the sugars.

Direct Catalyzed Condensation of Monosaccharides in Solution. In the presence of acids and water, the disaccharides are in equilibrium with the products of hydrolysis although the rate of attainment of equilibrium is very slow at room temperature. An excess of water favors the existence of the monosaccharides in the equilibrium mixture, whereas a high concentration of the sugar is favorable to the existence of disaccharides and oligosaccharides. A 25% solution of D-glucose in concentrated hydrochloric acid gives, after 15 hours at room temperature, a mixture from which a disaccharide osazone (isomaltose) may be isolated (*26*). As might be expected from the many positions available for formation of a disaccharide linkage and because each position allows for at least one pair of α,β-isomers, the products formed are probably complex mixtures. However, the available evidence indicates a preference for condensation between the hemiacetal (anomeric) hydroxyl and the primary hydroxyl groups. This type of reaction, called "reversion," is very important in industrial processes involving the hydrolysis of polysaccharides such as in the preparation of D-glucose from starch.

Most of the isomers theoretically possible by the condensation of two glucose units have been isolated (*26a*). (See also under Isomaltose.)

The specificity of the reaction may be greatly increased by the use of enzymes rather than acids as the catalysts. According to the enzyme employed, α- or β-glycosidic linkages may be synthesized at will, and even the position of condensation in the nonglycosyl sugar may be varied somewhat. Maltose and other α-D-glucosides are formed by the action of yeast α-D-glucosidase on concentrated D-glucose solutions (*27*). Similarly, gentiobiose and cellobiose are formed from D-glucose solutions through the catalytic action of α-D-glucosidases, and the relative proportions of the two isomers is affected by the concentration (*28*). Gentiobiose is also formed by the action of dried yeasts on D-glucose solutions (*29*).

In many cases the synthesis of oligosaccharides under natural conditions

24. A. Pictet and H. Vogel, *Helv. Chim. Acta* **10**, 588 (1927).

25. A. Pictet and H. Vogel, *Helv. Chim. Acta* **11**, 209 (1938); See also H. Bredereck *et al.*, *Chem. Ber.* **86**, 1277, 1286 (1953).

26. See E. Fischer, *Ber.* **23**, 3687 (1890).

26a. J. C. Sowden and A. S. Spriggs, *J. Am. Chem. Soc.* **78**, 2503 (1956).

27. A. C. Hill, *J. Chem. Soc.* **83**, 589 (1903).

28. E. Bourquelot, H. Hérissey, and J. Coirre, *Compt. rend.* **157**, 732 (1913); I. Vintilescu, C. N. Ionescu, and A. Kizyk, *Bull. soc. chim. Roumania* **17**, 283 (1935).

29. H. Pringsheim, J. Bondi, and J. Leibowitz, *Ber.* **59**, 1983 (1926).

probably takes place as a result of phosphorylase action. Such an action has been demonstrated by the *in vitro* synthesis of sucrose from α-D-glucose 1-phosphate and D-fructose in the presence of enzymes from bacteria such as *Pseudomonas saccharophila* (see Enzymic synthesis of disaccharides below).

Elimination of Water from Two Monosaccharide Units by Use of Dehydrating Agents. Acetylated sugars with free hydroxyl groups may be condensed with the elimination of a mole of water. Two moles of 2,3,4,6-tetra-*O*-acetyl-D-glucose combine (*30*) under the influence of phosphorus pentoxide in an inert solvent such as benzene with the formation of the octaacetate of 1-*O*-β-D-glucosyl-β-D-glucoside (β,β-trehalose) (see under Sucrose).

2. DETERMINATION OF STRUCTURE

To determine the molecular configuration of an oligosaccharide, one must first identify the monosaccharide units that enter into its composition. This can be done by applying appropriate tests on the hydrolysis products. Complete information as to the nature of the linkages must include knowledge of (1) the ring type of each constituent unit, (2) the particular hydroxyl or carbonyl group of each unit involved in the linkage of the units, and (3) the stereochemical configuration (α- or β-) of the glycosidic linkages involved.

The methylation method has been the principal means for determining the type of ring of the monosaccharide constituents and their points of attachment to one another in the oligosaccharide molecule. The usual procedure involves: (1) complete methylation of the disaccharide; (2) hydrolysis of the methylated disaccharide to partially methylated monosaccharide units, and their identification by comparison of their properties with those of known methylated compounds; (3) determination of the unmethylated positions in each unit, these being the positions which were available for ring formation and for linkage between units; and (4) determination of the ring type (pyranose or furanose) by supplementary evidence, such as determination of the rate of hydrolysis of the partially methylated lactone (*31*).

When a reducing disaccharide, such as maltose or cellobiose, is directly methylated, ambiguous results are obtained in regard to its configuration. Since a glucopyranose unit, linked to a glycosidic residue through C-4 and a glucofuranose unit linked through C-5, would produce the same methylated derivative, namely, 2,3,6-tri-*O*-methyl-D-glucose, the ring type as well as

30. E. Fischer and K. Delbrück, *Ber.* **42,** 2776 (1909); F. Klages and R. Niemann, *Ann.* **529,** 185 (1937).

31. W. N. Haworth, "The Constitution of Sugars," p. 24. Arnold, London, 1929; S. Baker and W. N. Haworth, *J. Chem. Soc.* **127,** 365 (1925).

the point of attachment in the reducing moiety remains undetermined. To avoid this uncertainty the aldobionic acid or alditol rather than the original disaccharide is methylated. Thus, methylation of maltose produces methyl hepta-*O*-methylmaltoside, which on hydrolysis gives 2,3,4,6-tetra-*O*-methyl-D-glucose and 2,3,6-tri-*O*-methyl-D-glucose. Methylated maltobionic acid produces 2,3,4,6-tetra-*O*-methyl-D-glucose and 2,3,5,6-tetra-*O*-methyl-D-gluconic acid (see under Maltose). The position of the free hydroxyl in the tetra-*O*-methyl-D-gluconic acid shows that the disaccharide must be connected at the 4-position of the residue.

The action of enzymes is valuable for the purpose of providing information concerning the configuration of the glycosidic linkage in oligosaccharides. In reducing disaccharides, only one glycosidic linkage is present, and the enzymes maltase (α-glucosidase) and β-glucosidase (Chapter X) are often used for the determination of the type of linkage. A mutarotation of the disaccharide during enzyme or acid hydrolysis also gives an indication of the linkage involved. If downward mutarotation is observed, the glycosidic linkage is considered to be of the α-D-type; upward mutarotation indicates a β-D-type. For nonreducing oligosaccharides in which dual glycosidic linkages are involved, conclusions from enzymic studies regarding the stereochemical nature of linkages are often uncertain. Often enzymes serve to reveal the configuration of the glycosidic linkage in certain disaccharides that are constituents of larger oligosaccharide molecules. Thus, the fact that yeast invertase splits the trisaccharide raffinose to melibiose and D-fructose indicates that the monosaccharide is joined with D-glucose through a sucrose linkage (see under Raffinose).

The results obtained from an oxidation with periodate are used to great advantage for the determination of the structure of oligosaccharides, particularly of nonreducing disaccharides (*32*). The structure of sucrose, determined by the methylation procedure as being D-glucopyranosyl-D-fructofuranoside, was confirmed by this means. In a disaccharide consisting of glucopyranose and fructofuranose glycosidically united through C-1 of the aldose and C-2 of the ketose, the D-glucose residue would possess three adjacent free hydroxyls, on its carbon atoms 2, 3, and 4, and the D-fructose residue would have two free hydroxyls, on carbon atoms 3 and 4. On oxidation of such a disaccharide with periodate, the D-glucose residue would consume two moles of periodate and form one mole of formic acid, and the D-fructose residue would consume one mole of periodate. A total of three moles of periodate would thus be consumed, and one mole of formic acid would be formed per mole of disaccharide. If the D-fructose residue were to

32. P. Fleury and J. Courtois, *Bull. soc. chim. France* **10,** 245 (1943); *Compt. rend.* **214,** 366 (1942); E. L. Jackson and C. S. Hudson, *J. Am. Chem. Soc.* **59,** 994 (1937); **62,** 958 (1940); R. M. Hann, W. D. Maclay, and C. S. Hudson, *ibid.* **61,** 2432 (1939).

TABLE I

EASE OF ACID HYDROLYSIS OF SOME OLIGOSACCHARIDES

Oligosaccharide	$k/a_{H^+} \times 10^6$ (sec.$^{-1}$)	Activation energy (cal./g.-mole)
α-D-Glucopyranosyl α-D-glucopyranoside (Trehalose)	0.864	40,180
6-*O*-β-D-Glucopyranosyl-D-glucopyranose (Gentiobiose)	1.24	33,390
4-*O*-β-D-Glucopyranosyl-D-glucopyranose (Cellobiose)	5.89	30,710
3-*O*-α-D-Glucopyranosyl-D-fructose (Turanose)	11.9	32,450
4-*O*-α-D-Glucopyranosyl-D-glucopyranose (Maltose)	16.8	30,970
4-*O*-β-D-Galactopyranosyl-D-glucopyranose (Lactose)	16.6	26,900
6-*O*-α-D-Galactopyranosyl-D-glucose (Melibiose)	15.5	38,590
α-D-Glucopyranosyl β-D-fructofuranoside (Sucrose)	14,600	25,830
Raffinose	11,200[a]	25,340
Melezitose	48,300[a]	25,600

[a] These figures presumably represent the hydrolysis of the sucrose linkage in these trisaccharides.

exist in the disaccharide in the pyranose form, it would also contain three free hydroxyl groups at C-3, C-4, and C-5, and, as in the case of the D-glucose, it should consume two moles of periodate and give rise to one mole of formic acid. In this case, a total of four moles of periodate would be consumed, and two moles of formic acid would be formed per mole of disaccharide. Actually on oxidation of the sucrose with sodium periodate, three moles of periodate are consumed and one mole of formic acid is formed.

Application of the periodate oxidation method to the determination of the structure of reducing sugars does not give definite results, because the molecules are unstable and tend to become completely degraded. However, the reducing group may be stabilized by forming a glycoside or phenylosotriazole, which may be treated with periodate in the same manner as reducing disaccharides. As an example, in the case of the phenylosotriazole of 3-*O*-D-glucopyranosyl-L-arabinose, the moiety possessing the osotriazole group is a straight chain compound and has a free —CH_2OH group adjacent to an HCOH group; on periodate oxidation such a structure produces one mole of formaldehyde; this result shows that neither the primary alcohol group nor the next adjacent secondary alcohol group is occupied by the linkage (*33*). When the phenylosotriazole under consideration is a hexose derivative, it can be concluded that the junction between the two monosaccharides is other than through C-6 or C-5, if formaldehyde is produced.

33. W. Z. Hassid, M. Doudoroff, A. L. Potter, and H. A. Barker, *J. Am. Chem. Soc.* **70,** 306 (1948).

3. EASE OF ACID HYDROLYSIS

As shown in Table I (*34*), there is considerable difference in the ease of hydrolysis of oligosaccharides; sucrose, with its fructofuranose ring, is particularly labile. The ease of hydrolysis of the sucrose linkage in comparison with that of the glycopyranosides makes it possible to hydrolyze preferentially the sucrose linkage in trisaccharides with the formation of a resistant disaccharide. Thus, turanose, a disaccharide, is prepared by the partial hydrolysis of the parent trisaccharide melezitose.

4. PREPARATION, PROPERTIES, AND STRUCTURES OF SOME OLIGOSACCHARIDES OF NATURAL ORIGIN (*6*, *35*)

A. Disaccharides

Cellobiose

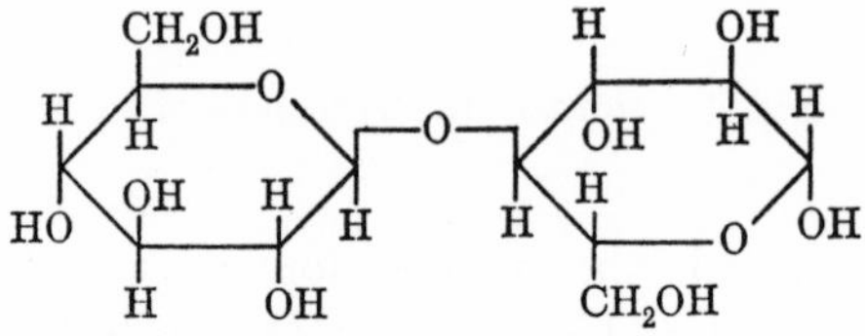
CH₂OH
H
OH
O
H
H
O
OH
H
H
OH
H
HO
H
H
OH
H
O
OH
H
OH
CH₂OH

Synonyms. 4-*O*-β-D-Glucopyranosyl-D-glucose.

Properties. β-Isomer: m.p. 225°C.; $[\alpha]_D^{20}$ +14.2° → +34.6° (*c*, 8; water). Reducing.

Identification. Phenylosazone, octaacetate.

Occurrence. The sugar is not known to exist in the free state in products of biological origin but is the basic repeating unit of cellulose and lichenin.

Preparation (*36*). Cellulose in the form of cotton or filter paper is simultaneously acetylated and acetolyzed by the action of acetic anhydride and sulfuric acid at low temperatures. Cellobiose octaacetate crystallizes from the reaction mixture and after separation is recrystallized from alcohol. The acetyl groups are removed by any of several methods, preferably with barium methoxide in methanol solution.

Crystalline cellobiose has been obtained from hydrolyzates of cellulose by a cell-free enzyme preparation from *Aspergillus niger* (*37*). An enzyme

34. E. A. Moelwyn-Hughes, *Trans. Faraday Soc.* **25**, 503 (1929).

35. For more detailed information concerning the occurrence and preparation of many of the individual oligosaccharides, the following references are particularly recommended: F. J. Bates and Associates, *Natl. Bur. Standards Circ.* **C440** (1942); "Beilsteins Handbuch der organischen Chemie," Vol. **31**, Springer, Berlin, 1938.

36. A. P. N. Franchimont, *Ber.* **12**, 1941 (1879); G. Braun, *Org. Syntheses* **17**, 34, 36 (1937).

37. R. L. Whistler and C. L. Smart, *J. Am. Chem Soc.* **75**, 1916 (1953).

preparation purified by adsorption on and elution from powdered cellulose, reacts with swollen cellulose to produce cellobiose as the major product for the first three hours of hydrolysis.

Structure. See discussion under Maltose.

Synthesis. By the reaction of 1,6-anhydro-β-D-glucopyranose (levoglucosan) with tetra-O-acetyl-D-glucosyl bromide and the subsequent hydrolysis of the anhydro ring with sulfuric acid, Freudenberg and Nagai (*38*) were able to synthesize cellobiose in small yield. The stereospecificity of the method provides evidence for the β-configuration of the D-glucosidic linkage. The exact position of the glucosidic linkage is not defined, however, as several unsubstituted hydroxyl groups are present in the 1,6-anhydro-β-D-glucose. A structurally definitive synthesis by the reaction of 2,3-O-isopropylidene-1,6-anhydro-β-D-mannopyranose (which contains only one free hydroxyl, at carbon 4) and tetra-O-acetyl-D-glucosyl bromide has been described (*39*). After rupture of the anhydro ring, a derivative of the 2-epimer of cellobiose is obtained (epicellobiose) which is carried to cellobiose through the intermediary cellobial (epicellobial). The method is similar to that used for the synthesis of lactose. (See under Lactose.)

Metabolism. (See Chapter XIV.) Absorption of the disaccharide in the gut of the rat takes place at about 6.8% of the rate of absorption of D-glucose (*40*). Normal rats form glycogen in the liver and muscle in equivalent amounts from cellobiose and D-glucose. These two sugars possess the same ability to lower an exogenous ketonuria.

Polymer Homologs (*41*). A product obtained by the acetolysis of cellulose has been resolved by chromatography into a series of crystalline acetates ranging in degree of polymerization from 1 to 6 inclusive.

Acetate	M.p. (°C.)	$[\alpha]_D$ (chloroform)
α-D-Glucopyranose	105–9	+97°
α-Cellobiose	225–6	+39.6°
α-Cellotriose	223–4	+22.6°
α-Cellotetraose	230–34	+13.4°
α-Cellopentaose	240–41	+4.2°
α-Cellohexaose	252–5	−0.23°

Epimelibiose

Synonyms. 6-O-α-D-Galactopyranosyl-D-mannose.

Properties. M.p. 201°C.; $[\alpha]_D^{25}$ +120.9° → +124.6° (*c*, 2; water). Reducing

38. K. Freudenberg and W. Nagai, *Ber.* **66,** 27 (1933).

39. W. T. Haskins, R. M. Hann, and C. S. Hudson, *J. Am. Chem. Soc.* **64,** 1289 (1942).

40. C. E. Vaniman and H. J. Deuel, Jr., *J. Biol. Chem.* **152,** 565 (1944).

41. For a recent study, and a list of pertinent references, see E. E. Dickey and M. L. Wolfrom, *J. Am. Chem. Soc.* **71,** 825 (1949).

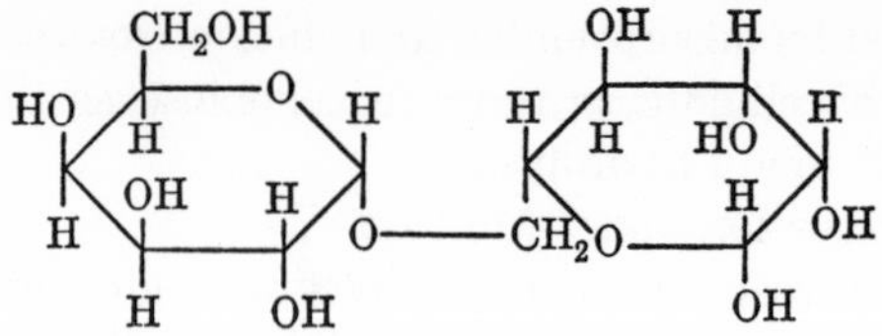

Identification. Reduction to epimelibiitol.

Occurrence. The disaccharide occurs as a unit in the polysaccharide guaran.

Preparation. The sugar may be prepared by charcoal-column fractionation of the partial acid hydrolysis products of guaran (*42*) and by the alkaline isomerization of melibiose (*43*).

Structure. The structure of epimelibiose has been established by periodate oxidation and by comparison of its osazone with that of melibiose. Reduction of epimelibiose gives epimelibiitol, m.p. 157–158°.

Gentiobiose

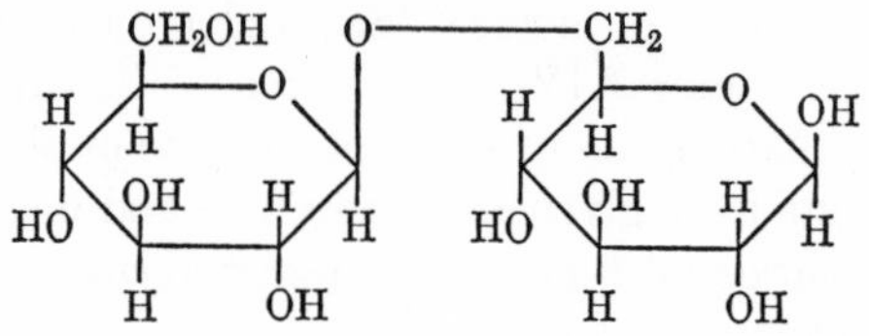

Synonyms. 6-*O*-β-D-Glucopyranosyl-D-glucose, "amygdalose."

Properties. α-Isomer; crystallizes associated with two moles of methanol; m.p. 85–86°C.; $[\alpha]_D^{20}$ +21.4° → +8.7° (*c*, 5; water). β-Isomer (solvent-free); m.p. 190–195°C. Not fermented by top yeasts. Reducing.

Identification. Phenylosazone, octaacetate.

Occurrence. The disaccharide is the sugar constituent of a number of glycosides of which the most important are amygdalin and crocin. The two D-glucose units of the trisaccharide gentianose, which is found free in the roots of plants of the *Gentian* species, are connected together in the same manner as gentiobiose. Gentiobiose is found in materials obtained by the action of acids and certain enzymes on D-glucose and on polymers such as starch and cellulose. In such materials it is probably a reversion product (see under Isomaltose).

Preparation (*44*). The sugar is obtained by partial acid or enzymic hydrolysis of gentianose and removal of the fructose by yeast fermentation.

42. R. L. Whistler and D. F. Durso, *J. Am. Chem. Soc.* **73,** 4189 (1951).

43. L. Hough, J. K. N. Jones, and E. L. Richards, *J. Chem. Soc.* p. 295 (1954).

44. C. S. Hudson and J. Johnson, *J. Am. Chem. Soc.* **39,** 1272 (1917); E. Bourquelot and H. Hérissey, *Compt. rend.* **135,** 290 (1902).

It is usually separated as the octaacetate. The hydrogenation of hepta-*O*-acetylamygdalin (*45*) and the isolation of the octaacetate of gentiobiose, from the acetylated mother liquors ("hydrol") of the preparation of D-glucose from starch, have been suggested for the preparation of the disaccharide. The best method, however, is probably the synthetic method of Helferich as modified by Reynolds and Evans and described below. Enzymic synthesis by the action of almond emulsin on D-glucose is also recommended (*46*).

Synthesis (*47*). By the condensation of 1,2,3,4-tetra-*O*-acetyl-β-D-glucopyranose with tetra-*O*-acetyl-D-glucosyl bromide, a linkage is established between carbon 6 of the first molecule and carbon 1 of the second molecule, and octa-*O*-acetylgentiobiose is formed.

Structure (*48*). Methylation of gentiobiose followed by acid hydrolysis gives the well-known 2,3,4,6-tetra-*O*-methyl-D-glucose and a tri-*O*-methyl-D-glucose which yields a crystalline methyl tri-*O*-methyl-D-glucoside. The latter substance is identical with that formed by the methylation and detritylation of methyl 6-*O*-trityl-D-glucopyranoside and must be methyl 2,3,4-tri-*O*-methyl-D-glucoside. This evidence shows that the disaccharide linkage of gentiobiose connects carbon 1 of one glucose unit and carbon 6 of the second glucose unit. It is confirmed by the above synthesis under conditions such that the linkage can be formed only between these two carbons.

The β-configuration for the glucosidic linkage is shown by the hydrolysis of gentiobiose by the β-D-glucosidase of almond emulsin and by its synthesis under conditions favorable to the formation of β-D-glucosides (Koenigs-Knorr synthesis).

Isomaltose

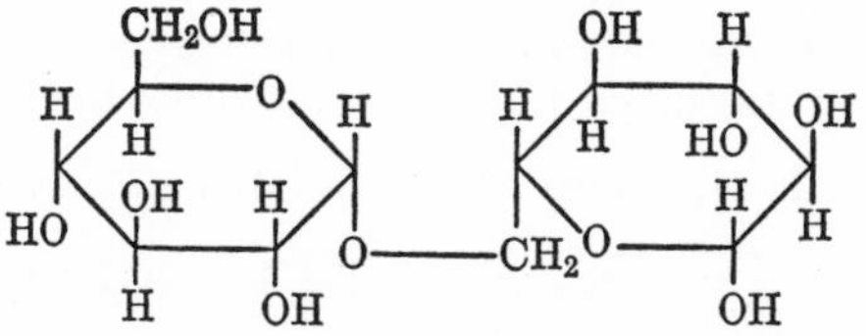
CH₂OH
H
O
H
H
OH
H
HO
H
OH
O
OH
H
H
OH
H
HO
H
CH₂
O
H
OH

Synonyms. Brachiose, 6-*O*-α-D-glucopyranosyl-D-glucose.

Properties. Amorphous, $[\alpha]_D^{24}$ +103.2° (*c*, 3.8; water); crystalline, $[\alpha]_D^{25}$ +120° (*c*, 1.2; water). Not fermentable by yeasts. Reducing.

Identification. Octaacetate; octa-*p*-nitrobenzoate.

45. M. Bergmann and W. Freudenberg, *Ber*. **62**, 2783 (1929).

46. B. Helferich and J. F. Leete, *Org. Syntheses* **22**, 53 (1942).

47. D. D. Reynolds and W. L. Evans, *J. Am. Chem. Soc*. **60**, 2559 (1938); B. Helferich and W. Klein, *Ann*. **450**, 219 (1926).

48. W. Charlton, W. N. Haworth, and W. J. Hickinbottom, *J. Chem. Soc*. p. 1527 (1927); W. N. Haworth and B. Wylam, *ibid*. **123**, 3120 (1923).

Occurrence. This disaccharide exists as a unit in the polysaccharides amylopectin, glycogen, and especially certain bacterial dextrans (*Leuconostoc dextranicum*, *L. mesenteroides*) from which it may be obtained by partial hydrolysis. (See also Reversion, Chapters I, IV, and XII.)

Preparation. Isomaltose has been obtained as the crystalline β-octaacetate in 5% yield from partial acid hydrolyzates of a bacterial dextran (*49*); from Taka-amylase hydrolyzates of amylopectin (*50*) as the crystalline α- and β-octaacetates and the octa-*p*-nitrobenzoate; from the acid hydrolyzates of glycogen (*51*) and from hydrol (*52*). It has recently been prepared in 50% yield from enzymic hydrolyzates of the dextran from *Leuconostoc mesenteroides* by a separation procedure employing charcoal-column elution (*53*).

Structure. The methylation studies of Georg and Pictet (*54*) established their preparation to be a 6-*O*-D-glucopyranosyl-D-glucose (*55*). (See Synthesis). Although it follows from the nonidentity of isomaltose with gentiobiose that the former must be an α-D-glucoside, the complete proof of structure of isomaltose came only after the preparation of crystalline, well-defined derivatives. Thus, Wolfrom, Georges, and Miller (*56*) demonstrated the probable identity of their crystalline isomaltose octaacetate (from a $1 \rightarrow 6$ linked dextran) with that of Georg and Pictet and, by application of the Hudson Isorotation Rules, presented strong evidence for the α-D-glucosyl link in isomaltose. They also converted the isomaltose to its methyl glycoside, and on the basis of periodate studies showed that the latter must be the methyl 6-*O*-α-D-glucopyranosyl-β-D-glucopyranoside.

The synthesis of isomaltose from gentiobiose by anomeric isomerization (*57*) is consistent with the previously assigned structure.

Synthesis. The first syntheses that probably led to isomaltose as one of the end-products were carried out by condensing D-glucose in the presence of acids (*56*). E. Fischer coined the term isomaltose for the disaccharide he

49. M. L. Wolfrom, L. W. Georges, and I. L. Miller, *J. Am. Chem. Soc.* **69,** 473 (1947); **71,** 125 (1949).

50. E. M. Montgomery, F. B. Weakley, and G. E. Hilbert, *J. Am. Chem. Soc.* **69,** 2249 (1947); **71,** 1682 (1949).

51. M. L. Wolfrom, E. N. Lassettre, and A. N. O'Neill, *J. Am. Chem. Soc.* **73,** 595 (1951).

52. M. L. Wolfrom, A. Thompson, A. N. O'Neill, and T. T. Galkowski, *J. Am. Chem. Soc.* **74,** 1062 (1952).

53. A. Jeanes, C. A. Wilham, R. W. Jones, H. M. Tsuchiya, and C. E. Rist, *J. Am. Chem. Soc.* **75,** 5911 (1953).

54. A. Georg and A. Pictet, *Helv. Chim. Acta* **9,** 912 (1926).

55. A. Georg, *Compt. rend. soc. phys. et hist. nat. Genève* **47,** 94 (1930).

56. Reviewed by M. L. Wolfrom, L. W. Georges, and I. L. Miller, *J. Am. Chem. Soc.* **71,** 125 (1949).

57. B. Lindberg, *Acta Chem. Scand.* **3,** 1355 (1949).

obtained in the same manner, and which he characterized as the phenylosazone (sintered at 140°, m.p. 150–153°) (*58*). By a modified procedure, Georg and Pictet (*54*) obtained a sirupy disaccharide that gave an amorphous octaacetate, $[\alpha]_D^{20}$ +93.7° (*c*, 4.8; chloroform). The free sugar showed $[\alpha]_D^{23}$ + 104.6° → +99.7° (*c*, 5; water), and gave a phenylosazone with m.p. 160°.

Partial characterization of the disaccharide obtained by Georg and Pictet was made on the basis of methylation (*55*). Hydrolysis of the fully methylated sugar gave 2,3,4-tri-*O*-methyl-D-glucose and 2,3,4,6-tetra-*O*-methyl-D-glucose; the disaccharide was indicated as 6-*O*-D-glucopyranosyl-D-glucose. Subsequent workers have noted the heterogeneity of products produced in such acid-catalyzed condensations, and a careful chromatographic study of the acid reversion products of D-glucose has confirmed this fact (*59*). Isomaltose octaacetate has been synthesized in a 46% yield from gentiobiose octaacetate by anomeric isomerization in the presence of titanium tetrachloride (*57*).

A series of methyl glycosides of oligosaccharides having 1 → 6 linkage was made by the transfer of glucosyl groups from sucrose to methyl α-D-glucopyranoside (*59a*).

Lactose (*60*)

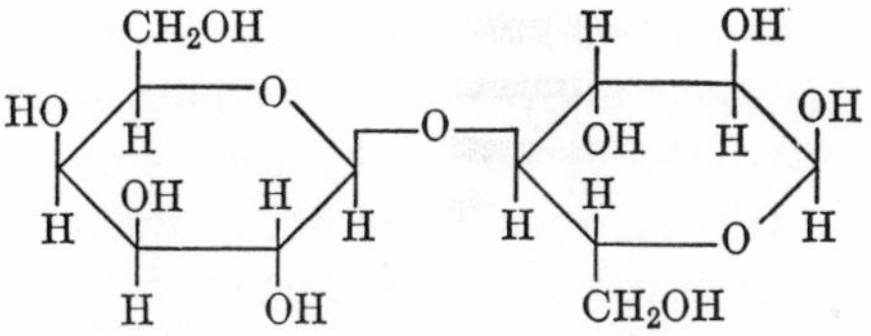
CH₂OH
HO
H
O
O
H
OH
OH
H
OH
H
OH
H
H
H
H
H
O
H
H
OH
CH₂OH

Synonyms. 4-*O*-β-D-Galactopyranosyl-D-glucose, milk sugar.

Properties. Monohydrate of α-isomer; m.p. 202°C.; $[\alpha]_D^{20}$ +85.0 → +52.6° (*c*, 8; water). Anhydrous β-isomer; m.p. 252°C.; $[\alpha]_D^{20}$ +34.9° → +55.4° (*c*, 4; water). Not fermentable by ordinary yeasts; fermented by lactose yeasts. Reducing.

Identification. Phenylosazone; hydrolysis and oxidation with nitric acid to mucic acid; benzylphenylhydrazone.

Occurrence. Found in the milk of all mammals to the extent of approximately 5%. It has been reported that a methanol extract of the longstyled pollen of forsythia flowers contains lactose (*61*).

58. E. Fischer, *Ber.* **23,** 3687 (1890); **28,** 3024 (1895).

59. A. Thompson, K. Anno, M. L. Wolfrom, and M. Inatome, *J. Am. Chem. Soc.* **76,** 1309 (1954).

59a. R. W. Jones, A. Jeanes, C. S. Stringer, and H. M. Tsuchiya, *J. Am. Chem. Soc.* **78,** 2499 (1956).

60. E. O. Whittier, *Chem. Revs.* **2,** 85 (1925–26)

61. R. Kuhn and I. Löw, *Ber.* **82,** 479 (1949).

Preparation (*62*). Whey, obtained as a by-product in the manufacture of cheese, upon evaporation deposits crystalline lactose, which is easily recrystallized from water.

The monohydrate of the α-isomer crystallizes from solutions at temperatures below 93–95° and the more-soluble β-isomer from aqueous solutions above this temperature (*63*).

Structure. The disaccharide, after acid or enzymic hydrolysis (β-D-galactosidase), gives one molecule each of D-galactose and D-glucose. If the sugar is first oxidized with bromine to lactobionic acid and then hydrolyzed, D-gluconic acid and D-galactose are the products obtained (*64*). This evidence establishes lactose as being a D-galactosyl-D-glucose.

After methylation and hydrolysis, the disaccharide yields a tri-*O*-methyl-D-glucose and a tetra-*O*-methyl-D-galactose. As the tetra-*O*-methyl-D-galactose is the same as that obtained by a similar procedure from methyl D-galactopyranoside, it must be 2,3,4,6-tetra-*O*-methyl-D-galactose. The tri-*O*-methyl-D-glucose is identical with that from maltose and is 2,3,6-tri-*O*-methyl-D-glucose. Since the open-chain lactobionic acid after methylation and hydrolysis gives tetra-*O*-methyl-D-glucono-1,4-lactone, the disaccharide linkage must be connected to carbon 4 of the D-glucose moiety (*65*) (see under Maltose). The principal evidence for the configuration of the glycosidic linkage rests on the known specificity of the galactosidases of almond emulsin. The sugar is hydrolyzed by both crude and purified almond emulsin, and the relative rate of hydrolysis by the two emulsins is proportional to the β-D-galactosidase and not to the α-D-galactosidase content. As the enzyme studies indicate the existence of a D-galactosidic linkage, lactose may be described as 4-*O*-β-D-galactopyranosyl-D-glucose. Additional support is given by the synthesis of lactose by a method ordinarily giving β-D-galactosides.

Synthesis. The synthesis of lactose by the condensation of D-glucose and D-galactose at high temperatures in the presence of acetic anhydride or zinc chloride has been reported (*66*). Fischer and Armstrong (*67*) obtained a D-galactosyl-D-glucose by the reaction of tetra-*O*-acetyl-D-galactosyl chloride, sodium ethoxide, and an aqueous solution of D-glucose. They obtained

62. See F. P. Nabenhauer, *Ind. Eng. Chem.* **22,** 54 (1930).

63. C. S. Hudson, *J. Am. Chem. Soc.* **30,** 1767 (1908); J. Gillis, *Rec. trav. chim.* **39,** 88, 677 (1920); R. W. Bell, *Ind. Eng. Chem.* **22,** 51 (1930); W. E. Stringer, *Food Inds.* **11,** 72, 262 (1939); P. F. Sharp and D. B. Hand, *U. S. Patent* 2,182,618 (Dec. 5, 1940).

64. E. Fischer and J. Meyer, *Ber.* **22,** 361 (1889).

65. W. N. Haworth and C. W. Long, *J. Chem. Soc.* p. 544 (1927).

66. E. Demole, *Ber.* **12,** 1935 (1879); Berthelot, *Bull. soc. chim. France* [2] **34,** 82 (1880); A. Pictet and H. Vogel, *Helv. Chim. Acta* **11,** 209 (1928).

67. E. Fischer and E. F. Armstrong, *Ber.* **35,** 3144 (1902).

an osazone which they considered to be melibiose osazone. The properties of the osazone have since made it probable that the product is lactose (*68*). A synthesis of more importance in providing information on the structure of lactose involves as the first step the reaction of tetra-*O*-acetyl-D-galactosyl bromide and 2,3-*O*-isopropylidene-1,6-anhydro-β-D-mannopyranose in an organic solvent and in the presence of silver carbonate (Koenigs-Knorr reaction) (*69*). Since the only unsubstituted hydroxyl is at carbon 4 of the anhydromannose, the condensation must take place at this point. After removal of the isopropylidene (acetone) group, the product is acetylated, and the anhydro ring is opened by the action of sulfuric acid in glacial acetic acid and acetic anhydride. The resulting substance is a disaccharide octaacetate epimeric with lactose and, hence, called epilactose. This substance is then converted to lactose through the glycal synthesis by oxidation of lactal with perbenzoic acid. In all probability, the initial condensation produces a β-D-galactosidic linkage since tetra-*O*-acetyl-D-galactosyl bromide condenses with alcohols with the formation of β-D-galactosides. The sequence is as follows:

2,3-*O*-Isopropylidene-1,6-anhydro-β-D-mannopyranose + tetra-*O*-acetyl-D-galactosyl bromide $\xrightarrow{Ag_2CO_3}$ 4-*O*-(tetra-*O*-acetyl-β-D-galactosyl)-2,3-*O*-isopropylidene-1,6-anhydro-β-D-mannopyranose $\xrightarrow{HOAc}$ 4-*O*-(tetra-*O*-acetyl-β-D-galactosyl)-1,6-anhydro-β-D-mannopyranose $\xrightarrow{Ac_2O}$ 4-*O*-(tetra-*O*-acetyl-β-D-galactosyl)-di-*O*-acetyl-1,6-anhydro-β-D-mannopyranose $\xrightarrow[HOAc\,-\,(Ac)_2O]{H_2SO_4}$ 4-*O*-(tetra-*O*-acetyl-β-D-galactosyl)-tetra-*O*-acetyl-D-mannose $\xrightarrow[HOAc]{HBr}$ 4-*O*-(tetra-*O*-acetyl-β-D-galactosyl)-tri-*O*-acetyl-D-mannosyl bromide $\xrightarrow[HOAc]{Zn}$ hexa-*O*-acetyllactal $\xrightarrow[acid]{perbenzoic}$ hexa-*O*-acetyllactose $\xrightarrow{OH^-}$ lactose

General Discussion. (See also Chapter XIV.) Enzymic syntheses of lactose from D-glucose have also been carried out (*70*). Mammary tissue and other tissues not only catalyze the condensation of two molecules of hexose but also the transformation of D-glucose to D-galactose.

Homogenates and a lyophilized protein fraction have been obtained from mammary gland, both of which synthesize an appreciable amount of lactose from glycogen and α-D-glucose 1-phosphate, whereas free D-glucose is not converted (*71*). Mammary tissue from lactating cows contains the following enzymes: phosphoglucomutase, uridyl transferase, galactowaldenase, and

68. H. H. Schlubach and W. Rauchenberger, *Ber.* **59,** 2102 (1926).

69. W. T. Haskins, R. M. Hann, and C. S. Hudson, *J. Am. Chem. Soc.* **64,** 1852 (1942).

70. G. A. Grant, *Biochem. J.* **30,** 2027 (1936); W. E. Petersen and J. C. Shaw, *Science* **86,** 398 (1937); D. Michlin and M. Lewitow, *Biochem. Z.* **271,** 448 (1934).

71. G. W. Kittinger and F. J. Reithel, *J. Biol. Chem.* **205,** 527 (1953); F. J. Reithel, M. G. Horwitz, H. M. Davidson, and G. W. Kittinger, *ibid.* **194,** 839 (1952).

a galactosyl transferase. The latter enzyme catalyzes the transfer of the galactosyl group from uridine diphosphate D-galactose to α-D-glucose 1-phosphate, forming lactose 1-phosphate (*72*). There is evidence indicating that D-glucose is transformed to D-galactose by the enzyme galactowaldenase present in the mammary gland by the reaction (*72a*): uridine diphosphate D-glucose $\rightleftharpoons$ uridine diphosphate D-galactose. It is possible that the mammary gland contains a phosphorylase which splits the phosphate from lactose 1-phosphate, thus giving rise to free lactose. (See Chapter XIII.)

The tolerance of normal humans for the oral administration of lactose is considerable. Urinary excretion takes place mainly after hydrolysis to D-glucose and D-galactose. When the sugar is injected intravenously into rabbits, it is excreted unchanged (*73*). Rats are unable to survive on a diet in which lactose is the sole source of carbohydrate; they develop diarrhea and alopecia and finally die (*74*). (For more discussion, see Chapter XIV.)

The conditions for the maximum conversion of lactose to hexose sugars have been studied by Ramsdell and Webb (*75*). Using 0.007 *M* HCl as the hydrolyzing agent and a temperature of 147°, 30% solutions of lactose are converted to hexose sugars to the extent of 93% of the theory in less than 65 minutes. A mixture of equal parts of D-glucose and D-galactose is soluble in water to the extent of 42% at 25°.

Maltose

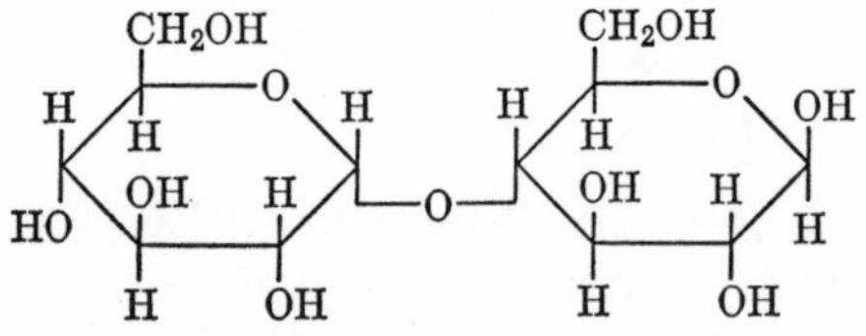

Synonyms. 4-*O*-α-D-Glucopyranosyl-D-glucose, malt sugar.

Properties. Obtained as a monohydrate of the β-isomer: m.p. 102–103°C.; $[\alpha]_D^{20}$ +111.7° → +130.4° (*c*, 4; water). Fermentable by yeasts in the presence of D-glucose (*75a*). Reducing.

Identification. Phenylosazone, β-naphthylhydrazone.

Occurrence. Maltose occasionally has been recorded as present in intact

72. R. Caputto and R. E. Trucco, *Nature* **168,** 1061 (1952).

72a. J. E. Gander, W. E. Petersen, and P. D. Boyer, *Arch. Biochem. and Biophys.* **60,** 260 (1956).

73. L. B. Winter, *J. Physiol. (London)* **71,** 341 (1931).

74. B. H. Ershoff and H. J. Deuel, Jr., *J. Nutrition* **28,** 225 (1944).

75. G. A. Ramsdell and B. H. Webb, *J. Dairy Sci.* **28,** 677 (1945).

75a. See: M. G. Blair and W. Pigman, *Arch. Biochem. and Biophys.* **48,** 17 (1954).

plants. However, since it is a product of the enzymic hydrolysis of starch and since both amylases and starch are found in the same plants, it may be a secondary product formed during the extraction process.

Preparation (*76*). Soluble starch, made from commercial starch by a mild treatment with acid, is hydrolyzed by the enzymes of barley flour to a mixture of maltose and dextrins (see under Maltotriose). These are separated by fractional precipitation with alcohol, and the crude maltose is recrystallized from aqueous alcohol. Commercial maltose contains considerable quantities of dextrins which are removed by fractional precipitation of an aqueous solution with alcohol.

Structure. The methylation of maltose leads to a methyl hepta-*O*-methylmaltoside which by acid hydrolysis is converted to 2,3,4,6-tetra-*O*-methyl-D-glucose and a tri-*O*-methyl-D-glucose (*77*). The tri-*O*-methyl-D-glucose does not form an osazone (methoxyl at carbon 2), and on methylation gives the well-known methyl 2,3,4,6-tetra-*O*-methyl-D-glucopyranoside. Of the many possible tri-*O*-methyl-D-glucoses, only three conform to these specifications. These are the 2,3,4-, the 2,3,6-, and the 2,4,6-tri-*O*-methyl-D-glucoses. The synthetic 2,3,4-tri-*O*-methyl-D-glucose differs from the product of the hydrolysis of the methylated maltose; its structure is determined through its synthesis by the methylation of 6-*O*-trityl-D-glucose and by its oxidation to tri-*O*-methylxylaric acid. Since the tri-*O*-methyl-D-glucose from the methylated maltose is oxidized by nitric acid to di-*O*-methyl-L-threaric acid, it must be the 2,3,6-tri-*O*-methyl-D-glucose. In agreement with this conclusion, the third possible isomer, 2,4,6-tri-*O*-methyl-D-glucose, which has been synthesized, gives neither of these dibasic acids when oxidized.

The identification of the tri-*O*-methyl-D-glucose from maltose as the 2,3,6-tri-*O*-methyl-D-glucose still leaves two possibilities for the structure of maltose, since the disaccharide bridge may be connected to carbon 4 or carbon 5. The position of the linkage is shown by the bromine oxidation of maltose to maltobionic acid which on methylation and hydrolysis yields, in addition to tetra-*O*-methyl-D-glucose, a tetra-*O*-methyl-D-gluconic acid. Inasmuch as this acid forms a lactone identical with methylated D-glucono-1,4-lactone, it must be 2,3,5,6-tetra-*O*-methyl-D-gluconic acid; the unsubstituted hydroxyl at carbon 4 represents the position of the disaccharide linkage (*78*).

The above evidence proves (*79*) that maltose consists of two D-glucose

76. T. S. Harding, *Sugar* **25,** 350 (1923); H. C. Gore, *U. S. Patent,* 1,657,079 (Jan. 24, 1928).

77. W. N. Haworth, J. V. Loach, and C. W. Long, *J. Chem. Soc.* p. 3146 (1927).

78. W. N. Haworth and S. Peat, *J. Chem. Soc.* p. 3094 (1926).

79. W. N. Haworth, C. W. Long, and J. H. G. Plant, *J. Chem. Soc.* p. 2809 (1927).

residues connected between carbons 1 and 4 by an oxygen bridge, but the configuration of the glucosidic linkage remains to be determined. This determination is necessary particularly because another important disaccharide, cellobiose, gives exactly the same final products as outlined above for maltose. The best proof of the configurations of the glucosidic carbon of these two disaccharides is obtained from studies of the enzymic hydrolysis. Maltose is hydrolyzed by the same yeast enzyme (α-D-glucosidase) as that which hydrolyzes methyl α-D-glucoside. The β-D-glucosidase of almond emulsin produces no significant cleavage. Cellobiose, however, is hydrolyzed by the same enzyme (β-D-glucosidase) as that acting on β-D-glucosides. From this evidence, maltose is given the formula of 4-*O*-α-D-glucopyranosyl-D-glucose and cellobiose the formula 4-*O*-β-D-glucopyranosyl-D-glucose. These formulas are confirmed by the high dextrorotation of maltose and the small rotation of cellobiose. As a rule, the α-D-glucosides are strongly dextrorotatory and the β-D-glucosides levorotatory. (Chapter I.)

Melibiose

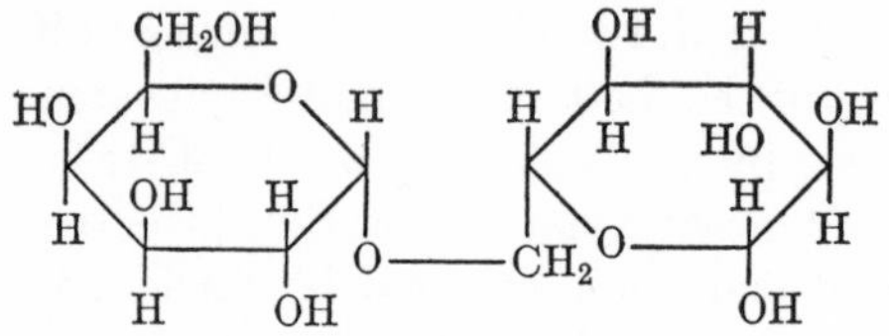
CH₂OH
OH
H
HO
O
H
H
H
OH
H
HO
OH
H
H
O
CH₂
O
H
H
H
OH
OH

Synonyms. 6-*O*-α-D-Galactopyranosyl-D-glucose.

Properties. Crystallizes as the dihydrate of the β-isomer; m.p. 82–85°C.; $[\alpha]_D^{20}$ +111.7° → +129.5° (*c*, 4; water). Fermentable by bottom yeasts but not by most top yeasts. Reducing.

Identification. Phenylhydrazone and osazone; octaacetate. Oxidation of hydrolysis products to give mucic acid.

Occurrence. The sugar occurs mainly as a constituent of the trisaccharide raffinose, although it has been found free in plant exudates from ash and mallow (*Malvus* sp.).

Preparation. Hydrolysis of raffinose by invertase yields melibiose (*80*) and D-fructose. By the use of bakers' yeast (top yeast), hydrolysis and simultaneous removal of the D-fructose by fermentation takes place. The sirup crystallizes directly or after purification through the octaacetate.

Structure. Hydrolysis of methylated melibionic acid gives 2,3,4,5-tetra-*O*-methyl-D-gluconic acid (identified by failure to form a lactone, and by nitric acid oxidation to tetra-*O*-methyl-D-glucaric acid) and 2,3,4,6-tetra-*O*-methyl-D-galactose (identical with the product obtained by hydrolysis of

80. C. S. Hudson and T. S. Harding, *J. Am. Chem. Soc.* **37,** 2734 (1915); H. G. Fletcher, Jr., and H. W. Diehl, *J. Am. Chem. Soc.* **74,** 5774 (1952).

methyl 2,3,4,6-tetra-*O*-methyl-D-galactopyranoside). Thus, the disaccharide linkage must connect carbon 1 of D-galactose and carbon 6 of the D-glucose residue (*81*). The α-configuration of the linkage is indicated by the susceptibility of melibiose to hydrolysis by yeast melibiase, an α-D-galactosidase. The anomeric configuration is confirmed by synthesis, as well as by rotatory changes during hydrolysis.

Synthesis. The condensation of 2,3,4,6-tetra-*O*-acetyl-D-galactopyranosyl bromide with 1,2,3,4-tetra-*O*-acetyl-D-glucopyranose in the presence of silver carbonate gives a disaccharide octaacetate which is different from the melibiose octaacetates (*82*). This compound probably has a β-galactosidic linkage, the customary result of the Koenigs-Knorr reaction as applied here. The use of quinoline as the acid acceptor favors the formation of the α-galactosidic linkage, and, when silver carbonate is replaced by quinoline in this disaccharide synthesis, melibiose octaacetate is formed (*83*). This synthetic melibiose octaacetate probably has the α-configuration since it differs from the product of the Koenigs-Knorr synthesis.

Planteobiose

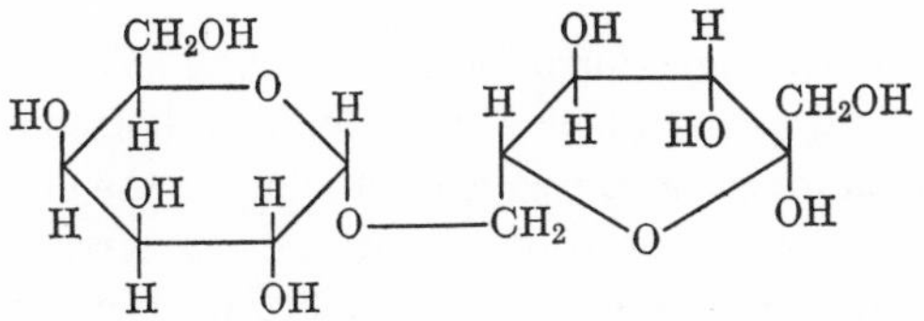
CH2OH
HO
H
O
H
OH
H
H
OH
O
CH2
OH
H
H
H
HO
CH2OH
OH
O

Synonyms. Melibiulose, 6-*O*-α-D-galactopyranosyl-D-fructose.

Properties. Amorphous; $[\alpha]_D + 125°$ (*c*, 1.8; water). Reducing.

Occurrence. The disaccharide is a unit in the structure of planteose, and may be prepared from the latter by partial acid hydrolysis.

Synthesis. Planteobiose is synthesized from melibiose by alkaline isomerization (*84*) and by the action of *Acetobacter suboxydans* on epimelibiitol (*85*).

Structure. Reduction of the ketone group in planteobiose gives a mixture of melibiitol (6-*O*-α-D-galactopyranosyl-D-glucitol) and epimelibiitol (1-*O*-α-D-galactopyranosyl-D-mannitol).

Sucrose

Synonyms. Saccharose, "sugar," cane sugar, beet sugar, α-D-glucopyranosyl β-D-fructofuranoside, β-D-fructofuranosyl α-D-glucopyranoside.

81. W. N. Haworth, J. V. Loach, and C. W. Long, *J. Chem. Soc.* p. 3146 (1927).
82. B. Helferich and H. Rauch, *Ber.* **59,** 2655 (1926).
83. B. Helferich and H. Bredereck, *Ann.* **465,** 166 (1928).
84. R. J. Suhadolnik, M. S. Thesis, Iowa State College, 1953.
85. R. J. Suhadolnik, D. French, and L. A. Underkofler, *Science* **117,** 100 (1953).

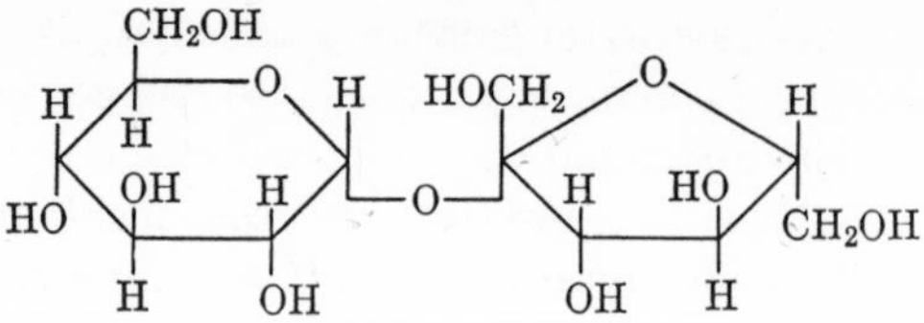

Properties. $[\alpha]_D^{20}$ +66.53 (*c*, 26; water); m.p. 160–186°C., depending on the medium used for purification (*86*). Nonreducing. Fermentable by yeasts.

Identification. Hexaacetate; diazouracil test (positive for sucrose or sucrose-containing oligosaccharides, i.e., raffinose, gentianose, and stachyose) (*87*). A sensitive specific method is based on the serological identification of a dextran produced by a sucrose-specific dextransucrase (*88*).

Occurrence. The sugar occurs almost universally throughout the plant kingdom in the juices, seeds, leaves, fruits, flowers, and roots of plants. Sucrose was reported in all of the 281 species of phanerogams studied by Bourquelot and his associates (*89*). Honey consists principally of sucrose and its hydrolysis products glucose and fructose (invert sugar). The principal sources of commercial interest are sugar cane, sugar beets, and the sap of maple trees. (See also p. 5, 6.)

Manufacture. Cane Sugar. Sugar cane (*Saccarum officinarum* L.) is a species of the family of grasses having a single stalk and often reaching a height of 18 feet. During harvesting, the cane is cut close to the ground and topped. In order to prevent losses due to the hydrolysis (inversion) of the sucrose, the stalks are processed as rapidly as possible. This is accomplished by first passing them through cutting machines and then through roll crushers which force out the juice. The pressed cane fiber (called bagasse) may be extracted with water and passed a second time through the rollers. The bagasse may be used as a fuel or for the preparation of paper products.

Although the juice varies considerably in composition, the following analysis may be taken as being representative:

Water	83.0%
Sucrose	15.0%
Reducing sugars	1.0%
Other organic material	0.5%
Ash	0.5%

The juice, originally acidic, is made slightly alkaline by the addition of lime, which acts to prevent hydrolysis of the acid-sensitive sucrose and

86. See: A. Pictet and H. Vogel, *Helv. Chim. Acta* **11**, 901 (1928).

87. H. W. Raybin, *J. Am. Chem. Soc.* **59**, 1402 (1937); D. French, G. M. Wild, B. Young, and W. J. James, *ibid.* **75**, 709 (1953). See also p. 525 and 526.

88. J. Y. Sugg and E. J. Hehre, *J. Immunol.* **43**, 119 (1942).

89. Quoted by C. Béguin, *Pharm. Acta Helv.* **1**, 90 (1926).

which also removes many impurities. This purification by the use of lime, called defecation, is the principal purification process in the preparation of the raw sugar. When the alkaline juice is heated, a heavy scum or cake which forms on the surface contains many of the impurities while still others settle out on the bottom. After separation of the impurities, clear juice is drawn into evaporating pans.

Subsequent to a preliminary evaporation of the purified juice in vacuum pans to a solution of about 50% solids, the sirup is transferred to vacuum pans in which the rate of evaporation and the temperature may be accurately controlled. The evaporation is continued until crystals appear, and then fresh sirup is added at a rate such that the original crystals grow without the formation of new crystal nuclei (false grain). When the desired growth has been obtained, the mass of crystals and sirup, called the massecuite, is dropped into centrifuges; the mother liquor is separated, and the crystals are washed with clear juice and finally removed. These crystals constitute the "raw sugar" of commerce and are the raw material for the refinery. Successive crops of crystals of decreasing purity are taken from the mother liquors until no more may be economically obtained. The final mother liquor (named "blackstrap") is a dark-colored viscous liquid which is sold as cattle food and which is also extensively employed as the source of carbohydrates in the preparation of industrial alcohol and rum since it still contains much fermentable sugar (*89a*).

The "raw sugar," as shipped to the refineries, is usually a brown, fairly coarse, crystalline product polarizing about 97°*S*. The principal task of the refinery is to remove the color and nonsugar impurities so as to obtain a high-quality white granulated sugar which is nonhygroscopic and is a smooth-pouring product. As a first step, the raw sugar is mixed with affination sirup and washed in centrifugals to remove the major amount of color and other impurities. The washed raw sugar, of about 99.5 purity, is then dissolved, and the resulting liquor clarified to remove the insoluble impurities. This may be accomplished by mechanical filtration, using diatomaceous earth as a filter medium, or by means of frothing-type clarifiers. In the latter case, a small amount of lime and phosphoric acid is added to precipitate and flocculate the impurities, which are then skimmed off the top of the solution. Following clarification, the washed raw sugar liquor is purified and decolorized by passage through columns of animal bone charcoal (bone black). This removes the soluble impurities, i.e., most of the organic coloring matter, and a portion of the inorganic mineral ash and organic nonsugar impurities. In some cases, decolorizing carbons may be used to remove color and ion-exchangers to remove mineral matter. The clarified, decolorized sugar liquor is crystallized in vacuum pans as described for raw sugar. The resulting

89a. See M. G. Blair ana . Pigman, *Arch. Biochem. and Biophys.* **42**, 278 (1953).

mixture of crystals and mother liquor is directed from the vacuum pans to centrifugals for separation of the sirup and final washing of the crystals. The wet white sugar is then dried and screened to predetermined particle sizes for various uses. Several crops of white crystals may be obtained from the original granulated liquors and sirups. Crystallization of highly refined lower-purity products results in the soft brown sugars of commerce. Other products are manufactured, such as powdered sugar, pressed and loaf sugars, liquid sugars, invert sirups, and various specialty products (*90*).

Beet Sugar. In other than tropical and subtropical countries, the sugar beet (*Beta vulgaris*) is the principal source of sucrose. After harvesting, the beets are taken to the mill, washed, and cut into slices called "cosettes." The cosettes are delivered from a central spout into a series of diffusion vessels. Here they are extracted with hot water utilizing the countercurrent principle. Fresh water passes first into the diffuser having the most exhausted charge; the solution then goes through the diffusion vessels in order of increasing sugar content and finally passes through the fresh charge of cosettes. The dark diffusion juice containing about 12% of sucrose is agitated with lime for several hours. Carbon dioxide is passed into the solution, and the precipitate, which contains most of the impurities, is separated by filtration. The light-yellow filtrate is decolorized by a treatment with sulfur dioxide, and after a final filtration is concentrated in multiple-effect vacuum pans. The crystals are developed during the evaporation in the same manner as for the cane sugar and are then separated from the mother liquors by centrifugation and finally dried. The evaporation and crystallization are carried out repeatedly with the mother liquors as long as enough sugar is obtained to make the process economical.

Additional quantities of sucrose may be obtained from the molasses by diluting it to a concentration of about 7% sugar, cooling to 12°, and adding lime (Steffen process). A difficultly soluble compound of sucrose with three moles of lime, tricalcium saccharate, crystallizes. The tricalcium saccharate, after separation from the final molasses, serves in the place of lime for the purification of the warm diffusion juice. Some beet sugar factories recover additional sugar from the molasses by a treatment with barium hydroxide, which forms the difficultly soluble barium saccharate. This saccharate is decomposed with carbon dioxide, and the insoluble barium carbonate is separated from the sucrose. The barium carbonate is reclaimed and reconverted to barium hydroxide. The final molasses is usually sold for cattle food or for industrial fermentations particularly when mixed with "blackstrap" molasses.

The sugar may be purified by recrystallization from aqueous or aqueous alcohol solutions (*91*).

90. Information supplied by T. R. Gillett.

91. F. J. Bates and Associates, *Natl. Bur. Standards Circ.* **C440** (1942).

Structure (*91a*). The sugar is hydrolyzed by acids and by enzymes to a mixture of equal amounts of D-fructose and D-glucose. The process is called inversion since the optical rotation changes from dextro to levo because of the high levorotation of the D-fructose. The mixture formed is called invert sugar. Octa-*O*-methylsucrose, obtained by the methylation of sucrose, does not undergo inversion of rotation on hydrolysis, and two dextrorotatory tetra-*O*-methylhexoses are obtained. The tetra-*O*-methyl-D-glucose is the well-known 2,3,4,6-tetra-*O*-methyl-D-glucose. The structure of the D-fructose derivative is shown by the following evidence. (For the structure of tetra-*O*-methyl-D-fructopyranose, see p. 214.) Oxidation with nitric acid gives a liquid tri-*O*-methyl-2-keto-D-gluconic acid, which in turn is oxidized by acid permanganate to a crystalline tri-*O*-methyl-D-arabono-1,4-lactone. This lactone is identical, except for the sign of the rotation, with the product obtained by the oxidation of tri-*O*-methyl-L-arabinose. Inasmuch as the tri-*O*-methyl-D-arabonic lactone from sucrose yields di-*O*-methyl-D-threaric acid (I) on further treatment with nitric acid, it must have the methyl

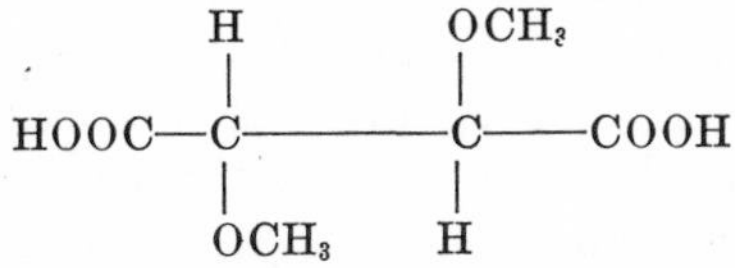
H
OCH3
HOOC—C
C—COOH
OCH3
H
(I)

groups at positions 2, 3, and 5; hence, the original methylated D-fructose from sucrose is the 1,3,4,6-tetra-*O*-methyl-D-fructofuranose. If the probable assumption is made that the sucrose has ring structures for the component sugars, then the connection between the hexose units must be between the anomeric carbons, and sucrose has the formula given above (*92*).

The above structure is confirmed by the results obtained by periodic acid oxidation (*93*). Sucrose consumes three moles of periodic acid, and one mole of formic acid is formed. (See earlier discussion in this chapter.) After bromine oxidation of the tetraaldehyde and subsequent hydrolysis, hydroxypyruvic, D-glyceric, and glyoxylic acids are obtained. (For a discussion of this method see p. 215.)

The configuration of the glycosidic linkages of sucrose is α- for the D-glucose component and β- for the D-fructose component. The hydrolysis of sucrose by yeast α-D-glucosidase and not by the β-D-glucosidase of almond emulsin supports the α-D-glucoside configuration. Similarly, the hydrolysis of the sugar by yeast invertase, an enzyme which hydrolyzes β- but not

91a. I. Levi and C. B. Purves, *Advances in Carbohydrate Chem.* **4,** 1 (1949).

92. J. Avery, W. N. Haworth, and E. L. Hirst, *J. Chem. Soc.* p. 2308 (1927); W. N. Haworth, E. L. Hirst, and A. Learner, *ibid.* p. 2432 (1927).

93. P. Fleury and J. Courtois, *Bull. soc. chim. France* [5] **10,** 245 (1943); *Compt. rend.* **216,** 65 (1943).

α-D-fructofuranosides, supplies evidence (*94*) for the β-D-fructofuranoside configuration. Comparisons made by use of the isorotation rules agree with the above evidence because only the α,β-configuration gives agreement between the calculated and observed rotations for sucrose and sucrose octaacetate (*95*).

Synthesis. In 1928, Pictet and Vogel (*96*) claimed to have accomplished the synthesis of sucrose by coupling tetra-*O*-acetyl-D-fructofuranose with tetra-*O*-acetyl-D-glucopyranose in the presence of a dehydrating agent. However, Zemplén and Gerecs (*97*) were not successful in achieving this synthesis by Pictet and Vogel's method. In attempting to condense the two acetylated monosaccharides, Irvine and co-workers (*95*, *98*) were unable to obtain sucrose octaacetate but did produce a disaccharide derivative with a different glycosidic linkage, the so-called isosucrose octaacetate. The acetylated derivative had a different melting point and specific rotation from those of sucrose octaacetate.

It was not until a quarter of a century later that an authentic chemical synthesis was accomplished by Lemieux and Huber (*23*). They synthesized sucrose by reacting 3,4,6-tri-*O*-acetyl-1,2-anhydro-α-D-glucopyranose with 1,3,4,6-tetra-*O*-acetyl-D-fructofuranose in a sealed tube at 100° for 104 hours. Chromatographic separation of the products of the synthesis gave a 5.5% yield of sucrose octaacetate. Lemieux also synthesized octaacetyl-β-D-maltose (*99*) by treatment of the same anhydride with 1,2,3,6-tetra-*O*-acetyl-β-D-glucose at 120° for 13 hours.

The *in vitro* enzymatic synthesis of sucrose was accomplished by Hassid, Doudoroff, and Barker (*100*). They found that a bacterial preparation from *Pseudomonas saccharophila* contains a phosphorylase capable of catalyzing the reversible reaction:

$$\text{Sucrose} + \text{inorganic phosphate} \rightleftharpoons \alpha\text{-D-glucose 1-phosphate} + \text{D-fructose}$$

Using α-D-glucose 1-phosphate and D-fructose, they prepared sucrose, which was isolated in crystalline form. (See Enzymic synthesis of oligosaccharides, p. 520).

Synonyms. α-D-Glucopyranosyl α-D-glucopyranose, "mycoside," mushroom sugar.

94. H. H. Schlubach and G. Rauchalles, *Ber.* **58,** 1842 (1925); C. B. Purves and C. S. Hudson, *ibid.* **59,** 49 (1937).

95. F. Klages and R. Niemann, *Ann.* **529**, 185 (1937); M. L. Wolfrom and F. Shafizadeh, *J. Org. Chem.* **21,** 88 (1956).

96. A. Pictet and H. Vogel, *Helv. Chim. Acta* **11,** 436 (1928); Ber. **62,** 1418 (1929).

97. G. Zemplén and A. Gerecs, *Ber.* **62,** 984 (1929).

98. J. C. Irvine, J. W. H. Oldham, and A. F. Skinner, *J. Am. Chem. Soc.* **51,** 1279 (1929); J. C. Irvine and J. W. H. Oldham, *ibid.* **51,** 3609 (1929).

99. R. U. Lemieux, *Can. J. Chem.* **31,** 949 (1953).

100. W. Z. Hassid, M. Doudoroff, and H. A. Barker, *J. Am. Chem. Soc.* **66,** 1416 (1944).

α,α-Trehalose

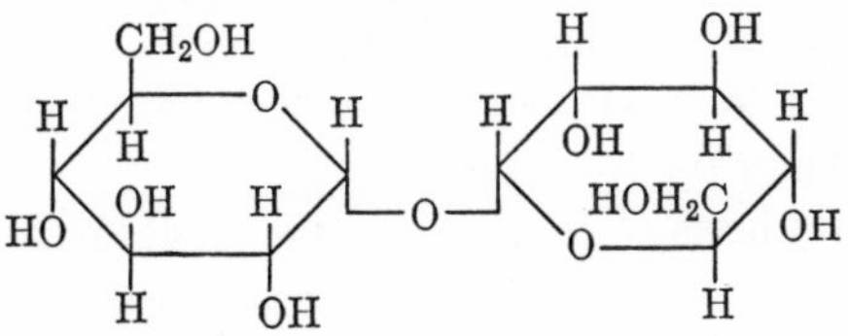

Properties of Dihydrate. Nonreducing; m.p. 97°C.; $[\alpha]_D^{20}$ +178.3° (*c*, 7; water). Fermentable by most yeasts.

Identification. Hexaacetate.

Occurrence (*101*). The sugar was originally separated from rye ergot and is a common constituent of fungi. It is found in young mushrooms, but as the plants develop the trehalose content is replaced by mannitol, and in aged or dried mushrooms the sugar is completely replaced by mannitol (*102*). Trehala manna, a source of trehalose, is not a true manna (plant secretion) but consists of an oval shell about the size of an olive formed by certain insects found in Syria. Probably the best source of the sugar is the "resurrection plant," *Selaginella lepidophylla*, a common plant of the southwestern United States, which contains free trehalose. As some workers have not been able to obtain the sugar from this source, it is probable that the harvesting time must be carefully controlled. Seaweeds are also reported to contain considerable quantities of the disaccharide.

Preparation (*103*). The sugar is extracted from trehala manna by the action of boiling 75% alcohol. After concentration, the extracts are purified by treatment with basic lead acetate and the excess lead removed with hydrogen sulfide. The filtered solution, after concentration, deposits crystals of trehalose. Essentially the same process is employed in obtaining the sugar from coarsely ground *Selaginella*, but the extraction may be carried out with water rather than alcohol. Yeast may be a better source (*103a*).

Hungarian ergot may be used as a source (*104*). The benzene-extracted ergot is treated with alcohol. The extracts are purified with activated carbon and evaporated; crystalline material is obtained by diluting the residue with aqueous alcohol and allowing the solution to crystallize.

Structure. Methylation and hydrolysis of trehalose produce two moles of 2,3,4,6-tetra-*O*-methyl-D-glucopyranose (*105*). The sugar consumes

101. H. A. L. Wiggers, *Ann.* **1,** 174 (1832).

102. E. Bourquelot, *Compt. rend.* **111,** 578 (1890).

103. T. S. Harding, *Sugar* **25,** 476 (1923).

103a. L. C. Stewart, N. K. Richtmyer, and C. S. Hudson, *J. Am. Chem. Soc.* **72,** 2059 (1950).

104. G. Zemplén, *Chem. Abstr.* **31,** 6204 (1937).

105. H. Schlubach and K. Maurer, *Ber.* **58,** 1179 (1925); (the 2,3,5,6-tetramethyl-

four moles of periodic acid, and two moles of formic acid are formed. Hence, the disaccharide must have a pyranose structure for each glucose component and have a glycosidic linkage connecting the two anomeric carbons. Consideration of the optical rotatory relationships indicates that both anomeric carbons have the α-configuration.

Synthesis. The synthesis of trehalose has been accomplished by heating a mixture of the anomers of 2,3,4,6-tetra-*O*-acetyl-D-glucose and 3,4,6-tri-*O*-acetyl-1,2-anhydro-D-glucose at 100°. Chromatographic separation of the deacetylated products gives α,α-trehalose, as well as α,β-trehalose (*106*). Earlier attempts at the synthesis had given both the α,β-isomer and the β,β-isomer (*107*).

Turanose (*108*)

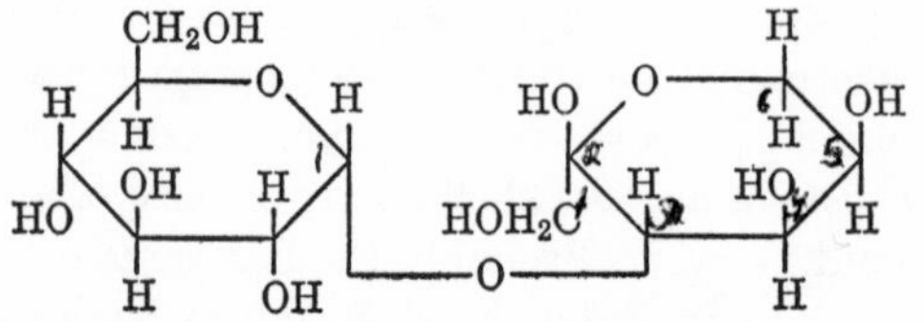
CH₂OH
H
O
H
H
OH
H
HO
H
OH
HO
O
H
OH
H
H
HO
HOH₂C
O
H
H

Synonyms. 3-*O*-α-D-Glucopyranosyl-D-fructose.

Properties. M.p. 157°C.;$[\alpha]_D^{20}$ +27.3° → +75.8° (*c*, 4; water). Not fermented by yeasts. Reducing.

Identification. Phenylosazone.

Occurrence. The trisaccharide melezitose yields on partial hydrolysis turanose and D-glucose.

Preparation (*109*). Melezitose is partially hydrolyzed by dilute sulfuric acid with the liberation of D-glucose and turanose. The D-glucose is removed by fermentation and the turanose crystallized directly.

Structure. As shown by G. Tanret, the sugar is hydrolyzed to D-fructose and D-glucose by yeast α-D-glucosidase and, hence, must be an α-D-glucoside. This conclusion receives confirmation from the lack of hydrolysis of the disaccharide by almond emulsin (*110*). The above evidence and the resistance of the sugar to oxidation by alkaline hypoiodite solutions, coupled with its reduction of alkaline copper salt solutions, show that the unsubstituted hemiacetal group belongs to the fructose component. The mutarotation of turanose resembles that of fructose and probably is caused

D-glucose of S. and M. is the compound now known as 2,3,4,6-tetra-*O*-methyl-D-glucose).

106. R. U. Lemieux and H. F. Bauer, *Can. J. Chem.* **32,** 340 (1954).

107. W. N. Haworth and W. J. Hickinbottom, *J. Chem. Soc.* p. 2847 (1931).

108. C. S. Hudson, *Advances in Carbohydrate Chem.* **2,** 1 (1946).

109. C. S. Hudson and E. Pacsu, *J. Am. Chem. Soc.* **52,** 2522 (1930).

110. M. Bridel and T. Aagaard, *Compt. rend.* **184,** 1667 (1927); T. Aagaard, *Chem. Abstr.* **24,** 1089 (1930).

by an interconversion between pyranose and furanose isomers rather than between α,β-isomers (*111*). Hence, the hydroxyls of carbons 5 and 6 of the fructose component must be unsubstituted. The formation of an osazone proves that free hydroxyls are present at both carbons 1 and 2 of the D-fructose moiety (*111*, *112*). This evidence eliminates all positions except carbons 3 and 4 for the disaccharide linkage. If the linkage involved carbon 4 of the D-fructose residue, the turanose would yield the same osazone as maltose, but actually the two osazones are quite different (*111*). Hence, the two monosaccharides must be connected by an oxygen bridge between carbon 3 of the D-fructose and carbon 1 of the D-glucose component. It is, then, 3-*O*-α-D-glucopyranosyl-D-fructose. This structure is confirmed by the ease of hydrolysis of the sugar by alkalies (*113*) and by the formation of tri-*O*-tritylturanose (*114*).

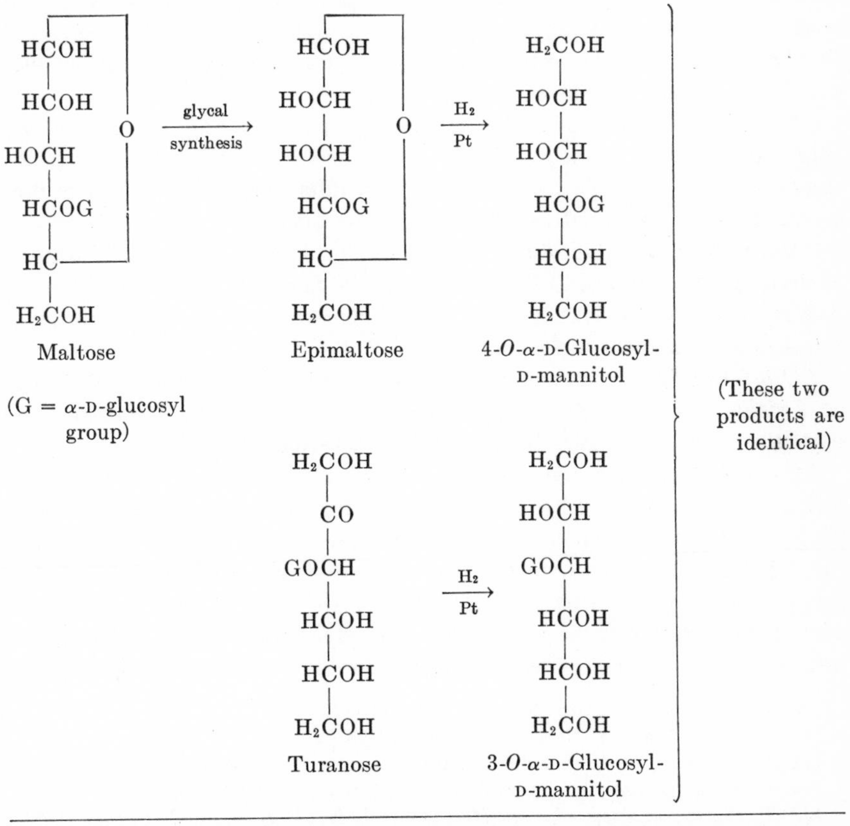
glycal
synthesis
H_2
Pt
Maltose
(G = α-D-glucosyl group)
Epimaltose
4-O-α-D-Glucosyl-D-mannitol
(These two products are identical)
Turanose
3-O-α-D-Glucosyl-D-mannitol

111. H.S. Isbell and W. W. Pigman, *J. Research Natl. Bur. Standards* **20,** 773 (1938).
112. E. Pacsu, E. J. Wilson, Jr., and L. Graf, *J. Am. Chem. Soc.* **61,** 2675 (1939).
113. H. S. Isbell, *J. Research Natl. Bur. Standards* **26,** 35 (1941).
114. E. Pacsu, *J. Am. Chem. Soc.* **53,** 3099 (1931).

By an ingenious application of stereochemical principles, the structure of turanose has been related to that of maltose, and a direct proof of its structure has been obtained (*115*). The proof involves the conversion of maltose to epimaltose by means of the glycal synthesis (see p.127), and the reduction of the epimaltose to the same product (3- or 4-*O*-α-D-glucosyl-D-mannitol) as that obtained by the reduction of turanose. The symmetry of mannitol is such that substitutions at the 3- and 4-positions of mannitol are equivalent substitutions. An outline of the important steps in the synthesis are given in the formulas on the previous page.

B. Miscellaneous Disaccharides

3-O-β-L-Arabopyranosyl-L-arabinose. $[\alpha]_D$ +220° (water); reducing; phenylosazone, m.p. 235°C.; obtained by graded hydrolysis of larch ε-galactan (*116*) and peach gum. The high positive rotation indicates that both L-arabinose units probably exist in the pyranose form. Hydrolysis of the hexa-*O*-methyl derivative gives 2,3,4-tri-*O*-methyl-L-arabinose and 2,4-di-*O*-methyl-L-arabinose (*117*).

6-O-α-L-Arabinosyl-D-glucose (*vicianose*). M.p. 210°C.; $[\alpha]_D$ +40° (water); obtained from a glycoside isolated from the seeds of *Vicia angustifolia* (*118*). Hepta-*O*-acetylvicianose is obtained by condensing 2,3,4-tri-*O*-acetyl-β-L-arabinosyl bromide with 1,2,3,4-tetra-*O*-acetyl-D-glucose.

3-O-α-D-Galactopyranosyl-L-arabinose. Amorphous, $[\alpha]_D$ +152° (water); phenylosazone, m.p. 240°C.; obtained by partial hydrolysis of *Acacia cyanophylla* gum (*119*). Hydrolysis of the methylated disaccharide gives 2,3,4,6-tetra-*O*-methyl-D-galactose and 2,4-di-*O*-methyl-L-arabinose.

3-O-β-D-Galactopyranosyl-D-galactose. From the partial hydrolyzate (*120*) of *Acacia pycuantha* gum. M.p. 159–160°C.; $[\alpha]_D$ + 62° (water). The structure was established by lead tetra-acetate oxidation.

4-O-α-D-Galactopyranosyl-D-galactose. M.p. 210–211°C.; $[\alpha]_D$ +177° (water), reducing; obtained by partial acid hydrolysis of okra mucilage. The methylated disaccharide yields, on hydrolysis, 2,3,4,6-tetra-*O*-methyl-D-galactose and 2,3,6-tri-*O*-methyl-D-galactose. Periodate oxidation of the disaccharide yields formaldehyde, showing that the carbon 5 of the reducing moiety cannot be involved in the glycosidic linkage. The optical rotation suggests an α-D-galactosidic linkage in the disaccharide (*121*).

115. C. S. Hudson, *J. Org. Chem.* **9**, 117, 470 (1944).
116. J. K. N. Jones, *J. Chem. Soc.* p. 1672 (1953).
117. P. Andrews, D. H. Ball, and J. K. N. Jones, *J. Chem. Soc.* p. 4090 (1953).
118. G. Bertrand and G. Weismeiller, *Compt. rend.* **150,** 180 (1910).
119. F. Smith, *J. Chem. Soc.* p. 744 (1939); J. K. N. Jones, *ibid.* p. 1672 (1953); A. J. Charlson, J. R. Nunn, and A. M. Stephen, *ibid.* p. 269 (1955).
120. E. L. Hirst and A. S. Perlin, *J. Chem. Soc.* p. 2622 (1954). A. S. Perlin, *Anal. Chem.* **27,** 396 (1955).
121. R. L. Whistler and H. E. Conrad, *J. Am. Chem. Soc.* **76,** 1673 (1954).

Two isomeric D-galactosyl-D-galactoses were obtained from the same source but have not been characterized.

4-O-β-D-Galactopyranosyl-3,6-anhydro-L-galactose (agarobiose). $[\alpha]_D -5.8°$ (water); reducing; obtained as a product of partial hydrolysis of the agar-agar like substance from *Gelidium amansii.* The structure is indicated by the fact that hexa-*O*-methylagarobiose yields methyl 2,3,4,6-tetra-*O*-methyl-D-galactopyranoside and 2,5-di-*O*-methyl-3,6-anhydro-L-galactose dimethyl acetal on methanolysis (*122*).

6-O-D-Galactopyranosyl-D-galactose. Octa-*O*-methyl ether, m.p. 101°C., $[\alpha]_D +42.9°$ (methanol); obtained by partial methanolysis of methylated larch (*Larix occidentalis*) gum. Hydrolysis yields 2,3,4,6-tetra-*O*-methyl-D-galactose and 2,3,4-tri-*O*-methyl-D-galactose (*123*).

2-O-β-D-Glucopyranosyl-D-glucose (sophorose). M.p. 180°C.; $[\alpha]_D +34.5° \rightarrow +19.9°$ (water); obtained by hydrolysis of a glycoside isolated from *Sophora japonica* (*124*). The sugar is identical with the synthetic disaccharide prepared by earlier workers (*125*).

3-O-β-D-Glucopyranosyl-D-glucose (laminaribiose). M.p. 204–206°C.; $[\alpha]_D^{16} +24.9° \rightarrow +18.6°$ (water); obtained by partial hydrolysis of the polysaccharide laminarin from seaweeds (*126*). The disaccharide has been synthesized by condensing 1,2:5,6-di-*O*-isopropylidene-D-glucose with 2,3,4,6-tetra-*O*-acetyl-D-glucosyl bromide (*127*).

4-O-D-Glucopyranosyl-L-rhamnose (scillabiose). Phenylosazone, m.p. 165° C.; obtained from a glycoside isolated from *Scilla maritima* L. Complete hydrolysis gives D-glucose and L-rhamnose (*128*).

4-O-β-D-Mannopyranosyl-D-mannose. M.p. 193.5–194°C.; $[\alpha]_D^{25} -7.7° \rightarrow +2.2°$ (water); reducing; from a partial enzymatic or acidic hydrolyzate of guaran. Hydrolysis of the methylated disaccharide gives 2,3,4,6-tetra-*O*-methyl-D-mannose and 2,3,6-tri-*O*-methyl-D-mannose. Hydrolysis of the mannobionic acid gives the same tetra-*O*-methyl-D-mannose and 2,3,5,6-tetra-*O*-methyl-D-mannolactone. As the disaccharide is not hydrolyzed by α-D-mannosidase, it must have the β-D-mannosidic linkage (*129*).

L-Rhamnosyl-D-galactose (robinobiose). Acid hydrolysis of the glycoside robinin yields a rhamnoside of kaempferol and robinobiose, an L-rhamnosyl-

122. C. Araki, *J. Chem. Soc. Japan* **65,** 533 (1944); **65,** 627 (1944). *Chem. Abstr.* **42,** 1210 (1948); **45,** 6162 (1951).

123. E. V. White, *J. Am. Chem. Soc.* **64,** 302 (1942).

124. J. Rabaté, *Bull. soc. chim. France* [5] **7,** 565 (1940); *Naturwissenschaften* **34,** 344 (1947).

125. K. Freudenberg *et al., Ber.* **69,** 1245 (1936); *Chem. Ber.* **84,** 144 (1951).

126. V. C. Barry, *Sci. Proc. Roy. Dublin Soc.* **22,** 423 (1941).

127. P. Bachli and E. G. V. Percival, *J. Chem. Soc.* p. 1243 (1952).

128. G. Zemplén, *Chem. Abstr.* **33,** 4202 (1939).

129. R. L. Whistler and J. Z. Stein, *J. Am. Chem. Soc.* **73,** 4187 (1951).

D-galactose. Enzymic hydrolysis of robinin yields a trisaccharide that must be L-rhamnosyl-D-galactosyl-L-rhamnose (*130*).

6-O-β-L-Rhamnosyl-D-glucose (*rutinose*). Obtained by enzymic hydrolysis of rutin. The structure was established by synthesis from 2,3,4-tri-*O*-acetyl-L-rhamnosyl bromide and 2,3,4-tri-*O*-acetyl-D-glucosyl chloride (*131*).

5(or 4)-O-β-D-Xylopyranosyl-L-arabinose. $[\alpha]_D$ −34° (water); reducing; phenylosazone, m.p. 216°C.; obtained by partial hydrolysis of peach gum and cholla gum (*116*). Hydrolysis of the methylated disaccharide yields 2,3,4-tri-*O*-methyl-D-xylose and 2,3-di-*O*-methyl-L-arabinose.

6-O-β-D-Xylosyl-D-glucose (*primeverose*). M.p. 209°C.; $[\alpha]_D$ +23° → −3.4° (water); obtained by partial hydrolysis of a glycoside from *Primula officinalis* (*132*) from madder root (*133*). (See Ruberythric acid.) The synthesis has been accomplished by coupling 2,3,4-tri-*O*-acetyl-α-D-xylosyl bromide with 1,2,3,4-tetra-*O*-acetyl-β-D-glucose (*134*).

4-O-β-D-Xylopyranosyl-D-xylose(*xylobiose*). M.p. 185–186°C.; $[\alpha]_D^{25}$ −32°→ +25.5° (water); obtained by partial hydrolysis of corn-cob xylan. Methylation of the xylobionic acid, followed by hydrolysis, gives 2,3,4-tri-*O*-methyl-D-xylose and 2,3,5-tri-*O*-methyl-D-xylono-1,4-lactone. These data, coupled with the rotatory properties, indicate the assigned structure (*135*).

In addition to the disaccharide, a series of crystalline oligosaccharides through xyloheptaose were obtained from the same source (*136*):

	M.p. (°C.)	$[\alpha]_D^{25}$ (water)
Xylotriose	205–6	−39° → −47°
Xylotetraose	219–20	−49° → −60°
Xylopentaose·½H_2O	231–2	−66°
Xylohexaose·2H_2O	236–7	−73°
Xyloheptaose·2H_2O	240–42	−74°

The structure of each oligosaccharide is established in the following manner. The degree of polymerization is indicated by reducing group determination. Slow hydrolysis of each homolog leads only to the lower members including xylobiose, whose structure is known, and eventually to D-xylose. Results of periodate oxidation are consistent with 1→4 links

130. G. Zemplén and A. Gerecs, *Ber.* **68**, 2054 (1935).
131. G. Zemplén and A. Gerecs, *Ber.* **68**, 1318 (1935); *ibid.* **67**, 2049 (1934).
132. A. Goris, M. Mascré, and C. Vischinniac, *Bull. sci. pharmacol.* **19**, 577, 648 (1912).
133. D. Richter, *J. Chem. Soc.* p. 1701 (1936).
134. C. M. McCloskey and G. H. Coleman, *J. Am. Chem. Soc.* **65**, 1778 (1943).
135. R. L. Whistler, J. Bachrach, and C. C. Tu, *J. Am. Chem. Soc.* **74**, 3059 (1952); R. L. Whistler and C. C. Tu, *ibid.* **74**, 3609 (1952).
136. R. L. Whistler and C. C. Tu, *J. Am. Chem. Soc.* **75**, 645 (1953).

between the pentose units. Since the xylan from which the oligosaccharides are formed is known to have the pyranose ring form, it is reasonable that the products of hydrolysis would have a similar structure.

C. Tri-, Tetra-, and Pentasaccharides

Gentianose

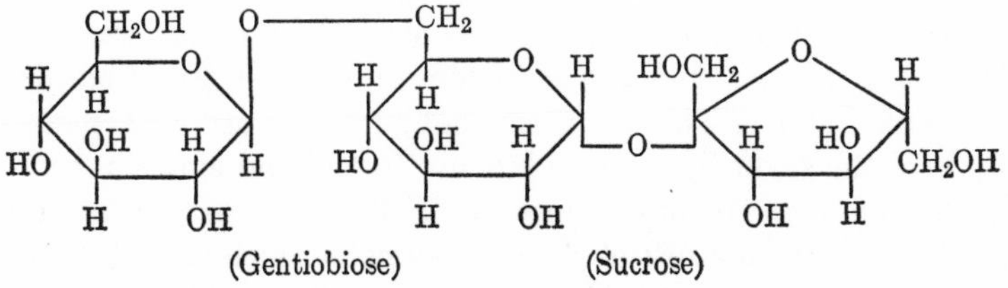
CH_2OH
O
CH_2
H
H
OH
H
HO
H
H
OH
H
H
OH
H
HO
H
OH
$HOCH_2$
O
H
H
HO
CH_2OH
OH
H
O
(Gentiobiose)
(Sucrose)

Synonyms. *O*-β-D-Glucopyranosyl-(1→6)-*O*-α-D-glucopyranosyl-(1→2)-β-D-fructofuranoside.

Properties. M.p. 209–211°C.; $[\alpha]_D^{20}$ +31.5 (water). Nonreducing.

Occurrence. The sugar is found in the rhizomes of many species of *Gentian*.

Preparation (*137*). Powdered gentian root is extracted with 90% alcohol and the sugar isolated from the extracts.

Structure. Gentianose yields two moles of D-glucose and one of D-fructose when completely hydrolyzed by acids. Partial acid hydrolysis or the action of invertase produces fructose and gentiobiose (*138*). The enzymes of almond emulsin cleave the disaccharide into D-glucose and sucrose. This evidence suffices to fix the structure of the trisaccharide. The two D-glucose units must be connected by a β-(1→6)-D-glucosidic linkage. The D-fructose unit must form one end of the molecule, be connected to the reducing carbon of the gentiobiose component through a sucrose linkage, and have a furanose structure.

Maltotriose

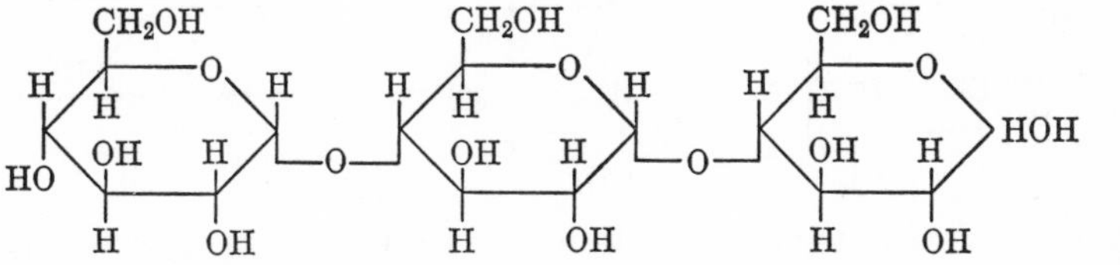

Synonyms. *O*-α-D-Glucopyranosyl-(1→4)-*O*-α-D-glucopyranosyl-(1→4)-D-glucose.

Properties. Amorphous; $[\alpha]_D^{23}$ +160° (water). Not fermented by a commercial bakers' yeast that ferments maltose. Reducing.

137. M. Bridel and M. Desmarest, *J. pharm. chim.* **9,** 465 (1929).
138. E. Bourquelot and H. Hérissey, *Compt. rend.* **135,** 399 (1902).

Identification. Hendecaacetate.

Occurrence. The trisaccharide is present as a unit in starch, and is prepared by chromatographic resolution of an enzymic hydrolyzate of the polysaccharide (*139*).

Structure. Hydrolysis of the methylated trisaccharide gives two moles of 2,3,6-tri-*O*-methyl-D-glucose and one mole of 2,3,4,6-tetra-*O*-methyl-D-glucose (*140*). Thus, there are two (1→4)-D-glucosidic linkages per molecule. Hydrolysis of maltotriitol leads to D-glucose, D-glucitol, maltose, and maltitol. (*141*). These results are consistent only with a trisaccharide of the structure given above. The anomeric configurations are confirmed by the hydrolysis of the sugar by maltase but not by almond emulsin.

Polymer Homologs. As for cellulose (see Cellobiose), partial hydrolysis of amylose leads to a mixture of linear polymers which may be separated chromatographically into fractions with degrees of polymerization from 1 to 7 (*142*).

Compound	$[\alpha]_D$ (water)
Maltotetraose	+ 177°
Maltopentaose	+ 180°
Maltohexaose	+ 184.7°
Maltoheptaose	+ 186.4°

The structures of these substances have not been assigned by any rigorous method. However, assuming no rearrangement during the hydrolysis, it is likely that they are linear polymers of α-(1→4)-linked D-glucose. Results of studies with salivary α-amylase are consistent with this structure (*143*).

Maltotetraose has been isolated as an amorphous solid, $[\alpha]_D$ +165.5° (water), from corn sirup concentrate by a combination of charcoal-column elution and cellulose-column chromatography. The structure was determined by periodate oxidation and by hydrolysis with β-amylase (*144*).

Manninotriose

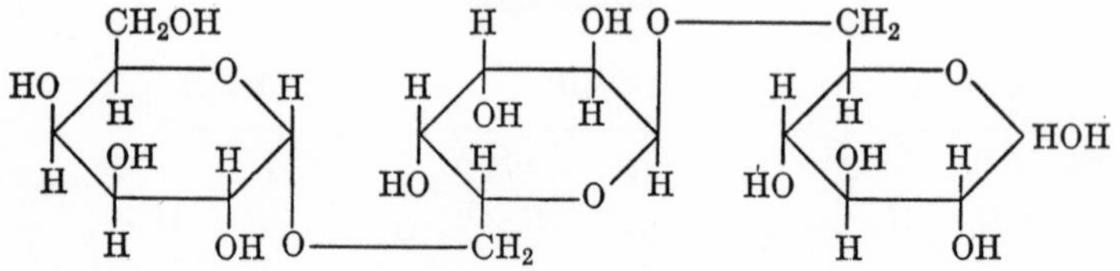

Synonyms. *O*-α-D-Galactopyranosyl-(1→6)-*O*-α-D-galactopyranosyl-(1→6)-D-glucose.

139. M. L. Wolfrom, L. W. Georges, A. Thompson, and I. L. Miller, *J. Am. Chem. Soc.* **71,** 2873 (1949); L. W. Georges, I. L. Miller, and M. L. Wolfrom, *ibid.* **69,** 473 (1947).

140. J. M. Sugihara and M. L. Wolfrom, *J. Am. Chem. Soc.* **71,** 3357 (1949).

141. A. Thompson and M. L. Wolfrom, *J. Am. Chem. Soc.* **74,** 3612 (1952).

142. W. J. Whelan, J. M. Bailey, and P. J. P. Roberts, *J. Chem. Soc.* p. 1293 (1953).

Properties. Amorphous; $[\alpha]_D$ +167° (*c*, 1.2; water). Reducing.

Identification. Phenylosazone, 1-phenylflavazole.

Occurrence. Besides being a component of stachyose, this trisaccharide has been found to occur free in the ash manna from *Fraxinus ornus* and *F. rotundifolia.*

Preparation. Manninotriose is most readily obtained by partial hydrolysis of stachyose, either by acid or invertase (*145*).

Structure. The monosaccharide units that make up this trisaccharide and their sequence was determined by Tanret (*145*), who showed that hydrolysis of the bromine oxidation product of manninotriose gave D-galactose and D-gluconic acid. On the basis of methylation studies Onuki proposed the structure D-Galp-(1→6)-D-Galp-(1→4)-D-G. This structure has been corrected in recent years. The significant evidence may be summarized as follows. Brewers' yeast α-D-galactosidase catalyzes the complete hydrolysis of manninotriose; this indicates that the two galactosidic linkages have the α-D-configuration (*146*). Periodate oxidation of the trisaccharide (*147*, *148*) and of manninotriitol (*148*) indicate a 1,6-linkage between the D-galactose and D-glucose residues. Partial acid hydrolysis of manninotriitol yields melibiitol and confirms the 1,6-linkage (*148*). Finally, Laidlaw and Wylam (*149*) have repeated Onuki's (*150*) methylation experiments and found 2,3,4-tri-*O*-methyl-D-glucose as one of the products of hydrolyzed permethylated stachyose, a result requiring that the D-glucose be unsubstituted at the 2-, 3-, and 4-positions.

Melezitose (*108*)

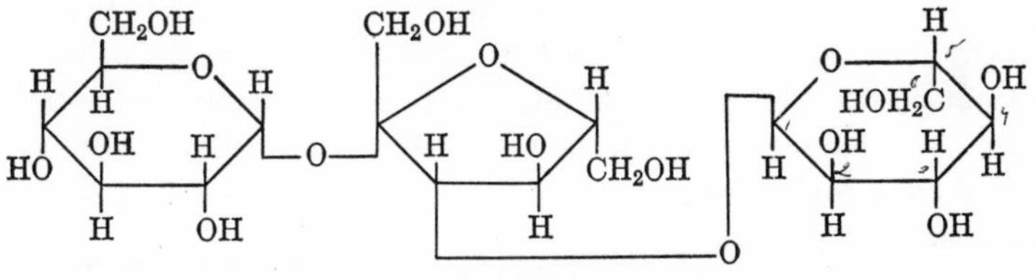
CH2OH
O
H
H
OH
HO
H
OH
O
CH2OH
H
HO
CH2OH
H
O
HOH2C
OH
H
(Sucrose)
(Turanose)

Synonyms. *O*-α-D-Glucopyranosyl-(1→3)-*o*-β-D-fructofuranosyl-(2→1)-α-D-glucopyranoside.

143. W. J. Whelan and P. J. P. Roberts, *J. Chem. Soc.* p. 1298 (1953).

144. R. L. Whistler and J. L. Hickson, *J. Am. Chem. Soc.* **76,** 1671 (1954).

145. C. Tanret, *Compt. rend.* **134,** 1586 (1902).

146. M. Adams, N. K. Richtmyer, and C. S. Hudson, *J. Am. Chem. Soc.* **65,** 1369 (1943).

147. H. Hérissey, A. Wickstrom, and J. E. Courtois, *Bull. soc. chim. biol.* **34,** 856 (1952); J. E. Courtois, A. Wickstrom, and P. LeDizet, *ibid.* **34,** 1121 (1952); H. Hérissey, A. Wickstrom, J. E. Courtois, and P. LeDizet, *Intern. Congr. Biochem. Abstracts Communs. 2nd Congr. Paris* p. 311 (1952).

Properties of Dihydrate. M.p. 153–154°C.; $[\alpha]_D^{20}$ +88.2° (*c*, 4; water). Not fermented by top (bakers') yeast. Nonreducing.

Identification. Hendecaacetate.

Occurrence. The sugar, discovered by Berthelot in 1859, is a constituent of the sweet exudations of many plants such as the "honeydew" of limes and poplars, and the manna exuded from insect-produced wounds of the Douglas fir, Virginia pine, larch, etc. In dry seasons when the supply of flower nectar is insufficient, bees may collect these mannas or honeydews, and the honeys may contain considerable quantities of melezitose (*151*). When the quantity of the trisaccharide is great, crystallization of the honey may take place in the comb. Probably because of the resistance of the melezitose to hydrolysis by invertase, honeys which contain this sugar will not serve as food for bees.

Preparation. Melezitose-rich honey provides the best source since the crystallized sugar is easily separated by dilution of the honey with alcohol followed by centrifugation (*151*). Mannas from various sources may be utilized by extracting the impurities with aqueous alcohol and then extracting the trisaccharide with water (*152*). The sugar crystallizes from the aqueous extracts after the addition of alcohol.

Structure. Complete acid hydrolysis leads to one mole of D-fructose and two moles of D-glucose (*152*). Dilute acid hydrolyzes the sugar to D-glucose and a disaccharide, turanose, and the ease of hydrolysis is about the same as that of sucrose (*153*). Since turanose is 3-*O*-α-D-glucopyranosyl-D-fructose (see under Turanose), the nature of one of the disaccharide linkages is established. A bacterial enzyme has been obtained from *Proteus vulgaris* that splits melezitose to D-glucose and sucrose; these products demonstrate the α-D-glucopyranosyl β-D-fructofuranoside linkage of the other half of the molecule (*154*). As confirming evidence may be cited the nonreducing character of melezitose and the fact that both disaccharide linkages are hydrolyzed by α-D-glucosidase (*155*).

Planteose

Synonyms. *O*-α-D-Galactopyranosyl-(1→6)-*O*-β-D-fructofuranosyl-(2→1)-α-D-glucopyranoside.

---

148. D. French, G. M. Wild, and W. J. James, *J. Am. Chem. Soc.* **75,** 3664 (1953).

149. R. A. Laidlaw and C. B. Wylam, *J. Chem. Soc.* p. 567 (1953).

150. M. Onuki, *Proc. Imp. Acad. (Tokyo)* **8,** 496 (1932); *Sci. Papers Inst. Phys. Chem. Research (Tokyo)* **20,** 201 (1933).

151. C. S. Hudson and S. F. Sherwood, *J. Am. Chem. Soc.* **42,** 116 (1920).

152. G. Tanret, *Bull. soc. chim. (France)* [3] **35,** 817 (1906).

153. C. S. Hudson and E. Pacsu, *J. Am. Chem. Soc.* **52,** 2522 (1930).

154. E. J. Hehre and A. S. Carlson, *Arch. Biochem. and Biophys.* **36,** 158 (1952); E. J. Hehre, *Advances in Carbohydrate Chem.* **8,** 277 (1953).

155. R. Weidenhagen, *Z. Ver. deut. Zücker-Ind.* **78,** 781 (1928).

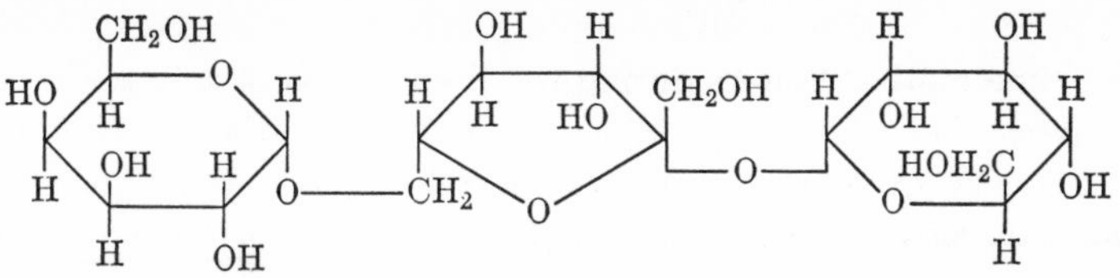
CH₂OH
O
HO
H
H
H
OH
H
H
O
H
OH
OH
H
H
H
HO
CH₂OH
CH₂
O
O
H
OH
H
H
OH
H
HOH₂C
H
O
OH
H

(Planteobiose) (Sucrose)

Properties of Dihydrate. M.p. 123–124°C.; $[\alpha]_D$ +129° (*c*, 4; water). Nonreducing.

Identification. Hendecaacetate.

Occurrence. Planteose occurs in the weed *Plantago* (*156*) and has been isolated in a pure form from the seeds of *P. ovata.*

Preparation. The sugar may be obtained by methanol extraction of the defatted seeds of *P. ovata*, followed by yeast fermentation of the extract to remove sucrose, and final isolation by the technique of charcoal-column elution (*157*).

Structure. Complete acid hydrolysis of planteose yields D-galactose, D-glucose, and D-fructose. Almond emulsin (α-D-galactosidase) catalyzes the hydrolysis of planteose to D-galactose and sucrose (*157*). Partial acid hydrolysis gives D-glucose and the reducing ketose disaccharide planteobiose. The latter has been shown to be 6-*O*-α-D-galactopyranosyl-D-fructose (see Planteobiose). Periodate oxidation of planteose oxidizes the D-fructose moiety, confirming that positions 3 and 4 of D-fructose are unsubstituted.

Raffinose

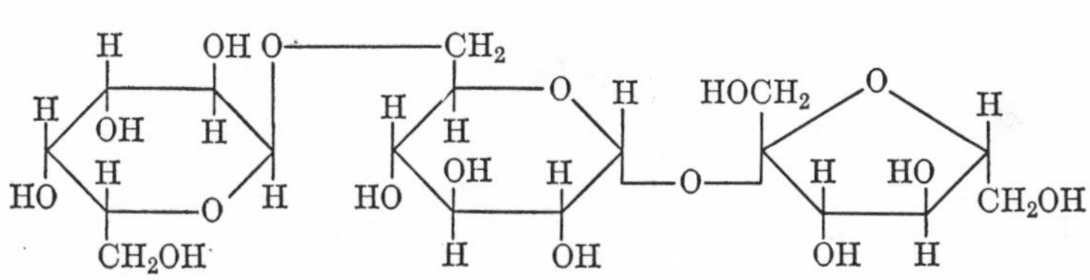
H
OH
O
CH₂
H
OH
H
H
HO
O
H
CH₂OH
H
O
H
H
OH
H
HO
H
OH
HOCH₂
O
H
O
H
HO
CH₂OH
OH
H

(Melibiose) (Sucrose)

Synonyms. Gossypose, melitose, melitriose, *O*-α-D-galactopyranosyl-(1→6)-*O*-α-D-glucopyranosyl-(1→2)-β-D-fructofuranoside.

Properties of Pentahydrate. M.p. 80°C.; $[\alpha]_D^{20}$ +105.2° (*c*, 4; water). Partially fermented by top yeast (bakers' yeast) with formation of melibiose; completely fermented by bottom yeast. Nonreducing.

Identification. X-ray diffraction powder pattern; hendecaacetate.

Occurrence. Raffinose occurs almost as widely in the plant world as

156. N. Wattiez and M. Hans, *Bull. acad. roy. med. Belg.* **8,** 386 (1943); *Chem. Abstr.* **39,** 4849 (1945).

157. D. French, G. M. Wild, B. Young, and W. J. James, *J. Am. Chem. Soc.* **75,** 709 (1953).

sucrose. It exists free in small amounts (0.05%) in sugar beets, but accumulates in the mother liquors during the preparation of sucrose.

Preparation. The sugar is available as a by-product of the barium process for the recovery of sucrose from beet molasses (see under Sucrose) and crystallizes directly from the final molasses (*158*). Cottonseed meal may also be utilized by extracting the sugar with water, precipitating it as a slightly soluble compound with calcium or barium hydroxide, and removing the metal ion by carbonation (*159*).

Structure. Complete acid hydrolysis gives one mole each of D-glucose, D-fructose, and D-galactose. Mild acid hydrolysis affects only one linkage, and melibiose and D-fructose result (*160*). Inasmuch as invertase produces the same end-products, a sucrose-type linkage must be present. Hydrolysis catalyzed by almond emulsin (α-D-galactosidase) gives sucrose and D-galactose and establishes the presence of the sucrose moiety (*161*). This evidence fixes the order of the monosaccharides and the nature of the interlinkages, since the structures of sucrose and melibiose are well established. Hydrolysis of the methylated sugar gives the expected partially

(Melibiose portion) (Sucrose portion)

O-α-D-Gal*p*-(1→6)-*O*-α-D-G*p*-(1→2)-β-D-Fru*f*

↑ ↑

hydrolyzed by α-D-galactosidase — hydrolyzed by invertase

methylated monosaccharides (*162*), while additional confirming evidence has been obtained by periodate oxidation studies (*163*).

Stachyose

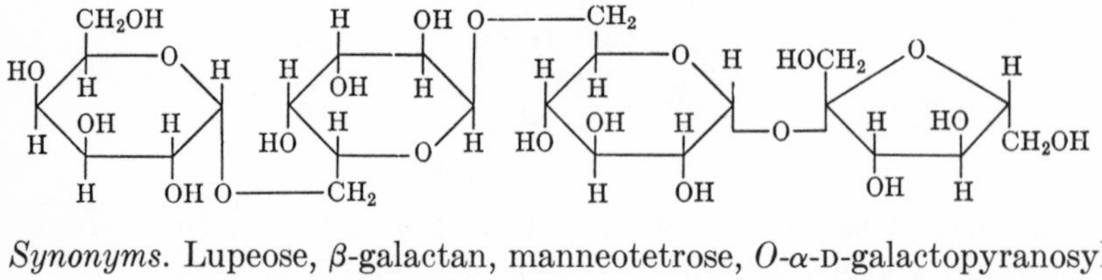
CH₂OH
HO
H
O
OH
H
H
OH
O
CH₂
HOCH₂
CH₂OH
HO

Synonyms. Lupeose, β-galactan, manneotetrose, *O*-α-D-galactopyranosyl-

158. T. S. Harding, *Sugar* **25,** 308 (1923); E. H. Hungerford and A. R. Nees, *Ind. Eng. Chem.* **26,** 462 (1934).

159. E. P. Clark, *J. Am. Chem. Soc.* **44,** 210 (1922); D. T. Englis, R. T. Decker, and E. B. Adams, *ibid.* **47,** 2724 (1925).

160. See C. Scheibler and H. Mittelmeier, *Ber.* **22,** 1680, 3120 (1889).

161. C. Neuberg, *Biochem. Z.* **3,** 528 (1907).

162. W. N. Haworth *et al., J. Chem. Soc.* **123,** 3125 (1923); *ibid.* pp. 1527, 3146 (1927).

163. J. E. Courtois and A. Wickstrom, *Bull. soc. chim. biol.* **32,** 759 (1950); H. Hérissey, A. Wickstrom, and J. E. Courtois, *ibid.* **33,** 642 (1951).

(1→6)-*O*-α-D-galactopyranosyl-(1→6)-*O*-α-D-glucopyranosyl-(1→2)-β-D fructofuranoside.

Properties. M.p. 167–170°C.; $[\alpha]_D^{20}$ +148° (*c*, 9; water). Partially fermentable by yeasts. Nonreducing.

Occurrence. The tetrasaccharide has been isolated from about forty different plant species, and is usually found associated with sucrose and raffinose. It has been reported in the roots of *Stachys* species, in the twigs of white jasmine, in the seeds of yellow lupine (*Lupinus lutens*), in soybeans (*Soja hispida*), in lentils (*Ervum lens*), and in ash manna (*Fraxinus ornus*).

Preparation (*164*). Ash manna, soybeans, and rhizomes of *Stachys tuberifera* have been utilized as sources of the sugar.

Structure. The tetrasaccharide structure of stachyose was assigned on the basis of cryoscopic measurements (*150*), and on the fact that it is cleaved by acid or invertase to a trisaccharide (manninotriose) and D-fructose in equimolar amounts (*165*). The structure previously given for stachyose, and based on the methylation studies of Onuki, must be revised with respect to the D-galactosyl → D-glucose linkage (see under Manninotriose). Laidlaw and Wylam (*149*) have found that completely methylated stachyose on hydrolysis yields 2,3,4,6-tetra-*O*-methyl-D-galactose, 2,3,4-tri-*O*-methyl-D-galactose, 2,3,4-tri-*O*-methyl-D-glucose, and 1,3,4,6-tetra-*O*-methyl-D-fructose. This result, as does the periodate oxidation study of Hérissey and associates (*166*), requires a 1→6 linkage between all units except the terminal D-glucosyl-D-fructose. The presence of a sucrose linkage between the latter was proved by the partial hydrolysis of stachyose with the α-D-galactosidase of almond emulsin to a mixture of raffinose and sucrose (*167*). This result confirms the previous conclusion based on the ease of hydrolysis of the D-fructose unit by acid and by invertase. The α-D-galactosidic linkages follow from the structure of manninotriose, as well as from the complete hydrolysis of stachyose by brewers' yeast emulsin which contains both invertase and α-D-galactosidase.

Verbascose

Synonyms. *O*-α-D-Galactopyranosyl-(1→6)-*O*-α-D-galactopyranosyl-(1→6)-*O*-α-D-galactopyranosyl-(1→6)-*O*-α-D-glucopyranosyl-(1→2)-β-D-fructofuranoside.

164. For a recent review of refinements in the methods of preparation see D. French, *Advances in Carbohydrate Chem.* **9,** 149 (1954).

165. C. Tanret, *Compt. rend.* **134,** 1586 (1902); *Bull. soc. chim. France* [3] **27,** 947 (1902); *ibid* [3] **29,** 888 (1903).

166. H. Hérissey, A. Wickstrom, and J. E. Courtois, *Bull. soc. chim. biol.* **33,** 642 (1951); *ibid.* **34,** 856 (1952).

167. D. French, G. M. Wild, and W. J. James, *J. Am. Chem. Soc.* **75,** 3664 (1953).

Properties. M.p. 253°C.; $[\alpha]_D^{20}$ +170° (water). Nonreducing.

Occurrence. This oligosaccharide has been isolated from the roots of the mullein, *Verbascum thapsus* (*168*).

Structure. Cryoscopic molecular weight values indicate that verbascose is a pentasaccharide (*169*). From methylation studies, Murakami concluded that verbascose was a D-galactosyl-substituted stachyose (at C-6 of the terminal D-galactose unit of stachyose). Hot dilute acetic acid removes the D-fructose unit from verbascose to give a tetrasaccharide verbascotetraose (m.p. 240°C.; $[\alpha]_D^{20}$ +191.4° (water)). This tetrose has been partially hydrolyzed, with removal of D-glucose, to give the crystalline trisaccharide galactotriose (*164*).

D. Miscellaneous Tri- and Tetrasaccharides

Cellotriose. See under Cellobiose.

Isomaltotriose. *O*-α-D-Glucopyranosyl-(1→6)-*O*-α-D-glucopyranosyl-(1→6)-D-glucose; amorphous solid, $[\alpha]_D^{20}$ +145° (water); has been isolated in a 20% yield from an enzymic hydrolysis of dextran (*53*).

Labiose. M.p. 126–128°C.; $[\alpha]_D$ +136.7° (water); obtained from the dry powdered tubers of *Eremostachys labiosa.* The trisaccharide is hydrolyzed by invertase and dilute acid to one mole of D-galactose and two moles of D-fructose (*170*).

Panose. See below.

Scorodose. A tetrafructoside from the bulbs of onion and garlic (*Allium*) (*171*).

5. ENZYMIC SYNTHESIS OF OLIGOSACCHARIDES

A. Synthesis of Sucrose by the Mechanism of Phosphorolysis.

Sucrose cannot be synthesized biologically to any considerable extent by a simple reversal of its hydrolysis. When the enzyme invertase is allowed to act upon a dilute solution of sucrose, such as exists in plant cells, the reaction in which invert sugar is formed goes almost to completion. Theoretically, when the equilibrium is reached a finite amount of sucrose might remain in solution, its concentration being determined by the free energy change of the reaction and the concentration of the hydrolysis products. The $\Delta F°$ for the hydrolysis of sucrose is of the order of −6600 cal. per mole; this means that the reaction has a strong tendency to favor hydroly-

168. E. Bourquelot and M. Bridel, *Compt. rend.* **151,** 760 (1910).
169. S. Murakami, *Acta Phytochim.* (*Japan*) **11,** 213 (1940); **13,** 161 (1943).
170. S. M. Stryskov, *Chem. Abstr.* **34,** 2798 (1940).
171. Y. Kihara, *Chem. Abstr.* **34,** 385 (1940).

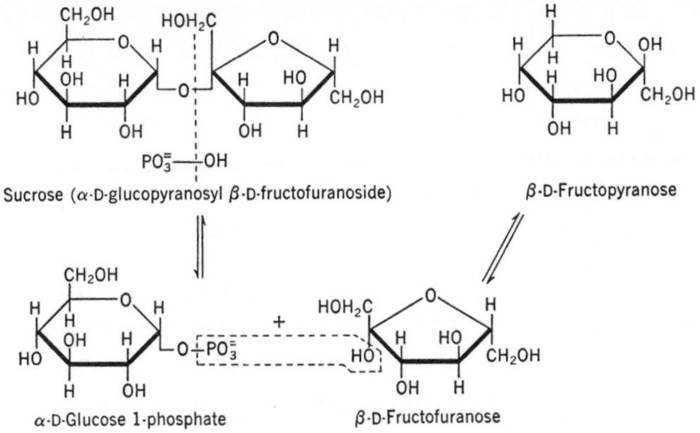
Sucrose (α-D-glucopyranosyl β-D-fructofuranoside)
β-D-Fructopyranose
α-D-Glucose 1-phosphate
β-D-Fructofuranose

FIG. 4

sis. This tendency is greatly reinforced by the high concentration of one of the reactants, water, in an aqueous environment. The combination of these factors is responsible for the practically irreversible nature of the hydrolysis of sucrose.

Evidence is now available showing that sucrose is synthesized in nature by a mechanism (or mechanisms) involving a reversal of *phosphorolysis* rather than that of hydrolysis. It is known that certain species of bacteria, namely *Pseudomonas saccharophila*, *P. putrifaciens*, and *Leuconostoc mesenteroides* (*171a*) contain a phosphorylase which, in the presence of inorganic phosphate, catalyzes the phosphorolytic decomposition of the disaccharide sucrose with the production of α-D-glucose 1-phosphate and D-fructose. The reverse reaction, the dephosphorolytic condensation of α-D-glucose 1-phosphate and D-fructose results in the formation of sucrose with the elimination of phosphoric acid, as shown in Figure 4. (For polysaccharide synthesis through the action of phosphorylases, see Chapter XII.)

The synthetic process for sucrose can be regarded as a condensation reaction in which the elements of water of hydrolysis are replaced by those of phosphoric acid. The process can also be considered as a transglucosidation reaction in which the D-glucosyl radical from α-D-glucose 1-phosphate is transferred to a D-fructofuranose radical, serving as an acceptor.

The free energy required for the formation of the glycosidic link in sucrose is available in the α-D-glucose 1-phosphate. Phosphorylated D-glucose is required because free D-glucose, on account of its low free energy level, cannot serve as part of the substrate for sucrose synthesis. The energy level of the D-glucose can be raised through combination with phosphate by using the energy drop from adenosine triphosphate (ATP) to

171a. W. Z. Hassid and M. Doudoroff, *Advances in Enzymol.* **10,** 123 (1950).

form D-glucose 6-phosphate through an enzymic reaction involving hexokinase. The latter ester can then be readily transformed by the aid of the enzyme phosphoglucomutase to α-D-glucose 1-phosphate. Thus, the free energy for the synthesis of sucrose is probably derived from a high-energy phosphorus bond of adenosine triphosphate.

The fact that sucrose can be synthesized from α-D-glucose 1-phosphate and D-fructose is consistent with the evidence presented by Isbell and Pigman (*172*) and Gottschalk (*173*) that D-fructose exists as an equilibrium mixture of the pyranose and furanose forms. The total system of sucrose synthesis can be represented by the equation (Fig. 4) which includes the equilibrium reaction of the two ring forms of D-fructose. The occurrence of D-fructose in the sucrose molecule as D-fructofuranose is an indication that sucrose phosphorylase is specific for the furanose configuration of that ketose (*174*, *175*).

In the phosphorolysis of sucrose the rupture of the bond in α-D-glucose 1-phosphate could occur either between the carbon and oxygen of the hexose phosphate or between the oxygen and phosphorus. Cohn (*176*), employing O^{18}-labeled inorganic phosphate, has determined the location of the bond that is broken in the reaction. By incubating oxygen-labeled inorganic phosphate with sucrose in the presence of the enzyme sucrose phosphorylase, and allowing the reaction to proceed to equilibrium, she demonstrated that the O^{18} concentration of the inorganic phosphate and of the D-glucose 1-phosphate, after equilibrium had been reached, was the same as the O^{18} concentration of the initial inorganic phosphate. This could occur only if the forward and reverse reactions do not involve a rupture of the bond between phosphorus and oxygen.

The equilibrium constant for the phosphorolysis of sucrose, expressed by the mass law equation:

$$K = \frac{[\text{sucrose}][\text{inorganic phosphate}]}{[\text{fructose}][\alpha\text{-D-glucose 1-phosphate}]}$$

is equal to 0.053 at pH 6.6 and 30° (*171*). Thus, the equilibrium favors the breakdown rather than the synthesis of sucrose. When α-D-glucose 1-phosphate and inorganic phosphate are present in equal concentrations in the equilibrium reaction mixture, the D-fructose concentration will be approximately twenty times that of sucrose. From the equilibrium constant,

172. H. S. Isbell and W. W. Pigman, *J. Research Natl. Bur. Standards* **20,** 773 (1938).

173. A. Gottschalk, *Advances in Carbohydrate Chem.* **5,** 49 (1950).

174. W. Z. Hassid, M. Doudoroff, and H. A. Barker, *J. Am. Chem. Soc.* **66,** 1416 (1944).

175. W. Z. Hassid and M. Doudoroff, *Advances in Carbohydrate Chem.* **5,** 29 (1950).

176. M. Cohn, *J. Biol. Chem.* **180,** 771 (1949).

the free energy change for the phosphorolytic reaction can be calculated by the equation:

$$\Delta F^0_{303^\circ} = -RT \ln K_{303^\circ} = -1385 \log 0.053 = 1770 \text{ cal.}$$

As in the formation of glycogen and starch, the energy needed for the formation of the glycosidic bond in sucrose may be derived from utilization of energy-rich phosphate bonds of compounds such as adenosine triphosphate. Assuming that the free energy change of the reaction is entirely due to the difference in bond energies of sucrose and α-D-glucose 1-phosphate, the energy of the glycosidic bond of sucrose can be estimated. Since the energy of the C—O—P bond of the ester is about 4800 cal., the value for the glycosidic bond in sucrose must be 4800 + 1770 cal. = 6570 cal. This relatively high value for a glycosidic bond may account for the distinctive role of sucrose in the metabolism of plants.

The system responsible for sucrose synthesis in plants does not seem to be a simple sucrose phosphorylase of the bacterial type capable of causing directly the reaction between α-D-glucose 1-phosphate and D-fructose. It appears that uridine diphosphate glucose is involved as a D-glucose donor in the reaction (*177–181*). Leloir and his co-workers (*177*) showed that wheat germ, corn germ, bean germ, and potato sprouts contain an enzyme that catalyzes the reversible formation of sucrose from uridine diphosphate glucose (UDPG) and D-fructose:

$$\text{UDPG} + \text{D-fructose} \rightleftharpoons \text{sucrose} + \text{UDP}$$

When a mixture of UDPG and D-fructose is subjected to the reaction of enzyme preparations from these plant sources in the presence of inorganic phosphate buffer at pH 7.0, a nonreducing disaccharide, identified as sucrose, is formed. The equilibrium constant, K, for this reaction at 37°C was found to be between 2 and 8, and the ΔF was estimated to be approximately −1000 cal. as compared to +1770 cal. for the sucrose phosphorylase reaction. In contrast to the sucrose phosphorylase reaction, the equilibrium of the reaction starting with UDPG and D-fructose is in favor of sucrose synthesis.

Leloir and Cardini (*177a*) found later that wheat germ contains another enzyme which will form sucrose phosphate when α-D-fructose 6-phosphate

177. C. E. Cardini, L. F. Leloir, and J. Chiriboga, *J. Biol. Chem.* **214,** 149 (1955).
177a. L. F. Leloir and C. E. Cardini, *J. Biol. Chem.* **214,** 157 (1955).
178. J. F. Turner, *Nature* **172,** 1149 (1953); **174,** 692 (1954).
178a. D. P. Burma and D. C. Mortimer, *Arch. Biochem. and Biophys.* **62,** 16 (1956).
179. J. G. Buchanan, *Arch. Biochem. and Biophys.* **44,** 140 (1953).
180. J. G. Buchanan *et al.*, *in* "Phosphorus Metabolism" (W. D. McElroy and B. Glass, eds.), Johns Hopkins Press, Baltimore, (1952).
181. E. W. Putman and W. Z. Hassid, *J. Biol. Chem.* **207,** 885 (1954).

is substituted for D-fructose:

$$\text{UDPG} + \text{D-fructose 6-phosphate} \rightleftharpoons \text{UDP} + \text{sucrose phosphate}$$

This finding is in accord with the results of experiments on *Canna* leaves supplied with labeled substrates, indicating that both of the immediate precursors of sucrose are phosphorylated compounds and that no free D-fructose is involved in the process of synthesis (*181*). Since phosphatase is also present in wheat germ, the sucrose phosphate formed in the plant may be rapidly dephosphorylated, resulting in the accumulation of free sucrose.

Working with algae and green leaves, Buchanan, Calvin, and others (*179*, *180*) detected chromatographically the presence of C^{14}-labeled sucrose phosphate and uridine diphosphate glucose after exposing the plants to $C^{14}O_2$ for short photosynthetic periods. This sucrose phosphate was believed to yield D-fructose 1-phosphate on hydrolysis (*179*), and hence would be different from the product synthesized by the wheat germ preparation. On the basis of the results of the various investigations, it appears that there is more than one mechanism for sucrose synthesis in nature.

Bean and Hassid (*181a*) showed that the same enzyme preparation from green peas, in addition to synthesis of sucrose from UDPG and D-fructose, and sucrose phosphate from the same nucleotide and D-fructose 6-phosphate, is capable of forming other disaccharides (sucrose analogs) when ketose monosaccharides other than D-fructose or D-fructose 6-phosphate are used as D-glucose acceptors. Thus, when D-rhamnulose, D-xylulose, and L-sorbose were used in the presence of this pea preparation and UDPG, D-glucosyl D-rhamnuloside, D-glucosyl D-xyluloside and D-glucosyl L-sorboside were formed, respectively. The latter two disaccharides are probably identical with those formed by the action of an enzyme present in *Pseudomonas saccharophila* from D-glucose 1-phosphate and the corresponding ketoses (*175*).

B. Synthesis of Analogs of Sucrose and Maltose by Sucrose and Maltose Phosphorylases

Sucrose phosphorylase is capable of synthesizing analogs of sucrose in which D-fructose is replaced by other ketose sugars (*171*). D-Xylulose (D-*threo*-pentulose), L-ribulose (L-*erythro*-pentulose), and L-sorbose can replace D-fructose in the reaction with α-D-glucose 1-phosphate, forming the corresponding nonreducing disaccharides, D-glucosyl D-xyluloside, D-glucosyl L-ribuloside, and D-glucosyl L-sorboside. Inasmuch as it has been shown that these disaccharides are nonreducing and that their ketose con-

181a. R. C. Bean and W. Z. Hassid, *J. Am. Chem. Soc.* **77,** 5737 (1955).

stituents exist in the furanose form, they can be considered as analogs of sucrose. The enzyme is also capable of combining α-D-glucose 1-phosphate with an aldose, L-arabinose, to form a reducing disaccharide with a 1→3 glucosidic linkage having no obvious structural relation to sucrose. Most of the known natural reducing disaccharides, such as maltose, lactose, and cellobiose, possess a 1→4 linkage; this 1→3 linkage is unique among disaccharides (*175*) which occur free in nature.

α-D-Glucopyranosyl α-L-sorbofuranoside. Like synthetic sucrose, this disaccharide is formed from α-D-glucose 1-phosphate and L-sorbose through the action of the *P. saccharophila* enzyme (*182*). The disaccharide is nonreducing and gives a positive Seliwanoff reaction. Its specific rotation is $[\alpha]_D$ +33°, and its m.p. is 178–180°C. It appears to be only very slightly affected by invertase, but it is easily hydrolyzed by acid. On oxidation of the carbohydrate with sodium periodate, three moles of the reagent are consumed, and one mole of formic acid is formed, but no formaldehyde is produced. These data are consistent with a nonreducing disaccharide structure in which the aldose moiety exists in the pyranose and the ketose moiety in the furanose form.

The nonreducing disaccharide gives a blue-green color with diazouracil, a reaction shown by Raybin (*183*) to be specific for sucrose and other compounds containing the same type of glycosidic linkage, such as raffinose, gentianose, and stachyose. The analogy of the synthetic nonreducing D-glucosyl L-sorboside to sucrose in its reaction with diazouracil and with the bacterial sucrose phosphorylase indicates that the local structure about the glycosidic linkage is the same as that of sucrose. Since β-D-fructose and α-L-sorbose have the same configuration for their second carbon atoms (*184*), the ketose portion of the disaccharide is desiginated as α-L-sorboside.

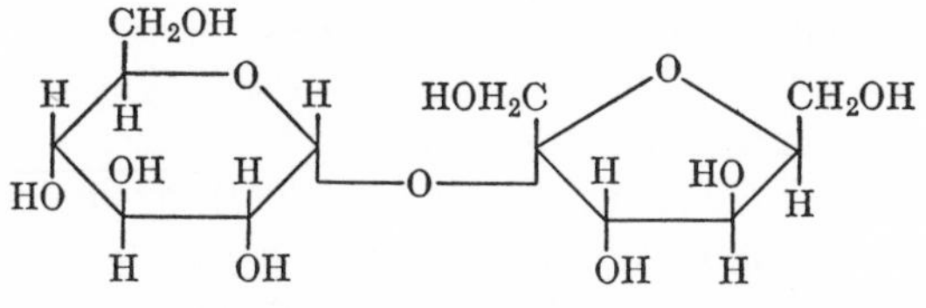

CH₂OH
H
O
H
H
HO
OH
H
O
H
OH
HOH₂C
O
CH₂OH
H
HO
H
OH
H

α-D-Glucopyranosyl α-L-sorbofuranoside

α-D-Glucopyranosyl β-D-xyluloside. The disaccharide synthesized from α-D-glucose 1-phosphate and D-xylulose by sucrose phosphorylase does not reduce Fehling solution; it is practically unaffected by invertase but

182. W. Z. Hassid, M. Doudoroff, H. A. Barker, and W. H. Dore, *J. Am. Chem. Soc.* **67**, 1394 (1945).

183. H. W. Raybin, *J. Am. Chem. Soc.* **55**, 2603 (1933); **59**, 1402 (1937).

184. C. S. Hudson, *J. Am. Chem. Soc.* **60**, 1537 (1938).

is easily hydrolyzed with acid (*185*). The specific rotation of the disaccharide is $[\alpha]_D$ +43°, and its m.p. is 156–157°C. Its rate of hydrolysis with acid is approximately 30% greater than that of sucrose. In the oxidation of the disaccharide with sodium periodate, two moles of periodate are consumed, whereby one mole of formic acid is produced. These data are consistent with a structure of a nonreducing disaccharide consisting of glucopyranose and xylulofuranose. As the disaccharide gives the Raybin reaction (*183*), the local structure about the glycosidic linkage in the glucosyl xyluloside is probably the same as that of sucrose.

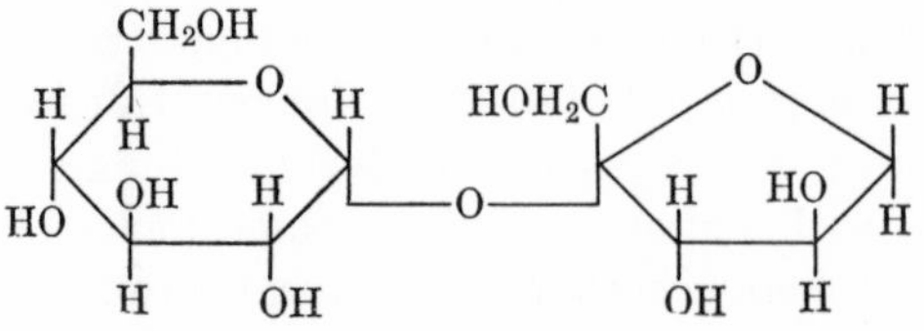

α-D-Glucopyranosyl β-D-xylulofuranoside

D-*Glucosyl* L-*ribuloside*. Using the same enzyme preparation from *P. saccharophila*, another nonreducing disaccharide consisting of D-glucose and L-ribulose can be synthesized from α-D-glucose 1-phosphate and L-ribulose (*186*). The disaccharide is not affected by invertase but is easily hydrolyzed with dilute acid. It gives Raybin's diazouracil reaction, indicating that it contains the same type of linkage as sucrose. There is good reason to believe that the structure of this disaccharide is α-D-glucopyranosyl α-L-ribulofuranoside (*187*).

*3-O-α-*D*-Glucopyranosyl-*L*-arabinopyranose*. Similar to the previously described nonreducing disaccharides, this reducing disaccharide is formed from α-D-glucose 1-phosphate and L-arabinose by means of *P. saccharophila* enzyme (*188*). It contains two molecules of water of crystallization, and its $[\alpha]_D$ in water is +156°. Unlike sucrose and the synthetic nonreducing disaccharides synthesized by the sucrose phosphorylase enzyme, it is difficultly hydrolyzable with acid. The phenylosatriazole derivative of the disaccharide (*189*) is hydrolyzed with acid to D-glucose and L-arabinose phenylosotriazole; this shows that the L-arabinose constitutes the free

185. W. Z. Hassid, M. Doudoroff, H. A. Barker, and W. H. Dore, *J. Am. Chem. Soc.* **68,** 1465 (1946).

186. M. Doudoroff, W. Z. Hassid, and H. A. Barker, *J. Biol. Chem.* **168,** 733 (1947).

187. The linkage pertaining to the L-ribuloside part of this disaccharide was incorrectly designated in the original publication (*186*) as the β-type.

188. W. Z. Hassid, M. Doudoroff, A. L. Potter, and H. A. Barker, *J. Am. Chem. Soc.* **70,** 306 (1948).

189. R. M. Hann and C. S. Hudson, *J. Am. Chem. Soc.* **66,** 735 (1944); W. T. Haskins R. M. Hann, and C. S. Hudson, *ibid.* **67,** 939 (1945).

reducing group in the disaccharide. On oxidation of the phenylosotriazole derivative of the disaccharide with sodium periodate three moles of the reagent are consumed with the formation of one mole each of formic acid and formaldehyde per mole of phenylosotriazole derivative. These data indicate that in the disaccharide D-glucose is linked through C–1 to C–3 of L-arabinose. Methylation of the disaccharide produces a methyl hexa-*O*-methyl derivative which, on hydrolysis, gives rise to 2,3,4,6-tetra-*O*-methyl-D-glucose and 2,4-di-*O*-methyl-L-arabinose. That the di-*O*-methyl-L-arabinose possesses the pyranose configuration is shown by the rapid rate of hydrolysis of the di-*O*-methyl-L-arabonolactone derivative to its acid and by the fact that no periodate is consumed when the lactone is oxidized with this reagent. On the basis of these results the structure of the disaccharide is designated as:

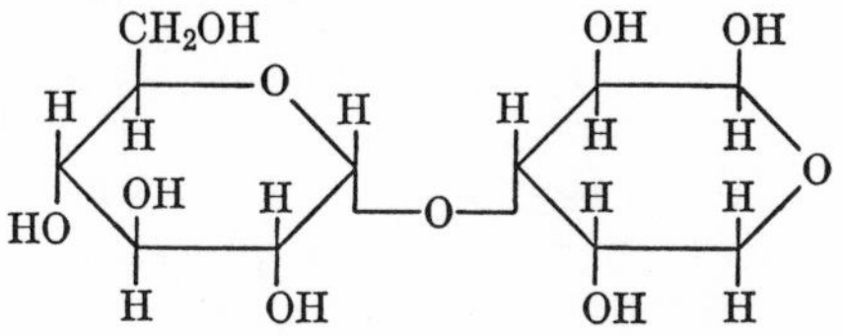
CH2OH
O
H
H
H
H
OH
H
HO
O
H
OH
OH
OH
H
H
H
H
O
OH
H

3-*O*-α-D-Glucopyranosyl-L-arabinopyranose

4-O-α-D-Glucopyranosyl-D-xylopyranose. Doudoroff and Fitting (*190*) found that the bacterium *Neisseria meningitidis* contains a phosphorylase (maltose phosphorylase) capable of catalyzing the reversible reaction:

$$\text{Maltose} + \text{inorganic phosphate} \underset{}{\overset{\text{maltose phosphorylase}}{\rightleftharpoons}} \beta\text{-D-glucose 1-phosphate} + \text{D-glucose}$$

This enzyme is unique in that it causes inversion of the anomeric linkage (α to β, and vice versa) when synthesis or degradation takes place.

Of a number of monosaccharides investigated, D-xylose appears to be the only sugar, besides D-glucose, that is capable of reacting with β-D-glucose 1-phosphate in the reverse direction in the presence of this enzyme to form a disaccharide.

The disaccharide (*190a*) thus formed reduces Fehling solution; it is soluble in water and has a specific rotation in water $[\alpha]_D$ +94.5°. On hydrolysis with acid it produces one mole of D-glucose and one mole of D-xylose. Oxidation with bromine and subsequent hydrolysis of the oxidation product results in the formation of D-glucose and D-xylonic acid, and shows that the D-xylose constitutes the reducing moiety of the disaccharide.

190. C. Fitting and M. Doudoroff, *J. Biol. Chem.* **199,** 153 (1952).

190a. E. W. Putman, C. Fitting Litt, and W. Z. Hassid, *J. Am. Chem. Soc.* **77,** 4351 (1955).

Complete methylation of the disaccharide produces a methyl hexa-*O*-methyl derivative, which on hydrolysis with acid gives rise to 2,3,4,6-tetra-*O*-methyl-D-glucose and 2,3-di-*O*-methyl-D-xylose. Since D-xylofuranose has never been encountered in nature, it is assumed that the D-xylose occurs in the disaccharide in the pyranose configuration. It is, therefore, concluded that the disaccharide is joined glycosidically through C–1 of D-glucose and C–4 of D-xylose and can be considered an analog of maltose. The decrease in specific rotation from +94.5° to +35.0° during the course of acid hydrolysis indicates that the two monosaccharide units are combined in the disaccharide through an α-glycosidic linkage. The structural formula for the disaccharide may be written as follows:

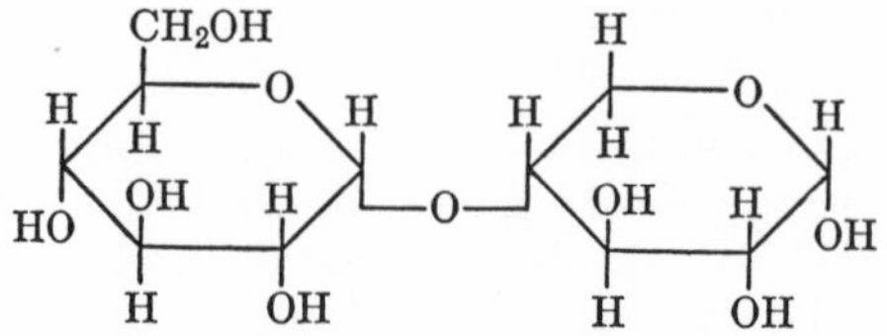
CH₂OH
H
O
H
H
H
O
H
H
H
OH
H
O
OH
H
HO
OH
H
OH
H
OH

4-*O*-α-D-Glucopyranosyl-D-xylopyranose

C. Synthesis of Disaccharides by Transglycosidation (*191*) Through the Action of Sucrose Phosphorylase (*191a*)

The process of enzymic transfer of sugar residues was named "transglycosidation" by Rabaté (*192*), who observed the transfer of D-glucose residues from various glycosides to such acceptors as ethanol, catalyzed by preparations from leaves of a number of species of plants. In the sucrose phosphorylase reaction, α-D-glucose 1-phosphate can be regarded merely as one of a number of "glucose donors" for the enzyme sucrose phosphorylase. This hexose phosphate does not appear to be an essential product or substrate of the enzyme activity for the synthesis of disaccharides. The enzyme can act not only as a "phosphorylase" but also as a "transglucosidase" capable of mediating the transfer of the D-glucose portion of substrates to a variety of "acceptors" (*193*).

The evidence for the double function of the enzyme was obtained from the fact that when P^{32}-labeled inorganic phosphate and nonradioactive α-D-glucose 1-phosphate are added to sucrose phosphorylase preparations

191. E. J. Hehre has suggested in *Advances in Enzymol.* **11,** 330 (1951) that the term "transglycosylation" describes more accurately the nature of the group transferred in the cases (phosphorylases) for which the mechanism of the reaction has been studied with O^{18}-labeled phosphate.

191a. For a recent review see J. Edelman, *Advances in Enzymol.* **17,** 189 (1956).

192. J. Rabaté, *Compt. rend.* **204,** 153 (1937); see Chapter X, also.

193. M. Doudoroff, H. A. Barker, and W. Z. Hassid, *J. Biol. Chem.* **168,** 725 (1947).

in the absence of ketose sugars, a rapid redistribution of the isotope occurs between the organic and inorganic fractions without liberation of D-glucose. D-Glucose, which is known to inhibit sucrose phosphorylase, is also found to inhibit the exchange reaction. Similarly, the presence of D-fructose is found to decrease the rate of exchange. Such a decrease in rate would be expected if D-fructose competed with phosphate for the D-glucose residue of α-D-glucose 1-phosphate. These observations indicate that the enzyme combines reversibly with the D-glucose portion of α-D-glucose 1-phosphate forming a D-glucose–enzyme complex and releasing inorganic phosphate according to the equation:

$$\alpha\text{-D-Glucose 1-phosphate} + \text{enzyme} \rightleftharpoons \text{D-glucosyl–enzyme} + \text{phosphate}$$

The equilibrium of the reaction would require that the energy of the α-D-glucose 1-phosphate linkage be preserved in the glycosyl–enzyme bond. The transfer of phosphate could not involve the formation of free D-glucose, because if this occurred approximately 4800 cal. would be released in the decomposition of the ester and would be required for its resynthesis. Since no external source of energy was available for the resynthesis of the ester, it must be concluded that the original bond energy is conserved in the glycosyl–enzyme complex.

It was also demonstrated (*194*) that, in a phosphate-free medium, sucrose phosphorylase brings about the exchange of added free C^{14}-labeled D-fructose, forming sucrose in which its D-fructose moiety proved to be radioactive:

$$\underset{\text{(sucrose)}}{\text{D-Glucosyl D-fructoside}^*} + \text{enzyme} \rightleftharpoons \text{D-glucose–enzyme} + \text{D-fructose}^*$$

In this reaction, as well as in the phosphorolysis reaction, the enzyme acts as a D-glucose acceptor and is able to catalyze the exchange of an ester bond for a glycosidic bond.

That the sucrose phosphorylase also functions as a transglucosidase can further be demonstrated by the fact that the enzyme will catalyze an exchange of glucosidic bonds between two different disaccharides in the absence of inorganic phosphate and α-D-glucose 1-phosphate. Thus, D-glucosyl L-sorboside, which had been originally synthesized from α-D-glucose 1-phosphate and L-sorbose, can also be formed by a reaction between sucrose and L-sorbose:

$$\underset{\text{(sucrose)}}{\text{D-Glucosyl D-fructoside}} + \text{L-sorbose} \rightleftharpoons \text{D-glucosyl L-sorboside} + \text{D-fructose}$$

194. H. E. Wolochow, E. W. Putman, M. Doudoroff, W. Z. Hassid, and H. A. Barker, *J. Biol. Chem.* **180**, 1237 (1949).

In a similar manner, sucrose can be prepared by a reaction between the synthetic disaccharide D-glucosyl D-xyluloside and D-fructose (*171*).

$$\text{D-Glucosyl D-xyluloside} + \text{D-fructose} \rightleftharpoons \underset{\text{(sucrose)}}{\text{D-glucosyl D-fructoside}} + \text{D-xylulose}$$

The mode of action of sucrose phosphorylase explains the observed role of arsenate in causing the hydrolytic decomposition of both sucrose and α-D-glucose 1-phosphate in the presence of the enzyme (*195*). Arsenate presumably acts as a D-glucose acceptor with the enzyme, to form an unstable D-glucose 1-arsenate compound, which hydrolyzes spontaneously to D-glucose and arsenate:

$$\text{Sucrose} + \text{arsenate} \rightarrow \text{D-glucose 1-arsenate} + \text{D-fructose}$$

$$\downarrow H_2O$$

$$\text{D-glucose} + \text{arsenate}$$

Hestrin, Feingold, and Avigad (*195a*) found that the levansucrase enzyme system of *Aerobacter levanicum* which utilizes the D-fructose moiety of sucrose, forming a polysaccharide (levan) and D-glucose, possesses a complementary property of catalyzing the reversible transfer of the D-fructosyl unit of β-D-fructofuranosyl aldosides of different configurations to the anomeric carbon position of an aldose.

When a cell-free solution of levansucrase was allowed to act on raffinose in the presence of D-glucose, in addition to the appearance of melibiose and a comparatively small quantity of levan, a rapid formation of a nonreducing disaccharide identified as sucrose occurred. This reaction proved to be reversible: raffinose + D-glucose ⇌ sucrose + melibiose.

A number of other aldoses were found to react similarly with raffinose in the presence of levansucrase. Thus, the interaction of raffinose and D-xylose resulted in the formation of a nonreducing disaccharide ($[\alpha]_D$ + 62°, in water), consisting of D-xylose and D-fructose. Periodate oxidation together with other data suggested that the compound is a sucrose analog, α-D-xylopyranosyl-β-D-fructofuranoside, to which the name "xylosucrose" was given. In addition to D-xylose, the following other aldoses were shown to be converted to the corresponding aldosyl-D-fructofuranosides on reaction with raffinose or sucrose in the presence of levansucrase: L-arabinose, D-glucose, D-galactose, and melibiose.

195. M. Doudoroff, H. A. Barker, and W. Z. Hassid, *J. Biol. Chem.* **170,** 147 (1947).
195a. S. Hestrin, D. S. Feingold, and G. Avigad, *J. Am. Chem. Soc.* **77,** 6710 (1955).

D. Synthesis of Oligosaccharides by Transglycosidation Through the Action of Hydrolytic Enzymes

Pigman (*75a, 196*) made the observation that enzymes from *Aspergillus oryzae*, *A. niger*, *Bacillus mesentericus*, and pancreas, which were formerly considered to be purely hydrolytic, are capable of synthesizing unfermentable substances from maltose, although not from D-glucose.

By the use of sensitive methods, it has been observed (*197–199*) that yeast invertase formed substances during the early stages of action on sucrose that are presumed to be trisaccharides. To explain their formation, it has been suggested that yeast invertase, in addition to being a hydrolytic enzyme, is also a fructose-transferring enzyme. Small amounts of oligosaccharides are synthesized by transfructosidation as a result of competition of the decomposition products of the substrate for the elements of water. The transfer probably occurs with a fructosyl–enzyme complex as the intermediate. Although at present there is no direct evidence that a fructosyl–enzyme compound is formed, the following scheme of enzyme action has been postulated (*199*).

$$\text{Fru-G} + \text{E} \rightleftharpoons \text{Fru-E} + \text{G}$$

$$\text{Fru-E} + \text{Fru-G} \rightleftharpoons \text{Fru-Fru-G} + \text{E}$$

$$\text{Fru-E} + \text{Fru-Fru-G} \rightleftharpoons \text{Fru-Fru-Fru-G} + \text{E, etc.}$$

$$\text{Fru-E} + H_2O \rightleftharpoons \text{Fru} + \text{E}$$

(Fru = D-fructose, E = enzyme, and G = D-glucose)

The last reaction, involving water, is assumed to be slow and irreversible; these properties account for the disappearance of the oligosaccharides in the later stages of the reaction. Thus, it appears that transfructosidase is analogous in its action to the proteolytic enzymes which catalyze transpeptidations (*200*) or to the phosphate transferring phosphatases (*201*).

Kestose or O-α-D-Glucopyranosyl-(1→2)-O-β-D-fructofuranosyl-(6→2)-β-D-fructofuranoside. This sugar is produced during the action of yeast invertase on a 50% sucrose solution and can be isolated by cellulose chromatography (*202*). The trisaccharide crystallizes from methanol and (with some dif-

196. W. W. Pigman, *J. Research Natl. Bur. Standards* **33,** 105 (1944).

197. J. S. D. Bacon and J. Edelman, *Arch. Biochem.* **28,** 467 (1950).

198. P. H. Blanchard and N. Albon, *Arch. Biochem.* **29,** 220 (1950).

199. E. H. Fischer, J. Kohtes, and J. Fellig, *Helv. Chim. Acta* **34,** 1132 (1951).

200. R. B. Johnston, M. J. Mycek, and J. S. Fruton, *J. Biol. Chem.* **185,** 629 (1950).

201. B. Axelrod, *J. Biol. Chem.* **176,** 295 (1948); J. Appleyard, *Biochem. J.* **42,** 596 (1948); O. Meyerhof and H. Green, *J. Biol. Chem.* **178,** 655 (1949).

202. N. Albon, D. J. Bell, P. H. Blanchard, D. Gross, and J. T. Rundell, *J. Chem. Soc.* p. 24 (1953); See also, J. S. D. Bacon, *Biochem. J.* **57,** 320 (1954).

ficulty) from water as fragile rhomboidal plates. It is not sweet. Its specific rotation in water is $[\alpha]_D$ +27.3°; m.p. 145°C.

Hydrolysis of the methylated kestose gives rise to 1,3,4,6-tetra-*O*-methyl-D-fructofuranose, 2,3,4,6-tetra-*O*-methyl-D-glucopyranose, and 1,3,4-tri-*O*-methyl-D-fructose.

A similar trisaccharide can be extracted from the tubers of the Jerusalem artichoke (*203*).

O-β-D-Fructofuranosyl-(2→6)-O-α-D-glucopyranosyl-(1→2)-β-D-fructofuranoside. This trisaccharide, which is composed of the same monosaccharide units as kestose, has a different configuration and is named "neokestose" (*204*). It is synthesized during the action of yeast invertase preparations on sucrose and isolated by chromatography on a carbon–Celite column. It is obtained as a nonreducing amorphous powder, having an $[\alpha]_D$ +22.2° (in water). Its structure is deduced from an analysis of the cleavage products of the mixed methylated sugars. It appears to be formed by enzymic transfer of a β-D-fructofuranosyl radical to sucrose. Invertase will, thus, transfer β-D-fructofuranosyl radicals to the primary alcoholic group of D-glucopyranose as well as those of D-fructofuranose.

O-α-D-Glucopyranosyl-(1→4)-O-α-D-glucopyranosyl β-D-fructofuranoside or α-maltosyl β-D-fructofuranoside. While the principal trisaccharides formed by yeast invertase from sucrose contain two D-fructose and one D-glucose molecules (*205*), the chief trisaccharide formed from sucrose by honey invertase contains two D-glucose and one D-fructose molecules (*206*). This sugar has been isolated from a honey invertase digest of sucrose; the yield was 11 % of the original weight of sucrose. The trisaccharide is nonreducing to Fehling solution and gives D-glucose and D-fructose on hydrolysis. Its configuration was deduced from the fact that on partial hydrolysis with yeast and honey invertase both maltose and sucrose are produced.

A similar trisaccharide composed of two D-glucose units and one D-fructose unit can be isolated by charcoal chromatography from the honeydew of the citrus mealy bug *Pseudococcus citri* when feeding on the sap of potato sprouts (*207*). Presumably this trisaccharide arises as a natural product in the digestive systems of many insects. Also there is chromatographic evidence for its presence in honeydews of cottonlike maple scale, *Pulvinaria vitis*, and in the spirea aphid, *Aphio spiralcola*.

O-α-D-Glucopyranosyl-(1→2)-O-β-D-fructofuranosyl-(1→2)-β-D-fructofuranoside (tentative structure). This nonreducing trisaccharide is produced as

203. R. Dedonder, *Compt. rend.* **232,** 1134 (1951).

204. D. Gross, P. H. Blanchard, and D. J. Bell, *J. Chem. Soc.* p. 1727 (1954).

205. H. C. S. de Walley, *Intern. Sugar J.* **54,** 127 (1952); L. M. White and G. E. Secor, *Arch. Biochem. and Biophys.* **36,** 490 (1952).

206. J. W. White and J. Maher, *J. Am. Chem. Soc.* **75,** 1259 (1953).

207. H. E. Gray and G. Fraenkl, *Science* **118,** 304 (1953).

the result of the action of "Takadiastase" on sucrose (*208*). The trisaccharide appears to be formed by enzymic transfer of a D-fructofuranosyl radical to sucrose. The sugar, isolated as a sirup, has a specific rotation $[\alpha]_D$ +28° (in water). Methylation and subsequent hydrolysis of the compound produces 1,3,4,6-tetra-*O*-methyl-D-fructose, 2,3,4,6-tetra-*O*-methyl-D-glucose, and 3,4,6-tri-*O*-methyl-D-fructose in equimolar proportions. From the ease of hydrolysis by dilute acid and by yeast invertase preparations free from α-D-glucosidase, the D-glucose radical is assumed to be combined as in sucrose. The β-linkage is deduced from the accepted specificity of yeast invertase.

O-α-D-Glucopyranosyl-(1→6)-O-α-D-glucopyranosyl-(1→4)-α-D-glucopyranose. Cultures of *A. niger* NNRL 337 contain an enzyme system which can use maltose to synthesize an unfermentable reducing trisaccharide, consisting entirely of D-glucose units, sometimes called panose (*209*). The trisaccharide is crystalline, has an $[\alpha]_D$ +154° (mutarotates downward) and a m.p. 213°C. (dec.). Partial hydrolysis of this oligosaccharide and of its aldonic acid followed by chromatography on paper indicated the presence of isomaltose, maltose, and D-glucose in the former and isomaltose (no maltose) and D-glucose in the latter. Further evidence for the presence of one α,1→6 and one α,1→4 linkage was based on the relative positions of the spots from maltotriose, the unknown trisaccharide, and a possible trisaccharide from the α,1→6-dextran series (*210*). On the basis of these data, a tentative structure for the trisaccharide was formulated as 4-*O*-α-isomaltopyranosyl-D-glucose. Definite proof for this structure was obtained by the isolation of crystalline β-isomaltose octaacetate from the partial hydrolysis of the acetylated reduced trisaccharide derivative (*211*).

An enzyme in liver converts maltose to maltotriose and maltotetraose (*211a*).

E. Miscellaneous Oligosaccharides

Inulobiose, a reducing disaccharide with the probable structure of 1-*O*-β-D-fructofuranosyl-D-fructofuranose, has been isolated from a partial acid hydrolyzate of inulin by paper chromatographic methods (*212*). This disaccharide can also be prepared from D-fructose and raffinose by a carbo-

208. J. S. D. Bacon and D. J. Bell, *J. Chem. Soc.* p. 2528 (1953).

209. S. C. Pan, L. W. Nicholson, and P. Kolachov, *J. Am. Chem. Soc.* **73,** 2547 (1951).

210. D. French, *Science* **113,** 352 (1951).

211. M. L. Wolfrom, A. Thompson, and T. T. Galkowski, *J. Am. Chem. Soc.* **73,** 4093 (1951).

211a. K. V. Giri, A. Nagabhushanam, V. N. Nigam, and B. Belavadi, *Science* **121,** 898 (1955).

212. J. H. Pazur and A. L. Gordon, *J. Am. Chem. Soc.* **75,** 3458 (1953).

hydrate transferring enzyme, transfructosidase, from the mold *Aspergillus oryzae* (*213*). (See also p. 684.)

The inulobiose was prepared by precipitation from aqueous solution with acetone. It dissolves readily in water and tastes sweeter than sucrose. Its specific rotation is $[\alpha]_D$ $-32.5°$ (in water). The specific rotation of the octaacetyl derivative is $[\alpha]_D$ $-6.5°$ (in chloroform).

A reducing disaccharide, consisting of D-glucose and D-fructose, named *leucrose* (*214*), is formed in the reaction mixture to the extent of about 3% during the synthesis of dextran from sucrose by an enzyme isolated from the microorganism *Leuconostoc mesenteroides*. Its specific rotation is $[\alpha]_D$ $-6.8°$ (in water); m.p. 161–162°C. Methylation studies show that its structure is 5-*O*-α-D-glucopyranosyl-D-fructopyranose.

Aspergillus niger (strain 152), which produces an intracellular polyglucan (*215*), contains a transglucosidase responsible for the synthesis of a number of oligosaccharides. When maltose is used as a substrate in the presence of a cell-free extract of this mold, the following oligosaccharides are produced: isomaltose (6-*O*-α-D-glucopyranosyl-D-glucose), panose (*O*-α-D-glucopyranosyl-(1→6)-*O*-α-D-glucopyranosyl-(1→4)-α-D-glucopyranose), and isomaltotriose. This indicates that the mold contains an intracellular transglucosidase analogous to the extracellular enzymes produced by *A. niger* NRRL-337 (*209*) and by *A. oryzae* (*216*).

Another trisaccharide formed from sucrose by *A. niger* has been characterized as *O*-α-D-glucopyranosyl-(1→2)-*O*-β-D-fructofuranosyl-(1→2)-β-D-fructofuranoside (*217*).

During the action of an enzyme extract from yeasts on lactose two disaccharides and two trisaccharides are produced (*218*). The compounds were isolated by paper-chromatographic procedures. From partial and complete hydrolysis of the products and their aldonic acids, the following arrangements of the monosaccharide units in the oligosaccharides are identified: 6-*O*-D-galactosyl-D-glucose, 6-*O*-D-galactosyl-D-galactose, *O*-D-galactosyl-(1→6)-*O*-D-galactosyl-(1→4)-D-glucose, and *O*-D-galactosyl-(1→6)-*O*-D-galactosyl-(1→6)-D-glucose.

When culture filtrates of *Penicillium chrysogenum* are allowed to act on maltose as a substrate, the maltose appears to be completely converted to isomaltose, 6-*O*-α-D-glucopyranosyl-D-glucose, and other saccharides

213. J. H. Pazur, *J. Biol. Chem.* **199**, 217 (1952).

214. F. H. Stodola, E. S. Sharpe, and H. J. Koepsell, *J. Am. Chem. Soc.* **78**, 2514 (1956).

215. S. A. Barker, E. J. Bourne, and M. Stacey, *J. Chem. Soc.* p. 3084 (1953).

216. J. H. Pazur and D. French, *J. Biol. Chem.* **196**, 265 (1952).

217. S. A. Barker, E. J. Bourne, and T. R. Carrington, *J. Chem. Soc.* p. 2125 (1954).

218. J. H. Pazur, *J. Biol. Chem.* **208**, 439 (1954).

(*219*). The products are separated by fractionation on a column of charcoal (Norit A).

When filtrates from cultures of several species of *Aspergillus* and *Rhizopus* were allowed to act on maltose and starch, the synthesis of unfermentable sugars, isomaltose, cellobiose, panose, and two unknown sugars, was demonstrated by paper chromatography (*220*).

Enzymes of *A. macerans* form cyclic six-, seven- and eight-membered dextrins from starch substances (p. 681).

219. K. V. Giri, K. Saroja, R. Venkataraman, and P. L. Narasimha Rao, *Arch. Biochem. and Biophys.* **51,** 62 (1954).

220. K. Aso and K. Shibasaki, *Tohoku J. Agri. Research* **3,** 349 (1953).

X. NATURALLY OCCURRING GLYCOSIDES AND GLYCOSIDASES*

Helmut Baumann and Ward Pigman

From a biological standpoint, the natural glycosides comprise one of the important groups of the carbohydrates. Bourquelot states that of 281 species of phanerogams investigated in his laboratories glycosides were found to be present in 205 species (*1*). Many of the colored pigments of flowers, the naturally occurring dyestuffs and aromatic principles, and drugs such as the heart-stimulating (cardiac) glycosides are of glycosidic nature.

Numerous conjectures of the function of glycosides in plants have been made (*2*). Glycosides may serve as reserve deposits for sugars, particularly in seeds. Other possible functions are as controls for osmotic pressure and for the stabilization of labile aglycons. By analogy with the use of glucosides, or particularly glucuronides, for detoxification by animals (see p. 599), it has been suggested that plant glycosides play a similar role by removing toxic materials or end-products of metabolic processes. Moreover, in a few cases, glycosides appear to perform an important function in the regulation of the general plant metabolism in the role of the so-called "plant hormones."

Plant glycosides are known to be localized in the cell vacuoles. Frey-Wyssling suggests that the aglycons are end-products of metabolic processes. The aglycons usually are lipophilic in character, but they also contain hydrophilic groups and are surface-active. These characteristics lead to the supposition that the aglycons will tend to be deposited along with the lipides in the surface of the border layer of the cytoplasm next to the vacuoles. Because their accumulation in this layer might be detrimental to the functions of the cell, it is likely that glycosidation occurs and the glycosides, now hydrophilic, pass into the aqueous phase of the vacuoles, which act as a disposal ground for the waste products of metabolism.

Although most common in plant materials, glycosides are also found in

* Translated in part by Joe Clayton.

1. Quoted by C. Béguin, *Pharm. Acta Helv.* **1,** 90 (1926).

2. For a discussion of the subject see A. Frey-Wyssling, *Naturwissenschaften* **33,** 500 (1942).

substances of animal origin; among the best-known animal sources are brain tissue (cerebrosides) and urine. Naturally occurring oligosaccharides, a type of glycoside, are discussed in a separate chapter (Chapter IX). Because the principal interest in the glycosides resides in the chemistry of the aglycon (the nonsugar portion), the naturally occurring glycosides are considered in the present chapter along with the enzymes (glycosidases) which act as catalysts for their hydrolysis and synthesis and which often accompany the glycosides in natural products. General methods of synthesis and the definitions and properties of glycosides are considered in an earlier chapter (Chapter IV). The so-called "nitrogen glycosides" (glycosylamines) are covered elsewhere (Chapter VIII).

Part I

GLYCOSIDES (3)

1. ANTHOCYANIDIN, FLAVANOL, AND CAROTENOID GLYCOSIDES (*4*)

Many plant pigments occur as glycosides which on acid or enzymic hydrolysis yield a sugar, usually glucose, or a mixture of sugars, and the anthoxanthins which include the flavones, the flavonols, the flavanones, the isoflavones, and the xanthones. The soluble red, violet, and blue pigments of flowers, fruits, and leaves which have been termed anthocyanins give a sugar and an anthocyani*din* (the aglycon) on hydrolysis. Before the widespread adoption of coal-tar base dyes, these substances had considerable value as dyestuffs. The subject is well reviewed, and the methods for the determination of the structures of these glycosides and their aglycons are given adequately elsewhere (*4*). The synthesis of peonin (V), the anthocyanin pigment of the dark-red peony, is outlined below (*5*):

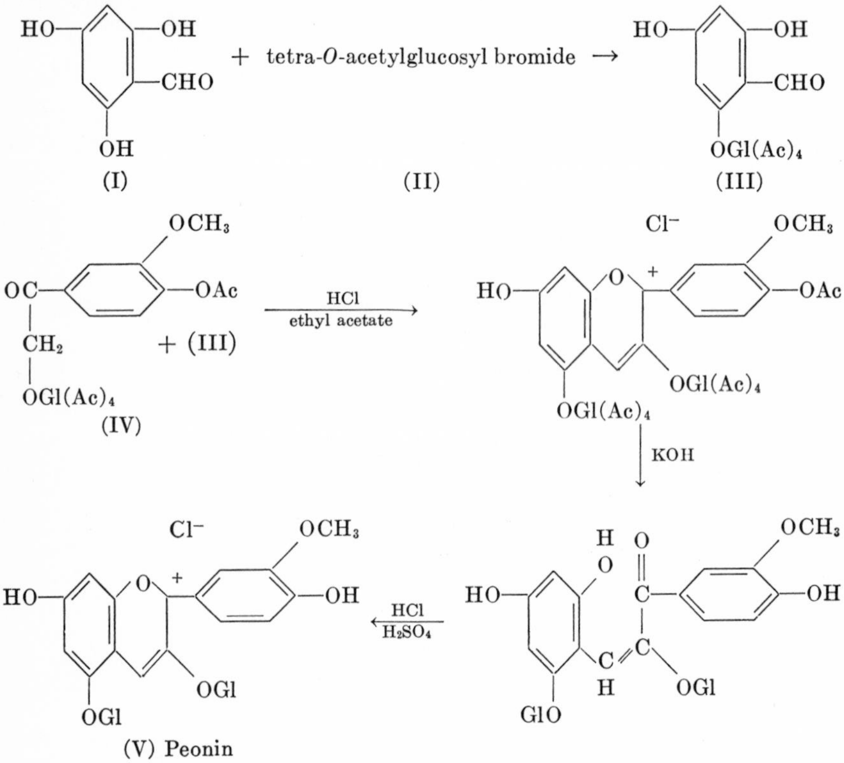
HO
OH
CHO
OH
(I)
+ tetra-O-acetylglucosyl bromide →
(II)
OGl(Ac)4
(III)
OCH3
OC
OAc
CH2
OGl(Ac)4
(IV)
+ (III)
HCl
ethyl acetate
Cl⁻
O
+
KOH
HCl
H2SO4
OGl
GlO
H
C
(V) Peonin

(Gl(Ac$_4$) = tetra-*O*-acetylglucosyl group; Gl = glucosyl group.)

In many types of plant tissue, colorless materials are present which, upon treatment with mineral acids, are converted to red substances exhibiting many of the properties of anthocyanidins. The colorless compounds were given the names of leucoanthocyanins and leucoanthocyanidins by Rosenheim (*6*). These compounds probably represent a heterogeneous class. They may have an important part in bleaching and color-stabilization problems, particularly in the western areas of the United States, where many woods have a reddish rather than the more usual yellowish cast. Although work has been done, particularly by the Robinsons, the structures of the leucoanthocyanins have not been established definitely.

Quercitrin, a flavonol glycoside from the bark of certain oak trees, is used for the preparation of L-rhamnose (see under this sugar). It has the structure:

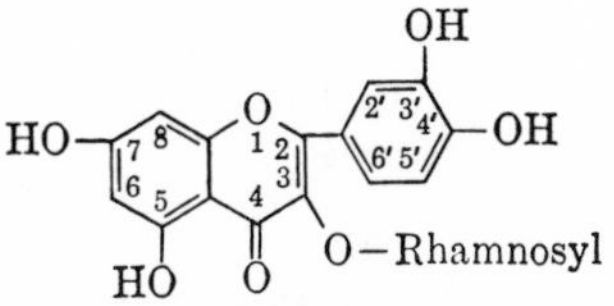
OH
HO
O
1
2
3
4
7
8
6
5
2′
3′
4′
6′
5′
OH
O–Rhamnosyl
HO
O

Quercitrin

The aglycon is known as quercetin. A number of natural glycosides yield quercitin derivatives on hydrolysis. Thus, xanthorhamnin obtained from the ripe fruit of *Rhamnus infectoria* yields one mole of rhamnetin, two moles of L-rhamnose, and one of D-galactose. Rhamnetin is the 7-methyl ether of quercetin. Glycosides of the 3′-methyl ether of quercetin, isorhamnetin glycosides, also are naturally occurring. From crocus pollen, the 3,4′-diglucoside of isorhamnetin has been isolated (*7*). Rhamnazin is the 3′, 7-dimethyl ether.

One of the flavanone glycosides, hesperidin, has been called vitamin P, which may be concerned with the regulation of capillary permeability and

3. General references: E. F. Armstrong and K. F. Armstrong, "The Glycosides." Longmans, Green, New York, 1931; J. J. L. van Rijn and H. Dieterle, "Die Glycoside," 2nd ed. Borntraeger, Berlin, 1931; K. Paech and M. V. Tracey, "Modern Methods of Plant Analysis," Vol. 2. Springer, Berlin, 1955; R. J. McIlroy, "The Plant Glycosides." Longmans, Green, New York, 1951.

4. K. P. Link, *in* "Organic Chemistry" (H. Gilman, ed.), 2nd ed., p. 1315. Wiley, New York, 1943; E. F. Armstrong and K. F. Armstrong, "The Glycosides." Longmans, Green, New York, 1931; R. Robinson, *Ber.* **67A**, 85 (1934).

5. R. Robinson and A. R. Todd, *J. Chem. Soc.* p. 2488 (1932); for a discussion of the structure of flavylium chlorides of the type of (V), see R. L. Shriner and R. B. Moffett, *J. Am. Chem. Soc.* **63**, 1694 (1941).

6. See W. W. Pigman, E. Anderson, R. Fischer, M. A. Buchanan, and B. L. Browning, *Tappi* **36**, 4 (1953).

7. See R. Kuhn, I. Loew, and H. Trischmann, *Ber.* **77**, 196, 202, 211 (1944).

fragility (*8*). The glycoside is found in the peels of citrus fruits and on hydrolysis yields one mole each of glucose, rhamnose, and the aglycon hesperitin. The sugar units in the hesperidin are united in disaccharide fashion to form 6-*O*-(β-L-rhamnosyl)-D-glucose (rutinose), and the hesperidin is hesperitin β-rutinoside (*9*). The flavanone exists in equilibrium with its chalcone isomer, the chalcone being formed in alkaline solution and the hesperidin existing in acid solution:

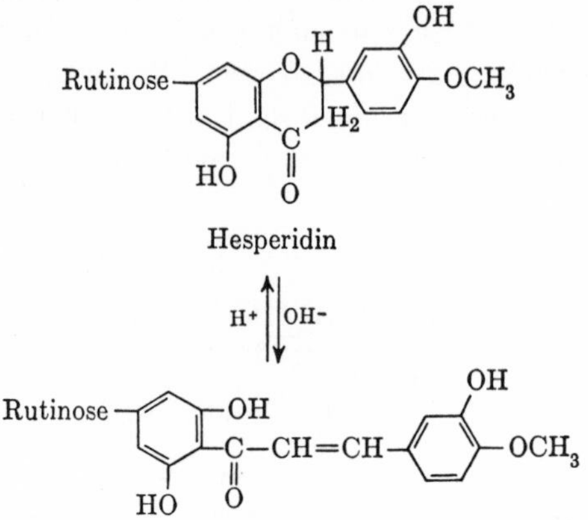
OH
H
O
Rutinose
OCH3
H2
C
HO
O
Hesperidin
H+
OH-
OH
Rutinose
OH
C—CH=CH
OCH3
HO
O
Hesperidin chalcone

The chalcone takes up hydrogen readily and the reduced form loses hydrogen when shaken in air. The reduced chalcone also gives up hydrogen to the well-known oxidation-reduction coenzymes (see Cozymase) and may play such a role in biological systems.

The hesperidin frequently is accompanied by another glycoside, eriodictyol glycoside. This substance has been shown to be closely related to hesperidin. The methoxyl group (see above formula) is replaced by a hydroxyl group, and the sugar component is L-rhamnose rather than rutinose (*10*). The glycoside rutin is 3-(3,5,7,3′,4′-pentahydroxyflavone) rutinoside.

Several of the glycosides of this group have shown the ability to reduce capillary fragility and permeability. In vitamin C–deficient states, a response to the vitamin may be improved if its injection is accompanied by one of these glycosides. Earlier it was thought that the active material

8. C. Z. Wawra and J. L. Webb, *Science* **96,** 302 (1942); A. Szent-Györgyi, *Z. physiol Chem.* **255,** 126 (1938); G. J. Martin, *Ann. N. Y. Acad. Sci.* **61,** 637 (1955); H. Scarborough and A. L. Bacharach, *Vitamins and Hormones* **7,** 1 (1949).

9. G. Zemplén and A. K. Tettamanti, *Ber.* **71,** 2511 (1938); G. Zemplén and R. Bognár, *Ber.* **76,** 773 (1943).

10. A. Mager, *Z. physiol. Chem.* **274,** 109 (1942).

was hesperidin, so-called vitamin P, and rutin was also active in many cases. More recent investigations indicate that the active principle is quercetin, the aglycon of rutin. The activity of the glycosides is more equivocal because of the necessity of *in vivo* hydrolysis of the glycosidic linkages for the production of the active material. Griffith (*11*) reported a high degree of improvement in hypertensive patients treated with quercetin, even for cases showing no previous response to rutin. The subject is highly controversial (*8*).

Some of the above and similar compounds exhibit a powerful influence on the sexual processes of the green alga *Chlamydomonas*. Thus the glucoside from crocus pollen (see above) in dilutions as low as 1 mg. in 6×10^9 ml. of water (about 80 molecules per cell) immobilizes the gametes of the alga, and the cilia drop off. The yellow aglycon acts on the bisexual cells and imparts to them the property of being able to conjugate only after the addition of male gametes (*7*).

The coloring principle of saffron, crocin, which was isolated from the hila of *Crocus sativas*, is the ester of a carotenoid pigment (crocetin), and has the structure (*12*):

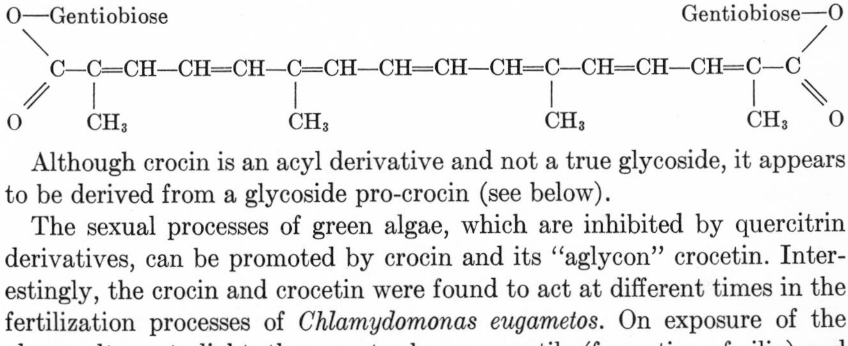
O—Gentiobiose
Gentiobiose—O
C—C=CH—CH=CH—C=CH—CH=CH—CH=C—CH=CH—CH=C—C
O
CH3
CH3
CH3
CH3
O

Although crocin is an acyl derivative and not a true glycoside, it appears to be derived from a glycoside pro-crocin (see below).

The sexual processes of green algae, which are inhibited by quercitrin derivatives, can be promoted by crocin and its "aglycon" crocetin. Interestingly, the crocin and crocetin were found to act at different times in the fertilization processes of *Chlamydomonas eugametos*. On exposure of the algae cultures to light, the gametes became motile (formation of cilia) and copulated (*13*). Kuhn and co-workers showed that a substance which is liberated upon exposure to light and affects these sexual processes of the gametes can be replaced by crocin. Moreover, crocin produced cilia formation and crocetin the copulation. The *cis*- and *trans*-isomers of crocetin behaved differently, *cis*-crocetin influencing the female and *trans*-crocetin the male gametes. Crocin itself arises in the plant upon exposure to light; a pro-crocin is assumed to be an intermediate from which picrocrocin and crocin are formed.

11. See J. Q. Griffith, Jr., *J. Am. Pharm. Assoc. Sci. Ed.* **42,** 68 (1953); J. Nashski and C. F. Krewson, *ibid.* **42,** 66 (1953).

12. P. Karrer, F. Benz, and M. Stoll, *Helv. Chim. Acta* **16,** 297 (1933); P. Karrer and K. Mizi, *ibid.* **12,** 985 (1929).

13. R. Kuhn, F. Moewus, and D. Jerchel, *Ber.* **71,** 1541 (1938).

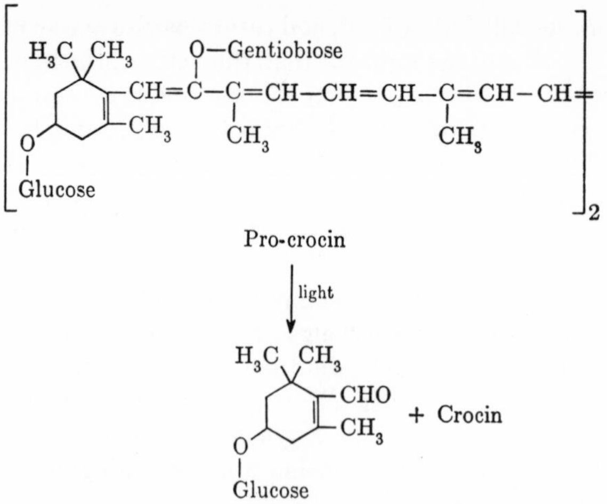
H3C CH3
O—Gentiobiose
CH=C—C=CH—CH=CH—C=CH—CH=
CH3
CH3
CH3
O
Glucose
2
Pro-crocin
light
H3C CH3
CHO
CH3
+ Crocin
O
Glucose

Picrocrocin

The glucose in picrocrocin has a β-glucosidic linkage, since picrocrocin is hydrolyzed to the corresponding alcohol by almond emulsin. Upon treatment with acids and alkalies, safranal, a doubly unsaturated aldehyde, is formed.

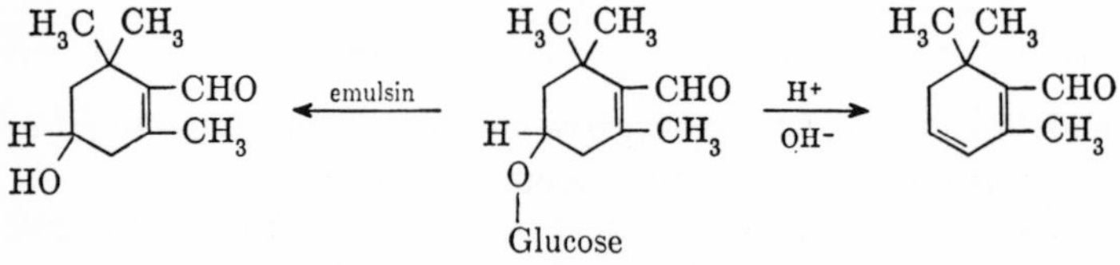
H3C CH3
CHO
CH3
H
HO
emulsin
H3C CH3
CHO
CH3
H
O
Glucose
H+
OH-
H3C CH3
CHO
CH3

Aglycon Picrocrocin Safranal

The sexual substances of the green algae *Chlamydomonas eugametos* show the same effects as their alkaline and acid hydrolytic products. Actually these substances can be replaced by picrocrocin, the aglycon, and safranal (*14*). Upon addition of picrocrocin, the gametes become all female. Safranal and the aglycon, which has a ten times enhanced activity, permit only male cells to be formed. Quantitative studies showed that the natural material of the green algae is closely related to picrocrocin, and differs only in the sugar component. The investigation of the natural sexual substance has not been completed, since it occurs in very small amounts. Only 1.2 molecules of crocin per gamete suffice to produce these effects.

These compounds comprise a new class of substances which, analogous to the steroids in the animal kingdom, serve as sexual hormones. The close relationship to carotene and vitamin A is interesting.

14. R. Kuhn, F. Moewus, and G. Wendt, *Ber.* **72,** 1702 (1939); R. Kuhn and I. Loew, *ibid.* **74,** 219 (1941).

2. INDICAN

In addition to the anthocyanins, another important source of dyes is the naturally occurring indican which on hydrolysis yields indoxyl and glucose. The indoxyl upon oxidation is converted to the dye indigo. The preparation of indigo from plants involves the extraction of the glucoside, its enzymic hydrolysis by microorganisms, and the oxidation of the indoxyl to indigo by air. The synthesis by Robertson (*15*) of indican, illustrated below, furnishes the final evidence needed for the structural determination and demonstrates the glycoside to be 3-hydroxyindole β-D-glucoside.

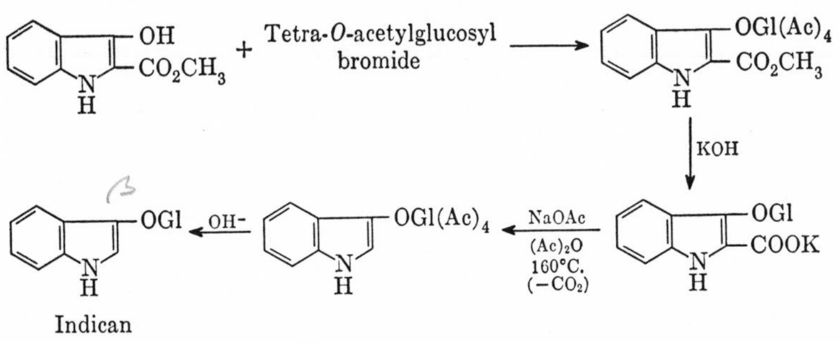
OH
CO_2CH_3
N
H
+
Tetra-*O*-acetylglucosyl bromide
OGl(Ac)$_4$
CO_2CH_3
KOH
OGl
COOK
NaOAc
$(Ac)_2O$
160°C.
$(-CO_2)$
OGl(Ac)$_4$
OH-
OGl
Indican

($Gl(Ac)_4$ = tetra-*O*-acetylglucosyl group; Gl = glucosyl group)

Normal metabolism of tryptophan in animals leads to the production of indoxyl glucosiduronic acids (and sulfate) in the urine (*2*).

3. AGLYCONS RELATED TO PHENANTHRENE

A. Cardiac Glycosides (*16*)

These glycosides are of considerable medical interest because of their stimulatory action on the heart. Some of the many plant families in which the presence of these glycosides has been demonstrated are: Liliaceae, Ranunculaceae, Scrophulariaceae, and Apocynaceae. The most important sources are certain species of *Strophanthus* and *Digitalis* (foxglove), the latter providing most of the drugs of therapeutic value. Many if not all of the cardiac glycosides have a deoxysugar as one of the component sugars and usually this sugar is attached directly to the aglycon. The known sugar components are listed later in this chapter (p. 552). The general formula of

15. A. Robertson, *J. Chem. Soc.* p. 1937 (1927).

16. W. H. Strain, *in* "Organic Chemistry" (H. Gilman, ed.), 2nd ed., p. 1427. Wiley, New York, 1943; R. Tschesche, *Fortschr. Chem. org. Naturstoffe* **1,** 1 (1945); H. Heusser, *ibid.* **7,** 87 (1950); L. F. Fieser and M. Fieser, "Natural Products Related to Phenanthrene," 3rd ed., p. 507. Reinhold, New York, 1949. See series of more than 134 articles by T. Reichstein and co-workers "Glycoside und Aglycone" in *Helv. Chim. Acta* (1938 to 1954).

a cardiac glycoside may be expressed as follows (*17*):

Aglycon-(deoxysugar)$_m$-(glucose)$_n$

Acids hydrolyze the linkage between the aglycon and the sugars in the cardiac glycosides, and di- and trisaccharides can be isolated. It is stated that this linkage is not hydrolyzed by the enzymes in the same plant, but instead only the glycosidic bonds between the sugars are split. Many of the

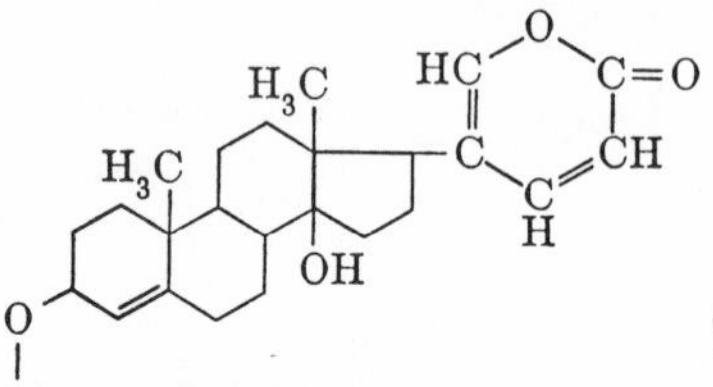

Rhamnose-β-glucose

Proscillaridin *A* Scillabiose

Scillaren *A*,
principal glycoside
of *Scilla maritima*[18]

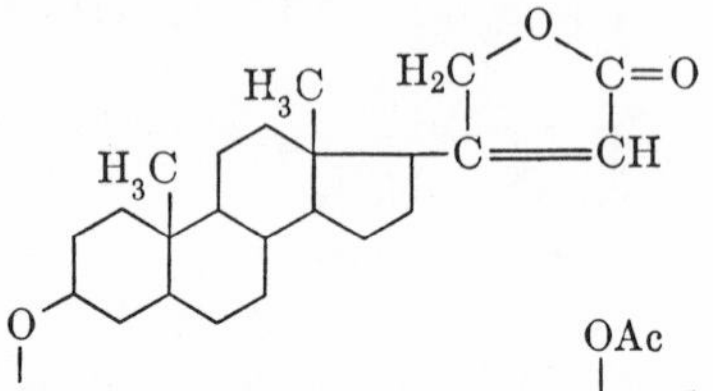

Digitoxose-digitoxose-digitoxose-β-glucose

Acetyl-digoxin

Lanata-glycoside *C*,
glycoside from *Digitalis lanata*

products which have been obtained from the above-mentioned plants are undoubtedly partially degraded due to the loss of glucose by enzymic action during the process of preparation. The structures of several typical cardiac glycosides and of the degradation products are given in the accompanying formulas. It will be noted that the aglycons are lactones all very similar in structure. The aglycon ring structures are similar to those of the sterols, vitamin D, sex hormones, bile acids, neutral saponins, and the adrenal corticosteroids, all being derived from the hydrocarbon cyclopentanoperhydrophenanthrene.

When administered to persons with impaired heart function, cardiac

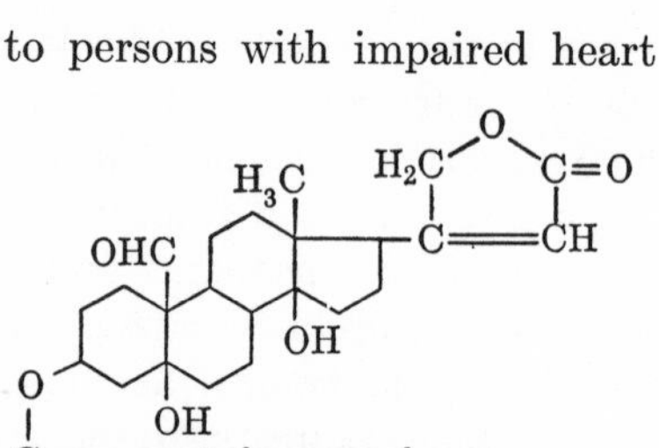

Cymarose-β-glucose-α-glucose

Strophanthobiose

Cymarin Strophanthotriose

k-Strophanthin-β

k-Strophanthoside from *Strophanthus kombé*

17. A. Stoll and J. Renz, *Enzymologia* **7**, 362 (1939).

TABLE I

Biological Activity of Strophanthidin Glycosides

Substance	Mean lethal dose (cat assay) (micrograms/kg.)	Mean systolic dose (frog assay) (micrograms/kg.)
Strophanthidin	306.2	2.71
Strophanthidin β-glucoside	91.3	0.583
Strophanthidin β-glucoside tetraacetate	1166	18.77
Strophanthidin β-xyloside	109.5	0.64
Strophanthidin β-xyloside triacetate	591.6	8.07
Strophanthidin L-arabinoside	94.5	0.308
Strophanthidin L-arabinoside triacetate	1230	6.33
Strophanthidin β-galactoside tetraacetate	1692	11.29
Strophanthidin cymaroside (cymarin)	110.1	0.60

glycosides produce an increased intensity of heart beat and a decreased rate. Some of these glycosides have been used as arrow poisons.

The influence of the nature of the glycosidic group of the strophanthidin glycosides on their biological activity is illustrated in Table I. The mean lethal dose (cat assay) and the mean systolic dose (frog assay) for a number of natural and synthetic glycosides are compared with those for the unsubstituted aglycon (strophanthidin) (*19*). It is of interest that the glucoside and L-arabinoside are more active than the natural product (the cymaroside).

Several synthetic glycosides of adrenal corticosteroids have been prepared (*20*). The deoxycorticosterone glucoside is more soluble in water than the aglycon and exhibits full physiological activity in maintaining the life of adrenalectomized rats (*21*). Synthetic glucosides of cholestanol and epicholestanol (*22*) and the methyl esters of several sterol galactosiduronic acids (*23*) are reported.

B. Saponins (*24*)

The saponins are an important class of glycosides widely distributed in plants. Saponin solutions foam easily. Given intravenously they are poison-

18. A. Stoll, *Helv. Chim. Acta* **35,** 1934 (1952).

19. F. C. Uhle and R. C. Elderfield, *J. Org. Chem.* **8,** 162 (1943).

20. W. S. Johnson, *J. Am. Chem. Soc.* **63,** 3238 (1941).

21. K. Miescher, W. H. Fischer, and C. Meystre, *Helv. Chim. Acta* **25,** 40 (1942).

22. R. P. Linstead, *J. Am. Chem. Soc.* **62,** 1766 (1940).

23. H. Sell and K. P. Link, *J. Biol. Chem.* **125,** 235 (1938).

24. W. H. Strain, *in* "Organic Chemistry" (H. Gilman, ed.), 2nd ed., p. 1454. Wiley, New York, 1943; L. Kofler, "Die Saponine" Springer, Vienna, 1927; R. Tschesche, *Fortschr. Chem. org. Naturstoffe* **1,** 1 (1945); L. F. Fieser and M. Fieser, "Natural Products Related to Phenanthrene," 3rd ed. Reinhold, New York, 1949.

ous and possess hemolytic action. They are nontoxic, as a rule, when administered orally, probably because of lack of absorption from the intestine. Their use as fish poisons depends on this fact, and fish which have been killed by the addition of plant extracts containing saponins to fish-bearing waters may be safely consumed by humans.

Two classes are recognized, the so-called neutral saponins (digitalis saponins), which have as aglycons substances derived from cyclopentanoperhydrophenanthrene, and the acid saponins, which have as aglycons substances derived from triterpene. The aglycons are called sapogenins. Most of the investigations have been devoted to the determination of the structures of the neutral saponins.

The formulas of a typical neutral saponin, sarsasaponin from *Radix sarsaparillae* (*25*), and the acid saponin of sugar beets (*Beta vulgaris*), the "glucuronide" of oleanolic acid (*26*), are given.

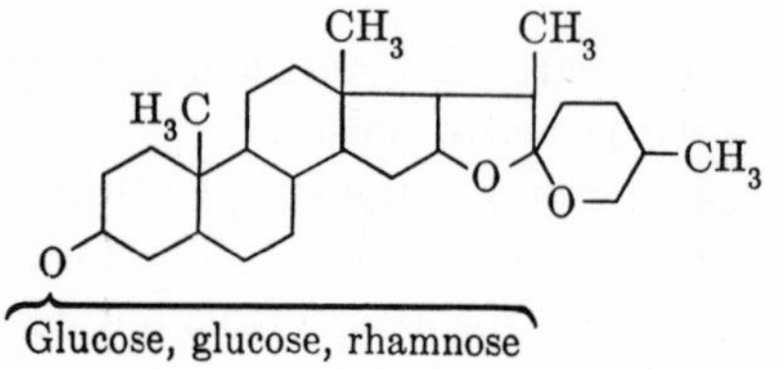
CH3
CH3
H3C
CH3
O
O
O
Glucose, glucose, rhamnose

Sarsasaponin

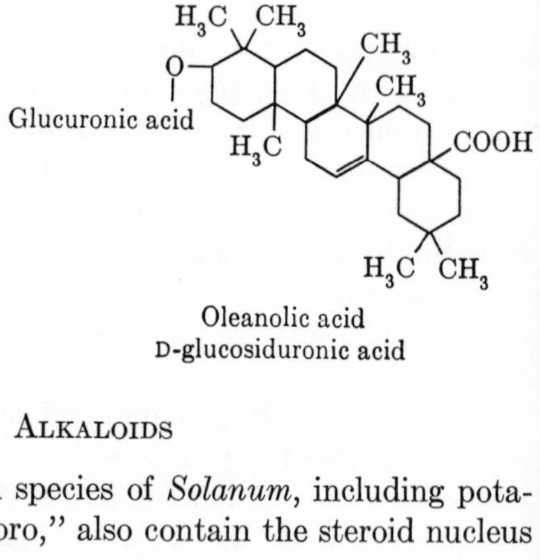
H3C CH3
CH3
CH3
O
Glucuronic acid
H3C
COOH
H3C CH3

Oleanolic acid
D-glucosiduronic acid

C. Solanum Alkaloids

The solanum alkaloids occurring in species of *Solanum*, including potatoes, "Dead Sea Apple," and "poro-poro," also contain the steroid nucleus

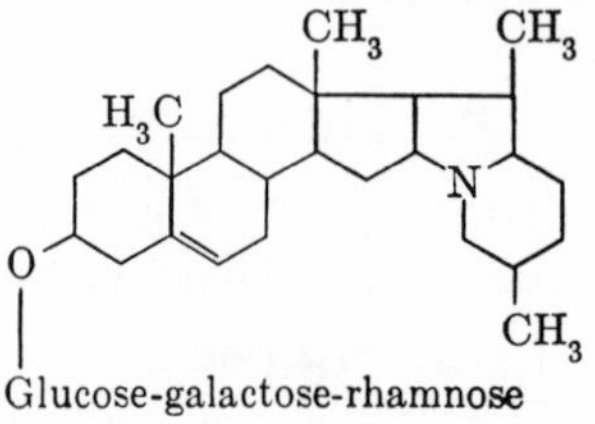
CH3
CH3
H3C
N
O
CH3
Glucose-galactose-rhamnose

Solanin

25. R. E. Marker and E. Rohrmann, *J. Am. Chem. Soc.* **61**, 846 (1939); F. C. Uhle and W. A. Jacobs, *J. Biol. Chem.* **160**, 342 (1945).

26. K. Rehorst, *Ber.* **62**, 519 (1929); O. Jeger, *Fortschr. Chem. org. Naturstoffe* **7**, 1 (1950).

and exist as glycosides (*27*). An alkaloid, whose structure shows a certain similarity to the saponins, is obtained by the total hydrolysis of solanin, the glycosidic alkaloid of *Solanum sodomaeum*, along with sugars (*28*).

Dihydrosolagenin (demissidin), combined with a tetrasaccharide, was found in *Solanum demissum* (*29*). This tetrasaccharide, also found in tomatin, the glycosidic alkaloid of tomato plants, is a xylosyl-glucosyl-glucosyl-galactose (*30*).

Plants containing demissin are not affected by the larva of the potato beetle (*29*). This doubtlessly arises from the presence of the alkaloid, since, normally, potato leaves are avoided when they have a gelatinous layer containing demissin. Crossbreeding between species containing solanin and demissin does not lead to the expected resistance, because the demissin content decreases in the hybridization (*31*).

4. SUBSTITUTED-PHENYL GLYCOSIDES

Many substituted phenols are found as the aglycons of naturally occurring glycosides. Arbutin (hydroquinone β-D-glucoside) and methylarbutin (*p*-methoxyphenyl β-D-glucoside) are extracted from the leaves of the bearberry (*Arctostaphylos uva-ursi*) and frequently occur together in other plants, particularly those of the family Ericaceae. The substances have been synthesized by the reaction between the corresponding salt of the phenol and tetra-*O*-acetylglucosyl halide (*32*). The leaves of certain varieties of *Pyrus* (pear family) turn black when they fall, but others assume an intermediate yellow color. These differences are believed to be due to variations in the arbutin and methylarbutin content. Leaves with considerable amounts of arbutin form hydroquinone by enzymic hydrolysis, and the hydroquinone is then oxidized by the air directly to a black product. The hydroquinone methyl ether obtained from the methylarbutin oxidizes first to a transient yellow substance before the black color develops.

Salicin is a glucoside found in willow bark (*Salix*) and in poplar bark (*Populus*). Particularly in the poplar bark, it is found accompanied by a second glucoside, populin. Salicin is *o*-hydroxymethylphenyl β-D-glucoside,

27. G. Oddo and G. Caronna, *Ber.* **67,** 446 (1934); L. H. Briggs, R. Newbold, and N. E. Stace, *J. Chem. Soc.* p. 3 (1942); L. H. Briggs and J. J. Carroll, *ibid.* p. 17 (1942).

28. V. Prelog and S. Szpilfogel, *Helv. Chim. Acta* **25,** 1306 (1942); *ibid.* **27,** 390 (1944); F. C. Uhle and W. A. Jacobs, *J. Biol. Chem.* **160,** 243 (1945).

29. R. Kuhn and I. Loew, *Chem. Ber.* **80,** 406 (1947).

30. R. Kuhn and I. Loew, *Chem. Ber.* **86,** 1027 (1953). For later work on solanins see: R. Kuhn *et al., Chem. Ber.* **88,** 1492 (1955).

31. S. M. Prokoshew, E. T. Petochenko, G. S. Il'in, V. Z. Baranova, and N. A. Lebedva, *Chem. Abstr.* **46,** 8201, 8722 (1952).

32. A. Michael, *Ber.* **14,** 2097 (1881); C. Mannich, *Arch. Pharm.* **250,** 547 (1912).

while populin is the 6-benzoyl derivative (*33*). The salicin is hydrolyzed easily by enzymes in almond emulsin, but populin is unaffected (*34*). However, it is claimed that an enzyme present in *Populus monilifera* hydrolyzes populin to salicin and benzoic acid (*35*). These substances have had some medicinal application as remedies for fever and acute rheumatism, and probably are metabolized to the widely used salicylates.

5. VANILLIN AND COUMARIN GLUCOSIDES

Vanillin, the aromatic principle of vanilla extract, occurs in many plants as the glycoside and, in particular, in the vanilla bean (*Vanilla planifolia* Andrews) of commerce. The curing of the beans is essentially an enzymic hydrolysis with the formation of the free vanillin. The glucoside and related glucosides have been synthesized (*36*), and the vanillin β-D-glucoside is the most easily hydrolyzed of all the glycosides cleaved by almond emulsin. An old but now little-used method for the production of vanillin depends on the oxidation of the glucoside, coniferin, which occurs in the sap of fir trees.

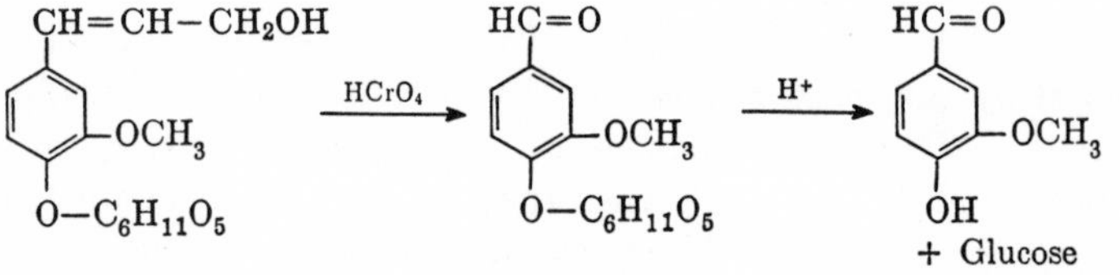
CH=CH−CH₂OH
OCH₃
O−C₆H₁₁O₅
HCrO₄
HC=O
OCH₃
O−C₆H₁₁O₅
H+
HC=O
OCH₃
OH
+ Glucose

Coniferin | Vanillin β-glucoside (Glucovanillin) | Vanillin

The significance of coniferin itself and the other glycosides of hydroxycinnamic alcohols, which have been known for a long time, has been indicated only recently (*37*). Freudenberg showed that the phenols (coniferyl and sinapin alcohols) liberated in the hydrolysis are very easily dehydrogenated by enzymes and in the process polymerize to ligninlike materials (dehydrogenative polymerization). As the first step the following compounds

33. P. Piria, *Ann.* **56**, 35 (1845); N. K. Richtmyer and E. Yeakel, *J. Am. Chem. Soc.* **56**, 2495 (1934).

34. W. W. Pigman and N. K. Richtmyer, *J. Am. Chem. Soc.* **64**, 374 (1942).

35. T. Weevers, *Koninkl. Akad. Wetenschappen Amsterdam* **12**, 193 (1909).

36. See B. Helferich, H. E. Scheiber, R. Streeck, and F. Vorsatz, *Ann.* **518**, 211 (1935).

37. K. Freudenberg, H. Reznik, H. Boesenberg, and D. Rasenack, *Ber.* **85**, 641 (1952); K. Freudenberg and D. Rasenack, *Ber.* **86**, 756 (1953).

were isolated:

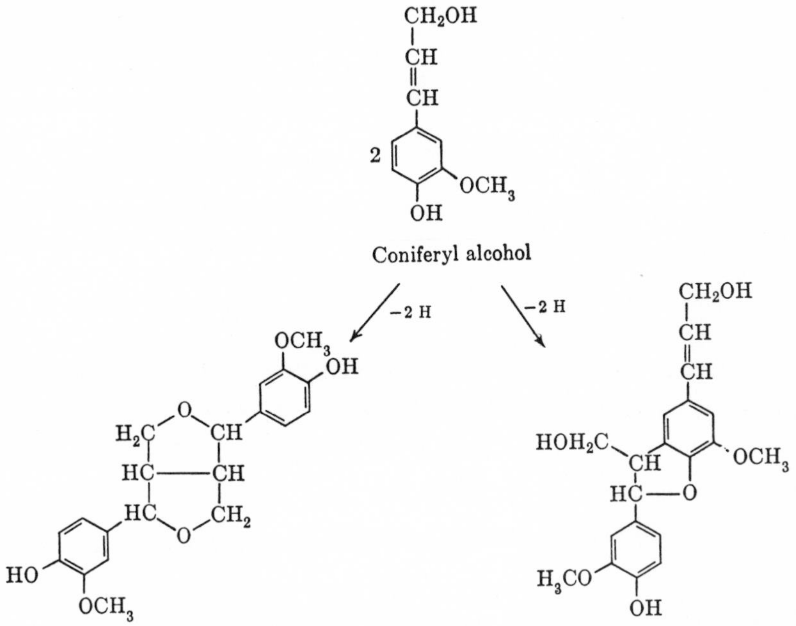
CH2OH
CH
CH
2
OCH3
OH
Coniferyl alcohol
−2 H
−2 H
OCH3
OH
H2C
O
CH
HC
CH
HC
CH2
O
HO
OCH3
CH2OH
CH
CH
HOH2C
CH
OCH3
HC
O
H3CO
OH

Pinoresinol

Dehydrodiconiferyl alcohol

Since the β-glucosidases have been demonstrated in the cambium layer of conifer stems and the dehydrogenating enzymes have been found in an inner layer, an increase in the lignification progressing from the outer layers to the inner layers may be explained.

It is usually considered that the aromatic principle coumarin, which is found in many plants, occurs as the glucoside. Since it has no free hydroxyl group, it is probably present in the wood as the glucoside of *o*-coumaric acid (*trans*) or *o*-coumarinic acid (*cis*). In the recovery from hydrolyzed plant extracts, both acids form the lactone coumarin, the *o*-coumaric acid being isomerized into the *cis* form, *o*-coumarinic acid. The glycoside of the unsubstituted *o*-coumaric acid has been isolated only from the blossoms of *Melilotus altissima* (*38*). On the other hand glycosides of hydroxy- and methoxy-substituted coumarin are widely abundant. These *cis-trans* rearrangements have been studied especially with the naturally occurring glucosides of furocoumarinic acid (*39*).

38. C. Charaux, *Bull. soc. chim. biol.* **7**, 1056 (1925).
39. A. Stoll, A. Perreira, and J. Rentz, *Helv. Chim. Acta* **33**, 1637 (1950).

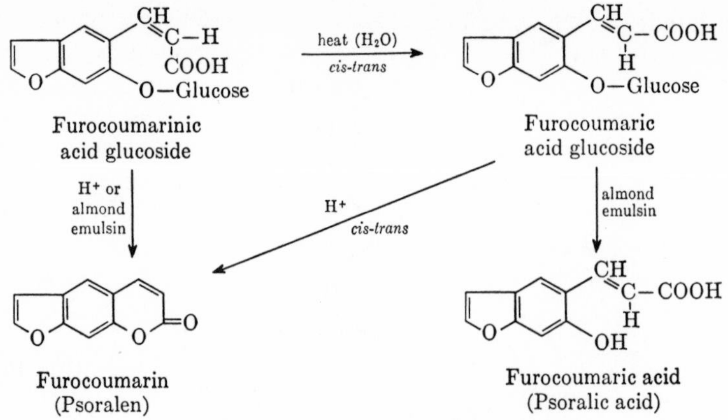
heat (H_2O)
cis-trans
Furocoumarinic acid glucoside
Furocoumaric acid glucoside
H+ or almond emulsin
H+
cis-trans
almond emulsin
Furocoumarin (Psoralen)
Furocoumaric acid (Psoralic acid)

6. CYANOGENETIC GLYCOSIDES

One of the earliest known glycosides is amygdalin, the effective principle of "oil of bitter almonds." Most plants belonging to Rosaceae (apricot,

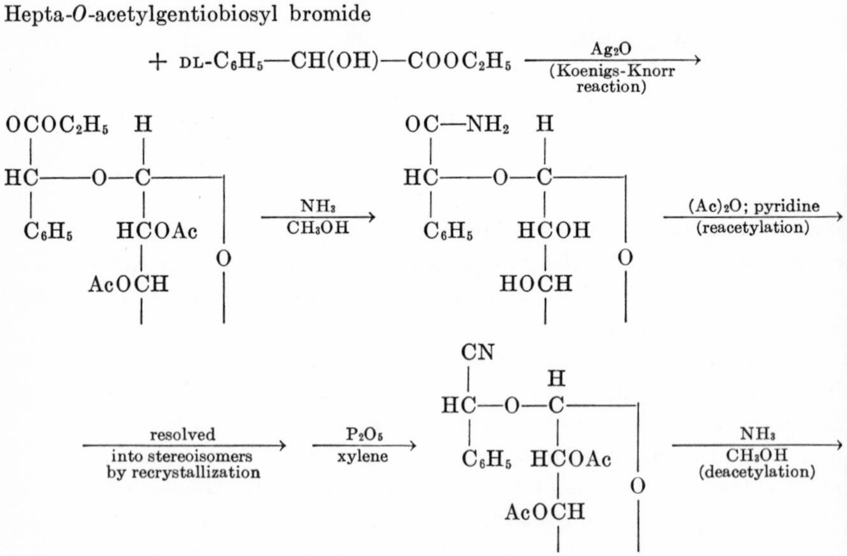
Hepta-O-acetylgentiobiosyl bromide
+ DL-C6H5—CH(OH)—COOC2H5
Ag2O
(Koenigs-Knorr reaction)
NH3
CH3OH
(Ac)2O; pyridine
(reacetylation)
resolved into stereoisomers by recrystallization
P2O5
xylene
NH3
CH3OH
(deacetylation)

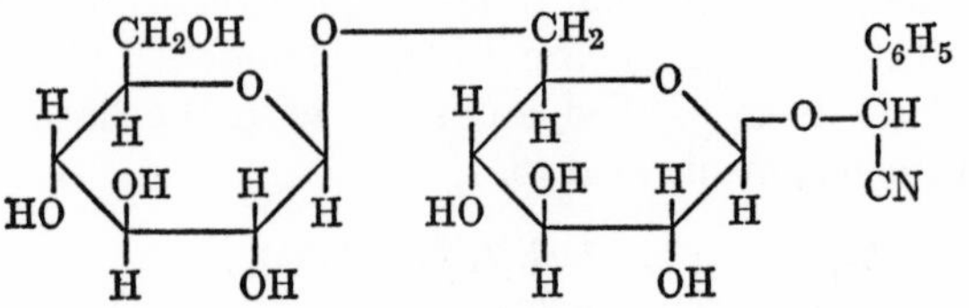

Amygdalin

bitter almond, plum, peach, etc.) contain considerable quantities of the glycoside or other cyanogenetic glycosides in the kernels, leaves, and woody portions. Acid or enzymic hydrolysis converts amygdalin to one mole each of benzaldehyde and hydrogen cyanide and two moles of glucose. The enzymic hydrolysis of amygdalin is of particular interest because it was one of the earliest-observed instances of enzymic action (*40*). The responsible substance was named "emulsin," a term now suggested for mixtures of enzymes (see p. 563).

Since the amygdalin may be synthesized (*41*) from hepta-*O*-acetylgentiobiosyl bromide and ethyl DL-mandelate by the procedure outlined above, the glycoside is undoubtedly D(levo)-mandelonitrile β-D-gentiobioside (*42*).

The enzymic hydrolysis by almond emulsin (β-glucosidase component) requires the preliminary hydrolysis of the gentiobiose into glucose and mandelonitrile β-D-glucoside before the aglycon group is removed (*43*), but the hydrolysis by other enzymes may follow a different course.

It is claimed that yeast extracts will hydrolyze amygdalin to mandelonitrile β-glucoside which is identical with the glucoside prunasin found in wild cherry bark (*Prunus serotina*). A glucoside isomeric with prunasin and called sambunigrin is found in elder leaves (*Sambucus niger*). These glucosides differ only in the nature of the aglycon group; that for prunasin is D(levo)-mandelonitrile β-glucoside whereas that for sambunigrin is L(dextro)-mandelonitrile β-glucoside. In alkaline solution these two isomeric glucosides are racemized to a mixture of the two which is called prulaurasin (*44*). The synthesis of these substances from the synthetic ethyl mandelates and tetra-*O*-acetylglucosyl bromide has been accomplished (*45*).

7. HYDROXYANTHRAQUINONE GLYCOSIDES

These important substances are found in many plant materials, and the aglycons have had considerable value as dyestuffs. Ruberythric acid, the principal constituent of madder (the ground root of *Rubia tinctoria*), is hydrolyzed by the enzymes of *Primula officinalis* and *P. vulgaris* emulsin to alizarin (1,2-dihydroxyanthraquinone) and primeverose (6-glucose β-xyloside). Since methylation of the ruberythric acid and acid hydrolysis yields alizarin 1-methyl ether, the glycoside is 2-alizarin β-D-primevero-

40. F. Wöhler and J. Liebig, *Ann.* **22,** 1 (1837).

41. R. Campbell and W. N. Haworth, *J. Chem. Soc.* p. 1337 (1924); G. Zemplén and A. Kunz, *Ber.* **57,** 1357 (1924); R. Kuhn and H. Sobotka, *ibid.* **57,** 1767 (1924).

42. For the configuration of mandelic acid see K. Freudenberg, F. Brauns, and H. Siegel, *Ber.* **56,** 193 (1923).

43. R. Weidenhagen, *Ergeb. Enzymforsch.* **1,** 197 (1932).

44. See R. J. Caldwell and S. L. Courtauld, *J. Chem. Soc.* **91,** 666, 671 (1907).

45. E. Fischer and M. Bergmann, *Ber.* **50,** 1047 (1917).

side (*46*). This structure has received a final proof in the synthesis of the glycoside from alizarin and hexa-*O*-acetylprimeverosyl bromide in an aqueous acetone–KOH solution (*47*). Other glycosides present in madder are: purpurin (1,2,4-trihydroxyanthraquinone D-glucoside) and rubiadin glucoside (*48*) (3-(1,3-dihydroxy-2-methylanthraquinone) D-glucoside).

TABLE II

COMMON AND SYSTEMATIC NAMES OF THE DEOXYSUGARS OF THE CARDIAC GLYCOSIDES

Common name	Systematic name
D-Allomethylose (*49*)	6-Deoxy-D-allose
L-Talomethylose (*50*)	6-Deoxy-L-talose
L-Acovenose (*51*)	6-Deoxy-3-*O*-methyl-L-talose
L-Rhamnose	6-Deoxy-L-mannose (Chapter II)
L-Acofriose (*52*)	6-Deoxy-3-*O*-methyl-L-mannose
D- and L-Fucose	6-Deoxy-D- and L-galactose (Chapter II)
D-Digitalose (*53*)	6-Deoxy-3-*O*-methyl-D-galactose
D-Antiarose (*54*)	6-Deoxy-D-gulose
D-Quinovose	6-Deoxy-D-glucose (Chapter II)
L-Thevetose (*55*)	6-Deoxy-4-*O*-methyl-L-glucose
D-Digitoxose (*56*)	2,6-Dideoxy-D-*ribo*-hexose
D-Cymarose (*57*)	2,6-Dideoxy-3-*O*-methyl-D-*ribo*-hexose
D-Diginose (*58*)	2,6-Dideoxy-3-*O*-methyl-D-*lyxo*-hexose
L-Oleandrose (*59*)	2,6-Dideoxy-3-*O*-methyl-L-*arabo*-hexose
D-Boivinose (*60*)	2,6-Dideoxy-D-*xylo*-hexose
D-Sarmentose (*61*)	2,6-Dideoxy-3-*O*-methyl-D-*xylo*-hexose

46. D. Richter, *J. Chem. Soc.* p. 1701 (1936).

47. G. Zemplén and R. Bognar, *Ber.* **72,** 913 (1939).

48. E. T. Jones and A. Robertson, *J. Chem. Soc.* p. 1699 (1930).

49. F. Micheel, *Ber.* **63,** 347 (1930); A. Hunger and T. Reichstein, *Helv. Chim. Acta* **35,** 1073 (1952).

50. J. Schmutz and T. Reichstein, *Helv. Chim. Acta* **34,** 1264 (1951); J. Schmutz, *ibid.* **31,** 1719 (1948).

51. C. Tamm and T. Reichstein, *Helv. Chim. Acta* **34,** 1224 (1951).

52. H. Muhr, A. Hunger, and T. Reichstein, *Helv. Chim. Acta* **37,** 403 (1954).

53. O. T. Schmidt and E. Wernicke, *Ann.* **556,** 179 (1944); F. Reber and T. Reichstein, *Helv. Chim. Acta* **29,** 343 (1946).

54. K. Doebel, E. Schlitter, and T. Reichstein, *ibid.* **31,** 688 (1948); P. A. Levene and J. Compton, *J. Biol. Chem.* **111,** 325, 335 (1935).

55. M. Frèrejacque and V. Hasenfratz, *Compt. rend.* **222,** 815 (1946); F. Blindenbacher and T. Reichstein, *Helv. Chim. Acta* **31,** 1669 (1948).

56. F. Micheel, *Ber.* **63,** 347 (1930); B. Iselin and T. Reichstein, *Helv. Chim. Acta* **27,** 1203 (1944).

57. R. C. Elderfield, *J. Biol. Chem.* **111,** 527 (1935); D. A. Prins, *Helv. Chim. Acta* **29,** 378 (1946).

The presence of these glucosides along with the ruberythric acid in madder is the probable explanation for the well-known color difference between the natural and the synthetic alizarin.

8. SUGAR COMPONENTS OF NATURAL PLANT GLYCOSIDES

The most frequently encountered sugar component of glycosides is D-glucose, but practically all of the naturally occurring sugars are found in plant glycosides. Peculiarly enough, three of the most common sugars (D-galactose, D-mannose, and D-fructose) are only rarely encountered. Galactose is reported to occur in certain saponins and trisaccharide glycosides (robinose and rhamninose). A mannoside is found in some seaweeds. Fructose is reported to be the sugar of certain saponins. In contrast, the 6-deoxy-L-mannosides and 6-deoxy-D- and L-galactosides (L-rhamnosides and D- and L-fucosides) are often found in plant products. Of the pentoses, L-arabinose and D-xylose are frequent and D-arabinose infrequent constituents of glycosides. Glucuronic acid is often a constituent.

In addition to the sugars mentioned, a group of deoxysugars and branched-chain sugars is found as constituents of the digitalis glycosides. The deoxysugars found in the digitalis glycosides are all derived from 6-deoxyaldoses. In addition, either the hydroxyl group on carbon atom 2 is replaced by a hydrogen atom (dideoxysugars) or the hydroxyl group on carbon 3 is methylated. In Table II the known deoxysugars of the cardiac glycosides are listed. The structures of acovenose and acofriose are still doubtful, but all the others have been proven through synthesis.

A sugar interesting because of its unusual branched-chain structure is apiose, which occurs conjugated with the 5,7,4′-trihydroxyflavone as the glycoside apiin in the leaves and seed of parsley (*62*). Other branched-chain sugars known are hamamelose, streptose, cordecypose, and mycarose (Chapter II). The structure of apiose is shown by the reduction of apionic acid with phosphorus and hydrogen iodide to 3-methylbutyric acid (*63*). The single asymmetric carbon of apiose probably has the configuration of D(levo)-lactic acid.

---

58. C. W. Shoppee and T. Reichstein, *Helv. Chim. Acta* **25,** 1611 (1942); C. Tamm and T. Reichstein, *ibid.* **31,** 1630 (1948).

59. G. Hesse, *Ber.* **70,** 2264 (1937); F. Blindenbacher and T. Reichstein, *Helv. Chim. Acta* **31,** 2061 (1948).

60. O. Schindler and T. Reichstein, *Helv. Chim. Acta* **35,** 730 (1952); H. R. Bollinger and T. Reichstein, *ibid.* **36,** 302 (1953).

61. W. A. Jacobs and N. M. Bigelow, *J. Biol. Chem.* **96,** 355 (1932); H. Hauenstein and T. Reichstein, *Helv. Chim. Acta* **33,** 446 (1950).

62. See C. S. Hudson, *Advances in Carbohydrate Chem.* **4,** 57 (1949).

63. O. Th. Schmidt, *Ann.* **483,** 115 (1930).

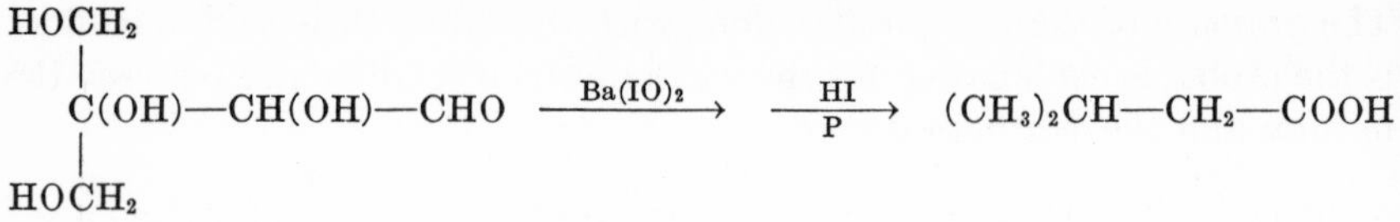

$$\begin{array}{c} \text{HOCH}_2 \\ | \\ \text{C(OH)—CH(OH)—CHO} \xrightarrow{\text{Ba(IO)}_2} \xrightarrow[\text{P}]{\text{HI}} (\text{CH}_3)_2\text{CH—CH}_2\text{—COOH} \\ | \\ \text{HOCH}_2 \end{array}$$

Apiose

In the plant materials from which the glycosides are obtained by extraction, the corresponding enzymes are often to be found. If care is not taken to destroy the enzyme, hydrolysis of the glycoside may take place and erroneous conclusions be drawn concerning the sugars present. Hydrolysis is prevented by rapid heating of the aqueous or alcoholic solutions to the boiling temperature. Because this precaution has not always been taken, many reported monosaccharide constituents may really be disaccharides or trisaccharides. In many instances it is known that the sugar portion of the glycoside is a di- or trisaccharide. In other instances an oligosaccharide structure is assumed if several molecules of a sugar are formed from a single mole of the glycoside although, if the aglycon is a polyhydroxyphenol, the glycoside may be a di- or triglycoside. The structures of some di- and trisaccharides found as constituents of glycosides are described in the chapter on oligosaccharides.

The naturally occurring glucosides have almost exclusively the beta configuration for the glucosidic carbon and as a result are levorotatory. Dextrorotating phillyrin from *Forsythia suspensa* and *Olea fragrans* is believed (*64*) to be an α-D-glucoside, for it is hydrolyzed by yeast α-glucosidase and not by almond emulsin. Alkyl glycosides are rare, but the ethyl α-D-galactoside has been obtained (*65*) by the extraction of the phosphatides of yellow sweet lupines; floridoside, a crystalline glycoside found in red algae (*Florideae*), is considered to be 2-glycerol α-D-galactoside (*66*). Methyl β-D-glucoside has been isolated from the fresh leaves of *Scabiosa succisa* (*67*). A D-glyceric acid α-mannoside occurs in algae of the genus *Polysiphonia* (*68*).

9. THIOGLYCOSIDES AND THIOSUGARS (*69*)

Black mustard (*Brassica nigra* Koch) contains a glucoside, sinigrin, which is hydrolyzed by enzymes present in the plant to allyl isothiocyanate,

64. F. Kolle and T. Hjerlow, *Pharm. Zentr.* **71**, 705 (1930).

65. E. Nottbohm and F. Mayer, *Vorratspflege u. Lebensmittelforsch.* **1**, 243 (1938).

66. H. Colin, *Bull. soc. chim. France* [5] **4**, 277 (1937).

67. N. Wattiez, *Chem. Abstr.* **19**, 3284 (1925).

68. H. Colin and J. Augier, *Compt. rend.* **208**, 1450 (1939).

69. For reviews see J. Gadamer, *Arch. Pharm.* **235**, 44 (1897); H. Will and W. Körner, *Ann.* **125**, 257 (1863); A. L. Raymond, *Advances in Carbohydrate Chem.* **1**, 129 (1945).

potassium hydrogen sulfate, and glucose. The presence of this glucoside explains the odor of allyl isothiocyanate which develops when the seed is bruised and moistened. According to J. Gadamer, the structure is:

$$\underset{\text{CH}_2{=}\text{CH—CH}_2\text{—N}{=}\overset{\displaystyle|}{\text{C}}\text{—S—}(\text{C}_6\text{H}_{11}\text{O}_5)}{\overset{\text{OSO}_3\text{K}}{}}$$

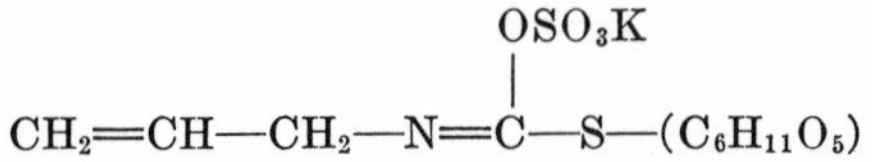

Almond emulsin does not hydrolyze the glucoside, but mustard-seed emulsin contains an enzyme, myrosin, which catalyzes the hydrolysis. It seems probable that the linkage is beta and indeed enzymic hydrolysis produces β-glucose. However, silver nitrate and silver carbonate produce α-glucose, presumably as a result of a Walden inversion (70). The hydrolytic action of sodium hydroxide leads to "thioses" (1-thiosugars).

Many of the plants of *Cruciferae* produce sinigrin and other sulfur-containing glycosides. These compounds comprise the so-called mustard-oil glycosides and are described in more detail elsewhere (*3,69*).

Synthetic thioglucosides are prepared by the action of thiophenol on acetylglycosyl bromides in the presence of sodium hydroxide (*71, 72*). They are extremely resistant to acid hydrolysis, and this resistance probably explains the lack of hydrolysis by almond emulsin (*71, 73*). By treatment of sugar thiols with mercuric chloride, thioglycosides also may be synthesized (Chapter V):

$$\begin{array}{ccc}
\text{HC(SC}_2\text{H}_5)_2 & & \text{HC—SC}_2\text{H}_5 \\
| & \xrightarrow[\text{H}_2\text{O}]{\text{HgCl}_2} & | \\
\text{HCOH} & & \text{HCOH} \qquad \text{O} \\
| & & |
\end{array}$$

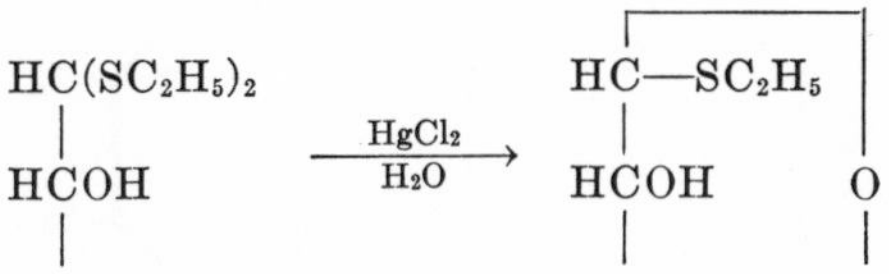

Many aromatic 1-thio-β-D-glucosides have been tested as antimalarials. Some show a slight positive action, but the effect is too small to be of value (*74*).

The sulfur analogs of the sugars are known as thiosugars (*75*). When the sulfur replaces the oxygen of the anomeric hydroxyl, the compounds are sometimes distinguished as "thioses," e.g., "glucothiose" and "cellobiothiose." In addition to the thioglucosides discussed above, the only naturally occurring derivative of a thiosugar is the 5-thiomethylribose

70. W. Schneider, H. Fischer, and W. Specht, *Ber.* **63**, 2787 (1930).

71. E. Fischer and K. Delbrück, *Ber.* **42**, 1476 (1909); C. B. Purves, *J. Am. Chem. Soc.* **51**, 3627 (1929).

72. W. Schneider, J. Sepp, and O. Stiehler, *Ber.* **51**, 220 (1918).

73. W. W. Pigman, *J. Research Natl. Bur. Standards* **26**, 197 (1941).

74. E. M. Montgomery, N. K. Richtmyer, and C. S. Hudson, *J. Org. Chem.* **11**, 301 (1946).

75. W. Schneider, R. Gille, and K. Eisfeld, *Ber.* **61**, 1244 (1928).

Synthesis of Streptidine

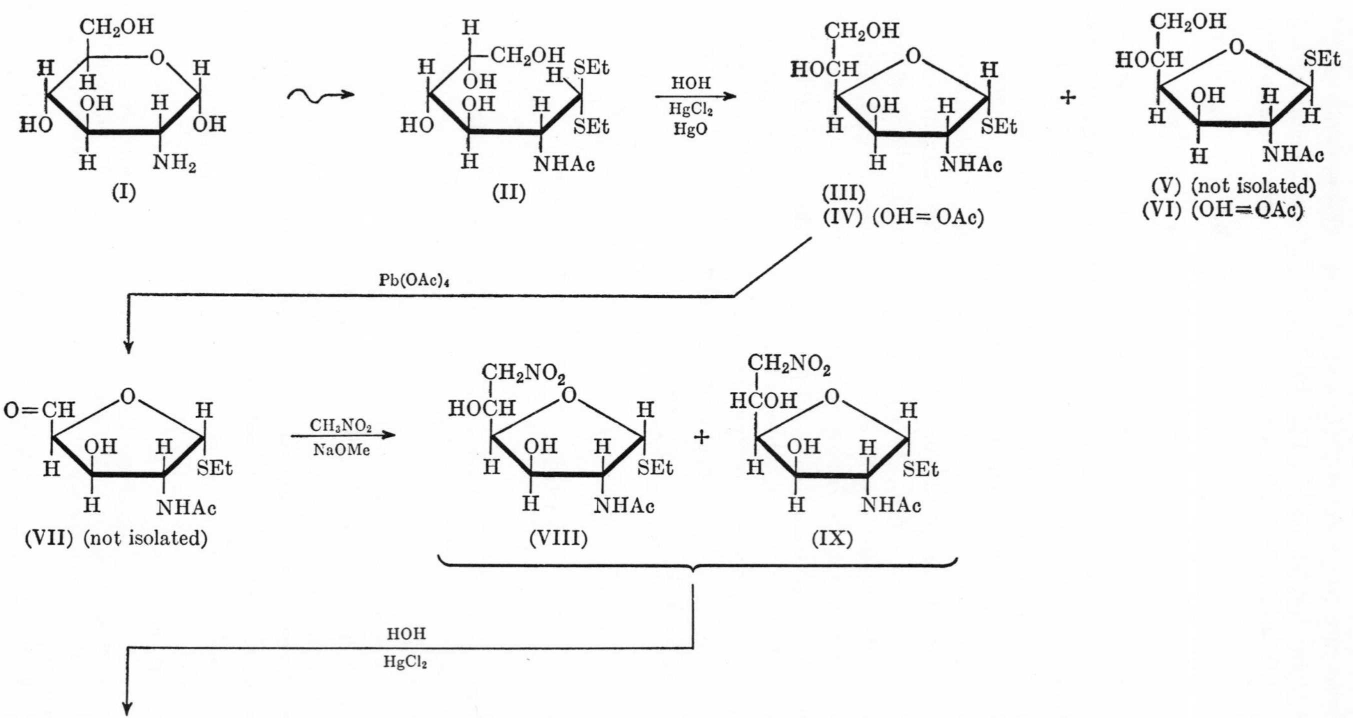
(I)
(II)
HOH
$HgCl_2$
HgO
(III)
(IV) (OH = OAc)
(V) (not isolated)
(VI) (OH=OAc)
$Pb(OAc)_4$
(VII) (not isolated)
CH_3NO_2
NaOMe
(VIII)
(IX)
HOH
$HgCl_2$

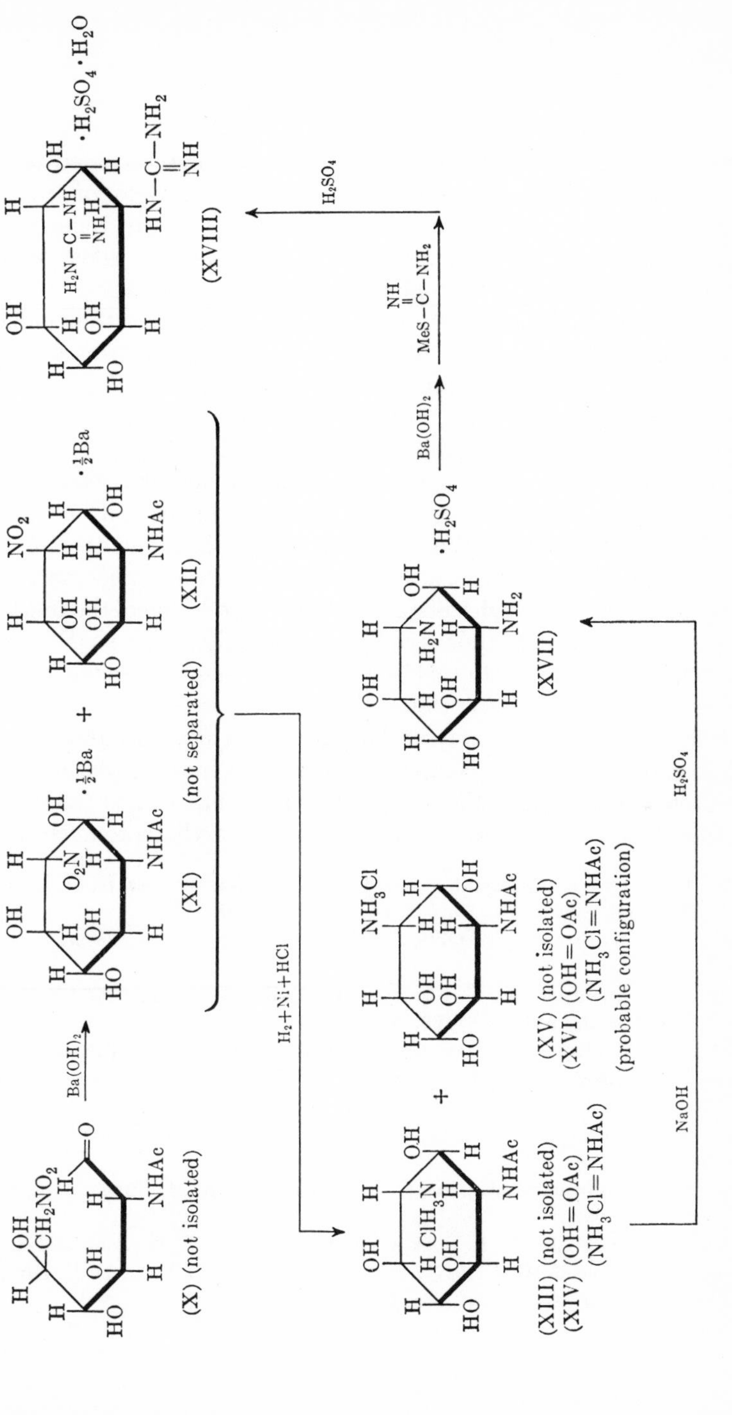

reported to occur, combined with adenosine, in yeast extracts (see under Nucleosides).

10. STREPTOMYCIN (*76*)

Streptomycin, an important antibiotic, was first prepared as a crude concentrate by Waksman and co-workers from cultures of *Streptomyces griseus*, a soil organism. Acid hydrolysis of streptomycin yields streptidine and streptobiosamine. Wolfrom and co-workers (*77*) have synthesized streptidine (XVIII) from D-glucosamine (I) by the series of reactions shown on pages 556 and 557. This synthesis establishes the configuration of five of the asymmetric centers (C-2 to C-6 inclusive) as a completely *trans* relation. From the nature of the cyclization reactions, the remaining center is very probably *trans* to the adjacent nitrogen atoms. On this basis, streptidine is a diguanidino-*scyllo*-inositol.

Streptobiosamine, upon hydrolysis, yields *N*-methyl-L-glucosamine and streptose. The structure of *N*-methyl-L-glucosamine was confirmed by synthesis (*78*). In 1948, Wolfrom (*79*) and Folkers and their co-workers (*80*) independently established the structure of streptose as 5-deoxy-3-formyl-L-lyxose. The high resistance toward acetylation of the free hydroxyl group in tetra-*O*-acetyldideoxydihydrostreptobiosamine suggested that it was tertiary in nature. On this basis, *N*-methyl-L-glucosamine was assigned to the C-2 position of streptose (*81*).

Although the position of the linkage between the streptose and streptidine units has not been completely settled, the most probable structure of streptomycin is given in the accompanying formula (XIX) (*79, 80, 82, 83*).

Another antibiotic (streptomycin B, mannosylstreptomycin), isolated

76. For a review of the subject and detailed references see R. U. Lemieux and M. L. Wolfrom, *Advances in Carbohydrate Chem.* **3**, 337 (1947).

77. M. L. Wolfrom, S. M. Olin, and W. J. Polglase, *J. Am. Chem. Soc.* **72**, 1724 (1950).

78. F. A. Kuehl, Jr., E. H. Flynn, F. W. Holly, R. Mozingo, and K. Folkers, *J. Am. Chem. Soc.* **68**, 546 (1946); **69**, 3032 (1947).

79. M. L. Wolfrom and C. W. DeWalt, *J. Am. Chem. Soc.* **70**, 3148 (1948).

80. F. A. Kuehl, Jr., M. N. Bishop, E. H. Flynn, and K. Folkers, *J. Am. Chem. Soc.* **70**, 2613 (1948).

81. N. G. Brink, F. A. Kuehl, Jr., E. H. Flynn, and K. Folkers, *J. Am. Chem. Soc.* **68**, 2405 (1946).

82. M. L. Wolfrom, M. J. Cron, C. W. DeWalt, and R. M. Husband, *J. Am. Chem. Soc.* **76**, 3675 (1954).

83. F. A. Kuehl, Jr., R. L. Peck, C. E. Hoffhine, Jr., E. W. Peel, and K. Folkers, *J. Am. Chem. Soc.* **69**, 1234 (1947); F. A. Kuehl, Jr., R. L. Peck, D. E. Hoffhine, Jr., and K. Folkers, *J. Am. Chem. Soc.* **70**, 2325 (1948).

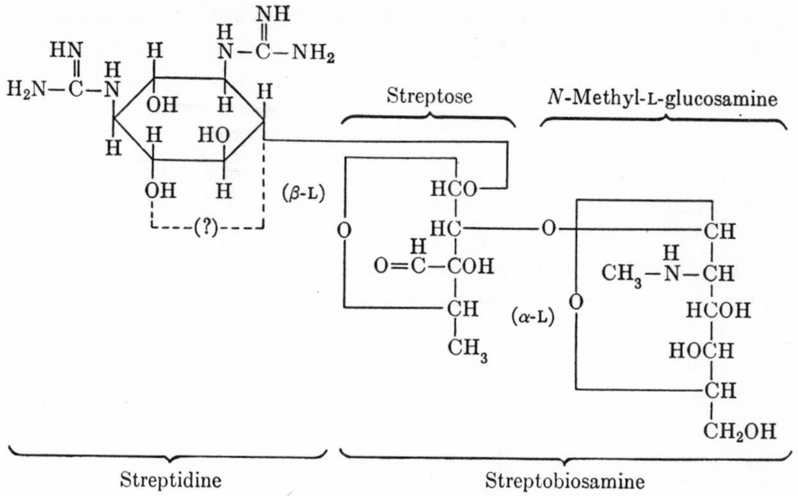
Streptose
N-Methyl-L-glucosamine
(β-L)
(α-L)
Streptidine
Streptobiosamine

(XIX)
Streptomycin

from streptomycin concentrates by Fried and co-workers (*84*), has been assigned (*85*) the structure (XX).

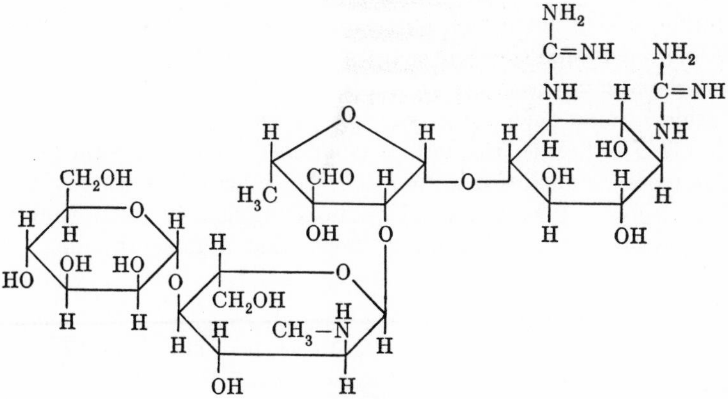

(XX)
Streptomycin B

Several derivatives of streptomycin have been prepared (*86*). These have

84. J. Fried and E. Titus, *J. Biol. Chem.* **168,** 391 (1947).

85. J. Fried and H. E. Stavely, *J. Am. Chem. Soc.* **74,** 5461 (1952).

86. I. A. Solomons and P. P. Regna, *J. Am. Chem. Soc.* **72,** 2974 (1950); W.. A Winsten, C. I. Jarowski, F. X. Murphy, and W. A. Lazier, *J. Am. Chem. Soc.* **72,** 3969 (1950).

less activity or more toxicity than the parent compound, except for dihydrostreptomycin, which also has widespread clinical use. In dihydrostreptomycin, the aldehyde group of the streptose unit is reduced to CH_2OH.

11. CEREBROSIDES (*87*)

A group of poorly defined substances known as cerebrosides, glycolipides, and gangliosides has been found in the lipide ("Protagon") fraction of brain, nerve tissue, spleen, and the stroma of erythrocytes. The investigations of Thudichum, Thierfelder, Levene, Klenk, and others have established that the cerebrosides normally consist of one mole each of a nitrogenous base (sphingosine), of a fatty acid, and of a sugar. The cerebrosides are separated from the accompanying gangliosides on the basis of the greater solubility of the gangliosides in water. In gangliosides, more than one mole of monosaccharide is present (*88*).

The fatty acid components are usually lignoceric acid, $CH_3(CH_2)_{22}$—COOH (of kerasin), 2-hydroxylignoceric acid (of phrenosin), Δ^{15}-lignoceric acid (of nervone), behenic acid, or stearic acid.

Sphingosine has been shown to be 2-amino-1,3-dihydroxy-4-*trans*-D-*erthro*-octadecene (*89*).

The sugar components are D-galactose and D-glucose in glycosidic linkage with the primary hydroxyl of the sphingosine (*90*). Hexosamines have also been found, and probably exist partially as a component of an attached acid termed neuraminic acid (see under Sialic acid, Chapter XII).

The presence of a neuraminic acid residue may be characteristic of gangliosides. Some evidence exists that in some pathological conditions, e.g., Gaucher's disease, the hexose component may be D-glucose rather than the more common D-galactose (*91*). The glycosidic nature is indicated by the hydrolysis of cerebrosides by almond emulsin (*92*, *93*). Methylation of a cerebroside from ox brain has shown that a galactopyranose ring is present (*93*).

87. J. C. Cowan and H. E. Carter, *in* "Organic Chemistry" (H. Gilman, ed.), Vol. 3, p. 236. Wiley, New York, 1953; H. J. Deuel, Jr., "The Lipids." Interscience, New York, 1951, 1955; H. Thierfelder and E. Klenk, "Die Chemie der Cerebroside und Phosphatide." Springer, Berlin, 1930.

88. E. Klenk, *Z. physiol. Chem.* **273,** 76 (1942); E. Klenk and F. Rennkamp, *ibid.* **273,** 253 (1942); E. Klenk and K. Lauenstein, *ibid.* **295,** 164 (1953).

89. H. E. Carter, F. J. Glick, W. P. Norris, and G. E. Phillips, *J. Biol. Chem.* **170,** 285 (1947); G. Fodor and D. Banfi, *Helv. Chim. Acta* **37,** 1471 (1954).

90. H. E. Carter and F. L. Greenwood, *J. Biol. Chem.* **199,** 283 (1952); T. Nakayama, *J. Biochem.* (*Japan*) **37,** 309 (1950).

91. N. Halliday, H. J. Deuel, Jr., L. J. Tragerman and W. E. Ward, *J. Biol. Chem.* **132,** 171 (1940); A. W. Devor, *Arch. Biochem. and Biophys.* **50,** 217 (1954).

92. B. Helferich, H. Appel, and R. Gootz, *Z. physiol. Chem.* **215,** 277 (1933).

93. J. Pryde and R. W. Humphreys, *Biochem. J.* **20,** 825 (1926).

The formulas of a typical ganglioside and cerebroside as proposed by Klenk (*88*) are given in the accompanying formulas:

Kerasin (a cerebroside from cattle spleen):

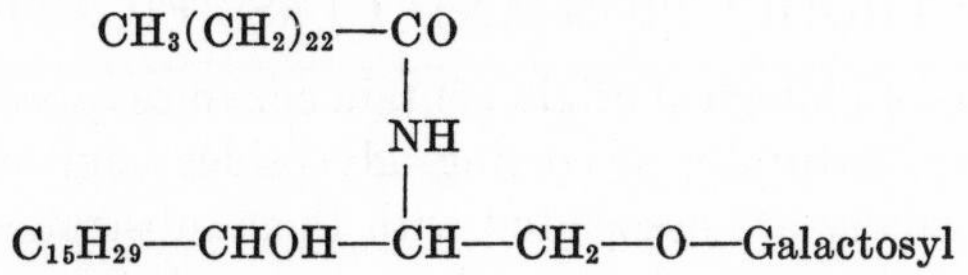
CH3(CH2)22—CO
NH
C15H29—CHOH—CH—CH2—O—Galactosyl

Ganglioside of brain and spleen:

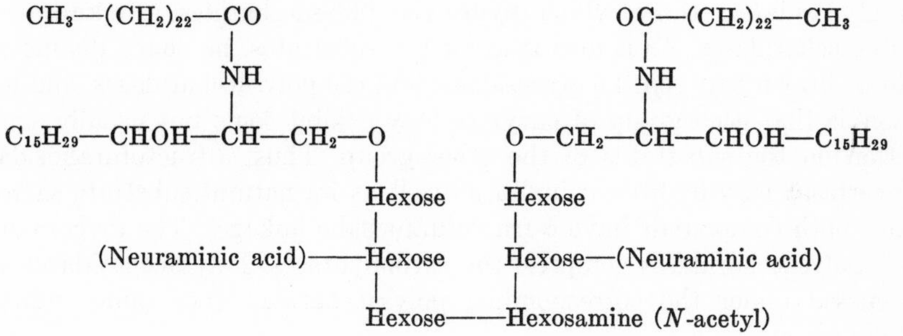
CH3—(CH2)22—CO
OC—(CH2)22—CH3
NH
NH
C15H29—CHOH—CH—CH2—O
O—CH2—CH—CHOH—C15H29
Hexose
Hexose
(Neuraminic acid)——Hexose
Hexose—(Neuraminic acid)
Hexose——Hexosamine (N-acetyl)

Part II

GLYCOSIDASES (1)

1. INTRODUCTION AND CLASSIFICATION

Many materials of biological origin contain enzymes capable of catalyzing the hydrolysis of naturally occurring glycosides and oligosaccharides. These enzymes usually are associated with their substrates, and to obtain the latter it is necessary to destroy the enzymes before hydrolysis takes place. Enzymes which hydrolyze glycosides and oligosaccharides are known as glycosidases; those which hydrolyze polysaccharides are known as polysaccharidases. As is also true for the substrates, no sharp distinction can be drawn between the glycosidases and the polysaccharidases, and it is possible that each group of enzymes may exhibit some but usually slight action on the substrates of the other group. Thus, β-fructofuranosidase (invertase) may hydrolyze inulin as well as its natural substrate sucrose since both compounds have β-fructofuranosidic linkages. The glycosidases and polysaccharidases comprise the carbohydrases. Polysaccharidases are discussed under the corresponding polysaccharides. (See under Starch, Cellulose, etc.)

From the historical standpoint the glycosidases are of particular interest since they were the first enzymes to be known. Planche (1810, 1820) showed that the extracts of certain plants will cause guaiacum tincture to become blue. It was then demonstrated that extracts of the bitter almond hydrolyze the glycoside amygdalin also found in the bitter almond (Robiquet and Boutron-Chalard, 1830). The active principle of the bitter almond was further investigated and named emulsin (Liebig and Wöhler, 1837; Robiquet, 1838). Although a diastase in germinated barley was described in 1815 by Kirchoff, salivary amylase by Leuchs in 1831, and other cereal diastases in 1833 (Payen and Persoz), the first of the proteases (pepsin) was not reported until 1836 by Schwann.

The glycosidases are not of great industrial importance at present although the polysaccharidases are of the utmost interest from this standpoint. The amylases play important roles in the fermentation and baking industries and are of considerable biological importance. Other polysaccharidases such as cellulases and inulases are of considerable potential importance, for the corresponding polysaccharides are widely distributed. Of the glycosidases, β-fructofuranosidase or invertase, which hydrolyzes

1. For more detailed information see W. W. Pigman, *Advances in Enzymol.* **4,** 41 (1944); J. B. Sumner and K. Myrbäck, eds., "The Enzymes." Academic Press, New York, 1950, especially Vol. I, Part I; S. P. Colowick and N. O. Kaplan, eds., "Methods in Enzymology." Academic Press, New York, 1955. (In 4 vols.)

sucrose, is the most important although α-glucosidase (maltase) should be of considerable interest because of the common occurrence of maltose in commercial products. Most of the research carried out with these enzymes has centered around the amylases, the β-glucosidase and other enzymes of almond emulsin, and yeast invertase. The glycosidases provide excellent enzymes for specificity studies since the number of substrates which may be synthesized is practically limitless and since the compounds are well defined, easily prepared, and usually crystalline. Although the glycosidases offer these advantages to the investigator, studies in this field suffer from the lack of purity of the enzymes and particularly in not having crystalline enzymes.

The historical name "emulsin" as applied to the active principle of the preparation from almonds has gradually assumed the meaning of a crude mixture of glycosidases from any source. Helferich and Vorsatz (*2*) have used the term "emulsin" in this sense, but the definition has been broadened to include other enzymes. It is suggested that the partially purified enzyme mixtures obtained from seeds, microorganisms, and animal organs and tissues be termed emulsins. Commercial "enzymes" are known as emulsins according to this definition. Almond emulsin is a mixture of enzymes prepared from almonds and not the β-glucosidase therein. Commercial invertase is a yeast emulsin and Takadiastase is an *Aspergillus oryzae* emulsin.

The individual glycosidases of the emulsins are named according to the α- or β-hexoside which they hydrolyze, as α- or β-hexosidases. Thus, β-glucosidases (earlier emulsin or prunasin) catalyze the cleavage of β-glucosides, and α-glucosidases the cleavage of α-glucosides.

2. MECHANISM OF ACTION

The most widely accepted theory of enzyme action is based on the formation of an intermediate compound or adsorption complex between enzyme and substrate (Brown, 1902; Henri, 1903). Since both conceptions of the nature of the enzyme-substrate complex can lead to the same kinetic equations, the distinction seems unimportant at present. In the following development of the kinetic equations, the original scheme of Michaelis and Menten (1913) will be followed and compound formation will be considered to take place. However, in later discussions, the process will be considered as a type of adsorption.

A. Kinetic Equations and Effect of Substrate Concentration

In order to develop the kinetic equations, consider the hydrolysis of a glucoside (S) by an enzyme (E) to an alcohol or phenol (ROH) and glucose.

2. B. Helferich and F. Vorsatz, *Z. physiol. Chem.* **237,** 254 (1935); W. W. Pigman, *J. Research Natl. Bur. Standards* **30,** 159 (1943).

The reactions may be represented:

$$S + E \rightleftarrows ES \tag{1}$$

$$ES + H_2O \rightarrow E + ROH + \text{Glucose} \tag{2}$$

Since a certain portion of both enzyme and substrate always is combined, the concentration of free enzyme $[E]$ and substrate $[S]$ at any time is given by the following equations, where the total enzyme concentration is represented by "e" and the total substrate concentration by "A."

$$[S] = [A] - [ES] \tag{3}$$

$$[E] = e - [ES] \tag{4}$$

If $[S]$ is much greater than e (or $[ES]$) as is usually the case:

$$[S] = [A] \tag{5}$$

The equilibrium constant for reaction (1) is given by:

$$[E]\,[S]/[ES] = K_m \tag{6}$$

or

$$[ES] = [E]\,[S]/K_m \tag{6'}$$

By substitution of equation (4) in (6′):

$$[ES] = (e - [ES])\,[S]/K_m$$

Solving for the concentration of the enzyme-substrate compound, $[ES]$:

$$[ES] = \frac{e[S]}{K_m + [S]} \tag{7}$$

If equation (2) represents the rate-determining reaction, the velocity of the reaction is given by:

$$v = k[ES] \tag{8}$$

In dilute solution, the water concentration remains constant and can be neglected. Substitution of equation (7) in (8) gives:

$$v = \frac{k \cdot e \cdot [S]}{K_m + [S]} \tag{9}$$

If V is the velocity when $[S]$ is much larger than K_m (i.e., at high substrate concentrations), then:

$$V = ke, \quad \text{and} \quad k = V/e \tag{10}$$

Equation (9), then becomes:

$$v = \frac{V[S]}{K_m + [S]} \tag{11}$$

or,

$$K_m = [S]\left(\frac{V}{v} - 1\right) \tag{12}$$

K_m, as may be seen from equations (1) and (6), is the dissociation constant of the enzyme-substrate compound (ES) and has a characteristic value for each enzyme. It is known as the Michaelis constant, and the reciprocal $1/K_m = K_M$, is termed the association constant. Equation (12) has been used extensively for the calculation of enzymic dissociation constants, but the method has been much improved by Lineweaver and Burk (*3*), who employ the reciprocal of equation (11) for the calculation:

$$1/v = (K_m/V[S]) + 1/V \tag{13}$$

This equation is of the form $y = ax + b$, where $y = 1/v$, $a = K_m/V$, $x = 1/[S]$, and $b = 1/V$. The plot of $1/v$ versus $1/[S]$ should yield a straight line with the y intercept as $1/V$ and the slope as K_m/V. The enzyme dissociation constant is determined by measurement of the initial velocity ($k[S]$) of decomposition of the substrate at different initial substrate concentrations. From the plot of $1/v$ against $1/[S]$, the dissociation constant K_m is calculated.

If the hydrolysis follows the first-order equation, at least as a first approximation, the velocity is given by $v = k'[S]$, where k' is the observed "first-order" constant for each value of A. Substituting this relation in equation (13), one finds:

$$(1/k')V = K_m + [S] \tag{14}$$

If the reciprocal of the observed first-order reaction constant is plotted against the initial substrate concentration $[A]$, for a number of experiments carried out at various substrate concentrations, the intercept on the A (concentration) axis, gives $-K_m$ (see Fig. 1).

This may be seen by making $1/k' = 0$, in equation (14), since then $[S] = -K_m$. It is obvious that $1/k'$ instead of $(1/k')V$ may be employed since K_m is determined under such conditions that both quantities are zero. This equation is probably the most convenient form to use for the determination of enzyme dissociation constants. This form was first suggested by Veibel (*4*), but the development of the equation as given here is original.

The dissociation constants for the hydrolysis of a series of alkyl β-glucosides by the β-glucosidase of almond emulsin have been measured by Veibel and Lillelund (*5*) and are given in Table III.

3. H. Lineweaver and D. Burk, *J. Am. Chem. Soc.* **56,** 658 (1934).
4. S. Veibel, *Enzymologia* **3,** 147 (1937).
5. S. Veibel and H. Lillelund, *Z. physiol. Chem.* **253,** 55 (1938).

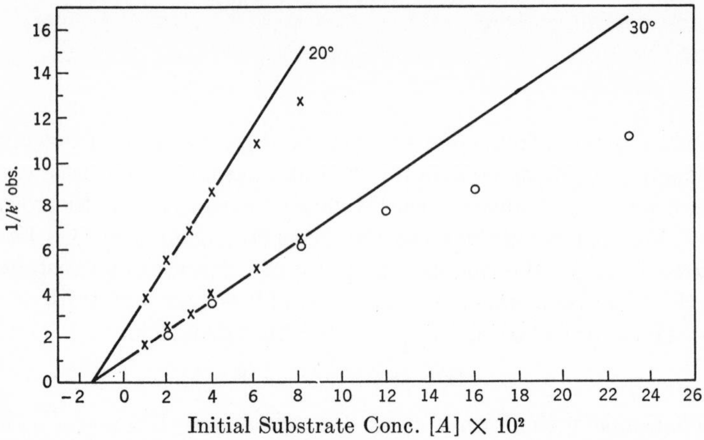

1/k' obs.
Initial Substrate Conc. [A] × 10²
20°
30°

FIG. 1. Plot of concentration ($A \times 10^2$) versus the reciprocal of the observed first-order reaction constant ($1/k$) for the hydrolysis of isobutyl β-glucoside by sweet-almond emulsin.

TABLE III

DISSOCIATION CONSTANTS FOR THE HYDROLYSIS OF β-GLUCOSIDES BY SWEET-ALMOND β-GLUCOSIDASE

β-Glucoside	K_m
CH_3—	0.62
CH_3CH_2—	0.25
$CH_3CH_2CH_2$—	0.16
$CH_3(CH_2)_2CH_2$—	0.060
$CH_3(CH_2)_3CH_2$—	0.025
$(CH_3)_2CH$—	0.40
$CH_3(C_2H_5)CH$— (levo)	0.048
$CH_3(C_2H_5)CH$— (dextro)	0.041
$(CH_3)_2CHCH_2$—	0.017
$(CH_3)_3C$—	1.46
$C_2H_5(CH_3)_2C$—	0.15
$CH_3(C_2H_5)_2C$—	0.079
$(C_2H_5)_3C$—	0.057

B. MECHANISM

A mechanism (*6*) for the action of the glycosidases is illustrated in Fig. 2. This mechanism is based on the concept of the intermediate formation of a compound or complex between the enzyme and substrate and embodies the

6. W. W. Pigman, *J. Research Natl. Bur. Standards* **27,** 1 (1941); *Advances in Enzymol.* **4,** 41 (1944); see also M. A. Jermyn, *Science* **125,** 12 (1957).

suggestion of Euler (*7*) that, in the formation of the enzyme-substrate complex, two areas of the enzyme molecule are involved. In the figure, these two areas are represented by the ovals. It is assumed that the glycoside is adsorbed (*8*) on these two areas, the aglycon group being taken up by area II and the sugar radical by area I. The area I exhibits extremely specific adsorption, but area II adsorbs many types of groups.

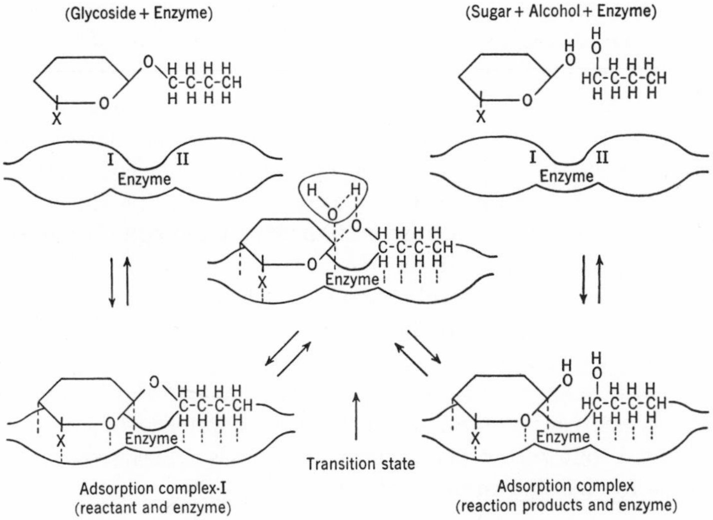
(Glycoside + Enzyme)
(Sugar + Alcohol + Enzyme)
Enzyme
Enzyme
Transition state
Adsorption complex-I
(reactant and enzyme)
Adsorption complex
(reaction products and enzyme)

FIG. 2. Possible mechanism for the enzymic hydrolysis of an alkyl glucoside.

As shown in the figure, the first stage of the reaction may take place with the adsorption of the glycoside on the two areas of the enzyme surface. Next, a molecule of water (or hydronium ion) adds to the glycosidic linkage. Cleavage of the glycosidic linkage then is assumed to take place with the formation of a complex consisting of enzyme, sugar, and alcohol. Dissociation of the sugar and alcohol from the surface of the enzyme comprises the final stage of the reaction.

According to this mechanism, the enzymic hydrolysis is similar to the acid hydrolysis, but, through the formation of the intermediate complex, a preliminary activation of the substrate molecule takes place. The activation

7. H. von Euler, Z. *physiol. Chem.* **143,** 79 (1925).

8. The term adsorption is used in a very general sense, and the combination may take place through hydrogen and electrostatic bonds, van der Waals' forces, and possibly even weak covalent bonds. As shown by Hitchcock, the same kinetic equations result from consideration of the process as the formation of a chemical compound or as a simple adsorption [D. I. Hitchcock, *J. Am. Chem. Soc.* **48,** 2370 (1926)].

energy required in the second phase of the reaction, which corresponds to the reaction which takes place during acid hydrolysis, therefore is lowered. Thus, the activation energy for the acid-catalyzed hydrolysis of methyl β-glucoside is 32,610 cal. as compared with only 12,200 cal. for the enzyme-catalyzed reaction (*9*). The total activation energy may be considered to be derived from two sources: (1) from the formation of the enzyme-substrate complex, and (2) from the addition of the solvent or hydronium ion. During the period of combination of the enzyme and glycoside, which probably is very short, the translational and the vibrational energies of the substrate molecule are restricted and may be one source of energy during the preliminary activation. The substrate molecule primarily is the source of this energy. However, activation may also result from molecular distortion or "straining" of the substrate molecule. Thus, it might be considered that in the enzyme-substrate complex, the two components of the glucoside would be kept further apart than corresponds to the normal equilibrium distance in the free glycoside. Also, if the two active areas on the enzyme move relative to one another, the substrate molecule would be "strained." For such activation, the source of the necessary energy would be the thermal energy of the enzyme.

The glycoside-enzyme complex in the second and third stages of the mechanism may react with an alcohol instead of water (*10*). The free sugar is not formed, but rather the glucosyl radical is transferred and a new glycoside is formed according to the equation:

$$R_1\text{—O—Glucose} + R_2\text{—OH} \rightleftarrows R_2\text{—O—Glucose} + R_1\text{—OH}$$

Enzymes which catalyze such group-transferring reactions are characterized by the prefix "trans," in this case as a "transglucosidase." They may be identical with the ordinary glucosidases. Such group-transfer has been observed also for other glycosidases and particularly for oligosaccharides. A reverse transfer of this type from oligosaccharides would seem to be the most likely mechanism of synthesis of glycosides. A more extensive discussion of this subject is given in Chapter IX.

An amplification of the general mechanism is given in Fig. 3, which illustrates the details of a possible transition state such as that given in a more generalized form in the center of Fig. 2. The enzyme protein is considered to incorporate in some way a sugar residue, which would correspond to the area I of Fig. 2. As indicated later in this section, the presence of such a residue would explain the high specificity shown by many of the glyco-

9. S. Veibel and E. Frederiksen, *Kgl. Danske Videnskab. Selskab. Mat. fys. Medd.* **19,** No. 1 (1941).

10. K. Takano and T. Miwa, *J. Biochem.* (*Japan*) **37,** 435 (1950); *Symposia on Enzyme Chem. Japan* **4,** 76 (1950); J. Rabaté, *Compt. rend.* **204,** 153 (1937).

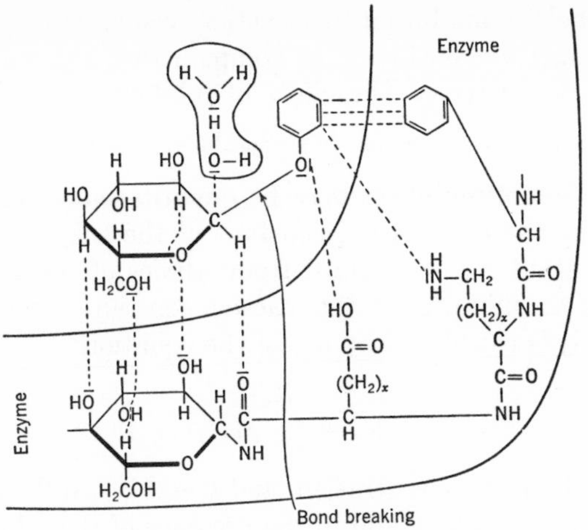
Enzyme
Enzyme
Bond breaking

FIG. 3. Possible transition state.

sidases. The area of general absorption (area II of Fig. 2) is considered to be composed of polar and aromatic groups of a peptide chain, illustrated here as phenyl and amino groups. In addition to the activation energy provided by the restriction of the kinetic energies, the action might be facilitated by the presence on the enzyme surface of polar groups which would encourage an electron shift in the bond broken during the hydrolytic action. Such a mechanism has been proposed by Swain (see Chapter I). In Fig. 3, these groups are presented as an electron-attracting proton of a carboxyl group and an electron-repelling oxygen of a carbonyl group. When steric requirements are met, such groups would promote the electron transfer from the carbon to the oxygen in the bond broken during hydrolysis. This exact mechanism has no direct supporting evidence, but it agrees with the current evidence obtained from studies of specificity and with current concepts of enzyme action.

The linkage broken is that between the carbon 1 of glucose and the oxygen, as shown by experiments with H_2O^{18}. After treatment of salicin with β-glucosidase in solution containing H_2O^{18}, the heavy oxygen was found attached to the glucose (*10a*).

The mechanism described in Figs. 2 and 3 accounts for most of the characteristics of enzyme-catalyzed reactions and will be used in the present chapter for this purpose. As previously described, the Michaelis equation and its modifications usually account for the influence of glycoside concentration on the rate of reaction. The action of various substances such as

10a. S. S. Springhorn and D. E. Koshland, Jr., Abstracts American Chemical Society Meeting, Minneapolis, p. 37c. (September 1955).

sugars and alcohols in inhibiting the reaction also agrees with this mechanism, for they may be considered to compete with the substrate for the active areas of the enzyme. The effect of inhibitors may be written as:

Glucoside + inhibitor + enzyme ⇄ glucoside-enzyme + inhibitor-enzyme

Frequently, the inhibiting effect may be quantitatively accounted for by the calculation of the dissociation constant of the enzyme-inhibitor compound. The constant K_I is obtained from studies of the influence of the concentration of the inhibitor on the reaction constant at various substrate concentrations. It is calculated by use of the equation:

$$K_{m_I} = \frac{K_m \cdot [I]}{(K_m + [S])[(k/k_I) - 1]}$$

where I is the inhibitor concentration, and k and k_I are the observed reaction constants in the absence and in the presence of the inhibitor (*4*). The other terms have their usual meanings. Since the products of hydrolysis of glycosides often are inhibitors, the reaction constants calculated from the first-order equation may decrease somewhat during the reaction.

In the development of the kinetic equations it was assumed that the concentration of the solvent (water) remains constant throughout the reaction. At high substrate concentrations this is not true, however, and there is a deviation from the theoretical equations. In the case of the inversion of sucrose by yeast invertase, the effect of the sucrose and water concentration was investigated by Nelson and Schubert (*11*), who found that the velocity of hydrolysis increases with substrate concentration to about 5% sucrose but thereafter decreases steadily. As shown by these investigators, however, the decrease may be accounted for by the decrease in the water concentration as the sugar concentration increases.

C. Influence of Hydrogen Ion Concentration

The enzymic hydrolysis of carbohydrates and derivatives is influenced markedly by the hydrogen-ion concentration. There is an optimal region of pH, and at higher and lower values the activity decreases. Fig. 4 gives the pH activity curves for the hydrolysis of sucrose, raffinose, and inulin by purified yeast invertase (*12*).

An explanation (*13*) for the influence of the hydrogen-ion concentration is that these enzymes are amphoteric and that only the undissociated molecule is catalytically active; on this basis, equations have been developed

11. J. M. Nelson and M. P. Schubert, *J. Am. Chem. Soc.* **50,** 2188 (1928).

12. M. Adams, N. K. Richtmyer, and C. S. Hudson, *J. Am. Chem. Soc.* **65,** 1369 (1943).

13. L. Michaelis and M. Rothstein, *Biochem. Z.* **110,** 217 (1920).

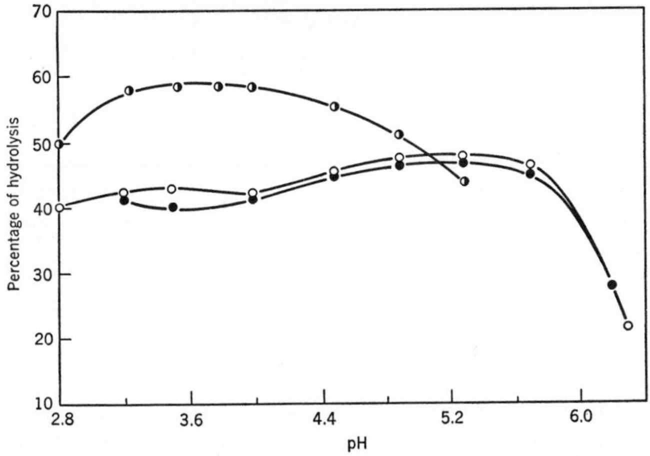
70
60
50
40
30
20
10
Percentage of hydrolysis
2.8
3.6
4.4
5.2
6.0
pH

FIG. 4. pH-Activity curves for the hydrolysis of sucrose (circles), raffinose (filled circles), and inulin (half-filled circles).

which express quantitatively the effect of the pH. This explanation also applies to the mechanism of Fig. 4. As another possible explanation, the effect may be considered to be due to the opposing influence of two factors. Thus, on the alkaline side of the catenary, the rate increases with increase of acidity. This behavior would be expected if hydrogen ion is a catalyst for the reaction. However, an opposing factor would be the competition of hydrogen ions for the adsorbing groups in the active areas of the enzyme. At acidities on the alkaline side of the catenary, it would be expected that the dissociation constants would be essentially independent of the hydrogen-ion concentration; on the acid side there would be a marked increase in the dissociation constants (less association).

D. MEASUREMENT OF ACTIVITY AND INFLUENCE OF ENZYME CONCENTRATION

As shown by equation (9) (given earlier in this chapter), the initial velocity at any fixed substrate concentration is directly proportional to the enzyme concentration. In general, the velocity constant calculated according to the first-order equation exhibits a similar relation as would be expected because $v = k_{obs.}[S]$. Table IV shows the results obtained for different concentrations (g) of *Aspergillus niger* emulsin with sucrose as the substrate (*14*). Since the reaction constant often varies somewhat with the degree of hydrolysis, the extrapolated initial value should be used or several values over the range 30 to 50% hydrolysis should be averaged. The k/g ratio usually may be employed for the expression of enzyme activity under

14. W. W. Pigman, *J. Research Natl. Bur. Standards* **30,** 159 (1943).

TABLE IV

INFLUENCE OF ENZYME CONCENTRATION ON THE REACTION CONSTANT

Emulsin concentration (g/50 ml.)	$k \times 10^4$ (first-order equation)	$k/g \times 10^4$
0.438	131	300
0.0438	13.1	300
0.00876	2.66	300
0.00438	1.09	250

carefully specified experimental conditions. Weidenhagen (*14*, *15*) has suggested a set of standard conditions which it would seem well to adopt until more favorable conditions are known. In general, he proposes the use of 0.1388 M substrate solutions at the optimal pH and at 30°C. The enzyme concentration (g) is taken as the grams of emulsin or pure enzyme present in 50 ml. of reaction mixture. Reaction constants calculated from the first-order equation over the interval 30 to 50% hydrolysis are used to calculate the activity from the relation:

$$E.V. = \text{enzyme value} = \frac{k}{g \cdot \log 2}$$

The enzyme value thus obtained is the reciprocal of the time for 50% hydrolysis under the given conditions and with one gram of emulsin in 50 ml. For several of the important glycosidases, the following substances have been selected as the standard substrates: maltose (α-glucosidase), salicin (β-glucosidase), melibiose (α-galactosidase), lactose (β-galactosidase), and sucrose (invertase).

Because many substrates are too insoluble for the "standard conditions" to be employed and because many glycosides are available in only small quantities, it is common in specificity studies to use smaller concentrations. Particularly, in the investigation of the specificity of β-glucosidase, 0.052 M glucoside concentrations have been employed. The other experimental conditions are the same, however. The same formula is used for the calculation of activity, which in this case is called the enzyme efficiency or "Wertigkeit."

E. TEMPERATURE INFLUENCES

The rate of an enzyme-catalyzed reaction increases as the temperature is raised above room temperature; but, in contrast to ordinary chemical reactions, the rate reaches a maximum and finally falls off as the tempera-

15. R. Weidenhagen, *in* "Handbuch der Enzymologie" (F. F. Nord and R. Weidenhagen, eds.), p. 538. Akademische Verlagsges., Leipzig, 1940.

TABLE V

COMPARISON OF ACTIVATION ENERGIES FOR THE HYDROLYSIS OF β-GLUCOSIDES BY β-GLUCOSIDASE AND BY ACID

(Data of Veibel and Frederiksen)

β-Glucoside	Activation energy (calories/mole)	
	Enzymic hydrolysis	Acidic hydrolysis
CH_3—O—Gl	12,200	32,600
$CH_3CH_2CH_2$—O—Gl	13,500	32,400
$(CH_3)_2CH$—O—Gl	13,100	32,100
$(C_2H_5)_2CH$—O—Gl	10,600	31,500
$(CH_3)_3C$—O—Gl	20,000	30,800
$(CH_3)_2C(C_2H_5)$—O—Gl	20,000	29,900

ture continues to increase. This decrease in rate usually arises from the destruction of the enzyme at the higher temperatures. Although "optimal temperatures" are given in the literature for some enzymes, these temperatures are not true constants. They will vary according to the conditions employed, e.g., according to the relative amounts of enzyme and substrate.

In the region of the increase of reaction constants with increase of temperature, the rates of increase for the enzyme-catalyzed reactions are less than those for the corresponding acid-catalyzed reactions. This difference in rates is reflected by the smaller values for the activation energies for the reactions brought about by enzymes as compared with those catalyzed by acids. In Table V, the activation energies are given (*9*) for the hydrolysis of a number of β-glucosides by the β-glucosidase of almond emulsin.

3. CHEMICAL COMPOSITION OF GLYCOSIDASES

Unfortunately, crystalline glycosidases are still unknown, but a highly purified β-glucosidase and an invertase (β-fructofuranosidase) have been described.

A. β-GLUCOSIDASE

From almond emulsin, enzymes with a β-glucosidase value as high as 16 have been prepared. (The ordinary almond emulsins have a value of 1 or less.) The properties of such preparations have been studied by Helferich and associates (*16*). The elementary composition agrees with that of protein substances, but the hydrogen content is somewhat greater than usual. The protein nature of the material also agrees with the action of the anions of neutral salts on the enzymic activity since the order of activation by

16. B. Helferich, *Ergeb. Enzymforsch.* **7,** 98 (1938).

these anions is similar to the well-known lyotropic series. The inactivation of the enzyme by formaldehyde may also be due to its protein character.

Against neutral reducing agents, the enzyme is quite resistant, but oxidizing agents destroy it rapidly. Hydrocyanic acid, hydrogen sulfide, and glutathione have no destructive action, but ozone and osmium tetroxide as well as ultraviolet light bring about rapid inactivation. A quantitative investigation of the ozone inactivation gives an equivalent weight of 800 to 1100 for the enzyme. Since the absorption spectrum of the enzyme and the rate of inactivation by ozone are similar to those for tryptophan, it is possible that this amino acid constitutes an important part of the enzyme structure. The destructive action of osmium tetroxide seems to be of a different character from the action of ozone since it does not parallel the tryptophan destruction and since a considerable part of the activity of the oxidized enzyme may be restored by reduction with hydrogen sulfide or cysteine.

Even highly purified β-glucosidase preparations contain 3 to 6% of carbohydrate material as estimated by the orcinol reaction, but there seems to be no direct correlation between the activity and the carbohydrate content (*17*). The carbohydrate constituent is of particular interest since Helferich (*18*) has suggested that it may constitute the holding group ("Haftstelle") of the enzyme and be responsible for the adsorption of the glycoside. In terms of the mechanism proposed earlier in this chapter, this suggestion means that the very specific area (I) may consist of a carbohydrate group built into the protein structure. Adsorption of the sugar radical of a glycoside then would be analogous to the deposition of molecules on seed nuclei in a supersaturated solution. Although such a role for the carbohydrate would explain the marked influence of changes in the sugar radical of the glycoside on the rate of hydrolysis, the concept admittedly is without much experimental foundation.

In view of the important role of dialyzable coenzymes in certain enzyme systems, it is important to note that there is no evidence for a coenzyme playing a part in the hydrolysis of β-glycosides. When solutions of purified β-glucosidase buffered at various pH's between 2.75 and 10.35 are dialyzed, the activity of the solution remains the same as that of a similar undialyzed solution. Although a decrease of activity takes place at the greater acidities and alkalinities, this decrease is due to an irreversible destruction of the enzyme. In confirmation of this conclusion, the addition of material passing through the membrane or of boiled enzyme does not restore the activity (*19*). The β-glucosidase activity is destroyed by treatment with diazo-

17. B. Helferich and W. W. Pigman *Z. physiol. Chem.* **259**, 253 (1939).

18. B. Helferich, W. Richter, and S. Grünler, *Ber. Verhandl. sächs. Akad. Wiss. Leipzig Math. naturw. Kl.* **89**, 385 (1937).

19. B. Helferich, R. Hiltmann, and W. W. Pigman, *Z. physiol. Chem.* **259**, 150 (1939).

methane, with trypsin, and by acetylation (*20*). The enzyme is most stable at pH 6 to 7.5; at pH 9.5 and 3.5, solutions of the enzyme are appreciably inactivated after several days at 30°C (*19, 21*).

B. Yeast Invertase

Several reports of the preparation of highly active yeast invertase preparations have been made. The activity of these preparations is such that the time values are less than 0.2 minute. (A time value of 0.2 minute corresponds to an enzyme value of about 700; commercial invertases usually have enzyme values of 10 or less.) Those of Adams and Hudson (*22*) are reported to give typical protein reactions as well as a positive Molisch test for carbohydrates. The most active preparations contain only 6.9% of reducing material after an acid hydrolysis, but others contain as much as 30 to 50% carbohydrate. Invertase preparations with large carbohydrate contents fail to give the usual protein precipitation tests and are not coagulated by heating. Although such preparations are of appreciably less activity than those with smaller carbohydrate contents, the activity of all is closely the same when based on the nitrogen content.

4. ENZYMES OF ALMOND EMULSIN

A. Preparation and Purification

Almond emulsin is prepared from defatted crushed almonds by extraction with water and precipitation of the extracts with alcohol. The dried powder is known as almond emulsin. A preparation of considerably more activity is obtained by treatment of the almond meal with zinc sulfate solution and precipitation of the enzymes from solution by the addition of tannin. The tannin is separated from the enzyme by extraction of the precipitate with acetone, and the solid residue is the "Rohferment" of Helferich (*23*) which has been used for many of the studies of the specificities of the enzyme components of almond emulsin. The "Rohferment" usually has a β-glucosidase value of about 1.

Purification of the "Rohferment" gives preparations 10 to 16 times more active (β-glucosidase value 10 to 16) and some of the enzyme constituents of the cruder preparations are lost in the purification process. It should be noted that almond emulsin is not a definite substance but is a mixture of enzymes which are present in variable proportions depending on the method and extent of purification. Various methods for the purification may be used

20. B. Helferich, P. E. Speidel, and W. Toeldte, *Z. physiol. Chem.* **128,** 99 (1923).
21. B. Helferich and A. Schneidmüller, *Z. physiol. Chem.* **198,** 100 (1931).
22. M. Adams and C. S. Hudson, *J. Am. Chem. Soc.* **65,** 1359 (1943).
23. B. Helferich, S. Winkler, R. Gootz, O. Peters, and E. Günther, *Z. physiol. Chem.* **208,** 91 (1932).

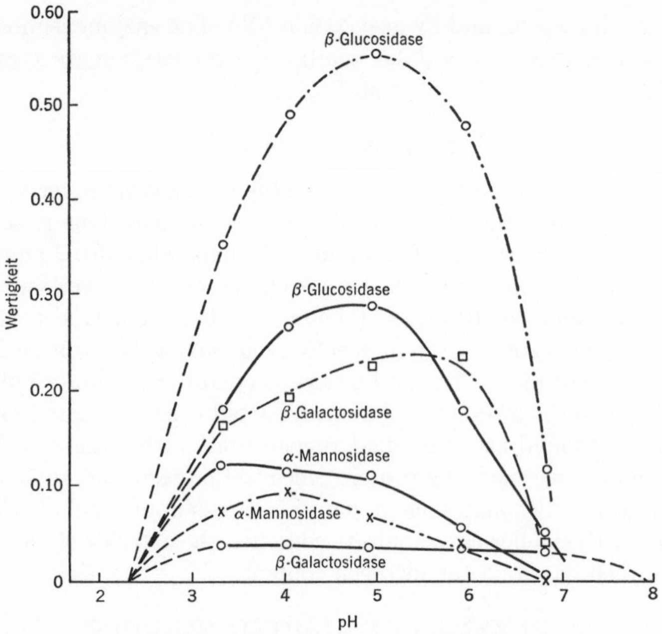

0.60
0.50
0.40
0.30
0.20
0.10
0
Wertigkeit
β-Glucosidase
β-Glucosidase
β-Galactosidase
α-Mannosidase
α-Mannosidase
β-Galactosidase
2
3
4
5
6
7
8
pH

FIG. 5. The relation of pH to the activity of the principal enzymes of almond emulsin. The full lines give data for the "Rohferment" and the broken lines data for the highly purified emulsin. The upper curve for purified β-glucosidase has been constructed at one-quarter of its real value.
(Data of K. Hill.)

singly or in combination. The preparations of highest activity (*24*) have been obtained from the "Rohferment" by adsorption of the enzymes on silver hydroxide and, after desorption by action of ammonium sulfide, removal of certain of the impurities by their preferential adsorption on activated carbon.

B. Optimal pH

According to the measurements of K. Hill (*25*), the maximal activity for almond β-glucosidase is shown at pH 5.0 and for α-mannosidase at 3.3 to 5. The position of the pH optimum for the β-galactosidase exhibits an influence of purification; thus, the "Rohferment" shows its maximal activity over a broader interval (pH 3.3 to 7) than that for the purified product (pH 5 to 6) (see Fig. 5).

24. B. Helferich and S. Winkler, *Z. physiol. Chem.* **209,** 269 (1932); B. Helferich and W. W. Pigman, *Z. physiol. Chem.* **259,** 253 (1939); B. Helferich and M. Hase, *ibid.* **274,** 261 (1942).

25. K. Hill, *Ber. Verhandl. sächs. Akad. Wiss. Leipzig Math. naturw. Kl.* **86,** 115 (1934).

The influence of buffer type and concentration on the optimal pH for β-glucosidase activity has been investigated by Viebel and Lillelund (*26*) using the *o*-cresyl and *n*-butyl β-glucosides. The optimal pH for the hydrolysis of these glucosides varies between 4.0 and 5.0. The hydrolysis takes place more rapidly in citrate- than in acetate-buffered solution. The two glucosides exhibit an appreciable difference in the optimal pH for the solutions in acetate buffers. The hydrolysis rates in acetate-buffered solutions are affected by the concentration of the buffer to an extent of about 10% in the range 0.04 to 0.12 *M* although there is little effect of buffer concentration to be observed for the citrate-buffered solutions.

C. Enzymes Present

In addition to β-glucosidase, the enzyme which hydrolyzes β-glucosides, other enzymes are present in the "Rohferment" and in the purified preparations. The methods used for establishing the presence of different enzymes in the emulsins are based on the production of changes in the relative rates of hydrolysis of several glycosides as a result of some treatment given to the enzyme preparation. Thus, in the purification of crude almond emulsins, the activity towards β-glucosides and β-galactosides increases but that towards α-galactosides decreases. This change of activity is taken as evidence for the presence of a special enzyme (α-galactosidase) different from the β-glucosidase. Also, when solutions of almond emulsin are heated or exposed to ultraviolet light, their ability to hydrolyze α-mannosides may be unaffected although the ability to hydrolyze β-glucosides may be greatly diminished. Hence, the existence of a special α-mannosidase is postulated. By similar methods, the presence of two other glycosidases is indicated. These enzymes are β-glucuronidase and "β-(*N*-acetyl)-glucosaminidase" which hydrolyze the β-glycosidic derivatives of glucuronic acid and *N*-acetylglucosamine. The enzyme preparations also catalyze the cleavage of β-galactosides. There is as yet no definite evidence that β-galactosidase differs from β-glucosidase. In the subsequent discussion, however, they will be considered to be different.

The four principal glycosidases in almond emulsin (β-glucosidase, β-galactosidase, α-galactosidase, and α-mannosidase) are probably responsible for the hydrolysis of the pentosides and some other glycosides. Of the pentosides, the L-arabinosides, the β-D-xylosides, and α-D-lyxosides are hydrolyzed by almond emulsin. The D-arabinosides and the β-L-xylosides are not affected, and the D- and L-ribosides and L-lyxosides have not been tested. It is of considerable interest that the hydrolyzable pentosides are configurationally related to hydrolyzable hexosides (i.e., they belong to the same homomorphous series) and may be considered to be derived from

26. S. Veibel and H. Lillelund, *Enzymologia* **9**, 161 (1940).

them by substitution of the primary alcoholic groups by hydrogen atoms (see Chapter I).

α-D-Mannose type: α-D-mannose, α-D-lyxose

β-D-Galactose type: β-D-galactose, α-L-arabinose

α-D-Galactose type: α-D-galactose, β-L-arabinose

β-D-Glucose type: β-D-glucose, β-D-xylose

Since L-arabinose and D-xylose are found in natural products, it would be possible that special L-arabinosidases and D-xylosidases exist; the existence of a special D-lyxosidase seems improbable since the sugar is not a natural product. In the case of the D-lyxosides, the hydrolysis most probably is due to the α-mannosidase component of almond emulsin (*27*). The stability of the enzyme to heat supports this conclusion. The simplest explanation for the hydrolysis of the other pentosides is that they also are cleaved by the corresponding hexosidases. This concept receives support from studies of the effect of purification on the relative rates of hydrolysis of the hexosides and pentosides (*23*). Thus, purification of the cruder preparations of almond emulsin increases their ability to hydrolyze α-L-arabinosides and β-D-xylosides in the same relative proportions as for the configurationally related β-galactosides and β-glucosides. The α-galactosidase activity decreases, however, in the same proportion as the ability to catalyze the cleavage of the β-L-arabinosides. Although this evidence does not eliminate the possibility of special pentosidases, particularly in enzyme preparations from other sources, it makes their postulation in almond emulsin unnecessary.

It has never been conclusively demonstrated that only a single component in almond emulsin is responsible for the cleavage of all β-glucosides, i.e., that several β-glucosidases are not present, but most of the available evidence supports this concept. Apricot emulsin as well as three almond emulsins of different purity were investigated (*28*) for their action on β-glucosides which had the following substances as the aglycons: methanol, glucose, phenol, and saligenin. As shown in Table VI, the relative rates of hydrolysis of the series of glucosides by the four enzyme preparations is the same within the experimental error. The earlier work of Willstätter, Kuhn, and Sobotka (*29*) led to the same conclusion. However, later work (*30*) which should be checked, indicates that several β-glucosidases may be present.

27. W. W. Pigman, *J. Am. Chem. Soc.* **62,** 1371 (1940).

28. B. Helferich, R. Gootz, and G. Sparmberg, *Z. physiol. Chem.* **205,** 201 (1932).

29. R. Willstätter, R. Kuhn, and H. Sobotka, *Z. physiol. Chem.* **129,** 33 (1923).

30. L. Zechmeister, G. Tóth, P. Fürth, and J. Bársony, *Enzymologia* **9,** 155 (1941).

D. Specificity of the β-Glucosidase

Influences of Substitution and of Configurational Changes in the Sugar Radical of Glucosides. A number of β-glucosides have been prepared in which the hydroxyl groups on carbons 2, 3, and 4 have been substituted by methoxyl and tosyloxy groups. For all such compounds, the derivatives have been found to be "unhydrolyzable" (*31*). Thus, the 3-*O*-methyl and the 2,4,6-tri-*O*-methyl derivatives of phenyl β-glucoside as well as the 2-tosyl, 3-tosyl, and 4-tosyl derivatives of vanillin β-glucoside are not appreciably hydrolyzed by almond emulsin even after 100 hours or more (*32, 33*).

When substitutions are made at carbon 6 of β-glucosides, the effects are quite different than those arising from substitutions at the ring carbons (2, 3, 4, 5). In the accompanying formula, this type of substitution is represented by variations in the nature of the atoms or groups represented by *X*:

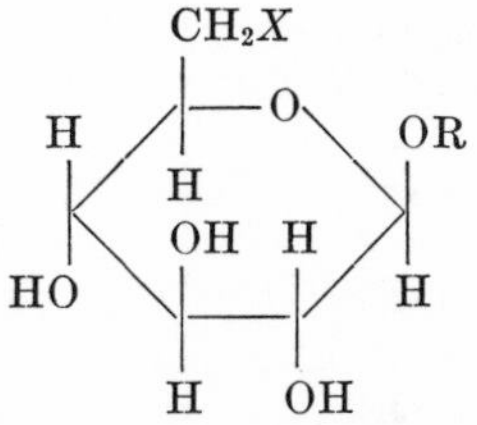
CH₂X
O
H
OR
H
OH
H
HO
H
H
OH

The ease of hydrolysis of a series of such 6-substituted β-glucosides (*34*) is compared in Table VII.

In general there seems to be a correlation between the size of the group *X* and its influence on the rate of hydrolysis as may be seen by a comparison of the rates of hydrolysis and the volumes of the groups as given by Biltz. It appears that the effect of groups substituted for the hydroxyl of carbon 6 is a steric effect, and that such substitutions produce only quantitative changes in the rate of hydrolysis (*33, 34*). However, when the substituent groups are quite large, e.g., benzoyl and tosyl groups, the rate of hydrolysis becomes so slow as to be immeasurable. It is of interest that apparently the

31. In most instances, under stringent experimental conditions utilizing high enzyme concentrations and long time periods, the minimum enzyme efficiency ("Wertigkeit") which is significant is about 10^{-5}. This is about 1/33,000 the rate of hydrolysis of a fairly easily hydrolyzable glucoside (phenyl β-glucoside with E.E. = 0.33). A compound with enzyme efficiency of 10^{-5} or less is usually considered to be "unhydrolyzable."

32. B. Helferich and S. Grünler, *J. prakt. Chem.* [2] **148,** 107 (1937).

33. W. W. Pigman and N. K. Richtmyer, *J. Am. Chem. Soc.* **64,** 374 (1942).

34. B. Helferich, S. Grünler, and A. Gnüchtel, *Z. physiol Chem.* **248,** 85 (1937).

TABLE VI

EFFECT OF PURIFICATION ON THE RATES OF HYDROLYSIS OF A SERIES OF β-GLUCOSIDES

β-Glucoside	Enzyme value (or relative enzyme value)			
	Apricot emulsin	Almond emulsin		
		I	II	III
Methyl β-glucoside	0.013 (1)	0.012 (1)	0.021 (1)	0.13 (1)
Cellobiose	0.034 (2.6)	0.040 (3.3)	0.052 (2.5)	0.27 (2.1)
Phenyl β-glucoside	0.076 (5.8)	0.070 (5.8)	0.13 (6.2)	0.67 (5.2)
Salicin	0.44 (32)	0.42 (35)	0.67 (32)	3.4 (26)

TABLE VII

COMPARATIVE RATES OF HYDROLYSIS OF 6-SUBSTITUTED β-GLUCOSIDES

Substituent group (group *X*)	Phenyl 6-*X*-β-glucoside (*E.E.*)	Vanillin 6-*X*-β-glucoside[a]	Volume of group *X*[b] (Biltz)
H	0.56	—	5.8
OH	0.3	39	9.4
F	0.03	(6)	15.9
Cl	—	2.5	16.5
Br	0.003	1.5	19.5
OCH_3	0.0023	—	24.4
I	—	0.17	24.3

[a] Calculated in the same manner as for the enzyme efficiencies but employing 0.00104 *M* substrate solutions.

[b] Molecular volume in milliliters.

most easily hydrolyzed glycoside types are those with $X = H$, i.e., the 6-deoxyglucosides.

A similar type of substitution is the replacement of the primary alcohol group ($—CH_2OH$) of hexosides by H or $CHOH—CH_2OH$ to form the pentosides or heptosides of similar ring configuration. The evidence available for believing that the α- and β-L-arabinosides, the β-D-xylosides, and α-D-lyxoside are acted on by β- and α-galactosidase, β-glucosidase, and α-mannosidase, respectively, has been cited previously. The preparation of the phenyl D-*glycero*-β-D-*galacto*-heptoside (phenyl β-D-α-mannoheptoside) has made it possible to test the influence of the substitution of a $—CH_2OH$ group for the hydrogen attached to carbon 6 on the ease of hydrolysis of phenyl β-galactoside. As would be expected from the presence of the β-galactopyranoside ring, this heptoside is hydrolyzed by almond emulsin at a slow but significant rate (*35*) (*E.E.* = 0.00022 as compared with 0.032 for phenyl β-galactoside).

Changes of Ring Structure and Configuration. When the structure of a hydrolyzable pyranoside is changed to that of a furanoside, the latter is unaffected by the enzyme. Thus, the α- and β-D-glucofuranosides are unaffected (*36*) by almond emulsin as well as by yeast α-glucosidase (yeast maltase). Similarly, yeast invertase catalyzes the cleavage of sucrose and other β-fructofuranosides, but not that of the known fructopyranosides (*37*).

The influence of the configuration of the carbons forming the pyranose rings of hydrolyzable glycosides has also been investigated. In no known instance is the enantiomorphous modification of a hydrolyzable glycoside acted upon by the same enzyme. The best examples, at present, are the pairs of β-D- and β-L-arabinosides and the α-D- and α-L-arabinosides. Although the L-isomers are easily cleaved, the D-isomers remain unaffected even after long periods of time (*23, 38*). A similar difference exists for the hydrolyzable D-xylosides and the unhydrolyzable L-xylosides (*39*). The earlier work of E. Fischer showed that the L-glucosides are unaffected by enzymes.

It is of interest to consider the effect of variations in the configuration of a single asymmetric center. Data are available for making this comparison as a result of studies of the action of almond emulsin on the phenyl α-D-taloside and the methyl D-gulosides, none of which was found (*35, 40*) to be appreciably hydrolyzed. Inasmuch as the α-D-talosides differ from the hydrolyzable α-D-mannosides only in the configuration of a single carbon atom (carbon 4), it seems that the change in configuration of only a single asymmetric center is sufficient to prevent enzymic action. This is substantiated by the lack of enzymic cleavage of the gulosides which differ from the hydroyzable galactosides only in the configuration of carbon 3.

The experiments cited illustrate the extreme specificity of the almond emulsin enzymes to slight changes in the sugar portion of gylcosides. At present it seems that these influences may be summarized by the statement that *hydrolyzable glycosides must belong to one of the naturally occurring types* (p. 44) *and none of the ring hydroxyls may be substituted by other groups.* Conversely, enzymes are to be expected in natural products corresponding to each of the naturally occurring types, and it is probable that no enzymes exist for the hexoside types which are not naturally occurring. However,

35. W. W. Pigman, *J. Research Natl. Bur. Standards* **26,** 197 (1941).
36. E. Fischer, *Ber.* **47,** 1980 (1914); W. N. Haworth, C. R. Porter, and A. C. Waine, *J. Chem. Soc.* p. 2254 (1932).
37. R. Weidenhagen, *Z. Ver. deut. Zucker-Ind.* **82,** 921 (1932).
38. B. Helferich H. Appel, and R. Gootz, *Z. physiol. Chem.* **215,** 277 (1933).
39. B. Helferich, E. Günther, and W. W. Pigman, *Ber.* **72,** 1953 (1939).
40. B. Helferich, W. W. Pigman, and H. S. Isbell, *Z. physiol. Chem.* **261,** 55 (1939).

it is not to be expected that individual enzyme preparations will contain all of the possible enzymes; instead enzymes usually will be found in biological materials in association with their substrates.

Aglycon Specificity. The marked influence of changes in the rings of hydrolyzable glycosides on enzymic action has been emphasized in the preceding section. The effect of variations in the aglycon group are quite different, however, and it is unusual to find that structural changes completely inhibit enzymic cleavage although occasionally the rate is very slow. In the mechanism described previously, the concept of a general unspecific adsorption on the area II was developed to agree with the experimental work which has been done on the influence of the structure of the aglycon group. In the following discussion of this work, the β-glucosides will be divided into those yielding glucose and an alcohol on hydrolysis (alkyl β-glucosides) and those giving glucose and a phenol (aryl β-glucosides).

Alkyl β-Glucosides. The enzymic hydrolysis of numerous alkyl β-glucosides has been studied. Many of the results obtained are summarized (*41*) in Fig. 6. It is of considerable interest that in the various homologous series the rate of hydrolysis increases with increasing chain length. The *n*-alkyl series shows a progressive increase in the rate of hydrolysis with increasing chain length of the aglycon group until the chain length reaches about 7 carbon atoms. Thereafter, however, the rate decreases. On the basis of the postulated mechanism previously given (Fig. 2), this occurrence of an optimal chain length for maximal hydrolysis is to be ascribed to a counterbalancing of the beneficial effects of increased chain length on the formation of the enzyme-substrate complex by the disadvantageous influence of slow dissociation of the products of hydrolysis from the enzyme's surface. That is, the rate-determining reaction for the *n*-nonyl glucoside may be the dissociation of the *n*-nonyl alcohol from the surface of the enzyme rather than the decomposition of the glucosidic linkage.

This explanation of the influence of increasing chain length or molecular weight of the aglycon receives support from a comparison of the dissociation constants of the enzyme – alkyl glucoside complex with the number of carbons in the aglycon group. In Fig. 7, such a comparison is made using the data reported by Veibel and Lillelund (*5*). In the various series, the adsorption increases rapidly with the increasing size of the aglycon group. The increase in adsorption is indicated by a decrease in the dissociation constants. The highest association (adsorption) is shown by the *n*-alkyl

41. This figure is taken from W. W. Pigman and N. K. Richtmyer, *J. Am. Chem. Soc.* **64,** 369 (1942) and W. W. Pigman, *Advances in Enzymol.* **4,** 41 (1944). It incorporates results of Veibel and associates and some of Helferich. Some new data by Helferich and Goerdeler, *Ber. Verhandl. sächs. Akad. Wiss. Leipzig Math. phys. Kl.* **92,** 75 (1940) are included. The results of Veibel at various concentrations has been interpolated at the standard concentration (0.052 *M*).

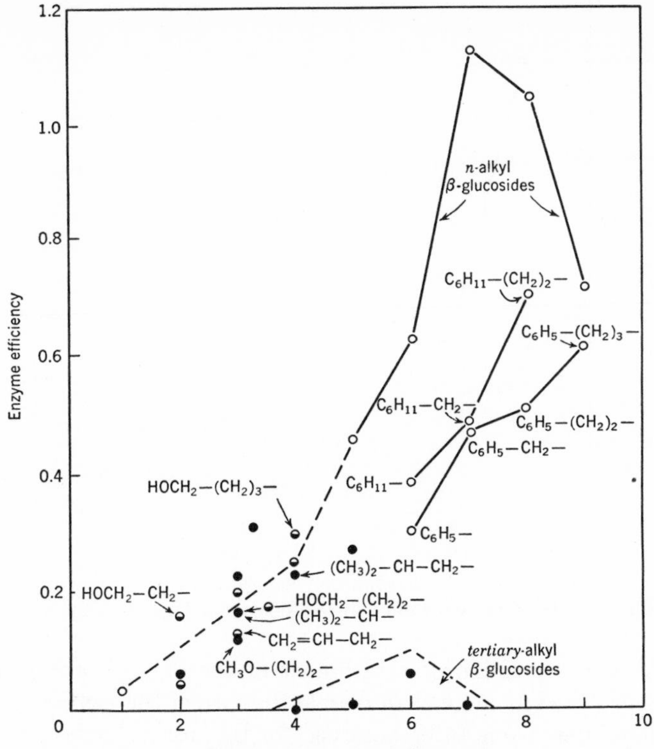

1.2
1.0
0.8
0.6
0.4
0.2
0
2
4
6
8
10
Enzyme efficiency
n-alkyl
β-glucosides
C6H11—(CH2)2—
C6H5—(CH2)3—
C6H11—CH2—
C6H5—(CH2)2—
C6H5—CH2—
HOCH2—(CH2)3—
C6H11—
C6H5—
(CH3)2—CH—CH2—
HOCH2—CH2—
HOCH2—(CH2)2—
(CH3)2—CH—
CH2=CH—CH2—
CH3O—(CH2)2—
tertiary-alkyl
β-glucosides
Carbon Atoms in Aglycon

FIG. 6. The relationship between the enzyme efficiency and the number of the carbon atoms in the aglycon groups of alkyl β-glucosides. Circles represent data of Pigman and Richtmyer; filled circles are data of Veibel, and half-filled circles are data of Helferich.

series and the association becomes less as the extent of branching increases. This influence of branching might be expected as the straight chains should have a greater opportunity to accommodate themselves to the adsorbing atoms of the active areas on the enzyme. A summary of the effect of various groups in the aglycon radicals of alkyl β-glucosides and additional discussion is given elsewhere (*1*).

In Table VIII, values are given for the ease of hydrolysis of some disaccharides which have β-glucosidic or β-galactosidic linkages (*1*). For comparison, several other glycosides are included.

The marked influence of the effect of structural and configurational changes in the aglycon group is very evident. Thus, cellobiose and 4-mannose β-glucoside differ only in the configuration of a single carbon atom (carbon 2 of the aglycon group); yet there is more than a 60-fold difference in the ease of hydrolysis of the two compounds. Gentiobiose and cellobiose

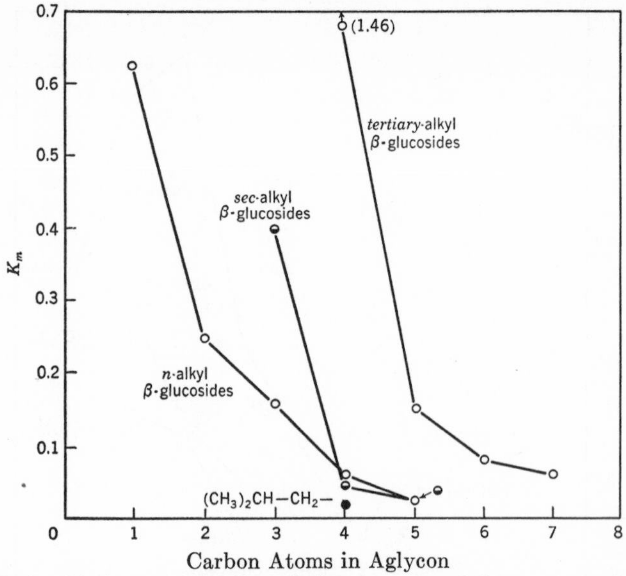
(1.46)
tertiary-alkyl
β-glucosides
sec-alkyl
β-glucosides
n-alkyl
β-glucosides
(CH₃)₂CH—CH₂—
K_m
0.7
0.6
0.5
0.4
0.3
0.2
0.1
0
1
2
3
4
5
6
7
8
Carbon Atoms in Aglycon

FIG. 7. Relationship between the dissociation constant of the enzyme-substrate complex and the number of carbon atoms in the aglycon groups of alkyl β-glucosides.

differ only in the position of attachment of the aglycon group, but the latter is hydrolyzed at more than double the rate of the gentiobiose.

The same difference is to be observed for the disaccharides and derivatives of the β-galactoside series. Here, the effects of breaking the pyranose ring of the aglycon of lactose by oxidation to lactobionic acid or reduction to lactositol may be observed. As may be seen from the table, these compounds are hydrolyzed much more slowly than lactose. The formation of the glycosidic derivatives of lactose, even though such a change is remote from the linkage undergoing hydrolysis, appreciably accelerates the hydrolysis (compare lactose, phenyl lactoside, and protocatechuic aldehyde lactoside).

Aryl β-Glucosides. In Table IX are recorded the results of Helferich and associates from their study of the influence of substitution in the benzene ring of phenyl β-glucoside on the ease of enzymic hydrolysis (*1*). It should be noted that β-glucosidases from some sources other than almond emulsin exhibit quite different specificities; hence, the conclusions drawn apply only to sweet-almond β-glucosidase. The principal effects of substituent groups are summarized in the following generalizations for which phenyl β-glucoside is taken as the standard for the comparison.

(1) The rate of hydrolysis is increased by the introduction of "*meta*-directing groups" in any position, and aldehyde groups exhibit the greatest effect.

TABLE VIII

RATE OF ENZYMIC HYDROLYSIS OF DISACCHARIDES AND RELATED COMPOUNDS WITH β-GLUCOSIDIC AND β-GALACTOSIDIC LINKAGES

β-Glucosides			β-Galactosides		
Substrate	Structure	$E.E. \times 10^3$	Substrate	Structure	$E.E. \times 10^3$
Cellobiose	4-Glucose β-glucoside	159, 180	Lactose	4-Glucose β-galactoside	11.2
Gentiobiose	6-Glucose β-glucoside	75	Lactulose	4-Fructose β-galactoside	(14)
Celtrobiose	4-Altrose β-glucoside	(23)	Neolactose	4-Altrose β-galactoside	(2.8)
	4-Mannose β-glucoside	2.3	Lactositol	4-Sorbitol β-galactoside	0.84
Phenyl α-cellobioside	4-(Phenyl α-glucoside) β-glucoside	160	Lactobionic acid	4-(Gluconic acid) β-galactoside	0.41
Phenyl β-glucoside		330	Phenyl β-lactoside	4-(Phenyl β-glucoside) β-galactoside	23
			Protocatechuic aldehyde β-lactoside	4-(Protocatechuic aldehyde β-glucoside) β-galactoside	80
			Phenyl β-galactoside	Phenyl β-galactoside	32–49

(2) In all cases known, the rate of hydrolysis is decreased by the introduction of an amino group in any position. Acetylation of the amino group reduces its inhibiting influence.

(3) With the single exception of the amino group, all groups, when substituted in the *ortho* position, increase the ease of enzymic hydrolysis.

(4) Although the "*meta*-directing groups" increase the ease of hydrolysis when in the *para* position (but less than when in the *ortho* position), other groups have an inhibiting action.

(5) The substitution of groups in the *meta* position results in influences intermediate between those of the same groups in the *ortho* and *para* positions, but the general effect is to increase the ease of hydrolysis.

(6) Compounds with two groups in addition to the glucosidic group in the aromatic nucleus usually exhibit an additive influence of the two groups. Thus, for a group like methyl, the *ortho* effect is strongly positive and the *para* effect is weakly negative. The 2,4-dimethylphenyl β-glucoside is

TABLE IX

INFLUENCE OF SUBSTITUTIONS IN THE AROMATIC NUCLEUS ON THE HYDROLYSIS OF PHENYL β-GLUCOSIDE BY SWEET-ALMOND β-GLUCOSIDASE

Monosubstituted				Disubstituted	
	Enzyme efficiency				
Group X	Ortho subst. 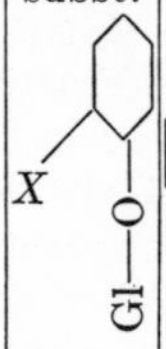	Meta subst. 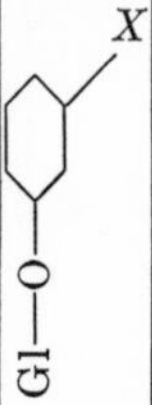	Para subst. 	Groups and position	Enzyme efficiency
None (H)	0.33	0.33	0.33	4-CHO (monosubstituted)	4.2
CHO—	8.6	—	4.2	4-CHO, 2-OH	9.7
CH_3—	4.3	0.55	0.12	4-CHO, 2-OCH_3	13
CH_3O—	3.5	—	0.27	4-CHO, 2-$C_6H_5CH_2O$—	2.3
CH_3CO—	3.3	—	1.1	4-CH_3—CH=CH—, 2-OCH_3—	1.1
CH_3CH_2—	2.3	—	0.08	3-CHO, 6-OCH_3	11
$CNCH_2$—	2.0	—	1.2	3-CHO, 6-OC_2H_5—	2.5
$HOCH_2$—	2.0	—	—	6-CH_3, 2-CH_3—	0.1
CH_3OCO—	1.6	1.5	1.5	4-CH_3, 2-CH_3—	1.4
HOCO—	1.6	0.60	0.43	2-CH_2OH (monosubstituted)	2.0
$AcNHCH_2$—	0.88	1.48	0.13	2-CH_2OH, 4-Cl	0.48
HO—	0.56	0.47	0.059	2-CH_2OH, 4-Br	0.60
$HOCOCH_2$—	0.13	—	0.64	2-CH_2OH, 4-I	0.62
NH_2—	—	—	0.055		
NO_2—	—	—	0.53		
NH_2CH_2—	0.036	0.05	0.027		

hydrolyzed at a rate intermediate between those for the two corresponding monosubstituted compounds.

As is shown by the values given for the acid hydrolysis of some of these compounds (Table X), there appears to be no correlation between the ease of enzymic and of acid hydrolysis. If the influences of these groups were merely on the glucosidic linkage, such a parallelism might be expected.

Since the substituent groups undoubtedly exert an influence on the glucosidic linkage undergoing hydrolysis as well as on the formation and stability of the enzyme-substrate complex, the interpretation of the results is difficult. It would seem, however, that the main influences would be on

TABLE X

COMPARISON OF THE RATES OF ACID AND ENZYME HYDROLYSIS OF SOME AROMATIC β-GLUCOSIDES

Aglycon group	Enzyme efficiency	Acid hydrolysis $k \times 10^4$
C_6H_5—	0.34	23
2-$CNCH_2C_6H_4$—	2.0	4.9
4-$CNCH_2C_6H_4$—	1.2	16
2-$CH_3COC_6H_4$—	3.3	110
4-$CH_3COC_6H_4$—	1.1	8
2-$CHOC_6H_4$—	8.6	9
4-$CHOC_6H_4$—	4.2	8
2-OH-4-$CHOC_6H_3$—	10	13
6-OCH_3-3-$CHOC_6H_3$—	11	43
2-OCH_3-4-$CHOC_6H_3$—	13	35
4-CH_3—C_6H_4—	0.12	21
2-CH_3—C_6H_4—	4.3	18
2-CH_2OH—C_6H_4—	1.9	11

the formation and stability of the enzyme-substrate complex. As the *ortho* position is closest to the linkage undergoing hydrolysis, the formation of weak bonds between the enzyme and groups in the *ortho* position would tend to facilitate hydrolysis. This influence would be less for groups in the *meta* position and still less for those in the *para* position. The inhibiting influence of the amino group might be ascribed to its ionic charge and the formation of a bond with the enzyme so stable that the dissociation of the products of hydrolysis from the enzyme would be inhibited.

5. OCCURRENCE AND SPECIFICITY OF OTHER β-GLUCOSIDASES

Although almond emulsin is the classical source of glycosidases and has received the most study, these enzymes are widely distributed in seeds, in animal tissues and organs, and in microorganisms. Although enzymes similar to the almond-emulsin glycosidases occur in many natural products, there is no reason for assuming that enzymes from the different sources which act on the same substrates should be identical. Instead it might be anticipated that the living tissues would develop enzymes best suited for the particular glycoside or disaccharide actually being synthesized or hydrolyzed. As will be shown in the subsequent discussion, the effect of changes in the aglycon groups of glycosides on the rate of enzymic hydrolysis is quite different for enzymes from different sources, i.e., the aglycon specificities vary. Unfortunately, there is practically no information on the effects

TABLE XI

COMPARISON OF THE SPECIFICITY OF β-GLUCOSIDASES FROM DIFFERENT SOURCES

Source of emulsin	β-Glucoside							
	Phenyl		Salicyl		*o*-Cresyl		*p*-Cresyl	
	f[a]	Ratio	f[a]	Ratio	f[a]	Ratio	f[a]	Ratio
Prunus armeniaca (apricot)	2.47	1.0	30.7	12.5	59.8	24.2	1.27	0.51
Amygdalus communis (sweet almond)	2.10	1.0	29.1	13.9	52.5	25.0	1.20	0.57
Prunus persica (peach)	0.315	1.0	3.16	10.0	5.84	18.5	0.169	0.53
Cycas revoluta (sago palm)	0.0226	1.0	0.176	7.65	0.394	17.4	0.0114	0.50
Papaver somniferum (opium poppy)	0.00459	1.0	0.0163	3.54	0.0268	5.82	0.00411	0.89
Glycine hispida (soybean)	0.00073	1.0	0.00181	2.48	0.00071	0.97	0.00146	2.0
Cucurbita moschata (squash)	0.00913	1.0	0.00503	0.55	0.00421	0.46	0.00897	1.00
Aspergillus oryzae (Takadiastase)	0.110	1.0	0.0962	0.88	0.0139	0.13	0.0722	0.59
A. oryzae	1.058	1.0	0.843	0.80	0.013	0.12	0.749	0.71
A. niger	2.99	1.0	0.965	0.32	0.0772	0.025	4.34	1.46
Ergot	0.148	1.0	0.0523	0.35	0.0349	0.24	0.148	1.0

[a] "f" is a measure of the ease of hydrolysis similar to the enzyme value and enzyme efficiency.

of changes in the sugar portion of glycosides on the enzymic hydrolysis for any enzymes except those from almond emulsin.

A comparison of the specific action of β-glucosidases from a number of sources on four different β-glucosides has been made by Miwa, Cheng, Fujisaki, and Toishi (*42*) and their results are summarized in Table XI. The table records the ease of hydrolysis as "f" values and also as relative values with the ease of hydrolysis of the phenyl β-glucoside being taken as unity for each enzyme preparation. The apricot, sweet-almond, and peach β-glucosidases are markedly affected by substitution in the *ortho* position as is demonstrated by the values for the salicyl and *o*-cresyl β-glucosides; *para* substitution is much less effective and inhibits the hydrolysis. The fungal β-glucosidases exhibit an inhibitory effect of *ortho* substitution;

42. T. Miwa, C. Cheng, M. Fujisaki, and A. Toishi, *Acta Phytochim.* (*Japan*) **10**, 155 (1937); see also K. Kobayashi, *J. Biochem.* (*Japan*) **18**, 41 (1944); *ibid.* **19**, 65, 71 (1947).

TABLE XII

COMPARISON OF THE SPECIFICITES OF β-GLUCOSIDASE OF SNAIL AND ALMOND EMULSIN

β-Glucoside	Sweet-almond emulsin		Snail emulsin	
	E.E.	Ratio	*E.E.*	Ratio
Phenyl	0.33	1.0	0.028	1.0
Salicyl	1.7	5.2	0.034	1.2
Vanillin	13	39	0.151	5.4
p-Cresyl	0.12	0.36	0.026	0.9
o-Cresyl	4.3	13	0.035	1.3
Ethyl	0.045	0.14	0.0056	0.2

those from the other plant sources seem to be intermediate in character between the two extremes, and to be much less affected by structural changes in the aglycon groups.

The digestive juices of the snail (*Helix pomatia*) contain a β-glucosidase in addition to an active cellulase. In Table XII, the action of the snail emulsin on several β-glucosides is compared with that of sweet-almond emulsin (*43*). The snail β-glucosidase reacts similarly to that in almond emulsin, but the influence of variations in the aglycon structure is much less.

The β-glucosidase which occurs as an impurity in highly purified yeast invertase hydrolyzes gentiobiose, but it exhibits no activity for the hydrolysis of cellobiose although almond emulsin hydrolyzes the latter disaccharide the more rapidly. Phenyl β-glucoside is cleaved at about the same rate as gentiobiose (*12*) in contrast to the results for almond emulsin for which the former glucoside is the more easily hydrolyzed. The glucoside phlorizin is only slowly acted upon by almond emulsin (in comparison with salicin) and by emulsins from cattle, horse, and pig liver, and intestinal mucosa, and pig and cattle kidneys. However, it is easily cleaved by a preparation from horse kidneys (*44*). Aqueous extracts of ground rabbit livers and kidneys exhibit considerable β-glucosidase activity, and the optimal pH is around 6; in contrast, extracts of spleens, lungs, testicles, and muscles have only slight ability to hydrolyze β-glucosides (*45*).

The β-glucosidase found in extracts of *Irpex lacteus*, on the basis of specificity studies, apparently is responsible for the hydrolysis of phenyl β-D-glucoside, salicin, and cellobiose (*46*).

43. B. Helferich and J. Goerdeler, *Ber. Verhandl. sächs. Akad. Wiss. Leipzig Math. phys. Kl.* **92,** 75 (1940).

44. E. Hofmann, *Biochem. Z.* **285,** 429 (1936).

45. K. Aizawa, *J. Biochem. (Japan)* **30,** 89 (1939).

46. T. Kobayashi, K. Wakabayashi, and K. Nisizawa, *Research Repts. Fac. Textiles Sericult. Shinshu Univ.* **2,** 102 (1952).

6. ALFALFA AND COFFEE EMULSINS; β-GALACTOSIDASES

The glycosidase system of alfalfa (lucerne) seeds (from *Medicago sativa*) has been studied by K. Hill (*25*). It differs from sweet-almond emulsin in having only traces of a β-glucosidase although it has a very active β-galactosidase and an α-galactosidase. The α-mannosidase and the "β-*N*-acetylglucosaminidase" activities are similar to those of almond emulsin.

The optimal pH for the alfalfa β-galactosidase is close to 3.4 and the maximal range is rather short. For the α-galactosidase and the α-mannosidase, the optimal pH covers a rather broad region between 3.3 and 5.0. As is also true for almond emulsin, the α-mannosidase is more stable to heat and ultraviolet light than the other enzyme components.

A comparison of the aglycon specificity of the alfalfa and the sweet-almond β-galactosidases is made (*25, 47*) in Table XIII. It will be noted that the alfalfa β-galactosidase is affected less by structural variations in the aglycon and is not particularly influenced by *ortho* substitution.

Coffee emulsin resembles the alfalfa emulsin more closely than almond emulsin; although the β-glucosidase action is weak, the β-galactosidase, α-mannosidase, and particularly the α-galactosidase activities are appreciable. In contrast to the ease of hydrolysis by almond emulsin of vanillin β-galactoside as compared with phenyl β-galactoside, there is little difference in the ease of hydrolysis of the two galactosides by coffee emulsin. The coffee α-galactosidase exhibits its maximal activity over a wide range of pH, 3 to 6, but the β-galactosidase has its maximum activity near 3.5 to 4 and the α-mannosidase between 4.5 and 5.5 (*48*).

The β-galactosidases found in numerous plant and animal tissues and in microorganisms have been compared by Nisizawa (*49*). On the basis of studies of their specificity and inhibition, these enzymes have been classified in two main groups: those exhibiting a considerable effect of structural changes on the rate of action (almond-emulsin type), and those showing relatively little effect of substrate changes ("Taka" or *Aspergillus oryzae* type). Within each of these groups, considerable variation exists in the specificity, inhibition, and pH effects. The β-galactosidase of snail emulsin (*Eulota peliomphala*) appears to have both types of these enzymes. These results are very similar to those noted above for the β-glucosidases.

Although in almond emulsin no definite evidence exists for separate β-glucosidase and β-galactosidase components, the corresponding "Taka" enzymes (from *A. oryzae*) are inactivated differently (*50*). In view of cur-

47. B. Helferich and H. E. Scheiber, *Z. physiol. Chem.* **226**, 272 (1934); B. Helferich and R. Griebel, *Ann.* **544**, 191 (1940); B. Helferich, H. E. Scheiber, R. Streeck, and F. Vorsatz, *ibid.* **518**, 211 (1935).

48. B. Helferich and F. Vorsatz, *Z. physiol. Chem.* **237**, 254 (1935).

49. K. Nisizawa, *J. Fac. Textiles Sericult. Shinshu Univ. Ser. C* **1**, 1 (1951).

50. K. Nisizawa, *Sci. Repts. Tokyo Bunrika Daigaku* **6**, 43, 29 (1942).

TABLE XIII

COMPARISON OF THE SPECIFICITY OF THE β-GALACTOSIDASES OF ALFALFA AND ALMOND EMULSINS

Glucoside	Almond emulsin		Alfalfa emulsin	
	E.E.	Relative *E.E.*	*E.E.*	Relative *E.E.*
Phenyl β-galactoside	0.040	1.0	0.17	1.0
o-Cresyl β-galactoside	0.69	17	0.13	0.76
p-Cresyl β-galactoside	0.02	0.5	0.14	0.82
Protocatechuic aldehyde galactoside	7.5	190	0.36	2.1
Vanillin β-galactoside	1.35	34	—	—
Phenyl β-lactoside	0.023	0.6	0.029	0.17
Protocatechuic aldehyde β-lactoside	0.08	2.0	0.021	0.12
Lactose	0.009	0.2	0.004	0.024

rent concepts of enzyme specificity, the existence of different types of active sites in the same molecule certainly is a distinct possibility.

7. YEAST GLYCOSIDASES

The best-known glycosidase component of yeasts is β-fructofuranosidase (invertase, β-*h*-fructosidase, sucrase, saccharase), which hydrolyzes β-fructofuranosides including sucrose. Live yeasts provide an excellent source of invertase and are used in commercial operations for the inversion of sucrose. Alcoholic fermentation can be avoided by using high sugar concentrations of the order of 50%. Invertase preparations are made by allowing yeast to autolyze in the presence of an antiseptic such as toluene, and for this purpose the invertase content of the yeasts can be increased greatly by development of the yeasts in aerated sucrose solutions (*51*). According to the procedure of Adams and Hudson (*22*), the yeast is allowed to autolyze under toluene at 25°C. for several days; the liquid is filtered and immediately dialyzed at 28 to 30°C. for several days (cellophane diaphragms). At the conclusion of the dialysis, the solutions are allowed to age one or two weeks and inert material is then thrown out by acidification to pH 3.7 to 3.9 with acetic acid. The final stage of purification consists of adsorption on bentonite at pH 3.6 to 4.1 and elution at pH 5.4 to 5.6. By this procedure, invertase preparations are obtained with invertase values of about 1000 as compared with values of about 10 for commercial preparations. (The time value for the best preparations was about 0.16.)

The preparation and the reaction kinetics of invertase have received a

51. R. Willstätter, C. D. Lowry, Jr., and K. Schneider, *Z. physiol. Chem.* **146**, 158 (1925); R. Weidenhagen, *Z. angew. Chem.*, **47**, 581 (1934).

TABLE XIV

KINETICS OF HYDROLYSIS OF SUCROSE, RAFFINOSE, AND INULIN BY PURIFIED YEAST INVERTASE PREPARATIONS

Time (min.)	Sucrose		Raffinose		Inulin	
	Hydrolysis (per cent)	$k^a \times 10^4$	Hydrolysis (per cent)	$k^a \times 10^4$	Hydrolysis (per cent)	$k^a \times 10^4$
20	26.2	66.0	—	—	22.2	54.5
22	—	—	28.7	66.9	—	—
30	37.6	68.3	36.1	64.9	—	—
40	48.0	71.0	44.6	64.1	39.6	54.7
50	57.2	73.7	—	—	48.4	57.5
55	—	—	55.8	64.4	—	—
60	64.6	75.2	—	—	54.8	57.5
75	74.2	78.5	—	—	—	—
80	—	—	68.2	62.2	—	—
140	—	—	85.1	59.0	—	—
150	95.0	86.7	—	—	88.2	61.9
300	100.0	—	96.9	50.5	97.4	52.8
1440	—	—	100.4	—	100.0	—

[a] Calculated in minutes and common logarithms by use of first-order equations.

great deal of study (*52*), particularly by Willstätter, Kuhn, Euler, Josephson, Hudson, Myrbäck, Nelson, Weidenhagen, and their associates. The specificity and properties of yeast invertase have been restudied by Adams, Richtmyer, and Hudson (*12*). The optimal pH for the hydrolysis of sucrose and raffinose is probably around 5.0 to 5.5, although earlier workers found it to be somewhat lower (3.5 to 5.5). However, the rate of decrease toward the acid side is quite small, and even at pH 2.8 the enzyme is quite active (see Fig. 4, earlier in this chapter).

As shown in Table XIV, the results of Adams, Richtmyer, and Hudson indicate that under the "standard conditions," the first-order reaction constants decrease for raffinose, increase for sucrose, and remain fairly constant for inulin.

Specificity studies of yeast invertase are complicated by the difficulty of preparing β-fructofuranosides, and the studies have been limited to the naturally occurring di- and oligosaccharides containing β-fructofuranoside residues. Sucrose, raffinose, and stachyose have such residues in an unsubstituted condition (terminal positions) whereas melezitose has a substituted β-fructofuranoside residue (central position). Inulin is a polymeric β-

52. For discussions of the earlier work see J. M. Nelson, *Chem. Revs.* **12,** 1 (1933); R. Weidenhagen, *in* "Handbuch der Enzymologie" (F. F. Nord and R. Weidenhagen, ed. 5), p. 512. Akademische Verlagsges., Leipzig, 1940.

fructofuranoside with 1,2′-linkages. All of these compounds with the exception of the melezitose are hydrolyzed by yeast invertase preparations. For an invertase preparation from bakers' yeast with enzyme value of 791, the ease of hydrolysis of sucrose, raffinose, inulin, and stachyose is in the proportion, 100:23:0.036:6.8. For a similar preparation from brewers' yeast, the proportion is 100:12.5:0.006:3.1 (*12*). Although it is probable that sucrose, raffinose, and stachyose are hydrolyzed by yeast invertase, and that the different ratios observed for the two preparations are due to variation in the invertase molecule present in the brewers' and the bakers' yeasts, it is possible that the inulin hydrolysis may be due to another enzyme component, an inulase. Support for the existence of a special inulase is given by the marked difference between the optimal pH for the inulin and for the sucrose hydrolysis. Thus, that for the sucrose inversion lies between 5.0 and 5.5 while that for the inulin hydrolysis lies between 3.2 and 4.0. For yeasts, the ratio of invertase to inulase activity is quite large (2,800 to as high as 28,300), but for fungal emulsins, particularly those from *Aspergillus niger*, the ratio may be as low as about 5 (*14*).

Bottom (or brewers') yeasts contain an enzyme which hydrolyzes melibiose, an α-galactoside, and which is absent from top (bakers' or ale) yeasts (*53*). This enzyme, called α-galactosidase or melibiase, is carried along with invertase when the latter is purified, and purified brewers' yeast invertase provides a good source of the enzyme (*12*). The optimal pH region is fairly broad, and a pH of 4.5 is probably the best for most substrates. For such a preparation, with a melibiase value of 4.8, the relative ease of hydrolysis of melibiose, phenyl α-galactoside, and methyl α-galactoside is in the proportion, 100:123:3.3. A comparison of the action of α-galactosidases from several sources on melibiose and phenyl α-galactoside (*54*) is made in Table XV. In contrast with the invertase preparations from brewers' yeast, those from bakers' yeast are inactive towards melibiose and the methyl and phenyl α-galactosides (*12*); the α-galactosidase activity must be less than 10^{-4}.

In addition to invertase (β-fructofuranosidase) and the α-galactosidase of brewers' yeast, purified yeast invertase preparations contain a β-glucosidase and the otherwise unknown β-mannosidase. However, there is no evidence for the existence of a β-galactosidase, an α-mannosidase, an α-glucosidase, or an α-fructofuranosidase (*12*). Phenyl β-fructopyranoside also is not appreciably hydrolyzed by yeast invertase (*37*).

Yeasts are also a good source of an α-glucosidase. However, yeast α-glucosidase (maltase) as ordinarily prepared loses its activity very rapidly.

53. A. Bau, *Chem.-Ztg.* **19,** 1873 (1895); E. Fischer and P. Lindner, *Ber.* **28,** 3034 (1895).

54. R. Weidenhagen and A. Renner, *Z. Ver. deut. Zucker-Ind.* **86,** 22 (1936).

TABLE XV

COMPARISON OF EASE OF ENZYMIC HYDROLYSIS OF PHENYL α-GALACTOSIDE AND MELIBIOSE BY α-GALACTOSIDASES FROM SEVERAL SOURCES

Source of enzyme	Relative ease of hydrolysis of melibiose compared to phenyl α-galactoside
Bottom yeast	0.67
Sweet almond	1.1
Bitter almond	0.8
Barley malt	0.15
Aspergillus oryzae	<0.1

For this reason yeast invertase preparations contain little if any of this enzyme, and to obtain it very mild autolysis conditions must be employed. Dried yeasts seem to be a particularly good source (*55*). Such preparations contain considerable quantities of invertase, but if the low-temperature autolysate is treated with limited portions of activated aluminum hydroxide, the α-glucosidase is preferentially adsorbed and then may be eluted with solutions of secondary phosphates (*56*).

Although the yeast invertase exerts its optimal activity at about pH 4 to 5, the yeast α-glucosidase optimum is between 6 and 7, and the activity decreases very rapidly outside of these limits (*56*). Thus, at the optimum for invertase action, the α-glucosidase is practically inactive. However, at pH 6.5, there is appreciable invertase action.

It is of interest that α-glucosidase, purified by adsorption and elution, at pH 6.5 is able to hydrolyze sucrose at even a greater rate than maltose. The enzyme might be classified as an invertase as it inverts sucrose, but this term is reserved for β-fructofuranosidases. The hydrolytic action (*56*) of α-glucosidase on sucrose (β-fructofuranosyl α-glucopyranoside) is ascribed to the presence of an α-glucosidic linkage in the sugar.

Enzymes which hydrolyze maltose and α-glucosides are widely distributed in plant and animal products and microorganisms (*57*). The products which have been studied are crude and often only slightly active mixtures of various enzymes. Such preparations have been utilized for testing the action of α-glucosidase on sucrose. Since they may contain

55. R. Willstätter and E. Bamann, *Z. physiol. Chem.* **151,** 242, 273 (1926); J. R. Krieble, E. L. Skau, and E. W. Lovering, *J. Am. Chem. Soc.* **49,** 1728 (1927).

56. R. Weidenhagen, *Ergeb. Enzymforsch.* **2,** 90 (1933).

57. See H. Pringsheim and F. Loew, *Z. physiol. Chem.* **207,** 241 (1932); R. Weidenhagen, *Z. Ver. deut. Zucker-Ind.* **78,** 788 (1928); S. Hestrin, *Enzymologia* **8,** 193 (1940); K. Aizawa, *J. Biochem. (Japan)* **30,** 89 (1939).

TABLE XVI
COMPARISON OF THE RELATIVE EASE OF HYDROLYSIS OF SEVERAL α- AND β-GLUCOSIDES BY YEAST α-GLUCOSIDASE AND ALMOND β-GLUCOSIDASE

Enzyme	Aglycon group				
	CH_3	4-Glucose	Phenyl	Saligenin	*o*-Cresyl
Yeast α-glucosidase	1	2.3	12	(2.4)	11.7
Almond β-glucosidase	1	2.1	5.2	26	60

invertases as well as α-glucosidases and since the activities of these emulsins are usually low, the results have but little significance. Although sucrose is hydrolyzed by many such preparations, it is uncertain whether this is due to an invertase or an α-glucosidase component or both.

As previously mentioned, substitution of a group in the *ortho* position of phenyl β-glucoside usually produces a marked increase in ease of hydrolysis of the glucoside by almond β-glucosidase. Although the specificity of yeast α-glucosidase has not received much study, it appears that the hydrolysis of phenyl α-glucosides is not greatly affected by *ortho* substitution. In Table XVI, the relative ease of enzymic hydrolysis of several α- and β-glucosides with the same aglycon groups are compared (*58*).

Adaptation and Heredity (*59*). Yeasts of different species or even of different strains within a species appear to differ as to the enzymes they possess, for they do not all utilize the same sugars. Several studies (*60–63*) of the progeny of hybrid yeasts have been directed toward showing gene control of the enzymes involved in fermentation. For example, five genes (not all in the same yeast) are reported to be involved in maltose fermentations. The relationship of the genes to the fermentability of galactose, melibiose, melezitose, raffinose, methyl α-D-glucoside, and sucrose was also investigated. The data are difficult to interpret because they are complicated by the phenomenon of adaptation, i.e., the acquisition of the ability to ferment a sugar not ordinarily fermented after being grown in its

58. B. Helferich, U. Lampert, and G. Sparmberg, *Ber.* **67,** 1808 (1934).

59. See S. Spiegelman, *in* "The Enzymes" (J. B. Sumner and K. Myrbäck, eds.), Vol. I, Part 1, p. 267. Academic Press, New York, 1950.

60. R. B. Gilliland, *Nature* **173,** 409 (1954); B. D. Mundkur and C. C. Lindegren, *Am. J. Botany* **36,** 722 (1949); N. J. Palleroni and C. C. Lindegren, *J. Bacteriol.* **65,** 122 (1953).

61. B. D. Mundkur, *Ann. Missouri Botan. Garden* **36,** 259 (1949).

62. S. Hestrin and C. C. Lindegren, *Arch. Biochem.* **29,** 315 (1950); **38,** 317 (1952).

63. S. Spiegelman, *Cold Spring Harbor Symposia Quant. Biol.* **11,** 256 (1946); *Proc. 2nd Natl. Cancer Conf.* p. 1345 (1952).

presence. In addition, deviations of the segregations from Mendelian ratios are found; these are variously attributed to faulty technique, to "gene conversions" (*61*), or to a transmission of self-duplicating substances ("plasmagenes") in the cytoplasm (*63*). Also, di- and trisaccharides may be utilized through "transglycosidation" (Chapter IX) or through hydrolysis to the constituent monosaccharides.

Hestrin and Lindegren (*62*) have described a hybrid yeast capable, after adaptation, of fermenting methyl α-D-glucoside and apparently incapable of fermenting maltose at a significant rate. Another hybrid fermented maltose but did not readily attack methyl α-D-glucoside. They ascribed these results to the existence of an α-glucosidase which does not split maltose. A cell-free extract of the former yeast rapidly cleaved methyl α-D-glucoside and phenyl α-D-glucoside but attacked maltose only very feebly (*62*). Work of Spiegelman, Sussman, and Taylor (*64*) with fractional precipitation also points toward the presence of two different α-glucosidases in some yeast strains. One fraction of the enzymes of a maltose-adapted yeast was said to split maltose and phenyl α-D-glucoside but to be unable to split methyl α-D-glucoside. The second fraction was claimed to be very active against methyl α-D-glucoside but not to effect maltose or phenyl α-D-glucoside appreciably. The evidence is quite clear that, generally, enzymes of a given type have variable relative specificities. It is doubtful that the conditions of this work were sufficiently strenuous to prove that the α-glucosidases represent a case of absolute specificity.

8. β-GLUCURONIDASES (β-D-GLUCO-PYRANOSIDURONASES) (*65*)

Enzymes which hydrolyze the β-glycosides of D-glucuronic acid are common constituents of the tissues and fluids of the higher and lower animals and plants, including microorganisms. In man and other higher animals, the highest concentrations of the enzyme are found in liver, spleen, endocrine glands, and the tissues of reproduction.

Calf spleen and liver (*66*), *Escherichia coli* (*67*), and almond emulsin (*68a*, *b*) are the sources of the most-studied preparations of β-glucuronidases. Commercial preparations from animal tissues are available (*69*);

64. S. Spiegelman, M. Sussman, and B. Taylor, *Federation Proc.* **9,** 120 (1950).

65. W. H. Fishman, *Advances in Enzymol.* **16,** 361 (1955); H. G. Bray, *Advances in Carbohydrate Chem.* **8,** 251 (1953).

66. P. Bernfeld and W. H. Fishman, *J. Biol. Chem.* **202,** 757 (1953).

67. H. J. Buehler, P. A. Katzman, and E. A. Doisy, *Proc. Soc. Exptl. Biol. Med.* **76,** 672 (1951).

68a. C. Neuberg and W. Neimann, *Z. physiol. Chem.* **44,** 114 (1905).

68b. B. Helferich and G. Sparmberg, *Z. physiol. Chem.* **221,** 92 (1933).

69. S. L. Cohen, M. M. Goldfine, F. Toussaint, K. Friedman, and I. Noma, *Endocrinology,* **54,** 353 (1954).

these have clinical diagnostic use for the hydrolysis of urinary 17-hydroxycorticosteroids and 17-ketosteroids conjugated with glucuronic acid (*70*).

The β-glucuronidase (β-D-glucopyranosiduronase) of bovine liver and of spleen have been purified highly (*66*, *71*); the calf-liver enzyme has been estimated to have a purity of 85% (*71*). Various aromatic glucosiduronic acids have been used for the activity measurements (*65*), with the phenolphthalein D-glucosiduronic acid being chosen very commonly for this purpose. The optimal pH usually falls in the range 4.5 to 5.0. The enzyme is probably different from β-glucosidase, but additional definitive evidence is required (*68b*). (See also p. 318.)

The widespread occurrence of this class of enzymes in living tissues has aroused considerable interest in their function and significance. Fishman's suggestion (*65*) of a role in the synthesis of glucosiduronic acids seems incompatible in terms of the probable energy requirements, and Levvy's and Teague's views (*72*) of a purely hydrolytic function seem more likely. However, a transglycosidation mechanism is also highly probable. The amount of β-glucuronidase in tissues seems to be associated with the rapidity of metabolism and increases during rapid proliferation of cells. As a result, these enzymes have been of special interest in studies of cancer.

9. ENZYMIC SYNTHESIS OF GLYCOSIDES

The hydrolysis and synthesis of a glycoside may be represented by the equation:

$$ROG + H_2O \rightleftarrows ROH + GOH \qquad \begin{array}{l} R = \text{alkyl group} \\ G = \text{glycosyl group} \end{array}$$

The equilibrium constant, K, is given by:

$$K = \frac{(ROH)(GOH)}{(ROG)(H_2O)}$$

Obviously, the presence of a high concentration of alcohol facilitates the synthesis and high concentration of water the hydrolysis. In the Fischer method for the synthesis of the glycosides (Chapter IV), the catalyst is an acid, but, as shown by the excellent work of Bourquelot, Hérissey, and Bridel, enzymes also may be employed with some advantages over the use of acids. When acids are used, all the various isomers are formed, and the equilibrium is very complex although certain constituents predominate under the equilibrium conditions. The enzymes are very much more selective in their catalysis. Almond emulsin catalyzes the synthesis and hydroly-

70. E. M. Glenn and D. H. Nelson, *J. Clin. Endocrinol.* **13**, 911 (1953).

71. P. Bernfeld, J. S. Nisselbaum, and W. H. Fishman, *J. Biol. Chem.* **202**, 763 (1953); E. E. B. Smith and G. T. Mills, *Biochem. J.* **54**, 164 (1953).

72. R. S. Teague, *Advances in Carbohydrate Chem.* **9**, 185 (1954).

sis of β-glucosides because of the β-glucosidase present, but no enzyme is present for the synthesis of α-glucosides (α-glucosidase). On the other hand, some yeast emulsins (yeast α-glucosidase preparations) contain an active α-glucosidase and practically no β-glucosidase. As a result almond emulsin, as shown by Bourquelot, may be used for the selective synthesis of β-glucosides and yeast α-glucosidase for the α-glucosides. By this means, the following β-glucosides, among others, were obtained in crystalline condition, in some instances for the first time: ethyl, geranyl, cinnamyl, butyl, hexyl, 2-ethoxyethyl, mannitol, allyl, propyl, and glucose β-D-glucosides (*73*). Many α-glucosides including the methyl, mannitol, and 1,2-propanediol α-glucosides (*74*) have been obtained by employment of yeast α-glucosidase as a catalyst.

For the synthesis of β-glucosides, the reactive form of glucose is β-glucose; the concentration of this form determines the reaction rate and the position of the equilibrium (*75*). The equilibrium constants for the synthesis of several glucosides are as follows:

β-Glucoside	Av. *K*
Methyl	0.149
2-Ethoxyethyl	0.378
Mannitol	0.051

The *in vivo* synthesis of glycosides, as discussed earlier in this chapter (and Chapter IX), probably occurs by transglycosidation, because of the smaller changes in free energy. The glycosidases presumably are purely hydrolytic in their natural function or act as "transglycosidases."

The specific action of the enzymes is advantageous in many applications, but it is also a limitation to their general use. Only a few types of glycosides can be synthesized by this method (glucoside, mannoside, and galactoside types) because of the limited number of glycosidases which occur in nature. These biological catalysts are also heat sensitive and insoluble in organic solvents. In special instances, however, their application is very advantageous. Thus, selective hydrolysis has been used to separate mixtures of α- and β-glucosides and of methyl fructosides (*76*) and the enzymic synthesis

73. E. Bourquelot and M. Bridel, *Ann. chim. phys.* [8] **29,** 145 (1913); B. Helferich and U. Lampert, *Ber.* **68,** 2050 (1935); I. Vintilescu, C. Ionescu, and A. Kizyk, *Bull. soc. chim. România* **16,** 151 (1934); I. Vintilescu, C. Ionescu, and M. Solomon, *ibid.* **17,** 267 (1935).

74. E. Bourquelot, *Ann. chim.* **3,** 287 (1915); I. Vintilescu, C. Ionescu, and A. Kizyk, *Bull. soc. chim. România* **17,** 131 (1935).

75. I. Vintilescu, C. Ionescu, and A. Kizyk, *Bull. soc. chim. România* **17,** 137 (1935); *Ber.* **67,** 990 (1934).

76. E. F. Armstrong and K. F. Armstrong, "The Carbohydrates," p. 21. Longmans, Green, New York, 1934; C. B. Purves and C. S. Hudson, *J. Am. Chem. Soc.* **56,** 702, 708, 1969, 1972 (1934).

of glucosides and galactosides has been made the basis of a method for the determination of these sugars in plant extracts (*77*).

10. IN VIVO SYNTHESIS OF GLYCOSIDES

An interesting group of experiments has been reported by L. P. Miller, who has demonstrated that glucosides are synthesized in many plants when the aglycon is supplied in the nutrient solution or as a vapor in contact with the plant. Potato tubers, gladiolus corms, and wheat synthesize 2-chloroethyl β-glucoside when exposed to ethylene chlorohydrin (*78*). Although gentiobiose is not known to occur in gladiolus corms or tomatoes, the presence of *o*-chlorophenol induces the formation of the *o*-chlorophenyl β-gentiobioside by these plants. In the presence of both *o*-chlorophenol and ethylene chlorohydrin, both 2-chloroethyl β-glucoside and *o*-chlorophenyl β-gentiobioside are synthesized simultaneously by gladiolus corms (*79*). Bottle gourd (*Lagenaria leucantha*), radish, corn, tobacco, and dandelion plants form 2,2,2-trichloroethyl β-D-glucoside from added chloral hydrate (*80*). The glycosides are separated as their crystalline acetates from the juices of the plants after the treatment. Previously, similar results had been obtained by Ciamician and Ravenna (*81*), who inoculated maize and other plants with phenols and separated the corresponding glucosides from the plants. Thus, the injection of saligenin resulted in the synthesis of salicin.

Many phenols and alcohols when injected into animals are detoxified by conjugation as glucosiduronic acids, the glycosides of glucuronic acid (*82*, *72*). Phenolphthalein, cinnamic acid, and sulfapyridine when injected into rabbits may be recovered from the urine as the corresponding glucosiduronic acids (*83*). This procedure has been extensively used for the preparation of glucosiduronic acids. Since *d*- and *l*-menthol and *d*- and *l*-isomenthol are conjugated under the above conditions to different extents (the formation of the *d*-menthol and *d*-isomenthol glucosiduronic acids being greater), the biological method may be utilized for the resolution of the inactive materials (*84*).

77. M. Bridel and J. Charpentier, *J. pharm. chim.* [7] **30,** 33 (1924).

78. L. P. Miller, *Contribs. Boyce Thompson Inst.* **12,** 25 (1941).

79. L. P. Miller, *Contribs. Boyce Thompson Inst.* **12,** 163 (1941).

80. L. P. Miller, *Contribs. Boyce Thompson Inst.* **12,** 167 (1941); **12,** 359, 465 (1942); **13,** 185 (1943).

81. G. Ciamician and C. Ravenna, *Atti reale accad. Lincei* **25,** 3 (1916).

82. R. T. Williams, "Detoxication Mechanisms" Wiley, New York, 1947.

83. R. T. Williams, *Biochem. J.* **34,** 272 (1940); A. A. Di Somma, *J. Biol. Chem.* **133,** 277 (1940); I. Snapper, T. F. Yü, and Y. T. Chiang, *Proc. Soc. Exptl. Biol. Med.* **44,** 30 (1940); J. Scudi, *Science* **91,** 486 (1940).

84. R. T. Williams, *Biochem. J.* **34,** 48, 690 (1940).

11. BOURQUELOT BIOCHEMICAL DETERMINATION OF GLYCOSIDES AND OLIGOSACCHARIDES IN PLANT MATERIALS (*85*)

An interesting method has been used extensively by Bourquelot, Bridel, Hérissey, and associates for the analysis of glycosides and oligosaccharides in plant materials. The method depends upon the selective action of enzyme preparations from various sources in hydrolyzing certain of the components of plant extracts. Yeast emulsin (invertase) is usually used first and is followed by almond emulsin. Enzyme preparations from other sources such as *Rhamnus cathartica* emulsin (also called rhamnodiastase) and mustard-seed emulsin have special applications. The yeast emulsin (invertase) hydrolyzes sucrose and oligosaccharides such as gentianose, raffinose, and stachyose which have sucrose linkages in the molecule. Almond emulsin acts on β-glucosides, β-galactosides, α-mannosides, and to lesser extent on α-galactosides. Emulsins prepared from plants of the *Rhamnus* type apparently contain disaccharidases which hydrolyze glycosides of primeverose (6-glucose β-D-xyloside) and rutinose (6-glucose β-L-rhamnoside) into disaccharide and aglycon. Those from the mustard seeds have special enzymes hydrolyzing thioglycosides. Hydrolysis resulting from each of the treatments is shown by measurements of the reducing power and of the optical rotation before and after each treatment. These results are expressed quantitatively as the "index of enzymic reduction" which is the amount of reducing sugar formed per degree of rotation change (reducing sugar in grams/change of rotation produced by the enzyme) under specified conditions. This index differs for the various glycosides and compound sugars and may be used for the qualitative and quantitative estimation of the substances present in the plant extracts when too many are not present. The existence of many glycosides and oligosaccharides has been demonstrated by this method, many for the first time, and many plant species have been investigated. In 1920, Bourquelot summarized the results of the application of the method to 281 species of phanerogams and reported that 205 of these species contained glycosides hydrolyzable by almond emulsin. All were reported to contain sucrose, and raffinose and stachyose were common constituents.

In carrying out the hydrolysis in alcoholic solution it was observed that the hydrolysis was incomplete, and this led to the discovery of the synthesizing action of enzymes mentioned above. The enzymic synthesis then was utilized in methods for the biochemical determination of glucose and galactose by converting them to the corresponding glycosides.

85. E. Bourquelot, *Compt. rend.* **171**, 423 (1920); M. Bridel and C. Charaux, *Pharm. Acta Helv.* **1**, 107 (1926); C. Béguin, *ibid.* **1**, 65, 90 (1926).

In its present stage of development, the biochemical method probably leaves much to be desired, but additional study should make it a valuable tool for the analysis of the complex mixtures occurring in plant extracts. Methods (*86*) for the estimation of raffinose in the presence of sucrose have been described which depend on selective enzymic hydrolysis.

86. C. S. Hudson and T. S. Harding, *J. Am. Chem. Soc.* **37,** 2193 (1915); H. S. Paine and R. T. Balch, *Ind. Eng. Chem.* **17,** 240 (1925).

XI. THE IDENTIFICATION AND THE QUANTITATIVE DETERMINATION OF CARBOHYDRATES (1)

G. Ray Noggle*

1. QUALITATIVE IDENTIFICATION

A. Separation of Sugar Mixtures

Many methods have been employed for the identification of sugars. When only a single sugar is present in the material undergoing examination, the methods customary to organic chemistry may be used. Thus, derivatives may be prepared, and the properties can be compared with those of known materials. The optical rotation of the unknown or of its derivative provides one of the best properties for the identification. Mixtures are much more difficult to analyze. Distillation as a means of fractionation is limited because of the ease of decomposition and of the low volatility of sugars and derivatives. However, the methyl ethers and the propionic esters can be distilled without decomposition, and they are sometimes used for the separation of sugar mixtures (*1a*). Another method of separation is the fractional crystallization of the sugar mixture or of a derivative of the mixture.

Ketoses may be separated from contaminating aldoses by oxidation of the latter with bromine and removal of the aldonic acids with an ion-exchange resin (*2*). Ion-exchange resins are also useful in the recovery of sugar acids and of some nitrogen-containing derivatives of sugars.

* The section on histochemistry was prepared by Robert W. Mowry.

1. General references: C. A. Browne and F. W. Zerban, "Sugar Analysis." Wiley, New York, 1941; F. J. Bates and Associates, *Natl. Bur. Standards Circ.* **C440,** (1942); Z. Dische, *in* "Methods of Biochemical Analysis" (D. Glick, ed.), Vol. II, p. 313. Interscience, New York, 1955.

1a. C. D. Hurd, R. W. Ligett, and K. M. Gordon, *J. Am. Chem. Soc.* **63,** 2656, 2657, 2659 (1941); C. D. Hurd, D. T. Englis, W. A. Bonner, and M. A. Rogers, *ibid.* **66,** 2015 (1944); for the application of the methyl ethers to the analytical separation of sugars see C. D. Hurd and S. M. Cantor, *ibid.* **60,** 2677 (1938); see also Chapters IX and XII for products obtained by the hydrolysis of polysaccharides and oligosaccharides.

2. J. C. Sowden and R. Schaffer, *J. Am. Chem. Soc.* **74,** 499 (1952).

The introduction of chromatographic techniques (*3*) to the carbohydrate field has made available powerful new tools for separating and identifying the compounds in sugar mixtures. Several rather distinct types of chromatography are now recognized: column chromatography, partition chromatography, adsorption chromatography, paper chromatography, ion-exchange chromatography, ionography, and others. All of these techniques have been applied to carbohydrate analysis.

In general two types of problems are encountered in regard to the application of chromatography to carbohydrate analysis. If only a small amount of material (milligrams or even micrograms) is available, the paper-chromatographic technique is used to separate the sugars present in a mixture. If more material is available or if larger amounts of sugars are to be separated for preparative purposes, column chromatography is used. Column chromatography has been used for the separation of sugar derivatives as well as directly for free sugars. The free sugars are colorless, but the passage of adsorption bands out of the column may be detected by measurements of the density or refractive index of the eluate. The column technique is considerably improved by employing a fraction collector to collect consecutive samples of the eluate from the column. Various analytical and chromatographic procedures can be used to analyze separate aliquots of effluent. Streak reagents may be used to indicate the positions of bands of adsorbed material on extruded columns. Charcoal (*4*), cellulose (*5*), starch, silicates (*5a*), and other materials are widely used as adsorbents (*6*).

Ion-exchange chromatography has also been used to separate components of sugar mixtures (*7*). The carbohydrates form complexes with borate ions (*8*) which behave as anions and can be separated on an anion-exchange

3. H. H. Strain, "Chromatographic Adsorption Analysis," Interscience, New York, 1942; T. I. Williams, "An Introduction to Chromatography." Chemical Publishing, New York, 1947; L. Zechmeister and L. Cholnoky, "Principles and Practice of Chromatography" (translated by A. L. Bacharach and F. A. Robinson). Wiley, New York, 1948; "Chromatographic Analysis," *Discussions Faraday Soc.* **No. 7** (1949); E. Lederer and M. Lederer, "Chromatography." Elsevier, New York, 1953; for a review of column chromatography as applied to sugar separations see W. W. Binkley and M. L. Wolfrom, *Sugar Research Foundation Sci. Rept.* **10,** (1948).

4. R. L. Whistler and D. F. Durso, *J. Am. Chem. Soc.* **72,** 677 (1950).

5. L. Hough, J. K. N. Jones, and W. H. Wadman, *J. Chem. Soc.* p. 2511 (1949); *ibid.* p. 1702 (1950).

5a. B. W. Lew, M. L. Wolfrom, and R. M. Goepp, Jr., *J. Am. Chem. Soc.* **68,** 1449 (1946); W. H. McNeely, W. W. Binkley, and M. L. Wolfrom, *ibid.* **67,** 527 (1945); L. W. Georges, R. S. Bower, and M. L. Wolfrom, *ibid.* **68,** 2169 (1946).

6. For a detailed discussion see D. J. Bell, *in* "Modern Methods of Plant Analysis" (K. Paech and M. V. Tracey, eds.), Vol. II, p. 1. Springer, Berlin, 1955.

7. J. X. Khym and L. P. Zill, *J. Am. Chem. Soc.* **74,** 2090 (1952).

8. J. Böeseken, *Advances in Carbohydrate Chem.* **4,** 189 (1949); H. S. Isbell, J. F. Brewster, N. B. Holt, and H. L. Frush, *J. Research Natl. Bur. Standards* **40,** 129 (1948).

resin. The method has been used to separate the sugars in plant extracts (*9*) and phosphorylated sugars (*10*). The borate complexes have also been separated by a modified form of electrophoresis (*11*).

By far the most widely used chromatographic technique in the carbohydrate field is paper chromatography (*12, 13*). This method, first used for the analysis of amino acids (*14*), was used in 1946 by Partridge (*15*) to separate a mixture of sugars. The method enables the rapid separation of the components of some complex mixtures. Very small amounts of material can be used, and relatively simple equipment is needed. In addition the technique can be used as an aid in establishing the homogeneity of a sample and the identification of an unknown substance.

The method involves the following steps. A small drop of the material in solution is placed at one end of a strip of filter paper. After drying, the paper is treated with a suitable solvent so that the solvent moves gradually over the sugar spot and along the paper; this process is called "development." After a time the paper is removed from contact with the solvent and dried; the spots on the paper are identified by appropriate methods.

Whatman No. 1 filter paper has been generally used for sugar chromatography, but other grades of Whatman paper as well as other types of filter paper may be useful for some particular problem. Both ascending and descending developments have been used. Temperature control is useful during the development of the chromatogram, but if adequate internal standards are used this is not a prerequisite for successful chromatography. A simple one-demensional chromatogram usually will not separate all of the components in a complex mixture. Frequently the separation can be improved by multiple development of the chromatogram in the same direction with the same or different solvents. Alternatively, the chromatogram can be developed two-dimensionally with two different solvents run at right angles to each other.

9. G. R. Noggle and L. P. Zill, *Arch. Biochem. and Biophys.* **41,** 21 (1952).

10. J. X. Khym and W. E. Cohn, *J. Am. Chem. Soc.* **75,** 1153 (1953).

11. H. J. MacDonald, "Ionography." Yearbook Publishing, Chicago, 1955.

12. J. N. Balston and B. E. Talbot, "A Guide to Filter Paper and Cellulose Powder Chromatography." Reeve Angel, London, 1952; F. Cramer, "Papierchromatographie." Verlag Chemie, Weinheim, 1953 (also translated in English by L. Richards, Macmillan, London, 1954); R. J. Block, E. L. Durrum, and G. Zweig, "A Manual of Paper Chromatography and Paper Electrophoresis." Academic Press, New York, 1955.

13. L. Hough, *in* Methods of Biochemical Analysis (D. Glick, ed.), Vol. I, p. 205. Interscience, New York, 1954; G. N. Kowkabany, *Advances in Carbohydrate Chem.* **9,** 303 (1954); C. L. Comar, "Radioisotopes in Biology and Agriculture," p. 360. McGraw-Hill, New York, 1955; also see reference *6*.

14. R. Consden, A. H. Gordon, and A. J. P. Martin., *Biochem. J.* **38,** 224 (1944).

15. S. M. Partridge, *Nature* **158,** 270 (1946).

TABLE I

Some Solvents for Paper Chromatography of Carbohydrates
(From Bell(*6*))

Solvent components[a]	Reference
Phenol, water-saturated (lower layer used)	(*16*)
n-Butanol, water-saturated	(*16*)
Ethyl methyl ketone, water-saturated	(*16*)
Ethyl acetate(2) – pyridine(1) – water(2)	(*17*)
Ethyl acetate(3) – acetic acid(1) – water(3)	(*17*)
n-Butanol(5) – ethanol(1) – water(4)	(*18*)
Amyl alcohol mixture (fusel oil)(3) – acetic acid(1) – water(1)	(*19*)
n-Butanol(3) – pyridine(1) – water(1.5)	(*19*)
n-Butanol(5) – pyridine(3) – water(3) – benzene(1)	(*20*)
n-Propanol(7) – ethyl acetate(1) – water(2)	(*21*)

[a] When the solvent mixture forms two layers, the upper one is employed for development. The figures following the components indicate the volume ratios taken for the mixture.

A large number of different solvent systems have been used for paper chromatography of carbohydrates. Some of the most useful are listed in Table I. The system *n*-butanol(40)–ethanol(11)–water(19) is also good (*5*).

Mixtures of methylated sugars are most often encountered in the hydrolyzates of methylated polysaccharides prepared for structural studies. Their separation is discussed in this connection in Chapter XII.

Of particular interest to the biochemist has been the separation and identification of the phosphorylated sugars. These components have been examined with the aid of paper chromatography, and Table II shows some of the solvent systems that have been used. The general topic of the separation of sugar phosphates is adequately covered by Benson (*22*).

After the separation of the sugars on the filter paper by the different solvents, the sugars are identified by their relative position and by specific color tests. The position of the sugar spot is generally given in terms of a constant, R_f, which is defined as the ratio of the distance moved by the spot to the distance moved by the solvent front. Often it is impossible to determine the distance moved by the solvent front (it may be permitted to

16. S. M. Partridge, *Biochem. J.* **42,** 238 (1948).
17. M. A. Jermyn and F. A. Isherwood, *Biochem. J.* **44,** 402 (1949).
18. E. L. Hirst and J. K. N. Jones, *Discussions Faraday Soc.* **No. 7,** 268 (1949).
19. A. Jeanes, C. S. Wise, and R. J. Dimler, *Anal. Chem.* **23,** 415 (1951).
20. H. C. S. deWhalley, N. Albon, and D. Gross, *Analyst* **76,** 293 (1951).
21. N. Albon and D. Gross, *Analyst* **77,** 410 (1952).
22. A. A. Benson, *in* "Modern Methods of Plant Analysis" (K. Paech and M. V. Tracey, eds.), Vol. II, p. 113. Springer, Berlin, 1955.

TABLE II

SOME SOLVENTS FOR PAPER CHROMATOGRAPHY OF SUGAR PHOSPHATES (*22*)

Solvent components[a]	Reference
Ethyl acetate(3) – acetic acid(3) – water(1)	(*23*)
Methyl cellosolve(7) – methyl ethyl ketone(2) – 3*N* NH_4OH(3)	(*23*)
Ethyl acetate(1) – formamide(2) – pyridine(1)	(*23*)
t-Butanol(80) – picric acid(2 g.) – water(20)	(*24*)
Isopropyl ether(90) – 90% formic acid(60)	(*25*)
Phenol(72 g.) – water(28 g.)	(*22*)
Butanol(100) – propionic acid(50) – water(70)	(*22*)
Methanol(80) – 88% formic acid(15) – water(5)	(*26*)
Methanol(60) – 28% NH_4OH(10) – water(30)	(*26*)

[a] The figures following the components indicate ratios of volumes taken for the mixture.

drip off the end of serrated paper), and under these conditions an R_x value is determined. This is the ratio of the distance moved by the sugar spot to the distance moved by some internal standard. The R_f or R_x values are not absolute constants but depend on a number of variables, all of which may not be controlled during a separation. The R_f values are useful for comparing separations within a single run under similar conditions of development (*27*). A number of tables of R_f or R_x values for various carbohydrates (*28*) and sugar phosphates (*22*) have been compiled.

The use of color reagents to detect sugars on paper chromatograms has several functions. The color reveals the position of the sugar so that R_f values can be determined, and in certain cases the color will indicate the nature of the sugar, e.g., as a ketose or aldose. Many different spray reagents have been devised, but they fall into four general types (*28*): (1) reagents that depend on the reducing power of the sugar; (2) acids that act on the sugar to produce a derivative which reacts with aromatic amines or phenols; (3) reagents that cleave the sugar to fragments which are detected; (4) reagents that are specific for certain structural features.

Kowkabany (*28*) suggests that for identification of the spots the following color reagents have the greatest general usefulness: silver nitrate – ammonia, aniline hydrogen phthalate, *p*-anisidine hydrochloride, *o*-phenylenediamine dihydrochloride, benzidine – acetic acid, 3,5-dinitrosalicylic

23. D. C. Mortimer, *Can. J. Chem.* **30,** 653 (1952).
24. A. T. Wilson, Doctoral Thesis, University of California (1954).
25. C. S. Hanes and F. A. Isherwood, *Nature* **164,** 1107 (1949).
26. R. S. Bandurski and B. Axelrod, *J. Biol. Chem.* **193,** 405 (1951).
27. E. C. Bate-Smith and R. G. Westall, *Biochim. et Biophys. Acta* **4,** 427 (1950).
28. G. N. Kowkabany, *Advances in Carbohydrate Chem.* **9,** 303, (1954).

acid and sodium hydroxide, and 3,4-dinitrobenzoic acid with sodium carbonate. Under prescribed conditions, the naphthoresorcinol – trichloroacetic acid reagent is useful for detecting ketoses. Nonreducing sugars can be detected by potassium permanganate and sodium carbonate, sodium metaperiodate, and lead tetraacetate.

Unequivocal identification of unknown compounds cannot be made on the basis of chromatography alone. Even if the R_f values of all sugars were available, many have about the same R_f values, even with different solvents. Moreover, new sugars are still being discovered. Material sufficient for the necessary confirmatory tests may be obtained from the use of large heavy sheets of paper or from the use of column chromatography. Information from paper chromatograms is an aid in the calculations needed for the operation of celulose columns. Adsorption chromatography is also to be recommended. Activated carbon (*4*) is particularly good for the separation of sugars differing in degree of polymerization. Magnesol (*5a*) (a hydrated magnesium silicate) has proved very versatile in the separation of acetylated sugars.

B. Color Reactions (*1*)

The presence of "carbohydrates" is indicated by the development of colors when the unknown is treated with strong sulfuric acid and an appropriate phenol, *N*-base, or related compound, such as: α-naphthol, resorcinol, orcinol, phloroglucinol, anthrone, and carbazole. The test employing α-naphthol is known as the Molisch test for carbohydrates, but is instead a test for saccharides. Functional derivatives, such as acids and amino compounds, do not give the typical colors. The colored substances probably are condensation products between the phenols (or other compound) and furfural, hydroxymethylfurfural, and similar products formed from the sugars by the action of the acids (Chapter I). This type of reaction can be used for the quantitative estimation of carbohydrates (see below). The reaction is given by the simple sugars, the oligosaccharides, and by many polysaccharides. Many of the reagents used in paper chromatography operate through similar reactions.

Strong sulfuric and hydrochloric acids convert carbohydrates to dark-colored substances which probably are condensation products of furfural, hydroxymethylfurfural, etc. (Chapter I).

The colors produced from ketoses, pentoses, and uronic acids in the presence of phenols and acids as well as other reagents often are enough different from those formed from aldohexoses so that they may be used for the classification of unknown materials. The ketoses, pentoses, and uronic acids usually form colored products under conditions milder than those required for the aldohexoses. Tauber's benzidine test for pentoses and uronic acids involves the heating of benzidine in glacial acetic acid with the sugar. A cherry-red color forms in the presence of pentoses and glucuronic acid, whereas hexoses give a yellow to brown color. Phloroglucinol gives a violet-red color with pentoses and uronic acids in the presence of hydrochloric acid. Orcinol may be used to distinguish between pentoses and uronic acids. The Seliwanoff test for ketoses is carried out by heating the unknown with hydrochloric acid and resorcinol. A fiery-red color develops if a ketose is present.

A particularly important color reaction is the Raybin diazouracil test for sucrose (see under Sucrose). An alkaline solution of diazouracil turns green in the presence of sucrose. The only known interfering substances are raffinose, gentianose, and stachyose.

The reduction of metallic salts provides a convenient test for "reducing" sugars. In alkaline solution, the sugars reduce the salts of copper, silver, mercury, and other metals to the metal or to a suboxide. The well-known Fehling and Tollens solutions are of this character. The sugar and some of the products resulting from isomerization in alkaline solution (see Chapter I) are oxidized to the corresponding acids. The formation of the metal or

$$2Cu(OH)_2 + \begin{array}{c} HCO \\ | \\ -C- \\ | \end{array} \rightarrow \begin{array}{c} HOCO \\ | \\ -C- \\ | \end{array} + Cu_2O + H_2O$$

oxide is taken as evidence for the presence of reducing sugars. Similar reactions are given by many substances other than carbohydrates. The application of this test to the quantitative determination of sugars is described in the next section.

Strong alkalies cause solutions of reducing sugars to turn dark brown, particularly when the solutions are hot. The nature of the products is unknown.

Reducing sugars reduce nitrophenols to deeply colored derivatives. Picric acid, $C_6H_2OH(NO_2)_3$, is transformed to the deep-red salt of picramic acid, $C_6H_2(NO_2)_2(NH_2)OH$. For *o*-dinitrobenzene, the test is so sensitive that 6 parts per 1,000,000 of reducing sugars may be detected.

Methylene blue solutions are decolorized by alkaline solutions of reducing sugars. Safranine changes from red to a yellow color under similar conditions.

C. Derivatives

The reaction products of the reducing sugars and aromatic hydrazines are very useful derivatives for identification purposes. One mole of hydrazine may react to give the sugar hydrazone, or two residues may be introduced to give the osazones. Phenylhydrazine is the most common hydrazine used for this purpose, but other hydrazines are used (Chapter II, Table I). The choice of hydrazine depends upon the sugar present since the products differ greatly in their ease of isolation. For example, mannose phenylhydrazone is difficultly soluble, whereas the glucose phenylhydrazone is quite soluble.

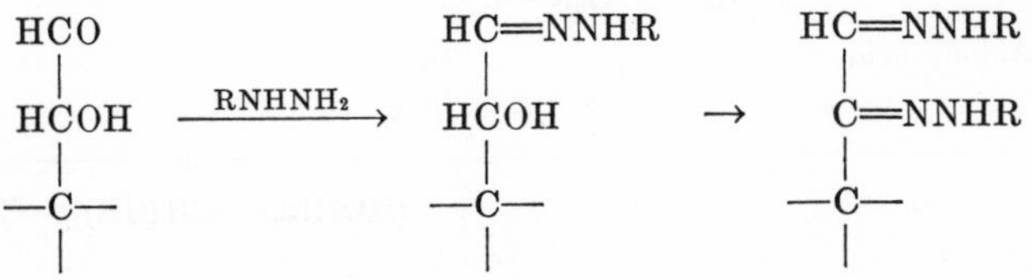
HCO
HCOH
—C—
RNHNH₂
HC=NNHR
HCOH
—C—
HC=NNHR
C=NNHR
—C—

The osazones are much less soluble than the hydrazones. However, it should be noted that three sugars (e.g., glucose, mannose, and fructose) give the same osazone because of the loss of asymmetry at carbon atom 2. (For further details of this reaction, the reader is referred to the discussion of nitrogenous derivatives, Chapter VIII.)

The 2,4-dichlorophenylhydrazones of a great many sugars were isolated and characterized by Mandl and Neuberg (*29*). The hydrazones were easy to crystallize and gave good melting points. The same authors were able to differentiate between L-arabinose and D-ribose by means of their diphenylhydrazones. Reactions with *p*-bromophenylhydrazine or 1-benzyl-1-phenylhydrazine also often lead to crystalline derivatives.

The hydrazones and osazones rarely have sharp melting points, and disparities in reported values are often encountered. Moreover, optical rotations are frequently difficult to determine because of slow, complex mutarotations. Confirmation of the identity through a comparison of X-ray patterns or through other derivatives is desirable. The osotriazoles (Chapter VIII) prepared from the osazones by the reaction of copper sulfate generally have properties quite suitable for qualitative analyses. Isolation of the more-soluble osotriazoles is facilitated by adsorption on and elution from activated carbon (*29a*).

The benzimidazole derivatives prepared from the aldonic acids have been suggested for the identification of sugars and acids (*30*). The benzimidazoles are made by oxidation of the sugars to the aldonic acids, and subsequent condensation of the aldonic acids with *o*-phenylenediamine.

29. I. Mandl and C. Neuberg, *Arch. Biochem. and Biophys.* **35,** 320 (1952).

29a. M. G. Blair and J. C. Sowden, *J. Am. Chem. Soc.* **77,** 3323 (1955).

30. See S. Moore and K. P. Link, *J. Biol. Chem.* **133,** 293 (1940); R. J. Dimler and K. P. Link, *ibid.* **150** (1943); see also N. K. Richtmyer, *Advances in Carbohydrate Chem.* **6,** 175 (1951).

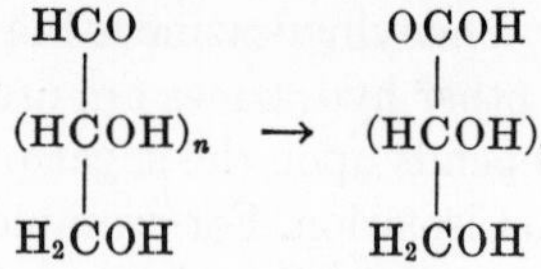

$$
\begin{array}{ccc}
\text{HCO} & & \text{OCOH} \\
| & & | \\
(\text{HCOH})_n & \rightarrow & (\text{HCOH})_n \\
| & & | \\
\text{H}_2\text{COH} & & \text{H}_2\text{COH}
\end{array}
$$

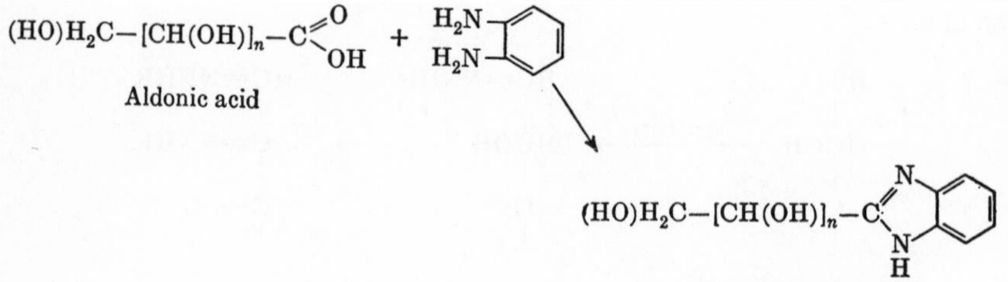

$$(\text{HO})\text{H}_2\text{C}-[\text{CH}(\text{OH})]_n-\text{C}\diagdown{}^{\text{O}}_{\text{OH}} \quad + \quad {}^{\text{H}_2\text{N}}_{\text{H}_2\text{N}}$$

Aldonic acid

$$(\text{HO})\text{H}_2\text{C}-[\text{CH}(\text{OH})]_n-\text{C}$$

H

Aldobenzimidazole

The separation of small quantities of the aldobenzimidazoles is facilitated by the formation of the insoluble copper salt from which the copper may be removed by exposure to hydrogen sulfide. The melting points and optical rotations of the benzimidazoles and of the corresponding hydrochlorides differ sufficiently for the different sugars so that the identification usually is assured. Fructose under the conditions outlined above is likely to be oxidized with the production of small quantities of D-arabobenzimidazole. Characteristic derivatives of hexuronic and saccharic acids also are obtained by condensation with o-phenylenediamine.

Derivatives of particular value for the identification of many important sugars are mentioned in Chapters II, VIII, and IX under the description of the individual sugars and for Polyols in Chapter V.

2. QUANTITATIVE DETERMINATION

Many of the qualitative tests may be applied to the quantitative determination of sugars. The color developed in the presence of acids and phenols or the amount of metal or metallic oxide formed by the reduction of the salts of heavy metals by the sugars can be measured. Some of these methods can also be used on a micro-scale to determine quantitatively the sugar eluted from paper chromatograms. In some cases, difficultly soluble derivations such as the osazones or hydrazones can be weighed directly. Because of the absence of a stoichiometric relation for the methods, they are not completely satisfactory. Complete descriptions of many of the methods described will be found in the article by Bell (6).

A. OPTICAL ROTATION (1)

When sugars or their derivatives are reasonably pure, and in particular are free of optically active impurities, the measurement of the optical rotation provides the most convenient method for their identification and analysis. This method of "direct polarization" finds wide application in the analysis of raw and purified cane and beet sugar. The specific rotation $[\alpha]$ of a sugar in solution at 20°C. and measured with the D line of the sodium lamp is given by:

$$[\alpha]_D^{20} = \frac{100\alpha}{l \times c}$$

(α = observed optical rotation; l = length of tube in decimeters; c = weight of sugar (grams) in 100 ml. of solution at 20°C.). When the specific rotation is known, the concentration, c, may be calculated from:

$$c = \frac{100\alpha}{l \times [\alpha]_D^{20}}$$

Usually the specific rotation varies somewhat with the concentration (c), and this effect must receive consideration.

The method is very easily applied when a saccharimeter is used for the measurement of the rotation. In this procedure, the weight of impure sugar which is taken for the analysis is the same as the amount of pure sugar which will read 100°S. under the same conditions. The observed optical rotation gives directly the percentage of sugar in the sample. Thus, a reading of 90°S. would mean that the original material contained 90% of the sugar. The weight of a sugar which will read 100°S. on a saccharimeter when made up to 100 ml. at 20°C. and read in a 2-dm. tube is known as the normal weight. For sucrose, the normal weight is 26.00 g.

Mixtures of several sugars are more difficult to analyze by optical rotation methods, but sometimes the analysis is possible if the rotations of the components vary in a different manner when the solvent, the acidity, or the temperature is changed. The change in solvent may be brought about by the addition of salts (Chapter V) which markedly affect the rotations. If the specific rotations of the two components are known under two sets of conditions, the solution of two simultaneous equations will give the relative percentages of components x and y:

$$\text{Condition 1: } x[\alpha_x] + y[\alpha_y] = 100[\alpha_{obs}].$$

$$\text{Condition 2: } x[\alpha'_x] + y[\alpha'_y] = 100[\alpha'_{obs}].$$

One of the most important sugar mixtures which can be analyzed by the optical rotatory method is the mixture of sucrose and its hydrolysis products, glucose and fructose. The process of hydrolysis of sucrose into glucose and fructose is known as inversion because of the change of the sign of rotation which takes place during the hydrolysis. Mixtures of this type are found in invert sirups, honey, etc. The polarimetric method for this purpose is based on the optical rotatory power of the original material and of the completely hydrolyzed product. From the known rotations of sucrose and of its hydrolysis products, the quantity of sucrose in the original mixture

$$\underset{\text{Sucrose}}{C_{12}H_{22}O_{11}} + H_2O \rightarrow \underbrace{\underset{\text{Glucose}}{C_6H_{12}O_6} + \underset{\text{Fructose}}{C_6H_{12}O_6}}_{\text{Invert sugar}}$$

may be calculated. This method originally was devised by Biot (1842), but it was greatly improved by Clerget and bears the name of the Clerget method. Acids have been employed as the catalysts for the hydrolysis reaction. However, the instability of fructose under acid conditions, and the marked influence of acids and salts on its optical rotation are likely to lead to erroneous results unless the conditions are carefully controlled. The inversion by yeast invertase gives more accurate results.

The results are calculated from the formula:

$$S = \frac{100(P - P')}{133 - 0.5(t - 20)}$$

where P and P' are the observed optical rotations before and after acid hydrolysis and t is the temperature (°C.) at which the rotations are measured. The constant 133 is the Clerget constant. The percentage of sucrose is given by S. The method must be carried out under carefully standardized conditions (*1*).

B. Reducing Sugar Methods (*1*)

a. Oxidation by Metallic Salts in Alkaline Solution

The principal chemical methods for quantitatively determining the sugars make use of the reducing action of sugars on alkaline solutions of the salts of certain metals. Although many metallic salts, including those of copper, silver, mercury, and bismuth, undergo this type of reaction, copper has been employed by far the most extensively in sugar analysis. The reaction might be visualized as the case of an aldehyde or ketone being oxidized by withdrawal of oxygen from the base formed by the action of the alkali upon the salt. The reduced base is precipitated either as the free metal or as the suboxide:

$$RCHO + Ag_2O \rightarrow 2\ Ag + RCOOH$$

$$RCHO + 2\ CuO \rightarrow Cu_2O + RCOOH$$

However, the reaction does not proceed stoichiometrically. It has been shown previously (see Chapter I) that sugars with free aldehyde and ketone groups quickly undergo change even in weakly alkaline solution. Glucose, fructose, and mannose undergo a mutual interconversion until equilibrium is established. This interconversion is explained by the formation of an enol form. Upon prolonged action the double bond may descend farther along the chain, and cleavages of the carbon chain may occur. Strong alkalinity produces more deeply seated changes forming saccharinic acids and their lactones. In the presence of cupric salts in alkaline solution, the enediols are oxidized at the expense of the cupric ions which are reduced and precipitated as insoluble cuprous oxide. The carbon chain of the sugar is ruptured with the formation of acids with shorter chains. Since the enediol bond of a hexose at the time the molecule is ruptured may be either at the 1,2- or 2,3-position and since the hydroxyls may have altered their positions, numerous acids are produced.

Under such circumstances it is amazing that the reaction has quantitative value. But it has been found that, although the products are many and variable, it is possible to standardize the conditions so that the amount of cuprous oxide may be used as a measure of the quantity of sugar.

Copper solutions became important for the purpose of sugar analysis after Trommer (1841) used alkaline copper sulfate to distinguish between grape sugar (glucose) and cane sugar (sucrose). In 1844, Barreswil reported the important discovery that the addition of potassium tartrate to alkaline copper sulfate solution greatly increases the stability. The reaction of the tartrate with the copper salt is still not clearly understood, but it is generally assumed that complex salts are formed. Cupric tartrate is precipitated when a solution of copper sulfate is added to a chemically equivalent amount of sodium tartrate in solution. If a second equivalent of sodium hydroxide is added, the precipitated cupric tartrate dissolves. Since the resulting solution is neutral to litmus, the whole cupric tartrate residue acts as an ion to neutralize the alkali. That the copper is a constituent of the anion is shown by electrolysis of the solution; under these conditions the copper migrates to the anode. The reagent used for sugar analysis must contain additional alkali because the sugar enol is formed only in alkaline solution.

Citrates, oxalates, salicylates, glycerol, and cane sugar also stabilize alkaline solution of cupric salts. Some of these, citrates in particular, have been used in the preparation of copper solutions for sugar analysis.

The copper method was further improved in 1848 by Fehling, who worked out analytical details of the alkaline copper method essentially as they now are used. Fehling gave as stoichiometrical equivalents: 5 molecules of copper to 1 molecule of glucose. But apparently he did not realize that the amount of copper which is reduced varies with experimental conditions and is quantitative only within a narrow range of concentrations and of reaction times. The ratio 1:5 was employed subsequently until Soxhlet in 1878 showed that the ratio varies with the degree of excess of copper present during the reaction. Soxhlet's method was also an improvement in that he kept the copper solution and the alkaline tartrate solution in separate containers; the solutions were mixed at the time of analysis. The composition of the Fehling (Soxhlet) reagents is as follows:

Fehling solution A: 34.639 g. crystalline copper sulfate ($CuSO_4 \cdot 5H_2O$) made up to 500 ml. with water.

Fehling solution B: 173 g. Rochelle salt and 50 g. NaOH made up to 500 ml. with water.

Since the copper reduction method has become used so generally for sugar analysis, numerous modifications have been described which are based on the same fundamental principles but which differ in analytical details. Fehling solution is rather unstable. Hence, efforts have been made to improve its stability. Many organic products other than sugars cause either a precipitation of cuprous oxide or prevent its precipitation even if sugars are present. Consequently, other copper solutions are frequently employed, especially in biological analysis. Copper sulfate or acetate usually is used as the source of the cupric ion. Potassium hydroxide has been substituted for sodium hydroxide in the method of Allihn and in its modifications. Citrates or carbonates have been used instead of sodium or potassium hydroxide to produce reagents having less alkalinity as for the solutions of Benedict and of Soldaini. Among other copper solutions recommended for testing sugars, copper ammonium tartrate and ammoniacal copper sulfate may be mentioned. But with all the numerous modifications the Fehling-Soxhlet solution is the most widely used of the copper solutions. No other has been found to equal it for general usefulness in sugar analysis although others may be more suitable under specific circumstances.

The amount of copper which is reduced by various sugars has been found to vary according to the alkalinity, the temperature, the time of heating, the sugar concentration, the nature of the sugar, the type of the tartrate (D, L, or *meso*), the amount of contact with air, etc. Fehling solution approximates the degree of alkalinity which has been found to give the largest deposit of cuprous oxide. Two of the most important variables are the temperature and the time of heating. Initially, the reduction is very rapid as the temperature is raised to 75°C. The rapid phase is followed by a slow secondary reduction which continues for a long time. However, the rate of reduction is very slow at the later time periods. In most methods the solution is allowed to boil until a point is reached at which a small variation in the time will exert only a negligible influence on the results. Because of the arbitrary establishment of the conditions and the absence of a stoichiometric relation between the quantity of sugar and the cuprous oxide formed, close adherence to the conditions described for the various methods is required. Under standardized conditions, the amount of cuprous oxide is proportional to the initial quantity of sugar. For many methods, tables have been published which relate the quantity of sugar and the amount of cuprous oxide or copper. The multiplicity of tables arises from the fact that many investigators have confined their work to one single sugar for one individual set of conditions. The early tendency was to devise a particular method for each sugar under examination. This procedure requires different reagents and procedures for each sugar and renders impossible the interpretation of copper equivalents for mixtures of sugars. This difficulty led to the establishment of unified procedures for which the same reagents and procedure are used regardless of the nature of the sugar. Empirical copper equivalents have been determined for the sugars of common occurrence and for the most frequently occurring sugar mixtures. Among the unified methods are those of Munson and Walker (the most common method in the United States), of Quisumbing and Thomas, of Bertrand, of Brown, Morris, and Millar, of Lane and Eynon, and of Scales (modified).

After the establishment of standard conditions for the reduction, considerable variation is possible in the method for determining the cuprous oxide. It may be weighed directly or ignited to cupric oxide. It may be further reduced to metallic copper by hydrogen, by alcohol vapor, or by electrolysis in nitric acid solution. In other procedures, the cuprous oxide is dissolved after filtration and is determined volumetrically by use of ferric salts and permanganate, iodine and thiosulfate, thiocyanate and silver salts, dichromate and ferrous salts, or the cyanide method. In the cyanide method, the excess of cupric ion is determined. Several processes have also been worked out for the determination of the extent of the reduction without filtration of the cuprous oxide. Titration may be made of the cuprous ion or of the excess cupric ion. Ferric-ion oxidation of the dissolved cuprous oxide is employed in the Bertrand method. The Scales, the Shaffer-Hartmann, and the Shaffer-Somogyi methods employ iodometric determination of the cuprous ion in the presence of citrates which form complex ions with cupric ions. The Folin-Wu method and its modification according to Benedict require measurement of the color produced by cuprous salts and a tungstic acid reagent.

Instead of measuring the copper reduced by a given amount of sugar, the copper solution may be titrated directly by the addition of sugar to the boiling copper solution. The end-point is distinguished by the discharge of the blue color (methods of Violette and of Pavy), by spot tests with ferrocyanide (Soxhlet), or by the internal indicator methylene blue (Lane and Eynon). Other indicators have been suggested; in the case of very dark molasses, the end-point preferably is determined electrometrically. Main's "pot method" was devised because it is difficult to standardize the time of heating and the rate of ebullition. The temperature is regulated by a boiling water-bath, and the reduction is carried out in test tubes provided with floats, variable amounts of sugar being added to constant amounts of copper reagent. The same principle is used, but constant amounts of sugar solution are added to variable quantities of copper reagent in the method of Reischauer and Kruis.

Although the reduction of cupric salts in alkaline solution is common to all aldoses and ketoses (as well as aldehydes and hydroxyketones), conditions may be established for which a preferential oxidation of monosaccharides occurs. In the Barfoed method, copper acetate in neutral or slightly acid solution oxidizes monosaccharides but affects disaccharides such as maltose only to a minor degree. The Steinhoff method for the selective determination of glucose, maltose, and dextrins in mixtures depends on the determination of glucose by the Barfoed reagent, the sum of dextrose and disaccharides (maltose) by use of Fehling solution, and the total sugar after complete acid hydrolysis.

Descriptions of the procedures followed in the various methods and tables relating the sugar quantity to the amount of cuprous oxide or copper are given in the standard works on analysis (*1*).

b. Oxidation with Potassium Ferricyanide

A number of important methods are based on the oxidation of sugars by ferricyanide ion in alkaline solution. The method is open to the same objections as the copper reduction methods, namely, the lack of a stoichiometric reaction and the dependence of the method on arbitrarily chosen conditions. The ferricyanide may be used to titrate the sugar solution directly by the use of picric acid or of methylene blue as an indicator. Or, the reduced ferrocyanide may be precipitated as the zinc salt, and the excess ferricyanide determined iodometrically. The Hagedorn-Jensen method and the Hanes modification utilize the latter procedure. In the Folin-Malmros micro method, Prussian blue is formed and determined colorimetrically. Extensive application of the ferricyanide method has been made in the determination of the diastatic power of amylase preparations and in blood analysis.

$$4\ K_3Fe(CN)_6 + 4\ KOH \rightarrow 4\ K_4Fe(CN)_6 + 2\ H_2O + 2\ O\ \text{(consumed)}$$

$$2\ H_3Fe(CN)_6 + 2\ HI \leftrightharpoons 2\ H_4Fe(CN_6) + I_2$$

$$2\ K_4Fe(CN)_6 + 3\ ZnSO_4 \rightarrow K_2Zn_3[Fe(CN)_6]_2 + 3\ K_2SO_4$$

C. Colorimetric Procedures

A great many reactions are known which will give colored products with sugars. By the use of a colorimeter or spectrophotometer very sensitive methods of quantitative analysis of sugars have been developed. A number of these procedures have been used to estimate the sugars separated and eluted from paper chromatograms.

The formation of colored products by the reaction of sugars and phenols in the presence of strong acids has been mentioned previously as a qualitative test for carbohydrates. Carbazole or anthrone may be used instead of a phenol. Methods employing orcinol (3,5-dihydroxytoluene) and carbazole have been described in detail (*31*). Dische (*32*) described a modified carbazole reaction for determining ketohexoses, ketopentoses, trioses, and glycolic aldehyde as well as a method for determining heptoses.

Because of a difference in ease of reaction and of the colors produced by carbazole, conditions may be selected also for the determination of uronic acids with little or no interference from the sugars (*32*).

The absorption curves for the different sugars after treatment with orcinol or carbazole and strong acid differ considerably. Hence, the shape of the absorption curve frequently is of value in the identification of an unknown sugar even in the presence of amino acids and other materials.

Anthrone has been used extensively for the colorimetric determination of saccharides, reducing and nonreducing (*33*). The sugar is converted to a furfural derivative with sulfuric acid which then reacts with the anthrone to form a colored solution. The method will determine sugars in the range of 0 to 80 micrograms.

The colorless triphenyltetrazolium ion is reduced by sugars to insoluble, red triphenylformazan. The red formazan is then dissolved in isopropanol and determined colorimetrically (*34*).

Additional discussion of such methods is given in Chapter XII, Part II.

D. Special Methods

a. Determination of Aldoses by Hypoiodite

Romijn (1897) first showed that aldoses are quantitatively oxidized by iodine in weakly alkaline solution under carefully controlled conditions. Ketoses and nonreducing sugars are only slightly attacked. Equations illustrating the reaction are given below (see also Chapter VI).

The iodine and alkali form hypoiodite and iodide:

$$I_2 + 2\,NaOH \rightarrow NaIO + NaI + H_2O$$

31. M. Sørensen and G. Haugaard, *Biochem. Z.* **260,** 247 (1933); S. Gurin and D. B. Hood, J. *Biol. Chem.* **139,** 775 (1941); **131,** 211 (1939).

32. Z. Dische and E. Borenfrend, *J. Biol. Chem.* **192,** 583 (1951); Z. Dische, *ibid.* **204,** 983 (1953); **167,** 189 (1947); **183,** 489 (1950).

33. D. L. Morris, *Science* **107,** 254 (1948); A. Loewus, *Anal. Chem.* **24,** 219 (1952).

34. K. Wallenfels, *Naturwissenschaften* **37,** 976 (1950); R. A. Fairbridge, K. J. Willis, and R. G. Booth, *Biochem. J.* **49,** 423 (1951).

Part of the hypoiodite is converted into iodate and iodide, the amount depending on the concentration, the time, and the temperature:

$$3\ NaIO \rightarrow NaIO_3 + 2\ NaI$$

The hypoiodite reacts with the aldose:

$$RCHO + NaIO + NaOH \rightarrow RCOONa + NaI + H_2O$$

Since sodium iodate cannot oxidize the sugar in alkaline solution, some active iodine is lost as far as the sugar oxidation is concerned. If the entire quantities of alkali and iodine are admitted simultaneously, much iodine is transformed to iodate and a deficiency may result for the sugar oxidation. If iodine is present in too great an excess, over-oxidation can occur, and the alcoholic groups are slowly oxidized to carboxyl or carbonyl groups.

Although some iodine may be lost by the side reaction, this iodine is measured along with the excess when the solution is acidified and titrated with thiosulfate:

$$NaIO + NaI + H_2SO_4 \rightarrow I_2 + Na_2SO_4 + H_2O$$

$$NaIO_3 + 5\ NaI + 3\ H_2SO_4 \rightarrow 3\ I_2 + 3\ Na_2SO_4 + 3\ H_2O$$

$$I_2 + 2\ Na_2S_2O_3 \rightarrow 2\ NaI + Na_2S_4O_6$$

Slater and Acree found that the iodine consumption can be confirmed by titrating with alkali the free acid left after the completion of the thiosulfate titration:

$$HCl + NaOH \rightarrow NaCl + H_2O$$

$$\text{Aldonic lactone} + H_2O \rightleftarrows RCOOH$$

$$RCOOH + NaOH \rightarrow RCOONa + H_2O$$

Although the stoichiometric nature of this reaction is an advantage over the empirical nature of the copper reductions, this procedure does not have as great a versatility of application, and it also must be used under carefully controlled conditions. Alcohol, glycerol, mannitol, formic acid, lactic acid, dextrin, amino acids, and many other substances take up iodine. Hence, the method cannot be applied directly to impure sugar products of unknown composition. Under well-defined conditions and in the absence of interfering materials, the method is stoichiometric. This method has been used for micro-determination of sugars on paper chromatograms (*35*).

b. Determination of Reducing Aldose Sugars by the Kiliani Reaction

This reaction has been made the basis of a stoichiometric method for determining reducing aldose sugars (*36*). The sugar is reacted with cyanide.

35. J. R. Hawthorne, *Nature* **160**, 714 (1947); O. G. Ingles and G. C. Israel, *J. Chem. Soc.* p. 810 (1948); p. 1213 (1949).

Ammonia from the hydrolysis of the nitrile is steam-distilled into alkali. One ammonia is equal to one aldose reducing group. (See also Chapter XII.)

c. Determination of D*-Glucose with* D*-Glucose Oxidase*

D-Glucose is quantitatively oxidized to D-gluco-δ-lactone by D-glucose oxidase in the presence of molecular oxygen. The lactone is converted to D-gluconic acid, which is titrated with standard alkali (*37*).

d. Determination of Pentoses and Pentosans

Pentose sugars and pentosans may be quantitatively estimated by conversion into furfural by distillation with hydrochloric acid. The amount of furfural is determined gravimetrically after precipitation with phloroglucinol, barbituric acid, or thiobarbituric acid, or volumetrically by titration with bromine or phenylhydrazine. Approximately theoretical yields of furfural are obtained if the furfural is removed rapidly from the reaction mixture by steam distillation:

$$\underset{\text{Pentose}}{C_5H_{10}O_5} \rightarrow \underset{\text{Furfural}}{C_5H_4O_2} + 3\,H_2O$$

Hexoses yield hydroxymethylfurfural, and methyloses yield methylfurfural. These substances are not produced in quantitative yields, and they interfere with the furfural determination. (See Chapters I and VI.)

e. Determination of Sugars as Hydrazones and Osazones (See also Chapter VIII)

The solubility of the different hydrazones and osazones or of similar derivatives in the presence of impurities has prevented their general employment for the quantitative separation of the sugars. In certain cases, however, where they are characterized by great insolubility, they may be used for fairly accurate quantitative determinations. Arabinose may be determined by precipitating it with diphenylhydrazine, mannose with phenylhydrazine, and fructose with methylphenylhydrazine. Some osazones may be determined volumetrically. Glucosazone, for example, is reported to be reduced stoichiometrically by titanium trichloride to isoglucosamine.

f. Fermentation Methods

The selective fermentation of sugars by microorganisms is utilized for the qualitative and quantitative determination of sugar mixtures. Ordinary

---

36. V. L. Frampton, L. P. Foley, L. L. Smith, and J. G. Malone, *Anal. Chem.* **23,** 1244 (1951); A. P. Yundt, *Tappi* **34,** 95 (1951).

37. R. L. Whistler, L. Hough, and J. W. Hylin, *Anal. Chem.* **25,** 1215 (1953).

TABLE III

FERMENTATIVE CHARACTERISTICS OF SOME MICROORGANISMS (*39*)

Organism	D,L-Glyceric aldehyde	D-Arabinose	L-Arabinose	D-Ribose	L-Ribose	D-Lyxose	D-Xylose	L-Rhamnose	D-Glucose	D-Mannose	D-Galactose
Bacillus megatherium	A	0	A	A	0	0	A	0	A	AG	0
Serratia marcescens	AG	A	A	A	0	A	0	0	A	A	A
Escherichia coli	A	AG	AG	AG	AG	AG	AG	AG	AG	AG	AG
Aerobacter aerogenes	A	AG	AG	AG	AG	AG	AG	AG	AG	AG	AG
Bacterium friedländeri	AG	AG	AG	AG	AG	AG	AG	AG	AG	AG	AG
Proteus vulgaris	A	A	0	0	A	A	A	0	A	A	0
Salmonella aertrycke	AG	A	AG	AG	A	AG	AG	AG	AG	AG	AG
S. enteritidis	A	A	AG	AG	A	A	AG	AG	AG	AG	A
S. choleraesuis	A	A	0	AG	0	AG	AG	AG	AG	AG	AG
S. paratyphi	A	0	AG	AG	A	A	A	AG	AG	AG	AG
S. schottmülleri	A	A	AG	AG	AG	AG	AG	AG	AG	AG	AG
Eberthella typhi	A	0	0	A	0	0	0	0	A	A	0
E. dysenteriae Flexner	A	0	A	A	A	0	0	0	A	A	0
E. dysenteriae Sonne	A	A	A	A	A	A	A	A	A	A	A
Sarcina lutea	A	0	0	0	0	A	0	0	0	0	0
Staphylococcus aureus	A	0	A	A	A	0	A	0	A	0	0
Staph. albus	A	0	A	A	A	A	A	0	A	A	A
Saccharomyces cerevisiae	0	0	0	0	0	0	0	0	AG	AG	0
Torula cremoris	0	0	0	0	0	0	0	0	AG	AG	0

A, acid formation observed.
G, gas formation observed.
0, no reaction.

yeasts ferment glucose at alkalinities up to pH 8, although maltose is only slowly fermented above pH 7.2. This difference has been made the basis of the Somogyi method for the determination of glucose, maltose, and dextrins in products such as are obtained by the hydrolysis of starch (*37a*). The determination of the reducing power of a sample before fermentation, after fermentation at pH 7.5, and after fermentation at pH 5.0, provides a method for the selective determination of maltose, glucose, and unfermentable (dextrin) material. Instead of reducing sugar determinations, measurements of the alcohol concentration may be used to measure the degree of fermentation (*37b*). Mixtures such as are obtained by the hydrolysis of starch also may be analyzed by the use of a yeast which will not ferment maltose, and one which will act on this sugar (*38*).

TABLE IV

FERMENTATIVE CHARACTERISTICS OF SOME MICROORGANISMS (*39*)

Organism	Sorbitol	D-Gluconic acid	Dulcitol	D-Galactonic acid	Mucic Acid	Inositol	Erythritol	Methyl α-D-glucoside	Glucosamine	D-Glucononose
Bacillus megatherium	0	A	0	0	0	0	0	0	0	0
Serratia marcescens	A	A	0	0	0	A	A	0	A	0
Escherichia coli	AG	AG	AG	AG	A	0	0	0	AG	0
Aerobacter aerogenes	AG	AG	0	0	AG	AG	0	AG	AG	0
Bacterium friedländeri	AG	AG	AG	AG	AG	AG	0	AG	AG	0
Proteus vulgaris	0	AG	0	0	0	0	0	AG	0	A
Salmonella aertrycke	AG	AG	AG	AG	AG	0	0	0	A	0
S. enteritidis	AG	A	AG	A	A	0	0	0	A	0
S. choleraesuis	AG	AG	0		0	0	0	0	A	0
S. paratyphi	AG	AG	A	0	0	0	0	0	A	0
S. schottmülleri	AG	AG	AG	AG	A	AG	0	0	A	0
Eberthella typhi	A	A	0	0	0	0	0	0	0	0
E. dysenteriae, Flexner	A	A	0	A	0	0	0	A	0	0
E. dysenteriae, Sonne	0	A	0	A	A	0	0	0	0	0
Sarcina lutea	0	0	0	0	0	0	0	0	0	0
Staphylococcus aureus	0	A	0	0	0	0	0	0	A	0
Staph. albus	A	A	A	0	A	A	A	A	A	A
Saccharomyces cerevisiae	0	0	0	0	0	0	0	A	0	0
Torula cremoris	0	0	0	0	0	0	0	0	A	A

A, acid formation observed.
G, gas formation observed.
0, no reaction.

Wise and Appling (*40*) determine D-galactose in the presence of D-mannose, D-glucose, D-fructose, D-xylose, L-arabinose, and D-glucuronic acid by use of a yeast (*Saccharomyces carlsbergensis*) which ferments D-galactose and one (*S. bayanus*) which does not. Both yeasts ferment the mannose, glucose, and fructose but have no action on the xylose, arabinose, and

37a. I. E. Stark and M. Somogyi, *J. Biol. Chem.* **142,** 579 (1942); I. E. Stark, *ibid.* **142,** 569 (1942).

37b. W. W. Pigman, *J. Research Natl. Bur. Standards* **33,** 105 (1944); M. G. Blair and W. Pigman, *Arch. Biochem and Biophys.* **42,** 278 (1953); **48,** 17 (1954).

38. See for example A. S. Schultz, R. A. Fisher, L. Atkin, and C. N. Frey, *Ind. Eng. Chem. Anal. Ed.* **15,** 496 (1943).

39. L. Sternfeld and F. Saunders, *J. Am. Chem. Soc.* **59,** 2653 (1937); see also C. M. McCloskey and J. R. Porter, *Proc. Soc. Exptl. Biol. Med.* **60,** 269 (1945).

40. L. E. Wise and J. W. Appling, *Ind. Eng. Chem. Anal. Ed.* **16,** 28 (1944).

glucuronic acid. Mixtures of this type are obtained by the hydrolysis of plant gums.

The accompanying Tables III and IV illustrate the marked specific action of bacteria and yeasts on sugars and derivatives. By the proper application of microorganisms, it is possible to provide evidence for the presence of a given sugar in an unknown mixture. Thus as shown in the accompanying tables, an evidence of fermentation by *Torula cremoris* combined with an absence of fermentation by ordinary yeasts (*S. cerevisiae*) would be indicative of the presence of glucosamine. In turn, the fermentation characteristics of a microorganism is used for its identification. The latter use provides the main application for many of the rarer sugars.

3. ISOTOPE PROCEDURES

A. Synthesis of Labeled Sugars

C^{14}-labeled sugars have been prepared both by biosynthetic and synthetic methods (Chapter II). P^{32}-labeled sugar phosphates have also been produced biosynthetically (*22*). Biosynthetically produced C^{14}-labeled sugars are of limited value because of the distribution of label between the various carbon atoms. The 3,4-C^{14}-labeled glucose isolated from liver glycogen (*41*) is an exception.

B. Degradation of Labeled Sugars

The usefulness of isotopically labeled sugars depends upon having adequate methods of accurately determining the position of the label in the sugar molecule. A number of methods are available for degrading sugars. Wood, Lifson, and Lorber (*41*) used a combination of microbiological and chemical techniques to degrade labeled glucose isolated from rat liver glycogen. The glucose was fermented to lactic acid with *Lactobacillus casei*. The lactate was then oxidized with $KMnO_4$ to acetaldehyde and CO_2, and the acetaldehyde then was degraded to iodoform and formic acid. It is not possible by this method to distinguish between carbon atoms 1 and 6, 2 and 5, and 3 and 4.

A chemical method (*41*) of degrading glucose was developed to distinguish between carbon atoms 3 and 6. D-Glucose was converted to the methyl D-glucopyranoside which was then oxidized with periodic acid at room temperature to convert carbon atom 3 to formic acid. A second periodic acid oxidation of the hydrolyzed dialdehyde, which was also produced, gave carbon atom 6 as formaldehyde.

Aronoff and Vernon (*42*) converted glucose to the glucosazone which was then degraded with periodate. This oxidation gave the bis(phenyl-

41. H. G. Wood, N. Lifson, and V. Lorber, *J. Biol. Chem.* **159,** 475 (1945).

42. S. Aronoff and L. P. Vernon, *Arch. Biochem.* **28,** 424 (1950).

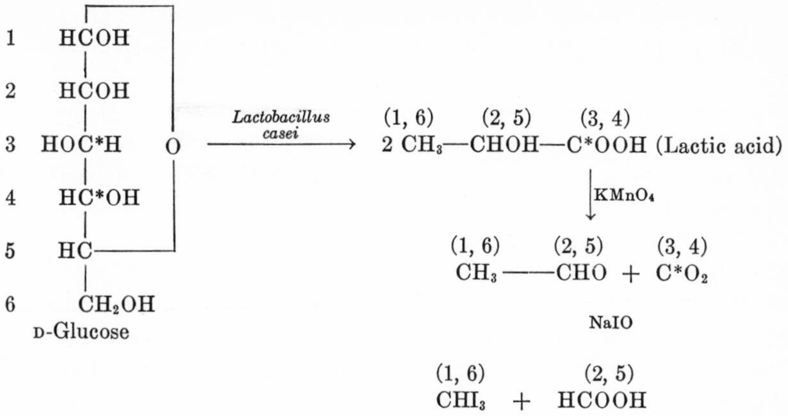
1 HCOH
2 HCOH
3 HOC*H
4 HC*OH
5 HC
6 CH₂OH
D-Glucose
Lactobacillus casei
(1, 6) (2, 5) (3, 4)
2 CH₃—CHOH—C*OOH (Lactic acid)
KMnO₄
(1, 6) (2, 5) (3, 4)
CH₃——CHO + C*O₂
NaIO
(1, 6) (2, 5)
CHI₃ + HCOOH

hydrazone) of mesoxaldehyde derived from carbon atoms 1, 2, and 3 of glucose, formic acid from carbon atoms 4 and 5, and formaldehyde from carbon atom 6. The formaldehyde was precipitated with Dimedon. The bis(phenylhydrazone) of mesoxaldehyde was further degraded with alcoholic KOH. Vittorio, Krotkov, and Reed (*43*) had difficulty with this latter degradation and modified the procedure.

Various other chemical methods of degrading glucose have been devised (*44*). All are rather difficult and require a good deal of chemical manipulation. A combination biological and chemical method of degrading glucose was described by Gunsalus and Gibbs (*45*). The procedure is based on the finding that *Leuconostoc mesenteroides* ferments D-glucose to form one mole each of lactate, ethanol, and CO_2 :

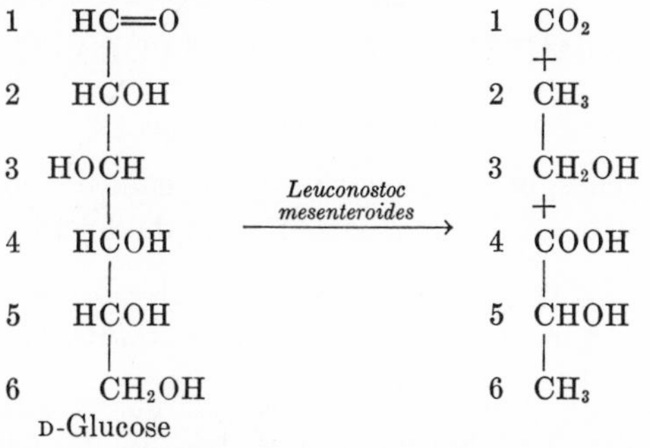
1 HC=O
2 HCOH
3 HOCH
4 HCOH
5 HCOH
6 CH₂OH
D-Glucose
Leuconostoc mesenteroides
1 CO₂
+
2 CH₃
3 CH₂OH
+
4 COOH
5 CHOH
6 CH₃

43. P. V. Vittorio, G. Krotkov, and G. B. Reed, *Science* **115,** 567 (1952).

44. Y. J. Topper, A. B. Hastings, *J. Biol. Chem.* **176,** 1255 (1949); S. Abraham, I. L. Chaikoff and W. Z. Hassid, *ibid.* **195,** 567 (1952); J. C. Bevington, E. J. Bourne, and C. N. Turton, *Chemistry & Industry*, p. 1390 (1953); C. T. Bishop, *Science* **117,** 715 (1953); F. W. Minor, G. A. Greathouse, H. G. Shirk, A. M. Schwartz, and M. Harris, *J. Am. Chem. Soc.* **76,** 1658 (1954); J. C. Sowden, *J. Am. Chem. Soc.* **71,** 3568 (1949).

45. I. C. Gunsalus and M. Gibbs, *J. Biol. Chem.* **194,** 871 (1952).

The ethanol and lactic acid can be degraded by conventional chemical methods to give the distribution of label in each of the carbon atoms of D-glucose.

Methods for degrading ribulose (D-*erythro*-pentulose) and sedoheptulose (D-*altro*-heptulose) have been devised by Bassham and associates (*46*). Biological methods of degradation depending on the action of bacteria to produce small fragments such as ethanol, acetic acid, formic acid, lactic acid, etc., are of rather wide use in the sugar field.

The distribution of radioactive carbon in D-fructose-1,6-C^{14} has been determined by its oxidation in alkaline solution to D-arabonic acid with the loss of C-1 (*46a*). Degradations of the phenylosotriazoles are also useful for separating the activities at these two positions and for the determination of C-3 (*44*).

Degradation of the benzimidazole derivatives of saccharinic (*46b*) or aldonic acids (*46c*) leads to an easy determination of the specific activities of C-1, C-2, and the terminal carbon. Since the aldoses can be readily converted to aldonic acids in high yield (Chapter VI), the method of degradation is also applicable to these sugars. The terminal carbon can be isolated by periodate oxidation to formaldehyde. The original C-1 and C-2 appear in 2-benzimidazolecarboxylic acid, which is obtained by permanganate oxidation. Decarboxylation produces benzimidazole which contains only the original C-1. Acetic acid (*46d*), sometimes encountered in the degradation of deoxysugars, can also be degraded through the benzimidazole derivative. The resulting 2-methylbenzimidazole is condensed with benzaldehyde to form a more easily oxidized derivative, 2-styrylbenzimidazole.

4. HISTOCHEMISTRY OF CARBOHYDRATES* (*47–50*)

A. Purposes and Principles

In its broadest sense, histochemistry is the chemical study of morphologically defined plant or animal material. The methodology varies. The form

* Prepared by Robert W. Mowry.

46. J. A. Bassham, A. A. Benson, L. D. Kay, A. Z. Harris, A. T. Wilson, and M. Calvin, *J. Am. Chem. Soc.* **76**, 1760 (1954).

46a. H. L. Frush and H. S. Isbell, *J. Research Natl. Bur. Standards* **51**, 167 (1953).

46b. J. C. Sowden and D. J. Kuenne, *J. Am. Chem. Soc.* **75**, 2788 (1953).

46c. I. A. Bernstein, K. Lentz, M. Malm, P. Schambye, and H. G. Wood, *J. Biol. Chem.* **215**, 137 (1955).

46d. S. Roseman, *J. Am. Chem. Soc.* **75**, 3854 (1953).

47. D. Glick, "Techniques of Histo- and Cytochemistry." Interscience, New York, 949.

48. G. Gomori, "Microscopic Histochemistry." U. of Chicago Press, Chicago, 1952.

of the tissue sample may vary from thin microtome slices to fractions obtained by ultracentrifugation. Historically, histochemistry has developed as the more limited application of microchemical reactions to thin slices of tissue under conditions that preserve tissue detail; at the same time the reactions must yield *in situ* products that can be seen or localized in their proper position within the tissues and cells. Methods of this kind have demonstrated the location of many important chemical substances inside the tissues and cells of healthy and diseased animals and plants. Animal tissues, particularly, have been studied by these methods.

The technical advantages include the multiplicity of individual objects in a single tissue section that can be separately evaluated and the ease with which multiple specimens can be tested simultaneously. As the average tissue section is extremely thin, numerous determinations are possible on a single small sample of tissue. The disadvantages include the difficulties of quantitation, the limitations imposed by solubility, and a current insufficiency of dependable methods.

Tissue carbohydrates must be kept undissolved and preferably unchanged during the processes of histologic fixation, section-cutting, and chemical treatment. Any solution of the original, intermediary, or final products of tissue carbohydrates defeats their accurate localization in tissues and cells. The reaction products of microchemical methods must be highly colored or black in order to be seen with the microscope. Reproducibility and confirmation by alternative methods are the usual tests for satisfactory localization.

B. Fixation and Preparation of Sections

To preserve dead tissue with a minimal disturbance of cellular detail from autolysis, the histologist commonly uses chemical solutions known as "fixatives." Most fixatives "harden" tissues by denaturation or precipitation of proteins. They retard autolysis and polysaccharide degradation by the inactivation of most enzymes.

Many different fixatives are in use, each with special advantages or purposes and limitations. The solution and diffusion of carbohydrates must be minimized. Fixation may induce undesirable changes in the chemical structure. The Altmann-Gersh procedure (*51*) of freezing and vacuum-drying in the cold immobilizes even ordinarily diffusible substances and probably causes minimal chemical and tissue changes (*50*, *52a*). But, the

49. R. D. Lillie, "Histopathologic Technic and Practical Histochemistry." Blakiston, New York, 1954.

50. A. G. E. Pearse, "Histochemistry." Little, Brown, Boston, 1953.

51. I. Gersh, *Anat. Record* **53**, 309 (1932).

52a. L. G. E. Bell, *Intern. Rev. Cytol.* **1**, 35 (1952).

apparatus required is quite expensive, bothersome, and subject to frequent technical failures. Refinements of apparatus may overcome some of these objections (*52b*, *52c*).

Few intact tissues are sufficiently thin that enough light is transmitted to reveal cellular details at high magnifications of the microscope. Although some tissues are easily studied in smears, spreads, and squash preparations, most of them require sectioning. Even after fixation, the tissue block must be hardened before thin sections can be cut. The simplest method of hardening fresh or fixed tissue for the cutting of sections is by freezing. Such "frozen-sections" are used by many workers (*53*). For the study of tissue carbohydrates, most workers prefer the thinner sections, greater permanency, and convenience of sections cut after paraffin infiltration.

In preparation for paraffin infiltration water and fats are removed after fixation from the small blocks of tissue by consecutive extractions with alcohol and fat solvents, such as xylene. The tissue blocks are then placed in several changes of molten paraffin. After the displacement of xylene by paraffin is complete, the tissue blocks in paraffin are removed from the oven and hardened by cooling. Sections can be cut easily by a rotary microtome at a thickness of 5 to 7 microns (0.005 to 0.007mm.). When water-soluble carbohydrates are to be studied, it is important to cut and mount the paraffin sections on slides without exposure to water. In ordinary work, the paraffin ribbons are floated on water and lifted on slides for mounting. Paraffin is removed from the tissue sections prior to microchemical tests by consecutive baths in several changes of xylene and alcohols.

C. Methods for the Histochemical Demonstration of Carbohydrates

Oldest of all the histochemical tests is the iodine reaction (*50*) with starch, applied to plant histology in the early nineteenth century by Caventon and Raspail. For almost all purposes, it has been replaced by methods that give better color and contrast, and more permanent preparations. Still, the iodine reaction is used in a modern histochemical method for phosphorylase (*54*).

More than seventy-five years ago, it was discovered that "amyloid" was colored red by a basic dye that is normally blue. Soon, it was learned that metachromasia, or the property of causing a change in the color of a pure dye when bound, is shown by many but not all mucinous substances when stained with any one of a number of thiazine dyes. Metachromatic

52b. M. S. Burstone, *J. Natl. Cancer Inst.* **17,** 49 (1956).
52c. E. W. Emmart and L. R. Crisp, *Rev. Sci. Instr.* **27,** 315 (1956).
53. A. H. Coons, E. H. Leduc, and M. H. Kaplan, *J. Exptl. Med.* **93,** 173 (1951).
54. T. Takeuchi and H. Kuriaki, *J. Histochem. Cytochem.* **3,** 153 (1955).

dyes, Best's carmine stain (*55*) for glycogen, and various empirical mucin stains have been widely used for over fifty years without much knowledge of their theoretical basis.

A more critical approach to histochemical problems was heralded by the publication of Lison's "Histochemie Animale" in 1936 (*56*). Some of Lison's original studies dealt with the meaning of metachromasia, the effects of fixatives on glycogen, and other topics of carbohydrate histochemistry. Other milestones in histochemistry were the alkaline phosphatase method of Gomori (*57*) and the periodic acid – Schiff method for carbohydrates developed by McManus (*58*), Lillie (*59*), and Hotchkiss (*60*). The technical performance and fruitful results of these two methods did much to show the possibilities of histochemistry in histology and pathology.

Histochemical methods for carbohydrates are best applied to the poorly soluble polysaccharides of high molecular weight. Because of diffusion and solution, monosaccharides and disaccharides are not shown by the present methods. Methods that lead to the selective or nearly selective coloration of broad classes of carbohydrates are the most frequently used. As the coloring methods are not specific, they are often used together with other procedures for the presumptive identification of particular linkages or chemical groupings. Examples of discriminatory procedures are the extraction of glycogen by diastase (*61*) or the acetylation (*62*) of glycols before the periodic acid – Schiff reaction.

a. Oxidation Reactions

The formation of insoluble aldehydes from vicinal glycols or their amino derivatives by oxidants that include periodic acid, chromic acid (*63*), lead tetraacetate, (*49*) and many others is well known and widely used in histologic studies. (See Chapter VI for further information about these oxidants.) Although Schiff's leucofuchsin (*49*) is almost always used for the coloration of the insoluble aldehydes produced by oxidation, other indicators can be used (*50*). The requisite vicinal glycol groupings are usually plentiful in carbohydrates but are not always present and are not limited to carbohydrates.

55. C. M. Bensley, *Stain Technol.* **14,** 47 (1939).
56. L. Lison, "Histochemie animale," Gauthier-Villars, Paris, 1936.
57. G. Gomori, *Proc. Soc. Exptl. Biol. Med.* **42,** 23 (1939).
58. J. F. A. McManus, *Nature* **158,** 202 (1946).
59. R. D. Lillie, *J. Lab. Clin. Med.* **32,** 910 (1947).
60. R. D. Hotchkiss, *Arch. Biochem.* **16,** 131 (1948).
61. R. D. Lillie and J. Greco, *Stain Technol.* **22,** 67 (1947).
62. J. F. A. McManus and J. E. Cason, *J. Exptl. Med.* **91,** 651 (1950).
63. H. Bauer, *Z. Mikroscop. anat. Forsch.* **33,** 143 (1933).

Periodic acid (see Chapter VI) has been the most widely used oxidant, following its introduction to histochemistry by McManus (*58*) and Lillie (*59*). The work of Hotchkiss was important in clarifying the chemical basis and limitations of the histochemical reaction (*60*). Further studies by McManus (*64*) and others soon led to the widespread, almost routine use of the periodic acid – Schiff reaction in histology and pathology. Some histologic features are not as well shown by any other method. Lillie showed the similarity of the various oxidant-Schiff methods used in histochemistry and proved the superiority of periodic acid over chromic acid and potassium permanganate (*65*). He showed that both chromic acid and permanganate tend to destroy whatever aldehydes are produced, probably by oxidation to carboxyl groups and carbon dioxide. With periodic acid, secondary oxidation is small even after the lapse of many hours at room temperature.

In McManus' or Lillie's procedures, periodic acid is used in water and allowed to act on tissue sections for only five or ten minutes, respectively. Hotchkiss prescribed periodic acid in either water or 70% alcohol for ten minutes. The sulfurous acid rinse that Hotchkiss interposed between the periodic acid and Schiff's reagent was shown by McManus to be not only unnecessary but deleterious as some aldehydes undergo sulfite-blockade (*64*). In histochemical studies on partly hydrolyzed dextran and other water-soluble carbohydrates, Mowry has found periodic acid to work well in 90% alcohol (*66*) and in other solvents that include glacial acetic, methanol, and diethyl ether. He showed that the time of oxidation for the optimal demonstration varies considerably for different substances in these solvents (*67a*). Cartilage ground substance is unusual in giving a much stronger periodic acid-Schiff reaction when the oxidation is performed in glacial acetic acid instead of water. The vast literature on the histochemical uses of periodic acid was reviewed recently by McManus (*67b*).

After oxidation, the tissue slides are washed and tested for aldehydes. Schiff's reagent is almost always used. Insoluble aldehydes are colored red. The intensity of color is generally assumed to indicate the amounts of aldehyde produced and of the presumed vicinal glycols initially present. Other aldehyde reactions, such as the formation of some colored Schiff bases (*49*), or the reduction of alkaline silver nitrate (*48*), have sometimes been used. The relative intensity of reaction at particular tissue sites will differ somewhat with various aldehyde reagents. After oxidation by periodic acid, glycogen is difficult to color by certain organic amines (Schiff-base

64. J. F. A. McManus, *Stain Technol.* **23,** 99 (1948).
65. R. D. Lillie, *Anat. Record* **108,** 239 (1950).
66. R. W. Mowry, *Am. J. Pathol.* **29,** 523 (1953).
67a. R. W. Mowry, *J. Natl. Cancer Inst.* **13,** 230 (1952).
67b. J. F. A. McManus, *Intern. Rev. Cytol.* **6,** in press (1957).

formation) but is always deeply colored by the ordinary Schiff's leucofuchsin reagent.

As so many substances and structures are colored by the periodic acid – Schiff reaction, there is great need for further procedures to distinguish between them. Intense reactions in tissue sections are strong presumptive evidence of carbohydrates although some lipides and amino acid groupings may interfere. In animal tissues, the strongest reactions are seen for glycogen, ingested starch, injected dextran, epithelial mucins, cell walls of fungi, and other sites known to contain carbohydrates. Duplicate sections can be treated with diastase, pectinases (*68*), lipid solvents, or various chemical reagents prior to periodic oxidation as confirmatory or partially discriminatory procedures.

Other demonstration methods may offer a clue to the degree of esterification of a carbohydrate. Whereas dextran is intensely periodic–Schiff positive and nonmetachromatic, highly sulfated dextran is periodic–Schiff negative but intensely metachromatic (*69a*).

Differences in the degree of reaction that follow changes in histochemical conditions may eventually offer clues to the spatial relations of the adjacent hydroxyls, the positions of the 1,2-glycols in the carbon chains, and the position of glycosidic linkages. Boric acid added to lead tetraacetate in glacial acetic is said to selectively inhibit the oxidation of *cis* hydroxyls under histochemical conditions (*69b*).

b. *Reactions of Acidic Groups*

The most familiar examples of the identification of acidic groups are the use of Toluidine Blue O for metachromasia and various other basic dyes. Naturally occurring acidic carbohydrates include components of the ground substance of cartilage, the connective tissue mucins, mast cell granules, and most of the epithelial mucins (*70*). (see Chapter XII). Sulfate esters and some other acidic groups in carbohydrates confer an acid charge and the property of basophilia or the capacity of binding basic dyes from relatively dilute solutions. Metachromasia is a special category of basophilia and is discussed later.

When acyl groups are introduced into carbohydrates by the esterification of hydroxyl groups, some degree of reciprocal relation should exist between the extent of esterification and the intensity of the periodic acid – Schiff reaction. Whenever the hydroxyl groups are sufficiently numerous, partial esterification may take place without any great decrease in the relative

68. J. F. A. McManus and J. E. Cason, *Arch. Biochem. and Biophys.* **34**, 293 (1951).
69a. R. W. Mowry, *J. Histochem. Cytochem.* **2**, 470 (1954).
69b. P. H. Staple, *Nature* **176**, 1125 (1955).
70. G. B. Wislocki, H. Bunting, and E. W. Dempsey, *Am. J. Anat.* **81**, 1 (1947).

number of vicinal glycols available for periodic acid cleavage. Complete esterification, whether with sulfate or acetyl groups, precludes a positive periodic acid – Schiff reaction. For example, partially hydrolyzed dextran in tissue sections gives an intensely positive periodic acid – Schiff reaction but is uncolored by toluidine blue and other basic dyes. Fully sulfated dextran of similar molecular weight gives a negative test for vicinal glycols but is strongly basophilic and metachromatic (*69a*). A comparable range of histochemical properties is seen in the ground substance of cartilage (*71*) and may possibly reflect varying degrees of sulfation of chondroitin (*72*). Sufficiently prolonged sulfation abolishes the periodic acid – Schiff reaction in tissue sections.

Similarly, desulfation should lead to a decrease in the acidic properties and the appearance of more hydroxyl groups. If the new hydroxyl groups are in the correct position, an enhanced periodic acid – Schiff reaction may result. Although sulfation methods have been applied to histochemical studies with the resulting induction of metachromasia (*73*) and basophilia (*74*), attempts at desulfation by saponification have not been satisfactory (*75*), probably because of anhydro ring formation.

Some acidic polysaccharides and glycoproteins contain no sulfate esters but contain carboxyl groups, typically in their uronic (usually glucuronic) acid moieties. Hyaluronic acid is an example (see Chapter XII). Carboxyl groups are more weakly acid and probably are never as numerous per molecule as sulfate groups may be when hydroxyl groups are extensively esterified. Although such carbohydrates with carboxyl groups are probably plentiful in animal tissues, satisfactory methods for their unequivocal identification have not been developed.

The degree of basophilia possessed by various acidic carbohydrates will depend on their degree of acidity relative to the staining environment. The degree of basophilia has been determined for various substances in staining solutions of different pH values in the hope of distinguishing sulfated from nonsulfated acid carbohydrates in tissue sections (*76*). The pH below which staining does not occur, the "extinction-point," is a convenient index for comparing various acidic substances (*50*). Variables such as the dye concentration and the ionic strength must be rigidly controlled.

Perhaps the most important source of difficulty in the identification of

71. G. Loewi, *J. Pathol. Bacteriol.* **65,** 381 (1953).

72. E. A. Davidson and K. Meyer, *J. Biol. Chem.* **211,** 605 (1954).

73. H. Kramer and G. M. Windrum, *J. Histochem. Cytochem.* **2,** 196 (1954).

74. J. F. A. McManus and R. W. Mowry, *Lab. Invest.* **1,** 208 (1952).

75. R. W. Mowry, unpublished work.

76. E. W. Dempsey, H. Bunting, M. Singer and G. B. Wislocki, *Anat. Record* **98,** 417 (1947).

acidic carbohydrates is the possibility that acid groups may be masked by basic proteins and other cations or by lactone formation. Even if acidic groups are not fully concealed, the net effect may be quantitatively modified. A blocking of acidic groups of tissue carbohydrates in the presence of various proteins, especially histones, has been shown *in vitro* by a number of workers, notably French and Benditt (*77*). Other investigators have reported enhancement of basophilia or metachromasia when sections of certain tissues were subjected to trypsin (*78*) or to pepsin (*79a*) solutions before staining. The extent to which blockade of potential acid groups actually occurs and persists during histologic procedures is not established. The possibility of an interference with or modification of acidic groups may be a serious limitation or fallacy in the estimation of relative acidity by the determination of either the dye-binding at various pH levels or the "extinction-point." The close agreement between the amounts and distribution of sulfated polysaccharides as judged histochemically and by careful autoradiography in S^{35}-injected mice suggests that masking of sulfate groups is not extensive (*79b*).

Metachromatic Dyes. Metachromasia is a curious phenomenon consisting of a definite change in the color of Toluidine Blue O and certain other basic dyes when bound by particular acid substances. This spectacular property has been much studied but with little clarification until recently. Lison stated that metachromasia which survived the action of alcohol and certain other extractives was due to the sulfate esters of high-molecular-weight carbohydrates (*80*). This view has been widely adopted. It is now clear that metachromasia is not confined to the sulfate esters of carbohydrates but is shown by the nucleic acids (*81*), hexametaphosphate (*82*), cysteic acid (*83*), carboxymethylcellulose (*84a*), and other substances. In spite of nonspecificity, the coloration of sulfated polysaccharides in tissue sections by metachromatic dyes is both useful and elegant. Toluidine blue has been used also for the detection of acidic carbohydrates on filter paper (*84b*).

It is not completely clear whether or not metachromasia due to sulfated carbohydrates can be distinguished in tissue sections from that due to acidic carbohydrates bearing only carboxyl groups. Examples of substances

77. J. E. French and E. P. Benditt, *J. Histochem. Cytochem.* **1,** 321 (1953).

78. R. H. Follis, Jr., *Proc. Soc. Exptl. Biol. Med.* **76,** 272 (1951).

79a. H. Hayashi, T. Funaki, and I. Morimoto, *Mie Med. J.* **4,** Suppl. 2, 143 (1955).

79b. R. C. Curran and J. S. Kennedy, *J. Pathol. Bacteriol.* **70,** 449 (1955).

80. L. Lison, *Compt. rend.* **118,** 821 (1935).

81. N. Weissman, W. H. Carnes, P. S. Rubin, and J. Fisher, *J. Am. Chem. Soc.* **74,** 1423 (1952).

82. J. M. Wiame, *J. Am. Chem. Soc.* **69,** 3146 (1947).

83. R. D. Lillie, R. Bangle, and E. R. Fisher, *J. Histochem. Cytochem.* **2,** 95 (1954).

84a. L. Michaelis, *Cold Spring Harbor Symposia Quant. Biol.* **6,** 131 (1947).

84b. D. Hamerman, *Science* **122,** 924 (1955).

exhibiting metachromasia believed due to nonsulfated acidic carbohydrates are synovial fluid, Wharton's jelly of umbilical cord (see Chapter XII), and the capsular substances (*84c*) of pneumococci, *Cryptococcus neoformans*, and staphylococci. Hyaluronic acid is probably weakly metachromatic despite conflicting reports (*85a*) (see Chapter XII, however). Bignardi induced metachromasia in certain neutral polysaccharides by prolonged chromic acid oxidation, probably with the formation of carboxyl groups from aldehydes (*85b*). Stronger and more uniform metachromasia of this type resulted when sections were first oxidized by periodic acid and then treated briefly in chromic acid (*85c*). Metachromasia or basophilia induced by such oxidation is not seen if stained in toluidine blue below pH 3–4; metachromatic basophilia induced by sulfation of the same substances is relatively unaffected by staining at very low pH levels (*85c*).

The staining of acidic carbohydrates by basic dyes is abolished in most cases by exposure to dilute HCl in methanol for a variable period, depending on the temperature. This "methylation" procedure was derived from the earlier work of Fraenkel-Conrat and Olcott (*85d*) by Mowry and extended by Fisher and Lillie from the same laboratory (*85e*).

Walton and Ricketts studied the effects of molecular weight and of varying degrees of esterification on the metachromasia of dextran sulfates in aqueous solution (*86*). Irrespective of molecular weight, a linear relation was found between the intensity of metachromasia and the degree of sulfation. This was taken as proof that polymerization of neither the dye nor the substrate are required for metachromasia. Carboxylated dextrans were feebly metachromatic compared to the corresponding sulfate esters. The conditions of testing were not the same as ordinarily used in histologic work but could be adapted.

A comprehensive theory of metachromasia in aqueous solutions that unifies much previous work has been developed by Schubert (*87a*) and applied histochemically in an extensive review of the subject (*87b*).

Techniques for the histologic use of metachromatic dyes vary greatly. Some workers complain of capricious and inexplicable variations in results. Some batches of dye are said to perform poorly. Most of the faults are

84c. R. W. Mowry, and C. H. Winkler, *Am. J. Pathol.* **32,** 628 (1956).

85a. B. Sylvén and H. Malmgren, *Lab. Invest.* **1,** 413 (1952).

85b. For references and additional discussion, See G. Gomori, *Brit. J. Exptl. Pathol.* **35,** 377 (1954).

85c. R. W. Mowry, *J. Histochem. Cytochem.* **4,** in press (1956).

85d. H. Fraenkel-Conrat and H. S. Olcott, *J. Biol. Chem.* **161,** 259 (1945).

85e. E. R. Fisher, and R. D. Lillie, *J. Histochem. Cytochem.* **2,** 81 (1954).

86. K. W. Walton and C. R. Ricketts, *Brit. J. Exptl. Pathol.* **35,** 227 (1954).

87a. M. Schubert and A. Levine, *J. Am. Chem. Soc.* **77,** 4197 (1955).

87b. M. Schubert and D. Hamerman, *J. Histochem. Cytochem.* **4,** 159 (1956).

prevented by the rigid control of the pH, dye concentration, dehydration, and tissue fixation. Although the choice of dye is probably not important, Toluidine Blue O is the favorite of most workers and is widely available from lots certified by the Biological Stain Commission. Although most often used as a 0.05 to 0.5% solution in water, toluidine blue has been used in high concentrations of alcohol to prevent the solution of water-soluble, alcohol-insoluble acid polysaccharides, e.g., heparin and dextran sulfate (*69a*). For consistent results, it is best to use the dye in dilute buffers of known pH; with alcoholic solutions, a knowledge and control of the pH is most important. As thionine forms precipitates with phosphates, other buffers must be used with this dye (*49*). When sections are compared after staining at various pH levels, broad groups of substances show fairly consistent differences in metachromasia, depending on the pH. For each substrate, there is probably an optimal range of pH for maximum metachromasia. The treatment of sections after staining greatly influences the results (*88*). For example, Mowry has found that more metachromasia is retained if alcohol-dehydrated sections are allowed to dry in air before clearing in xylene.

Hale's Dialyzed Iron and Related Methods. Hyaluronic acid was said by Hale to combine with "dialyzed iron"* in acetic acid solution (*89*). After the sections were rinsed, the classical HCl – potassium ferrocyanide reaction was used to color (as Prussian blue) the sites of iron-binding. The need for fixatives that would not dissolve hyaluronic acid was emphasized. The specificity was established by exposing duplicate portions of tissue to streptococcal hyaluronidase, presumable filtrates, before staining. This prevented coloration of hyaluronic acid but not that of other acidic carbohydrates.

Modifications of Hale's procedure produce less background coloration but still color acidic carbohydrates in general (*90*). Some substances, notably the mucins of the gastrointestinal tract and other epithelial structures, are colored more strongly and consistently than with the metachromatic dyes. As with basic dyes, the pH of the iron reagent is most important in determining the sites of iron-binding. By the use of dilute (0.1%) dialyzed iron in 1% acetic acid, the binding is largely limited to acidic carbohydrates without interference from the substances that are usually blue or orthochro-

* While Hale's iron oxide reagent was identified only as "dialyzed iron (B.D.H.)," most other workers have used 5% dialyzed iron oxide (Fe_2O_3), as formerly supplied by Merck and Co., Inc.

88. H. Kramer and G. M. Windrum, *J. Histochem. Cytochem.* **3,** 227 (1955).
89. C. W. Hale, *Nature* **1,** 802 (1946).
90. J. F. Rinehart and S. K. Abul-Haj, *Arch. Pathol.* **52,** 189 (1951).

matic with toluidine blue (*75*). This is advantageous when the action of enzymes or chemical reagents is being assessed.

As the blue color of the iron methods contrasts sharply with the magenta of the periodic acid – Schiff reaction, the combination of the two methods permits the coloration of both acidic groups and 1,2-glycols in the same tissue section. Although credit for the combined reaction belongs to Ritter and Oleson (*91*), the coloration of acidic carbohydrates in their procedure lacks selectivity. The difficulty of obtaining "dialyzed iron" from commercial sources will probably limit its usefulness in histology.

A quantitative colorimetric test for acidic carbohydrates based on iron-binding has been devised (*92*).

*Alcian Blue 8GS**. This is a derivative of chloromethylated copper phthalocyanin, probably a tetraalkylthiouronium or pyridinium salt (*93a*). First used as a stain for mucin by Steedman (*93b*), Alcian blue acts like a basic dye but is unusually fast and resistant to various chemical agents. The coloration of acidic carbohydrates by the original procedure is not very selective. Stronger and more selective coloration of acidic carbohydrates results when a lower pH and dye concentration are used (*93c*, *93d*).

Staining for thirty minutes in filtered 0.1% Alcian blue in 3% acetic acid, pH 2.5–2.8, colors the mucins of connective tissues, most epithelium, and certain microbial capsules (*84b*) deep blue to turquoise, with little or no staining of nucleic acids. Results with the Alcian blue stain resemble more those obtained with the better variants of the dialyzed iron procedure than those obtained with metachromatic dyes. In the case of epithelial mucins, Alcian blue has much greater sensitivity than toluidine blue.

Tests on pure substances and histological studies indicate that Alcian blue colors polysaccharides containing only glucuronic groups, in addition to those containing sulfate groups (*75*). The affinity of Alcian blue for various neutral polysaccharides after sulfation is variable, possibly due to steric factors. Methylation prevents the staining of acidic carbohydrates by Alcian blue, but a longer treatment is required than necessary to prevent metachromasia (*75*).

The Alcian blue stain followed by the periodic acid – Schiff reaction (*84c*,

* This patented dye is made by Imperial Chemical Industries, London, England; it can be obtained from a number of firms that supply dyes used in biological work.

91. H. B. Ritter and J. J. Oleson, *Am. J. Pathol.* **26,** 639 (1950).

92. N. Di Ferrante, *J. Biol. Chem.* **209,** 579 (1954).

93a. K. Venkataraman, "Chemistry of Synthetic Dyes." Academic Press, New York, 1952.

93b. H. F. Steedman, *Quart. J. Microscop. Sci.* **91,** 477 (1950).

93c. R. W. Mowry quoted by J. F. A. McManus, *in* "Connective Tissue in Health and Disease" (G. Asboe-Hansen, ed.), p. 31. Munksgaard, Copenhagen, 1954.

93d. R. W. Mowry, *J. Histochem. Cytochem.* **4,** in press (1956).

93c) is a simpler and more selective procedure for the coloration of both acidic groups and vicinal glycols than the Ritter-Oleson method (*91*) described above. The combination procedure gives a more complete demonstration of carbohydrates, e.g., epithelial mucins, than either method used alone. Alcian blue can be used at different pH levels for the study of dye-binding capacity and in acidified 70% alcohol for staining water-soluble, alcohol-insoluble substances (*75*).

The use of Alcian blue for the detection of acidic carbohydrates on paper after electrophoresis has been described (*93e, 93f*). Cystine and cysteine are said to be selectively colored by Alcian blue in sulfuric acid after the preliminary treatment of tissue sections with performic acid (*93g*).

Empirical Methods. Mayer's mucihematein and mucicarmine methods (*94*) are classical and widely used stains for mucus. Both mixtures contain aluminum salts whose binding by acidic groups may contribute to the staining action. These methods are not as selective or dependable as others of this group and are not recommended for histological studies. It is of interest that the mucicarmine stain has been recommended for detecting both acid and neutral polysaccharides on filter paper (*84b*).

c. *Nucleic Acids* (*50*)

Nucleoproteins consist of basic proteins in saltlike linkages with nucleic acids (Chapter VIII). Because nucleoproteins are probably present in all cells and vital to growth, there is tremendous biological interest in the histochemical detection of the nucleic acids. Chromosomes, sperm heads, and certain viruses consist largely of nucleoprotein. Two nucleic acid types occur in plant and animal cells: deoxyribonucleic acid (DNA), typically present in the nucleus, and ribonucleic acid (RNA), typically found in the cytoplasm and in the nucleolus (see, however, Chapter VIII). Both contain phosphoric acid groups and purine and pyrimidine bases but differ in the pentose moieties.

Deoxyribonucleic Acid (*DNA*). The staining of nuclei by basic dyes is well known and presumably depends on phosphoric acid groups. The binding of basic dyes by DNA takes place even at relatively low pH values (1–2) and is hard to explain. Although the nuclei are ordinarily easy enough to recognize, need exists for methods that selectively color DNA. Two methods have been widely used and seem well established. One depends on the Feulgen reaction and the other on the methyl green – pyronine stain.

Feulgen and Rossenbeck reported that brief hydrolysis of tissue sections

93e. C. Rizzoli, *Boll. soc. ital. biol. sper.* **31,** 426 (1955).

93f. L. Feeney and W. K. McEwen, *Stain Technol.* **31,** 135 (1956).

93g. C. W. M. Adams, and J. C. Sloper, *J. Endocrinol.* **13,** 221 (1956).

94. F. B. Mallory, "Pathological Technic," p. 129. Saunders, Philadelphia, 1942.

in 1 *N* HCl at 60°C. hydrolyzed the base-purine linkage and the deoxyribose could be colored by Schiff's reagent (*95*). This procedure is in common use under the name of the Feulgen reaction for DNA. In practice the color produced is most selective and quite adequate for microscopic study. Though gradually accepted and now widely used by histologists, the specificity of the Feulgen reaction has been much debated and challenged on chemical grounds. It is now clear that the reaction is reasonably specific (*96*) and reliable, provided the customary precautions are taken (*97*). In the Feulgen procedure, the hydrolysis is believed to cleave the purine – sugar linkages, thereby generating an aldehyde group, which in the case of deoxyribose reacts readily with the leucofuchsin reagent. Naturally occurring aldehydes, fortunately rare in tissue sections, are easily ruled out by Schiff-treatment of duplicate sections. The optimal time of hydrolysis varies for different fixatives and must be empirically determined for each set of conditions. Prolonged hydrolysis leads to the loss of DNA from tissue sections and must be avoided. Under the conditions of the Feulgen procedure, the aldose of RNA does not become Schiff-positive.

The other method used for the differential coloration of DNA and RNA is the methyl green – pyronine stain derived from the work of Pappenheim and Unna and applied to histochemical studies by Brachet (*98*). Methyl green has a well-established affinity for DNA but does not stain RNA or depolymerized DNA to any appreciable extent (*99*, *100*). By staining in a suitable mixture of methyl green and pyronine, a red dye, excellent contrast is obtained between the blue-green DNA and the red RNA. Recent improvements in technic are said to yield more consistent results (*101*, *102*). Only a few fixatives yield good results with the method. The basis for the differential staining is attributed by Kurnick (*100*) to differences in the degree of polymerization between DNA and RNA.

The quantitative estimation of DNA by photometry has been extensively studied, usually with the Feulgen reaction. Much progress has been made in this direction (*103*). Ultraviolet absorption also has been used for the

95. R. Feulgen and H. Rossenbeck, *Z. physiol. Chem.* **135,** 203 (1924).

96. W. G. Overend and M. Stacey, *Advances in Carbohydrate Chem.* **8,** 45 (1953).

97. R. E. Stowell, *Stain Technol.* **20,** 45 (1945).

98. J. Brachet, *Compt. rend.* **133,** 88 (1940).

99. A. W. Pollister and C. Leuchtenberger, *Proc. Natl. Acad. Sci.* (*U. S.*) **35,** 111 (1949).

100. N. B. Kurnick, *J. Gen. Physiol.* **33,** 243 (1950).

101. N. B. Kurnick, *Stain Technol.* **27,** 233 (1952); N. B. Kurnick, *Intern. Rev. Cytol.* **4,** 221 (1955).

102. E. B. Taft, *Stain Technol.* **26,** 205 (1951).

103. See A. W. Pollister and L. Ornstein, *in* "Analytical Cytology" (R. C. Mellors, ed.), p. **1**/3. Blakiston, New York, 1955.

quantitative estimation of nucleic acids in plant and animal cells (*104a*).

Although crystalline deoxyribonuclease is now available from commercial sources, its use for the selective removal of DNA from tissue sections is not yet established. Further studies are needed (*104b*).

Ribonucleic Acid (*RNA*). Cytoplasmic basophilia is a normal property of most cells and is usually ascribed to RNA. As no method colors only RNA, its specific recognition requires the use of purified ribonuclease, introduced to histochemistry in the work of Brachet (*98*, *105*).

Basophilia that is removed from duplicate sections by treatment in ribonuclease solution before staining is attributed to RNA. Nonspecific extraction is detected in control sections stained after exposure to the solvent without enzymes. To minimize the extraction of RNA by the buffer alone, Pearse advises a digestion temperature no higher than 37°C. (*50*). The particular method used to color the RNA is not critical. As the use of ribonuclease is expensive and somewhat troublesome, various chemical extractives of doubtful specificity, e.g., acids, have been proposed as alternatives (*106*, *107*).

d. *Miscellaneous*

Reduced ascorbic acid possesses the unusual property of reducing silver nitrate in acid solution (*50*). The specificity of the reaction is questioned less than the accuracy of histochemical localization (*108*, *109*). Since ascorbic acid is so soluble, diffusion is likely. The use of paraffin ribbons of frozen-dried tissue, fresh unfixed frozen-sections (*109*), and whole blocks of fresh tissue (*110*) placed directly in an acetic acid – alcohol solution of silver nitrate have each been recommended by various workers. The blocks of tissue can be sectioned after silver nitrate treatment. Positive reactions are considered qualitatively reliable, but negative tests do not prove the absence of ascorbic acid.

"Amyloid" is a substance of uncertain composition (*111*) sometimes found in diseased connective tissues. The name is derived from its resemblance to starch in turning blue when exposed to iodine and dilute sulfuric acid. This method of staining is so poor that it is now seldom used. A

104a. See J. I. Nurnberger, *in* "Analytical Cytology" (R. C. Mellors, ed.), p. 4/1. Blakiston, New York, 1955.

104b. B. Jackson and F. I. Dessau, *Stain Technol.* **30,** 9 (1955).

105. J. Brachet, *Compt. rend.* **133,** 90 (1940).

106. R. O. Erickson, K. B. Sax, and M. Ogur, *Science* **110,** 472 (1949).

107. E. R. Fisher, *Stain Technol.* **28,** 9 (1953).

108. C. B. Reiner, *Proc. Soc. Exptl. Biol. Med.* **80,** 455 (1952).

109. O. Eränkö, *J. Histochem. Cytochem.* **2,** 167 (1954).

110. H. W. Deane and A. Morse, *Anat. Record* **100,** 127 (1948).

111. R. B. Giles and E. Calkins, *J. Clin. Invest.* **34,** 1476 (1955).

number of different stains are in use, but most of them give inconstant and poorly selective results. "Amyloid" may possibly contain a sulfated saccharide moiety; such a structure might account for the fairly consistent metachromasia shown better with methyl violet (*112a*) than with other basic dyes such as toluidine blue. The wide variation in staining properties seen with "amyloids" suggests that their chemical composition is also variable. Carnes and Forker hold that the metachromasia of "amyloid" is fundamentally different from that of chondroitin sulfate (*112b*).

The two oldest methods, namely the iodine reaction for starch and Best's carmine stain for glycogen (*55*), are still not explained. Results by the latter method are often so good that it is still used by many workers. Substances stained by Best's carmine are strongly periodic acid – Schiff positive and not colored by the acidic group reactions. Both periodic acid oxidation and acetylation prevent Best's carmine coloration of glycogen (*75*). Whereas this suggests strongly that glycols are involved, further work is needed to explain and possibly improve the usefulness of both staining methods.

D. The Use of Enzymes in the Identification of Carbohydrates in Tissues

As the methods in use for the coloration of carbohydrates in tissue sections lack sufficient specificity, additional evidence is needed for the presumptive identification of particular polysaccharides and glycoproteins. Various enzymes have been applied to either tissue sections or fresh tissue for the purpose of either solubilizing or blocking particular substrates. To rule out nonspecific solution, duplicate "control" sections are exposed to the solvent without enzyme or to an enzyme solution that has been inactivated. Afterwards, both the "digested" and the "control" sections are stained by a suitable method and then compared. Sections known to contain the substrate should be tested along with the unknown. Material that is colored in the control section but absent after enzyme treatment is presumptively identified as a substrate of the enzyme used.

Ideally, this technic requires a pure, preferably substrate-specific enzyme. The tissue substrate should be insoluble in the various histological reagents but susceptible to the action of the enzyme despite the effects of fixation, alcohol dehydration, and paraffin embedding. The lack of removal or any effect by even an impure enzyme preparation that is known to be active against a particular substrate may be helpful in ruling out certain possibilities; this requires the assumption that the histological processing, especially fixation, has not rendered the substrate "indigestible" in the

112a. B. Highman, *Arch. Pathol.* **41**, 559 (1946).
112b. W. H. Carnes and B. R. Forker, *Lab. Invest.* **5**, 21 (1956).

tissue. For example, the ease with which RNA can be removed from tissue sections by ribonuclease varies considerably with different fixatives (*113*). It is not yet known to what extent fixation may affect the digestibility of other carbohydrates in tissue sections. Collodion films sometimes used in histology to prevent the detachment of sections from the slide must not be used as the films hinder access of the enzyme to the substrate.

Probably the best-known method of this type is the application of saliva to tissue sections, used by Bauer to confirm the staining of glycogen by Schiff's reagent after chromic acid oxidation (*63*). Preferable for many reasons is the use of a buffered solution of malt diastase (*61*). There is need for refining the diastase test for starch and glycogen by the use of purer enzymes in more dilute solutions. After either periodic acid oxidation or acetylation, glycogen in sections is no longer removable by diastase. There is no evidence that the type of fixative influences the action of diastase on glycogen or starch significantly.

Because of the great and continuing biological interest in the acid carbohydrates of connective tissue, there has been an intensive effort to localize by histochemical methods the various carbohydrates that have been characterized by the chemical studies of Meyer and others (see Chapter XII). Although it is not yet settled completely whether hyaluronic acid is stainable by any of the customary methods, most workers have assumed it to be metachromatic with toluidine blue. Hyaluronidases (see Chapter XII) from various sources have been used (*50*). Much of the earlier work was done with impure preparations and needs verification. Bull-testis hyaluronidase can be obtained in concentrated form and has been most often used. As bull-testis hyaluronidase depolymerizes both hyaluronic acid and chondroitin sulfates of types A and C, metachromasia that is abolished by this enzyme has been considered due to one of these (*114*). As the optimal conditions for the histochemical application of bull-testis hyaluronidase have not been systematically explored, technical directions vary greatly and need to be standardized.

The hyaluronidases of bacterial origin are said to depolymerize only hyaluronic acid (*114*) and have been applied to a few histochemical studies (*115*). Unfortunately, only impure or crude filtrates of cultures have sometimes been used. There is need for more histochemical observations made with purified preparations of these specific hyaluronidases. The attempts to demonstrate hyaluronic acid illustrate the confusion that can arise from an insufficiently critical interpretation of results obtained with impure enzymes whose actions are poorly understood and with demonstration

113. R. D. Lillie, *Anat. Record* **103**, 611 (1949).
114. K. Meyer and M. M. Rapport, *Advances in Enzymol.* **13**, 199 (1952).
115. H. Bunting, *Ann. N. Y. Acad. Sci.* **52**, 977 (1950).

methods not proven capable of revealing the substrate. The effects of various fixatives on the susceptibility of hyaluronic acid and the chondroitin sulfates to the hyaluronidases is not yet established.

McManus (*68*) found that pretreatment of tissue sections with crude fungal pectinase prevented the coloration of various tissue carbohydrates by the periodic acid – Schiff reaction. Prior acetylation of tissue sections prevented this effect of "pectinase." Blockage of "pectinase" action by acetylation was reversible if saponification was performed before the enzyme treatment. There will undoubtedly be wider histochemical use of pectinases and the many other carbohydrases (see Chapters X and XII) as purer preparations and further knowledge of their indications and limitations are obtained.

XII. POLYSACCHARIDES (1)

Part I

General Aspects and Phyto and Microbial Polysaccharides

Roy L. Whistler and W. M. Corbett

Polysaccharides are high-molecular-weight carbohydrates. They may be viewed as condensation polymers in which monosaccharides (or their derivatives such as the uronic acids and aminosugars) have been glycosidically joined with the elimination of water according to the empirical equation:

$$n\ C_6H_{12}O_6 \rightarrow [C_6H_{10}O_5]_n + (n - 1)H_2O$$

From the reverse direction this equation states that polysaccharides, on complete hydrolysis, yield only simple sugars (or their derivatives). Polysaccharides and oligosaccharides (Chapter IX) are thus, to this extent, defined similarly. However, the term polysaccharide is limited generally to those monosaccharide condensation polymers which contain ten or more monosaccharide residues. As was seen in Chapter IX, oligosaccharides contain two to nine sugar residues. Obviously this limitation of the two terms is completely arbitrary. It is justified on the basis that, as found in nature, most oligosaccharides contain two or three monosaccharide units in contrast to most polysaccharides which contain a hundred to several thousand monosaccharide units. Carbohydrates containing 5 to 15 sugar residues have not been found in nature although they surely occur, at least in small amounts. A few natural polysaccharides contain 30 to 100 sugar residues but most contain more.

1. NOMENCLATURE AND CLASSIFICATION

In the early periods of carbohydrate chemistry no systematic nomenclature existed. A polysaccharide name coined at that time usually reflected the origin of the polysaccharide or sometimes emphasized some property of the isolated substance. Illustrative examples of such polysaccharide nomenclature are found in the terms cellulose, the principal

1. For a comprehensive review of polysaccharide chemistry see R. L. Whistler and C. L. Smart, "Polysaccharide Chemistry." Academic Press, New York, 1953.

component of cell walls in plants, and starch, a name derived from the Anglo-Saxon "stercan" meaning to stiffen. Names like these were not designed with a view toward their being put into a systematic nomenclature. Yet they have been used so extensively that they must be accepted in spite of their deficiencies.

Progress toward a systematic nomenclature has produced the significant ending *-an* to designate that a substance is a polysaccharide. (The ending *-osan* signifies a simple sugar anhydride (see Chapter VII).) Thus, another word for polysaccharide is the generic term *glycan*. This term is evolved from the generic word glycose, meaning a simple sugar, and the ending *-an*, signifying a sugar polymer. Although not all older polysaccharide names employ this ending, it is found generally in names of polysaccharides composed of one or two sugar types: araban for an arabinose polymer, xylan for polymers of xylose, mannan for those of mannose, galactan for those of galactose, and galactomannans for galactose-mannose combinations. Until recently certain polymers of fructose were called fructosans. The name of the fructose polymers has been correctly shortened to fructans.

Persistent because of its wide use in the literature is the term pentosan, which designates polysaccharides composed of pentose sugar residues. This obviously unsystematic term has so far not been shortened to pentan or glycopentan. Cellulosan as a term for polysaccharides closely associated with cellulose is little used in modern carbohydrate literature.

Many polysaccharide names ending with the unsystematic and undesirable *-in* ending have been changed to end in *-an* as a step toward uniformity. Such terms are laminaran, carrageenan, lichenan, isolichenan, asparagan, senistran, graminan, tritican, kritesan, phlean, secalan, poan, pyrosan, and irisan. Names which have not been changed because of their long-standing and wide use are: pectin, amylopectin, inulin, chitin, heparin, and chondroitin.

The systematic name glucan does not refer to a specific polysaccharide but signifies only that the polysaccharide is composed of glucose residues. The manner of linkage and the arrangement are not specified. The name is a group name only and applies as well to cellulose as to glycogen, laminaran, or other glucose polymers. The polysaccharide can be defined more specifically if a source designation is also employed as part of the name. Thus, a more definite polysaccharide is specified in each case by the designation beechwood xylan, yeast mannan, or peanut araban.

Polysaccharides of the same type differ at least slightly from one source to another. Sometimes the differences are quite marked, as with starches. There is a well-known and readily apparent difference among starches from different plants. A particular starch is meant, however, by banana starch or corn starch.

Ideally, the polysaccharides should be classified according to their chemical composition and structure as has been suggested by Whistler (*1*). In such a classification, polysaccharides hydrolyzing to only one monosaccharide type are termed homoglycans while polysaccharides hydrolyzing to two or three or more monosaccharide types are termed heteroglycans with prefixes of di-, tri-, and so on to designate the number of different types of sugar units. At present there is no proof that more than five or six types of sugar units occur in a single polysaccharide. The number of types of sugar units contained in a polysaccharide can easily be determined by chromatographic examination of the hydrolyzate, provided, of course, that the polysaccharide is pure. In this structural classification the first logical subclassification separates polysaccharides as to whether they are linear or branched. This separation can readily be made by performing several simple tests. The easiest test is that of film formation. An aqueous polysaccharide solution when spread on a glass plate and dried will be brittle if a branched polysaccharide is present. Films from linear molecules will be strong, undergo folding without breaking and when plasticized can be stretched with the development of birefringence and a detectable "fibrous" X-ray pattern. Linear polysaccharides also show streaming birefringence when their solutions are stirred and viewed between crossed polarizing plates. Methylation studies may further reveal whether a molecule is branched.

Unfortunately, many polysaccharides have not been examined in rigorously pure conditions, and often examination has not extended to characterization of films. Therefore, at times, it is useful to classify polysaccharides according to source.

In subsequent discussion, the polysaccharides will be discussed from the standpoint of their sources as:

Phytopolysaccharides (Phytoglycans)

Bacterial and Fungal Polysaccharides

Zoöpolysaccharides (Zoöglycans) and Conjugates (Glycoproteins and Glycolipides)

The phytopolysaccharides and the bacterial and fungal polysaccharides will be considered in Part I of this chapter, and the zoöpolysaccharides in Part II. This classification, however, has the definite disadvantage that some polysaccharides of identical or similar structure are separated according to their origin. Thus, amylopectin (plants) and glycogen (animals) are separated. Chitin is found in lower animals, microorganisms, and fungi. Cellulose, although considered typical of plants, is also produced by some bacteria and lower animals.

2. THE STRUCTURES OF POLYSACCHARIDES

A. General Concepts

Though polysaccharides may be viewed as condensation polymers formed by the combination of monosaccharides with the elimination of the elements of water, the naturally occurring polysaccharides are far less complicated than would occur if the combination of monomers took place in random fashion. In fact many simplifying features are apparent on careful examination of all known polysaccharide structures. The basic reasons for such simplified and ordered arrangements stem from the action of those specific synthesizing enzymes which produce the monosaccharides and those enzymes which connect the monosaccharides, by various and sometimes complex routes, to polymer structures. Methods by which enzymes produce polysaccharides are given on page 703.

In the condensation of monosaccharides to form natural polymers, the hydroxyl on the anomeric carbon always participates in the condensation. Since most polysaccharides are composed of aldose sugar units, this discussion will be confined to such units. The hydroxyl on carbon atom 1 (anomeric carbon) may condense with any hydroxyl other than that at C-1 on an adjoining monosaccharide unit. In this way, a linear chain can be formed with a free C-1 hydroxyl group at one end. A complete randomness of linkage with the various hydroxyl groups has never been found in nature. Most frequently, a particular mode of linkage is repeated uniformly through the chain. Even the stereoconfiguration of C-1 remains constant in most observed cases. Thus, in amylose, there is a uniform α-D-1→4 linkage, in cellulose a uniform β-D-1→4 linkage, and in laminaran an essentially uniform β-D-1→3 linkage.

A further and highly simplifying fact in polysaccharide chemistry is that of the multitude of stereoisomeric monosaccharides only a very few are found in natural polysaccharides. Of the hexoses there are D-glucose, D-mannose, D-fructose, D-galactose, and infrequently L-galactose, and possibly D-idose or L-altrose. Of the pentoses there are D-xylose, L-arabinose, and infrequently D-arabinose. Of the modified simple sugars there are D-glucosamine, D-galactosamine, D-glucuronic acid, D-galacturonic acid, D-mannuronic acid, L-fucose, and L-rhamnose. Even these monosaccharides do not occur at random in polysaccharides but rather are found in a systematic arrangement.

Frequently a polysaccharide consists of but a single type of sugar unit. The most abundant polysaccharides are of this type. Paramount, as an example, is cellulose, which is present in the world in a quantity equal to or greater than the quantity of all other polysaccharides. Yet cellulose consists of a chain of D-glucopyranose units linked uniformly together by β-D-1→4 bonds. The presence of another linkage, once in some 700 links, is not ruled out. Essentially cellulose is a linear chain represented by *A* in Fig. 1.

Sometimes the hydroxyl groups of C-1 from two sugars have apparently condensed with two hydroxyls other than C-1 on a third sugar unit in a polysaccharide. When this occurs a branch point is produced in the molecule. The molecule may contain a single branch as in *B* of Fig. 1 or it may contain numerous branch points. Sometimes the branch may be but a single sugar unit in length. The molecule then is a substituted linear polysaccharide with sugar units acting as the substituents. Such a structure is *C* in Fig. 1. In other instances a branch-on-branch structure may occur which may be likened to a bush; a small section is depicted in *D* of Fig. 1.

In no known instance do polysaccharides occur as a cage or three-dimensional net structure. They are either linear, cyclic, or branched. It is apparent that when a branch point is introduced the glycosidic bond connects different positions from those connected in the linear portions between branches. It is common to find the same kind of glycosidic linkage at all branch points in a homoglycan. If more than one type of sugar unit

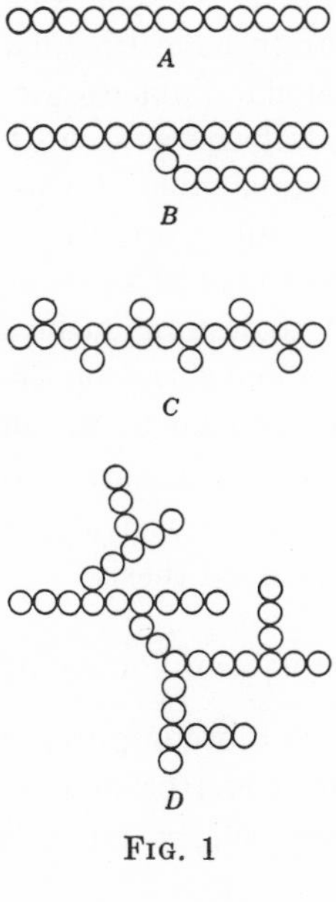
A
B
C
D

FIG. 1

is present it is usual for all units of the same sugar to be linked in the chain by the same sort of glycosidic bond.

Even in a linear homoglycan it is possible for more than one type of glycosidic linkage to be prevalent. In such a molecule the linkages do not occur randomly but are usually in an ordered arrangement.

If two or more types of sugars occur in a polysaccharide, the sugar units, generally, seem to be in an ordered arrangment. Thus, in linear diheteroglycans, polysaccharides composed of two kinds of sugars, the units seemingly are arranged in an alternating and regular fashion. Some diheteroglycans have the structural arrangment illustrated by *C* of Fig. 1. In this structure the principal chain may be composed of one type of sugar linked uniformly throughout, while the branches are composed of a second type of sugar which may be connected to the main chain by identical glycosidic bonds.

When more than two types of sugars are combined to produce a polysaccharide, they usually form a branch-on-branch structure exemplified by *D* in Fig. 1. Even here, some semblance of a simplifying order seems to exist. Thus, it is common to find hexose sugars and perhaps uronic acids in the main or central branches while the pentose sugars, D-xylose and L-arabinose, are in the side branches.

There are, then, in polysaccharides certain naturally imposed simplifications which greatly facilitate their understanding and their structural characterization. However, it is possibly correct to say that no polysaccharide is completely uniform. Even such seemingly regular molecules as cellulose and amylose appear to have irregularities or "anomalous links" in their structures. The irregular linkages are rare and may have a frequency of only 1 in each 700 linkages as seems to be true in some celluloses. Such rare irregularities are explainable on the basis that the various possible glycosidic bonds do not differ greatly in energy; hence, within the enzyme-substrate system there may at times occur a brief change, influential in causing an irregularity to develop in the chain growth. The irregularity may be due to a brief abnormal action on the part of the principal chain-synthesizing enzyme or may be due to the interference or the usurping action of a second enzyme. If enzymes are beyond reproach in the formation of irregular bonds, then quite conceivably such infrequent bonds could be produced by chance chemical synthesis.

B. Purification and Proof of Structure

Since polysaccharides do not occur pure, it is essential that they be purified before their structures can be determined. Unfortunately, much careful structural work, particularly methylations, has been done on products of unknown purity. Sometimes impurities may be easily removed, as in the case of cotton cellulose. In other instances, involving the simultaneous extraction of more than one polysaccharide, tedious procedures are necessary to effect separation and even then purification may be incomplete. Care must be taken when isolating polysaccharides from biological material to ensure that enzymic degradation does not occur. Enzyme action can be stopped by immersing the fresh tissue in hot ethanol.

Unfortunately, there are no specific tests for absolute purity of polysaccharides. A polysaccharide may be regarded as free from other polysaccharides if it may be separated by at least two suitable procedures into fractions each of which have the same physical and chemical properties. The principal methods for the fractionation of polymeric compounds are listed below. Most of these are applicable to polysaccharides or glycoproteins.

I. Solubility methods (*2*, *2a*).
  A. Fractional precipitation (by adding precipitant or by cooling).
  B. Fractional solution (by solvents of varying composition and at varying temperatures).
  C. Distribution between immiscible solvents (inclusive of Craig countercurrent distribution).

II. Ultracentrifugation (*2*, *2b*).

III. Ultrafiltration through graded membranes (dialysis and electrodialysis) (*2*, *2a*).

IV. Methods depending on electrical charge (applicable to polymers which can be ionized or converted to ionic complexes) (*2*, *2c*).
  A. Electrophoresis (inclusive of "mobility spectra" and "isoelectric spectra").
  B. Electroconvection.
  C. Ionography (electrophoresis in stabilized media).

V. Chromatographic adsorption, ion exchange, and partition chromatography (inclusive of paper chromatography) (*2*, *2a*, *2d*).

VI. Molecular distillation (*2*, *2a*).

2. L. H. Cragg and H. Hammerschlag, *Chem. Revs.* **39,** 79 (1946); A. C. Corcoran, ed., "Methods in Medical Research," Vol. 5. Year Book Publishers, Chicago, 1952.

2a. A. Weissberger, ed., "Techniques of Organic Chemistry," 2nd ed., Interscience, New York, 1954.

2b. A. E. Alexander and P. Johnson, "Colloid Science." Oxford U. P., New York, 1949.

2c. A. Kolin, *Proc. Natl. Acad. Sci.* (*U. S.*) **41,** 101 (1955); S. Raymond, *Proc. Soc. Exptl. Biol. Med.* **81,** 278 (1952); M. E. Adams, M. L. Karon, and R. E. Reeves, *J. Am. Chem. Soc.* **73,** 2350 (1951); H. J. McDonald, "Ionography." Year Book Publishers, Chicago, 1955.

2d. E. Lederer and M. Lederer, "Chromatography." Elsevier, New York, 1953.

a. Hydroxyl Groups

The main reactive group present in any polysaccharide is, of course, the hydroxyl group. However, there may be other groups of importance which may occur naturally or be produced by the process of isolation or any other treatment. The average number of hydroxyl groups per sugar residue is usually measured by the determination of the acetyl or methyl groups introduced by acetylation or methylation of the polysaccharide. An estimate of the number of free primary hydroxyl groups may be obtained by tosylation (*p*-toluenesulfonation) or tritylation (triphenylmethylation). Primary hydroxyl groups are generally tosylated some 20 times faster than secondary hydroxyl groups, and under suitable conditions esterification of primary hydroxyl groups only may be achieved. Estimation of the primary tosyl groups is made by reaction of the ester with sodium iodide whereby only primary tosyl groups are replaced by iodine. Primary hydroxyl groups can also be determined by measurement of the number of trityl groups introduced on reaction of the polysaccharide with trityl chloride. This reaction combined with carbanilation may be used to measure the number of both primary and secondary hydroxyl groups (*3*). Ultraviolet light absorption is used to estimate the number of carbanilate and trityl groups present.

Secondary hydroxyl groups cannot be determined directly. However, when adjacent hydroxyl groups (α-glycol groups) occur in the molecule, as in $1 \rightarrow 4$ glucans, they may be determined by oxidation with periodate or lead tetraacetate (see p. 699). Lead tetraacetate oxidations are restricted to nonaqueous solutions, whereas periodate is used for aqueous solutions. One mole of oxidant is consumed for each carbon bond broken.

b. Uronic Acids

Almost half of the known types of polysaccharides contain uronic acid units. Uronic acid residues may be determined by decarboxylation with 12% hydrochloric acid and the evolved carbon dioxide determined by absorption (*4*) or by manometric measurement (*5*). A micro-quantitative colorimetric method employing carbazole has been developed for uronic acids (*6*). (See also Part II of this chapter and Chapter XI.)

3. C. J. Malm, L. J. Tanghe, B. C. Laird, and G. D. Smith, *Anal. Chem.* **26,** 188 (1954).

4. R. L. Whistler, A. R. Martin, and M. Harris, *J. Research Natl. Bur. Standards* **24,** 13 (1940).

5. M. V. Tracey, *Biochem. J.* **43,** 185 (1948).

6. Z. Dische, *J. Biol. Chem.* **167,** 189 (1947); **183,** 489 (1950).

c. Other Acidic Groups

Native polysaccharides with acid groups other than the uronic type are not very common except for the sulfate esters. Total acidity may be estimated by direct titration, but erroneous results are obtained if the polysaccharide is alkali-labile as is the case with many oxidized polysaccharides. Addition of calcium acetate (*7*, *8*) or sodium bromide (*8*, *9*) to the polysaccharide solution increases the accuracy of the titration. Other methods for the estimation of carboxyl and other acidic groups involve determination of the amount of methylene blue absorbed, or determination of the amount of silver salt formed by exchange from a solution which contains silver in combination with a very weak acid. The sulfate content of polysaccharide sulfates, such as agar, is obtained by ordinary sulfate analysis of the completely hydrolyzed or ashed polysaccharide.

d. Carbonyl Groups

Although many methods have been devised for the estimation of carbonyl groups in polysaccharides, a simple stoichiometric method is not available. The number of aldehyde groups in a polysaccharide is usually measured with alkaline iodine (*10*). Chlorous acid is also useful (*11*). The oxidation can be followed by the consumption of oxidant or amount of acid formed. In one colorimetric method, 2,5-dinitrosalicylic acid in alkaline solution (*12*) is used. In another, the ferricyanide reduced by carbonyl groups is measured after conversion to Prussian blue (*12a*). Two principal sources of difficulty with these methods must be guarded against, over-oxidation and/or alkali-lability of the polysaccharide. Frequent empirical use has been made in cellulose chemistry of the copper number (a measure of copper reduction) and in starch chemistry of the alkali number (a measure of the alkali consumed in saccharinic acid formation). Saccharinic acid formation begins at the reducing terminal and progresses through successive removals of sugar moieties (see p. 653).

Several methods have been devised for the determination of total carbonyl groups under neutral conditions. In one method the polysaccharide

7. E. C. Yackel and W. O. Kenyon, *J. Am. Chem. Soc.* **64,** 121 (1942).

8. A. C. Ellington and C. B. Purves, *Can. J. Chem.* **31,** 801 (1953).

8a. A Schwebel, H. S. Isbell, and J. V. Karabinos, *Science* **113,** 465 (1951).

9. C. C. Unruh, P. A. McGee, W. F. Fowler, Jr., and W. O. Kenyon, *J. Am. Chem. Soc.* **69,** 349 (1947).

10. A. R. Martin, L. Smith, R. L. Whistler, and M. Harris, *J. Research Natl. Bur. Standards* **27,** 449 (1941).

11. H. F. Launer, W. K. Wilson, and J. H. Flynn, *J. Research Natl. Bur. Standards* **51,** 237 (1953).

12. K. H. Meyer, G. Noelting, and P. Bernfeld, *Helv. Chim. Acta* **31,** 103 (1948).

12a. S. Nussenbaum and W. Z. Hassid, *Anal. Chem.* **24,** 501 (1952).

is reacted with phenylhydrazine acetate and the combined nitrogen determined; in another, the polysaccharide is reacted with hydroxylamine hydrochloride or *O*-methylhydroxylamine hydrochloride and the amount of liberated hydrochloric acid measured. Still another procedure involves the reaction of the carbonyl groups with hydrogen cyanide; the number of combined groups is estimated by measurement of the ammonia liberated on hydrolysis of the cyanohydrins (*8*), or, if radioactive hydrogen cyanide is used, by the activity of the final polysaccharide (*8a*).

e. Other Groups

Methyl groups are frequently found as esters of uronic acids and sometimes as ethers of sugar residues. Ether-linked methyl groups and total methoxyl are determined by the Zeisel method (*13*). Methyl esters or glycosides may be differentiated from methyl ethers by the action of alkali and acid, respectively, which will saponify the ester or glycoside but have no effect on the ether. The ester or glycosidic methoxyl can be distilled as methanol and be determined colorimetrically after oxidation to formaldehyde and condensation with Schiff reagent (*14*).

Glucosamine and galactosamine in polysaccarides are measured usually by the method of Elson and Morgan after hydrolysis. The aminosugar is condensed with acetylacetone followed by *p*-dimethylaminobenzaldehyde (Ehrlich's reagent) (*15*). Aminopolysaccharides frequently occur as the *N*-acetates. In general, *N*-acetyl groups are more resistant to hydrolysis than *O*-acetyl groups, being hydrolyzed only by hot, aqueous, strong acids or bases (*15a*). (See also Chapter VIII and Sialic Acid, Part II.)

f. Nonreducing End Groups

The ratio of nonreducing to reducing end groups in a polysaccharide gives a measure of the extent of branching, for there will be one branch for each nonreducing end unit found above one. The ratio of glycosidic units to nonreducing end units gives the average chain length of the branches.

Periodate oxidation is useful for end-group assay (*16–18*). A linear

13. See F. J. Bates and associates, *Natl. Bur. Standards Circ.* **C440,** 509 (1942).

14. C. L. Hoffpauir and R. E. Reeves, *Anal. Chem.* **21,** 815 (1949).

15. See E. A. Kabat and M. M. Mayer, "Experimental Immunochemistry," p. 312. C. C Thomas, Springfield, Ill., 1948; N. F. Boas, *J. Biol. Chem.* **204,** 553 (1953).

15a. A. Chaney and M. L. Wolfrom, *Abstr. papers, Am. Chem. Soc., Atlantic City* p. 4D, 1956.

16. F. Brown, S. Dunstan, T. G. Halsall, E. L. Hirst, and J. K. N. Jones, *Nature* **156,** 785 (1945).

17. T. G. Halsall, E. L. Hirst, and J. K. N. Jones, *J. Chem. Soc.* p. 1427 (1947).

18. A. L. Potter and W. Z. Hassid, *J. Am. Chem. Soc.* **70,** 3488 (1948).

polysaccharide yields definite quantities of formic acid from the nonreducing terminal sugar and of formic acid and formaldehyde from the reducing terminal sugar (p. 700). The formaldehyde is produced in small yield, and, if precautions are not taken, is liable to be further oxidized. Formic acid may be titrated directly. Excess oxidant can be removed by ethylene glycol. The formic acid liberated from the reducing end groups of a highly branched $1 \rightarrow 2$, $1 \rightarrow 3$, or $1 \rightarrow 4$ polysaccharide will be negligible to that liberated from the nonreducing units, and the total formic acid produced may be taken as a measure of the branch length. This method is not applicable to $1 \rightarrow 6$ hexans, because each of the sugar units will liberate one mole of formic acid.

The original methylation method introduced by Haworth (*19*) is still of importance. Paper-chromatographic modifications have made the method applicable at a micro-scale. The nonreducing terminal group of a linear polysaccharide contains one more hydroxyl group than the preceding units, and, if branching occurs, the branch unit will contain one less hydroxyl group than the adjacent sugar units. These groups may be estimated by methylation of the polysaccharide followed by hydrolysis or methanolysis to give the methylated monosaccharides or glycosides. It is important that methylation be complete and that no degradation occur. Hydrolysis or methanolysis also must be carefully controlled to keep demethylation to a minimum (*20*).

Originally, quantitative separation of the various methylated glycosides was achieved by fractional distillation in high vacuum (*19*). In the case of amylopectin, methyl 2,3,4,6-tetra-*O*-methyl- and 2,3,6-tri-*O*-methylglucosides were isolated as well as a small quantity of a mixture of methyl di-*O*-methylglucosides. The yield of di-*O*-methylglucoside, derived from the branching points, should be equal to the yield of the tetra-*O*-methylglucoside, from the nonreducing terminal groups, but in practice it is greater. This is due to incomplete methylation and to demethylation during methanolysis.

Other methods have been described for the separation of methylated sugars. These include partition between an organic solvent and water (*21*, *22*) and separation on columns of alumina (*22*), silica gel (*23*), or charcoal (*24*). A micro method now generally adopted has come into being

19. W. N. Haworth and H. Machemer, *J. Chem. Soc.* p. 2270 (1932).
20. K. Freudenberg and H. Boppel, *Ber.* **73,** 609 (1940).
21. J. Y. Macdonald, *J. Am. Chem. Soc.* **57,** 771 (1935).
22. F. Brown and J. K. N. Jones, *J. Chem. Soc.* p. 1344 (1947).
23. D. J. Bell and A. Palmer, *Nature* **163,** 846 (1949).
24. B. Lindberg and B. Wickberg, *Acta Chem. Scand.* **8,** 569 (1954); W. J. Whelan and K. Morgan, *Chemistry & Industry* p. 78 (1954).

with the application of paper chromatography to carbohydrates (*25*). The positions of the various methylated monosaccharides which have been separated on sheets of filter paper by development with a butanol solvent are revealed by spraying with suitable reagents. Such components may be partially identified by the distance traveled on the paper and by the color which they produce with various reagents. Quantitative estimation of the methylated sugars is obtained by elution of each from unsprayed sheets of filter paper and oxidation with alkaline iodine or periodate. Analysis of a mixture of methylated sugars may be obtained by spraying the papers to reveal the location of the various components and then measuring the amount of reflectance or light transmission of the various spots (*26*). (See also Chapter XI.) Only a very small percentage of tetra-*O*-methylhexose will be obtained on hydrolysis of a methylated polysaccharide of high molecular weight. Here greater accuracy in end-group determination may be obtained by concentration of the tetra-*O*-methylhexose, relative to the tri-*O*-methylhexose, by extracting the former from an aqueous solution with chloroform. By paper-sheet or cellulose-column chromatography of methylated polysaccharide hydrolyzates, sufficient amounts of the individual methylated monosaccharides may be obtained to prepare crystalline derivatives for identification (*27*).

g. Identification of Monosaccharides (see also Chapter XI)

Mixtures of sugars, such as occur in the hydrolyzates of polysaccharides, are frequently difficult to separate into the component sugars. Crystallizations, selective precipitations with chemical reagents, and fermentations have been used when applicable. A more general tool is chromatography, particularly when only small amounts of material are available for study. Some combinations are easily separated chromatographically and some, for example, fructose and mannose, only with considerable difficulty. Silicates and activated carbon are particularly useful for adsorption chromatography and cellulose (powder or paper) for partition chromatography of the sugars.

Paper chromatography provides a rapid, sensitive micro method often enabling trace components to be detected. On paper, artifacts have been detected which were produced by exposure of the sugar to alkali during neutralization of the hydrolyzates. Care should be taken to avoid even brief exposures of the sugars to alkalies. Neutralization through electrodialysis has been used to avoid this danger. Information as to the identity of the sugar is obtained from the distance of its movement and from the

25. E. L. Hirst, L. Hough, and J. K. N. Jones, *J. Chem. Soc.* p. 928 (1949).
26. E. F. McFarren, K. Brand, and H. R. Rutkowski, *Anal. Chem.* **23,** 1146 (1951).
27. L. Hough, J. K. N. Jones, and W. H. Wadman, *J. Chem. Soc.* p. 2511 (1949).

colors produced by different sprays (*28*). However, since many sugars move at the same rate even in several different solvents, confirmatory evidence is necessary. After elution, the monosaccharide at each location on a filter-paper chromatogram may be estimated by micro methods such as those with alkaline iodine (*25*), Somogyi's reagent (*29*), or periodate. The sugars may also be estimated by the density of the spots produced by various sprays (*26*). Unequivocal identification, however, depends on the recovery of a sufficient quantity of the pure sugar for the determination of its properties and those of its derivatives.

Monosaccharides may be separated by the addition of borax to form negatively charged complexes which are absorbed on columns of basic ion-exchange resins, from which the sugar complexes are preferentially eluted with dilute solutions of sodium borate (*30*). The complexes may also be separated by ionophoresis because of differences in dissociation constants (*31*). Individual sugars may be determined by selective fermentation or enzymic degradations.

h. Nature of the Glycosidic Linkages

Information on the nature of the glycosidic links present in a polysaccharide may be obtained by investigation of the products formed by the action of alkali, especially lime water. Thus, 1 → 4 hexans (e.g., hydrocellulose) produce isosaccharinic acids (*32*) and 1 → 3 hexans (laminaran) produce metasaccharinic acids (*33*).

Use has been made of the relationship between the optical rotation of D-glucans in water and cuprammonium hydroxide solution and that of the methyl mono-*O*-methyl-D-glucoside which is methylated on the same hydroxyl group as that involved in the glucosidic link of the glucan (*34*). See Table I.

The methods most used in identifying the nature of the glycosidic bridge are periodate oxidation and examination of hydrolysis products from the fully methylated polysaccharides. Identification of the *O*-methylsugars from the hydrolyzed *O*-methylpolysaccharides suggest the location of glycosidic linkages and acetal rings in the partially methylated monosaccharides. Determination of the amount of formic acid and formaldehyde

28. L. Hough, J. K. N. Jones, and W. H. Wadman, *J. Chem. Soc.* p. 1702 (1950).

29. A. E. Flood, E. L. Hirst, and J. K. N. Jones, *J. Chem. Soc.* p. 1679 (1948).

30. J. X. Khym and L. P. Zill, *J. Am. Chem. Soc.* **73,** 2399 (1951).

31. H. Michl, *Monatsh.* **83,** 737 (1952); R. Consden and W. M. Stanier, *Nature* **169,** 783 (1952).

32. J. J. Murumow, J. Sack, and B. Tollens, *Ber.* **34,** 1427 (1901).

33. W. M. Corbett, J. Kenner, and G. N. Richards, *Chemistry & Industry* p. 462 (1953); p. 1483 (1954).

34. R. E. Reeves, *J. Biol. Chem.* **154,** 49 (1944).

TABLE I

SHIFT IN OPTICAL ROTATION DUE TO COMPLEX FORMATION

Substance	$[\alpha]_{436}^{25}$ Water	$[\alpha]_{436}^{25}$ Cuprammonium hydroxide	Difference
Methyl 2-*O*-methyl-β-D-glucoside	−69°	+985°	+1054°
Methyl 3-*O*-methyl-α-D-glucoside	−46°	−86°	−40°
Laminaran	−29°	+34°	+63°
Methyl 4-*O*-methyl-β-D-glucoside	−36°	−1008°	−972°
Cellulose	−46°[a]	−1200°	−1154°
Soluble starch	+375°	−715°	−1090°
Glycogen	+366°	−597°	−963°
Methyl 6-*O*-methyl-β-D-glucoside	−48°	+161°	−209°

[a] In 1:1 mixture of water and triton B.

produced during periodate oxidation sometimes easily identifies the hydroxyl groups which are not involved in glycosidic linkage or ring formation (p. 700) (*35*, *36*).

Additional information can be gained by reduction and hydrolysis of the oxidation products resulting from the action of periodate. Information concerning the position of the linkages in dextrans was derived by analytical determinations of glycerol, erythritol, and glucose, which result, respectively, in this way from 1→6, 1→4, and 1→3 linked glucopyranoses (*37*).

Final proof of the nature of the glycosidic linkages is obtainable only by partial hydrolysis (or acetolysis) of polysaccharide derivatives to low-molecular-weight oligosaccharides, whose structures, if not already known, may be unambiguously determined (for method see p. 701). This procedure is particularly essential for establishing the order of linkages in a homoglycan containing different linkages and for establishing the order of sugar residues in a heteroglycan.

Establishment of the stereoconfiguration of the glycosidic bond is more complicated. Specific α- and β-glycosidase enzymes have been used with considerable success, and application of infrared spectrophotometry seems to be useful (*38*). In the latter method the presence of α-linked D-glucose

35. J. C. Rankin and A. Jeanes, *J. Am. Chem. Soc.* **76,** 4435 (1954).

36. J. J. Conell, E. L. Hirst, and E. G. V. Percival, *J. Chem. Soc.* p. 3494 (1950).

37. J. W. Sloan, B. H. Alexander, R. L. Lohmar, I. A. Wolff, and C. E. Rist, *J. Am. Chem. Soc.* **76,** 4429 (1954).

38. S. A. Barker, E. J. Bourne, M. Stacey, and D. H. Whiffen, *J. Chem. Soc.* p. 171 (1954).

units is said to be indicated by an absorption peak at 844 ± 8 cm.$^{-1}$, whereas β-linked residues are said to absorb at 891 ± 7 cm.$^{-1}$. In the case of α-glucans it may also be possible to determine the position of linkages by their characteristic absorption peaks.

Type of α-glucan linkage	Absorption (cm.$^{-1}$)
$1 \rightarrow 2$	Not determined
$1 \rightarrow 3$	793 ± 3
$1 \rightarrow 4$	930 ± 4: 758 ± 2
$1 \rightarrow 6$	917 ± 2: 768 ± 1

C. Molecular Size and Shape (*38a*)

Determination of molecular weights is possible by a variety of methods. Association of the molecules in solution gives rise to complications which may be minimized by the use of suitable solvents, low concentrations, and extrapolating data to infinite dilution. Since all polysaccharides possess a molecular-weight distribution, it is the average molecular weight which is usually measured. Physical and chemical methods based on osmotic pressure, depression of freezing point, and end-group assay count the molecules and give a number-average molecular weight, whereas light scattering and certain types of sedimentation methods give a weight average. In addition, sedimentation data give a Z-average molecular weight (*39*) and viscosity measurements a viscosity-average molecular weight (*40*). These may be defined as:

$$\text{Number-average, } M_n = \frac{\Sigma(n_i M_i)}{\Sigma n_i}$$

$$\text{Weight-average, } M_w = \frac{\Sigma(n_i M_i^2)}{\Sigma(n_i M_i)}$$

$$\text{Z-average, } M_z = \frac{\Sigma(n_i M_i^3)}{\Sigma(n_i M_i^2)}$$

$$\text{Viscosity-average, } M_v = \left[\frac{\Sigma(n_i M_i^{\beta+1})}{\Sigma(n_i M_i)}\right]^{1/\beta}$$

where n_i is the number of molecules of molecular weight M_i, and β is a constant equal to unity if Staudinger's law is obeyed.

M_n/M_w is a measure of the heterogeneity of the polysaccharide. For a perfectly homogeneous polymer the ratio would be unity, but the value

38a. See C. T. Greenwood, *Advances in Carbohydrate Chem.* **7**, 289 (1952).

39. W. D. Lansing and E. O. Kraemer, *J. Am. Chem. Soc.* **57**, 1369 (1935); I. Jullander, *Arkiv. Kemi Mineral Geol.* **21A**, No. 8 (1945).

40. P. J. Flory, *J. Am. Chem. Soc.* **65**, 372 (1943).

decreases as the heterogeneity of the polymer increases. Molecular weights determined by equilibrium methods, such as by osmotic pressure, are independent of the shape and flexibility of the molecule. On the other hand, kinetic measurements (as for example, determinations of viscosity), which are based on the properties of molecules in motion, may give rise to information concerning the shape and flexibility of the molecules.

a. Osmotic Pressure (2a, 2b)

Molecular weights of polysaccharides may be determined by measuring the osmotic pressure of dilute solutions. The osmotic pressure at infinite dilution, obtained by extrapolating a number of measurements at various low concentrations, is a function of the molecular weight as shown by the modified van't Hoff formula.

$$\pi = cRT/M + Bc^n$$

where π is the osmotic pressure in grams per cm.^{2}, c is the concentration of solute in grams per ml., M is the gram-molecular weight, B and n are constants, T is the absolute temperature, and R the gas constant. This method is limited to polysaccharides with molecular weights in the range 10,000 to 500,000 owing to diffusion through the membrane of molecules with molecular weights lower than 10,000, and to the small pressures produced by molecules with a molecular weight greater than 500,000.

b. Sedimentation Velocity (2, 2a, 2b)

A solution of macromolecules, when subjected to centrifugal forces many times greater than gravity, undergoes sedimentation in the plane of rotation. Disturbing effects caused by convection currents are minimized by the use of correctly shaped cells. The velocity of sedimentation is followed by observing the changes of light absorption or refractive index. By the use of high angular velocities, initial sedimentation may occur without diffusion effects becoming important. Solutions of homogeneous molecules produce sharp sedimentation boundaries, whereas a mixture of several components differing appreciably in average molecular weight will give separate boundaries for each component. However, if the individual molecular weights of a mixture of polymers spread over a wide range, a diffuse boundary occurs and the derived molecular weights will be only an approximation. Measurement of the position of the boundary at various times gives the velocity of sedimentation from which, by dividing it by the centrifugal acceleration, is obtained the sedimentation constant (S). This constant extrapolated to zero concentration at standard conditions is S_0. The molecular weight is derived from the equation:

$$M = \frac{S_0RT}{D_0(1 - V\rho)}$$

where V is the partial specific volume of the solute, ρ is the density of the solution, S_0 is the sedimentation constant at zero concentration and standard conditions, and D_0 is the diffusion constant.

The diffusion constant is independently evaluated by observing the changes in concentration of a solution in a stationary tube as the solute diffuses into pure solvent with which the solution forms a liquid boundary. From this can be calculated the molar frictional coefficient (f).

$$f = \frac{RT}{D_0} = \frac{M(1 - V\rho)}{S_0}$$

By comparison of the value with that calculated for a spherical particle of the same weight and density, information may be obtained as to the polymer's molecular configuration.

c. Sedimentation Equilibrium (2, 2a, 2b)

Smaller centrifugal forces are required for this method, but several days of continuous running are necessary to reach an equilibrium between sedimentation and diffusion. The molecular weight is calculated from the equation:

$$M = \frac{2RT \ln (C_2/C_1)}{(1 - V\rho)\omega^2(x_2^2 - x_1^2)}$$

where the terms have the same meaning as above, c_1 and c_2 are the concentrations of solute at distances x_1 and x_2, respectively, from the axis of rotation, and ω is the angular velocity. If the plot of c against x^2 deviates from a straight line, the polymer is heterogeneous. Measurement of the concentration by light absorption gives the weight-average molecular weight, whereas refractive methods give the Z-average molecular weight.

d. Viscosity (2a, 2b)

The viscosity of a solution increases with the molecular weight of the solute. By making measurements on solutions of low concentrations, Staudinger derived the following empirical equation:

$$\eta_{sp} = KMc \qquad \text{or} \qquad \frac{\eta_{sp}}{c} = KM$$

where

$$\eta_{sp} = \frac{\eta_{\text{solution}}}{\eta_{\text{solvent}}} - 1 = \eta_r - 1$$

η_{sp} = specific viscosity, K = constant for a particular homologous series, η_r = relative viscosity, M = molecular weight of solute, c = concentration of solute. The constant K shows reasonable constancy for a given homologous series but varies for different series, temperatures, and solvents. The reduced viscosity $\left(\frac{\eta_{sp}}{c}\right)$ varies with the concentration, and more accurate results are obtained if the intrinsic viscosity $[\eta]$ is used. This term is obtained by extrapolating the reduced viscosity to infinite dilution.

Originally the value of K for a particular series was derived by studying several lower members of the series. However, the value obtained did not hold for higher members and considerable error was introduced. A more desirable method is to evaluate the constant with the use of members of the series whose molecular weights have been obtained by osmotic pressure or ultracentrifuge methods. The more convenient viscosity method is thereafter used for determining the molecular weights of other members of the same series.

Deviation from Staudinger's equation occurs for molecular weights above 10,000, and a modified equation has been introduced:

$$[\eta] = KM^a$$

The constant a appears to be a function of the shape and solvation of the molecules. Theoretical calculations predict a to be 0.5 for a matted coil, 1.0 for a randomly linked chain, and 2.0 for a stiff chain. Experimental values vary from 0.53 for polystyrene in butanone to 1.5 for amylose in ethylenediamine. For polymers of molecular weight 100,000 to 1,000,000, the equation is further modified to give

$$[\eta] = K_1M^a - K_2M^{2a}$$

where $K_2 \ll K_1$ and is significant only for large molecules.

e. Light Scattering (*2a*, *2b*)

A beam of light on passage through a solution is partially scattered. This is due mainly to the radiation of light by loosely bound electrons of the solute molecules. The amount of light scattered by each particle is dependent on its particle size and may be related to the molecular weight by the equation:

$$\frac{Hc}{\tau} = \frac{1}{M} + \frac{2Bc}{RT}$$

where

$$H = \frac{32\pi^3\mu_0^2}{3N\lambda^4}\left(\frac{\mu - \mu_0}{c}\right)^2$$

c = concentration
τ = turbidity, defined by $I/I_0 = e^{-\tau l}$
M = molecular weight (above)
B = constant, identical with that of the modified van't Hoff equation
μ_0 = refractive index of solvent
μ = refractive index of solution
λ = wavelength of light
N = Avogadro's number

This equation only holds when the particle size is less than $\frac{1}{20}$ of the wavelength of the primary light. With particles greater than this critical size (e.g., a glucan with a D.P. greater than 50–60), scattering takes place from more than one point of the molecule to give interference and a dissymmetry in the angular distribution of scattered light. Dissymmetry is measured by comparing the scattered light intensity at two angles symmetrical to the 90° position. If the molecular configuration is known, a correction factor for the measured turbidity may be obtained and the molecular weight obtained.

f. Streaming Birefringence (2a, 2b)

In a solution subjected to a velocity gradient, there is a tendency for the particles to align themselves with their long axis parallel to the direction of flow. This results in a difference of refractive index in two directions at right angles. Although it is possible to obtain the molecular weight of polymers by the difference between the two refractive indices, streaming-birefringence measurements are more often used to obtain information on molecular shape. The apparatus for producing the velocity gradient consists of two concentric cylinders, one being stationary while the other rotates.

g. Other Methods

Cryoscopic methods for determination of molecular weights of high polymers are of no practical value because of the small depression of temperature, the sensitiveness of the measurements to low-molecular-weight impurities, and the tendency of the solute molecules to associate. Ultrafiltration through membranes of known pore size and various adaptations of the isopiestic method have been described but they are of limited application.

3. PHYTOPOLYSACCHARIDES (PHYTOGLYCANS)

A. Plant Cell Walls

Polysaccharides are components of almost all living things. They are present in greatest quantity in the higher orders of plants where they constitute approximately three-quarters of the dry weight. The majority of plant polysaccharides are components of the cell walls. In a typical tissue from either an annual or perennial plant, the cell walls consist of three morphologically distinct layers; namely, the intercellular cement, or middle lamella, the primary wall, and the secondary wall, as shown (*41*) in Fig. 2.

The middle lamella or intercellular layer contains cellulose, xylans, uronic acid – containing polysaccharides, and sometimes a mannan. Poly-

41. From H. W. Giertz, *World Paper Trade Rev.* **138,** 1451 (1952).

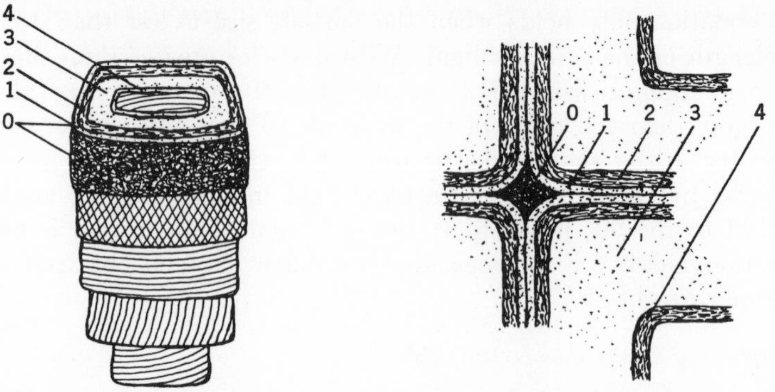
4
3
2
1
0
0 1 2 3 4

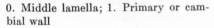

Side view—walls cut away.

Transverse section

0. Middle lamella; 1. Primary or cambial wall

2. Secondary wall: outer layer; 3. Secondary wall: middle layer; 4. Secondary wall: inner spiral layer

FIG. 2. Cell wall and intercellular layer

saccharides composed of pentose sugar units are the most prevalent but still constitute less than 15% of the layer. The most abundant middle lamellar substance is lignin which constitutes more than 70% of the layer. Lignin (*42*) is a three-dimensional, or net, plastic which is rich in aromatic rings and contains such groups as methoxyl, aromatic and aliphatic hydroxyls, and several types of unsaturation. The material may be a polymer in which the basic unit is a phenylpropyl radical:

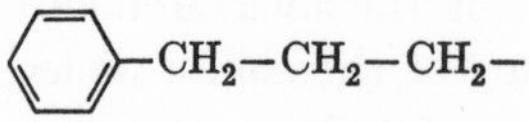
—CH2—CH2—CH2—

The origin of lignin is not known. One hypothesis is that in the aging tissue lignin is built up directly from simple sugars such as sucrose (*43*, *44*). Its postulated formation from pectin or other polysaccharides has never been experimentally verified. (See also p. 548).

The primary wall is a continuous, fairly pliable membrane forming the outside surface of the plant cell. It is about 0.5 micron in thickness and, thus, is only a small part of the cell. It is heavily lignified but is predominantly carbohydrate, with pectin, uronic acid – containing polysaccharides, and xylan or mannan in abundance and with cellulose in lesser amounts. For the most part the very long cellulose molecules are grouped into many fine threads (Fig. 3) which form a meshlike but coherent arrangement. They are intricately woven and mixed with the other polysaccharides,

42. F. E. Brauns, "The Chemistry of Lignin." Academic Press, New York, 1952.

43. M. Phillips and M. J. Gross, *J. Agr. Research* **51**, 301 (1935).

44. M. Phillips, M. J. Gross, B. L. Davis, and H. Stevens, *J. Agr. Research* **59**, 319 (1939).

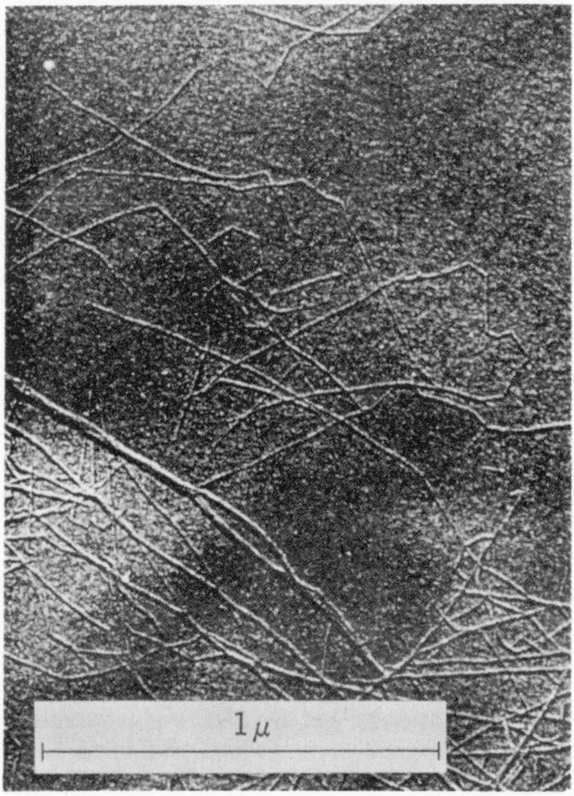
1 μ

FIG. 3. Cellulose threads from Swedish spruce (*45*)

lignin, protein, organic extractives (tannins, terpenes, alkaloids, fats, sterols, and other substances removable from the plant tissue by hot ethanol and benzene), and inorganic salts. The primary wall expands as the cell grows, but with the attainment of final cell size the primary wall may further thicken with the deposition of cellulose to form a laminated structure. In most seeds and many other organs the wall may attain considerable thickness and may contain large amounts of xylan, pectin, and uronic acid containing polysaccharides.

Fibrous and other highly differentiated cells, after their mature size and shape are fully attained, undergo formation of a massive inner or secondary wall. In a few instances, the wall is of a compound nature such as that shown in Fig. 2. Cellulose is the principal component of the secondary wall, but there is present in small amount the other components found in the primary wall. Especially in wood fibers, the secondary wall consists of three layers with the center layer the most massive. From superficial

45. B. G. Rånby, *Svensk Papperstidn.* **55**, 115 (1952).

examination, the massive center secondary wall may appear homogeneous. Closer inspection shows that it consists of a number of very thin concentric lamellae which in turn consist mainly of closely packed cellulose threads arranged more or less parallel and wound at a spiral angle around the fiber axis. Alternate layers are wound in opposite directions and in different spiral angles.

The major nonprotein fibers of commerce—cotton, wood, ramie, flax, hemp, and jute—are all cellulosic fibers. They differ in the amount of lignin, the degree of polymerization and crystallinity of the polysaccharides, and the shape of the fiber (see next section).

a. Cellulose (46, 47)

The individual threads making up the concentric lamellae or ultra-small layers in the cell wall have a diameter of about 77 Å. in wood and about 88 Å. in cotton (*48*). The tiny threads constituting the bulk of the cell wall consist predominantly of cellulose molecules which are themselves threadlike. The molecules are chains of D-glucose units linked uniformly by 1→4 β-D-glycosidic bonds.

In undegraded molecules of cotton cellulose some 3000 or more D-glucose units may be combined to form a chain with an extended length of 15,700 Å. and upward but with a cross-section of only about 4 Å. × 8 Å. These very long thin molecules can be coiled and twisted in numerous ways, but, because of the spacial arrangement between D-glucose units produced by the β-D-1→4 linkage, the chain is somewhat stiff and tends to remain more or less extended. An additional contribution to rigidity may be made by hydrogen-bonding between the oxygen atoms attached to carbon atoms 6 and 2 of the adjacent glucose residues. During their biosynthesis in the plant, the chains are grouped together to form the strings or threads visible with the electron microscope.

As the cellulose molecules are laid together, there are places where they are woven amongst each other in a random fashion, whereas a little farther on they are fitted together in perfectly ordered, crystalline arrangment. The tiny threads are, therefore, composed mainly of cellulose molecules lying roughly parallel but with disordered or amorphous regions mixed with ordered or crystalline regions. On X-ray analysis a pattern is obtained which shows definite arcs from the crystalline regions and a halo from the amorphous regions. The appearance of arcs demonstrates that the crystal-

46. See E. Ott, H. M. Spurlin, and M. W. Grafflin, eds., "Cellulose and Cellulose Derivatives." Interscience, New York, 1954.

47. See: L. E. Wise and E. C. Jahn, eds, "Wood Chemistry," 2nd ed. Reinhold, New York, 1952; A. G. Norman, "The Biochemistry of Cellulose, the Polyuronides, Lignin &c." Oxford U. P., New York, 1937.

48. B. G. Rånby, Ph.D Dissertation, Uppsala, 1952.

line regions are more or less oriented along the long axis of the plant cells. In the crystalline regions, the chains are directed alternately with "heads," in opposite directions. The dimensions of the unit cell are 10.3 Å. in the linear chain direction and 8.35 Å. and 7.9 Å. in the other directions. The unit cell has a length of two D-glucose units or one cellobiose unit.

The mixture of crystalline and amorphous regions give plant fibers their noteworthy physical properties. Within the crystalline regions, the closely packed chains are held together by numerous secondary forces, especially van der Waals' (*ca.* 8000 cal. per mole glucose unit) and hydrogen bonds (*ca.* 15,000 cal. per mole glucose unit). Although each individual hydrogen bond is relatively weak, three such bonds theoretically are possible per glucose unit. In the chain directions, primary valence forces hold the molecule together, the weakest being the carbon-oxygen glucosidic bonds with energies of the order of 50,000 cal. per mole. Plant fibers are consequently immensely strong with the tensile strengths of high grade steel. Even so, the strength of cellulose fibers can be increased by mercerization (treatment with caustic) under tension, a process which causes a reorientation of the chains toward each other.

The secondary bonding forces exert a peculiarly important influence on the reactions of cellulose. Because of the relative stiffness and the dense, tightly bound crystalline regions of cellulose fibers, they can be dissolved only by very energetic solvents, such as cuprammonium solution (copper hydroxide in ammonium hydroxide), which forms a soluble complex with cellulose, or acids such as 42% hydrochloric acid, strong sulfuric or phosphoric acids. Other than in the amorphous regions, cellulose is not very reactive chemically because the reagent molecules only slowly penetrate the crystalline portions. However, under some conditions the crystalline areas can be entered and soluble ethers or esters prepared (see p. 691). Cellulose can be made more reactive by precipitation from solution in an amorphous form or by swelling with alkali or concentrated solutions of certain salts. A thread made by spinning cellulose as it is reprecipitated from solution in cuprammonium is known as cuprammonium rayon or "Bemberg."

Cellulose is decomposed by cellulase enzymes found in germinating seeds, in fungal and bacterial extracts, and in the digestive juices of snails, crustacea, and certain fish (*49*). Enzymes for the utilization of cellulose by termites and ruminants are provided by the microflora of the digestive tracts. In the well-studied cases of cellulose decomposition, the initial degradation has been shown to be a hydrolytic cleavage of the cellulose chains, but further attack of the sugars by living organisms often leads

49. See W. Pigman, *in* "The Enzymes" (J. B. Sumner and K. Myrbäck, eds.), Vol. I, part 2, p. 725. Academic Press, New York, 1952.

to carbon dioxide and acidic materials. Cotton, wood, and other native celluloses exhibit a much greater resistance to enzymic hydrolysis than swollen or regenerated celluloses. For this reason, it has been common to use treated celluloses for measurements of cellulase activity, since the sensitivity is greatly increased (*49*). Karrer used cuprammonium rayon; Pringsheim swelled filter paper with lithium chloride or calcium thiocyanate; Walseth used cotton linters swollen with phosphoric acid; and Helferich and Goerdeler chose cellophane. Soluble, partially substituted celluloses are also being used, although an additional problem is introduced in the effect of the substituent group.

Enzymes, like acids, attack cellulose most rapidly in the amorphous areas and the reaction slows down as these areas are depleted. Striking differences, however, are observed in the courses of the degradations. A considerable portion of the cellulose sample can be degraded by enzymes to soluble fragments with the retention of a relatively high degree of polymerization. For example, Walseth (*50*) found that the degree of polymerization of a swollen cotton cellulose was reduced by enzymes only to about 1000 although there was a 38% loss of weight. The same sample was reduced by acid to a degree of polymerization of 80 with only an 8.3% loss of weight. The attack of each reactant is restricted to accessible areas. Presumably, the smaller molecules (the acid) can penetrate deeper into the cellulose structure. Another dramatic demonstration of the nature of enzymic attack is available in the attack of cotton cloth by mildew. A cotton cloth subjected to the action of the fungus *Chaetomium globosum* did not show a decrease in cuprammonium fluidity (a measure of D.P.), although a loss of 80% of its tensile strength occurred (*49*). In either case, the solubilized portion is rapidly converted to glucose or, in some cases with enzymes, to cellobiose:

$$\text{Cellulose} \xrightarrow{\text{Cellulase}} \text{Cellodextrins} \rightarrow \text{Cellobiose} \xrightarrow{\text{Cellobiase}} \text{D-Glucose}$$

With crude enzymes from *Aspergillus niger* under optimal conditions (for this enzyme, pH 4.5 at 47°C.), Walseth (*50*) was able to degrade a particularly reactive cellulose (preswollen with phosphoric acid) to the extent of 95% and to account for the loss of weight as D-glucose (by reducing-sugar determinations).

During the reaction brought about by some enzymes which have been separated from the crude extracts by fractional precipitation or by chromatographic adsorption, cellobiose rather than glucose accumulates (*49*, *51*).

50. C. S. Walseth, *Tappi* **35**, 228, 233 (1952).

51. D. R. Whitaker, *Arch. Biochem. and Biophys.* **43**, 253 (1953); R. L. Whistler and C. L. Smart, *J. Am. Chem. Soc.* **75**, 1916 (1953); K. Nisizawa and T. Kotayaski, *J. Agr. Chem. Soc. Japan* **27**, 239 (1953); P. Kooiman, P. A. Roelofsen, and S. Sweeris, *Enzymologia* **16**, 237 (1953).

Hence, the presence of glucose as the final product arises in some instances from the presence of a cellobiase, distinct from the cellulase, in the crude preparation. Evidence has been offered also for a random attack at any position in the chain rather than a splitting-off of successive small units from the end of the chains (*52*). Reese and co-workers (*53*) suggest that several enzymes take part in the degradation, the first of which is demonstrated, in the case of cotton, by its ability to attack the primary wall and, thus, to make the cellulose chains more available to hydrolytic attack (*54*).

In the decomposition of wood by enzymes, the reaction may proceed as an attack on the lignin or on the carbohydrate fraction. The so-called "white rots" of wood are believed to arise from fungal attack mainly on the lignin component, whereas the "brown rots" may result when the principal attack takes place on the carbohydrate fraction (*49*, *55*).

b. Hemicelluloses and Other Cell-Wall Polysaccharides (*46*)

Interlaced with cellulose in the primary and secondary walls are a number of other polysaccharides. Most of them are more soluble than cellulose even though they are held in the complex cellulose matrix by abundant secondary forces and by mechanical entanglements and entrapments. Polysaccharides extractable from the cell walls by alkaline solutions, such as 17.5% sodium hydroxide solution, are called hemicelluloses. (Cellulose is swollen, but not dissolved, by strong alkali.) The name hemicellulose was proposed in 1891 by Schulze (*56*), who was examining products extracted from leguminous seeds, brans, and green tissues. It was assumed that the easily extractable polysaccharides were destined for conversion to cellulose, and, thus, the name hemicellulose seemed appropriate. Today it is known that these polysaccharides are not precursors of cellulose. They are a group of unrelated polysaccharides which vary in amount and kind from plant to plant and even from tissue to tissue within the same plant. They consist of acidic and neutral molecules, some of low molecular weight and some of such high molecular weight that they are not easily extracted by strongly alkaline solutions. It is perhaps unfortunate that such a di-

52. See B. Norkrans, *Physiol. Plantarum* **3,** 75 (1950); *Symbolae Botan. Upsalienses* **11,** 1 (1950); J. H. Hash and K. W. King, *Science* **120,** 1033 (1954).

53. E. T. Reese and W. Gilligan, *Textile Research J.* **24,** 663 (1954); W. Gilligan and E. T. Reese, *Can. J. Microbiol.* **1,** 90 (1954); E. T. Reese and H. S. Levinson, *Physiol. Plantarum* **5,** 345 (1952); E. T. Reese, W. Gilligan, and B. Norkrans, *Physiol. Plantarum* **5,** 379 (1952); H. S. Levinson, G. R. Mandels, and E. T. Reese, *Arch. Biochem. and Biophys.* **31,** 351 (1951).

54. See also: P. B. Marsh, K. Bollenbacher, M. L. Butler, and L. R. Guthrie, *Textile Research J.* **23,** 878 (1953).

55. See: G. Fåhraeus, R. Nilsson, and G. Nilsson, *Svensk Botan. Tidskr.* **43,** 343 (1949).

56. E. Schulze, *Ber.* **24,** 2277 (1891); *Z. physiol. Chem.* **16,** 387 (1892).

TABLE II
PARTIAL ANALYSIS OF SOME WOODS AND PLANT TISSUES (*1*)

Tissue	Cellulose (%)	Pentosan (%)	Lignin (%)
Pine (Western yellow and white)	58	7	27
Yellow cedar	54	8	31
Redwood	48	8	34
White spruce	53	12	28
Mesquite	46	14	31
Hickory	56	19	23
Wheat straw	48	27	18
Corn stalk	40	26	16
Cottonseed hulls	35	21	17
Cotton fiber	98	<0.5	0

vergent mixture of polysaccharides are classified together, and it is entirely likely that the term hemicellulose will eventually be dropped, particularly once the individual polysaccharides are isolated and clearly identified.

Some of the pentosans from wastes which accumulate in the processing of agricultural products are converted by acids to furfural, a raw material of increasing industrial value and interest. These and other waste hemicelluloses such as those obtained from the pulping of wood represents a rich, almost untapped, source of raw material, much of which could be converted from a nuisance to a source of profit. (See also p. 799.)

Xylans. By far the most abundant polysaccharides in the hemicellulose group are the xylans (hemicellulose-A). These pentosans are composed either entirely or almost entirely of D-xylose units. Several types of xylans are extractable from different plant sources. Some are linear molecules, some contain one or more branches, and in some are combined one or more L-arabinose or D-glucuronic acid units. Xylans occur in practically all land plants and are present in some marine algae (*57*, *58*). They are most abundant in annual crops, particularly in agricultural residues such as corncobs, corn stalks, grain hulls, and stems. Here they occur in amounts ranging from 15 to 30%. Hardwoods contain 20 to 25% xylans whereas softwoods contain 7 to 12%. Spring wood has more pentosan than summer wood. Since xylans are the most abundant of the pentosans, their distribution is indicated by pentosan analysis. Although cellulose, pentosans, and lignin are the most abundant substances in plants, their relative amounts vary greatly from one plant tissue to another (Table II).

Xylan is precipitated on neutralization of an alkaline plant extract.

57. V. C. Barry and T. Dillon, *Nature* **146,** 620 (1940).
58. E. G. V. Percival and S. K. Chanda, *Nature* **166,** 787 (1950).

Purification is attained by redissolution in dilute sodium or potassium hydroxide solution and reprecipitation by addition of acid to pH 4.2 or of cold Fehling's solution. To avoid difficulties with lignin a delignified plant material is usually used for the initial alkaline extraction. After purification in this manner, the xylans are obtained as amorphous powders. However, Yundt (*59*) was able to obtain the xylans from barley straw and birch holocellulose in crystalline form after a mild degradation produced by autoclaving for 4 hours at 120° and pH 4.0. The crystalline polymers had a degree of polymerization of 35 to 39 (by end-group assay and by the osmotic pressure of a chloroform solution of the methyl derivative). Dry crystals showed double refraction and sharp X-ray diffraction patterns. Moist crystals (10 to 15% water) showed less sharp maxima and increased spacings, indicative of a distortion of the crystal lattices by a penetration of water molecules. Molar rotational shifts in the optical activity of cuprammonium solutions (after the method of Reeves) indicated that the polymers were essentially 1→4′-β-linked xylopyranose units. These crystalline xylans are hydrolyzed rapidly although incompletely by the enzymes of *Aspergillus niger*. The ultimate degree of hydrolysis depends upon the method used for the dispersion of the xylan. Retrogradation similar to that of the amylose of starch was noted.

From corncobs also, a xylan (*60, 61*) is obtained which is a linear chain of D-xylopyranose units connected by β-D-1→4 bonds:

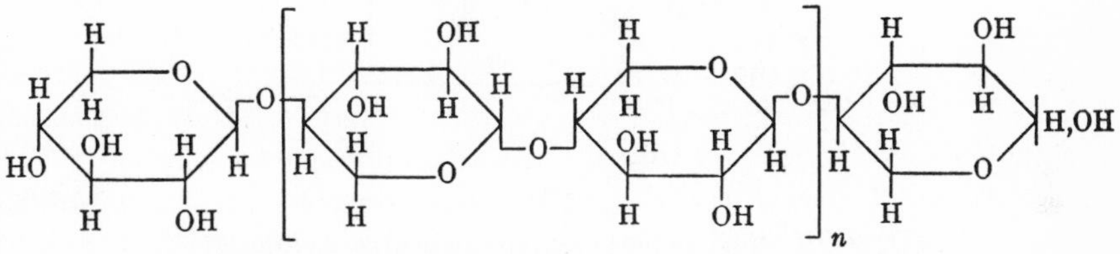

Thus, the molecule is identical in construction to cellulose with the exceptions that each ring unit lacks a projecting primary alcohol group and the molecular weight is low, not exceeding 30,000 (200 sugar units). The enzymes from *Aspergillus foetidus* have been separated into three components: one hydrolyzes corncob xylan primarily to xylobiose with no production of xylose; another hydrolyzes the xylan and xylooligosaccharides to D-xylose without the production of significant amounts of transient oligosaccharides; and a third hydrolyzes the xylan to a mixture of D-xylose and xylooligosaccharides (*62*).

59. A. P. Yundt, *Tappi* **34,** 89, 91, 92 (1951); see also C. T. Bishop, *Can. J. Chem.* **33,** 793 (1953).
60. R. L. Whistler, J. Bachrach, and D. R. Bowman, *Arch. Biochem.* **19,** 25 (1948).
61. R. L. Whistler and C. C. Tu, *J. Am. Chem. Soc.* **74,** 3609 (1952); **75,** 645 (1953).
62. R. L. Whistler and E. Masak, Jr., *J. Am. Chem. Soc.* **77,** 1241 (1955).

A xylan from esparto grass (*63*, *64*) is a singly branched chain of about 75 D-xylopyranose units linked β-D-1→4 in the main chain but with a 1→3 link at the point of branching. From the cell wall of pear wood, another similarly single-branched xylan is obtained which has about 115 D-xylopyranose units, but it contains, in addition, a terminal D-glucopyranosyluronic acid unit at one point (*65*). The xylan from the red seaweed (*57*, *58*) *Rhodymenia palmata* seems to be composed only of D-xylopyranose units

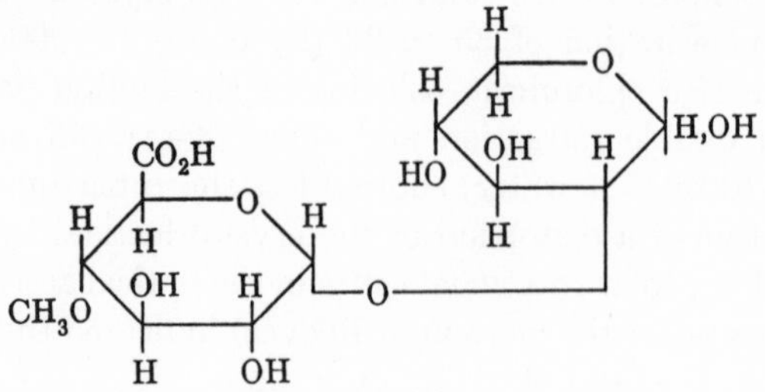

(I)

(I) 2-*O*-(4-*O*-Methyl-α-D-glucopyranosyluronic acid)-D-xylose (*66*)

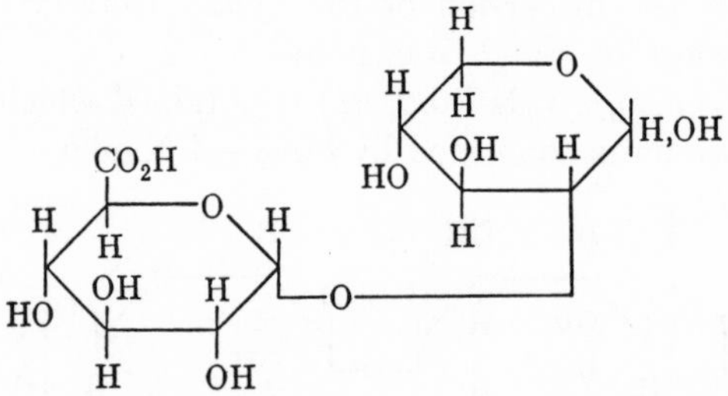

(II)

(II) 2-*O*-(α-D-Glucopyranosyluronic acid)-D-xylose (*67*)

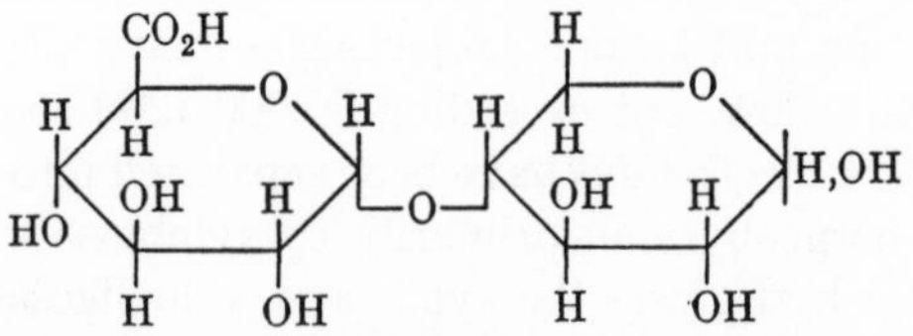

(III)

(III) 4-*O*-(α-D-Glucopyranosyluronic acid)-D-xylose (*67*)

63. S. K. Chanda, E. L. Hirst, J. K. N. Jones, and E. G. V. Percival, *J. Chem. Soc.* p. 1289 (1950).

64. S. K. Chanda, E. E. Percival, and E. G. V. Percival, *J. Chem. Soc.* p. 260 (1952).

65. S. K. Chanda, E. L. Hirst, and E. G. V. Percival, *J. Chem. Soc.* p. 1240 (1951).

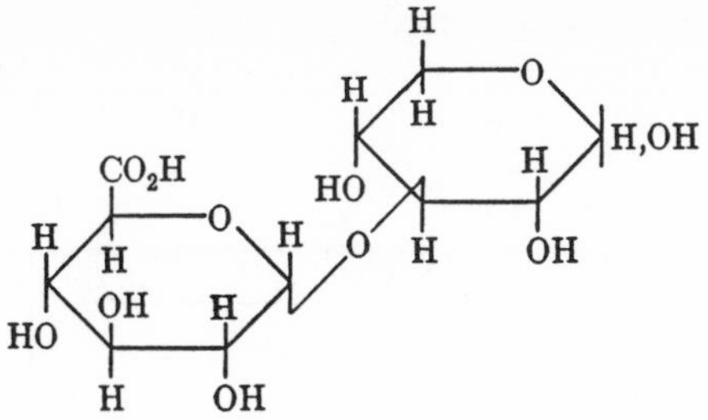

(IV)

(IV) 3-*O*-(α-D-Glucopyranosyluronic acid)-D-xylose (*65, 68*)

but has 1→3 and 1→4 linkages in the ratio of about 1:3. A xylan from wheat straw may be a chain of about 40 D-xylopyranose units to which are attached about 5 L-arabofuranose units and 3 D-glucuronic acid units (*69*). A polysaccharide extractable by water from wheat flour appears to be a chain of D-xylopyranose units linked by β-D-1→4 links with single L-arabofuranose units substituted along the chain and joined by 1→2 and 1→3 links (*70*). The L-arabinose and D-xylose units are present in the ratio of 3:5.

Acidic Hemicelluloses. After xylans are precipitated from an alkaline plant extract by neutralization, there remains dissolved a group of low-molecular-weight acidic polysaccharides. The acidic nature results from D-glucuronic acid units. Although the structures of these hemicelluloses (hemicellulose-B) are not fully known, it is apparent that D-glucuronic acid units are connected in a variety of ways to chains of D-xylopyranose units. The disaccharides (aldobiouronic acids) shown in formulas (I) to (IV) were isolated by partial acid hydrolysis of the hemicellulose and show the varied nature of the linkages which connect the D-glucuronic acid to the chain as a terminal unit. Sometimes the uronic acid unit is methylated, with the methyl ether group always at C-4. (For a further listing see Chapter VI.)

Mannans. A variety of other polysaccharides may occur in the cell walls of land plants. Among these are mannans, galactans, and pectic substances. In general, softwoods contain approximately 11% combined D-mannose, whereas hardwoods contain only about 1%. A linear mannan is also the chief constituent of the thickened cell walls of palm seeds, where it occurs as a food reserve and disappears on germination. A rich source is the endosperm of the tagua palm which is known as vegetable ivory and from which buttons have been made. This mannan is a linear chain of D-mannopyranose

66. R. L. Whistler, H. E. Conrad, and L. Hough, *J. Am. Chem. Soc.* **76,** 1668 (1954).
67. R. L. Whistler and L. Hough, *J. Am. Chem. Soc.* **75,** 4918 (1953).
68. G. A. Adams, *Can. J. Chem.* **30,** 698 (1952); C. T. Bishop, *ibid.* **31,** 134 (1953).
69. G. A. Adams and A. E. Castagne, *Can. J. Chem.* **29,** 109 (1951).
70. A. S. Perlin, *Cereal Chem.* **28,** 382 (1951).

units linked by β-1→4 bonds (*71*):

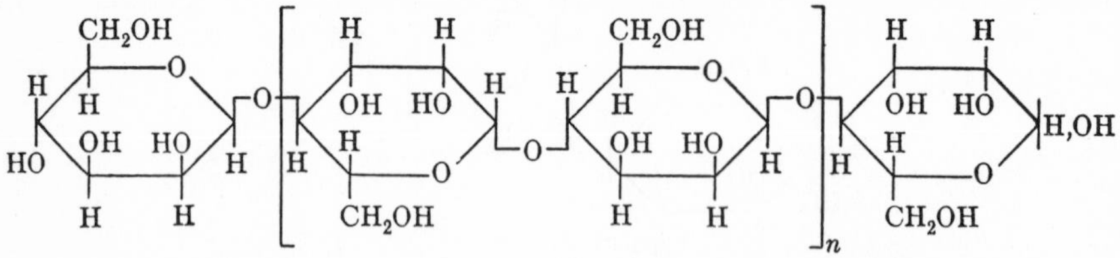

A similar substance (*72*, *73*) found in the tubers of orchids is salep mannan. Yet another similar, though perhaps slightly branched, mannan occurs (*74*) abundantly in the red alga *Porphyra umbilicalis*, a commercial seaweed harvested as a food in the British Isles, Hawaii, Japan, and elsewhere. These mannans of higher plants are quite different from the highly branched mannan of yeast, known as yeast gum (*75*), which contains 1→2, 1→3, and 1→6 linkages. A mannan from *Torula utilis* grown on a synthetic medium containing D-glucose-1-C^{14} as the sole source of carbon showed no radioactivity (*76*).

Pectic Substances (*46*, *77*). An important group of substances commonly called pectins is found in the primary cell wall and intercellular layers of all land plants, and, in some ways, seems to correspond to the hyaluronic acid of the ground substance of much animal tissue. Because of the immense gelling power of pectic substances, they are widely used for the gelation of fruit juices to form jellies.

The content of pectic substance in woody tissues is low because the volume of the pectic-containing layers is small. However, it occurs in fairly large amounts (10%) in the inner bark of black spruce (*78*). In soft tissues, like those of apple and other fruits devoid of secondary walls, the primary walls and middle lamella constitute a higher proportion of the total tissue, and the content of pectic substances is proportionately large. They are abundant in the rinds of citrus fruit, from which they are extracted as a by-product of citrus fruit production. Extraction is made usually with dilute hydrochloric acid solution. Crystalline salts of galacturonic acid have been

71. F. Klages, *Ann.* **509,** 159 (1934); **512,** 185 (1934).

72. H. Pringsheim and A. Genin, *Z. physiol. Chem.* **140,** 299 (1924).

73. F. Klages and R. Maurenbrecher, *Ann.* **535,** 175 (1938).

74. J. K. N. Jones, *J. Chem. Soc.* p. 3292 (1950).

75. E. Salkowski, *Ber.* **27,** 496 (1894); W. N. Haworth, R. L. Heath, and S. Peat, *J. Chem. Soc.* p. 833 (1941).

76. J. C. Sowden, S. Frankel, B. H. Moore, and J. E. McClary, *J. Biol. Chem.* **206,** 547 (1954).

77. See E. L. Hirst and J. K. N. Jones, *Advances in Carbohydrate Chem.* **2,** 235 (1946).

78. W. Pigman, E. Anderson, and R. L. Leaf, Jr., *J. Am. Chem. Soc.* **70,** 432 (1948).

isolated after the action of enzymes both on the citrus and on the spruce pectins (*78*).

Pectic substances are a mixture of three polysaccharides: a galactan, the methyl ester of a galacturonan, and an araban. The latter is of relatively low molecular weight and apparently is a chain of 1→5 linked α-L-arabofuranose units, half of which bear an additional 1→3 linked α-L-arabofuranose residue as a one-unit side chain. The galactan seems to be a chain of some 120 D-galactopyranose units united to one another by 1→4 β-links. In part, the molecules are mechanically mixed, and in part they are combined by primary links of unknown nature. Experimental evidence indicates that many of the prominent properties of pectin such as gelation, film formation, and high viscosity are derived principally from the galacturonan chain and that araban and galactan act mainly as diluents.

Pectins dispersed in water exist as negatively charged hydrophilic colloids stabilized by water layers held by the negative electrostatic fields. Addition of sugar decreases the stability of the pectin because the dehydrating action of the sugar disturbs the water bound to the pectin. Added hydrogen ions further upset the bonding by reducing the negative charge on the pectin. Consequently, a gel forms as a result of the tendency of aggregations of pectin molecules to crystallize. The gel consists of a giant ramified network of partially associated, partially hydrated micella. A second type of gel is formed when calcium or other divalent ions are added, for they may cross-link chains through ionic linkages between carboxyl groups.

The properties of pectic substances are altered by partial or complete demethylation, which increases the number of free carboxyl groups. Pectic acid is the completely demethylated galacturonan. It is a linear chain of 1→4 linked α-D-galactopyranosyluronic acid units.

Pectic enzymes (*79, 80*) are divided into two general classes: pectases and pectinases. The pectases hydrolyze the methyl ester group, whereas the pectinases cleave glycosidic links. The chains are attacked randomly, but more than one enzyme system may be involved (*81*). For instance, purified yeast polygalacturonase depolymerizes pectic acid to galacturonic acid (16%) and di- and trigalacturonic acids, whereas fungal polygalacturonase converts the oligosaccharides to monomers (*82*). Polymethylgalacturonase hydrolyzes pectin to a mixture of polymeric products, the cleavage amounting to about 26% of total hydrolysis. Similarly, an extracellular enzyme

79. See Z. I. Kertesz, *in* "The Enzymes" (J. B. Sumner and K. Myrbäck, eds.) Vol. I, Part 2, p. 745. Academic Press, New York, 1951.

80. W. W. Reid, *J. Sc. Food Agr.* **1,** 234 (1950).

81. E. Schubert, *Biochem. Z.* **323,** 78 (1952).

82. B. S. Luh and H. J. Phaff, *Arch. Biochem. and Biophys.* **33,** 212 (1951); H. J. Phaff and B. S. Luh, *ibid.* **36,** 231 (1952).

from *Neurospora crassa* fragments pectin to a molecular weight of about 4,000 (*83*).

B. Plant Reserve Foods

Plants store polysaccharides as food reserve in all types of cell but primarily in special storage cells or organs such as parenchymous cells or roots, tubers, and pith. The most important of these food reserves are starches, fructans, mannans, and galactomannans. The mannans are sometimes food reserves and sometimes structural material in the plant cell wall. In animals the chief reserve polysaccharide is glycogen, which in chemical structure is much like one of the components of starch (see Part II of this chapter.).

a. Starches (*84*, *85*)

Within the protoplast of many plant cells are inclusions in the form of starch granules. These granules are the principal food reserves of plants and are, hence, most abundant in such storage organs as seeds, which may contain as much as 70% starch, and fruits, tubers, roots, and stem pith, which may contain as much as 30%. Starches are unique among the carbohydrates in occurring as discrete granules, whose characteristics vary from one plant source to another. Canna and potato starches are among those with the largest granules whereas rice, buckwheat, and dasheen are representative of the smaller granule types. In most granules there is a spot or intersection of two or more lines or creases (see Fig. 4). This point of intersection, termed the hilum, is sometimes surrounded by rings or onionlike laminated structures. In polarized light, granules are anisotropic, showing a dark cross which has its intersection at the hilum.

Starches can be obtained from most plants by filtering the pulped or rough-ground plant on coarse cloth and centrifuging or settling the starch granules from the filtrate. They may be distinguished by an examination of the size and shape of the granules (Fig. 4), the temperatures at which they gelatinize in water, the rate of swelling in various solvents, the degree of isotropism evident in polarized light, and the extent to which they combine with iodine.

Starch granules are largely composed of carbohydrate but contain minor constituents, which may influence the properties of the granules. Cereal starches usually contain 0.5 to 1% fatty acids. These acids are adsorbed on

83. E. Roboz, R. W. Barrett, and E. L. Tatum, *J. Biol. Chem.* **195**, 459 (1952).

84. See R. W. Kerr, ed., "Chemistry and Industry of Starch," 2nd Ed. Academic Press, New York, 1950.

85. See J. A. Radley, "Starch and its Derivatives." Chapman and Hall, London, 1953.

the carbohydrate and may be completely removed by extraction with suitable organic solvents. Phosphorus in amounts of 0.01 to 0.2% may also be present in starch granules. In corn, wheat, and rice starches, the phosphorus may be removed by extraction with warm water and alcohol and seems to be present as glycerol monophosphate. In other starches, such as potato, arrowroot, tapioca, and sago, the phosphorus is bound as esterified phosphate at carbon atom 6 of the various D-glucose units.

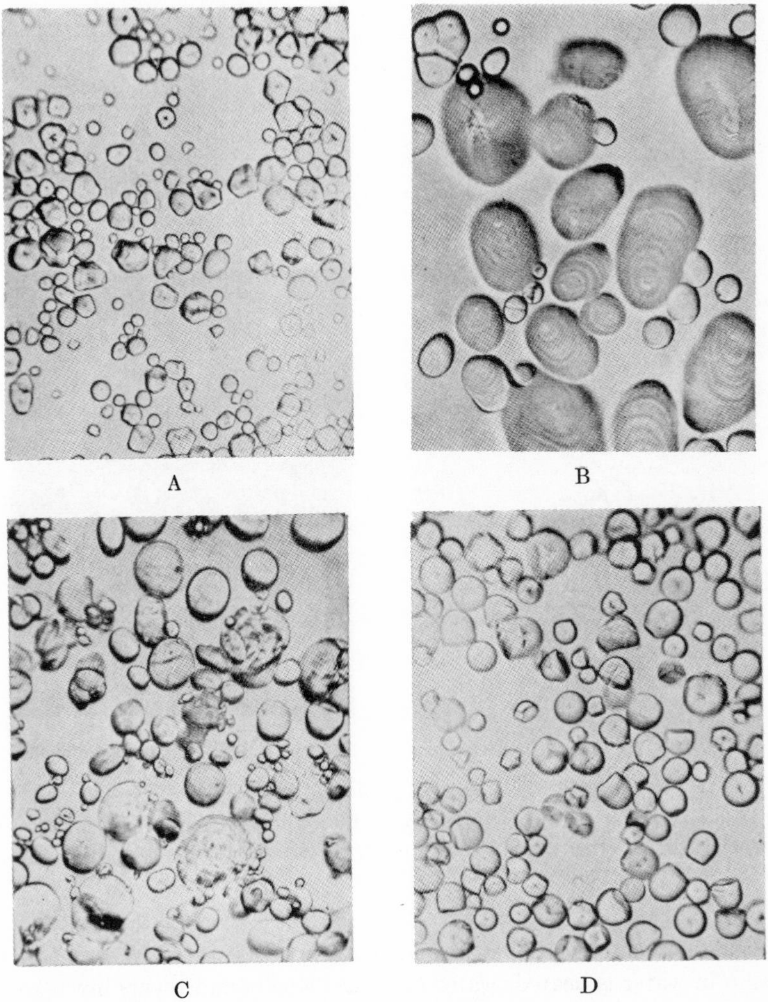
A
B
C
D

FIG. 4. Microphotographs of starch granules (× 200)
A. Corn starch. B. Potato starch. C. Wheat starch. D. Tapioca starch.

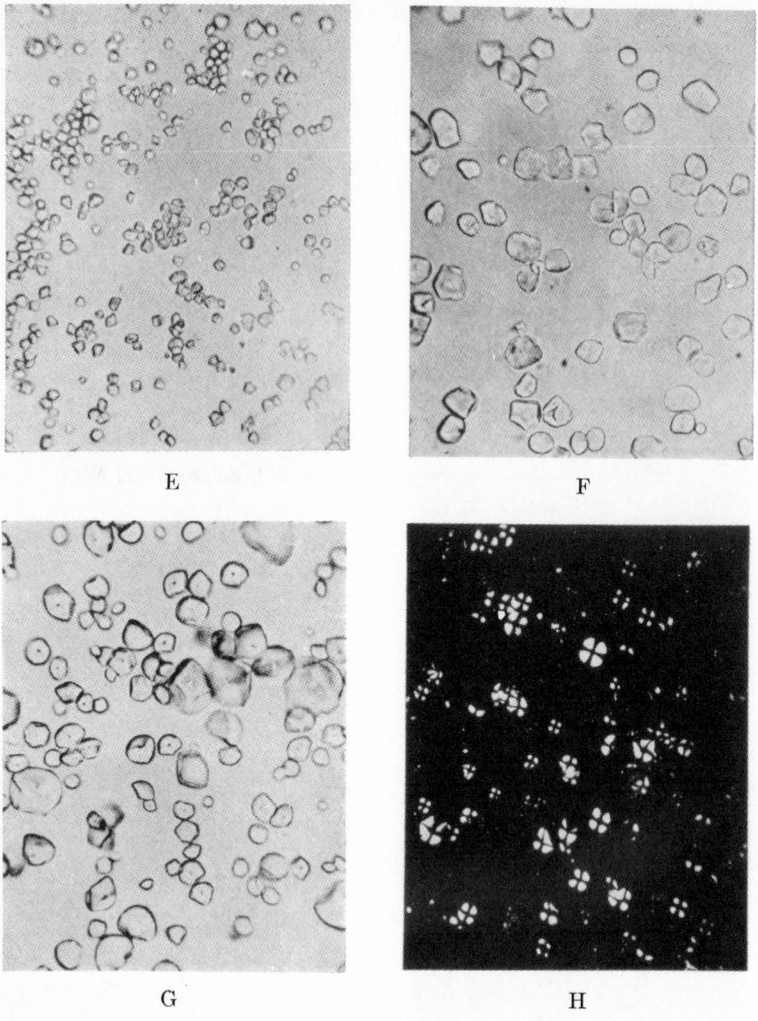

FIG. 4. (*Continued*)

E. Rice starch. F. Waxy maize starch. G. Sweet potato starch. H. Tapioca starch in polarized light. (Reproduced from "Chemistry and Industry of Starch" (R. W. Kerr, ed.), 2nd ed. Academic Press, 1950.)

Unmodified starch granules are insoluble in cold water. When their suspension in water is heated, water is at first slowly and reversibly taken up and limited swelling occurs. Then, at a definite temperature, which is distinctive for different types of starch (64 to 71° for corn starch; 82 to 83° for sweet potato starch), the granules undergo irreversibly a sudden rapid swelling and at the same time lose their birefringence. Because they swell to several hundred times their original volume, the viscosity of the suspension increases greatly. A small amount of starch diffuses from the granule into the solution. As the temperature of the suspension is raised, the final phase of the reaction is indicated by a more rapid diffusion of starch from some granules and by a rupture of others, leaving numerous formless sacs which are presumed to be artifacts of the swelling process.

The chief nonfood uses of starch depend on its ability to form pastes. Starch pastes are complicated colloidal systems, in which there are present not only highly swollen granules but free starch molecules, the empty granule sacs, and aggregates leached or spewed from the swollen granules. Because of the differences in the size and form of the granules, starches from different sources may vary greatly as to the type of paste which they produce even when they are of almost identical chemical composition.

Starches also differ in their chemical composition. They are not single substances, but, except in rare instances, are mixtures of two structurally different polysaccharides. One is a linear molecule termed amylose, and the other is a branched or bush-shaped structure termed amylopectin. Both are composed of D-glucopyranose units. In amylose 250 to 300 units are uniformly linked by 1→4 α-glucosidic bonds, which tend to induce a spiraling of the molecule in a helix-like fashion. In amylopectin the majority of the units are connected 1→4 with α-links, but there are 1→6 α-glycosidic bonds (amounting to about 4% of the total) at the branch points. The structure is a branch-on-branch arrangement of a thousand or more D-glucopyranose units similar to arrangement *D* shown in Fig. 1. There is an average of about one branch for approximately every 25 glucose units. The position of branching has been difficult to establish with certainty because of the low percentage of the 1→6 links. The assignment of the 1→6 position was made from methylation data. This linkage was confirmed later by the isolation of a 1→6 α-linked disaccharide, isomaltose, from enzymic hydrolyzates prepared under conditions such that enzymic synthesis was thought to be precluded (*86*). Isomaltose has also been isolated from acid hydrolyzates in amounts greater than were made by reversion in control experiments (*87*).

Separation (*88*) of amylose and amylopectin can be made by adding to a hot starch dispersion certain agents such as butanol, nitropropane, nitrobenzene, and thymol, which form a complex with amylose and cause it to

86. E. M. Montgomery, F. B. Weakley, and G. E. Hilbert, *J. Am. Chem. Soc.* **69,** 2249 (1947); **71,** 1682 (1949).

87. M. L. Wolfrom, J. T. Tyree, T. T. Galkowski, and A. N. O'Neill, *J. Am. Chem. Soc.* **72,** 1427 (1950); **73,** 4927 (1951).

88. T. J. Schoch, *Cereal Chem.* **18,** 121 (1941); E. J. Wilson, Jr., T. J. Schoch, and C. S. Hudson, *J. Am. Chem. Soc.* **65,** 1320 (1943); R. L. Whistler and G. E. Hilbert, *J. Am. Chem. Soc.* **67,** 1161 (1945).

precipitate in semicrystalline form. The amylose complex is collected by centrifugation, and the amylose is regenerated by washing with ethanol. Traces of residual amylose are removed from the amylopectin fractions by adsorption on cotton.

The quantity of amylose may be determined in starches or other mixtures by a characteristic reaction with iodine. Amylose combines with iodine to form a deep-blue complex, which is responsible for the color of starch indicators. Amylopectin solutions are colored blue-violet or purple. The intensity of the amylose–iodine complex can be measured in a spectrophotometer, or titrimetric measurements can be made of the amount of iodine taken up in forming the amylose–iodine complex.

Amylose chains differ from cellulose in that the 1→4 glycosidic linkages are of the α-D- rather than of the β-D-type. This difference is reflected in the tendency of amylose chains to coil in contrast to the linear extension of the chains in the cellulose model. Evidence indicates that a chair conformation (C1, see Chapter I) is the usual conformation for glucopyranosides in cellulose, sucrose, and many simple glycosides. However, steric hindrance occurs when attempts are made to join scale models of D-glucopyranose units through 1→4 α-glycosidic links. Boat conformations B1 and 3B seem most likely from steric considerations. Only one of these (3B) has the hydroxyls projected at angles such that complexing with cuprammonium would be expected. Amylose, in contrast to cellulose, does not dissolve in cuprammonium, but undergoes swelling. If it is dissolved in alkali, however, cuprammonium can be added with the formation of the clear deep-blue solution, typical of cuprammonium complexes. Reeves (*89*) has suggested that during the alkali treatment a change in ring conformation may take place, the change being from a mixture of B1 and 3B to all 3B, the ring conformation originally suggested by Freudenberg and Cramer.

The majority of starches have nearly identical ratios of amylose to amylopectin. The most prevalent composition—found in corn, wheat, arrowroot, potato starches, etc.—is 20 to 28% amylose and 72 to 80% amylopectin. So-called waxy or glutinous starches from waxy varieties of corn, sorghum, rice, barley, and millet contain only amylopectin, or if amylose is present it is so in amounts of not more than about 6%. On the other hand, a few starches, such as special mutant varieties of corn, are known that contain up to 65 to 77% amylose (*90*).

The relative amounts of amylose and amylopectin are significant in relationship to the application of a starch. The two forms differ markedly with regard to enzymic cleavage (see below) and with regard to "retrogradation," a term applied to the reassociation which takes place between starch

89. R. E. Reeves, *J. Am. Chem. Soc.* **76,** 4595 (1954).
90. G. M. Dunn, H. H. Kramer, and R. L. Whistler, *Agronomy J.* **45,** 101 (1953).

molecules in solution. As retrogradation takes place, starch solutions become increasingly cloudy, increasingly resistant to enzyme action, and lower in viscosity. Finally, they undergo precipitation. Amylose molecules, because of their linear nature, can coalesce and, hence, retrograde much more readily than the branched or bush-shaped amylopectin molecules. Whole starches retrograde at an intermediate rate and differ from each other in various physical properties (*91*). Some of the starches, such as white potato, sweet potato, and tapioca, undergo a partial fractionation by an initial preferential precipitation of amylose. Waxy corn starch, which is a low-molecular-weight amylopectin, retrogrades extremely slowly.

Retrogradation effects are encountered in industrial pastes as well as in the more familiar puddings and gravies. Retrogradation may also be an important factor in the hardening of bread as it becomes stale. Anti-staling agents (*92*) used in dough mixes are retrogradation inhibitors.

Techniques for the separation of amylose and amylopectin have not been developed to commercial feasibility. Instead, selections and improvements of the starch source are made. Waxy corn has been developed especially to provide a starch free of the difficulties, particularly retrogradation, caused by amylose.

The physical properties of starch suspensions and starch gels may also be greatly altered by modifying the starch in a variety of ways such as by oxidation, by heating (partial pyrolysis), and by hydrolysis with acids or enzymes (*93*). When a loss of viscosity has been produced without disruption of granules, the products are "thin-boiling starches." More highly degraded starches are called dextrins and are without granule structure. The decrease in chain length is attended by increased solubility and, hence, a lowered speed of retrogradation. Adhesiveness may also be improved. For Lintner soluble starch, the size of the molecule is decreased by a mild acid hydrolysis; for Zulkowsky starch, the modification is effected by heating the starch with glycerol at 190°. "British gums" or "Torrefaction dextrins" are produced by a high-temperature treatment. Oxidized starches and dextrins are discussed in more detail in a later section (p. 696). In the textile industry, starches and modified starches are employed for sizing yarns to protect them during the weaving operations, for sizing finished goods to improve appearance, and for thickening printing pastes. In paper manufacture, starch is added to the pulp in the beater to assist in hydration of the fibers and to cause them to adhere more closely; in addition, starches may be applied to finished sheets as a part of a surface coating generally

91. R. L. Whistler and C. Johnson, *Cereal Chem.* **25**, 418 (1948).

92. E. C. Edelmann, W. H. Cathcart, and C. B. Berquist, *Cereal Chem.* **27**, 1 (1950); B. G. Carson, L. F. Marrett, and R. W. Selman, *Cereal Chem.* **27**, 438 (1950).

93. See W. W. Pigman, R. W. Kerr, and N. F. Schink, *U. S. Patent*, 2,609,326 (1952).

along with clay or other pigments. In box manufacturing, starch adhesives are widely used.

The long linear chain structure of amylose is reflected in the film-forming properties of its acetate. Films prepared from acetylated whole starch and amylopectin are quite brittle, whereas those from butanol-precipitated amylose are similar to films from high-grade cellulose acetates (*94*).

A little more than half of the starch consumed in the United States is degraded to low-molecular-weight compounds by acid hydrolysis. A high degree of conversion to D-glucose (dextrose) may be brought about and the crystalline sugar isolated, or the hydrolysis may be stopped at an earlier stage and the corn sirup marketed. Large quantities of these products find application in bakery products, jams, ice cream, jellies, and miscellaneous uses.

In preparing derivatives of whole starch, the granules are reacted directly only at the risk of extensive degradation. Consequently, it is desirable to swell or disorganize the granules by some type of pretreatment employing either water, aqueous chloral hydrate, aqueous pyridine, formamide, or alkali. A readily reactive form of whole starches or of the components is obtained by precipitation of their aqueous solutions with ethanol.

Much of the present concept of the structures of amylose and amylopectin was arrived at through a study of the degradation of starch by enzymes (*95*). Starch enzymes are biologically important from their function of supplying carbohydrate for the metabolic needs of plants and animals. Amylases also have great industrial significance, for they are involved in the preparation of industrial and beverage alcohol from grains, in bread making, in the preparation of certain textile sizes, adhesives, etc., and in desizing operations.

Liquefying (α-) amylases are found with great frequency in plants. The enzymes of the pancreas (pancreatic amylase or amylopsin), saliva (salivary amylase or ptyalin), and many bacteria have similar actions. The dormant grains usually are much richer in the saccharogenic (β-) amylase than in the liquefying (α-) amylase. On germination, however, α-amylase increases rapidly during the early phases of growth. If both α- and β-amylases are present in the seed during germination, the liquefying activity develops more rapidly than the saccharifying ability. The best sources of the saccharogenic enzymes are ungerminated soybeans, potatoes, rye, barley, and wheat, whereas malted preparations from sorghum, maize, and oats are said to contain only the liquefying amylase. It is possible to inactivate either

94. R. L. Whistler and G. E. Hilbert, *Ind. Eng. Chem.* **36,** 796 (1944).

95. For a review of the amylases, see K. Myrbäck and G. Neumüller *in* "The Enzymes" (J. B. Sumner and K. Myrbäck, eds.), Vol. 1, Part 1, p. 653. Academic Press, New York, 1950. Several reviews are given in the *Advances in Carbohydrate Chem.*

of the enzyme types in a mixture with retention of the activity of the other. For example, malt α-amylase is rapidly inactivated by acids at room temperature in contrast to malt β-amylase, which is resistant to short acid treatments. On the other hand, malt β-amylase is rapidly inactivated by heat at 70° while malt α-amylase is resistant to a short heat treatment at 70°. The malt β-amylase is more readily inactivated if calcium ions are added.

Several of the amylases have been isolated in crystalline and apparently pure form. These include salivary, pancreatic, bacterial, and malt α-amylases and sweet potato β-amylase (*96*).

Amylases (also known as diastases) attack intact starch granules only with difficulty. A probable explanation is that the rate is slow because the reaction is heterogeneous in nature and because the granules are not penetrated by the enzyme. Consequently, it is generally the practice to gelatinize (cook) the starch before the addition of much if any of the enzyme. Industrially, the addition of a portion of malt or liquefying amylase during the cooking process may be advantageous to decrease the difficulty of handling.

The most readily demonstrated characteristics of the liquefying or α-amylases and the saccharifying or β-amylases are signified by their names. The action of the liquefying enzyme consists of a fast phase and a slow phase. There is a very rapid drop in viscosity accompanied by a comparatively small increase in reducing power (formation of low-molecular-weight dextrins) and followed by a slow appearance of fermentable sugars. The name α was derived from the downward mutarotation of the products. The saccharifying or β-amylases, on the other hand, cleave starch in such a manner as to increase the reducing power rapidly and to produce fermentable sugars with only a slow decrease in viscosity. The products from this reaction mutarotate upward.

The high yields of maltose obtained by the action of β-amylases on amylose (*97*), which has a straight-chain structure, suggest that these enzymes act by a continuous process of cleavage of the maltose groups from the ends of the chain. Although short amylose-like chains consisting of four to eight D-glucose residues are readily converted to maltose, the β-amylases do not hydrolyze maltotriose (*98*). Evidence that the maltose is cleaved from the

96. A. K. Balls, R. R. Thompson, and M. K. Walden, *J. Biol. Chem.* **163,** 571 (1946); A. K. Balls, M. K. Walden, and R. R. Thompson, *U. S. Patent,* 2,496,261 (1951); K. H. Meyer, E. H. Fischer, and P. Bernfeld, *Experientia* **3,** 106, 455 (1947); S. Schwimmer and A. K. Balls, *J. Biol. Chem.* **179,** 1063 (1949).

97. K. H. Meyer, W. Brentano, and P. Bernfeld, *Helv. Chim. Acta* **23,** 845 (1940); M. Samec, *Z. physiol. Chem.* **236,** 103 (1935).

98. K. Myrbäck and K. Ahlborg, *Biochem. Z.* **311,** 213 (1942); M. A. Swanson, *J. Biol. Chem.* **172,** 805 (1948).

nonreducing end is provided by the initially rapid cleavage of the highly branched amylopectin and also from the cleavage of amylose or its fragments after oxidation of the aldehydo end group to carboxyl with hypoiodite (*99*).

As shown above, the β-amylases cannot cleave or by-pass the 1→6 glucosidic linkages of amylopectin or glycogen. There is an indication from their action that amylose also has links other than the 1→4 α-glucosidic linkages (*100*). Whereas crude β-amylase can completely degrade pure amylose if retrogradation is avoided, purified β-amylases (crystalline sweet potato and an amorphous soybean β-amylase) are reported to degrade amylose fractions from several sources only to the extent of 70%. A β-glucosidase, "Z-enzyme," was obtained from the crude soybean amylase which was able to attack the anomalous links.

The β-amylases in the absence of the α-amylases are incapable of degrading whole starches completely. The hydrolysis proceeds rapidly until about 50 to 55% of the theoretical amount of maltose is produced and then very slowly until a limit of about 61 to 68% is reached (*101*). The solution is still viscous and the residue, called a β-amylase limit dextrin, is unfermentable. The limit dextrin arises from the inability of β-amylase to act beyond a branch point in the randomly branched amylopectin molecule and may be envisaged as a pruned amylopectin structure. In the case of potato starch, the β-limit dextrin includes all the associated phosphate. The limit dextrin contains one end group for every 10 to 12 D-glucose residues (*102*), in contrast to one in every 25 or 30 residues for the original amylopectin. The initial attack of β-amylase on amylopectin is about 20 times as fast as on amylose (*103*). Maltose in amounts of 53 to 62% of the theoretical have been reported from the action of β-amylases on amylopectins separated from various starches (*104*). When the β-limit dextrin is cleaved by acid hydrolysis or by the action of α-amylase, the structure is opened and new chain ends are made available which can be further acted upon by β-amylase.

In contrast to the saccharogenic enzymes, the liquefying enzymes are

99. B. Bötenblad and K. Myrbäck, *Biochem. Z.* **307**, 129 (1941).

100. S. Peat, S. J. Pirt, and W. J. Whelan, *J. Chem. Soc.* p. 705 (1952); S. Peat, S. J. Pirt, and W. J. Whelan, *J. Chem. Soc.* p. 714 (1952); S. Peat, G. J. Thomas, and W. J. Whelan, *J. Chem. Soc.* p. 722 (1952).

101. W. W. Pigman, *J. Research Natl. Bur. Standards* **33**, 105 (1944); J. Blom, A. Bak, and B. Braae, *Z. physiol. Chem.* **241**, 273 (1936).

102. K. H. Meyer, M. Wertheim, and P. Bernfeld, *Helv. Chim. Acta* **24**, 212 (1941).

103. R. H. Hopkins and B. K. Jha, *Biochem. J.* **46**, 319 (1950).

104. J. E. Hodge, E. M. Montgomery, and G. E. Hilbert, *Cereal Chem.* **25**, 19 (1948); K. H. Meyer, P. Bernfeld, P. Rathgeb, and P. Gurtler, *Helv. Chim. Acta* **31**, 1536 (1948).

distinguished by the rapidity with which they decrease the viscosity of solutions and cause the formation of low-molecular-weight fragments or dextrins. They are of the first importance in most industrial processes employing amylases. Malt α-amylases and possibly other liquefying enzymes act by splitting the starch molecules to units of about six D-glucose residues in length. Although the enzyme is not able to hydrolyze 1→6 links, it can by-pass them and also esterified phosphate. Hence, if 1→6 linkages and esterified phosphate are present, they accumulate in the dextrins, which are the principal products in the early stage of the reaction. The initial hydrolysis is not confined to the outer branches, but the longer inner branches are attacked simultaneously (*105*).

A considerable amount of maltose is formed by the extended action of liquefying enzymes. D-Glucose is also believed to be formed by some of the α-amylases. Malt α-amylase hydrolyzes starches to fermentable sugars in only about 90% of the theoretical yield, but complete fermentation of the starch occurs if this malt enzyme and the yeast are allowed to work together (*101*). However, pancreas and *Bacillus mesentericus* emulsins appear to be incapable of converting starches completely to fermentable sugars even in the presence of yeasts. These crude enzyme preparations and also *Aspergillus niger* and *A. oryzae* enzymes have been shown to synthesize unfermentable substances from maltose (*101, 106*). (See also Chapter IX).

α-Amylases rapidly alter starch in such a way that the solution is no longer colored by iodine. This stage in the degradation is designated as the *achroic point*, and the reducing value calculated as maltose is termed the *achroic R-value*. In the case of malt α-amylase acting on starch, the achroic R-value is reached when about 7% of the D-glucosidic linkages are hydrolyzed. At the achroic point the hydrolytic dextrins of starch resulting from the action of malt α-amylase are composed of 6 or 7 D-glucose units each (*107*). The time required for the starch to be hydrolyzed to the achroic point may be used as a measure of the enzyme activity (*108*). As the hydrolysis progresses toward the achroic point, the color of the solution with iodine changes rapidly from blue through violet to red-brown and finally through orange to deep yellow.

Bacteria-free filtrates of *Aerobacillus macerans* (*Bacillus macerans*) produce from starch cyclic dextrins, known as Schardinger dextrins, in yields

105. R. L. Lohmar, *J. Am. Chem. Soc.* **76,** 4608 (1954).

106. S. C. Pan, L. W. Nicholson, and P. Kolachov, *J. Am. Chem. Soc.* **73,** 2547 (1951); M. L. Wolfrom, A. Thompson, and T. T. Galkowski, *J. Am. Chem. Soc.* **73,** 4093 (1951).

107. C. S. Hanes and M. Cattle, *Proc. Roy. Soc.* **B125,** 387 (1938).

108. J. Wohlgemuth, *Biochem. Z.* **9,** 1 (1908); R. M. Sandstedt, E. Kneen, and M. J. Blish, *Cereal Chem.* **16,** 712 (1939); W. J. Olson, R. Evans, and A. D. Dickson, *Cereal Chem.* **21,** 533 (1944).

as high as 60% from whole starch and 70% from the straight-chain amylose. Three crystalline dextrins have been isolated and are called α, β, and γ. They appear from X-ray, periodate, and other data to be composed of six, seven, and eight D-glucose units, respectively, linked in a cycle with α-glycosidic 1→4 bonds. They are also known as cyclohexaamylose, cycloheptaamylose, and cyclooctaamylose. The cycles are about equal in size to the repeating unit of the postulated helical coil of amylose (*109*).

Certain glycosidases and phosphorylases which are found in plants and animals are essential in the metabolism of amylose, amylopectin, and glycogen. They bring about the synthesis and storage of the polysaccharides and later, when energy is demanded for the functioning of the organism, they depolymerize the polysaccharides to α-D-glucose 1-phosphate, which then enters into the energy-supplying metabolic cycle of the particular organism. (See also Chapters XIII, IX, Glycogen, and below under Synthesis.)

The phosphorylases (P-enzyme) act reversibly on either α-D-glucose 1-phosphate or amylose in the presence of inorganic phosphate, converting one to the other as equilibrium conditions dictate. α-D-Glucose 1-phosphate is converted to amylose with the release of inorganic phosphate, whereas in the reverse reaction inorganic phosphate is combined with D-glucose during its liberation to produce the α-D-glucose 1-phosphate ester.

One step of the reversible reaction is shown in the accompanying formulas:

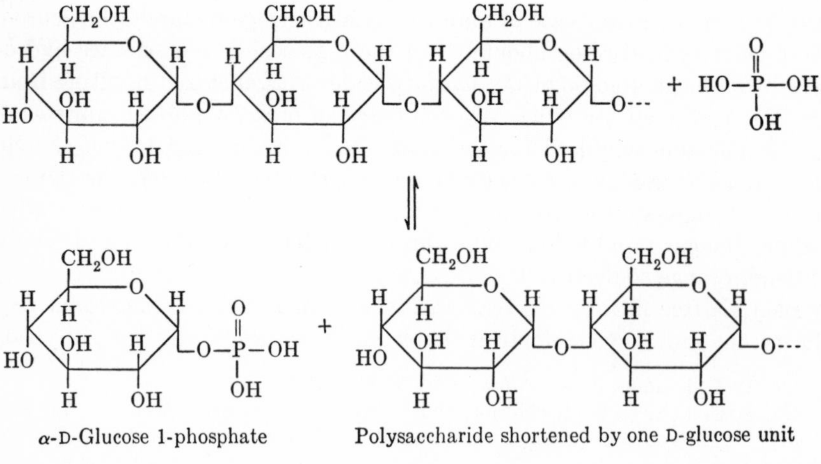

α-D-Glucose 1-phosphate   Polysaccharide shortened by one D-glucose unit

Potato phosphorylase has been shown to degrade amylose to glucose in

109. K. Freudenberg, E. Plankenhorn, and H. Knauber, *Ann.* **558,** 1 (1947); D French, D. W. Knapp, and J. H. Pazur, *J. Am. Chem. Soc.* **72,** 5150 (1950).

the presence of arsenate, presumably through formation of an unstable glucose 1-arsenate (*109a*).

Although phosphorylase can completely degrade amylose, it is to be noted that amylopectins and glycogens are only partially broken down to an enzyme-resistant limit dextrin. Thus, like β-amylase, phosphorylase evidently meets obstruction at or near 1→6 links. To cleave a 1→6 link and set free the single D-glucose unit which is joined to the chain as a stub, a special debranching factor (R-enzyme, isoamylase, or amylo-(1→6)-glucosidase) is required. This enzyme is found in the bean, potato (*110*), autolyzed brewer's yeast (*111*), and muscle (*112*). This branching enzyme plays a prominent role generally in the depolymerization of amylopectins and glycogens.

As might be expected, phosphorylases have been observed in numerous biological materials from animals and higher plants and in various bacteria, protozoa, and yeasts (*113*). An especially good source is the extract of potatoes (*114*). The phosphorylase can be concentrated from potato extract by means of fractional precipitation with ammonium sulfate.

b. Fructans (*115*)

A number of D-fructofuranose polymers occur as reserve foods in the roots, stems, leaves, and seeds of various plants, particularly those in the Compositae and Gramineae families. Dahlia tubers and the tubers of the Jerusalem artichoke are rich in fructans, as are the rhizomes and stems and leaves of grasses such as rye grass. The high fructan content of many easily grown but otherwise practically useless plants has stimulated much work on the preparation of crystalline fructose or fructose sirups. The polysaccharides are of low molecular weight and are readily water soluble. Most of them are branched. They may be classified according to the linkages of the principal chain into two groups, those with 2→1 links and those with 2→6 links. To the first group belong inulin, asparagosan, asphodelan, graminan, irisan, sinistran, tritican, and kritesan. To the second group belong phlean, levan, poan, secalan, and pyrosan.

Inulases, which are found in fungal enzyme preparations and particularly in *Aspergillus niger* extracts, hydrolyze inulin to give nearly theoretical

109a. J. Katz and W. Z. Hassid, *Arch. Biochem.* **30,** 272 (1951).

110. P. N. Hobson, W. J. Whelan, and S. Peat, *Biochem. J.* **47,** xxxix (1950).

111. B. Maruo and T. Kobayashi, *Nature* **167,** 606 (1951).

112. G. T. Cori and J. Larner, *Federation Proc.* **9,** 163 (1950).

113. For a more complete list of phosphorylase occurrences see E. J. Hehre, *Advances in Enzymol.* **11,** 297 (1951).

114. C. S. Hanes, *Proc. Roy. Soc.* **B128,** 421 (1940); **B129,** 174 (1940).

115. See E. J. McDonald, *Advances in Carbohydrate Chem.* **2,** 253 (1946).

yields of D-fructose. Hydrolysis of inulin by bakers' yeast invertase (*116*) and inulase from *A. niger* (*117*) produces also 1.7 and 1.5% D-glucose, respectively. If the glucose is not an integral part of the inulin molecule, it must be an integral part of an associated molecule which is hydrolyzed at approximately the same rate as inulin. Perhaps one end of the inulin chain is terminated by a sucrose unit. This would account for the observations that in the treatment of lower members of the inulin homologous series with yeast invertase, there is a delayed appearance of free D-glucose. An inulase preparation from *Sterigmatocystis nigra*, when allowed to act on inulin, produces a transient appearance of free sucrose (*118*). The hydrolysis may take place by the following mechanisms:

(1) Hydrolysis of the fructan linkages of sucrose-terminated fructans to lower members and sucrose.

(2) Hydrolysis of D-fructosylsucrose to sucrose and D-fructose.

(3) Hydrolysis of sucrose to D-glucose and D-fructose.

Two enzymes seem to be necessary for the complete hydrolysis of glucofructans; one enzyme hydrolyzes fructan units and the other enzyme hydrolyzes the sucrose units (*119*).

c. *Galactomannans* (*1*)

Polysaccharides composed of D-galactose and D-mannose are commonly found as food reserves in the endosperms of legumes. Good sources are the seeds of clovers, lespedeza, birdsfoot, trefoil, and alfalfa. Seeds of guar and of the carob tree (locust tree) are important commercial sources. These two galactomannans consist of a linear chain of D-mannopyranose units linked β-1→4 with attached D-galactopyranose units linked α-1→6 as single-unit side chains. In guar there is one D-galactose unit on every other D-mannose unit. These polysaccharides are excellent solution thickeners.

C. Plant Exudates (*1*)

When a plant is wounded there often exudes from the opening a viscous, sticky fluid which tends to cover and seal the incision. On drying in air the fluid thickens and hardens to a brittle, translucent, glassy mass. These exudates, plant gums, are in deciduous plants, often composed of polysaccharides. They are practically always highly branched structures (*D* in Fig. 1) composed of two to five types of monosaccharides. Almost all exu-

116. M. Adams, N. K. Richtmyer, and C. S. Hudson, *J. Am. Chem. Soc.* **65,** 1369 (1943).

117. P. Ohlmeyer and H. Pringsheim, *Ber.* **66,** 1292 (1933); W. W. Pigman, *J. Research Natl. Bur. Standards* **30,** 159 (1943).

118. R. Dedonder, *Bull. soc. chim. biol.* **34,** 157 (1952).

119. G. Legrand and C. Lewis, *Compt. rend.* **232,** 1439 (1951); J. Edelman and J. S. D. Bacon, *Biochem. J.* **49,** 446 (1951).

dates contain uronic acid units in more or less abundance. Commercial gums include not only plant exudates but also.seaweed polysaccharides and certain seed polysaccharides such as those from guar and locust bean. All exudates and other polysaccharides commercially listed as gums can absorb water to become viscous adhesive masses. Most of the important tree gums are obtained from either wild or cultivated species of the Leguminosae or *Acacia* though other plant families are also important.

a. Gum Arabic (*1*)

Gum arabic, one of the most important polysaccharide gums of commerce, exudes from thorny shrublike trees of the genus *Acacia*, found in the semiarid regions of the Sudan and Senegal regions. It is harvested by hand picking. A possible structure for arabic acid (*120*) based on extensive chemical work is illustrated.

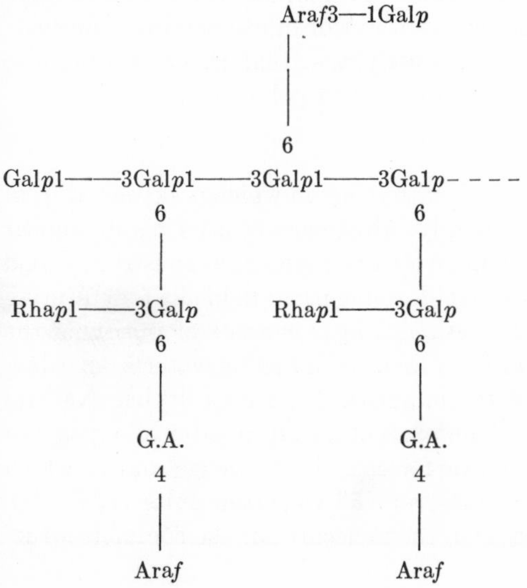
Araf3—1Galp
6
Galp1——3Galp1——3Galp1——3Galp- - - -
6
6
Rhap1——3Galp
Rhap1——3Galp
6
6
G.A.
G.A.
4
4
Araf
Araf

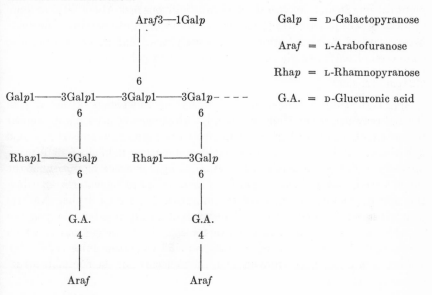

Galp = D-Galactopyranose

Araf = L-Arabofuranose

Rhap = L-Rhamnopyranose

G.A. = D-Glucuronic acid

b. Tragacanth (*1*)

Gum tragacanth is one of the oldest known drugs. It is widely used in the pharmacological, cosmetic, and textile-printing industries. It is obtained from semidesert thorny shrubs of the Astragalus family which grow abundantly in Iran, Turkey, and other Near Eastern countries. Tragacanth forms a thick viscid mucilaginous gel but only partly dissolves in water. The water-soluble fraction is called tragacanthin whereas the water-insolu-

120. E. L. Hirst, *J. Chem. Soc.* p. 70 (1942); T. Dillon, D. F. O'Caellachain, and P. O'Colla, *Proc. Roy. Irish Acad.* **55B,** 331 (1953).

ble fraction which constitutes 60 to 70% of the gum is called bassorin. A structural formula for the gum can not yet be advanced.

D. Algae (Seaweeds) (*121*)

Algae grow in abundance in both fresh water and salt water but occur in greatest profusion in shallow sea water. The multicellular algae or seaweeds have been examined more extensively than unicellular organisms and are of great commercial importance. Most polysaccharides isolated from seaweeds are those of the cell wall. Cellulose is sometimes absent from seaweeds, but usually it is found in the inner cell wall where it occurs in amounts ranging from 1 to 20%. To a large extent, the seaweeds use polysaccharides other than cellulose as their cell wall structural elements. When cellulose is present it is confined mainly to the inner wall whereas other polysaccharides make up the exterior wall and cover all exterior surfaces of the plant causing them to have a slippery mucilaginous feel. About 80% or more of most seaweeds are extractable by hot water or dilute alkaline solutions. Most seaweed polysaccharides are homoglycans; that is, polysaccharides composed of only a single sugar as the repeating polymer unit.

a. Agar (*1, 121*)

Agar is the sulfuric acid ester of a linear galactan which is extracted from the red seaweed of the Gelidium family. Most agar-bearing plants appear to contain about 40% of galactan on an air-dry basis. Agar is used as a food by Orientals, but its main use is as a gel-forming agent in media for culturing microorganisms. Commercial production of agar consists of purifying the raw seaweeds, extracting the agar from them with boiling water, congealing the agar by cooling, freezing out the impurities, and then drying. Natural agar consists principally of the calcium salt of a sulfuric ester of a galactan in which about nine 1→3 links occur for each 1→4 linkage and in which there is one sulfate group for about every 53 galactose units (*122, 123*). Both L- and D-galactose units occur in the molecule but the complete structure is not yet known.

b. Carrageenan (*1, 121*)

Hot water extraction of the red marine alga *Chondrus crispus*, commonly known as Irish moss, removes a hydrocolloid material which has been called carrageenan. This substance, produced commercially, is used as a stabilizer and homogenizer in toothpastes, ice creams, chocolate sirups, chocolate milk, bakery products, and in other foods. However, the hot water extract

121. See T. Mori, *Advances in Carbohydrate Chem.* **8,** 315 (1953).
122. W. G. M. Jones and S. Peat, *J. Chem. Soc.* p. 225 (1942).
123. V. C. Barry and T. Dillon, *Chemistry & Industry* p. 167 (1944).

is a mixture of at least five different polysaccharides (*123a*). The two main components are separable; one termed κ-carrageenan is precipitated as a gel on addition of potassium chloride and the other termed λ-carrageenan is separated from the supernatant by addition of appropriate amounts of ethanol (*123b*). In κ-carrageenan is found a D-galactose 4-sulfate residue joined by a β-1→4 link to a 3,6-anhydro-D-galactose residue, which in turn is joined by an α-1→3 link to another D-galactose 4-sulfate residue to form a chain of alternating units but with an occasional D-galactose 4-sulfate residue bearing as a substituent on position C-6 a single D-galactose 3,4-disulfate unit. λ-Carrageenan is composed almost entirely of monosulfated D-galactose units.

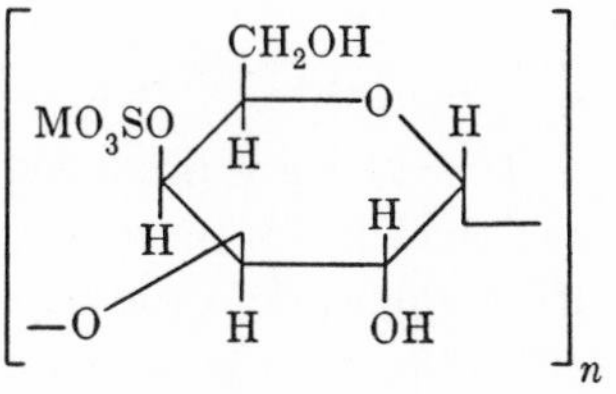

CH_2OH
MO_3SO
O
H
H
H
H
—O
H
OH
n

M = Metallic ion

c. *Alginic Acid* (*1*, *121*)

Alginic acid for the most part is a linear polymer of D-mannuronic acid units linked by β-1→4 bonds. It is present in numerous marine algae and is commercially extracted by a solution of sodium carbonate from *Macrocystis pyrifera*, the giant kelp from the southern coast of California. Very large amounts of algin are produced for industrial and food uses. It is suited to the stabilization of ice cream, sirups, cheese, chocolate milk, icings, sherbets, and other food products. It is widely used as an emulsifier in foods and as salad dressing. It is an excellent paper coating and textile size. Recently it has been used as an edible sausage casing. The properties of algin derive from its high molecular weight (50,000 to 185,000), from its linear structure, and from its acidic nature. The polysaccharide gels easily and forms insoluble salts with heavy metal ions and alkaline earths.

d. *Laminaran* (*1*, *121*)

Laminaran is a reserve carbohydrate in some brown algae. Large amounts are present in the fronds of species of the Laminaria. At certain seasons of the year almost a half of the frond weight is laminaran. At other times when

123a. D. B. Smith and W. H. Cook, *Arch. Biochem. and Biophys.* **45,** 232 (1953); D. B. Smith, W. H. Cook, and J. L. Neal, *Arch. Biochem. and Biophys.* **53,** 192 (1954); D. B. Smith, A. N. O'Neill, and A. S. Perlin, *Can. J. Chem.* **33,** 1352 (1955).

123b. A. N. O'Neill, *J. Am. Chem. Soc.* **77,** 2837, 6324 (1955).

the plant is drawing on its food reserves the amount of stored laminaran diminishes. It may be extracted by a dilute hydrochloric acid solution and be precipitated by alcohol. A neutral solution will slowly precipitate out laminaran due to aggregation of the long linear molecules. Chemical work suggests that the molecule is essentially a regular chain of β-1→3 linked D-glucopyranose units.

An enzyme which will cleave the 1→3 links of laminaran has been reported to occur in unfractionated specimens of wheat β-amylase (*124*). The enzyme preparation hydrolyzes laminaran to D-glucose in 70% yield, and crude soy β-amylase hydrolyzes laminaran to 72.3% D-glucose. There is a strong indication that the Z-enzyme of soybean and the laminaranase of wheat are identical (*100*).

4. FUNGAL AND BACTERIAL POLYSACCHARIDES (*1*)

A great variety of polysaccharides are produced by fungi and bacteria. Although some of these polysaccharides serve as reserve foods, many are fabricated into the structural framework of the fungi or the capsular sheath of bacteria. Other polysaccharides appear to have no definite function in the organism but seemingly are simply by-products of metabolism. Polysaccharides with interesting immunological properties occur in the capsules of pneumococci and tubercle bacilli. Many organisms produce polysaccharides with antigenic properties. These exact a specific response when injected into the animal body. Most polysaccharides synthesized by microorganisms are branched molecules which usually contain not more than three different monosaccharide types in a particular structure.

A. Aspergillus Polysaccharide

Extraction of the common black mold *Aspergillus niger* removes an intracellular polysaccharide which is a linear chain of D-glucypyranose units joined alternately by α-1→4 and α-1→5 bonds (*125*).

B. Leuconostoc Polysaccharides

When *Leuconostoc mesenteroides* grows in a sucrose solution it produces ropy slimes which are polysaccharides called dextrans. These slimes were known for years by manufacturers of sirups, molasses, and sugar. Great care is exercised to prevent bacteria from growing and hence to prevent slimes from developing in sugar solutions. In recent years, however, dextrans have been found of immense clinical value as plasma volume expanders in cases of hemorrhage or shock. Large quantities of dextran solution have been successfully injected into the blood stream of disabled

124. T. Dillon and P. O'Colla, *Nature* **166,** 67 (1950).
125. S. A. Barker, E. J. Bourne, and M. Stacey, *J. Chem. Soc.* p. 3084 (1953).

combat troops. For this purpose native dextran of molecular weight up to 4,000,000 is hydrolyzed by acid or by enzymes (*125a*) to a molecular-weight average of 76,000. Its effectiveness as a plasma expander is temporary. About 72 hours after injection 65 to 70% of the dextran has been excreted in the urine, 4 to 6% has been expired, and the remainder retained by the reticuloendothelial system, the polynuclear leucocytes, and the liver parenchyma (*126*). The polysaccharides may be antigenic in man, for they appear to produce a typical antibody response (*127*).

In commercial production, enzymes from a strain of *Leuconostoc mesenteroides* are used to synthesize dextran from sucrose, water, essential minerals, and vitamins (see under Synthesis, below). The native dextran so obtained is then carefully hydrolyzed to the proper molecular-weight average and recovered by fractional precipitation from solution with methanol (*128*).

Some other microorganisms also produce dextrans. The structures of dextran molecules vary with the type and strain of organism which produces them. All are branched molecules composed of D-glucopyranose units. However, they differ quantitatively with regard to the nature of the glycosidic bonds, although the main bond is the α-1→6 bond. In the analyses of dextrans produced by 96 microorganisms (mostly strains of *L. mesenteroides*), the percentages of 1→6 bonds present in the individual dextrans varied from 50 to 97%; the percentages of 1→4 and 1→3 bonds were fewer and varied over the range 0 to 50%, and 0 to 40%, respectively (*129*). The α-D-configuration for the linkage in one dextran was shown by the isolation of isomaltose from a hydrolyzate (*129a*).

The composition, particularly the molecular weight, is affected by the temperature of the medium, concentrations of sucrose and fructose, and by the addition of primers, such as low-molecular-weight dextrans or maltose (*130*). Periodate techniques (p. 700) have been particularly valuable for rapid analyses of these substances.

125a. V. Whiteside-Carlson and W. W. Carlson, *Science* **115,** 43 (1952).

126. V. Friberg, W. Graf, and B. Aberg, *Acta Pharmacol. Toxicol.* **9,** 220 (1953).

127. E. A. Kabat and D. Berg, *Ann. N. Y. Acad. Sci.* **55,** 471 (1952); P. H. Mauer, *Proc. Soc. Exptl. Biol. Med.* **83,** 879 (1953); see also V. Whiteside-Carlson, L. V. Farina, and W. W. Carlson, *J. Bacteriol.* **68,** 135 (1954).

128. G. H. Bixler, G. E. Hines, R. M. McGhee, and R. A. Shurter, *Ind. Eng. Chem.* **45,** 692 (1953).

129. A. Jeanes, W. C. Haynes, C. A. Wilham, J. C. Rankin, E. H. Melvin, Marjorie J. Austin, J. E. Cluskey, B. E. Fisher, H. M. Tsuchiya, and C. E. Rist, *J. Am. Chem. Soc.* **76,** 5041 (1954.)

129a. M. L. Wolfrom, L. W. Georges, and I. L. Miller, *J. Am. Chem. Soc.* **71,** 125 (1949).

130. H. M. Tsuchiya, N. N. Hellman, H. J. Koepsell, J. Corman, C. S. Stringer, S. P. Rogovin, M. O. Bogard, G. Bryant, V. H. Feger, C. A. Hoffman, F. R. Senti, and R. W. Jackson, *J. Am. Chem. Soc.* **77,** 2412 (1955).

C. Pneumococcus Polysaccharides

Capsules of pneumococci consist largely of a polysaccharide slime, but they contain in addition some protein and small amounts of other substances. The type-specificity and virulence of the pneumococci are due to their capsular polysaccharides (see Chapter VIII). The specificity of reaction for different pneumococcal types is due to variation in the capsular polysaccharide molecules. The antigenic polysaccharides are isolable from the bacteria but are more often prepared from the culture broth into which they are liberated by bacterial autolysis. Though there are more than 70 known types of pneumococci, little is known of the structures of their capsular polysaccharides save that from type III pneumococcus. This is shown to be a linear molecule of D-glucose and D-glucuronic acid units in equal amounts. They are linked alternately so that the molecule may be regarded as a chain of aldobiouronic acid units (*131*):

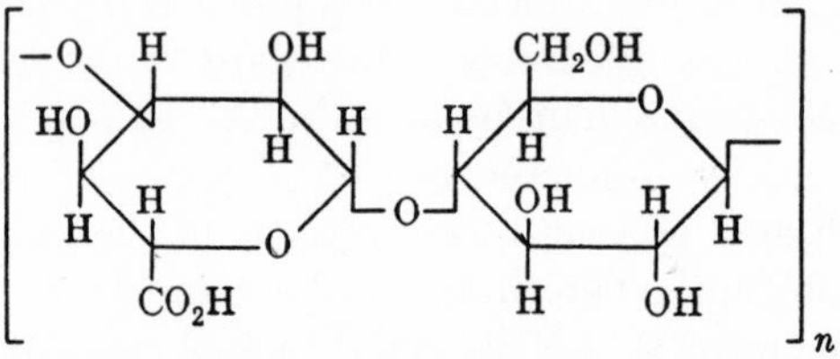
—O
H
OH
HO
H
H
H
H
H
O
CO₂H
O
CH₂OH
O
H
H
OH
H
H
H
OH
n

While the compositions of other pneumococcal polysaccharides have not been fully clarified, the composition of several have been determined as follows:

Type I	D-Galacturonic acid (28%), aminosugar, and acetic acid.
Type II	D-Glucose, L-rhamnose (40%), and D-glucuronic acid.
Type IV	D-Glucose and *N*-acetylhexosamine.
Type VIII	D-Glucose and D-glucuronic acid in 7:2 ratio.
Type XIV	D-Galactose and *N*-acetyl-D-glucosamine.

D. Crown-Gall Polysaccharide

The crown-gall organism, *Phytomonas tumefaciens*, produces a low-molecular-weight polysaccharide of D-glucose, which is of interest because it has predominantly 1→2 glycosidic linkages (*131a*).

5. GENERAL REACTIONS

Since polysaccharides are constituted of monosaccharide units, they undergo approximately the same chemical reactions as simple sugars. How-

131. R. D. Hotchkiss and W. F. Goebel, *J. Biol. Chem.* **121,** 195 (1937); R. E. Reeves and W. F. Goebel, *J. Biol. Chem.* **139,** 511 (1941).

131a. R. E. Reeves, *J. Biol. Chem.* **154,** 49 (1944); E. W. Putman, A. L. Potter, R. Hodgson, and W. Z. Hassid, *J. Am. Chem. Soc.* **72,** 5024 (1950).

ever, they have fewer hydroxyl groups per monosaccharide unit and possess only one available reducing group per molecule. Similar reactivity is exhibited only when the polysaccharides are in solution or are in the form of a highly dispersed gel in which the carbohydrate molecules are free to contact the reacting chemicals. In the solid state most polysaccharide molecules bind strongly to each other by secondary forces to form such a compact stable mass that reagents cannot easily penetrate and react with active centers. When a solid polysaccharide is treated with a solution of a reactive substance, the exposed surface polysaccharide molecules react first, while the reagent slowly diffuses into the remainder of the solid phase. Amorphous regions are penetrated and react first, while crystalline regions, if present, are penetrated slowly, if at all. Surface molecules exposed for a long period to the reagent may suffer decomposition, whereas interior molecules may be incompletely reacted. In the formation of derivatives such as ethers or esters, it is sometimes observed that unequal substitution has occurred not only between molecules but between segments of individual molecules. Thus, a molecule existing in the solid state with a portion in an amorphous region and a portion in a crystalline region may be completely substituted on the first portion and unsubstituted or incompletely substituted on the second portion. Partial reaction may sometimes be advantageous, as for the modification of cellulose fibers.

However, polysaccharides are normally pretreated to bring them into a reactive condition prior to chemical reaction. Pretreatment may consist of a simple swelling or gelatinization but sometimes consists in transforming the polysaccharide to a reactive dry powder of low density and low intermolecular cohesiveness. This transformation is frequently accomplished by freeze-drying an aqueous dispersion or by precipitating the polysaccharide solution by pouring a solution of it into eight or ten volumes of well-stirred ethanol, followed by repeated washing with fresh quantities of ethanol, and drying of the filtered product in a desiccator over calcium chloride. Such a fluffy, completely amorphous product is found to be easily penetrated and is reactive toward most reagents.

A. Esterification (See also Chapter III)

Polysaccharides are capable of ester formation with either organic or inorganic acids. Reaction may, in general, be effected by any of the well-known esterification procedures after their adaptation and modification to fit the possible special requirements of carbohydrate macromolecules. The esters produced are derivatives of high polymers and as such portray typical macromolecular properties in addition to natural ester behavior. Esterification with organic acids usually alters the properties from hydrophilic to hydrophobic, and, hence, alters the solubility so that the ester is no longer soluble in water but is soluble in organic liquids.

Preparative methods for polysaccharide esters ordinarily involve the treatment of the reactive polysaccharide with acids, acid anhydrides, or acid chlorides and a promoting agent. The promoting agent may be a catalyst; with acid anhydrides and acid chlorides, it may be a tertiary organic base and with acid chlorides it may be an alkali hydroxide. Use of substituted acid anhydrides as impelling agents to promote esterification by higher fatty acids is often used in industrial processes. Direct esterification by an acid alone produces, in most instances, only a minor degree of substitution and induces extensive depolymerization.

Cellulose is the only polysaccharide which is esterified in quantity in commercial practice. The first important plastic was celluloid, compounded of a mixture of camphor and a partially nitrated cellulose, known as pyroxylin. Pyroxylin is used in the manufacture of lacquers, collodion, and artificial leather. Highly nitrated cellulose, approximating the trinitrate stage, is known as guncotton. Cellulose acetates are of particular importance for spinning into acetate yarns, for the production of photographic films, and for the production of plastics. Plastics from mixed esters such as acetate–butyrate are often superior because they are tougher and are of greater shock resistance. Various starch esters with less than one substituent per D-glucose unit are produced commercially on a limited scale.

a. Acetates

Laboratory acetylation to produce a fully esterified polysaccharide is accomplished most easily if the polysaccharide has been pretreated to make it more reactive or if a gelatinizing agent such as formamide is incorporated in the acetylation reagents (*132*). With a fluffy, nonhorny polysaccharide, acetylation can be accomplished with 3.2 parts of acetic anhydride and 3.7 parts of pyridine per part of polysaccharide either at room temperature on long standing or at 100° for 2 to 4 hours. Acetylation by the normal procedures may be accompanied by some depolymerization, but with trifluoroacetic anhydride (*132a*) as the catalyst only about one bond per thousand is broken. However, the acetyl content of the product is liable to be 2% lower than the theoretical value, possibly due to the introduction of a few trifluoroacetyl groups.

Commercial cellulose acetate is produced from purified cotton linters or wood pulp which are pretreated with acetic acid at a temperature less than 50° to bring about partial swelling and increased reactivity. Acetylation is accomplished with a mixture of acetic acid, acetic anhydride, and sulfuric acid (or sometimes perchloric acid). The amount of acetic anhydride

132. J. F. Carson and W. D. Maclay, *J. Am. Chem. Soc.* **68**, 1015 (1946).

132a. K. S. Barclay, E. J. Bourne, M. Stacey, and M. Webb, *J. Chem. Soc.* p. 1501 (1954).

is enough to esterify the cellulose and react with any moisture present at the end of the pretreatment. Temperature is controlled to prevent excessive depolymerization. In the intermediate stages of acetylation, the sulfuric acid combines (*132b*) quantitatively with the cellulose to form the acid sulfate. In the final stages the acid sulfate groups are gradually replaced by acetyl groups, but the end-product contains some sulfur. At the conclusion of the reaction, water is added to react with excess acetic anhydride and bring the water content of the solution to 5 to 10%. The mixture is then held at a temperature of 40°, or slightly above, to reduce the number of acetyl groups to between 2.1 and 2.6 per D-glucose unit. Partial deacetylation is performed because cellulose triacetate is soluble in only a few solvents, such as glacial acetic acid and chlorinated hydrocarbons, whereas the partially deacetylated cellulose acetate is soluble in such low-cost commercial solvents as acetone. During deacetylation, the sulfur content of the cellulose derivative is reduced to about 0.01%.

b. Nitrates

Polysaccharides are usually nitrated by a mixture of nitric and concentrated sulfuric acids at 20° or below. The extent of nitration depends upon the ratio of the acids used, the temperature of the reaction, and the amount of water present (*133*). Although some degradation and sulfonation occur during the reaction, this method is used for the commercial production of cellulose and starch nitrates which are the only industrially made polysaccharide nitrates. Sulfonic ester groups introduced during the nitration would cause the product to be unstable, and, hence, they are hydrolytically removed by heating the ester in dilute mineral acid. Phosphoric acid is a better catalyst than sulfuric acid, because it produces a higher-molecular weight nitrate and does not tend to esterify with the polysaccharide (*134*). Both cellulose and starch nitrates esterified to about the triester stage are important explosives. Pyroxylin has 1.9 to 2.5 nitrate groups per D-glucose unit.

Nitrates of both cellulose and starch can be prepared by the action of dinitrogen pentoxide on the respective polysaccharide (*135, 136*).

Denitration can be achieved by strong sulfuric acid, but depolymerization of the carbohydrate also occurs. Alkaline hydrolysis gives rise to a mixture of polysaccharide fragmentation products as well as inorganic nitrates and nitrites. Nitrate groups are removed without appreciable degradation

132b. C. J. Malm, L. J. Tanghe, and B. C. Laird, *Ind. Eng. Chem.* **38,** 77 (1946).
133. G. Lunge, *J. Am. Chem. Soc.* **23,** 527 (1901).
134. E. Berl and G. Rueff, *Cellulose Chem.* **12,** 53 (1931).
135. R. Dalmon, J. Chedin, and L. Brissaud, *Compt. rend.* **201,** 664 (1935).
136. G. V. Caesar and M. Goldfrank, *J. Am. Chem. Soc.* **68,** 372 (1946).

under alkaline reducing conditions (*137*). Reductive denitration by sodium hydrogen sulfide was used in the old process for manufacturing rayon from cellulose nitrate. After spinning into fibers had been completed, the nitrate groups were removed to produce a stable and insoluble cellulose filament.

Polysaccharide nitrates are prepared in the laboratory for the viscometric estimation of molecular weight and for fractionation according to chain length (*138*). For these purposes it is necessary that depolymerization be kept to a minimum. This is achieved by nitration of the polysaccharide with a mixture of nitric acid, acetic acid, and acetic anhydride at low temperatures (*139*).

c. *Xanthates*

Polysaccharides react with carbon disulfide and sodium hydroxide to give dithiocarbonic acid esters known as xanthates:

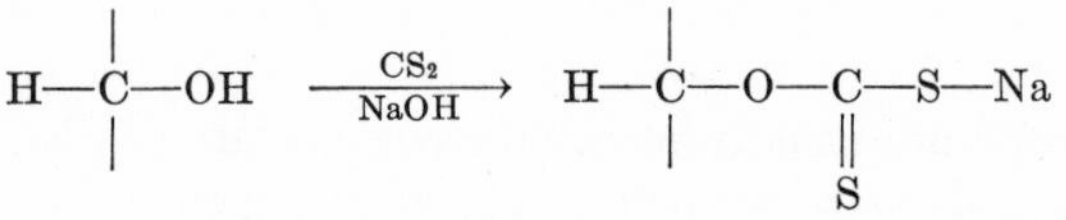
H—C—OH
CS2
NaOH
H—C—O—C—S—Na
S

The xanthate group appears to become preferentially attached to C-2 of D-glucose units in cellulose. Diazomethane replaces the xanthate groups with methyl groups so that subsequent hydrolysis yields 2-*O*-methyl-D-glucose (*140*). A high degree of xanthation is obtained when the polysaccharide is dispersed and esterified with carbon disulfide in tetraalkylammonium hydroxide (*140*).

Polysaccharide xanthates, the product of a weak acid and strong base, decompose spontaneously owing to the formation of free polysaccharide xanthic acid. The decomposition is greatly accelerated by the addition of mineral acid.

Cellulose xanthate is used in making viscose rayon from wood-pulp or cotton linters. Sheets of pulp are steeped in 18% sodium hydroxide solution to give soda cellulose. Shredded soda cellulose is then oxidized by atmospheric oxygen at 25 to 30° for 1 to 3 days by allowing the crumbs to stand in open containers. This process, known as aging, reduces the chain length of the cellulose and gives it a greater solubility. Cellulose xanthate is prepared by reacting the aged cellulose with carbon disulfide for 1 to 3 hours at 20 to 30°; the excess carbon disulfide is then removed by evacuation.

137. B. Rassow and E. Dörr, *J. prakt. Chem.* **108,** 169 (1924).

138. J. Duclaux and E. Wollman, *Bull. soc. chim. France* **27,** 414 (1920).

139. J. Harland, Unpublished work, British Cotton Industry Research Association; see A. Sharples, *J. Polymer Sci.* **13,** 393 (1954).

140. T. Lieser, *Ann.* **470,** 104 (1929); *Chem.-Ztg.* **60,** 387 (1936).

A sodium hydroxide solution of cellulose xanthate, termed viscose, is made suitable for spinning by storage at 15 to 20° for 1 to 3 days, during which time partially regenerated cellulose is produced by spontaneous elimination of some xanthate groups. The "ripened" cellulose xanthate solution is then forced through a spinneret into an acidic bath which decomposes the cellulose xanthate and coagulates the regenerated cellulose to produce fine filaments.

d. Other Esters

It is possible to react almost any acid with a polysaccharide to produce an ester, and a great variety of polysaccharide esters have been produced. Polysaccharide esters of aliphatic acids are readily prepared by reacting the free acid with the polysaccharide in the presence of an impelling agent consisting of a mixture of chloroacetic anhydride, chloroacetic acid, and magnesium perchlorate (*141*). Mixed esters, especially the acetate–propionate and acetate–butyrate, possess high solubilities, and since the solids possess shock resistance they are replacing cellulose acetate in the manufacture of lacquers, plastics, and films. Mixed esters in which a dibasic acid is incorporated have cross linkages and, hence, possess low solubilities and produce brittle plastics. Carbamate groups are stable to both acid and alkali and are produced by treatment of a polysaccharide with an isocyanate in pyridine solution:

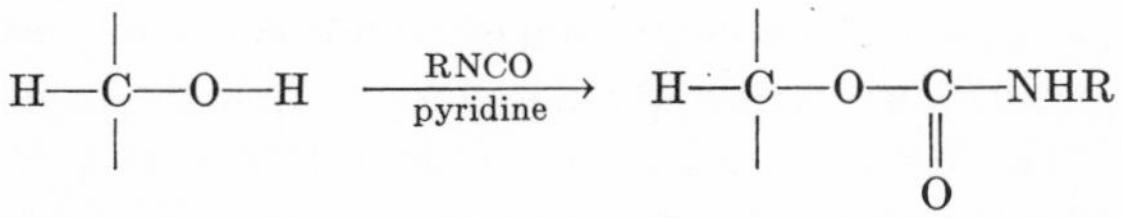
H—C—O—H
RNCO
pyridine
H—C—O—C—NHR
O

Esters of aromatic acids have not been developed commercially because of their high cost.

B. Etherification (See also Chapter VII)

Hydroxyl groups of polysaccharides are etherified readily by low-molecular-weight alkyl halides, alkyl sulfates, vinyl derivatives, and epoxides. Although a wide variety of ethers may be made, very few have found industrial importance. The cellulose ethers of industrial importance are the methyl, ethyl, cyanoethyl, and carboxymethyl ethers.

Ethyl and methyl cellulose ethers are prepared commercially by reacting alkali cellulose with ethyl or methyl chloride, respectively. Carboxymethylcellulose is formed by the interaction of salts of monochloroacetic acid with alkali cellulose. Cyanoethylcellulose, a compound of potential importance

141. H. T. Clarke and C. J. Malm, *British Patent* 313,408 (1929); *U. S. Patent*, 1,880,808 (1932).

in the textile industry, is prepared from alkali cellulose and acrylonitrile:

$$\text{H—}\overset{|}{\underset{|}{\text{C}}}\text{—O—H} + \text{CH}_2\text{=CH—CN} \rightarrow \text{H—}\overset{|}{\underset{|}{\text{C}}}\text{—O—CH}_2\text{—CH}_2\text{—CN}$$

Methyl and ethyl ethers of cellulose with a degree of substitution (D.S.) of 0.1 to 0.35 are used as emulsifying agents and paper sizes. Hydroxyethylcellulose (D.S., 0.5) is also used as a size. Highly substituted ethylcelluloses (D.S., 2.2 to 2.6) are of great importance in the plastics, film, and lacquer industries. Carboxymethylcellulose (D.S., 0.5 to 0.75) is used as a thickener in foods, and the sodium salt is added to washing powders in which its action in laundering is to prevent redeposition of soil in the fabric.

Polysaccharide methyl ethers are used extensively in determinations of the molecular structure of polysaccharides (see p. 651). Methyl ethers are most frequently prepared by reacting an alkaline suspension of the polysaccharide with dimethyl sulfate. Methyl *p*-toluenesulfonate has also been used (*142*). The heterogeneous reaction is greatly facilitated by extremely vigorous stirring, for there is a competing reaction in the destruction of the methylating agent by the base.

Degradation of the polysaccharide during methylation can be minimized by performing the reaction at low temperatures and in an atmosphere of nitrogen. Methylation is facilitated by simultaneous deacetylation and methylation of the polysaccharide acetate dispersed in an inert solvent (*143*). Fully methylated polysaccharides are obtained only after repeated methylations, which are often completed by a final methylation with a mixture of silver oxide and methyl iodide. Resistant hydroxyl groups may be methylated by the alternate addition of sodium metal and methyl iodide to the polysaccharide dispersed in liquid ammonia (*144*, *145*).

C. Oxidation (See also Chapter VI)

Polysaccharides can be oxidized even by such a mild oxidant as atmospheric oxygen. The rate of oxidation is greatly enhanced by alkalies and by various heavy metal ions. Mild oxidations are beneficial when properly employed for producing new and useful properties in polysaccharides. As an example, starch is mildly oxidized by small amounts of bleaching powder to produce improved textile sizes. Atmospheric oxidation of alkali-treated cellulose reduces the chain length of commercial cellulose to the point where its xanthate can be dissolved in a strong alkaline solution and can be used

142. J. W. Weaver and C. A. Mackenzie, *Ind. Eng. Chem.* **46**, 1490 (1954).

143. W. N. Haworth, E. L. Hirst and H. A. Thomas, *J. Chem. Soc.* 821 (1931).

144. K. Freudenberg and H. Boppel, *Ber.* **71**, 2505 (1938).

145. J. E. Hodge, S. A. Karjala, and G. E. Hilbert, *J. Am. Chem. Soc.* **73**, 3312 (1951).

for spinning into rayon fibers. On the other hand, there are instances where mild oxidations are decidedly detrimental. The best example is the tendering or weakening of rayon and cotton textile fibers during bleaching or the weakening of fabrics exposed to air and light. In both of these instances, weakening of the fibers is due to the oxidative depolymerization of the cellulose molecules or to oxidative sensitization of the molecules so that they fragment on treatment with mild alkali, such as may be encountered in laundering.

Polysaccharides may be attacked in several ways by an oxidant. Oxidation of anomeric carbon atoms may occur with a resultant rupture of glycosidic links. Oxidation of secondary alcoholic groups may also occur to produce carbonyl groups or, on rupture of carbon–carbon bonds, aldehyde or carboxyl groups. Oxidation of primary alcohol groups produces uronic acid residues. Amylose is reported to contain anomalous oxygen-sensitive glycosidic bonds not found in amylopectin (*146*). Many oxidants produce more than one type of oxidation, but usually one type predominates. Often the nature of the oxidation is influenced by the temperature, pH, and concentration of reactants.

A number of methods have been devised for the determination of the nature of the groups formed by the oxidation of cellulose (*147*). These include:

(1) Determination of carbonyl groups by reaction with hydroxylamine hydrochloride and titration of the liberated hydrochloric acid, or determination of aldehyde groups by oxidation with hypoiodite or chlorous acid and by reaction with diamines and subsequent fixation of dyes.

(2) Determination of combined uronic acid groups by evolution of carbon dioxide.

(3) Measurement of residual hydroxyl groups by acetylation and nitration.

(4) Measurement of carboxyl groups by direct titration or by partition methods based on calcium acetate, silver phenolates, or methylene blue.

In oxygen-free alkali, oxidized polysaccharides which contain carbonyl functions are quickly degraded to saccharinic acids, dihydroxybutyric acid, lactic acid, formic acid, and other similar compounds of low molecular weight. The low viscosity of oxycelluloses in cuprammonium hydroxide solutions results from the immediate molecular fragmentation caused by a cleavage of bonds sensitized to alkali through the presence of carbonyl groups introduced by the earlier oxidation (*148*).

If one of the ring hydroxyl groups in a 1→4 linked glycan is oxidized to a

146. H. Baum and G. A. Gilbert, *Chemistry & Industry* p. 489 (1954).

147. See C. C. Unruh and W. O. Kenyon, *Textile Research J*. **16,** 1 (1946).

148. G. F. Davidson, *J. Textile Inst.* **29,** T195 (1938).

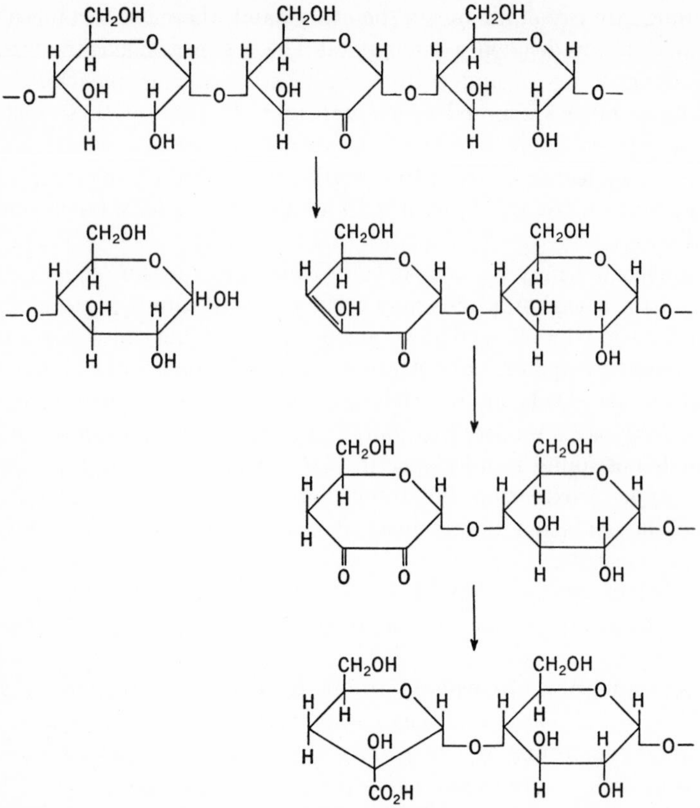
CH₂OH
O
H
OH
OH
CO₂H

FIG. 5. A proposed mechanism for the cleavage of an oxidized polysaccharide with alkali.

carbonyl group, both α-alkoxycarbonyl and β-alkoxycarbonyl groups will be present. The former will give rise to reducing properties (*149*) and the latter to alkali sensitivity (*150*, *151*). Alkaline cleavage of the polysaccharide may proceed according to the scheme shown in Fig. 5. (See also Chapter I.)

Products obtained by the action of oxidizing agents on raw starches are of considerable industrial importance, particularly as sizing materials, but their chemical natures are still unknown. Because of the increased fluidity of dispersions of oxidized starches as compared with untreated starches, they are classified with acid-treated ("acid-modified") starches as "thin-boiling starches." In addition they produce clearer solutions with a lower

149. J. Kenner and G. N. Richards, *J. Chem. Soc.* p. 2240 (1953).
150. J. F. Haskins and M. F. Hogsed, *J. Org. Chem.* **15**, 1264 (1950).
151. W. M. Corbett and J. Kenner, *J. Chem. Soc.* p. 2245 (1953).

congealing rate and more adhesiveness than is observed with unmodified starches. Commercially oxidized starches, however, still retain granular structures, are difficultly soluble in cold water, and give the usual colors in the presence of iodine.

Two general types of oxidation are used for the commercial processes: hypochlorite (and halogen) and peroxide. In the first type, a slightly alkaline starch slurry is reacted with sodium or calcium hypochlorite at 32 to 52°C. When the desired degree of oxidation is reached, sodium bisulfite is added to neutralize the oxidizing agent, and the product is ready for use after the water has been removed. Oxidative modification of starch also may be brought about by the action of alkaline peroxides, permanganates, persulfates, and perborates; the reactions may take place in the wet or dry states, but elevated temperatures are necessary.

Although the course of the oxidizing action of hypochlorites and halogens in the preparation of commercial oxidized starches is generally unknown, there is no doubt that it is quite complex. Whereas alkaline hypoiodite is used for end-group estimation (oxidation of aldehyde to carboxyl), conditions must be controlled to minimize over-oxidation (*10*, *152*). Hypochlorite oxystarches have been shown to contain carboxyl, aldehyde, and a small quantity of ketone groups (*153*). Bromine, also, under suitably controlled conditions oxidizes principally aldehyde groups. However, bromine oxidation of starches and starch derivatives has been shown to form among other products glucuronic acid residues from oxidation of the primary hydroxyl groups (*154*, *155*). This reagent may lead also to a cleavage of the carbon chains, as is evidenced by the separation of dibasic acids with carbon chains shorter than six atoms in length. The bromine-oxidized starch also forms an oxime derivative. This reaction has been attributed to the formation of a ketone group during the oxidation process.

Some oxidants are rather specific in their action and tend to bring about a preferred type of oxidation. A few such oxidants are periodate ion, lead tetraacetate, bismuthate ion, or trivalent silver, which oxidize adjacent secondary alcohol groups with chain cleavage to dialdehydes, and nitrogen dioxide, which preferentially oxidizes primary alcohol groups to carboxyl groups.

Periodate ion (see Chapter VI) is a useful oxidant in the determination of polysaccharide structures since it indicates the number of α-glycol groups present. (See also p. 648.) Thus, 1→4 linked glycans such as starch or cellulose have free hydroxyl groups at C-2 and C-3 of each sugar unit and are

152. M. Levine, J. F. Foster, and R. M. Hixon, *J. Am. Chem. Soc.* **64,** 2331 (1942).
153. M. E. McKillican and C. B. Purves, *Can. J. Chem.* **32,** 312 (1954).
154. V. Syniewski, *Ann.* **441,** 277 (1925).
155. F. F. Farley and R. M. Hixon, *Ind. Eng. Chem.* **34,** 677 (1942).

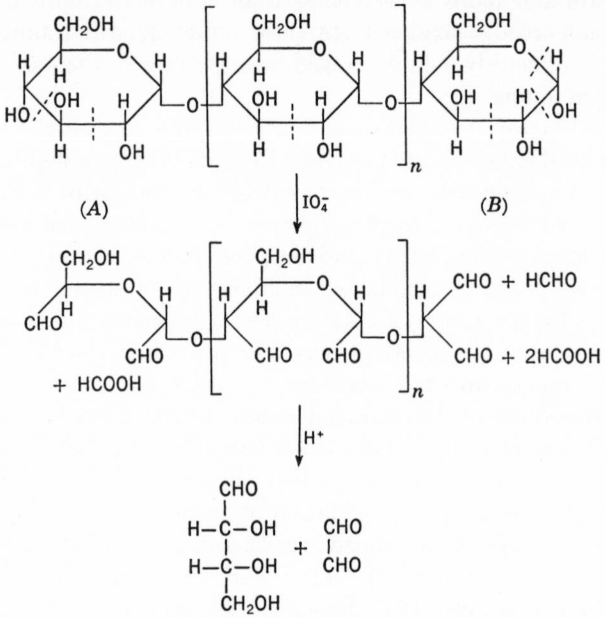

FIG. 6. Periodate oxidation of a 1→4 glucan.

oxidized at these positions with chain cleavage (Fig. 6). The nonreducing end units (*A*) are broken twice with the formation of one molecule each of formic acid. The reducing end unit (*B*) yields two molecules of formic acid and one molecule of formaldehyde. The estimation of formaldehyde and formic acid produced by the terminal groups has been utilized for the determination of chain lengths of polysaccharides. Formic acid is determined by direct titration (*16*, *17*). Formaldehyde is estimated gravimetrically as its dimedon derivative (*156*) or colorimetrically by its chromotropic acid complex (*157*). Hydrolysis of periodate-oxidized starch, cellulose, or glycogen leads to glyoxal and D-erythrose as illustrated in Fig. 6.

In a 1→3 linked glycan such as laminaran, the intermediate sugar units in the chain do not possess α-glycol groups, and, hence, oxidation will occur only on the end units of the chain (*35*, *36*). The amount of periodate consumed in an oxidation is perhaps best determined by reacting the excess reagent with iodide in neutral solution and titration of the iodine liberated with thiosulfate (*158*). Cellulose, starch, and most other polysaccharides rapidly consume the expected amount of periodate, but further oxidation

156. D. Aminoff and W. T. J. Morgan, *Biochem. J.* **48,** 74 (1951).
157. J. F. O'Dea and R. A. Gibbons, *Biochem. J.* **55,** 580 (1953).
158. J. C. P. Schwarz, *Chemistry & Industry* p. 1000 (1954).

continues slowly and must be taken into consideration in using periodate for structural investigations.

Periodate-oxidized polysaccharides are sensitive to alkaline degradation but lose this property on reduction of the aldehydic groups to alcohols or on their oxidation to carboxylic acids with chlorous acid or bromine.

Periodate-oxidized cellulose shows no carbonyl absorption bands in the expected region of the infrared (*159*). It is believed that the aldehyde groups are present in the hydrated form. Cyclization may occur to give a product of the type illustrated in formula (I).

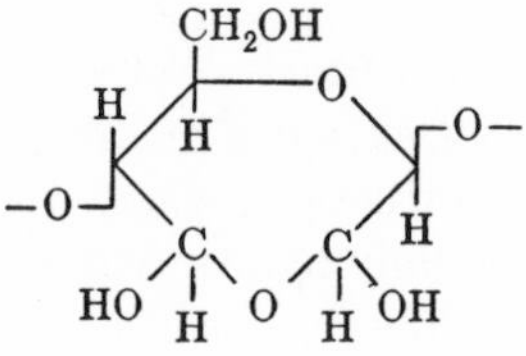

(I)

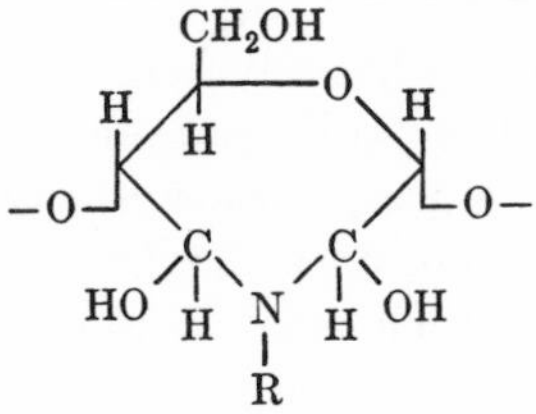

(II)

Reaction of periodate-oxidized starch with isonicotinoylhydrazine, thiosemicarbazide, or *p*-aminobenzoic acid produces gelatinous nitrogen-containing polysaccharides with units of the type (II). However, with phenylhydrazine a different type of reaction occurs which is known as the Barry reaction (*160*). Complete degradation occurs with the separation of glyoxal bis(phenylhydrazone). This reaction has been used for determining the structures of 1→3 polysaccharides, in which the nonreducing end group is first oxidized by periodate and then removed by treatment with phenylhydrazine to give glyoxal bis(phenylhydrazone) and a new polysaccharide with one less sugar unit.

Nitrogen dioxide oxidizes the primary hydroxyl groups of polysaccharides to uronic acids (*161*). Side reactions occur to an extent of 10 to 15%, presumably to produce carbonyl groups. These oxidized polysaccharides have some applications, based principally on their conversion to a soluble form by salt formation.

D. Depolymerization

a. Hydrolysis

Acids in contrast to enzymes (see above under Cellulose) cause a more or less random hydrolytic cleavage of the glycosidic bonds in polysaccha-

159. J. W. Rowen, F. H. Forziati, and R. E. Reeves, *J. Am. Chem. Soc.* **73**, 4484 (1951).

160. V. C. Barry, *Nature* **152**, 537 (1943).

161. P. A. McGee, W. F. Fowler, Jr., C. C. Unruh, and W. O. Kenyon, *J. Am. Chem. Soc.* **70**, 2700 (1948); W. W. Pigman, B. L. Browning, W. H. McPherson, C. R. Calkins, and R. L. Leaf, Jr., *J. Am. Chem. Soc.* **71**, 2200 (1949).

rides. Usually there is a gradual decrease in viscosity and an increase in reducing power as determined on material recovered at successive stages. Mono- and oligosaccharides are present at once in the hydrolysis liquors. The concentration of oligosaccharides increases and later decreases according to kinetic laws, while the concentration of monosaccharides continues to increase until the hydrolysis is complete. In practice, complete conversion of a polysaccharide to its constituent monosaccharides is difficult because of the decomposition of monosaccharides and because some random and partial repolymerization or "reversion" takes place with the formation of oligosaccharides.

The rate of hydrolysis of a polysaccharide is a function of its structure. In general, α-D-glycosidic linkages are hydrolyzed more readily than β-D-linkages. Polysaccharides, such as arabans and fructans, whose sugar units occur as furanosides may be rapidly and completely hydrolyzed under mild conditions, such as in 1% mineral acid at 80°. Polysaccharides consisting of pentose units in the pyranose form are more resistant, but hot 3% nitric acid causes complete hydrolysis. More concentrated acids, especially hydrochloric acid, decompose the pentoses to furfural. Stronger hydrolytic conditions are necessary for polysaccharides of hexopyranoside units. Usually normal sulfuric or hydrochloric acid at 100° is sufficient, but in certain cases more drastic conditions are necessary.

Glycuronans, polysaccharides composed of uronic acid units, are the most acid-resistant polysaccharides and are only slowly hydrolyzed by normal hydrochloric acid. Heteroglycans containing uronic acid units undergo more extensive hydrolysis elsewhere in the molecule than at the glycuronopyranosidic bond; consequently, aldobiouronic acids accumulate as resistant disaccharides in hydrolysis mixtures. (See pp 668 and 669.) To complete the hydrolysis of the aldobiouronic units, acid concentrations of 4% at 120° for 10 to 24 hours may be necessary (*162*). Naturally acidic polysaccharides undergo autohydrolysis when their aqueous solutions are boiled.

If a polysaccharide is not water soluble, it may be dissolved in 40 to 43% hydrochloric acid solution at 0° or in cold 72% sulfuric acid. When the product has become water soluble the solution is diluted to about 1 *N* and the hydrolysis completed at 100°.

b. Acetolysis

Acetolysis of polysaccharides yields, in addition to acetates of the constituent monosaccharides, various oligosaccharide acetates and particu-

162. W. A. G. Nelson, and E. G. V. Percival, *J. Chem. Soc.* p. 58 (1942); E. Anderson, F. H. Russell, and L. W. Seigle, *J. Biol. Chem.* **113,** 683 (1936); S. Morell, L. Baur, and K. P. Link, *J. Biol. Chem.* **105,** 15 (1934).

larly disaccharide acetates, in which glycosidic linkages characteristic of the parent polysaccharide molecule are preserved unchanged. Beside these products, acetates of monosaccharide aldehydrols have also been isolated in certain cases (*163*). The various acetolysis products from heteroglycans can be isolated by chromatography on a mixture of Magnesol and Celite (*164*). To minimize decomposition of the carbohydrate, the polysaccharide acetate is dissolved at 0° in acetic anhydride or an acetic acid–acetic anhydride mixture containing 3 to 5% sulfuric acid. After several hours, the temperature of the acetolysis solution is allowed to rise to 25° for completion of the reaction which may take up to 30 days. The reaction time may be reduced by increasing the sulfuric acid concentration, but this causes an increase in destruction of carbohydrate.

6. SYNTHESIS (See also Chapter IX)

Most laboratory syntheses of polysaccharides have been effected by means of enzymes, but study has been made of their formation as products of acid reversion.

A. Enzymic Synthesis of Polysaccharides

The enzymic synthesis of polysaccharides (*165*) from simple substrates is a process of transglycosylation in which sugar residues are transferred from a glycosyl donor to a polysaccharide or oligosaccharide receptor. The reaction may be expressed by the following scheme, where Gt represents a sugar residue, X an aglycon group, and Gr-O-H a carbohydrate receptor molecule:

$$\text{Gt—O—X} + \text{H—O—Gr} \rightleftharpoons \text{Gt—O—Gr} + \text{X—O—H}$$

The addition of the sugar residue to the receptor molecule may not involve a direct addition but may proceed through a "glycosyl–enzyme" complex. So far, only homoglycans have been prepared in the laboratory by use of enzymes.

$$\text{Gt—O—X} + \text{enzyme} \rightleftharpoons \text{Gt—enzyme} + \text{H—O—X}$$
$$\text{Gt—enzyme} + \text{H—O—Gr} \rightleftharpoons \text{Gt—O—Gr} + \text{enzyme}$$

Although an oligosaccharide primer is helpful in initiating the formation of amylose from D-glucose 1-phosphate it is not clear whether a primer is of assistance in initiating all polysaccharide syntheses. Many of the en-

163. R. L. Whistler, E. Heyne, and J. Bachrach, *J. Am. Chem. Soc.* **71,** 1476 (1949).

164. W. W. Binkley and M. L. Wolfrom, *Sugar Research Foundation Sci. Rept. Ser.* **No. 10** (1948).

165. For reviews see E. J. Hehre, *Advances in Enzymol.* **11,** 297 (1951); S. Peat, *Advances in Enzymol.* **11,** 339 (1951); M. Stacey, *Advances in Enzymol.* **15,** 301 (1954); S. A. Barker and E. J. Bourne, *Quart. Revs.* **7,** 56 (1953).

zymes are obtained only as crude mixtures which undoubtedly contain impurities of "priming" power. The general requirement for primers in various enzyme systems will be determinable when pure enzymes become available for study.

a. Amylose-Type Polysaccharides (See above under Starch)

Phosphorylases, which occur in a wide variety of sources, converts D-glucose 1-phosphate into an amylose type of polysaccharide with the formation of inorganic phosphate (*166*). The over-all reaction may be expressed as:

$$n\ (C_6H_{11}O_5 \cdot OPH_2O_3) \rightleftharpoons (C_6H_{10}O_5)_n + n\ H_3PO_4$$

D-Glucose 1-phosphate	Amylose-type polysaccharide	Phosphoric acid

In some instances, sugars and their derivatives may act as competitive inhibitors by functioning as receptors for the D-glucose unit undergoing transfer. The enzymic synthesis of amylose molecules preferably requires a polysaccharide or oligosaccharide primer. The synthetic polysaccharide is built unit by unit from the receptor's (primer's) nonreducing terminal group. Structural requirements of the receptor molecule vary for different phosphorylases. Potato phosphorylase requires a receptor (*167*, *168*) (1) to be a 1→4 linked α-glucan, (2) to have nonreducing terminal groups, and (3) to have chains of 3 to 20 D-glucose units. In contrast, jack-bean phosphorylase can function with amylose as a receptor molecule.

Amylomaltase (*169*), an enzyme isolated from *Escherichia coli*, synthesizes amylose-type molecules from maltose. Equilibrium is reached at about 60% conversion, the amylose-type product having an average chain length of 10 D-glucose units:

$$n\ C_{12}H_{22}O_{11} \rightleftharpoons (C_6H_{10}O_5)_n + n\ C_6H_{12}O_6$$

D-Maltose	Amylose-type polysaccharide	D-Glucose

However, if the D-glucose formed is destroyed by glucose dehydrogenase, the reaction goes to completion, and a polysaccharide is produced which closely resembles normal amylose.

166. W. Z. Hassid and R. M. McCready, *J. Am. Chem. Soc.* **63,** 2171 (1941); W. Z. Hassid, G. T. Cori, and R. M. McCready, *J. Biol. Chem.* **148,** 89 (1943).

167. D. E. Green and P. K. Stempf, *J. Biol. Chem.* **142,** 355 (1942); E. J. Bourne, D. A. Sitch, and S. Peat, *J. Chem. Soc.* p. 1448 (1949).

168. E. C. Proehl and H. G. Day, *J. Biol. Chem.* **163,** 667 (1946); J. M. Bailey, W. J. Whelan, and S. Peat, *J. Chem. Soc.* p. 3692 (1950).

169. J. Monod and A. M. Torriani, *Ann. Inst. Pasteur* **78,** 65 (1950).

b. Amylopectin-Type Polysaccharides (see also p. 682–3)

Only linear polysaccharides are formed by phosphorylases, but amylopectin and glycogen may be synthesized from D-glucose 1-phosphate by the joint action of phosphorylase and a branching enzyme. The first enzyme of this type, Q-enzyme, was isolated from potatoes but since has been isolated from various sources. Q-Enzyme can only synthesize α-D-1→6 links and has no action upon D-glucose 1-phosphate. Through the joint action of phosphorylase and varying amounts of Q-enzyme, the extent of branching in the resultant polysaccharide can be varied over a wide range (*170*).

Amylose when treated with Q-enzyme is converted into amylopectin in the absence of phosphate. This observation indicates that the enzyme is not a phosphorylase. Q-Enzyme can split the amylose chain into two fragments and, by a transglycosylation mechanism, transfers one fragment to a second amylose chain to which it is joined through a 1→6 α-D-glucosidic linkage. Branching occurs only when the amylose chains contain more than 40 D-glucose units (*171*). Q-enzyme may be associated with a second enzyme (D-enzyme) which brings about disproportionation but without producing branching (*171a*).

An enzyme capable of synthesizing and cleaving 1→6 α-D-glucosidic linkages is reported to occur in rabbit muscle (*172*).

Amylosucrase (*173*) from *Neisseria perflava* utilizes sucrose for the synthesis of polysaccharides with properties intermediate between those of glycogen and amylopectin (*174*). Apparently, there are two enzymes responsible for this synthesis; one enzyme converts sucrose into an amylose-type polysaccharide and the other enzyme, which is of the Q-enzyme type, breaks the straight chains to produce highly branched molecules. The resultant branched polysaccharides have about 12 D-glucose units for each nonreducing end unit.

c. Cyclic Dextrins

Enzymes from *Bacillus macerans* act on either the linear or branched components of starch to form cyclic dextrins termed Schardinger dextrins

170. S. A. Barker, E. J. Bourne, S. Peat, and I. A. Wilkinson, *J. Chem. Soc.* p. 3022 (1950).

171. S. Nussenbaum, W. Z. Hassid, G. T. Cori, and B. Illingworth, *J. Biol. Chem.* **2,** 190 (1951); S. Nussenbaum and W. Z. Hassid, *ibid.* **196,** 785 (1952).

171a. S. Peat, W. J. Whelan, and W. R. Rees, *J. Chem. Soc.* p. 44 (1956); S. Peat, W. J. Whelan, and G. W. F. Kroll, *ibid.* p. 53 (1956).

172. A. N. Petrova, *Biokhimiya* **14,** 155 (1949); **17,** 129 (1952); A. N. Petrova and E. L. Rozenfeld, *ibid.* **15,** 309 (1950).

173. E. J. Hehre and D. M. Hamilton, *J. Biol. Chem.* **166,** 777 (1946); *J. Bacteriol.* **55,** 197 (1948).

174. S. A. Barker, E. J. Bourne, and M. Stacey, *J. Chem. Soc.* p. 2884 (1950).

(*175*). The principal dextrins formed contain either 6 or 7 D-glucopyranose units linked in a ring (see above under Starch). In the presence of suitable "cosubstrates" such as D-glucose, D-maltose, and sucrose, the reaction reverses to produce linear polysaccharides (*176*). The *macerans* enzyme is similar in action to the Q-enzyme in that blocks of D-glucose units are transferred in contrast to individual D-glucose units.

d. Dextrans (See also above under *Leuconostoc* Polysaccharides)

Sucrose is converted into dextrans by various species of *Leuconostoc* or the dextran-sucrase enzymes isolated from these organisms (*177*). A 99% conversion of the D-glucose present in sucrose may be obtained by use of a pure enzyme. Phosphate plays no part in the synthesis, and the over-all action is not reversible:

$$\underset{\text{Sucrose}}{n\ C_{12}H_{22}O_{11}} \longrightarrow \underset{\text{Dextran}}{(C_6H_{10}O_5)_n} + \underset{\text{D-Fructose}}{n\ C_6H_{12}O_6}$$

The structures of the dextrans may be controlled by the type of enzyme preparation employed, by the type of initial receptor molecules, or by the addition of branched low-molecular-weight dextrans which produce products of low molecular weight (*178*). Some dextrans appear to have D-fructose end groups which are introduced into the molecule by sucrose acting as a receptor to initiate dextran synthesis.

e. Mycodextran

Mycodextran or nigeran is a unique glucan which is synthesized from maltose by *Aspergillus niger*. The essentially unbranched polysaccharide contains alternately arranged α-D-1→4 and α-D-1→3 linkages. It is possible that a few 1→6 bonds are present. The end-group assay of mycodextran shows an average chain length of 300 to 350 D-glucose units (*125*).

f. Levans

Levan-sucrase isolated from species of *Aerobacter* or *Bacillus* synthesizes a fructan (levan) from sucrose or raffinose but not from D-fructose, invert

175. F. Schardinger, *Zentr. Bakteriol. Parasitenk., Abt. II* **14,** 722 (1905); **22,** 98 (1909); E. B. Tilden and C. S. Hudson, *J. Am. Chem. Soc.* **61,** 2900 (1939).

176. D. French, J. H. Pazur, M. L. Levine, and E. Norberg, *J. Am. Chem. Soc.* **70,** 3145 (1948).

177. E. J. Hehre, *Proc. Soc. Exptl. Biol. Med.* **54,** 18 (1943); W. W. Carlson, C. L. Rosano, and V. Whiteside-Carlson, *J. Bacteriol.* **65,** 136 (1953).

178. H. J. Koepsell, H. M. Tsuchiya, N. N. Hellman, A. Kazenko, C. A. Hoffman, E. S. Sharpe, and R. W. Jackson, *J. Biol. Chem.* **200,** 793 (1953).

sugar, or inulin. The over-all reaction (*179*) may be expressed by the following equation:

$$n\ C_{12}H_{22}O_{11} \rightarrow (C_6H_{10}O_5)_n + n\ C_6H_{12}O_6$$

Sucrose → Levan + D-Glucose

Incomplete hydrolysis of sucrose by yeast invertase preparations produces, in addition to D-glucose and D-fructose, a number of oligosaccharides which are then hydrolyzed to different ratios of D-glucose and D-fructose (*180*, *181*). Thus, one action of yeast invertase is to transfer D-fructosyl units to form 2→6 D-fructofuranose linkages. (See also Chapter IX.)

g. Inulin

Thus far, inulin has not been synthesized by enzymes *in vitro*. However, by the action of a transfructosidase from *Aspergillus oryzae* upon sucrose (*182*, *183*) a trisaccharide has been obtained and shown to be 1-*O*-inulobiosyl-D-glucoside [*O*-D-fructofuranosyl-(2→1)-*O*-D-fructofuranosyl-(2→1) D-glucopyranoside] (*184*). (See also Chapter IX.)

h. Galactans

No galactans of high molecular weight have yet been synthesized by enzymes *in vitro*. Galactotransferases (*185*, *186*) from several sources have been isolated which will produce a galactosyllactose from lactose according to the equation (see Chapter IX):

$$2\ \text{Lactose} \rightarrow \text{galactosyllactose} + \text{D-glucose}$$

i. Cellulose

Although cellulose is abundantly synthesized by plants and a host of microorganisms, the mechanism of its enzymic synthesis is still obscure. That a complex mechanism is involved is illustrated by the fact that a cellulose produced by *Acetobacter xylinum* acting on D-glucose-1-C^{14} had 82% of the activity in C-1 of the D-glucose units and the remainder equally distributed between C-3 and C-4. A distribution of label was also shown with D-mannitol-1-C^{14} or D-glucose-2-C^{14} as substrates. Thus, some of the original

179. S. Hestrin and S. Avineri-Shapiro, *Nature* **152**, 49 (1943); *Biochem. J.* **38**, 2 (1944).
180. J. S. D. Bacon and J. Edelman, *Arch. Biochem.* **28**, 467 (1950).
181. P. H. Blanchard and N. Albon, *Arch. Biochem.* **29**, 220 (1950).
182. F. J. Bealing and J. S. D. Bacon, *Biochem. J.* **49**, lxxv (1951).
183. J. H. Pazur, *J. Biol. Chem.* **199**, 217 (1952).
184. J. S. D. Bacon and D. J. Bell, *J. Chem. Soc.* p. 2528 (1953).
185. K. Wallenfels and E. Bernt, *Naturwissenschaften* **38**, 306 (1951).
186. M. Aronson, *Arch. Biochem. and Biophys.* **39**, 370 (1953).

hexose units must be cleaved prior to cellulose formation (*187*). Cellulose (*188*) produced by *Acetobacter acetigenum* has an average chain length of 600 β-D-glucose units (*131*).

j. Miscellaneous

Pure maltose (but not maltose contaminated with D-glucose) is fermented incompletely with bakers' yeast. The behavior is explained in part by the formation of a nonfermentable substance with a lower reducing power than maltose, probably an oligosaccharide (*189*).

B. Acid Reversion

Acid hydrolysis of polysaccharides is an equilibrium process in which monosaccharides are in equilibrium with polysaccharides and oligosaccharides, some of which are formed by recondensation. Monosaccharides are favored in dilute solutions, whereas polymers are favored in concentrated solutions. By alteration of the concentration of substrates, the equilibrium of the reaction can be altered repeatedly from almost pure monosaccharide to a mixture of monomeric and polymeric carbohydrates (*190*). The rate at which equilibrium is reached for a given sugar concentration is dependent upon the temperature and the pH of the reaction mixture. Although a complex mixture of recondensation products is formed because all free hydroxyl groups on each sugar can participate, condensation preferably occurs through primary hydroxyl groups. Thus, a 25% solution of D-glucose in concentrated hydrochloric acid produces a mixture of disaccharides of which the main components are isomaltose and gentiobiose (*191*). (See under Glucose, Chapter II). A 50% solution of D-glucose in 5% hydrochloric acid on rapid evaporation at 0 to 45° is said to give in 15 to 20% yield a glucan containing some 42 sugar units (*192*). Cationic resins also can cause condensation of D-glucose (*193*).

187. F. W. Minor, G. A. Greathouse, H. G. Shirk, A. M. Schwartz, and M. Harris, *J. Am. Chem. Soc.* **76,** 5052 (1954); F. W. Minor, G. A. Greathouse, and H. G. Shirk, *ibid.* **77,** 1244 (1955); see also S. Hestrin and M. Schramm, *Biochem. J.* **58,** 345 (1954).

188. R. Kaushal and T. K. Walker, *Biochem. J.* **48,** 618 (1951).

189. M. G. Blair and W. Pigman, *Arch. Biochem. and Biophys.* **48,** 17 (1954).

190. W. R. Fetzer, E. K. Crosby, C. E. Engel, and L. C. Kirst, *Ind. Eng. Chem.* **45,** 1075 (1953).

191. E. Fischer, *Ber.* **28,** 3024 (1895).

192. E. Pacsu and P. T. Mora, *J. Am. Chem. Soc.* **72,** 1045 (1950).

193. G. Zemplén and L. Kisfaludy, *Acta Chim. Acad. Sci. Hung.* **4,** 79 (1954).

Part II

Animal Polysaccharides (Zoöpolysaccharides or Zoöglycans) and Glycoproteins

WARD PIGMAN AND DAVID PLATT*

1. DISTRIBUTION AND CLASSIFICATION

The complex carbohydrates of animal tissues include a wide range of compounds of interesting and varied distribution. The nuclei and cytoplasm of all cells contain relatively large amounts of nucleic acids believed vital to protein synthesis and cell growth. As a reserve storage for metabolic processes and energy production, glucose is found in most cells, notably in muscle and liver as the polymer glycogen. The cytoplasmic granules that distinguish the mast cell from all other cells may consist of heparins. Certain hormones and enzymes are known to consist partly of carbohydrates. The clear viscid secretion of "mucus" that coats and protects the respiratory, digestive, and reproductive passages probably owes its distinctive properties to a high content of high-molecular-weight carbohydrates. The supporting or connective tissues, such as cartilage and bone, contain important amounts of acidic carbohydrates, which owe their acidity usually to the presence of carboxyl or sulfate groups. Embryonic tissues and certain new growths of neoplasms appear to be rich in complex carbohydrates. On the basis of their carbohydrate components, the finer supporting structures (e.g., reticulum, basement membranes, and much so-called "ground substance") are demonstrated histologically. In health, all of the body fluids contain detectable quantities of carbohydrates or glycoproteins in fairly uniform amounts. Changes in the carbohydrates of the intercellular ground substance may play a significant part in derangements such as arthritis, arteriosclerosis, diabetes mellitus, and others. Polysaccharides are also significant in immunological or allergic reactions and the "resistance" to disease processes. In many lower animals, such as insects and crustacea, chitin is a major component of the structural substance.

Many of the zoöpolysaccharides exist in the living animal and in isolated products as loose salt complexes or chemically bonded with proteins (or with lipids or both). As a result, research into the composition of these materials has been made especially difficult because of the difficulties of purification, the lack of criteria for purity, the paucity of suitable analytical methods, and the general problem of the removal of the noncarbohydrate components.

* The sections on glycogen and chitin were prepared by R. Whistler and W. Corbett.

Relatively few zoöpolysaccharides have been isolated in pure condition, and few have had a fairly complete structural analysis. Glycogen, chitin, hyaluronic acid, heparin, chondroitin sulfates, and the blood-group polysaccharides are the best known and defined. The early work in this field has been summarized by P. A. Levene (*1*), who is also responsible for much of the nomenclature. Among the early workers were O. Schmiedeberg, F. Müller, O. Hammersten, C. Neuberg, P. A. Levene, and associates.

Systems of nomenclature for these substances have been proposed by Levene (*1*), Meyer (*2*), Stacey (*3*), Masamune (*4*), Winzler (*5*), and Blix (*6*).

The following classification is primarily a modification of those previously suggested, developed to follow general usage as far as possible and to reflect the new knowledge in the field:

Classification of Zoöpolysaccharides, Conjugates, and Related Compounds

I. Zoöglycans (Zoöpolysaccharides). The polysaccharides of animals, or the polysaccharide portion of glycoproteins and other combinations.
   A. Homozoöglycans (homozoöpolysaccharides) (glycogen, galactan, and chitin). Zoöpolysaccharides which contain only one type of monosaccharide or simple derivative (hexosamine).
   B. Heterozoöglycans (heterozoöpolysaccharides). Zoöpolysaccharides which contain two or more types of monosaccharide, hexosamine, or uronic acid. (Examples: Hyaluronic acid, chondroitin sulfate, heparin, blood-type polysaccharides, keratosulfate.)

II. Protein–Zoöpolysaccharide complexes.
   A. Mucoproteins. Dissociable complexes with salt linkages, or possibly mixtures.
   B. Glycoproteins. Stable combinations, covalently bonded and frequently synonymous with "mucoids." These or polysaccharides may constitute the carbohydrate components of the mucoproteins.

1. P. A. Levene, "The Hexosamines and Mucoproteins." Longmans, Green, London, 1925.

2. K. Meyer, *in* "Some Conjugated Proteins" (W. H. Cole, ed.), Rutgers Press, New Brunswick, 1953.

3. M. Stacey, *Advances in Carbohydrate Chem.* **2,** 161 (1946).

4. H. Masamune, *Tôhoku J. Exptl. Med.* **50,** 107 (1949). This paper is a summary of the work by H. Masamune and many associates in the series "Biochemical Studies of the Carbohydrates" over the period 1933 to 1949 at the Medical-Chemical Institute, Tohoku University, Sendai, Japan; 170 parts had appeared by 1955.

5. R. J. Winzler, *in* "Methods of Biochemical Analysis" (D. Glick, ed.), Vol. II, p. 279. Interscience, New York, 1955.

6. G. Blix, *Acta Physiol. Scand.* **1,** 29 (1940).

III. Zoöglycolipides.

IV. Zoöglycolipoproteins.

As indicated in the first part of the chapter, this type of classification based on the occurrence of polysaccharides offers some disadvantages, particularly in that some materials such as chitin, hyaluronic acid, and cellulose occur in plants or microorganisms as well as in animals. However, until more chemical work is done, a strictly chemical classification does not seem feasible. The conflicting classifications and nomenclature in this field need standardization and agreement.

Of the terms which have been used in this field, zoöpolysaccharide or zoöglycan (especially heterozoöpolysaccharide) corresponds most closely to the "mucopolysaccharide" of Meyer, who defines a mucopolysaccharide as one which contains a hexosamine unit.

The term "glycoprotein" has had diverse meanings. In its oldest and most general usage (*7a*), its significance is that of a conjugated carbohydrate protein; this usage in the sense of a firm combination is continued here. Meyer defines a glycoprotein as a firmly bound conjugate which contains less than 4% hexosamine; Masamune considers glycoproteins as dissociable complexes; Stacey gives the term "mucoprotein" approximately the same significance as the "glycoprotein" of Meyer. Some of the proteins of dissociable protein–carbohydrate complexes (mucoproteins according to Meyer) appear to contain small amounts of bound hexosamine and hexose; Masamune calls these proteins "glycidamins"; others have used "mucoid" for similar products. These terms, and others like mucin, should be used with caution, since it is questionable whether mixtures (if some of these products are such) should be given specific names. At this stage, names such as mucoproteins and mucins correspond somewhat to the term "hemicellulose" as used in plant products.

Mucus usually is the clear viscid secretion coating the surfaces of mucous membranes. Histologically, it appears to be produced usually by specific cells, such as "goblet cells." The "ground substance" (or intercellular material) of many connective tissues is physically similar to mucus, but the origin is uncertain, and it differs in staining properties. The staining characteristics of mucus are those for *vic*-glycol groups or acidic groups (Chapter XI) and are ascribed to the presence of mucins in the mucus. However, this terminology has undergone considerable changes (*7b*). The best-known mucins are those obtained from the mucous membranes, salivary glands, synovial fluids, eggs, and snails. The name "mucin" usually has the significance of a mucoprotein, especially of those in the secretions of the mucous membranes. Mucins are precipitated as a gummy, stringy mass by

7a. Committee on Protein Nomenclature, *J. Biol. Chem.* **4**, xlviii (1908).

7b. See for example K. Meyer, *Advances in Protein Chem.* **2**, 251 (1945).

TABLE I

OCCURRENCE OF SOME HETEROPOLYSACCHARIDES IN MESENCHYMAL TISSUES[a]

Group	Tissue	Hyaluronic acid	ChS-A[a]	ChS-B[a]	ChS-C[a]	Chondroitin	Keratosulfate
I	Vitreous humor	+					
	Synovial fluid	+					
	Mesothelioma	+					
II	Hyaline cartilage		+		+		
III	Heart valves			+	+		
	Tendon (pig and calf)			+	+		
	Aorta			+	+		
IV	Skin (pig and calf)	+		+			
	Umbilical cord	+			+		
V	Cornea		+			+	+

[a] ChS = Chondroitin sulfate.

weak acids and are soluble in alkalies and strong acids. They give a "mucin clot" when the secretion is diluted tenfold with a weak acid (1% acetic acid). The term mucoid usually means a water-soluble glycoprotein. The mucoids sometimes are precipitated by weak acids, but the flocculent precipitate is not a typical mucin precipitate.

Levene (*1*) classified many of these materials as chondroitin sulfates or mucoitin sulfates on the basis of the presence of sulfate groups and on the nature of the hexosamine components, D-galactosamine in chondroitins and D-glucosamine in mucoitins. In current practice, mucoitin as used earlier and by Masamune is known as the substance hyaluronic acid (Karl Meyer). The early described mucoitin sulfates (*1*), which are similar to the hyalurono-sulfates of Karl Meyer, appear to have been mixtures (*8*, *9*) of several materials; it would seem that the term mucoitin should be discarded. The usual components of "mucoitin sulfate" appear to be hyaluronic acid, the keratosulfate of Meyer (*10*) (apparently the same as the tendomucoid-α of Sasaki (*4*) and the corneal polysaccharide of Woodin (*11*)), and the limaçoitin sulfate of Masamune (*4*) (possibly one of the chondroitin sulfates B or C of Meyer) (*12*). On the other hand, Levene's chondroitin sulfate (*1*) is a definite substance, but two other compounds of apparently closely similar structure have been isolated (see below).

8. R. Satoh, *Tôhoku J. Exptl. Med.* **56**, 387 (1952).

9. W. P. Deiss and A. S. Leon, *J. Biol. Chem.* **215**, 685 (1955).

10. K. Meyer, A. Linker, E. A. Davidson, and B. Weissmann, *J. Biol. Chem.* **205**, 611 (1953).

11. A. M. Woodin, *Biochem. J.* **51**, 319 (1952).

12. K. Meyer and M. M. Rapport, *Science* **113**, 596 (1951).

The distribution of several of these zoöpolysaccharides in some tissues of higher animals is given (*13*) in Table I.

The free and bound heterozoöpolysaccharides contain only a rather restricted group of sugars in the basic units (*4*, *14*). Usually a hexuronic acid and a *N*-acetylhexosamine compose the apparent repeating units. Sometimes, the uronic acid is replaced by a hexose. Sulfate ester groups may be present. Known acids are D-glucuronic, D-galacturonic (*4*), and L-iduronic (*14a*) acids; the hexoses are D-mannose, D-galactose, and L-fucose. D-Glucosamine and D-galactosamine are the known hexosamines, occasionally occurring together. "Sialic acid" (see below) may be a frequent component of such materials. Remarkably, D-glucose apparently occurs rarely if ever in heterozoöpolysaccharides and glycoproteins. Since colorimetric identifications are often used for the component sugars and derivatives, the DL-allocation often is arbitrary; this is particularly true for fucose, which in a few known instances has been shown to be the L-isomer.

2. REASONABLY WELL-DEFINED ZOÖPOLYSACCHARIDES

A number of zoöpolysaccharides have been isolated in purified condition and the structures partially established. Many of these are bound with other tissue components in the natural condition. They are isolated from the macerated tissues or the secretions by extraction with alkalies or salts (especially calcium chloride). Mucins and many mucoids are precipitated by weak acids, and their polysaccharide components are subsequently recovered. If dissociable, proteins may be removed by precipitation with amyl alcohol – chloroform (Sevag) or formaldehyde (Masamune). Peptic or tryptic digestion may remove these and covalently bound proteins. Colorimetric, chromatographic, and isolation methods have been used for the identification of the component sugars (*5*, *14*, *15–16b*). (See also under Glucosamine, Chapter VIII, Uronic acids, Chapter VI and part I, Chapter XII.)

The action of enzymes on zoöpolysaccharides provides a valuable method

13. K. Meyer, *in* "Connective Tissues in Health and Disease" (G. Asboe-Hansen, ed.), p. 54 Munksgaard, Copenhagen, 1954.

14. I. Werner, *Acta. Soc. Med. Upsaliensis* **58,** 1 (1953).

14a. P. Hoffman, A. Linker, and K. Meyer, *Science* **124,** 1252 (1956).

15. H. Masamune and K. Ogawa, *Tôhoku J. Exptl. Med.* **60,** 11, 23, 33, 41 (1954); H. Masamune and M. Maki, *ibid.* **55,** 299 (1952); B. Weissmann, K. Meyer *et al., J. Biol. Chem.* **205,** 205 (1953); **208,** 417 (1954); E. A. Davidson and K. Meyer, *ibid.* **211,** 605 (1954).

16a. Z. Dische, *in* "Methods of Biochemical Analysis" (D. Glick, ed.), Vol. II, p. 313. Interscience, New York, 1955.

16b. R. W. Jeanloz, *in* "Proceedings of the Third International Congress of Biochemistry, Brussels, 1955" (C. Liébecq, ed.), p. 65. Academic Press, New York, 1956.

for their identification and characterization. Hyaluronidase preparations from different sources, probably because of the presence of variable amounts of other components such as β-glucuronidase, exhibit differing behaviors. The pneumococcal (type II) hyaluronidase and probably other bacterial hyaluronidases appear highly specific for known hyaluronic acid, whereas testicular hyaluronidase also hydrolyzes some of the chondroitin sulfates (A and C) (*9*, *12*). The hyaluronidases obtained from various sources also differ in their enzymic action on hyaluronic acid (see Hyaluronic acid).

Three homozoöpolysaccharides (glycogen, chitin, and lung galactogen) have been studied. The remaining heterozoöpolysaccharides are composed of more than one type of sugar residue. The well-defined products are described individually below. Complexes of these with proteins are covered in a subsequent section.

A. Glycogens

Glycogens are present in the cells of all animals and are the principal reserve polysaccharides of the animal world. In function and structure they correspond closely to the starches of plants. They occur abundantly in liver, tissues of the crayfish body wall, and to a lesser extent in muscle, yeast, and higher fungi. Sweet corn contains a low-molecular-weight amylopectin (*17*) which, because of its similarity to glycogen, is called "phytoglycogen." The properties of the glycogens vary according to the source; although glycogens of different origin may be similar in iodine staining power, optical rotation, and attack by enzymes, there is evidence that they are not identical. A portion of the glycogen in the cell is water soluble and a portion is insoluble, possibly because it is combined with protein. However, as glycogens occur with different degrees of polymerization, it is expected that they would have different solubilities.

Glycogens may be extracted from tissue with hot water, dilute trichloroacetic acid, or chloral hydrate but are usually removed by hot 30% potassium hydroxide solution. They are usually precipitated from the latter solution by alcohol. Some possibility exists that the alkaline extraction causes degradation (*18*, *19*).

Diffusion and sedimentation experiments suggest that glycogen molecules exist in solution as flat ellipsoids. The water-soluble portions have a molecular weight of about 5,000,000, whereas the insoluble glycogen fractions have molecular weights two or three times this figure. Methylation and periodate

17. W. Dvonch and R. L. Whistler, *J. Biol. Chem.* **181**, 889 (1949); W. Z. Hassid and R. M. McCready, *J. Am. Chem. Soc.* **63**, 1632 (1941).

18. W. N. Haworth and E. G. V. Percival, *J. Chem. Soc.* p. 2277 (1932).

19. D. J. Bell, H. Gutfreund, R. Cecil, and A. G. Ogston, *Biochem. J.* **42**, 405 (1948); M. R. Stetten, H. M. Katzen, and D. Stetten, Jr., *J. Biol. Chem.*, **222**, 587 (1956); see this article also for later work on molecular weights and metabolism.

oxidation show glycogens to be branched structures similar to amylopectins in that the molecules consist of chains of 1→4 linked α-D-glucopyranose units with α-1→6 links at the branch points (*20, 21*). The average length of a branch in a glycogen molecule is either 12 or 18 D-glucopyranose units, depending upon the source (*20–23*) of the glycogen, but in both types the branch lengths are less than the 25 to 27 units of amylopectin branches. Further evidence for the presence of 1→4 and 1→6 α-D-glucopyranosidic linkages is shown by the isolation in relatively large yields of maltose and isomaltose from partially hydrolyzed glycogen (*24*).

It has been reported that glycogens contain, in addition to D-glucose units, nitrogen, phosphorus, and uronic acid groups, but these reports have not been substantiated. Maltulose has been isolated from the products of α-amylase action on rabbit liver glycogen (*25*).

Amylases act on glycogen in a manner closely similar to that on amylopectin (see under Starch). As the storage product of carbohydrates in the animal body, glycogen is in equilibrium with other tissue components through the metabolic processes (Chapter XIII).

B. Chitin (*26, 27*)

Lower members of the animal world use the aminopolysaccharide chitin in structural tissues. It is also found in fungi and in insects. Chitin resembles cellulose in its chemical and biological properties.

Crab, shrimp, and lobster shells, waste products of the sea food industry, are the best sources of the polysaccharide. Calcium carbonate is first removed by hydrochloric acid and then protein and other organic impurities by extraction with sodium or potassium hydroxide solutions. Complete acid hydrolysis of chitin, although requiring drastic conditions, yields almost theoretical amounts of D-glucosamine and acetic acid (Chapter VIII), whereas controlled acid or enzyme hydrolysis produces *N*-acetyl-D-glucosamine. Acetolysis of chitin or acetylation of the partial acid hydrolysis products gives among other products chitobiose octaacetate which has been

20. W. N. Haworth, E. L. Hirst, and F. A. Isherwood, *J. Chem. Soc.* p. 577 (1937); W. N. Haworth, E. L. Hirst, and F. Smith, *J. Chem. Soc.* p. 1914 (1939).

21. K. Myrbäck, *Advances in Carbohydrate Chem.* **3,** 251 (1948).

22. D. J. Bell, *Biochem. J.* **29,** 2031 (1935); **30,** 2144 (1936); **31,** 1683 (1937).

23. T. G. Halsall, E. L. Hirst, and J. K. N. Jones, *J. Chem. Soc.* p. 1399 (1947).

24. M. L. Wolfrom, E. N. Lassettre, and A. N. O'Neill, *J. Am. Chem. Soc.* **73,** 595 (1951).

25. S. Peat, P. J. P. Roberts, and W. J. Whelan, *Biochem. J.* **51,** xvii (1952).

26. P. W. Kent and M. W. Whitehouse, "Biochemistry of the Aminosugars." Academic Press, New York, 1955.

27. R. L. Whistler and C. L. Smart, "Polysaccharide Chemistry." Academic Press, New York, 1953.

shown to consist of two *N*-acetyl-D-glucosamine units linked by a 1→4 β-glycosidic bond. This and other evidence suggests that chitin is a linear polymer of chitobiose.

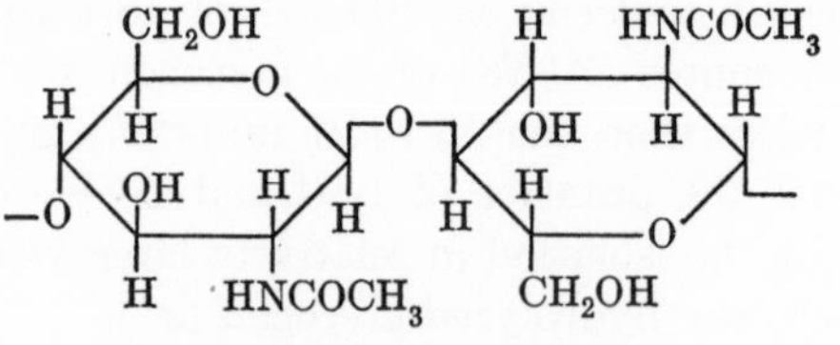
CH2OH
H HNCOCH3
O
H
H
O
OH
H
H
OH
H
O
H
H
H
O
H
HNCOCH3
CH2OH

Repeating unit of chitin

C. Galactan

A homozoöpolysaccharide composed of D-galactose has been isolated from beef lung (*28*). A galactan composed of D-galactose and L-galactose has been isolated from the eggs of *Helix pomatia*. Following methylation and hydrolysis, 2,4-di-*O*-methyl-D-galactopyranose and 2,3,4,6-tetra-*O*-methyl-DL-galactopyranose were isolated (*29*). On the basis of optical rotation data, the D/L ratio is indicated to be 6:1.

D. Hyaluronic Acid

Hyaluronic acid was first isolated by Karl Meyer from vitreous humor (*30*) and later from umbilical cord, synovial fluid, skin, cock's comb, certain fowl tumors, groups A and C hemolytic streptococci, and other sources (*31*). Historically, it has been a major and frequent if not universal component of Levene's so-called "mucoitin sulfates." The polysaccharide acts in animal tissue presumably as an integral part of the gel-like ground substance of connective tissue (and other tissues). Another important function of hyaluronic acid in animals is serving as a lubricant and shock absorbant in the joints.

Hyaluronic acid is generally prepared from umbilical cords. Most of the protein is removed by digestion with pepsin and trypsin, and the residual protein is separated by the chloroform – amyl alcohol procedure. Hyaluronic acid may be precipitated by fractionation with ammonium sulfate in the presence of pyridine (*32*). This step also removes a contaminating polysaccharide sulfate.

Hyalbiouronic acid, the deacetylated disaccharide obtained by action of

28. M. L. Wolfrom, D. I. Weisblat, J. V. Karabinos, and O. Keller, *Arch. Biochem.* **14,** 1 (1947).

29. D. J. Bell and E. Baldwin, *J. Chem. Soc.* p. 125 (1941); E. Baldwin and D. J. Bell, *ibid.* p. 1461 (1938).

30. K. Meyer and J. W. Palmer, *J. Biol. Chem.* **107,** 629 (1934).

31. K. Meyer and M. M. Rapport, *Advances in Enzymol.* **13,** 199 (1952).

32. R. W. Jeanloz and E. Forchielli, *J. Biol. Chem.* **186,** 495 (1950).

testicular hyaluronidase followed by mineral acid hydrolysis, has been characterized as 3-*O*-(β-D-glucopyranosyluronic acid)-2-amino-2-deoxy-D-glucose (*33*). Hyaluronic acid may be an unbranched or nearly unbranched polymer with the structure shown, but definite evidence for the linear nature has not been presented. The gelling properties of hyaluronic acid solutions would more likely be a property of a branched molecule, but cross-linking with salts (see Pectins) might cause gel formation.

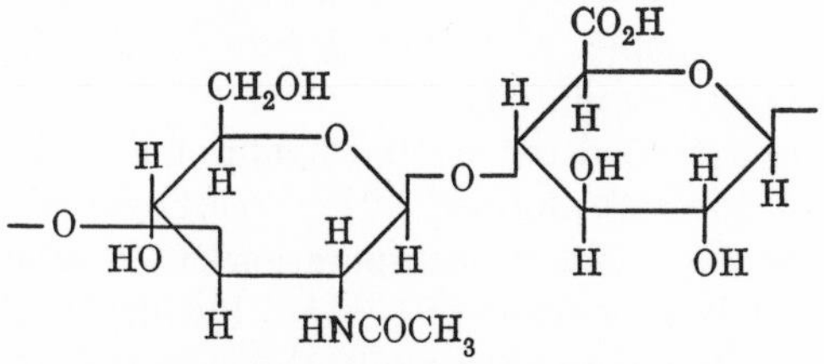
CO_2H
CH_2OH
O
H
O
H
H
OH
H
H
H
O
H
HO
H
H
OH
H
$HNCOCH_3$

Repeating unit of hyaluronic acid

Conflicting evidence has been presented indicating 1→3 (*34*), 1→4 (*35*), or mixed 1→3- and 1→4-linkages (*36*) between *N*-acetyl-D-glucosamine and D-glucuronic acid, but the evidence for the 1→4 linkage is the strongest (*36a*). The claim that hyaluronic acid was composed of a chitin core with polyglucosiduronic acid side chains (*37*) has been disproven by an analysis of the oligosaccharides formed by the action of testicular hyaluronidase (*38*).

In some samples of hyaluronic acid, the molar ratio of glucuronic acid to glucosamine appears to be greater than one (*39*). The molecular weight of umbilical hyaluronic acid as determined by light scattering has been reported as three to four million (*40*) and also as eight million (*41*).

Mucosin (*42*) and mucoitin (*43*) appear to be identical with hyalbiouronic acid and hyaluronic acid, respectively.

Very little is known about the biosynthesis of mammalian hyaluronic acid. Most of the work concerning the production of hyaluronic acid has been limited to that elaborated by group A streptococci. The C^{14} from glu-

33. B. Weissmann and K. Meyer, *J. Am. Chem. Soc.* **76,** 1753 (1954).
34. R. W. Jeanloz and E. Forchielli, *J. Biol. Chem.* **190,** 537 (1951).
35. K. H. Meyer, J. Fellig, and E. H. Fischer, *Helv. Chim. Acta* **34,** 939 (1951).
36. G. Blix, *Acta Chem. Scand.* **5,** 981 (1951).
36a. A. Linker, K. Meyer, and P. Hoffman, *J. Biol. Chem.* **219,** 13 (1956).
37. M. A. G. Kaye and M. Stacey, *Biochem. J.* **48,** 249 (1951).
38. B. Weissmann, K. Meyer, P. Sampson, and A. Linker, *J. Biol. Chem.* **208,** 417 (1954).
39. A. G. Ogston and J. E. Stanier, *Biochem. J.* **52,** 149 (1952).
40. T. C. Laurent and J. Gergely, *J. Biol. Chem.* **212,** 325 (1955).
41. B. S. Blumberg and G. Oster, *Science* **120,** 432 (1954).
42. T. Isikawa, *Tôhoku J. Exptl. Med.* **53,** 217 (1951).
43. M. Suzuki, *J. Biochem.* (*Japan*) **28,** 479 (1938).

cose-1-C^{14} or glucose-6-C^{14} was incorporated in approximately equal amounts at carbons 1 or 6, respectively, of the glucosamine and glucuronic acid moieties of the polysaccharide (*44*). These results indicate that glucose was converted to glucuronic acid and glucosamine without previous scission of the glucose. $C^{14}N^{15}$-Glucosamine was incorporated into the streptococcal hyaluronic acid without previous deamination (*45*). The pathway beginning with *N*-acetyl-D-glucosamine is uncertain. Some of the C^{14} of the acetyl-labeled sugar appeared in hyaluronic acid, but the streptococcal organism was shown to be capable of using acetate added free and also of deacetylating the acetyl aminosugar.

Studies have been carried out on the hyaluronic acid and chondroitin sulfate fractions of skin (*46a*) formed with C^{14}-carboxyl-labeled acetate as a carbon source. The major site of incorporation of C^{14} was in the *N*-acetyl moiety. The rate of incorporation of C^{14} into hyaluronic acid seems to be three times that of the incorporation into the chondroitin sulfate fraction.

Similar studies were carried out using C^{14} uniformly labeled glucose (*46b*). The results paralleled those obtained using the labeled acetate. The *N*-acetyl and glucosamine moieties of hyaluronic acid metabolized at the same rate. The components of chondroitin sulfate appeared to be converted into the polysaccharide at the same rate but at a rate slower than that for hyaluronic acid.

Of pronounced biological importance is the existence of an enzyme or enzymes (*31*) capable of hydrolyzing hyaluronates. The enzymes are very widespread, being found in a great variety of pathogenic organisms, in the venoms of many snakes and insects, in the salivary glands of leeches, and in certain insects. The enzymes are also found in animal tissues and are present at rather high concentrations in testes. Hyaluronidases are employed to aid the spreading and uptake of certain medicaments injected intramuscularly and subcutaneously. The enzymes are also of value in the treatment of traumatic swellings. Pneumococcal hyaluronidase hydrolyzes hyaluronic acid to disaccharide units consisting of a uronic acid and *N*-acetyl-D-glucosamine (*47*). Testicular hyaluronidase acts in a manner

44. S. Roseman, F. E. Moses, J. Ludowieg, and A. Dorfman, *J. Biol. Chem.* **203,** 213 (1953); S. Roseman, J. Ludowieg, F. E. Moses, and A. Dorfman, *J. Biol. Chem.* **206,** 665 (1954).

45. A. Dorfman, S. Roseman, F. E. Moses, J. Ludowieg, and M. Mayeda, *J. Biol. Chem.* **212,** 583 (1955).

46a. S. Schiller, M. B. Mathews, L. Goldfaber, J. Ludowieg, and A. Dorfman, *J. Biol. Chem.* **212,** 531 (1955).

46b. S. Schiller, M. B. Mathews, J. A. Cifonelli, and A. Dorfman, *J. Biol. Chem.* **218,** 139 (1956).

47. M. M. Rapport, A. Linker, and K. Meyer, *J. Biol. Chem.* **192,** 283 (1951); A. Linker and K. Meyer, *Nature* **174,** 1192 (1954).

similar to that of pneumococcal hyaluronidase by cleaving only *N*-acetylglucosaminidic bonds, but cleavage is less complete. The uronic acid present in the disaccharide isolated following the action of pneumococcal hyaluronidase appears to be a Δ-4,5-glucoseenuronic acid (*36a*), whereas D-glucuronic acid is found in the disaccharide produced by the action of testicular hyaluronidase.

E. Chondroitin Sulfates

Chondroitin sulfates are among the principal zoöpolysaccharides of the ground substance in mammalian tissue and in cartilage. Cattle nasal cartilage has been the chief source for the preparation of chondroitin sulfate (*1*), generally extracted by calcium chloride (*48*) or potassium chloride solution (*49*).

Three chondroitin sulfates have been isolated (*12*). These have been distinguished as A, B, and C (see Table I). Chondroitin sulfate A is the major chondroitin sulfate of bovine nasal septa and trachea. These products have been distinguished from each other on the basis of optical rotation and by their behavior to testicular hyaluronidase. The chondroitin sulfates A and C appear to consist of equimolar quantities of *N*-acetyl-2-amino-2-deoxy-D-galactose (*N*-acetylchondrosamine), D-glucuronic acid, and sulfuric acid. Chondrosine, the deacetylated disaccharide unit obtained by acid hydrolysis of presumed chondroitin sulfate A, is 3-0-(β-D-glucopyranosyluronic acid)-2-amino-2-deoxy-D-galactopyranose (*50*). Definite proof of the identification of the uronic component as glucuronic acid has not been offered for the C product. However, L-iduronic acid has been tentatively identified as the uronic acid of chondroitin sulfate B (*14a*).

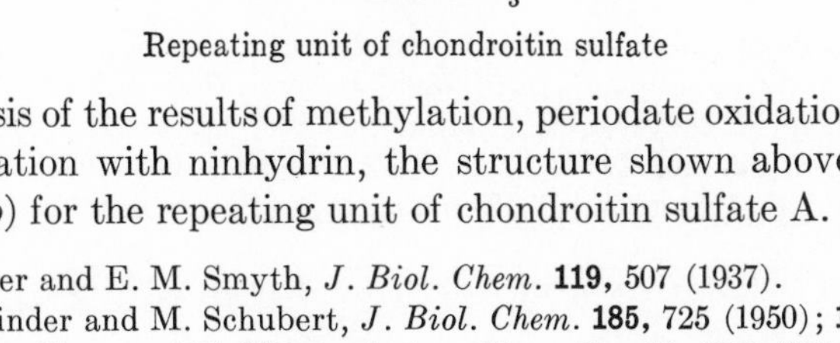

CO_2H
$HOSO_2$
OCH_2
O
H
OH
HNCOCH$_3$

Repeating unit of chondroitin sulfate

On the basis of the results of methylation, periodate oxidation, and oxidative deamination with ninhydrin, the structure shown above is proposed (*50, 51a, 51b*) for the repeating unit of chondroitin sulfate A.

48. K. Meyer and E. M. Smyth, *J. Biol. Chem.* **119,** 507 (1937).
49. J. Einbinder and M. Schubert, *J. Biol. Chem.* **185,** 725 (1950); **191,** 591 (1951).
50. E. A. Davidson and K. Meyer, *J. Am. Chem. Soc.* **76,** 5686 (1954).
51a. K. H. Meyer and G. Baldin, *Helv. Chim. Acta* **36,** 597 (1953).
51b. E. A. Davidson and K. Meyer, *J. Am. Chem. Soc.* **77,** 4796 (1955).

The linkage between repeating units appears to be of the 1→4 type (*51b*). The linkages of chondroitin sulfate are similar to the linkages in hyaluronic acid. The position of the sulfate group has not yet been established and may be at C-4 or C-6 of the galactosamine unit.

Highly purified chondroitin sulfuric acid from bovine cartilage has an osmotic molecular weight (*52*) of 43,300 in contrast to the less likely value of 260,000 estimated from viscosity data (*53a*).

Chondroitin, the nonsulfated polysaccharide, has been isolated from the corneal "hyaluronosulfate fraction" of Meyer (*54a*). It appears to be the desulfated chondroitin sulfate A or C. Chondrosine, the disaccharide obtained by the acid hydrolysis of this chondroitin, has an infrared absorption spectrum identical with that of the chondrosine of chondroitin sulfate A. An unsaturated acid is present in the disaccharide isolated following the action of pneumococcal hyaluronidase on chondroitin and desulfated chondroitin sulfate (*54b*).

So-called β-heparin, an anticoagulant isolated from the lung (*55*), is probably chondroitin sulfate B, for it contains approximately equimolar quantities of *N*-acetyl-D-galactosamine, a uronic acid (L-iduronic acid-?) and sulfuric acid (*14a*). It has about one-third of the anticoagulant activity of the usual heparin ("α-heparin").

Mixed digests of hyaluronic acid and chondroitin sulfate (A or C) with testicular hyaluronidase yield, in addition to the degradation products from the parent polysaccharides, products of transglycosylation, consisting of "hybrid" oligosaccharides and containing repeating units from both polysaccharides (*53b*).

F. Heparin (*56*)

Heparin ("α-heparin"), a blood anticoagulant, is found in liver, lung, thymus, spleen, and blood. It can be extracted from autolyzed beef liver by sodium hydroxide. After tryptic digestion of the proteins, heparin is precipitated with acidic ethanol (*57*). Heparin is usually crystallized as the barium salt. Purification through the free acid and reformation of the barium salt causes a decrease in the activity, as heparin is labile toward acidic

52. M. B. Mathews and A. Dorfman, *Arch. Biochem. and Biophys.* **42,** 41 (1953).

53a. G. Blix and O. Snellman, *Arkiv. Kemi Mineral. Geol.* **A19,** No. 32 (1945).

53b. P. Hoffman, K. Meyer, and A. Linker, *J. Biol. Chem.* **219,** 653 (1956).

54a. E. A. Davidson and K. Meyer, *J. Biol. Chem.* **211,** 605 (1954).

54b. A. Linker, K. Meyer, and P. Hoffman, *Abstr. Papers Am. Chem. Soc. Atlantic* City, p. 16D (1956).

55. R. Marbet and A. Winterstein, *Helv. Chim. Acta* **34,** 2311 (1951); I. Yamashina, *Acta Chem. Scand.* **8,** 1316 (1954).

56. J. E. Jorpes, "Heparin, Its Chemistry, Physiology and Application in Medicine." Oxford U. P., London, 1939; A. B. Foster and A. J. Huggard, *Advances in Carbohydrate Chem.* **10,** 336 (1955).

57. A. F. Charles and D. A. Scott, *Biochem. J.* **30,** 1927 (1936).

reagents. Heparin is a polymer of D-glucuronic acid and D-glucosamine. The amino group and some of the hydroxyls are sulfated (*58*). The D-glucuronic acid is decarboxylated during acid hydrolysis and liberates carbon dioxide. The molecular weight of heparin appears to be about 17,000 to 20,000. The probable repeating unit (*59*) is given in the accompanying formula.

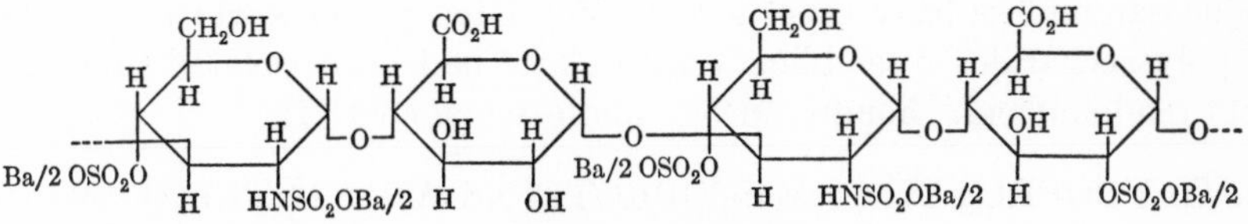
CH2OH
CO2H
CH2OH
CO2H
Ba/2 OSO2O
HNSO2OBa/2
OH
Ba/2 OSO2O
HNSO2OBa/2
OSO2OBa/2

Repeating unit of heparin

"β-Heparin," another anticoagulant, has been isolated from lung (*55a*). (See under Chondroitin sulfate.)

G. Blood-Group Polysaccharides (*60*)

The blood-group specific polysaccharides are found in the red blood cells, gastric mucin, saliva, ovarian cyst fluid, and other body secretions. Hog gastric mucin may be the most practical source (see Gastric mucin). These polysaccharides, combined with proteins, compose the A, B, O (H), Rh, and other antigens of the red blood cells and differentiate the various blood groups. If red cells of a specific type are brought in contact with their antibodies, agglutination of the red cells occur. The various blood-group substances are similar to each other in respect to the component simple sugar parts. D-Galactose, *N*-acetyl-D-glucosamine, and L-fucose were found to be present in the specific substances isolated from hog stomach (*61*). D-Mannose was apparently found in small amounts, but it is not an accepted constituent of the specific substance (*61*, *62*). Blood-group substance A, B, and O (H) isolated from ovarian cyst fluid showed the presence of L-fucose, D-galactose, D-glucosamine, D-galactosamine, and sialic acid (*63*). The presence of both glucosamine and galactosamine in the blood-group substances had been shown earlier (*64*).

58. J. E. Jorpes, H. Boström, and V. Mutt, *J. Biol. Chem.* **183,** 607 (1950).

59. M. L. Wolfrom, R. Montgomery, J. V. Karabinos, and P. Rathgeb, *J. Am. Chem. Soc.* **72,** 5796 (1950).

60. E. A. Kabat, "Blood Group Substances." Academic Press, New York, 1956. H. G. Bray and M. Stacey, *Advances in Carbohydrate Chem.* **4,** 37 (1949); E. A. Kabat and M. M. Mayer, "Experimental Immunochemistry." C. C Thomas, Springfield, Ill., 1948.

61. E. A. Kabat, A. Bendich, and A. E. Bezer, *J. Am. Chem. Soc.* **69,** 2163 (1947).

62. H. G. Bray, H. Henry, and M. Stacey, *Biochem. J.* **40,** 124 (1946).

63. R. A. Gibbons, W. T. J. Morgan, and M. Gibbons, *Biochem. J.* **60,** 428 (1955).

64. D. Aminoff and W. T. J. Morgan, *Nature* **162,** 579 (1948); D. Aminoff, W. T. Morgan, and W. M. Watkins, *Biochem. J.* **46,** 426 (1950).

H. Keratosulfate

Keratosulfate was isolated (*10*) upon fractionation of the so-called "hyaluronosulfate fraction" isolated from the cornea. It is composed of *N*-acetyl-D-glucosamine, D-galactose, and sulfuric acid, apparently combined in equimolar amounts. Attempts to hydrolyze keratosulfate by testicular and bacterial hyaluronidases, almond emulsin, crude β-glucuronidase, and β-glucosaminidase have been unsuccessful. Glycoproteins which contained zoöpolysaccharides resembling keratosulfate had been isolated previously from tendomucoid, chondromucoid, and osseomucoid (*4*).

3. GLYCOPROTEINS, MUCOPROTEINS AND INTERACTIONS OF ZOÖPOLYSACCHARIDES (*1, 4, 14*)

Knowledge of the role and state of combination of the glycoproteins and polysaccharides with other components of animal tissues and body fluids is a major prerequisite for an understanding of cellular and tissue composition and reactions. Some information is available, but mostly preliminary and frequently controversial results are available in this important field. The nomenclature is chaotic (p. 711).

The interaction of the components of ground substance, the amorphous matrix especially found between the cells of connective tissue, has received the most study (*65*). Collagen particularly has been studied. Collagen, reticulin, and elastin fibers (proteins) are embedded in a viscid ground substance, which appears to contain dissolved proteins, hyaluronic acid, and sulfate esters of other zoöpolysaccharides, especially of chondroitin sulfate. The soluble proteins present in connective tissue qualitatively are electrophoretically similar to those of blood serum (*66*). The metachromasia shown by the ground substance (Chapter XI) results from the presence of acidic substances. Synovial (joint) fluid appears to be closely related to ground substance, but is virtually devoid of sulfate esters (*67*).

Polar linkages seem to be the principal basis of association of the components of ground substance with the insoluble tissue components, for most of the dissolved components of ground substances and some of the fibrous elements are readily extracted by salt solutions or weak alkalies. Some type of interaction seems very probable, for extracted soluble collagen can be reversibly precipitated into several types of characteristic fibrils, the forms of which depend upon the precipitating conditions and upon the presence

65. See D. S. Jackson, *Biochem. J.* **54,** 638 (1953); J. T. Randall, ed., "Nature and Structure of Collagen." Academic Press, New York, 1953; G. Asboe-Hansen, ed., "Connective Tissue in Health and Disease." Munksgaard, Copenhagen, 1954; B. H. Persson, *Acta Soc. Med. Upsaliensis* **58,** No. 2, 1 (1953).

66. N. F. Boas, *Arch. Biochem. and Biophys.* **57,** 367 (1955).

67. L. Sundblad, *Acta Soc. Med. Upsaliensis* **58,** 113 (1953).

of certain glycoproteins or other materials (*68*). Chondroitin sulfate has been shown to precipitate the fibril form, whereas the addition of hyaluronic acid produced a fibrous precipitate with no axial periodicity. The hydrolysis of chondroitin sulfate by testicular "hyaluronidase" prior to extraction also greatly increases the ease of extraction of collagen from tendon (*65*).

The mucin precipitated from synovial fluids by weak acids appears to be a dissociable complex of hyaluronic acid and proteins. Electrophoretic studies of synovial fluids (at pH 8.6) have usually shown the presence of one fast-moving component considered to be free hyaluronic acid, but some fluids show a second fast component, possibly a hyaluronic acid – protein complex (*69*). On the basis of studies in the ultracentrifuge, the mucin possibly may exist in synovial fluid partially as a mucoprotein with a molecular weight of one to ten million (*70*). Electrophoretic and ultracentrifugal measurements at varying pH values provide two of the best ways of demonstrating interaction in such systems.

Masamune and associates (*4*) have provided some information concerning the nature of the combinations in other types of mucoproteins and of the proteins in the combinations. The mucoproteins of cartilage (chondromucoid) and of umbilical cord (funis mucin), removed from the tissues by aqueous extraction, are precipitated at pH 2 to 3. When the precipitated mucoproteins were extracted with solutions over the range pH 1 to 4, the composition of the residue did not remain constant; evidently the ratios of protein to carbohydrate in the mucoproteins are dependent upon the pH. Tendomucoid (from tendon) and osseomucoid (from bones) appear to be similar if not identical to chondromucoid.

Chondroitin sulfate could be separated from the chondromucoid. It remained in solution at pH 7 when chondromucoid was shaken with chloroform – amyl alcohol, whereas a second carbohydrate component (possibly keratosulfate or a closely related substance) remained with the protein fraction (*4*). Electrophoretic studies of chondromucoid show that the components associate in one kind of complex over the pH range 5 to 9 and that a different type of complex occurs below pH 4.85 (*71*). Shatton and Schubert (*72*) found both chondromucoid and free chondroitin sulfate in the extracts of bovine nasal cartilage; the mucoid was extracted first. Protein denaturants did not separate the protein portion of the mucoid. The protein was not collagen (*72*). Since hyaluronic acid does not appear to

68. J. Gross, *4th Josiah Macy Jr. Conf. on Metabolic Interrelations* p. 47 (1952).

69. D. Platt, W. Pigman, H. L. Holley, and F. M. Patton, *Arch. Biochem. and Biophys.* **64,** 152 (1956).

70. J. H. Fessler, A. G. Ogston, and J. E. Stanier, *Biochem. J.* **58,** 656 (1954).

71. S. M. Partridge, *Biochem. J.* **43,** 387 (1948).

72. J. Shatton and M. Schubert, *J. Biol. Chem.* **211,** 565 (1954).

bond with collagen, whereas chondroitin sulfate will, it appears that in neutral solutions sulfate but not carboxyl groups will produce bonding (*73*).

Similarly, the protein of funis (umbilical cord) mucin was precipitated by formaldehyde at pH 7, and the hyaluronic acid remained in solution. Other known sulfate esters (limacoitin sulfate and heparin) dissociated from the mucoproteins under similar conditions (*4*).

Although the polysaccharide sulfate esters of mucoproteins appear to be freely dissociable, the protein component may be a simple protein or a fairly firmly held conjugate with a second carbohydrate component. Such glycoproteins have been called "glucidamins" by Masamune and associates, although if the carbohydrate component is small or questionable they may be better considered as "simple" proteins. They usually contain a hexosamine residue. The coagulable proteins of serum, milk, bird eggs, phosphoproteins, and many plants are apparently of the latter type and may contain small amounts of firmly combined hexosamines and hexoses. The acidic polysaccharide components exist as anions in the mucoprotein complex. From a comparison of the number of total basic groups with the number of sulfate groups in the chondroitin sulfate of cartilage, the chondroitin sulfate appears to be mainly free (whale nasal cartilage) or combined with an equal number of basic groups (bull tracheal cartilage). In tendons and human umbilical cord, the basic protein groups are in great excess (*74*).

The nature of the proteins involved in mucoproteins and glycoproteins has received some preliminary study (*4*, *71*). A slight amount of evidence exists that the common protein components are albumins and globulins, except in mucous secretions. Pepsin and trypsin hydrolyze many of the mucoproteins or glycoproteins, but salivary mucoid and ovomucoid are quite resistant. At physiological pH (7.25 to 7.30), only fairly basic proteins would be expected to bond with carboxyl groups, and the sulfate bonding would be most probable for the common proteins.

Little or no information has been obtained concerning the stable (covalent) linkages in glycoproteins. The most likely are glycosylamine linkages formed from free amino groups and possibly stabilized by an Amadori rearrangement (Chapter VIII), glycosidic linkages through the hydroxyl groups of amino acids (such as serine, threonine, tyrosine, and hydroxyproline), and amide linkages from the amino groups of hexosamines.

In the following sections, the principal known glycoprotein or mucoprotein systems involving these products will be discussed.

A. Gastric Mucin

Gastric mucin is available commercially, as a product obtained from the mucosa of hog stomachs. The mucosal tissue is subjected to the action of

73. J. Einbinder and M. Schubert, *J. Biol. Chem.* **188,** 335 (1951).
74. T. Oh-Uehi and M. Utsushi, *Chem. Abstr.* **43,** 5104 (1949).

proteolytic enzymes and the mucin is precipitated from solution by alcohol (Meyer, Smyth, and Palmer (*75*) and Werner (*14*)). Apparently numerous biologically important zoöpolysaccharides, glycoproteins, and mucoproteins are present in the material.

Gastric mucin is the classical source of the so-called "mucoitin sulfates" of Levene (*1*) (see below). It has been an important source of the blood-group specific polysaccharides (see above), which appear to be the major known components (*76*). Other polysaccharide components are heparin, two chondroitin sulfates (*77*), and a zoöpolysaccharide composed of *N*-acetyl-D-glucosamine, D-galacturonic acid, and sulfuric acid (*78*).

"Mucoitin sulfate" has been considered to be composed of equimolar quantities of *N*-acetyl-D-glucosamine, D-glucuronic acid, and esterified sulfate (*1*). The mucoitin sulfate of gastric mucin was indicated by Levene as different from that of the cornea, vitreous humor, and umbilical cord. Such fractions have been reinvestigated by Meyer, who describes them as the "hyaluronosulfate fraction." Keratosulfate, chondroitin and its sulfate, heparin, and hyaluronic acid were isolated from such fractions. The gastric and corneal "mucoitin sulfates" in particular have been studied. (See previous discussion of "Mucoitin sulfate.")

B. Blood Serum Mucoids

The occurrence and composition of the glycoproteins in human blood serum have been reviewed by Winzler (*5*). Evidence for the existence of at least four such materials has been obtained by Schmid (*79*). One of these is present in serum to the extent of 0.5% and is the principal glycoprotein of the α_1-globulin fraction.

The α_1-glycoprotein (called orosomucoid by Winzler) was crystallized as a lead salt from fraction VI of the Cohn method 10 for serum fractionation. This product, probably the best characterized of the known glycoproteins, has the following analysis: N, 10.7%; polypeptide, 66%; hexose, 17.2%; hexosamine, 11.5%; phosphoric acid, 1.2%. The isoelectric point is at pH 2.7 (phosphate buffers; ionic strength, 0.1). The product is soluble in water, is stable at 100° in solution, and apparently has a low molecular weight (*79*). The carbohydrate components of "serum mucoid" had been indicated previously as: D-galactose, D-mannose, D-glucosamine, D-galactosamine, and L-fucose (*5*). Sialic acid or a precursor is also present.

75. K. Meyer, E. M. Smyth, and J. W. Palmer, *J. Biol. Chem.* **119,** 73 (1937).

76 K. Landsteiner and M. W. Chase, *J. Exptl. Med.* **63,** 813 (1936); K. Landsteiner and R. A. Harte, *ibid.* **71,** 551 (1940); W. T. J. Morgan and H. K. King, *Biochem. J.* **37,** 640 (1943).

77. H. Smith, R. C. Gallop, P. W. Harris-Smith, and J. L. Stanley, *Biochem. J.* **52,** 23 (1952); H. Smith and R. C. Gallop, *ibid.* **53,** 666 (1953).

78. R. Satoh, *Tôhoku J. Exptl. Med.* **56,** 387 (1952).

79. K. Schmid, *J. Am. Chem. Soc.* **75,** 60, 2532 (1953); **77,** 742 (1955).

A glycoprotein containing uronic acid, hexosamine, and one or more sugars has been found in human euglobulin (*80*).

A hyaluronidase inhibitor in human blood has been isolated and purified (*81*). This glycoprotein contains 4% hexosamine and 2% uronic acid and has a molecular weight of about 100,000.

C. Urinary Mucoids

Mörner isolated two water-soluble glycoproteins (called urinary mucoids) from urine by alcohol precipitation, redissolution, and precipitation with chloroform in the presence of acetic acid (*1, 4*). Interest in these substances was stimulated by the isolation of a purified urinary glycoprotein which proved to be a strong inhibitor of the hemagglutination by influenza virus and similar viruses (*82, 83*). Sialic acid (see below) is said to be removed from the glycoprotein by the virus.

The purified urinary glycoprotein dialyzes through cellophane membranes. Its minimum molecular weight (based on the L-fucose content) appears to be the formula weight of about 2,500 or some small multiple, probably less than 3 or 4. Paper chromatography of the hydrolysis products has shown the presence of D-galactose (5.4%), D-mannose (2.7%), and L-fucose (1%) (*83*). The hexosamine content is given as 7.6%, and both D-glucosamine and D-galactosamine may be present. Odin (*84*) has indicated that the identification of the hexosamine is in question and that sialic acid is also present to the extent of 7.3 to 9.4%.

A glycoprotein resembling the α_1-glycoprotein of blood serum has been isolated from the urine of patients with proteinuria (*85*). It contains D-glucosamine, D-mannose, and D-galactose as its carbohydrate constituents. Its electrophoretic behavior and immunochemical reactions greatly resemble those of the α_1-glycoprotein isolated by Schmid. It is clearly not the glycoprotein isolated from normal urine by Tamm and Horsfall.

D. Salivary Mucoproteins

One of the best-known mucins is that obtained from saliva and extracts of the submaxillary and sublingual glands. It is best prepared from neutral extracts of animal glands or from saliva by precipitation with weak acids (pH 2.5 to 3.5). It is purified by dissolution in stronger acids (pH 1 to 1.5)

80. J. Badin, M. Schubert, and M. Vouras, *J. Clin. Invest.* **34,** 1317 (1955).

81. J. K. Newman, G. S. Berenson, M. B. Mathews, E. Goldwasser, and A. Dorfman, *J. Biol. Chem.* **217,** 31 (1955).

82. I. Tamm and F. L. Horsfall, Jr., *Proc. Soc. Exptl. Biol. Med.* **74,** 108 (1950); *J. Exptl. Med.* **95,** 71 (1952).

83. A. Gottschalk, *Nature* **170,** 662 (1952).

84. L. Odin, *Nature* **170,** 663 (1952).

85. E. A. Popenoe, *J. Biol. Chem.* **217,** 61 (1955).

(*86*) and subsequent reprecipitation at pH 2.5 to 3.5. Animal salivary mucins have been studied in some detail, but little is known of the human mucins. According to Tanabe (*87*), the extracts of cattle glands also contain a mucoid which is not precipitated with the mucin. The sublingual mucin has a nitrogen content of 11 to 12% and a reducing value, after hydrolysis, corresponding to 15 to 16% of glucose. D-Glucosamine has been isolated from the acid hydrolyzates.

Preliminary electrophoretic studies at pH 6.1, 6.8, 7.5, and 8.0 on dissolved cattle submaxillary mucin show only one component (*6*). By treatment of cattle sublingual mucin with 2% sodium hydroxide at room temperature for 5 hours and subsequent fractionation, Tanabe obtained a glycoprotein and two so-called polysaccharides (II and III). "Polysaccharide II" (obtained in small amounts) appeared to be "mucoitin" (hyaluronic acid). "Polysaccharide III," obtained in a yield of 20% of the mucin, appeared to be a glycoprotein (N, 10%). It was reported to contain *N*-acetyl-D-glucosamine and probably galactose and glucuronic acid; possibly, this product is one of the blood-type substances. Polysaccharide I, obtained by alkaline hydrolysis of the first glycoprotein, in which it is present in small amounts (3%), was reported as a polymer of *N*-acetyl-D-glucosamine (1 part) and D-mannose (2 parts). The mucoid not precipitated with the mucin was found to be composed of products III and I. Similar products were obtained from cattle submaxillary glands.

Blix (*88*) found chemically that cattle submaxillary mucins contain three components. Two are "neutral" carbohydrates in small amounts, one of the blood-group type and the other a "dihexosehexosamine" type (possibly Tanabe-I). These "neutral" carbohydrates could be removed by reprecipitation of the mucin. The major component of the mucins is a glycoprotein, described as having 10% nitrogen and 16% hexosamine, identified by isolation of D-galactosamine. The purified mucin is said to contain 25 to 30% of sialic acid (see Sialic acid), which splits off fairly readily. The sialic acid or precursor may be bound to the galactosamine. Presumably the glucosamine isolated by other workers is a component of the sialic acid (or precursor) or of the accompanying polysaccharide.

Simmons (*89*) isolated a mucoid (glycoprotein) in fairly good yield from the extracts of pig submaxillary glands by alkaline extraction in the presence of sodium dodecyl sulfate. The product was separated and purified by fractional alcohol precipitation with ethyl and isopropyl alcohols at

86. O. Hammarsten, *Z. physiol. Chem.* **12,** 163 (1888).

87. Y. Tanabe, *J. Biochem.* (*Japan*) **28,** 227 (1938); **29,** 377, 381, 387 (1939); **30,** 11, 181 (1939).

88. G. Blix, *Z. physiol. Chem.* **240,** 43 (1936); G. Blix, L. Svennerholm, and I. Werner, *Acta Chem. Scand.* **6,** 358 (1952).

89. N. S. Simmons, Thesis, University of Rochester (1950).

pH 7 (acetate buffers). It was presumably a glycoprotein (9 to 10% N) containing 16% glucosamine; an amino acid analysis was made. Its relation to mucin is not clear, but it precipitates many proteins below their isoelectric points.

Blood-group specific substances have been isolated in amount of about 3 mg. per 100 cc. from the salivas of persons of the A, B, and O types (*90*). So-called "nonsecretors" excrete a similar polysaccharide which does not give the serological reactions typical of the blood-specific substances.

E. Gonadotropic Hormones and Thyroglobulin (*91*)

Four purified glycoprotein hormones with the ability to stimulate hormone production by the ovary or testes (gonadotropic activity) are well known. These are the interstitial cell-stimulating hormone (ICSH) and the follicle-stimulating hormone (FSH) of the anterior pituitary, the chorionic gonadotropin (HCG) of human pregnancy urine, and the gonadotropin of the blood serum of pregnant mares (PMSG). The protein and carbohydrate are firmly bound, and both portions of the molecule appear necessary for the hormonal actions. However, pepsin liberated an active dialyzable fragment from FSH.

A comparison of the partial composition of some of these materials is given below:

Gonadotropin	*N (%)*	*Hexose (%)*	*Hexosamine (%)*	*Mol. wt.*
ICSH (Sheep)	14.2	D-Mannose (4.5)	5.8	40,000
ICSH (Hog)	14.9	D-Mannose (2.8)	2.2	100,000
FSH (Sheep)	15.1	1.3	0.6	(70,000)
		1.2	1.5	67,000
PMSG (Horse)	10.7	D-Galactose (14.1–17.6)	8.4	—
HCG	12.0	D-Galactose (10.7)	5.2	100,000

Thyroglobulin has been shown probably to contain 2.4% glucosamine and two aldohexoses, galactose and mannose (*92*).

F. Ovomucoid

Ovomucoid was isolated originally by Mörner (*1*) from egg white by precipitation with weakly acidic alcohol after heat coagulation of other proteins. More recent isolation methods are based on fractionation with

90. K. Landsteiner and R. A. Harte, *J. Biol. Chem.* **140,** 673 (1941); R. A. Harte, *ibid.* **167,** 873 (1947).

91. C. H. Li, *Vitamins and Hormones* **7,** 223 (1949); C. H. Li and J. I. Harris, *Ann. Rev. Biochem.* **21,** 603 (1952); S. Gurin, C. Bachman, and D. W. Wilson, *J. Biol. Chem.* **128,** 525 (1939); **133,** 467, 477 (1940); H. Goss and H. H. Cole, *Endocrinology* **15,** 214 (1931); **26,** 244 (1940).

92. G. Lacombe and R. Michel, *Compt. rend. soc. biol.* **149,** 888 (1955).

ammonium sulfate (*93*). The carbohydrate moiety (*ca.* 25%) is bound firmly to the protein and can be separated only after drastic treatment. The constituents of the carbohydrate have been indicated as D-mannose, D-glucosamine (*94*), and D-galactose (*93*). Different hexosamine/hexose ratios have been reported, 1:1 (*95*) and 7:4 (*96*).

It appeared to be homogenous in the ultracentrifuge (*97*) but was shown to be heterogeneous when subjected to electrophoretic analysis (*97, 98*).

Ovomucoid is quite resistant to tryptic digestion. In fact, each of the three electrophoretic components exhibits pronounced antitryptic activity (*97*).

Upon methylation and hydrolysis, the polysaccharide obtained after the action of trypsin on ovomucoid yielded: *N*-acetyl-3,4,6-tri-*O*-methyl-D-glucosamine (7 moles), D-mannose (2 moles), 3,4,6-tri-*O*-methyl-D-mannopyranose (1 mole), and tetra-*O*-methyl-D-galactopyranose (1 mole). If correct, these results indicate a highly branched structure with every hydroxyl of some of the mannose units being substituted by a ring or glycosyl units (*96*).

4. GLYCOLIPIDES AND GLYCOLIPOPROTEINS (*3, 60*)

A number of biologically important compounds or complexes of carbohydrates with lipides and sometimes also with proteins have been found in animal tissues (and some bacteria). The Wassermann antigens and the Forssman antigens apparently are materials of this type. The cerebrosides and gangliosides (Chapter X) might be considered to belong to this group. All appear to contain a hexosamine residue.

The structure of an active fragment of blood-group A lipide from human liver has been indicated as a cephalin-tripeptide-heptasaccharide. The peptide is represented as glutamyl-seryl-glutamic acid; the peptide is connected by *N*-glycosyl linkages to a heptasaccharide composed of two moles of D-galactosamine, two of D-mannose, and three of D-galactose (*99*).

5. THE PROBLEM OF SIALIC ACID

Many tissues, fluids, mucoproteins, and glycoproteins have been shown to contain a material capable of reacting directly with Ehrlich's reagent,

93. M. Sørensen, *Biochem. Z.* **269,** 271 (1934).

94. S. Fränkel and C. Jellinek, *Biochem. Z.* **185,** 392 (1927).

95. H. Masamune and S. Hoshino, *J. Biochem.* (*Japan*) **24,** 219 (1936); O. Karlberg. *Z. physiol. Chem.* **240,** 55 (1936).

96. M. Stacey and J. M. Wooley, *J. Chem. Soc.* p. 184 (1940); p. 550 (1942).

97. E. Fredericq and H. F. Deutsch, *J. Biol. Chem.* **181,** 499 (1949); M. Bier, J. A. Duke, R. J. Gibbs, and F. F. Nord, *Arch. Biochem. and Biophys.* **37,** 491 (1952).

98. L. G. Longsworth, R. K. Cannan, and D. A. MacInnes, *J. Am. Chem. Soc.* **62,** 2580 (1940).

99. S. Hakomori, *Tôhoku J. Exptl. Med.* **60,** 331 (1954).

p-dimethylaminobenzaldehyde in hot strongly acid solution, to form a purple color. Materials giving a positive "direct Ehrlich test" have been isolated and crystallized and have been variously described as sialic acid, neuraminic acid, hemataminic acid, lactaminic acid, and gynaminic acid. This as yet uncharacterized component may play an important role in the cell structure and body functions.

In order to give a positive test with the Ehrlich reagent, hexosamines having a free amino group require previous treatment with an acylating agent followed by treatment with alkalies (see Hexosamines). The *N*-acylhexosamines require only the pretreatment with alkali, but crystalline sialic acid and similar materials and the previously unhydrolyzed glycoproteins react directly with Ehrlich's reagent to produce the purple color. The color obtained has an absorption maximum at 565 mμ (*100*) which differs from the absorption maximum at 530 obtained from hexosamines by the Elson-Morgan procedure (*101*).

Such materials may interfere with the determination of hexosamines (see Chapter VIII). With the colors produced by sialic acid as a reference, Werner and Odin (*100*) have estimated the amounts of sialic acid in several glycoproteins, including serum glycoprotein and ovomucin. They used Bial's orcinol, the direct Ehrlich reaction, diphenylamine, and tryptophan-perchloric acid.

In 1936, from the products of the mild hydrolysis of bovine submaxillary mucin, Blix (*88*, *102a*) isolated in minute yields a crystalline material which gave the "direct Ehrlich" test (see also under Salivary polysaccharides). This crystalline material was later named sialic acid. Submaxillary mucin may offer the best source of compounds related to or resembling sialic acid (*102b*). In 1941, Klenk crystallized a compound from brain gangliosides, called neuraminic acid (*103*). It appears to be closely related to sialic acid and has also been isolated from bovine submaxillary mucin, urinary glycoprotein, the gangliosides of spleen and other tissues, milk, and red blood cell stroma (*104*). Neuraminic acid occurs in combination with lactose in the mammary gland of the lactating rat (*105*). A hemataminic acid (*106*)

100. I. Werner and L. Odin, *Acta Soc. Med. Upsaliensis* **57,** 230 (1952).

101. J. Immers and E. Vasseur, *Acta Chem. Scand.* **6,** 363 (1952).

102a. G. Blix, E. Lindberg, L. Odin, and I. Werner, *Acta Soc. Med. Upsaliensis* **61,** 1 (1956).

102b. F. Zilliken, G. A. Braun, and P. György, *Arch. Biochem. and Biophys.* **63,** 394 (1956).

103. E. Klenk, *Z. physiol. Chem.* **268,** 50 (1941).

104. E. Klenk, *Z. physiol. Chem.* **273,** 76 (1942); E. Klenk and F. Rennkamp, *ibid.* **273,** 253 (1942); E. Klenk and K. Lauenstein, *ibid.* **291,** 147, 249 (1952); **295,** 164 (1953).

105. R. E. Trucco and R. Caputto, *J. Biol. Chem.* **206,** 901 (1954).

106. T. Yamakawa and S. Suzuki, *J. Biochem. (Japan)* **38,** 199 (1951).

and a lactaminic acid (*107*), very similar or identical to neuraminic acid, have also been described.

An *N*-acetylneuraminic acid has been isolated from bovine submaxillary mucin and the urinary glycoprotein (urinary mucoprotein of Tamm and Horsfall) following the enzymic action of the influenza virus on the glycoproteins (*108*). Gynaminic acid, from milk and meconium appear to be identical to the *N*-acetylneuraminic acid (sialic acid?) from sheep submaxillary gland and different from that from bovine submaxillary glands and lactaminic acid from bovine colostrum (*102b*, *109*).

2-Carboxypyrrole has been isolated from alkaline hydrolyzate of some mucoids (*110*). Gottschalk indicated that the 2-carboxypyrrole is an artifact formed during the hydrolysis of 4-hydroxypyrroline-2-carboxylic acid, which is unstable (*111*) but possibly is stabilized in the source material by a glycosidic linkage. No evidence for the presence of the pyrroline ring in the original glycoprotein was obtained.

A nonose structure has been proposed for sialic acid, neuraminic acid (*108*, *112*) and hemataminic acid (*106*). The structures for the compounds in the sialic acid family have yet to be established. They have been characterized as nitrogen-containing, monobasic, polyhydroxy, reducing acids (*102a*, *102b*, *108*). The empirical formula of sialic acid obtained from sheep submaxillary mucin appears to be $C_{11}H_{19}NO_9$ (*102a*, *102b*) with an *N*-acetyl group and is the same as that for gynaminic acid from human milk. Similar compounds isolated from the submaxillary glands of cattle, pig and horse differ in their X-ray diffraction patterns (*102a*). Hypoiodite titration indicates the presence of a reducing group (*102a*, *113*) and approximately one mole of hydrogen is taken up per mole of sialic acid on treatment with sodium borohydride (*102a*). Two moles of periodate were consumed by sheep sialic acid (*102a*) and gynaminic acid (*102b*) with the formation of one mole of formic acid (*102a*).

Sialic acid from bovine submaxillary glands upon enzymic degradation is reported to give equal amounts of pyruvic acid and *N*-acetylglucosamine

107. R. Kuhn, R. Brossmer, and W. Schulz, *Chem. Ber.* **87,** 123 (1954).

108. E. Klenk and H. Faillard, *Z. physiol. Chem.* **298,** 230 (1954); E. Klenk, H. Faillard, and H. Hempfried, *ibid.* **301,** 235 (1955); E. Klenk, H. Faillard, F. Weygand, and H. H. Schöne, *ibid.* **304,** 35 (1956).

109. F. Zilliken, G. A. Braun, and P. György, *Arch. Biochem. and Biophys.* **54,** 564 (1954).

110. A. Gottschalk, *Nature* **172,** 808 (1953); N. Hiyama, *Tôhoku J. Exptl. Med.* **51,** 317 (1949).

111. A. Gottschalk, *Nature* **174,** 654 (1954); *Biochem. J.* **61,** 298 (1955).

112. A. Gottschalk, *Nature* **176,** 881 (1955).

113. R. Heimer and K. Meyer, *Abstr. Papers Am. Chem. Soc., Atlantic City*, p. 71C (1956).

(*114*). Apparently a nonose structure as indicated above or some other combination, possibly glycosidic, of these components can be given for the various sialic-neuraminic acids and derivatives. These appear to differ in the number and type of acylating groups and in the presence of esters and acetal methyl groups.

114. R. Heimer and K. Meyer, *Proc. Natl. Acad. Sci. U. S.* **42,** 728 (1956).

XIII. PHOTOSYNTHESIS AND METABOLISM OF CARBOHYDRATES

G. R. Noggle

1. PHOTOSYNTHESIS

A. Introduction

The essential features of the photosynthetic reaction have been known since 1845 when it was recognized that the fundamental transformation of photosynthesis was the conversion of light energy into chemical energy and that the reaction could be written as follows:

$$\text{Carbon dioxide} + \text{water} \xrightarrow[\text{green plant}]{\text{light}} \text{organic matter} + \text{oxygen} + \text{chemical energy} \quad (1)$$

Since that time plant physiologists, biochemists, biophysicists, organic chemists, physicists, microbiologists, physical chemists, and others have contributed to the literature of photosynthesis (*1*).

The early work in photosynthesis was based on the assumption that carbon dioxide fixation was a process unique in green plants, and studies were made on the effect of various external factors such as light intensity, light quality, carbon dioxide concentration, and temperature. Certain internal factors were also recognized as affecting photosynthesis. Many fundamental studies on photosynthesis were concerned with the chemistry of the chlorophyll molecule. Enzymes were studied, and attempts were made to carry out cell-free photosynthesis by conventional biochemical techniques. While these studies contributed a great deal of information regarding the photosynthetic reaction, they did little to elucidate the mechanism of the process.

During the 1930's, however, research in the field of photosynthesis and in a number of allied sciences indicated that the concept of the nature of the problem of photosynthesis could be very profitably altered. The discovery in 1935 by Wood and Werkman (*2*) that propionic acid bacteria

1. A list of some general references on photosynthesis will be found at the end of Chapter XV (Bibliography).

2. H. G. Wood and C. H. Werkman, *J. Bacteriol.* **30,** 332 (1935).

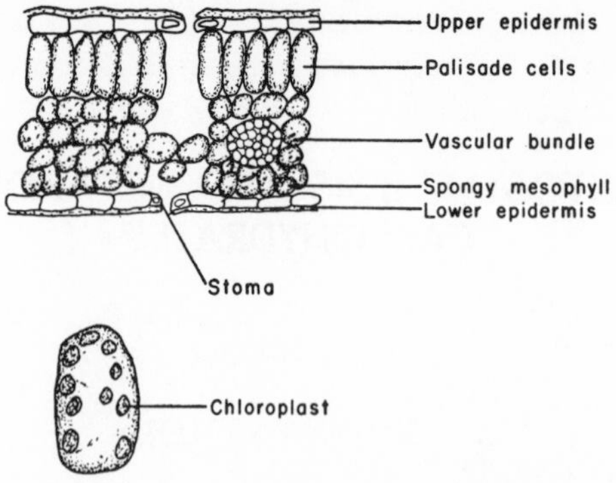
Upper epidermis
Palisade cells
Vascular bundle
Spongy mesophyll
Lower epidermis
Stoma
Chloroplast

FIG. 1. Cross-section of leaf (upper) and enlarged cell from the palisade tissue (lower) showing chloroplasts.

could fix carbon dioxide led to investigations (*3*) that have shown that practically all living organisms are capable of fixing carbon dioxide. It became possible to view carbon dioxide fixation by plants as a process similar to that occurring in other organisms and to apply to the photosynthesis problem concepts from bacterial and animal metabolism. The second discovery of major importance was the finding by Hill (*4*) that isolated chloroplasts, when illuminated, could liberate oxygen and reduce added oxidants. This discovery freed the plant physiologist of the notion that photosynthesis could only be studied in intact living plants.

Since 1940 many new techniques and methods have been applied to photosynthesis research. Isotope studies have been especially valuable in elucidating the path of carbon in photosynthesis. Advantage has been taken of new advances in the field of enzyme chemistry. It is the purpose of this section to outline the essential features of what is presently known about photosynthesis and to review the significance of some of the recent discoveries.

B. STRUCTURAL ASPECTS OF THE PHOTOSYNTHETIC APPARATUS

Photosynthesis in plants is carried on by the chloroplasts of the leaves. The distribution of the chloroplasts in the leaf of a land plant is shown in Fig. 1. The surface of the leaf is covered by a layer of waxy material called cutin. This waxy layer does not completely block the passage of gases and dissolved materials to and from the interior of the leaf, but the major exchange of gas and water vapor occurs through openings in the leaf known as stomata. Gases entering the stomata diffuse into the intercellular spaces and then come into contact with the chloroplast-containing cells.

3. M. F. Utter and H. G. Wood, *Advances in Enzymol.* **12,** 41 (1951).
4. R. Hill, *Nature* **139,** 881 (1937).

The leaves of water plants are not covered by cutin and contain no stomata. The epidermal cells very often contain chloroplasts as do the other cells in the leaf. Carbon dioxide enters the leaf in the dissolved state and comes into intimate contact with the chloroplast-containing cells.

The chloroplasts are embedded in the cytoplasm of the cell and are one of a number of cytoplasmic particles that are found in plant cells. There is no general agreement as to the nature of these various cytoplasmic particles (*5*). The term "mitochondria" is commonly used to denote one of these fractions, and a great deal of work has been carried out on their physiological role particularly with respect to the localization of enzymes (*6*). Comparable work with mammalian tissue has shown the mitochondrial fraction to be the site of action of a number of important enzyme systems (*7*).

The chloroplasts are small green bodies that vary somewhat in size and number per cell depending upon the species of plant and the environmental conditions under which the plant is grown. They are found in the higher plants, green algae, red algae, and brown algae, but not in blue-green algae nor the photosynthetic bacteria, where the chlorophyll appears in the form of grana. The structure and morphology of the chloroplasts have been discussed thoroughly in several recent reviews (*8*, *9*). In appearance they are discs or flat ellipsoids 3–10 μ across. The chloroplasts have a membrane, and within this membrane there may be several additional structures. The chlorophyll appears to be concentrated in bodies known as "grana" which are embedded in a colorless stroma.

The grana have been investigated by means of the electron microscope, and in spinach chloroplasts (*10*) approximately forty to sixty grana were found. The grana were thin discs about 6,000 Å. in diameter and 800 Å. thick. There is some evidence (*11*) that the grana themselves are made up of stacks of ten to twenty thin lamallae which are 75 to 100 Å. thick. The significance of the ultra-fine structure of the chloroplast is not thoroughly understood. If all of the chlorophyll is concentrated in the chloroplast then each granum, or each lamella in a granum, must contain several chlorophyll molecules. The close packing of the grana may then enable the light energy absorbed by one chlorophyll molecule to be passed along through a

5. E. H. Newcomer, *Botan. Rev.* **17,** 53 (1951).

6. D. R. Goddard and H. A. Stafford, *Ann. Rev. Plant Physiol.* **5,** 115 (1954).

7. A. L. Dounce, *in* "The Enzymes" (J. B. Sumner and K. Myrbäck, eds.), Vol. 1, Part 1, p. 187. Academic Press, New York, 1950.

8. S. Granick, *in* "Photosynthesis in Plants" (J. Franck and W. E. Loomis, eds.), p. 113. Iowa State College Press, Ames, 1949.

9. T. E. Weier and C. R. Stocking, *Botan. Rev.* **18,** 14 (1952).

10. S. Granick and K. R. Porter, *Am. J. Botany* **34,** 545 (1947).

11. S. Granick, *Chem. and Eng. News* **31,** 748 (1953).

number of chlorophyll molecules until the energy reaches an active center where reduction occurs (*11*). The structural properties of the chloroplast may be very important in any physical or chemical explanation of the mechanism of photosynthesis.

With the realization that the chloroplast was the site of at least part of the photosynthetic reaction, a great deal of work was done on the isolation of the chloroplasts. Such preparations are generally contaminated with nuclear and cytoplasmic material (*12*), and attempts to ascribe observed results solely to the chloroplasts should be viewed with caution. Accompanying the isolation studies have been analyses on the chemical and enzyme composition of the chloroplasts. On a dry-weight basis, the chloroplast contains about 45% protein and 25% lipid. The ash content is between 5 and 15% of the dry weight while the pigments account for 5 to 10%. The balance of the chloroplast is made up of carbohydrates, enzymes, and other unidentified compounds. The composition of the chloroplast material is quite variable and depends upon the plant species as well as upon the conditions of growth, i.e., nutrition, light, water, etc.

C. Kinetic Studies on Photosynthesis

From a consideration of the photosynthetic equation (1), it is apparent that the rate of photosynthesis may be determined by measuring the disappearance of carbon dioxide, the evolution of oxygen, or the increase in dry weight (synthesis of protoplasm). Rate studies, or reaction kinetics, have been widely utilized in studying photosynthesis, and such studies have been recently reviewed by Rabinowitch (*13*), who points out: "Photosynthesis is such a complex and heterogeneous process that it is probably impossible to make a complete analysis of its mechanism merely by measuring the rate of the over-all process under different conditions. However, this does not mean that kinetic measurements of photosynthesis are useless, but rather that they are most useful when combined with other biochemical and biophysical methods of approach. . . ."

Kinetic studies indicated that photosynthesis is dependent upon a number of external and internal factors. Of the external factors, carbon dioxide concentration, light, and temperature are the most important, whereas the chlorophyll concentration is probably the most important internal factor. The concentrations of various enzymes as well as certain undefined "protoplasmic factors" have also been suggested as limiting photosynthesis.

12. T. E. Weier and C. R. Stocking, *Am. J. Botany* **39,** 720 (1952); T. E. Weier, *Protoplasma* **42,** 260 (1953).

13. E. Rabinowitch, "Photosynthesis and Related Processes," Vol. II, Part 1, p. 831. Interscience, New York, 1951.

a. Carbon Dioxide Concentration

The average concentration of carbon dioxide in the air is roughly 0.03% by volume. The rate of photosynthesis increases as the carbon dioxide concentration is increased until the light intensity becomes a limiting factor. If the light intensity is increased, then the rate of photosynthesis is again increased by raising the CO_2 concentration. Prolonged exposure of plants to high concentrations of CO_2 is generally harmful.

b. Light

Two different effects of light on photosynthesis are recognized: the quantity or intensity of the light and the quality or spectral distribution of the light. The rate of photosynthesis increases as the light intensity is increased from zero until some other factor becomes limiting. Light-intensity curves are characterized by a linear increase in rate of photosynthesis at low light intensities. As the light intensity increases the curve flattens out, and an increase in light intensity does not bring about a corresponding increase in the rate of photosynthesis—a situation known as light saturation. At very high light intensities photosynthesis may actually be inhibited.

Plants kept in the dark do not carry out photosynthesis but do respire, i.e., evolve carbon dioxide and take in oxygen. As the darkened plants are given increasing amounts of light, photosynthesis will increase, and carbon dioxide will be utilized and oxygen evolved. At some particular light level, called the compensation point, the gas exchange due to respiration and to photosynthesis will exactly balance each other. Above the compensation point, photosynthesis exceeds respiration. In photosynthesis research, it was generally assumed that light had no effect on respiration and that "true photosynthesis" could be calculated by subtracting respiration gas-exchange values measured on a dark control. There was no direct way of measuring the photoeffect of respiration until Brown (*14*) used tracer oxygen to measure the respiratory rate. He found no evidence of photoinhibition or photoenhancement of respiration in several strains of *Chlorella* commonly used in photosynthesis research. The conditions of the experiment were similar to those that are ordinarily used in photosynthesis research. The practice of measuring photosynthesis by applying a correction for dark respiration appears to be valid, at least for *Chlorella*.

Studies on the effect of light of different wavelengths on photosynthesis have been carried out since the essential features of the process were first discovered. In their simplest form, such experiments consisted of measuring the rate of photosynthesis in plants placed in light that had passed through different colored filters. From these and more refined measure-

14. A. H. Brown, *Am. J. Botany* **40**, 719 (1953).

ments, it has been shown that plants carry out photosynthesis in light varying in wavelengths between 3900 Å. and 7600 Å.

The study of the wavelength dependence of photosynthesis has been extremely valuable in determining the role of the various pigments in photosynthesis. Such studies have been carried out by comparing the action spectrum of photosynthesis with the absorption spectrum of the plant. The photosynthetic action spectrum is determined by measuring the

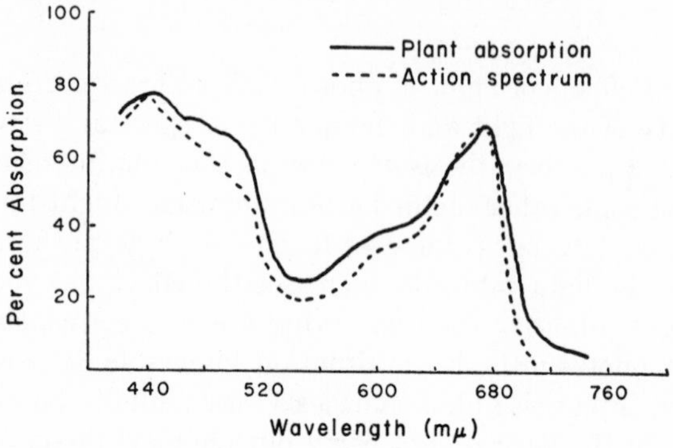
Plant absorption
Action spectrum
Per cent Absorption
100
80
60
40
20
440
520
600
680
760
Wavelength (mμ)

FIG. 2. Absorption spectrum of the green alga *Ulva taeniata*. The photosynthetic action spectrum, corrected to relative rates of equal incident quanta, was made to coincide with the absorption spectrum at 675 mμ. [From F. T. Haxo and L. R. Blinks (*15*)].

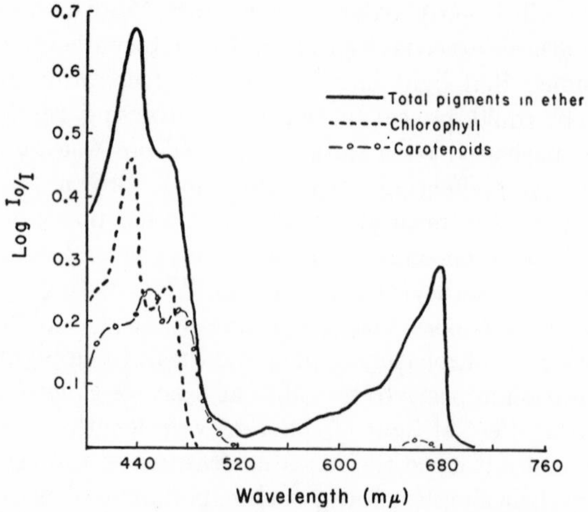
Total pigments in ether
Chlorophyll
Carotenoids
Log Io/I
0.7
0.6
0.5
0.4
0.3
0.2
0.1
440
520
600
680
760
Wavelength (mμ)

FIG. 3. Absorption spectra (in ether) of fat-soluble pigments in *Ulva taeniata*. The carotenoids were measured at the concentration obtaining in the total pigment extract. The chlorophyll curve was calculated by difference. [From F. T. Haxo and L. R. Blinks (*15*)].

relative rates of photosynthesis in light of different wavelengths. A comparison of the action spectrum of photosynthesis with the absorption spectrum of *Ulva taeniata* (*15*), a green alga, is shown in Fig. 2. In this figure the action spectrum is calculated in terms of equal incident quanta. The effect of this correction is to raise progressively the curve toward the blue region of the spectrum. These two curves show clearly that light is absorbed by some pigment which is then active in photosynthesis.

The nature of the fat-soluble pigment system present in *Ulva taeniata* is shown in Fig. 3. Carotene absorbs light in the blue region which is utilized in photosynthesis. Chlorophyll absorbs light in both the blue and red regions of the spectrum which is utilized in photosynthesis. Such studies with a wide variety of photosynthetic organisms have revealed that a number of different pigments may contribute to the absorption of light energy. Studies with extracted pigment systems are of limited value because the structural relationships of the various pigments within the chloroplast or grana are destroyed.

c. *Temperature*

If no other factor is limiting, the rate of photosynthesis increases with rising temperature up to the point at which permanent damage occurs to the plant. The maximum temperature tolerated by plants varies with the species as well as with the growing conditions. The decrease in photosynthetic rate at temperatures exceeding the maximum is thought to be connected with protoplasmic changes (enzyme denaturation, etc.) that alter the entire metabolism of the plant.

d. *Interaction of Factors*

From studies on the effect of temperature, carbon dioxide concentration, and light intensity, Blackman (*16*) showed that at low light intensities and high carbon dioxide concentrations the rate of photosynthesis was not sensitive to changes in temperature. Under these conditions the rate-limiting factor is light. At high light intensities and low carbon dioxide concentrations, the rate of photosynthesis is extremely sensitive to changes in the temperature. For these conditions, the rate-limiting factor is the carbon dioxide concentration. Blackman concluded that there were at least two distinctly different reactions in photosynthesis: a chemical reaction, requiring carbon dioxide and sensitive to temperature, and a photochemical reaction that is insensitive to temperature. The chemical reaction has been called the "dark reaction" or "Blackman reaction."

15. F. T. Haxo and L. R. Blinks, *J. Gen. Physiol.* **33,** 389 (1950).
16. F. F. Blackman, *Ann. Botany* (*London*) **19,** 281 (1905).

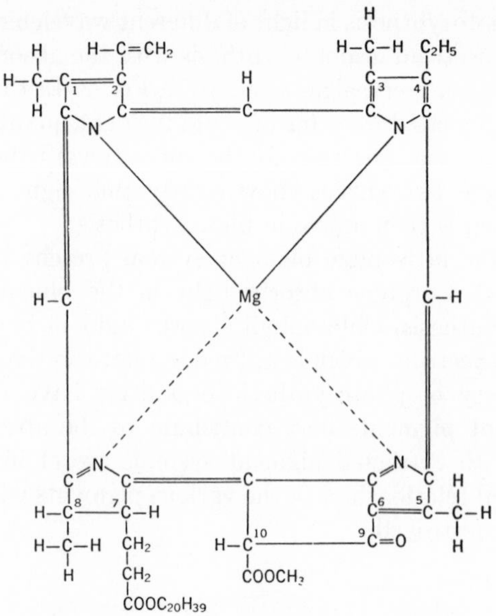

FIG. 4. Structural formula of chlorophyll-a.

e. Pigments

The fact that chlorophyll is essential for photosynthesis has been known for a long time, but it was not until the work of Willstätter and co-workers (*17*) in the early 1900's that the chemical nature of chlorophyll was established. These investigators showed that the chlorophyll in green plants was made up of two components, chlorophyll-a and chlorophyll-b, with the following composition:

Chlorophyll-a	$C_{55}H_{72}O_5N_4Mg$	mol. wt. 893
Chlorophyll-b	$C_{55}H_{70}O_6N_4Mg$	mol. wt. 907

The structural formula in Fig. 4 indicates the present concept of the chemical structure of chlorophyll-a (the numbering system is that of Hans Fischer). Chlorophyll-b differs from chlorophyll-a with respect to the group at position 3. The methyl group in chlorophyll-a is replaced by an aldehyde group (—CHO) in chlorophyll-b.

In addition to chlorophyll-a and -b, two other pigments are generally present in leaves: carotene, an orange pigment, and xanthophyll, a yellow

17. R. Willstätter and A. Stoll, "Investigations on Chlorophyll" (Translated by F. M. Schertz and A. R. Merz). Science Press, Lancaster, Pa., 1928; "Untersuchungen über die Assimilation der Kohlensäure." Springer, Berlin, 1918.

TABLE I

PRINCIPAL PIGMENTS FOUND IN PLANTS, ALGAE, AND PHOTOSYNTHETIC BACTERIA (*19*)

Pigments	Where found	Maximum absorption	Comments
Chlorophylls			
Chlorophyll-a	All green plants		The chlorophylls probably exist in a comlex with protein and lipide-like material
Chlorophyll-b	Green plants, green algae	Red and blue-violet	
Chlorophyll-c	Brown algae, diatoms		
Chlorophyll-d	Red algae		
Protochlorophyll	Etiolated plants	Near red, blue-violet	
Bacteriochlorophyll	Purple sulfur bacteria	Infra-red, blue-violet	Exists in several forms
Bacterioviridin	Green sulfur bacteria	Red and blue-violet	
Phycobilins			
Phycocyanin	Blue-green algae, red algae	Orange-red	Generally blue pigment
Phycoerythrin	Red algae, blue-green algae	Green	Generally red pigment
Carotenoids			
Carotene-α,β	Principal carotenoids of plants containing chlorophyll-a	Blue and blue-green	Approximately 6 to 8 different carotenes are known to occur in plants
Xanthophyll	Variable in most green plants	Blue and blue-green	Approximately 20 different xanthophylls are known

pigment. A number of other pigments are found in the algae and photosynthetic bacteria. These are summarized in Table I. Despite the fact that different chlorophylls are scattered throughout the plant kingdom, all of the organisms that carry out photosynthesis contain chlorophyll-a (bacteriochlorophyll in the bacteria). The other pigments present are believed to absorb light energy that is eventually utilized in photosynthesis. In a study involving the determination of the absorption and fluorescence spectra of photosynthetic bacteria and algae, Duysens (*18*) postulated that the various pigments pass light energy by means of inductive resonance to a pigment which is active in photosynthesis. The transfer of light energy is unidirectional and passes the energy with high efficiency. The following scheme of energy transfer was suggested for *Chlorella*, which contains

18. L. N. M. Duysens, Doctoral thesis, University of Utrecht, Netherlands (1952).

19. R. Hill and C. P. Whittingham, "Photosynthesis," p. 17. Wiley, New York, 1955.

chlorophyll-a and -b and some carotenoids:

$$\begin{array}{ccccccc} \text{Light} & & \text{Light} & & \text{Light} & & \\ \downarrow & & \downarrow & & \downarrow & & \\ \text{Carotenoids} & \xrightarrow{40\text{–}50\%} & \text{Chlorophyll-b} & \xrightarrow{100\%} & \text{Chlorophyll-a} & \rightarrow & \text{Photosynthesis} \\ \downarrow & & & & \downarrow & & \\ \text{Heat and other energy losses} & & & & \text{Fluorescence and other losses} & & \end{array}$$

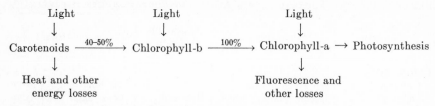

The energy absorbed by the carotenoids was transferred with 40 to 50% efficiency to chlorophyll-b, which transferred its energy with 100% efficiency to chlorophyll-a. In some organisms it was necessary to postulate two types of chlorophyll-a, one that could pass its energy to photosynthesis and an "inactive" chlorophyll-a which dissipated its energy to heat. The energy that flows into chlorophyll-a is thought to be transferred by inductive resonance to a pigment "reaction center" which participates in the dark reactions of photosynthesis.

Studies on the chemical structure of chlorophyll showed that it was closely related to heme, a pigment found in mammalian tissue. Subsequent work has indicated that a common biosynthetic pathway exists for the synthesis of porphobilinogen, a precursor to these two pigments. The steps leading to the formation of porphobilinogen were worked out by Shemin and co-workers (*20*) in a series of brilliant tracer experiments.

D. Bacterial Photosynthesis

The discovery that certain bacteria could carry out photosynthesis opened up a new field of photosynthetic research. It was found that certain green-, red-, purple-, and brown-colored bacteria could produce organic matter from carbon dioxide upon illumination. The formation of organic matter was not accompanied by oxygen evolution. As a result of work with the green sulfur bacteria, van Niel (*21*) showed that their CO_2 assimilation process was in close agreement with the following equation:

$$CO_2 + 2\,H_2S \xrightarrow{\text{light}} (CH_2O) + H_2O + 2\,S \qquad (2)$$

The similarity of this process to photosynthesis in green plants is obvious:

$$CO_2 + 2\,H_2O \xrightarrow{\text{light}} (CH_2O) + H_2O + O_2 \qquad (3)$$

van Niel then suggested a generalized formulation of photosynthesis as follows:

$$CO_2 + 2\,H_2A \xrightarrow{\text{light}} (CH_2O) + H_2O + 2\,A \qquad (4)$$

---

20. D. Shemin and C. S. Russell, *J. Am. Chem. Soc.* **75**, 4873 (1953).

21. C. B. van Niel, *in* "Photosynthesis in Plants" (J. Franck and W. E. Loomis, eds.), p. 437. Iowa State College Press, Ames, 1949.

In this equation, H_2A represents a hydrogen donor which reduces carbon dioxide with the aid of absorbed radiation, and A is the dehydrogenated donor.

Reaction (4) is a hydrogenation-dehydrogenation reaction which conforms to the principles of "comparative biochemistry" set forth by the Dutch microbiologist Kluyver. This concept, as stated by van Niel (*21*), "postulates as a fruitful central idea that all metabolic activities are intrinsically similar, and that each consists of a more or less extended series of inter- or intramolecular hydrogenation-dehydrogenation reactions." The comparative biochemistry principle has been extremely valuable in developing theoretical approaches to the photosynthetic reaction.

In addition to the pigmented bacteria, some colorless bacteria are able to fix carbon dioxide in the absence of light. These colorless bacteria, known as "chemosynthetic" or "chemoautotrophic" organisms, obtain energy for assimilating and reducing CO_2 by oxidizing NH_3, H_2S, and H_2.

From a consideration of the different types of photosynthesis that are carried on by green plants, photosynthetic bacteria, and adapted algae, van Niel (*22*) suggested a general mechanism involving three types of reactions common to all photosynthetic organisms. The first reaction is a photochemical step in which water is decomposed to produce a reducing system and an oxidizing system. The second reaction or reactions lead ultimately to the dark reduction of CO_2 by the photochemically produced reducing system. The third series of reactions leads to the eventual dark reduction of the photochemically produced oxidizing system. These reactions involve only one photochemical step, the separation of H and O or OH from water. The reduction of carbon dioxide is a dark reaction and can proceed with energy produced from a variety of sources. Photosynthetic organisms derive energy for the reduction of CO_2 from light by way of a pigment system. The chemosynthetic organisms are able to reduce CO_2 by energy derived from the oxidation of NH_3, H_2S, H_2, or other inorganic substances. Finally some organisms use energy obtained from the oxidation of organic material to reduce carbon dioxide.

A consequence of van Niel's formulation of photosynthesis is that the evolved oxygen should originate in the water and not from the carbon dioxide. Tracer studies with O^{18}-labeled water and carbon dioxide have been consistent with this view. In a recent review, however, Brown and Frenkel (*23*) have pointed out that, although the oxygen probably originates in the water molecule, the experimental evidence on this matter is not adequate to support or deny the theory that water is the sole source of photosynthetic oxygen.

22. C. B. van Niel, *in* "The Enzymes" (J. B. Sumner and K. Myrbäck, eds.), Vol. II, Part 2, p. 1074. Academic Press, New York, 1952.

23. A. H. Brown and A. W. Frenkel, *Ann. Rev. Plant Physiol.* **4,** 23 (1953).

$$\begin{array}{ccc}
[CH_2O]_n & & O_2 \\
\uparrow & & \uparrow \\
[CO_2] & \xleftarrow[\text{Chlorophyll}]{4\text{ H} \qquad \text{Light}} & [2\ H_2O] \\
\uparrow & & \uparrow \\
CO_2 & & 2\ H_2O
\end{array}$$

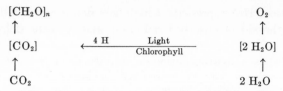

FIG. 5. Reactions of photosynthesis. (From Rabinowitch.*24*)

E. The Hill Reaction

It had been known for a long time that oxygen was evolved during the illumination of ground leaves, isolated chloroplasts, or aqueous suspensions of dried leaf powders. The amounts of oxygen evolved were small, and it remained for Hill (*4*) to show that illuminated isolated chloroplasts were able to produce considerable quantities of oxygen if an aqueous extract of an acetone powder of yeast or leaves was added. Subsequently it was shown that the yeast or leaf extract could be omitted if certain ferric salts were added. With ferric iron, the reaction proceeds as follows:

$$4\ Fe^{+++} + 2\ H_2O \xrightarrow[\text{chloroplasts}]{\text{light}} 4\ Fe^{++} + 4\ H^+ + O_2 \tag{5}$$

Additional work on this reaction, commonly called the "Hill reaction," has led to the conclusion that it probably represents the photochemical phase of photosynthesis. This reaction shares with photosynthesis the conversion of light energy into chemical energy, and the appearance of molecular oxygen.

Comparative studies on the Hill reaction and photosynthesis have led to the view that photosynthesis can be separated into two main groups of reactions as shown in Fig. 5. The right leg of the figure represents the photochemical phase which takes place in the chloroplast. The reactions include light absorption, energy transfer, and water photolysis with the concomitant production of oxygen and "active hydrogen." The "active hydrogen" drives the reaction represented on the left side of the figure, the final outcome being reduced carbon dioxide. The key reaction takes place in the chloroplast or grana where the energy from light is converted into chemical energy represented by "active hydrogen."

The nature of the "active hydrogen" or the mechanism of its production is not known. A widely accepted theory (*25*) of how light energy is transformed into chemical energy is that a "biradical" is formed from a molecule following light absorption. Such a biradical might have both oxidizing and reducing properties so that the result of such a compound XY absorb-

24. E. Rabinowitch, *Sci. American*, **179,** 24 (1948).

25. R. Hill and C. P. Whittingham, "Photosynthesis," p. 131. Wiley, New York, 1955.

ing light energy would be the formation of two radicals, XH and YOH. The mechanisms for the further reactions of these two radicals are not known. The XH reactions might be similar to other hydrogen transport reactions in metabolic systems.

The transfer of hydrogen or electrons in biological systems is relatively well understood, and it is of interest to examine some of the compounds involved in the transfer mechanism. Table II lists some of the compounds that might serve in the hydrogen transport system of the photosynthetic cell. Since it will be necessary to refer many times to these compounds, their structure is given at this point (see also Chapter VIII). The names of these compounds have not yet been systematized. Diphosphopyridine nucleotide (DPN^+) contains nicotinic acid amide, D-ribose, and adenosine 5-phosphate linked through a pyrophosphate group. Triphosphopyridine nucleotide (TPN^+, coenzyme II) contains a third phosphate group (Chapter VIII).

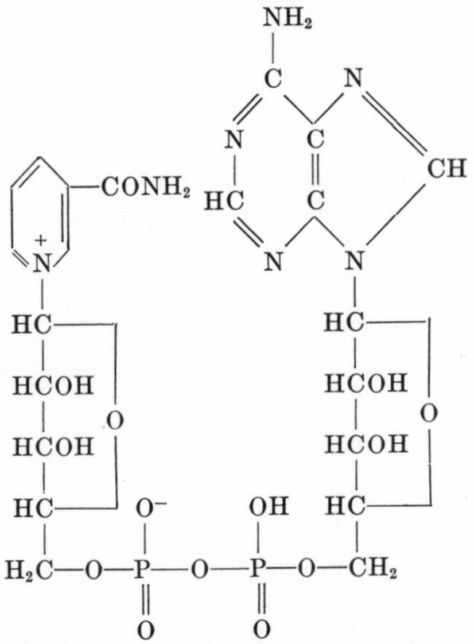

Diphosphopyridine nucleotide (DPN^+), oxidized form

In biological oxidations and reductions the reaction can be represented as follows:

$$XH_2 + Y \rightleftharpoons X + YH_2 \quad (6)$$

The hydrogen donor XH_2 is oxidized to X while the hydrogen acceptor Y is reduced to YH_2, the reaction being catalyzed by enzymes known as dehydrogenases. In some instances oxygen acts as the hydrogen acceptor, but in many other systems organic hydrogen acceptors or enzymes pass

TABLE II
THE STANDARD OXIDATION-REDUCTION POTENTIAL E_0' OF SOME BIOLOGICAL COMPOUNDS AT pH 7.0 REFERRED TO THE STANDARD HYDROGEN ELECTRODE

Electron donor	Electron acceptor	Potential E_0' (volts)
Water (H_2O)	Oxygen ($\frac{1}{2}$ O_2)	+0.81
Cytochrome *f* (reduced)	Cytochrome *f* (oxidized)	+0.38
Cytochrome *c* (reduced)	Cytochrome *c* (oxidized)	+0.28
Flavin nucleotide—bound to protein (reduced)	Flavin nucleotide (oxidized)	−0.06
Ascorbic acid	Dehydroascorbic acid	−0.06
Diphosphopyridine nucleotide, DPNH (reduced)	DPN^+ (oxidized)	−0.32
Triphosphopyridine nucleotide, TPNH (reduced)	TPN^+ (oxidized)	−0.324
Lipothiamide pyrophosphate, LTPP (reduced)	LTPP (oxidized)	−0.42
Hydrogen (H_2)	2 H^+	−0.42

the hydrogen from the hydrogen donor to the terminal hydrogen acceptor. The pyridine nucleotides act in this hydrogen transport role, probably by the following mechanism:

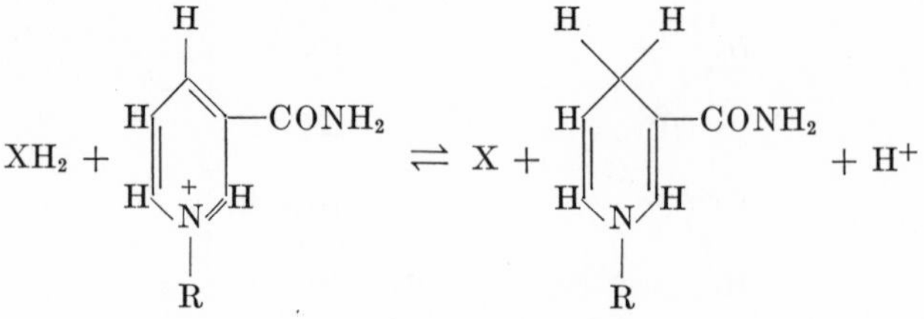

XH₂ +
H
H
CONH₂
H
+
N
H
R
⇌ X +
H H
H
CONH₂
H
N
H
R
+ H⁺

It is likely that the hydrogen from XH_2 dissociates into a hydride ion H^- ($= H^+ + 2\,e^-$) and a proton, H^+. The oxidized diphosphopyridine nucleotide then combines with the hydride ion leaving the proton in solution as hydrogen ion. These reactions can be summarized as follows:

$$\begin{aligned} DPN^+ + 2\,H^+ + 2\,e^- &\rightleftharpoons DPNH + H^+ \\ TPN^+ + 2\,H^+ + 2\,e^- &\rightleftharpoons TPNH + H^+ \end{aligned} \tag{7}$$

In the rest of the chapter DPN^+ (TPN^+) will be used to denote the oxidized forms of the pyridine nucleotides and DPNH (TPNH) to designate the reduced forms.

Under physiological conditions the reduced pyridine nucleotides are reoxidized by the flavoproteins. One such flavoprotein, flavin adenine dinucleotide, has the following structure:

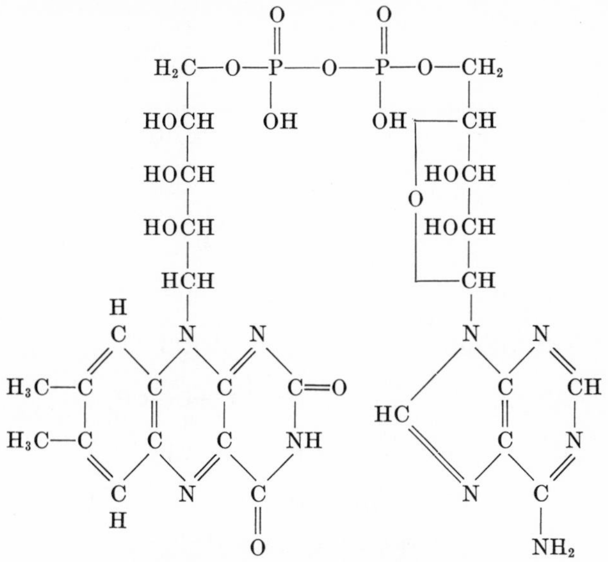

Flavin adenine dinucleotide (FAD)

The flavin component is riboflavin (vitamin B_2) or 6,7-dimethyl-9-D-ribityl-isoalloxazine.

Lipothiamide pyrophosphate (LTPP) is a compound postulated by Reed (*26*) to account for the biological activity of α-lipoic acid. It is not certain that such a compound does exist; however, α-lipoic acid and thiamine pyrophosphate do act in oxidation-reduction reactions.

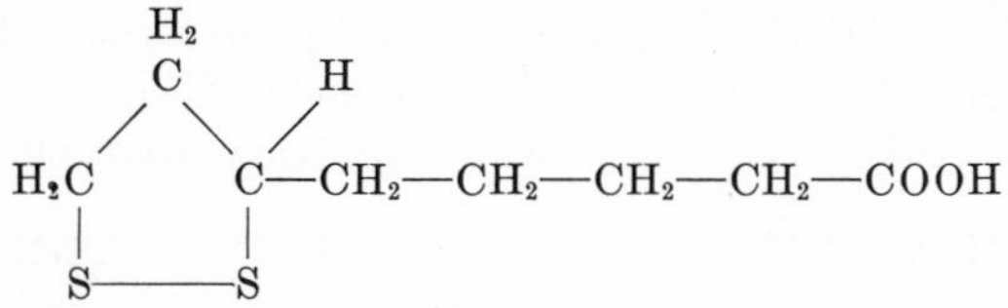

α-Lipoic acid (Thioctic acid, 6,8-Dithio-*n*-octanoic acid)

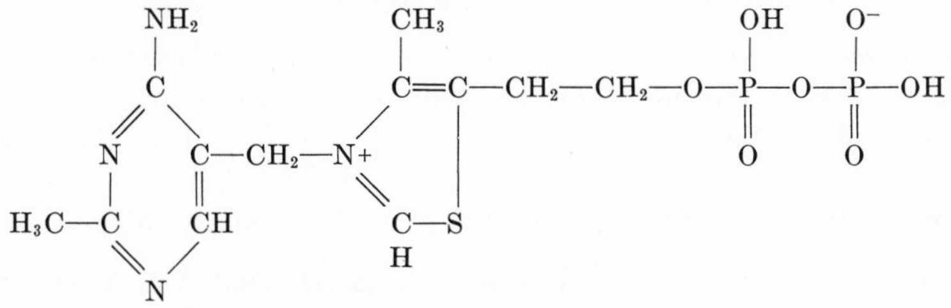

Thiamine pyrophosphate (TPP), Cocarboxylase

26. L. J. Reed, *Physiol. Revs.* **33,** 544 (1953).

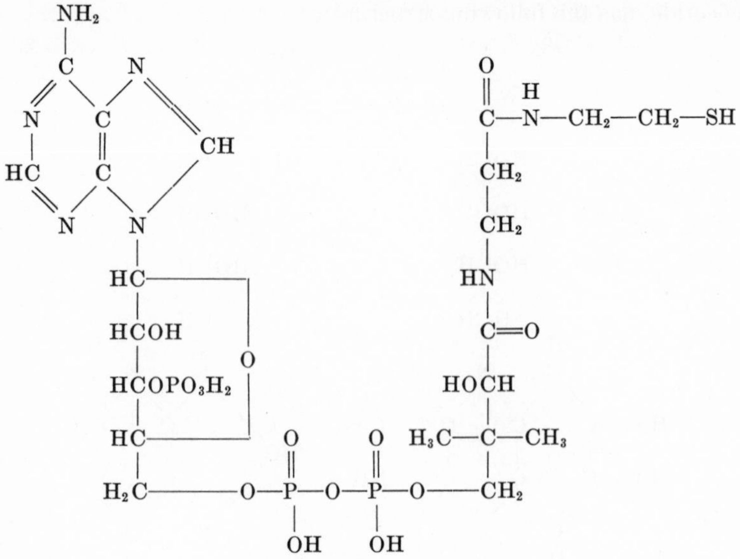

Coenzyme A(CoA, CoASH)

Attempts were made (*27*) to demonstrate that DPN^+ or TPN^+ could be reduced under conditions found in the Hill reaction. Such a reaction would occur as follows:

$$H_2O + DPN^+(TPN^+) \xrightarrow[\text{chloroplasts}]{\text{light}} \tfrac{1}{2}O_2 + DPNH(TPNH) \qquad (8)$$

These efforts were not successful until it was shown by Ochoa and Vishniac (*28*) that TPNH or DPNH could be demonstrated if the reaction was coupled with a second reaction that would remove the reduced pyridine nucleotides from the system. In the presence of the "malic enzyme," pyruvate, CO_2, and Mn^{++}, the following reactions took place:

$$H_2O + TPN^+ \xrightarrow[\text{chloroplasts}]{\text{light}} \tfrac{1}{2}O_2 + TPNH \qquad (9)$$

$$TPNH + \text{pyruvate} + CO_2 \xrightarrow[\text{"malic enzyme"}]{Mn^{++}} TPN^+ + \text{L-malate} \qquad (10)$$

The reaction was carried out with a suspension of chloroplasts from spinach leaves and "malic enzyme" from a pigeon-liver preparation. The reaction was followed by measuring the production of L-malic acid. In the dark, or in the absence of either the "malic enzyme" or TPN^+, no malic acid was observed. These results were confirmed by both Tolmach (*29*) and Arnon

27. A. S. Holt and C. S. French, *Arch. Biochem.* **19,** 368 (1948); A. H. Mehler, *Arch. Biochem. and Biophys.* **33,** 65 (1951).

28. S. Ochoa and W. Vishniac, *Nature* **167,** 768 (1951).

29. L. J. Tolmach, *Nature* **167,** 946 (1951).

(*30*). The experiments of Arnon were of interest since the "malic enzyme" was obtained from the same plant material that served as the source of the chloroplasts. Subsequent experiments (*31*) have shown that illuminated chloroplasts are able to carry out a great many reactions involving DPN^+ and TPN^+. These studies demonstrated that the photochemical system of green leaves could be linked to the glycolytic and respiratory systems of plants, but they did not prove that either DPN^+ or TPN^+ was directly reduced by light or that carbon dioxide was directly reduced by DPNH or TPNH. Anderson and Vennesland (*32*) found DPN^+ and TPN^+ present in green leaves in about equal amounts. The concentrations were such as would give about a 50% activation of the leaf TPN^+- or DPN^+-linked dehydrogenases.

The possibility that some of the energy derived from light might be stored in the form of "high-energy" phosphate bonds has been considered many times. One such compound of widespread occurrence in biological systems is adenosine triphosphate (ATP). The ATP molecule (see Chapter VIII) contains two "high-energy" bonds (designated by ~), each of which

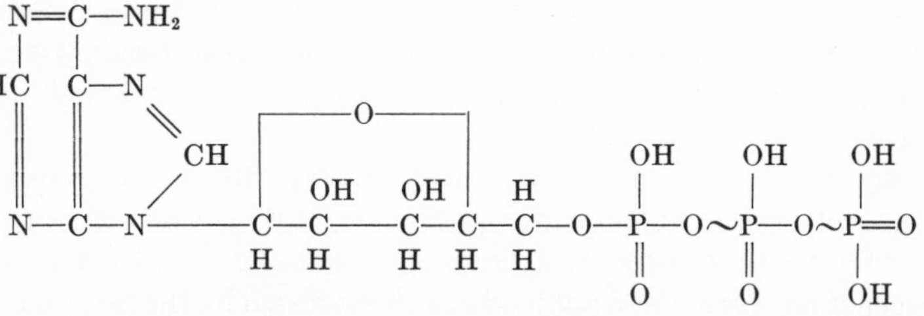

on hydrolysis has a ΔF value of about $-12{,}000$ cal. per mole. The energy released can be used in many different biosynthetic processes. Vishniac and Ochoa (*31*) demonstrated that the photochemical reduction of DPN^+ could be linked to oxidative phosphorylation and the formation of ATP. When a mitochondrial preparation from mung bean seedlings (*33*) was incubated with a spinach chloroplast preparation, ATP, DPN^+, and P^{32}-labeled phosphate, the radioactivity incorporated into ATP was increased fifteenfold upon illumination.

$$H_2O + DPN^+ \xrightarrow[\text{chloroplasts}]{\text{light}} \tfrac{1}{2}\, O_2 + DPNH \tag{11}$$

$$DPNH + \tfrac{1}{2}\, O_2 + 3\, ADP + 3PO_4^{---} \rightarrow DPN^+ + H_2O + 3\, ATP \tag{12}$$

$$\text{Net reaction:}\quad 3\, ADP + 3\, PO_4^{---} \xrightarrow{\text{light}} 3\, ATP \tag{13}$$

30. D. I. Arnon, *Nature* **167**, 1008 (1951).

31. W. Vishniac, and S. Ochoa, *in* "Phosphorus Metabolism" (W. D. McElroy and B. Glass, eds.), Vol. 2, p. 467. Johns Hopkins Press, Baltimore, 1952.

32. D. G. Anderson and B. Vennesland, *J. Biol. Chem.* **207**, 613 (1954).

33. A. Millerd, J. Bonner, B. Axelrod, and R. S. Bandurski, *Proc. Natl. Acad. Sci.* (*U. S.*) **37**, 855 (1951).

The ADP in the above reaction indicates adenosine diphosphate, which has the same structure as ATP but which has one less terminal phosphate group. By an entirely different procedure, Strehler (*34*) has been able to show that the ATP content of illuminated *Chlorella* is markedly increased following an anaerobic period in the dark. There seems to be little doubt that the production of "high-energy" phosphate bonds is connected to the photochemical phase of photosynthesis, but the mechanism of the reactions involved is not well understood at the present time.

An entirely different sort of mechanism for the photochemical step in photosynthesis was suggested by Calvin and Barltrop (*35*). It had been observed that when algae in a steady state of photosynthesis were fed radioactive carbon dioxide, the radioactivity could not be found in those products characteristic of the tricarboxylic acid cycle (Fig. 11, p. 777). If the algae were allowed to undergo photosynthesis for a short time in the presence of radioactive carbon dioxide and then placed in the dark, the radioactive carbon was found to appear in the members of the tricarboxylic acid cycle. These results were interpreted in terms of the reactions known to be necessary for pyruvic acid to enter into the tricarboxylic acid cycle. The pyruvic acid is oxidatively decarboxylated to yield acetyl-coenzyme A and CO_2. Acetyl-coenzyme A then enters the tricarboxylic acid cycle by condensing with oxalacetic acid.

The decarboxylation of pyruvic acid involves the participation of at least five cofactors, thiamine pyrophosphate (TPP), thioctic acid, coenzyme A, DPN^+, and Mg ions. According to Gunsalus (*36*) the formation of acetylcoenzyme A from pyruvic acid can be expressed by the reactions (14) to (17). The thioctic acid is designated as 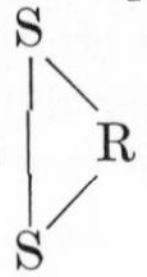 inasmuch as the two sulfurs are the reactive sites of the molecule. Calvin and Barltrop interpreted their tracer studies as indicating that light reduced the disulfide 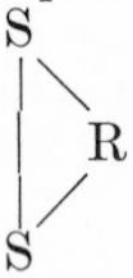 to the dithiol 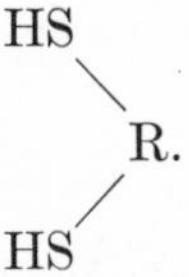. In the dithiol form, thioctic acid could not react with

34. B. L. Strehler, *in* "Phosphorus Metabolism" (W. D. McElroy and B. Glass, eds.), Vol. 2, p. 491. Johns Hopkins Press, Baltimore, 1952.

35. M. Calvin and J. A. Barltrop, *J. Am. Chem. Soc.* **74,** 6153 (1952).

36. I. C. Gunsalus, *J. Cellular Comp. Physiol.* **41,** Suppl. 1, 113 (1953); *in* "Mech-

$$CH_3COCOO^- + TPP^+ \rightleftharpoons [CH_3CO{:}TPP] + CO_2 \qquad (14)$$

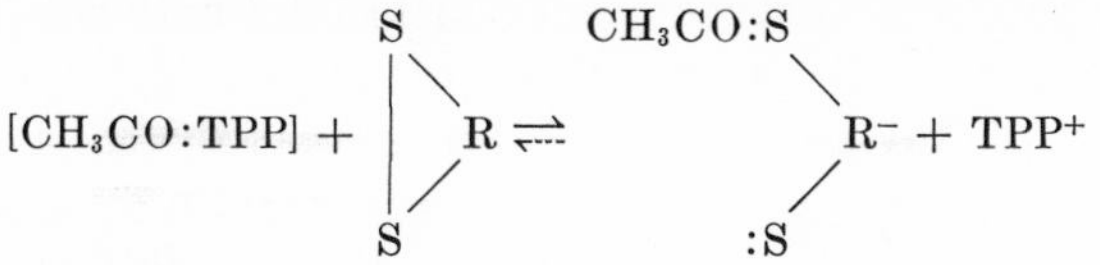

(15)

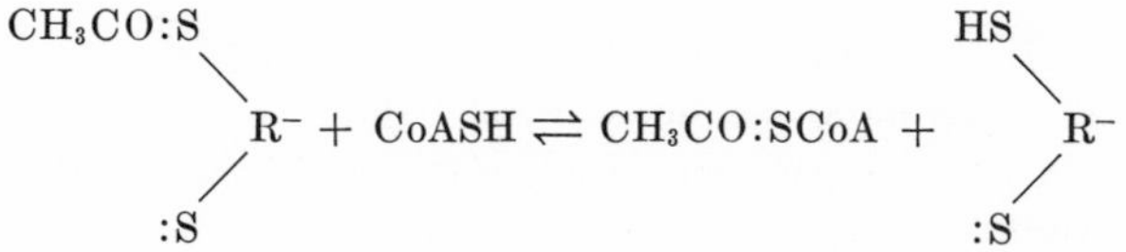

(16)

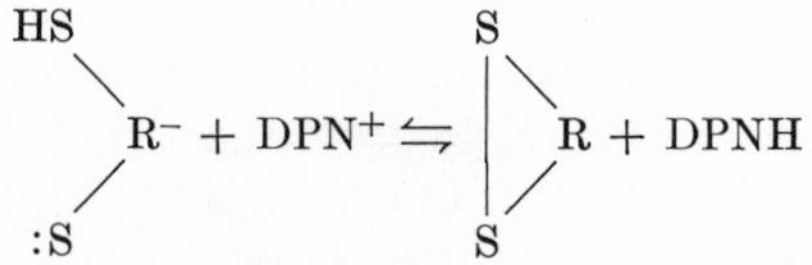

(17)

pyruvic acid to form acetyl-CoA. Such a reaction would prevent the pyruvic acid from entering the tricarboxylic acid cycle. In the dark, the dithiol would not be formed, and the pyruvic acid could enter the tricarboxylic acid cycle. Calvin and Barltrop also suggested that the thioctic acid might be involved in the primary quantum conversion act of photosynthesis by the following reaction:

$$\text{Light} + \text{chlorophyll} \rightarrow \text{excited chlorophyll} \qquad (18)$$

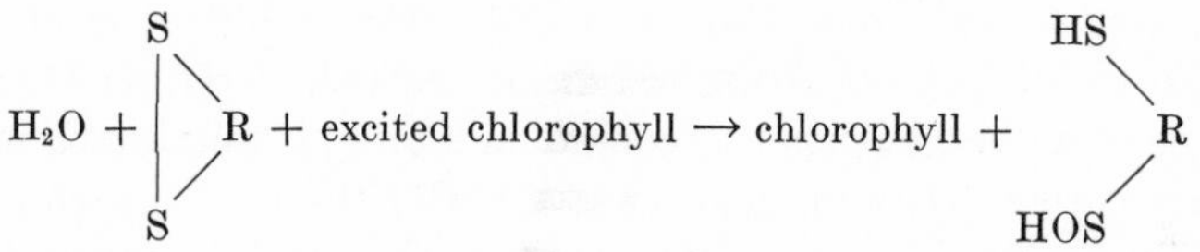

(19)

Additional studies by Calvin and co-workers (*37*) have given results that are consistent with this concept.

Thioctic acid has been found in green plants (*26*), but its biological form and distribution are not well established. Using S^{35}-labeled thioctic acid, it was shown (*38*) that *Scenedesmus* cells rapidly incorporated the thioctic acid into some bound form. In *Chlorella*, the thioctic acid became associated with a lipid fraction of the chloroplasts. Wessels (*39*) found that sulfhydryl enzyme inhibitors did not affect the Hill reaction. If thioctic acid is

anisms of Enzyme Action" (W. D. McElroy and B. Glass, eds.), p. 545. Johns Hopkins Press, Baltimore, 1954.

37. M. Calvin, *Federation Proc.* **13,** 697 (1954); D. F. Bradley and M. Calvin, *Arch. Biochem. and Biophys.* **53,** 99 (1954); D. F. Bradley and M. Calvin, *Proc. Natl. Acad. Sci.* (*U. S.*) **41,** 563 (1955).

38. R. C. Fuller, H. Grisebach, and M. Calvin, *J. Am. Chem. Soc.* **77,** 2659 (1955).

39. J. S. C. Wessels, *Philips Research Reports* **9,** 140, 161 (1954).

involved in photosynthesis, it might be expected that such inhibitors would influence the reaction. However, since little information is available regarding the distribution and localization of thioctic acid in the plant cell, it is not possible to say much about its role in photosynthesis.

F. The Path of Carbon in Photosynthesis

Very little progress was made on this aspect of photosynthesis before isotopic carbon became available. Carbon balance studies had shown that the amount of carbon dioxide that went into a leaf could be almost entirely recovered in the sugars and starch fraction. However, there was no information regarding the steps involved in these transformations. Early studies (*40*) with the short-lived carbon isotope C^{11} indicated that during photosynthesis the tracer was fixed principally in the carboxyl group of a complex molecule that contained a number of hydroxyl and carboxyl groups. When the long-lived carbon isotope C^{14} became available in 1945, these studies were extended by workers in a number of different laboratories.

The method of attack was stated by one group of workers (*41*) as follows. "First, the plants must be fed labeled carbon dioxide under as wide a variety of conditions as seems feasible, ranging from dark feeding after suitable pretreatments to increasingly long periods of photosynthesis in the presence of radioactive carbon. Included also should be a variation in the dark time following the administration of labeled carbon dioxide in the light. During the courses of these experiments, the kinetics of the total incorporation of the radioactive carbon dioxide should be studied under each set of conditions, following which an analysis of the plant substance is made in order to identify the compounds or substances into which the radioactive carbon has been incorporated. After these have been identified, the distribution of the radioactive atoms within each compound is to be determined."

Following this line of attack, Calvin and co-workers (*42*) showed that tracer carbon was very rapidly fixed in a large number of different compounds. For example, following a 30-second period of photosynthesis by the green alga *Scenedesmus* in the presence of $C^{14}O_2$, radioactivity was detected in a glyceric acid phosphate, phosphopyruvic acid, triose phosphate, sugar phosphates, sucrose, malic acid, glycolic acid, succinic acid, fumaric

40. M. D. Kamen, *in* "Photosynthesis in Plants" (J. Franck and W. E. Loomis, eds.), p. 365. Iowa State College Press, Ames, 1949.

41. A. A. Benson, M. Calvin, V. A. Haas, S. Aronoff, A. G. Hall, J. A. Bassham, and J. W. Weigl, *in* "Photosynthesis in Plants" (J. Franck and W. E. Loomis, eds.), p. 381. Iowa State College Press, Ames, 1949.

42. M. Calvin, J. A. Bassham, A. A. Benson, V. H. Lynch, C. Ouellet, L. Schou, W. Stepka, and N. E. Tolbert, *Symposia Soc. Exptl. Biol.* **5**, 284 (1951).

acid, citric acid, aspartic acid, alanine, serine, glycine, and lipides. The separation, isolation, and identification of the compounds was carried out by the use of paper chromatography and radioautography (*43*). These same workers also developed methods for degrading the isolated compounds to determine the distribution of the radioactive carbon within each compound.

Very brief exposures of plants to tracer carbon dioxide in the light resulted in the fixation of the tracer in only a few compounds. Of the activity fixed by *Scenedesmus* during a 5-second period of photosynthesis, 87% was incorporated into a glyceric acid phosphate, 10% in phosphopyruvic acid, and 3% in malic acid. The glyceric acid phosphate was originally believed to be D-glyceric acid 2-phosphate, but recent experiments indicate that it is probably D-glyceric acid 3-phosphate. It was suggested (*43*) that this compound was the major port of entry of carbon dioxide into plant metabolism. This has been confirmed by other workers (*44*). Degradation studies of the D-glyceric acid 3-phosphate established that most of the radioactivity was fixed in the carboxyl group with the α- and β-carbons being equally labeled.

As a result of the type of labeling found in the D-glyceric acid 3-phosphate, it was thought that the initial reaction was the carboxylation of some "two-carbon" compound. However, it was not possible to demonstrate the presence of any simple "two-carbon" compound that could be carboxylated to form the glyceric acid phosphate. Further studies (*45*) on the alcohol-soluble fraction of plants exposed briefly to tracer carbon dioxide revealed the presence of several additional compounds (Table III). One compound was identified as a D-sedoheptulose (D-*altro*-heptulose) phosphate, while the pentose phosphate was identified as D-ribulose (D-*erythro*-pentulose) phosphate (*46*). One of the sugar diphosphates was D-ribulose diphosphate. It was then suggested (*47*) that the pentose phosphates might be the source of the two-carbon compound that became carboxylated to form D-glyceric acid 3-phosphate. Subsequent research has shown this to be true.

The evidence for the participation of D-ribulose 1,5-diphosphate as a CO_2-acceptor in photosynthesis came from several sources. First, the data

43. A. A. Benson, J. A. Bassham, M. Calvin, T. C. Goodale, V. A. Haas, and W. Stepka, *J. Am. Chem. Soc.* **72**, 1710 (1950).

44. H. Gaffron, E. W. Fager, and J. L. Rosenberg, *Symposia Soc. Exptl. Biol.* **5**, 262 (1951).

45. J. G. Buchanan, J. A. Bassham, A. A. Benson, D. F. Bradley, M. Calvin, L. L. Daus, M. Goodman, P. M. Hayes, V. H. Lynch, L. T. Norris and A. T. Wilson, *in* "Phosphorus Metabolism" (W. D. McElroy and B. Glass, eds.), Vol. 2, p. 440. Johns Hopkins Press, Baltimore, 1952.

46. A. A. Benson, J. A. Bassham, M. Calvin, A. G. Hall, H. E. Hirsch, S. Kawaguchi, V. H. Lynch, and N. E. Tolbert, *J. Biol. Chem.* **196**, 703 (1952).

47. M. Calvin and P. Massini, *Experientia* **8**, 445 (1952).

TABLE III

ALCOHOL-SOLUBLE COMPOUNDS FOUND IN SOYBEAN LEAVES FOLLOWING A 10-SECOND PERIOD OF PHOTOSYNTHESIS

Compound	Per cent of radioactivity fixed
Glyceric acid phosphate	32
Sedoheptulose phosphate	24
Fructose phosphate	19
Triose phosphate	8
Glucose phosphate	6
Pentose phosphate	5
Sugar diphosphates	4
Enolpyruvic acid phosphate	3

of Bassham and co-workers (*48*) on the distribution of radioactive carbon in the early products of photosynthesis were consistent with such a view. It was necessary to assume certain enzymic reactions to obtain the observed labeling. The work of Horecker and co-workers (*49*) and Racker and co-workers (*50*) provided evidence for the existence of enzymes that catalyzed the reactions proposed by Bassham and co-workers. It was shown (*51*) that a cell-free sonic-treated *Chlorella* preparation catalyzed the carboxylation of D-ribulose 1,5-diphosphate to form D-glyceric acid 3-phosphate. The carboxylation enzyme was isolated and partially purified from spinach leaves (*51a*). Tracer experiments showed that in the presence of the carboxylation enzyme, D-ribulose 1,5-diphosphate was carboxylated to form two moles of D-glyceric acid 3-phosphate. Fager (*52*) also found that a cell-free algal extract fixed tracer carbon in the carboxyl group of glyceric acid phosphate but was unable to identify any of the intermediates. Weissbach and co-workers (*53*) prepared a soluble extract from spinach leaves that catalyzed the fixation of carbon dioxide into glyceric acid phosphate in the presence of D-ribose 5-phosphate. The fixation reaction was stimulated by

48. J. A. Bassham, A. A. Benson, L. D. Kay, A. Z. Harris, A. T. Wilson, and M. Calvin, *J. Am. Chem. Soc.* **76**, 1760 (1954).

49. B. L. Horecker and P. Z. Smyrniotis *J. Am. Chem. Soc.* **75**, 1009 (1953).

50. E. Racker, G. de la Haba, and I. G. Leder, *J. Am. Chem. Soc.* **75**, 1010 (1953); E. Racker, G. de la Haba, and I. G. Leder, *Arch. Biochem. and Biophys.* **48**, 238 (1954).

51. J. R. Quayle, R. C. Fuller, A. A. Benson, and M. Calvin, *J. Am. Chem. Soc.* **76**, 3610 (1954).

51a. A. Weissbach, B. L. Horecker, and J. Hurwitz, *J. Biol. Chem.* **218**, 795 (1956); W. B. Jakoby, D. O. Brummond, and S. Ochoa, *ibid.* **218**, 811 (1956).

52. E. W. Fager, *Biochem. J.* **57**, 264 (1954).

53. A. Weissbach, P. Z. Smyrniotis, and B. L. Horecker, *J. Am. Chem. Soc.* **76**, 3611 (1954).

TPN+, ATP, and Mg ions. Subsequent work (*53a*) has shown that D-ribose 5-phosphate is converted to D-ribulose 1,5-diphosphate by the action of ATP and two enzymes, phosphoriboisomerase and phosphoribulokinase. Both of these enzymes were isolated and purified from spinach extracts.

It was proposed (*48*) that there was a cyclic process involved in regenerating the carbon dioxide acceptor according to the following scheme:

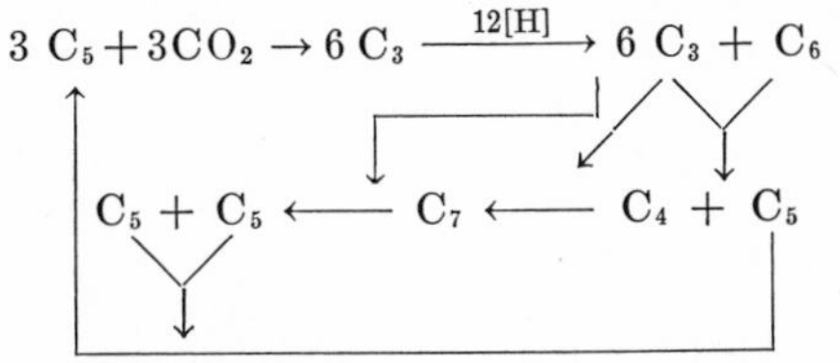
3 C5 + 3CO2 → 6 C3
12[H]
6 C3 + C6
C5 + C5
C7
C4 + C5

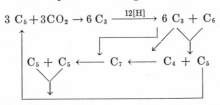

The details of all of the reactions of this cycle are not completely known but the steps shown in Table IV have been suggested (*94*). The enzymes necessary for these reactions have been found in plant tissues (see reviews by Racker (*54*) and Vishniac (*55*).

Racker (*56*) demonstrated the synthesis of carbohydrates from carbon dioxide and hydrogen in a cell-free system by bringing together many of the enzymes listed in Table IV. A spinach fraction furnished the phosphopentokinase, carboxydismutase, phosphopentosisomerase, transketolase, transaldolase, and hexose diphosphatase. To this fraction were added the other enzymes, DPN+, ATP, and a hydrogenase preparation. The hydrogenase enzyme furnished DPNH in the presence of hydrogen. When this mixture was incubated at 25° for 60 minutes, the synthesis of fructose 6-phosphate could be demonstrated.

The net result of all of the reactions listed in Table IV is the following:

$$3\ CO_2 + 9\ ATP + 4\ H_2O + 6\ TPNH + 6\ H^+ \rightarrow 1\ \text{triose-p} + 9\ ADP + 6\ TPN^+ + 8\ PO_4^{---} \quad (20)$$

In order to keep the reaction going it is necessary to generate continuously the TPNH and ATP. As discussed earlier (reaction (9)), it has been shown that illuminated chloroplast fragments are capable of reducing either DPN+ or TPN+. Similarly it has been shown (reactions (11) to (13)) that illuminated chloroplast fragments and mitochondrial preparations are able to bring about the synthesis of ATP.

On the basis of these results, it should be possible to prepare chloroplast

53a. A. Weissbach, P. Z. Smyrniotis, and B. L. Horecker, *J. Am. Chem. Soc.* **76,** 5572 (1954); J. Hurwitz, A. Weissbach, B. L. Horecker, and P. Z. Smyrniotis, *J. Biol. Chem.* **218,** 769 (1956); B. L. Horecker, J. Hurwitz, and A. Weissbach, *J. Biol. Chem.* **218,** 785 (1956).

54. E. Racker, *Advances in Enzymol.* **15,** 141 (1954).

55. W. Vishniac, *Ann. Rev. Plant Physiol.* **6,** 115 (1955).

56. E. Racker, *Nature* **175,** 249 (1955).

TABLE IV
REACTIONS INVOLVED IN THE CYCLIC REGENERATION OF THE CARBON DIOXIDE ACCEPTOR IN PHOTOSYNTHESIS[a]

Reaction	Enzyme system
1. 3 RuMP + 3 ATP → 3 RuDP + 3 ADP....	Phosphopentokinase
2. 3 RuDP + 3 CO_2 + 3 H_2O → 6 PGA.......	Carboxydismutase
3. 6 PGA + 6 ATP → 6 1,3-PGA + 6 ADP...	PGA kinase
4. 6 1,3-PGA + 6 TPNH + 6 H^+ → 6 Gald-p + 6 TPN^+ + 6 Pi......	Triose-p dehydrogenase
5. 2 Gald-p → 2 DHAP........................	Triose-p isomerase
6. Gald-p + DHAP → HDP....................	Aldolase
7. HDP + H_2O → HMP + Pi.................	HDP-ase
8. HMP + Gald-p → XuMP + EMP..........	Transketolase
9. EMP + DHAP → SDP....................	Aldolase
10. SDP → SMP + Pi.........................	SDP-ase
11. SMP + Gald-p → RiMP + XuMP	Transketolase
12. RiMP → RuMP............................	Phosphoriboisomerase
13. 2 XuMP → 2 RuMP........................	Phosphoketopentosisomerase

[a] The following abbreviations are used: PGA, D-glyceric acid 3-phosphate; RuMP, ribulose 5-phosphate; RuDP, ribulose 1,5-diphosphate; 1,3-PGA, D-glyceric acid 1,3-diphosphate; Gald-p, D-glyceraldehyde 3-phosphate; DHAP, dihydroxyacetone phosphate; HDP, fructose 1,6-diphosphate; HMP, either glucose 6-phosphate or fructose 6-phosphate; XuMP, xylulose 5-phosphate; EMP, erythrose 4-phosphate; SDP, sedoheptulose 1,7-diphosphate; SMP, sedoheptulose 7-phosphate; RiMP, ribose 5-phosphate; Pi, inorganic phosphorus; -p, organically bound phosphate.

preparations that would fix carbon dioxide when illuminated. The early experiments indicated that chloroplast preparations capable of carrying out the Hill reaction (photolyze water) could not reduce carbon dioxide. Recently Arnon and co-workers (*57*) reported that they were able to prepare chloroplast preparations that could photolyze water, fix carbon dioxide, and carry out photosynthetic phosphorylation (convert light energy into the high-energy phosphate bonds of ATP without the participation of respiration). An increasing order of complexity was observed for the reactions. Water photolysis could be carried out by preparations incapable of photosynthetic phosphorylation and CO_2 fixation. In turn, photosynthetic phosphorylation was found to proceed under conditions of low carbon dioxide concentration. Carbon dioxide fixation, however, occurred only under conditions which were compatible with active photolysis and phosphorylation.

Additional work on this reaction (*58*) has shown that the photosynthetic

57. D. I. Arnon, M. B. Allen, and F. R. Whatley, *Nature* **174,** 394 (1954).

58. F. R. Whatley, M. B. Allen, and D. I. Arnon, *Biochim. et Biophys. Acta* **16,** 605 (1955); D. I. Arnon, F. R. Whatley, and M. B. Allen, *ibid.* **16,** 607 (1955).

phosphorylation is an anaerobic process. Vitamin K, ascorbic acid, flavin mononucleotide, and Mg ions are required as cofactors. Menadione has been used as the principal vitamin K compound in these studies. Vishniac (*55*) suggested that photosynthetic phosphorylation may be the summation of two processes, the first being the reduction in light of the menadione followed by an oxidation coupled with phosphorylation. Arnon suggested the following scheme for the photosynthetic phosphorylation mechanism:

$$\begin{array}{ccccc} & & \text{Light energy} & & \\ & & \downarrow & & \\ 2\,[\text{H}] & \longleftarrow & [\text{H}_2\text{O}] & \longrightarrow & [\text{O}] \\ \downarrow & & & & \uparrow \\ \text{FMN} & \rightarrow \text{menadione} \rightarrow & \text{ascorbate} & \cdots & ? \end{array}$$

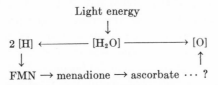

Between the ascorbic acid system and oxygen the cytochrome system may serve as an electron carrier. There is ample evidence (*59*) that a number of different cytochromes are associated with the chloroplasts. As the electrons pass through these electron carriers, ATP is generated from inorganic phosphorus and AMP.

It is inferred in these studies that the chloroplast is the photosynthetic unit and contains all of the enzymes and cofactors essential for reducing carbon dioxide to the carbohydrate level. Because of the known difficulties in obtaining chloroplast preparations free from contamination by mitochondria and other cytoplasmic particles, it would be well to withhold judgment on this question.

The carboxylation of ribulose diphosphate is not the only pathway for the entry of carbon dioxide into plant metabolism. The finding of C^{14}-labeled malic acid in short-term photosynthesis suggests another pathway. This may be related to the reaction described by Bandurski and Greiner (*60*) where "phosphoryl-enolpyruvate" was carboxylated to yield oxalacetate. Pathways of carbon dioxide fixation known to occur in other organisms (*3*) may be present in plants under special conditions. The relative importance of the various pathways depends on a number of factors: species of plant, age of plant, part of plant examined, growth conditions, experimental conditions, and others.

2. The Biosynthesis of Carbohydrates by Plants

The early workers in plant chemistry recognized that, as the result of photosynthesis, starch, sucrose, fructose, and glucose were formed. It was known that plants also synthesized fats, amino acids, proteins, organic

59. R. Hill, *Symposia Soc. Exptl. Biol.* **5,** 222 (1951); R. Hill, *Advances in Enzymol.* **12,** 1 (1951); L. P. Vernon and M. D. Kamen, *J. Biol. Chem.* **211,** 643 (1954); M. D. Kamen and L. P. Vernon, *ibid.* **211,** 663 (1954).

60. R. S. Bandurski and C. M. Greiner, *J. Biol. Chem.* **204,** 781 (1953).

acids, sugar alcohols, and many other products, but it was felt that some carbohydrate must be the first product of photosynthesis. Many attempts were made to identify this "first product." In experiments on sunflower leaves (*61*) it was possible to account for practically all of the carbon dioxide absorbed by the leaves by the increase in sucrose and starch. It was concluded that both carbohydrates were formed from an unknown common precursor.

New information on this problem has come from enzyme studies and isotope tracer studies. The work discussed in the preceding section disclosed that a great many different products were synthesized from carbon dioxide during photosynthesis. The nearest approach to a "first product" of photosynthesis is D-glyceric acid 3-phosphate. From this compound, through a whole series of enzyme-catalyzed reactions, the plant carries out the synthesis of the carbohydrates.

A. MONOSACCHARIDES

A large number of monosaccharides (see Chapter II) are found in plants, and any general biosynthetic scheme must account for the formation of trioses, tetroses, pentoses, hexoses, heptoses, deoxysugars, methyl sugars, branched-chain sugars, and aminosugars. While many free sugars are found in plants, their biosynthesis proceeds primarily through phosphorylated intermediates (*62*, *63*).

As a consequence of the widespread occurrence of the enzyme aldolase in plants, Tewfik and Stumpf (*64*) concluded that this enzyme played a major role in the sugar transformations of plants. Aldolase from mammalian tissue had been shown (*65*) to catalyze the following reaction:

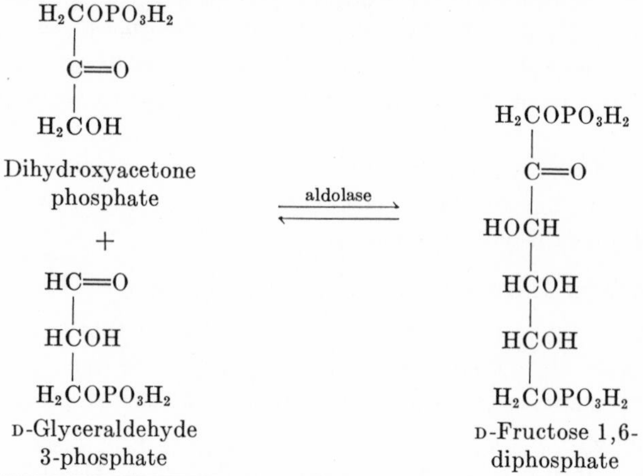
Dihydroxyacetone phosphate
aldolase
D-Glyceraldehyde 3-phosphate
D-Fructose 1,6-diphosphate

(21)

61. J. H. C. Smith, *in* "Photosynthesis in Plants" (J. Franck and W. E. Loomis,

It was shown that the enzyme, although specific for dihydroxyacetone phosphate, would react with a large number of different aldehydes. Thus, dihydroxyacetone phosphate reacted with D-glyceraldehyde, L-glyceraldehyde, and acetaldehyde to form D-fructose 1-phosphate, L-sorbose 1-phosphate, and a 5-deoxypentose 1-phosphate, respectively.

Hough and Jones (*66*) suggested that a series of aldol condensations would account for the biosynthesis of many of the monosaccharides. They reacted (*67*) glycolaldehyde and D-glyceraldehyde at room temperature in the presence of lime water and obtained chromatographic evidence for the formation of arabinose, xylose, ribose, and lyxose. DL-Ribose, DL-arabinose, and DL-xylose were isolated and characterized. (See also Chapters I and II.) Jones and co-workers (*68*) then studied a series of aldolase-catalyzed reactions between dihydroxyacetone phosphate and a number of different aldehydes. Glycolaldehyde formed D-xylulose (D-*threo*-pentulose), DL-lactaldehyde formed 6-deoxy-L-sorbose and 6-deoxy-D-fructose, D-erythrose formed D-sedoheptulose, D-threose formed D-*ido*-heptulose, and acetaldehyde formed 5-deoxy-D-xylulose. The aldolase preparation was obtained from pea seeds (*69*) and probably also contained other enzymes. All of the sugars that were formed had the D-xylulose structure and configuration for the first four carbon atoms. This *trans* configuration had also been noted for the sugars studied by Meyerhof (*65*). This aldolase reaction would not account for the biosynthesis of D-ribose which has a *cis* configuration. However, it is possible that D-xylulose may be a precursor in the biosynthesis of D-ribose.

Additional evidence for the aldolase reaction being involved in monosaccharide biosynthesis came from the isotope studies of photosynthesis. During short-term photosynthesis, the radioactivity from carbon dioxide appeared in a number of compounds in the following order: D-glyceric acid 3-phosphate, triose phosphate, hexose phosphates, and sucrose (*70*). The distribution of the tracer carbon in these compounds was compatible with

eds.), p. 53. Iowa State College Press, Ames, 1949.
62. H. G. Albaum, *Ann. Rev. Plant Physiol.* **3,** 35 (1952).
63. P. K. Stumpf, *Ann. Rev. Plant Physiol.* **3,** 17 (1952).
64. S. Tewfik and P. K. Stumpf, *Am. J. Botany* **36,** 567 (1949).
65. O. Meyerhof, K. Lohmann, and P. Schuster, *Biochem. Z.* **286,** 301, 319 (1936).
66. L. Hough and J. K. N. Jones, *Nature* **167,** 180 (1951).
67. L. Hough and J. K. N. Jones, *J. Chem. Soc.* p. 3191 (1951).
68. L. Hough and J. K. N. Jones, *J. Chem. Soc.* p. 4047 (1952); L. Hough and J. K. N. Jones, *ibid.* p. 4052 (1952); L. Hough and J. K. N. Jones, *ibid.* p. 342 (1953); P. A. J. Gorin and J. K. N. Jones, *ibid.* p. 1537 (1953); P. A. J. Gorin, L. Hough, and J. K. N. Jones, *ibid.* p. 2140 (1953).
69. P. K. Stumpf, *J. Biol. Chem.* **176,** 233 (1948).
70. A. A. Benson, *J. Chem. Educ.* **31,** 484 (1954).

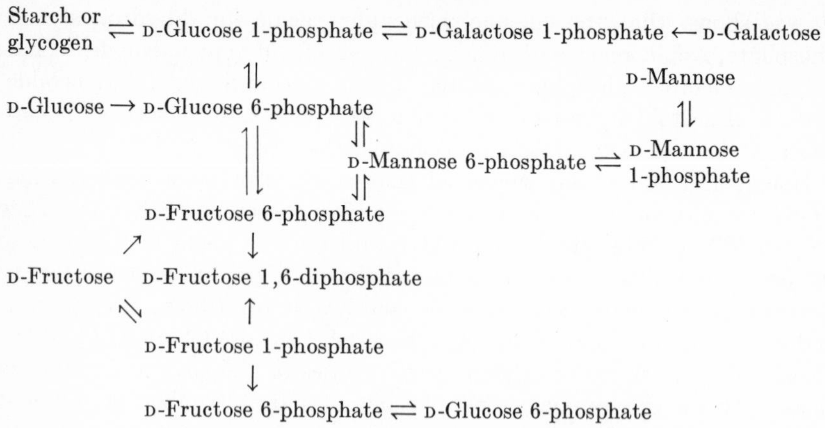
Starch or glycogen
D-Glucose 1-phosphate
D-Galactose 1-phosphate
D-Galactose
D-Mannose
D-Glucose
D-Glucose 6-phosphate
D-Mannose 6-phosphate
D-Mannose 1-phosphate
D-Fructose 6-phosphate
D-Fructose
D-Fructose 1,6-diphosphate
D-Fructose 1-phosphate
D-Fructose 6-phosphate
D-Glucose 6-phosphate

FIG. 6. The interconversion of some hexose sugars.

the proposal that the hexoses in plants were formed from D-glyceric acid 3-phosphate by a mechanism that is the reversal of glycolysis. The reaction sequence would be as follows: D-glyceric acid 3-phosphate → triose phosphate (D-glyceraldehyde 3-phosphate and dihydroxyacetone phosphate) → D-fructose 1,6-diphosphate → D-fructose 6-phosphate → D-glucose 6-phosphate → D-glucose 1-phosphate → starch. The enzymes that catalyze these reactions are known to occur in plant tissue, and plant extracts have been prepared that can carry out all of the glycolytic reactions.

Plants also contain the enzymes necessary for interconverting the hexoses. The reactions shown in Fig. 6 represent some of the known pathways for these interconversions. When barley plants were infiltrated (*71*) with D-glucose, D-fructose, D-galactose, or D-mannose, sucrose accumulated; hence the enzymes were present for interconverting these sugars. Mechanisms for these interconversions are discussed in several reviews (*72*, *73*) (see also Section 3B of this chapter).

The origin of pentose sugars in plants has always been of considerable interest. Both pentose and deoxypentoses are found in all cells. It had been observed that many plant gums contained pentose sugars. Accompanying this pentose was uronic acid. Since in some cases the pentose and uronic acid were frequently of the same homorphous series, D-glucuronic acid and D-xylose, it was suggested that the pentoses arose by a decarboxylation of the uronic acids. However, there is no evidence that this reaction represents an important pathway of pentose synthesis in plants.

71. R. M. McCready and W. Z. Hassid, *Plant Physiol.* **16,** 599 (1941).

72. W. Z. Hassid and E. W. Putman, *Ann. Rev. Plant Physiol.* **1,** 109 (1950).

73. L. F. Leloir, *in* "Phosphorus Metabolism" (W. D. McElroy and B. Glass, eds.), Vol. 1, p. 67. Johns Hopkins Press, Baltimore, 1951.

A condensation of C_2 and C_3 units has also been considered as a possible method of pentose synthesis. Aldolase-catalyzed reactions have led to pentose synthesis but such sugars have the *trans* configuration while D-ribose has a *cis* configuration. It is possible that D-xylulose can be epimerized to D-ribose by a reaction similar to that found to occur between D-galactose and D-glucose (*73*). Stumpf and Horecker (*73a*) found enzymes in D-xylose-adapted *Lactobacillus pentosus* cells that catalyzed the formation of D-ribose 5-phosphate from D-xylose. The first enzyme, xylose isomerase, converted D-xylose to D-xylulose. The second enzyme, xylulose kinase, in the presence of ATP catalyzed the formation of D-xylulose 5-phosphate. The formation of D-ribulose 5-phosphate from D-xylulose 5-phosphate is brought about by an enzyme known as phosphoketopentoisomerase. Finally D-ribose 5-phosphate is formed from D-ribulose 5-phosphate by the enzyme phosphoriboisomerase. Not all of these enzymes have been found as yet in plant tissue. It has been reported (*94*) that D-xylulose 5-phosphate labeled with C^{14} was formed after a few seconds exposure of the algae *Scenedesmus* to labeled bicarbonate. It seems likely that the above sequence of events could account for the biosynthesis of D-ribose in plants (*73b*).

With the discovery of the widespread occurrence in plants of the oxidative pathway of carbohydrate metabolism, new biosynthetic mechanisms were found. This oxidative pathway (also called the "hexose monophosphate shunt") will be referred to as the HMS pathway. The details of this pathway will be discussed in the next section of this chapter.

During the metabolism of D-glucose 6-phosphate by the HMS pathway, D-ribulose 5-phosphate and D-ribose 5-phosphate are formed (*74*). The two pentoses then react to from D-sedoheptulose 7-phosphate and D-glyceraldehyde 3-phosphate. The sedoheptulose phosphate and glyceraldehyde phosphate react to form D-fructose 6-phosphate and D-erythrose 4-phosphate. These reactions provide a cyclic mechanism which can be represented as follows:

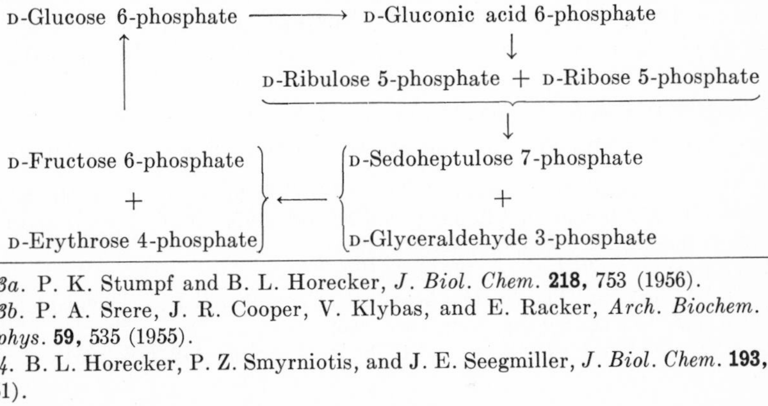
D-Glucose 6-phosphate
D-Gluconic acid 6-phosphate
D-Ribulose 5-phosphate + D-Ribose 5-phosphate
D-Fructose 6-phosphate
+
D-Erythrose 4-phosphate
D-Sedoheptulose 7-phosphate
+
D-Glyceraldehyde 3-phosphate

73a. P. K. Stumpf and B. L. Horecker, *J. Biol. Chem.* **218,** 753 (1956).

73b. P. A. Srere, J. R. Cooper, V. Klybas, and E. Racker, *Arch. Biochem. and Biophys.* **59,** 535 (1955).

74. B. L. Horecker, P. Z. Smyrniotis, and J. E. Seegmiller, *J. Biol. Chem.* **193,** 383 (1951).

Such a series of reactions not only provides for the synthesis of the pentoses, heptoses, and tetroses but also provides an additional pathway for the synthesis of hexoses. The enzymes for the above reactions have been found in plant tissue (*75*).

The biosynthesis of deoxyribose (2-deoxy-D-*erythro*-pentose) has not been demonstrated in plant tissue. Other deoxysugars have been synthesized through the action of the enzyme aldolase working on dihydroxyacetone phosphate and the appropriate aldehyde. Racker (*76*) found that *Escherichia coli* extracts catalyzed the following reaction:

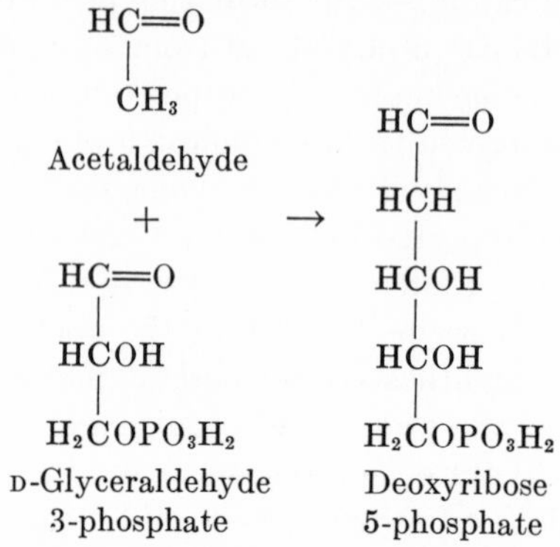
HC=O
CH3
Acetaldehyde
+
HC=O
HCOH
H2COPO3H2
D-Glyceraldehyde
3-phosphate
→
HC=O
HCH
HCOH
HCOH
H2COPO3H2
Deoxyribose
5-phosphate

(22)

A similar reaction may be involved in plants. The general problem of pentose biosynthesis is thoroughly discussed by Glock (*77*).

B. Oligosaccharides

See page 520, Chapter IX, for the biogenesis of these compounds.

C. Starch

Starch synthesis is closely related to sucrose synthesis (see Chapters IX and XII). Experiments with isotopically labeled sugars have shown that leaves can form starch from externally supplied glucose, fructose, and sucrose, as well as from several other compounds. Starch is also formed from carbon dioxide during photosynthesis. It was found (*78*) that when labeled carbon dioxide was fed to leaves, the starch became labeled before the free sugars. Labeled glucose and glucose 1-phosphate did not contribute an

75. M. Gibbs and B. L. Horecker, *J. Biol. Chem.* **208,** 813 (1954); B. Axelrod, R. S. Bandurski, C. M. Greiner, and R. Jang, *ibid* **202,** 619 (1953); N. E. Tolbert and L. P. Zill, *Arch. Biochem. and Biophys.* **50,** 392 (1954).

76. E. Racker, *J. Biol. Chem.* **196,** 347 (1952).

77. G. E. Glock, *in* "The Nucleic Acids" (E. Chargaff and J. N. Davidson, eds.), Vol. 2, p. 247. Academic Press, New York, 1955.

78. P. V. Vittorio, G. Krotkov, and G. B. Reed, *Science* **119,** 906 (1954).

appreciable amount of tracer carbon to the starch fraction. It was suggested that there was a common metabolic pool of hexose phosphates that contributed to both starch synthesis and sugar synthesis (*79*). However, within the cell, the active centers of starch synthesis and sugar synthesis were spatially separated so that under certain environmental conditions one pathway might predominate over the other.

D. Sugar Alcohols

A wide variety of sugar alcohols have been found in plant material (see Chapter V). However, not much is known about the biosynthesis of these compounds. Because the alcohols generally occur together with the structurally related sugars, it has been assumed that mechanisms are available for interconverting them. The following reaction (*80*), found to occur in animal tissue, may occur in plants:

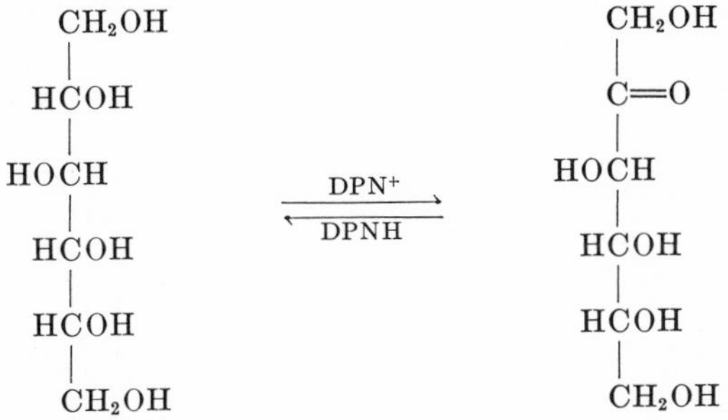

CH₂OH
HCOH
HOCH
HCOH
HCOH
CH₂OH
DPN+
DPNH
CH₂OH
C=O
HOCH
HCOH
HCOH
CH₂OH

Sorbitol D-Fructose (23)

E. Sugar Acids

As noted in Chapter VI, plants contain numerous types of acidic carbohydrates. The aldonic acids, uronic acids, and ascorbic acid are found in varying amounts in most plants. The uronic acids are found in greatest quantities in plant gums and mucilages (*81*) in association with hexose and pentose residues. The common occurrence of these three types of carbohydrates led to suggestions that the following (reaction (24)) metabolic pathways existed. There is little information available to substantiate these transformations. The presence of D-gluconic acid (as D-gluconic acid 6-phosphate) in plants is well established. The metabolism of this compound will be discussed in Section 3 of this chapter.

Ascorbic acid (L-xyloascorbic acid, vitamin C) is widely distributed in plant material, and the problem of its biosynthesis has been of great in-

79. H. K. Porter and L. H. May, *J. Exptl. Botany* **6,** 43 (1955).
80. R. L. Blakley, *Biochem. J.* **49,** 257 (1951).
81. J. K. N. Jones and F. Smith, *Advances in Carbohydrate Chem.* **4,** 243 (1949).

terest. Most of the experiments have been conducted by measuring the increase in ascorbic acid concentration following the feeding of various sus-

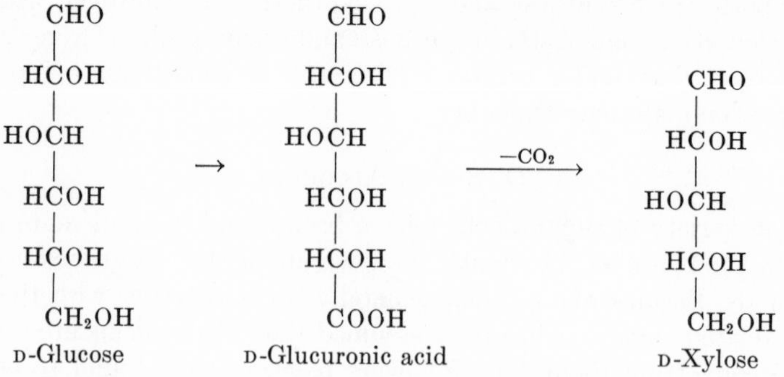
D-Glucose
D-Glucuronic acid
$-CO_2$
D-Xylose
(24)

pected precursors. D-Glucose has always given an increase in L-ascorbic acid in such experiments, while D-mannose, D-galactose, and L-sorbose have

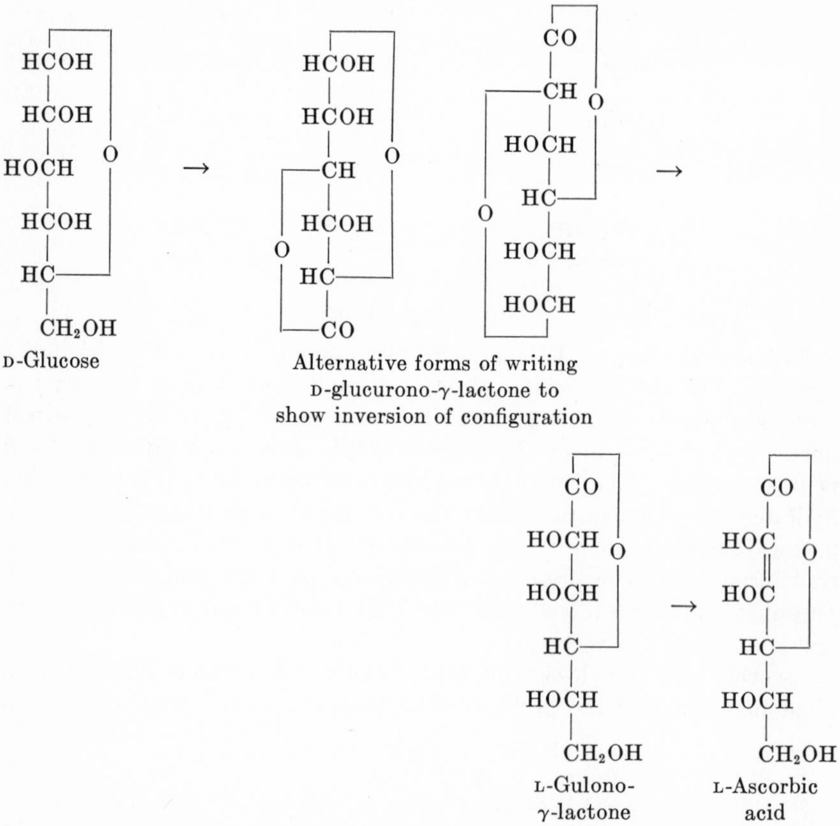
D-Glucose
Alternative forms of writing D-glucurono-γ-lactone to show inversion of configuration
L-Gulono-γ-lactone
L-Ascorbic acid

FIG. 7. Possible pathways of L-ascorbic acid synthesis in plants. (From Isherwood.)

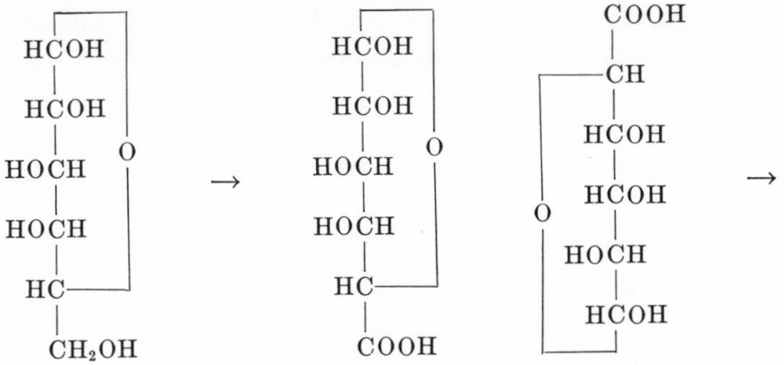

D-Galactose

Alternative forms of writing D-galacturonic acid to show inversion of configuration

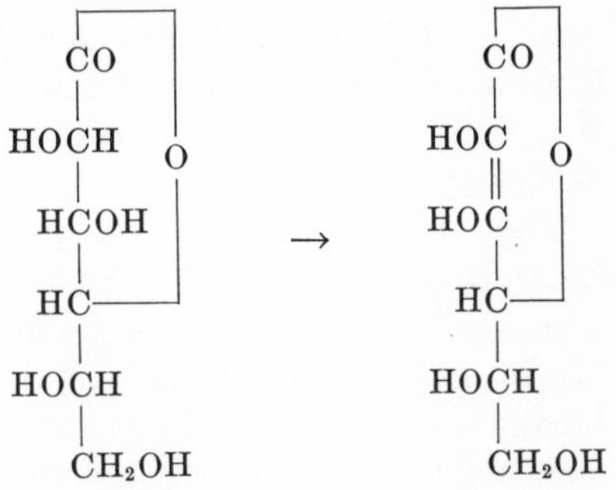

L-Galactono-γ-lactone

L-Ascorbic acid

FIG. 7. (Cont.)

given variable results. The question of the biosynthesis of L-ascorbic acid was recently investigated very thoroughly by Isherwood and co-workers (*82*). On the basis of feeding experiments, they consider the pathways shown in Fig. 7 to represent the most likely methods of ascorbic acid synthesis in plants. L-Gulono-, L-galactono- and D-glucurono-γ-lactones and D-galacturonic acid methyl ester were transformed into L-ascorbic acid when fed to cress seedlings. In the transformations of either D-glucose or D-galactose to L-ascorbic acid it is necessary to postulate that one of the intermediates is capable of effecting the conversion of the D-configuration to the L-configuration. D-Glucurono-γ-lactone and D-galacturonic acid can be written in alternative forms to show that this conversion is possible. Nothing is known of the enzymes that exist in plants to catalyze the reactions. D-Galactose and D-glucose can be interconverted in their phosphorylated forms, and the reactions of ascorbic acid synthesis probably occur as phosphorylated in-

82. F. A. Isherwood, Y. T. Chen, and L. W. Mapson, *Biochem. J.* **56**, 1 (1953).

termediates. The assumption that a lactone is involved as an intermediate in these reactions is not novel since it has been shown that glucono-δ-lactone 6-phosphate is an intermediate in the oxidation of D-glucose 6-phosphate. Results of tracer studies with D-glucuronolactone-C^{14} indicate that this lactone can be a direct precursor of L-ascorbic acid in the rat (*82a*).

3. CARBOHYDRATE BIOCHEMISTRY

A. Pathways for the Metabolism of Carbohydrates

a. Introduction

The breakdown of sugar by living cells has long been recognized as one of the major sources of energy for maintaining cellular activity. It became evident that this breakdown does not occur in one giant step, i.e., carbohydrate → carbon dioxide + water, but rather by a series of stepwise reactions involving a number of intermediate compounds. The elucidation of the nature of these intermediates represents a brilliant chapter in biochemistry.

The early work in this field was largely carried out on two types of material, muscle tissue and yeast cells. Through the efforts of such investigators as Hopkins, Meyerhof, Lohmann, Parnas, Embden, Harden, Neuberg, Warburg, the Coris, and others, the details of the individual steps of sugar breakdown were worked out (*83*, *84*). It was discovered that free sugars were not involved in the reactions but rather that the phosphorylated sugars took part. Certain phases of sugar breakdown in muscle tissue and in yeast cells were found to be identical although the end-products were different. Later work has shown that the pathways discovered in muscle tissue and yeast cells also prevail in plants, bacteria, molds, and animal tissue other than muscle (*85*). More recently several additional pathways of carbohydrate breakdown have been discovered. Many of the metabolic pathways of carbohydrates are reversible and provide mechanisms for the synthesis of the wide variety of compounds that go to make up the cell.

The term glycolysis was used to denote the disappearance of carbohydrate during metabolic activity. Warburg used the term to indicate the production of lactic acid from glucose in animal tissue. Glycolysis has also been used as a term to describe the sequence of reactions taking place in cells

82a. H. H. Horowitz and C. G. King, *J. Biol. Chem.* **205,** 815 (1953).

83. F. Dickens, *in* "The Enzymes" (J. B. Sumner and K. Myrbäck, eds.), Vol. 2, Part 1, p. 624. Academic Press, New York, 1951.

84. F. F. Nord and S. Weiss, *in* "The Enzymes" (J. B. Sumner and K. Myrbäck, eds.), Vol. 2, Part 1, p. 684. Academic Press, New York, 1951.

85. P. K. Stumpf, *in* "Chemical Pathways of Metabolism" (D. M. Greenberg, ed.), Vol. 1, p. 67. Academic Press, New York, 1954.

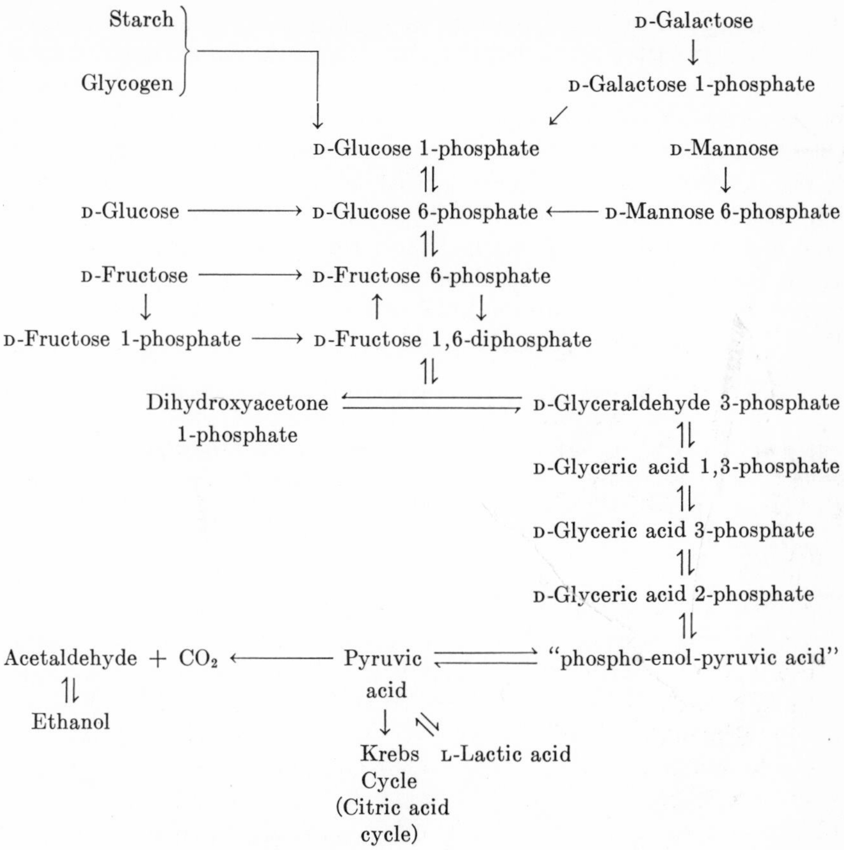
Starch
Glycogen
D-Galactose
D-Galactose 1-phosphate
D-Glucose 1-phosphate
D-Mannose
D-Glucose
D-Glucose 6-phosphate
D-Mannose 6-phosphate
D-Fructose
D-Fructose 6-phosphate
D-Fructose 1-phosphate
D-Fructose 1,6-diphosphate
Dihydroxyacetone 1-phosphate
D-Glyceraldehyde 3-phosphate
D-Glyceric acid 1,3-phosphate
D-Glyceric acid 3-phosphate
D-Glyceric acid 2-phosphate
Acetaldehyde + CO_2
Pyruvic acid
"phospho-enol-pyruvic acid"
Ethanol
Krebs Cycle (Citric acid cycle)
L-Lactic acid

FIG. 8. Embden-Meyerhof-Parnas scheme of glycolysis.

during the anaerobic breakdown. Weinhouse (*86*) has pointed out that glycolysis should not be used to designate a particular pathway of sugar utilization but rather only to denote sugar disappearance.

b. The Embden-Meyerhof-Parnas Scheme of Glycolysis

The best-known glycolytic pathway is that studied especially in muscle tissue and yeast cells. This pathway, sometimes known as the Embden-Meyerhof-Parnas (EMP) scheme, is shown in Fig. 8. The reactions take place under anaerobic conditions. In yeast the end-products are ethanol and carbon dioxide, whereas in muscle tissue the end-product is L-lactic acid. The EMP scheme is operative in a great many tissues and organisms and apparently represents the major pathway of carbohydrate breakdown.

86. S. Weinhouse, *Ann. Rev. Biochem.* **23,** 125 (1954).

The existence of the EMP pathway is based on several lines of evidence: the presence of the intermediates in the system, the isolation and characterization of one or more of the enzymes involved, and the metabolism or disappearance of one or more of the intermediates when added to a tissue extract.

The metabolism of isotopically labeled substrates has also been used to indicate the presence or absence of a particular glycolytic pathway. Koshland and Westheimer (*87*) studied the fermentation of glucose-1-C^{14} by yeast and found that the distribution of radioactivity in the fermented products was in accord with the EMP pathway. If the EMP path is operative, the fermentation should proceed as shown in reaction (25). They

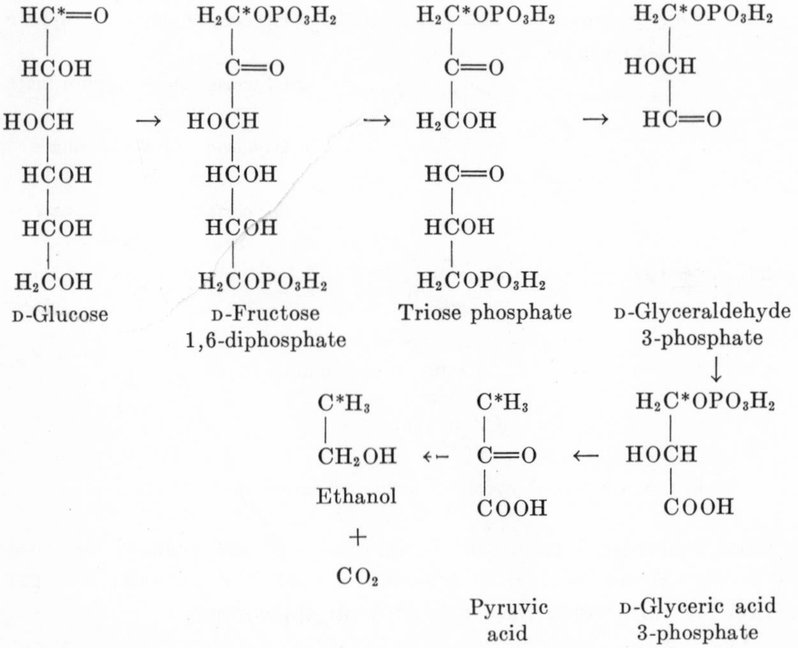
D-Glucose
D-Fructose 1,6-diphosphate
Triose phosphate
D-Glyceraldehyde 3-phosphate
Ethanol
+
CO_2
Pyruvic acid
D-Glyceric acid 3-phosphate

(25)

isolated the ethanol and found that the specific activity of the methyl group was about 95% that of the glucose used; these results gave quantitative support to the EMP pathway. Some radioactivity was found in the CO_2 and indicated another pathway of glycolysis.

The details of the Embden-Meyerhof-Parnas glycolytic pathway are thoroughly discussed in several recent articles (*83, 84, 86, 88*). The comparative biochemistry of glycolysis is discussed by Stumpf (*85*).

87. D. E. Koshland, Jr., and F. H. Westheimer, *J. Am. Chem. Soc.* **72,** 3383 (1950).

88. J. B. Neilands and P. K. Stumpf, "Outlines of Enzyme Chemistry" p. 246. Wiley, New York, 1955.

c. The Hexose Monophosphate Shunt (HMS) Scheme of Glycolysis

During work on the detailed analysis of glycolysis in various organisms, evidence accumulated for the existence of other pathways of carbohydrate breakdown than the EMP pathway. Enzymes were found which catabolized D-glucose in a number of different ways. The work of Warburg, Lipmann, and Dickens showed that D-glucose 6-phosphate was oxidized to D-gluconic acid 6-phosphate by a TPN-specific dehydrogenase. In yeast extracts the D-gluconic acid 6-phosphate is further oxidized in a reaction accompanied by carbon dioxide evolution. Scott and Cohen (*89*) demonstrated that D-ribose 5-phosphate was formed during this reaction. It was shown (*74*) that D-ribose 5-phosphate formation is preceded by D-ribulose 5-phosphate, and that an isomerase exists which catalyzes an equilibrium between these two pentose phosphates. The following reaction sequence (26) was suggested. The postulated keto-acid intermediate has not been detected. D-Gluconic acid 6-phosphate is formed from D-glucose 6-phosphate by way of the δ-lac-

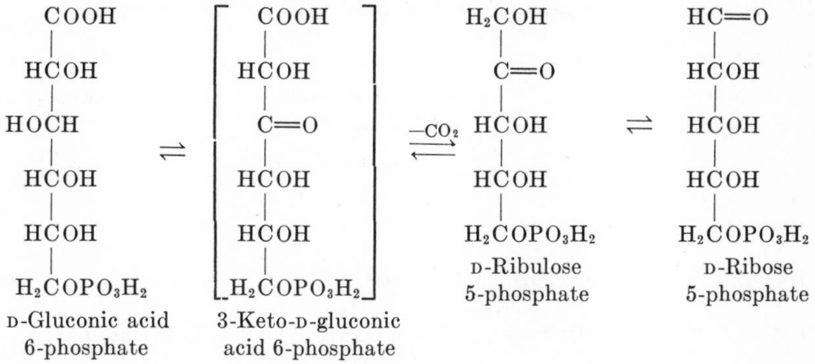
D-Gluconic acid
6-phosphate
3-Keto-D-gluconic
acid 6-phosphate
D-Ribulose
5-phosphate
D-Ribose
5-phosphate

(26)

tone (*90*), a reaction analogous to the bromine oxidation of glucose (Chapter VI) as follows:

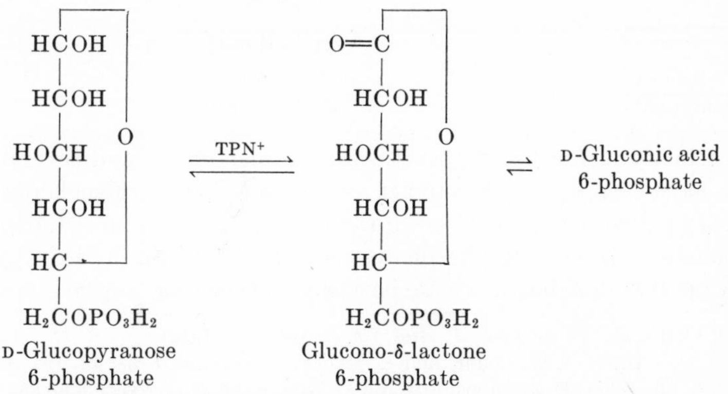
TPN+
D-Gluconic acid
6-phosphate
D-Glucopyranose
6-phosphate
Glucono-δ-lactone
6-phosphate

(27)

89. D. B. M. Scott and S. S. Cohen, *J. Biol. Chem.* **188**, 509 (1951).

Evidence from a number of sources indicated that pentose phosphates were metabolized in a series of reactions that resulted in the formation of hexose monophosphates and hexose diphosphates. Several enzyme steps are involved in these transformations. The reaction between D-ribulose 5-phosphate and D-ribose 5-phosphate to form D-sedoheptulose 7-phosphate and D-glyceraldehyde 3-phosphate is catalyzed by an enzyme known as transketolase (*91*). This enzyme is found in plant, animal, and bacterial cells. Thiamine pyrophosphate (TPP) and Mg ions are required as cofactors. The mechanism of the reaction was suggested (*92*) as shown in reaction (28).

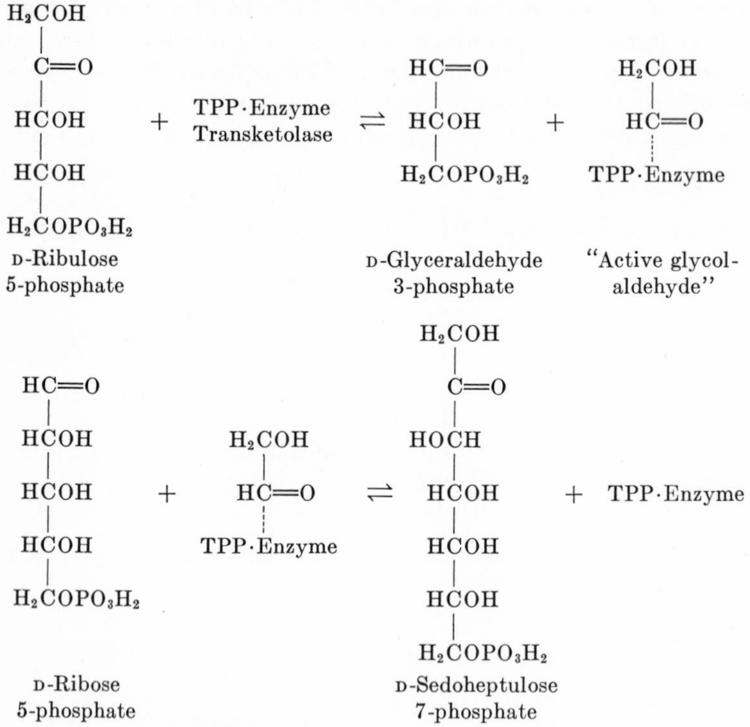
TPP·Enzyme
Transketolase
TPP·Enzyme
D-Ribulose 5-phosphate
D-Glyceraldehyde 3-phosphate
"Active glycolaldehyde"
TPP·Enzyme
TPP·Enzyme
D-Ribose 5-phosphate
D-Sedoheptulose 7-phosphate

(28)

The specificity of purified transketolase is rather broad, and several compounds have been shown (*93*) to act as donors of "active glycolaldehyde." Included in these compounds are D-ribulose 5-phosphate, D-sedoheptulose 7-phosphate, D-fructose 6-phosphate, L-erythrulose, and hydroxypyruvic acid. A number of aldehydes have been shown to act as "active glycolalde-

90. O. Cori and F. Lipmann, *J. Biol. Chem.* **194,** 417 (1952).
91. G. de la Haba, I. G. Leder, and E. Racker, *Federation Proc.* **12,** 194 (1953).
92. B. L. Horecker, P. Z. Smyrniotis and H. Klenow, *J. Biol. Chem.* **205,** 661 (1953).
93. B. L. Horecker, *The Brewers Digest* **28,** 214 (1953).

hyde" acceptors, including glycolaldehyde, D-erythrose 4-phosphate, D-ribose 5-phosphate, and D-glyceraldehyde 3-phosphate. The carbohydrates acted upon by transketolase have both *cis* and *trans* configurations at carbon atoms 3 and 4. However it has been reported (*73b*) that highly purified transketolase is specific for D-xylulose 5-phosphate. Plant transketolases may have the same specificity (*94*). The activity of D-ribulose 5-phosphate in the transketolase reaction is due to the presence of a phosphoketopentoepimerase which converts D-ribulose 5-phosphate to D-xylulose 5-phosphate.

The D-sedoheptulose 7-phosphate formed during the cleavage of the pentose phosphates is metabolized by the following reaction (29). The enzyme catalyzing this reaction is called transaldolase and is supposed to act by transferring a dihydroxyacetone group. Only D-sedoheptulose 7-phosphate and D-fructose 6-phosphate have been shown to act as dihydroxyacetone donors, and D-glyceraldehyde 3-phosphate and D-erythrose 4-phosphate as dihydroxyacetone acceptors (*95*).

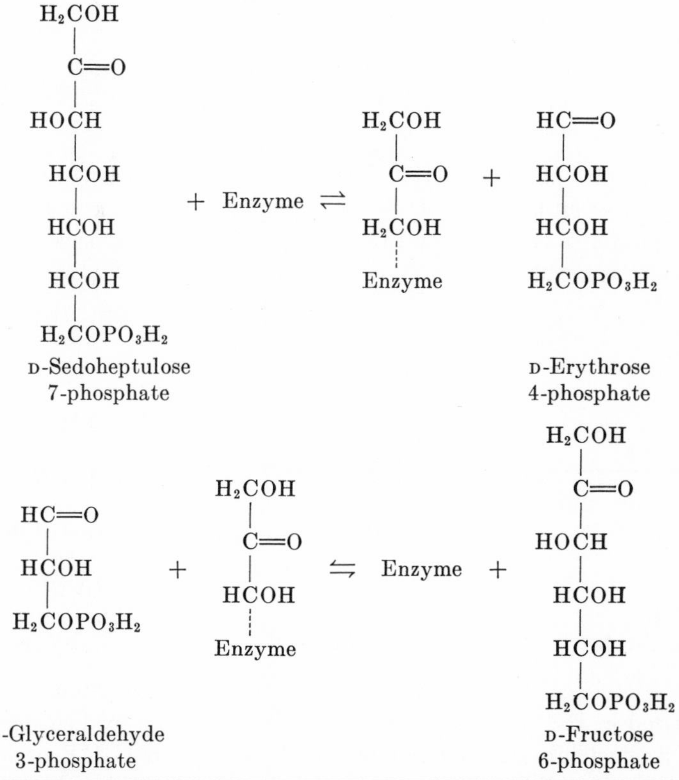
D-Sedoheptulose 7-phosphate
Enzyme
D-Erythrose 4-phosphate
D-Glyceraldehyde 3-phosphate
Enzyme
D-Fructose 6-phosphate

(29)

94. J. A. Bassham, S. A. Barker, M. Calvin, and U. S. Quarck, *Biochim. et Biophys. Acta* **21,** 376 (1956).

95. B. L. Horecker and P. Z. Smyrniotis, *J. Biol. Chem.* **212,** 811 (1955).

The tetrose phosphate formed in the preceding reaction (29) was identified as D-erythrose 4-phosphate (*96*) on the basis of its participation in several reactions. The tetrose phosphate was found to react in an aldolase-catalyzed reaction with dihydroxyacetone phosphate to yield D-sedohep-

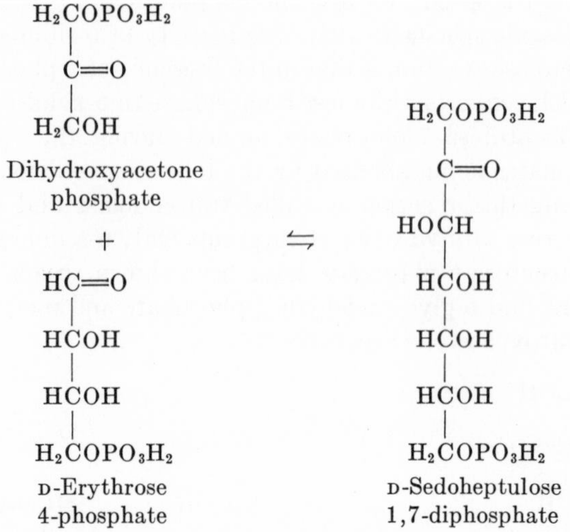
$H_2COPO_3H_2$
C=O
H_2COH
Dihydroxyacetone phosphate
HC=O
HCOH
HCOH
$H_2COPO_3H_2$
D-Erythrose 4-phosphate
$H_2COPO_3H_2$
C=O
HOCH
HCOH
HCOH
HCOH
$H_2COPO_3H_2$
D-Sedoheptulose 1,7-diphosphate

(30)

tulose 1,7-diphosphate (reaction (30)). The tetrose phosphate was also found to act as an acceptor of "active glycolaldehyde" derived from pentose phosphate. In this reaction (31), catalyzed by transketolase, D-fructose 6-phosphate is formed.

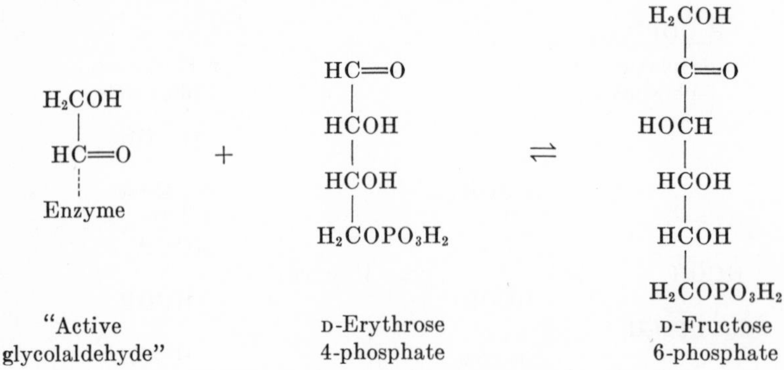
H_2COH
HC=O
Enzyme
"Active glycolaldehyde"
HC=O
HCOH
HCOH
$H_2COPO_3H_2$
D-Erythrose 4-phosphate
H_2COH
C=O
HOCH
HCOH
HCOH
$H_2COPO_3H_2$
D-Fructose 6-phosphate

(31)

The various reactions of the hexose monophosphate shunt have been summarized in Fig. 9. By this pathway it is possible to oxidize completely glucose 6-phosphate without having to go through the EMP pathway or the tricarboxylic acid cycle. A more detailed account of this oxidative path-

96. B. L. Horecker, P. Z. Smyrniotis, H. H. Hiatt, and P. A. Marks, *J. Biol. Chem.* **212,** 827 (1955).

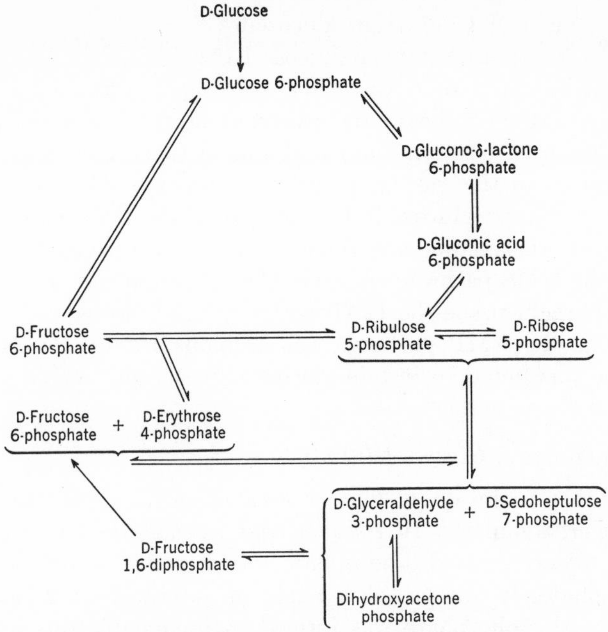
D-Glucose
D-Glucose 6-phosphate
D-Glucono-δ-lactone 6-phosphate
D-Gluconic acid 6-phosphate
D-Fructose 6-phosphate
D-Ribulose 5-phosphate
D-Ribose 5-phosphate
D-Fructose 6-phosphate
+
D-Erythrose 4-phosphate
D-Glyceraldehyde 3-phosphate
+
D-Sedoheptulose 7-phosphate
D-Fructose 1,6-diphosphate
Dihydroxyacetone phosphate

FIG. 9. The hexose monophosphate shunt scheme of glycolysis. [After Gunsalus, Horecker, and Wood (*97*).]

way will be found in several reviews (*93*, *97*). The relative importance of this pathway as compared to the EMP pathway has been studied with the aid of isotopically labeled substrates. As indicated by reaction (25), if glucose-1-C^{14} and glucose-6-C^{14} are respired by comparable tissue samples, the contribution of C^{14} to the CO_2 given off will be the same. If the HMS pathway is operative, the CO_2 from glucose-1-C^{14} will be initially higher in C^{14} than that from glucose-6-C^{14} by virtue of the following reaction (32):

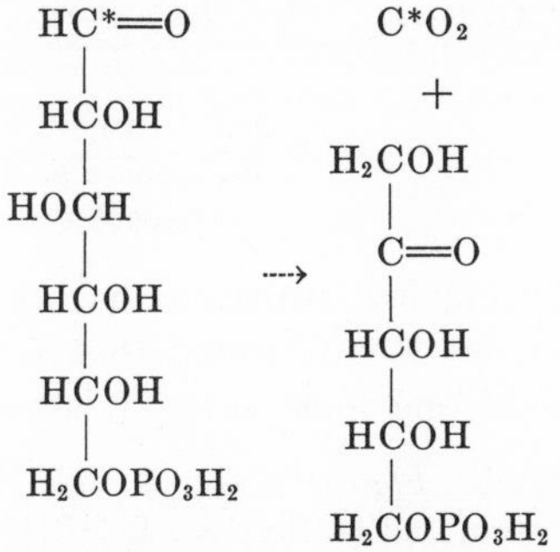
HC*=O
HCOH
HOCH
HCOH
HCOH
H2COPO3H2
C*O2
+
H2COH
C=O
HCOH
HCOH
H2COPO3H2

(32)

D-Glucose 6-phosphate → D-Ribulose 5-phosphate

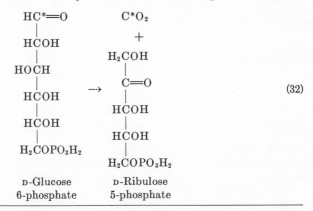

97. I. C. Gunsalus, B. L. Horecker, and W. A. Wood, *Bacteriol. Revs.* **19,** 79 (1955).

If the ratio $\frac{\text{Yield of } C^{14}O_2 \text{ from glucose-6-}C^{14}}{\text{Yield of } C^{14}O_2 \text{ from glucose-1-}C^{14}}$ is determined, a value of unity would be expected if the EMP pathway is operating. A value of less than one would indicate the existence of the HMS pathway. This technique has been used on plant and animal tissue to evaluate the relative importance of the various glycolytic pathways. Corn root tips were found (*98*) to convert glucose to CO_2 by way of the EMP glycolytic route. The tissues of other plants were found to respire glucose by both the EMP route and the HMS pathway. A study (*99*) of several rat tissues indicated that in diaphragm tissue the EMP pathway was followed, whereas in the kidney tissue the EMP pathway was accompanied by the HMS route. Liver tissue was found to respire glucose almost exclusively by the HMS route.

d. *Other Pathways of Glucose Utilization*

Several other pathways of glucose catabolism have been discovered in different microorganisms. In *Pseudomonas saccharophila* it was observed (*100*) that D-gluconic acid 6-phosphate was degraded to pyruvic acid and triose phosphate. It was postulated that an intermediate 2-keto-3-deoxy-D-gluconic acid 6-phosphate was formed. Subsequently this intermediate was isolated and characterized (*101*). The following pathway was suggested.

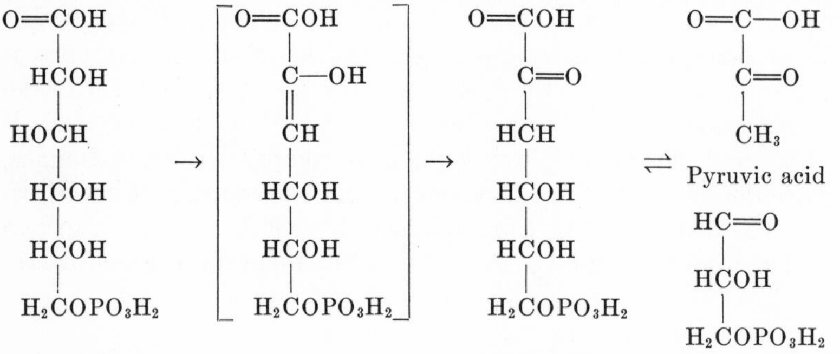
O═COH
HCOH
HOCH
HCOH
HCOH
H₂COPO₃H₂
O═COH
C—OH
CH
HCOH
HCOH
H₂COPO₃H₂
O═COH
C═O
HCH
HCOH
HCOH
H₂COPO₃H₂
O═C—OH
C═O
CH₃
Pyruvic acid
HC═O
HCOH
H₂COPO₃H₂
(33)

D-Gluconic acid 6-phosphate — 2-Keto-3-deoxy-D-gluconic acid 6-phosphate — D-Glyceraldehyde 3-phosphate

The use of isotopically labeled substrates has also revealed other pathways of glucose metabolism. It was found that *Leuconostoc mesenteroides* fermented glucose to yield one mole each of lactate, ethanol, and CO_2.

98. H. Beevers and M. Gibbs, *Plant Physiol.* **29**, 322 (1954).

99. B. Bloom, M. R. Stetten, and D. Stetten, Jr., *J. Biol. Chem.* **204**, 681 (1953); B. Bloom and D. Stetten, Jr., *J. Am. Chem. Soc.* **75**, 5446 (1953).

100. N. Entner and M. Doudoroff, *J. Biol. Chem.* **196**, 853 (1952).

101. J. MacGee and M. Doudoroff, *J. Biol. Chem.* **210**, 617 (1954).

Using C^{14}-labeled glucose (*102*), the following scheme was shown:

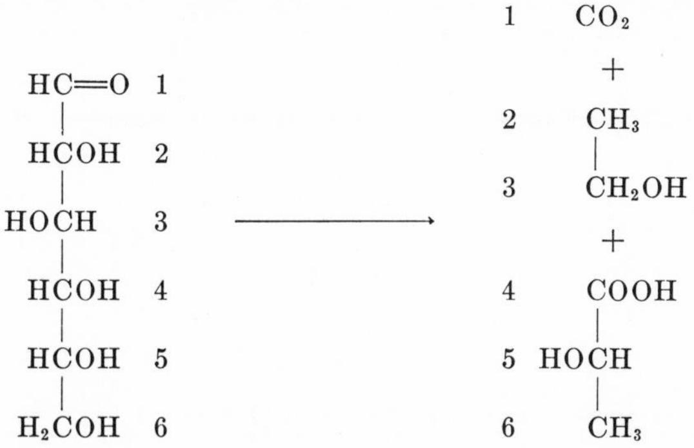

(34)

D-Glucose $\longrightarrow$ CO_2 + Ethanol + Lactic acid

Glucose-1-C^{14} yielded labeled carbon dioxide. Glucose-3,4-C^{14} gave carbinol-labeled ethanol and carboxyl-labeled lactate. Several enzymes have been isolated from the organism, but the mechanism of the reaction remains obscure.

Some microorganisms are able to oxidize glucose to gluconic acid and 2-ketogluconic acid without going through phosphorylated intermediates. The mechanism of these reactions are poorly understood. The pathways of carbohydrate metabolism in microorganisms are thoroughly discussed in a review by Gunsalus, Horecker, and Wood (*97*).

B. Interconversion of the Sugars

The glycolysis schemes shown in Figs. 8 and 9 indicate that D-glucose, D-fructose, and the trioses are the major sugars involved. It is known, however, that other carbohydrates may be converted to D-glucose and D-fructose and, thus, enter the glycolytic pathways. Sugars can also be synthesized from D-glucose and D-fructose, indicating that either the ensymes responsible for the interconversions are reversible or that other enzymes are present which catalyze the reverse reaction. Some of the relationships between the hexoses are shown in Fig. 6 (p. 760). Not all of the enzymes for these reactions have been isolated and characterized.

The transformation of D-galactose 1-phosphate to D-glucose 1-phosphate has been shown to be catalyzed by an enzyme known as galactowaldenase. Leloir and co-workers (*103*) demonstrated that the reaction required a coenzyme that was identified as uridine diphosphate glucose (*sym*-D-gluco-

102. I. C. Gunsalus and M. Gibbs, *J. Biol. Chem.* **194,** 871 (1952).

103. R. Caputto, L. F. Leloir, R. E. Trucco, C. E. Cardini, and A. C. Paladini, *J. Biol. Chem.* **179,** 497 (1949); R. Caputto, L. F. Leloir, C. E. Cardini, and A. C. Paladini, *ibid.* **184,** 333 (1950). For more recent work and concepts, see H. M. Kalckar, *Science* **125,** 105 (1957).

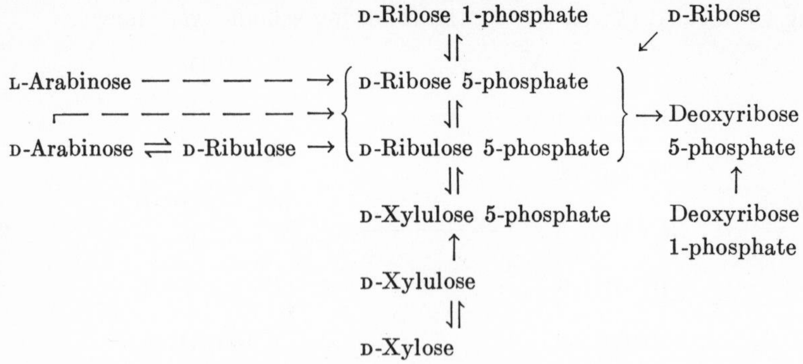
D-Ribose 1-phosphate
D-Ribose
L-Arabinose
D-Ribose 5-phosphate
Deoxyribose 5-phosphate
D-Arabinose
D-Ribulose
D-Ribulose 5-phosphate
D-Xylulose 5-phosphate
Deoxyribose 1-phosphate
D-Xylulose
D-Xylose

FIG. 10. Interrelationships of pentose and phosphates (After Glock, (77)).

pyranosyluridine 5′-pyrophosphoric acid, UDPG). It was postulated that the interconversion from D-galactose 1-phosphate to D-glucose 1-phosphate took place in two steps as follows:

$$\text{D-Galactose 1-phosphate} + \text{UDP glucose} \rightleftharpoons \text{D-glucose 1-phosphate} + \text{UDP galactose} \quad (35)$$

$$\text{UDP galactose} \rightleftharpoons \text{UDP glucose} \quad (36)$$

The conversion of D-glucose 1-phosphate to D-glucose 6-phosphate is catalyzed by an enzyme known as phosphoglucomutase (*104*). A cofactor for this reaction was identified as D-glucose 1,6-diphosphate (*105*). The following reaction mechanism was suggested:

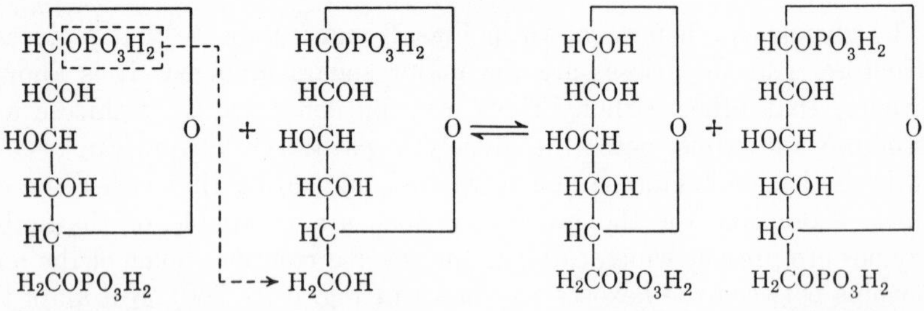
HCOPO3H2
HCOH
HOCH
HCOH
HC
H2COPO3H2
O
+
H2COH
HCOH

D-Glucose 1,6-diphosphate | D-Glucose 1-phosphate | D-Glucose 6-phosphate | D-Glucose 1,6-diphosphate

Only catalytic amounts of the diphosphates are required for the reaction. The phosphoglucomutase also acts on D-mannose phosphate and D-ribose phosphate and is thought to catalyze the interconversion of D-mannose 1-phosphate to D-mannose 6-phosphate and D-ribose 1-phosphate to D-ribose

104. G. T. Cori, S. P. Colowick, and C. F. Cori, *J. Biol. Chem.* **124,** 543 (1938).

105. C. E. Cardini, A. C. Paladini, R. Caputto, L. F. Leloir, and R. E. Trucco, *Arch. Biochem.* **22,** 87 (1949).

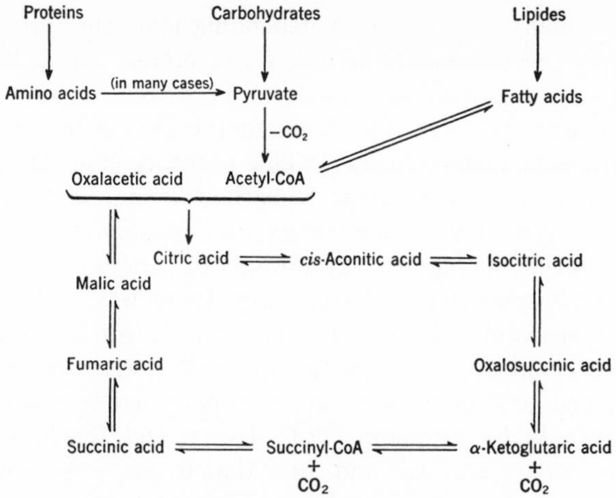

Proteins
Carbohydrates
Lipides
Amino acids
(in many cases)
Pyruvate
Fatty acids
$-CO_2$
Oxalacetic acid
Acetyl-CoA
Citric acid
cis-Aconitic acid
Isocitric acid
Malic acid
Fumaric acid
Oxalosuccinic acid
Succinic acid
Succinyl-CoA + CO_2
α-Ketoglutaric acid + CO_2

FIG. 11. The citric acid cycle.

5-phosphate. Complete discussion of these and other reactions involved in hexose interconversion are to be found in reviews by Racker (*54*) and Leloir (*73, 106*).

The problem of the interconversion of the pentoses and pentose phosphates has been extensively studied during recent years. Many of these findings are discussed in reviews by Lampen (*107*) and Glock (*77*) and summarized in Fig. 10.

D-Ribose can be formed by way of the HMS glycolytic pathway as well as by way of the condensation of two-carbon and three-carbon fragments. The deoxypentoses apparently arise only by the condensation of two-carbon and three-carbon fragments. The dotted lines in Fig. 10 indicate interconversions whose pathways are not thoroughly understood. In certain strains of bacteria, L-arabinose is metabolized but the intermediate products are not known.

The hexose monophosphate shunt pathway ties together hexose and pentose metabolism and provides reactions for the interconversion of these two groups of sugars. In addition this pathway also provides for the metabolism of the three-, four-, and seven-carbon sugars (*108*).

C. Pathways of Pyruvate Metabolism

Whether carbohydrate is metabolized by the EMP pathway or the HMS pathway, pyruvic acid is the common end-product. Pyruvate may be

106. L. F. Leloir, *Advances in Enzymol.* **14,** 193 (1953).

107. J. O. Lampen, *J. Cellular Comp. Physiol.* **41,** Suppl. 1, 183 (1953).

108. S. S. Cohen, *in* "Chemical Pathways of Metabolism" (D. M. Greenberg, ed.), Vol. 1, p. 173. Academic Press, New York, 1954.

metabolized in many different ways depending upon the type of organism and whether the conditions are aerobic or anaerobic. The details of many of these pathways are discussed in several recent reviews (*97*, *109*).

One of the major pathways of pyruvate metabolism is through the "Krebs cycle" or citric acid cycle (*110*, *111*). This pathway (Fig. 11) provides for the complete oxidation of pyruvate to carbon dioxide and water. During this oxidation, a great deal of the energy that is available from the carbohydrate is conserved as high-energy phosphate (*112*) by a process known as "oxidative phosphorylation." Originally there was some difficulty in explaining the mechanism for the entrance of pyruvate into the citric acid cycle. However, evidence of the participation of "active acetate" in carbohydrate, fat, and protein metabolism eventually led to the discovery of coenzyme A (CoA) by Lipmann (*113*). Lynen and Reichert (*114*) were able to isolate "active acetate" and show that it was acetyl-CoA. The formation of acetyl-CoA from pyruvate was discussed earlier (reactions (14) to (17)). The acetyl-CoA then condenses with oxalacetate and enters the citric acid cycle. The biochemistry of the formation of coenzyme A and its participation in a variety of biochemical reactions are discussed in a number of reviews (*115*).

109. E. S. G. Barron, *in* "Modern Trends in Physiology and Biochemistry" (E. S. G. Barron, ed.), p. 471. Academic Press, New York, 1952.

110. S. Ochoa, *Advances in Enzymol.* **15,** 183 (1954).

111. H. A. Krebs, *in* "Chemical Pathways of Metabolism" (D. M. Greenberg, ed.), Vol. 1, p. 109. Academic Press, New York, 1954.

112. F. E. Hunter, Jr., *in* "Phosphorus Metabolism" (W. D. McElroy and B. Glass, eds.), Vol. 1, p. 297. Johns Hopkins Press, Baltimore, 1951.

113. F. Lipmann, *J. Biol. Chem.* **160,** 173 (1945).

114. F. Lynen and E. Reichert, *Angew. Chem.* **63,** 47 (1951).

115. H. A. Barker, *in* "Phosphorus Metabolism" (W. D. McElroy and B. Glass, eds.), Vol. 1, p. 204. Johns Hopkins Press, Baltimore, 1951; E. R. Stadtman, *J. Cellular Comp. Physiol.* **41,** Suppl. 1, 89 (1953).

XIV. CARBOHYDRATES IN NUTRITION*

Harry G. Day and Ward Pigman

Part I

General Aspects

Carbohydrates are important in the nutrition of all people and nearly all domestic animals. The edible carbohydrates and fats provide approximately 90% of the calories in the diet of North Americans (*1*), and a large but variable percentage is furnished by the carbohydrates. No doubt a large portion of all the food energy ever used by humans was derived from starches and sugars, the major carbohydrates in nutrition.

The principal sources of useful dietary carbohydrates are cereals (especially rice, wheat, rye, and maize), potatoes, manioc, sugar cane, and sugar beets. The nutritional needs in humans and common domestic animals are such that some carbohydrates seem to be necessary for the maintenance of physiological well-being, at least in civilized societies. Carbohydrate foods generally provide the cheapest source of body energy and on economic grounds alone are essential to the diet of most people. The increasing complexity and industrialization of modern societies have led to a definite trend from "natural foods" to refined and semirefined carbohydrates. The refining process has decreased the cost of foodstuffs, improved their stability and availability, and, in some instances, has enhanced the palatability and usefulness. However, as a result of the increased use of refined foods, the nutritional requirements of humans must be known and considered. Good planning is necessary to avoid dietary imbalances and deficiencies when the refined products are used in substantial quantity. To some extent at least, it would seem to be the duty of the refiners of foodstuffs to provide the knowledge needed for the proper utilization of their products in the human diet.

Some of the information concerning the role of carbohydrates in nutri-

* The present chapter has required the examination of a very large amount of literature. Some efforts will be made to give credit for the findings used. Since the original sources are numerous and sometimes ill-defined, proper acknowledgement cannot always be given. A list of general references is given in Chapter XV.

1. "Recommended Dietary Allowances," Publ. 302, revised. National Research Council, Washington, D. C., 1953.

tion is presented in the current chapter. The actual pathways by which carbohydrates are converted into useful chemical energy in the body are discussed in more detail in Chapter XIII, particularly. Additional information is also provided under the individual sugars and polysaccharides, Chapters II, IX and XII. Carbohydrates also function as specifically active biological materials. These are discussed under the individual substances such as ascorbic acid.

1. CALORIC VALUE

Much of the information on the energy values of the carbohydrates and other classes of foodstuffs was developed in the later part of the 19th century. Rubner's (1885) and Atwater's (1899) estimates are generally used as the basis for calculations. The former showed that the oxidation of 1 g. of starch in a bomb calorimeter yielded approximately 4.1 kcal. (large calories). The bomb value for D-glucose was 3.76 kcal. On the basis of 185 dietary studies on groups of people in different parts of the United States, Atwater estimated the percentage of carbohydrate—as well as fat and protein—furnished by various groups of foodstuffs such as cereals, vegetables, meat, and milk. Then, on the basis of 97 digestion experiments on humans, he estimated the average coefficient of digestibility of some of the different carbohydrates, fats, and proteins in "an average mixed diet." By multiplying the values for the coefficients of digestibility by the heats of combustion, so-called metabolizable energy values were obtained for the components of the representative foods. From such data, averages were calculated in accordance with the proportions in which these components occurred in the "average mixed diet." Atwater concluded that this system gave figures suitable for the estimation of the caloric value of common foodstuffs. By this procedure, it became generally accepted that the figures should be 4, 9, and 4 kcal. per gram of edible carbohydrate, fat, and protein, respectively.

It is apparent that substantial errors may be introduced if the utilizability of the food components differ much from the calculations employed, or if there are differences in the utilizability of the energy liberated. For example, starch has a higher caloric value than glucose, as determined in a bomb calorimeter, because of the energy of the glycosidic bonds. But, the caloric value of the completely digested starch is the same as for D-glucose. The energy liberated by the hydrolysis of the glycosidic bonds during the digestive process in the intestine appears to be unavailable for any function other than the maintenance of the body temperature, because it is not coupled to phosphorylation mechanisms for the storage and transport of such energy. In some cases this is largely wasted heat energy. On the contrary, oxidation of glucose in the body is coupled to phosphorylation mechanisms which convert the energy into forms such as chemical bonds which can be used to do work. Thus, the effective fuel value of starches may not be very different from that of glucose or other utilizable monosaccharides.

2. DIGESTION AND ABSORPTION

In general all carbohydrates must be converted to their constituent monosaccharides before they can be absorbed by the gastrointestinal tract. The digestive processes are largely dependent on the action of suitable enzymes. However, the acidity of the stomach may be great enough at times to cause the nonenzymatic hydrolysis of sucrose, and probably some other disaccharides.

Digestion of the starches is initiated in the mouth through the action of α-amylase in the saliva. The attack is only on the glycosidic linkages in the interior of the susceptible polysaccharides thus forming oligosaccharides. The digestion is interrupted in the stomach due to the low pH, but in the intestines the pH is 7 or higher and digestion is resumed owing to various carbohydrases elaborated by the pancreas and small intestines. The resultant monosaccharides are transported across the intestinal mucosa to the blood and enter the liver by the portal vein. Varying degrees of digestion and assimilation may be effected by the microorganisms in the small intestines and large bowel.

Absorption of the major monosaccharides, D-glucose, D-fructose, and D-galactose, apparently involves phosphorylation in the intestinal mucosa and liberation of the sugar in the blood stream (*2*). The mechanism is believed to be analogous to the formation of urine in the renal tubules. Mannose and the pentoses seem to be absorbed only by diffusion (*3*).

3. STARCHES

Starches from different plant sources differ substantially in histologic features and in the chemical heterogeneity of the granule components. Relatively scant information is recorded on the utilization of starches as food for man and animals. Such information has shown that uncooked starches from the cereal grains are well utilized and that from raw potatoes, in contrast to the starch in cooked potatoes, is poorly utilized by human subjects (*4*).

In an extensive investigation of this problem by Booher and her associates (*5*), there was confirmation of the high digestibility of several starches

2. W. A. Darlington and J. H. Quastel, *Arch. Biochem. and Biophys.* **43,** 194 (1953).
3. F. Verzar and H. Sullman, *Biochem. Z.* **289,** 323 (1947).
4. C. F. Langworthy and H. J. Deuel, Jr., *J. Biol. Chem.* **52,** 251 (1922).
5. L. E. Booher, I. Behan, and E. McMeans, *J. Nutrition* **45,** 75 (1951).

TABLE I

Utilization of Raw (Uncooked) Starches at a Level of 63.7% in Diets Fed *ad Libitum* to Young Rats for Periods of 28 Days[a] (*5*)

Type of starch	Net body weight gain: Total (g. ± S.D.)	Net body weight gain: Grams per gram dry food	Starch coeff. of digestibility (%)
Wheat	127 ± 10.8	0.43	98.1
Wheat, acid-modified	131 ± 7.7	0.43	98.3
Wheat, oxidized	126 ± 6.8	0.41	98.4
Maize	121 ± 18.4	0.39	97.7
Maize, waxy	130 ± 5.2	0.42	98.3
Rice	130 ± 11.5	0.40	97.5
Cassava	123 ± 21.9	0.39	97.9
Sweet potato	109 ± 10.6	0.38	96.0
Arrowroot	91 ± 7.2	0.31	79.9
Sago palm	112 ± 13.6	0.32	65.3
Sago palm, ball-milled 2 hrs	135 ± 18.2	0.39	95.1
White potato	106 ± 13.0	0.31	—
White potato, ball-milled 40 hrs	111 ± 11.7	0.40	98.2
White potato, dextrinized	100 ± 12.6	0.31	59.2

[a] Basal diet: Starch 63.7%, casein 18.8%, roughage (Ruffex) 2.0%, cottonseed oil 9.4%, salt mixture 4.0%, cod-liver oil 1.0%, wheat-germ oil 0.5%, liver concentrate powder 0.6%, and a daily vitamin supplement.

from cereal grains and cassava roots, the degree of assimilability being about 98 % in test rats. As shown in Table I, no appreciable differences were observed between the raw starches from wheat, maize, rice, cassava, and sweet potatoes. Also, the high assimilation of raw wheat starch was not modified by partial hydrolysis with hydrochloric acid or partial oxidation with hypochlorite.

The results from this study and those of others (*6*) suggest that the relatively low utilizability of unmodified starches from potato, arrowroot, and sago is due to the degree of crystallization or character of the outermost layers of the starch granules. The factors which increase the digestibility of these starches must disrupt the granular structure. This may be accomplished by gelatinization as a result of cooking and by dextrinization as a result of chemical or enzymic hydrolysis. Ball-milling the starches with low digestibility, even for 2 hours, markedly raises the utilizability, but this does not appear to fragment greatly the polysaccharides molecularly, as indicated by the relatively slight changes in reducing power. These factors have often been neglected in animal experimentation, e.g., in dental

6. B. Jelinek, M. C. Katayama, and A. E. Harper, *Can. J. Med. Sci.* **30,** 447 (1952).

caries work, and undoubtedly affected the results, particularly in comparisons with human physiological conditions.

Owing to the structural differences between the major components of starch, amylose and amylopectin, it is possible that the utilizability of such polysaccharides may be affected by these differences. The scanty data which can be brought to bear on the question suggest that there are no differences in utilization under normal conditions. For example, Booher and associates (*5*) found no difference between waxy maize, which is all amylopectin, and common maize (corn) which is approximately 22% amylose and 78% amylopectin. Limit dextrins produced by the action of β-amylase on rice starch were utilized well by rats as determined by the deposition of glycogen in the liver following their administration via stomach tube or subcutaneous injection (*7*). The dextrins have a higher concentration of the 1,6-α-glucosidic linkages than the amylopectins from which they are formed.

It has been demonstrated that the intestinal mucosa of rabbits can account for the complete digestion of the amylose and amylopectin of starch (*8*). In this important study it was shown that glucose is the chief product of digestion, but maltose and two other oligosaccharides were present in the portal blood of rabbits digesting starch. Thus, maltose and some of the other oligosaccharides in the body are absorbed intact through the intestinal mucosa. More attention should be given to the utilizability of linear-type polysaccharides as compared with branched-chain substances.

A number of papers have been published on refection in experimental rats given certain diets containing large amounts of starch and devoid of B-complex vitamins. The first report was by Fridericia in 1926. The condition is characterized by the production of light-colored and bulky feces, and the ability to survive without a dietary source of the B-complex vitamins, if the animals have access to their feces. Also, there is a marked change in the microflora of the alimentary tract. Unmodified potato starch is the most effective in producing the condition, but raw rice starch also causes refection. Apparently the resistance of the starch to digestion is accompanied by a marked increase in the production of the necessary B-complex vitamins by the microorganisms of the lower alimentary tract.

4. DEXTRINS

Dextrins are formed by the partial hydrolysis, oxidation, or heat-treatment of starch. (See p. 677.) Various other reactions, such as polymerization, may be involved; thus various kinds of dextrins occur. Quantitatively

7. A. D. Deckard and R. C. Corley, *Proc. Indiana Acad. Sci.* **59,** 123 (1950).

8. J. Larner and C. M. McNickle, *J. Am. Chem. Soc.* **76,** 4747 (1954); *Federation Proc.* **14,** 242 (1955).

their dietary uses are not very important, but "malt-dextrin" mixtures and "corn sirups" are prescribed commonly in infant feeding. These products contain D-glucose, maltose, and other oligosaccharides in variable amounts.

Apparently dextrins are well utilized, but there is little if any scientific evidence that they are superior to some other carbohydrates in infant nutrition (*9*). It is reported that "the enthusiasm for malt-dextrin mixtures goes back to the Germen chemist Liebig, who, when his own child developed diarrhea, tried the effect of feeding dextrinized starch, following which the diarrhea ceased."

5. MALTOSE

This disaccharide needs to be hydrolyzed before it can be utilized, although small amounts may pass directly through the intestinal mucosa (*8*). The commercial foods for infants and children, which contain partially hydrolyzed starch or cereal—so-called "dextri-maltose"—may furnish considerable amounts of free maltose. There seems to be little, if any, evidence that this sugar has any unique nutritional qualities.

6. SUCROSE

Although sucrose is present in nearly all edible plants, a considerable proportion of the amount used as a food is refined sugar. Hockett (*10*) has estimated that sucrose, in the purified form and as it occurs in fruits, vegetables, molasses, and sirups, constitutes about one-fourth of the carbohydrate consumed in the United States. Its stability in transit and storage, pleasing taste, low cost, and versatility in the production and preservation of foods makes this sugar of outstanding economic and dietary significance.

Among the remarkable properties of sucrose is the rapidity of digestion and absorption from the digestive tract. For a long time it was assumed without question that glucose is utilized more rapidly because it is the "physiological" sugar and requires no digestive process. This was in spite of the fact that sucrose given orally caused a marked rise in the respiratory quotient within 4 minutes, whereas with glucose the elevation occurred only after 20 minutes (*11*). The first more direct experiment showing the rapid utilization of sucrose was by Rabinowitch (*12*). Diabetics being treated with protamine zinc insulin and who suffered hypoglycemia before breakfast were given 10 g. of sucrose in solution by mouth. Blood samples were taken immediately before the ingestion of sugar and other samples were removed at 1-minute intervals until the patients felt better. Marked elevations in blood sugar had occurred in all subjects within 5 minutes.

9. L. E. Holt, Jr., *Advances in Chem. Ser.* **No. 12,** 104 (1955).
10. R. C. Hockett, *Advances in Chem. Ser.* **No. 12,** 114 (1955).
11. H. L. Higgins, *Am. J. Physiol.* **41,** 258 (1916).
12. I. M. Rabinowitch, *J. Nutrition* **29,** 99 (1945).

TABLE II

Effect of Different Sugars in a Synthetic Milk on the Growth and Survival of Day-Old Pigs for Nine Days (*13*)

	Sugar used in "milk"			
	Glucose	Sucrose	Fructose	Glucose + fructose
No. of pigs	7	7	7	6
No. of deaths	1	6	5	1
Av. initial wt. (kg.)	1.24	1.29	1.33	1.29
Av. gain per pig (kg.)	1.12	−0.32	−0.31	0.49
Solids intake per pig (kg.)	1.53	0.43	0.61	1.46

The sucrase (invertase) necessary for the digestion of sucrose is secreted by the intestinal mucosa. Apparently the activity is not great enough to permit the utilization of sucrose in newborn animals. At least it has been shown (*13*) that newborn Duroc pigs were unable to survive on a synthetic milk diet containing sucrose as the only source of carbohydrate, whereas survival and growth occurred in pigs given glucose or an equimolar mixture of glucose and fructose. A summary of the findings (*13*) is given in Table II.

It is evident that under these conditions with newborn pigs, neither sucrose nor fructose is capable of promoting growth or appreciable survival even during a rather short period of time. Because the growth response to a mixture of glucose and fructose was only about one-half that for glucose alone, it is apparent that glucose does not promote the utilization of fructose under these conditions. Experiments should be done to determine the activity of sucrase and fructokinase, and perhaps related enzymes, in the intestines of young animals to determine when the activity becomes high enough to account for good utilization of sucrose and fructose.

7. D-GLUCOSE (DEXTROSE)

D-Glucose has a central position in animal nutrition because it is the principal carbohydrate metabolite; it is utilized directly by the tissues, and it is absorbed from the alimentary tract in far greater amounts than any other monosaccharide under nearly all situations. Under most dietary conditions much of it enters the body as the structural unit of starch, but owing to its use in candies and as a sweetening agent, with sucrose, in many fruits, carbonated beverages, and various confections, considerable amounts

13. D. E. Becker, D. E. Ullrey, S. W. Terrill, and R. A. Notzold, *Science* **120**, 345 (1954).

of free D-glucose may be consumed. Apparently D-glucose could serve satisfactorily in meeting at least 50% of the entire energy needs of humans and various animals. The utilization of this sugar has tended to be accepted as a basis for the evaluation of other carbohydrates. Commercial "glucose" is a mixture of D-glucose and oligosaccharides (p. 93). As used herein, glucose is the pure sugar, D-glucose.

8. D-FRUCTOSE (LEVULOSE)

Owing to its great sweetness and high utilizability in the body, D-fructose has been of special interest in nutrition for many decades. In the first quarter of this century, a large demand for this ketose was predicted if economical methods could be developed for its production. In addition to sucrose, many plants store the sugar in their tubers in the form of fructosans, of which inulin is the most common. Fructose can be prepared (p. 96) most conveniently from dahlia tubers and from Jerusalem artichokes, but the yield from the latter is not as favorable as from the former. Acid hydrolysis is commonly employed to liberate the fructose.

In one study designed to compare the utilization of fructose with glucose (*14*), young rats were given an experimental diet containing 68% of the test sugar. The fructose-fed rats grew at the same rate as those given glucose. Also, the total glycogen in the tissues was the same in the two groups. However, the livers of the animals given fructose were 22% heavier than those fed glucose.

Whether or not fructose or fructose-containing substances are ingested, the blood contains appreciable amounts of the sugar. In the blood of fetal sheep and newborn babies, the level of fructose is considerably higher than in adults (*15*). It is remarkable that fructose is the principal sugar of seminal fluid. Spermatozoa, but none of the somatic cells, derive energy from fructose (*16*).

In many respects the metabolism of fructose is different from glucose. This has been revealed over a number of years, but the proportion of papers on fructose since approximately 1945 is unusually large, several of which are reviewed by Hockett (*10*). Fructose is rapidly removed from the blood and has a low renal threshold in humans (*17*). Another favorable fact is that the infusion of fructose in hospitalized adults during the post-operative period is followed by a much smaller loss as urinary sugar than with glucose (*18*).

Nutritional interest in fructose has been focused upon its potential use-

14. G. Bachmann, J. Haldi, W. Wynn, and C. Ensor, *J. Nutrition* **16,** 229 (1938).
15. J. S. D. Bacon and D. J. Bell, *Biochem. J.* **42,** 397 (1948).
16. T. Mann, *Biochem. J.* **40,** 481 (1946).
17. J. J. Weinstein and J. H. Roe, *J. Lab. Clin. Med.* **40,** 39 (1952).
18. J. A. Moncrief, K. B. Coldwater, and R. Elman, *Arch. Surg.* **67,** 57 (1953).

fulness in persons with impaired utilization of D-glucose, notably those with diabetes mellitus. Even as early as 1896, Minkowski noted that fructose is utilized to a greater degree than glucose by the diabetic animal. It has been shown that liver slices of diabetic animals are impaired in their ability to oxidize glucose, but their capacity to oxidize fructose is unchanged from normal. In patients with diabetes mellitus or parenchymal hepatic disease, the impairment of fructose tolerance was relatively small and not at all comparable to the dimunition in tolerance of the same patients to glucose (*19*). The livers from rats made diabetic by the administration of alloxan were able to oxidize fructose at a normal rate, but the metabolism of glucose under similar conditions was greatly inhibited (*20*). In another study it has been reported that alloxan-diabetic rats utilize more fructose than glucose (*21*). The effect is not transitory because it could be demonstrated even after fructose had been fed for 25 consecutive days. Moreover, the nitrogen utilization was greater in the animals given fructose than in those fed glucose. However, there is evidence that the advantages of orally administered fructose decrease after some time (*22*).

The vast amount of research on the intermediary metabolism of fructose and glucose has demonstrated that fructose follows at least one pathway in the liver which is independent of glucose metabolism. (See Chapter XIII for additional discussion.) This pathway involves the direct conversion of fructose 1-phosphate to dihydroxyacetone phosphate and glyceraldehyde (*23*). It apparently can occur without the aid of any of the enzymes required in the glucose to triose phosphate. These findings and clinical evidence (*24*) suggest that the metabolism of fructose may be somewhat more independent of the influence of insulin than the metabolism of glucose. Nevertheless, it has not been demonstrated that fructose is a thoroughly reliable substitute for other carbohydrates in the feeding of diabetics. Although the research results show some promise, fructose apparently can serve as a diabetic food only under limited circumstances, and under all conditions the metabolic status of diabetic patients must be determined periodically. The evidence suggests that fructose may prove to be preferable to glucose in the parenteral nutrition of certain patients in whom glucose utilization is impaired.

A relatively large amount of dietary niacin is required by the rat when

19. L. H. Smith, Jr., R. H. Ettinger, D. Seligson, and S. Lightcap, *J. Clin. Invest.* **32,** 273 (1953).

20. S. S. Cernick and I. L. Chaikoff, *J. Biol. Chem.* **188,** 389 (1951).

21. E. Geiger and J. J. Pinsky, *Metabolism Clin. Exptl.* **4,** 166 (1955).

22. H. P. Sarett and L. P. Snipper, *J. Nutrition* **52,** 525 (1954).

23. H. G. Hers, T. Kusaka, and C. deDuve, *2nd Intern. Congr. Biochem. Paris* p. 291 (1952).

24. M. Miller, W. R. Drucker, J. E. Owens, J. W. Craig, and H. Woodward, Jr., *J. Clin. Invest.* **31,** 115 (1952).

TABLE III
EFFECT OF NIACIN ON UTILIZATION OF SOME CARBOHYDRATES BY RATS (*25*)

No. of rats	Carbohydrate	Growth per wk. per rat (gm.)	
		No niacin added	2 mg. per cent niacin added
10	Fructose	1.5 ± 0.7	12.0
10	Sucrose	3.3 ± 0.94	17.2
15	Glucose	9.4 ± 0.71	23.0
10	Starch	12.9 ± 1.04	22.7

fructose is the only dietary carbohydrate. This was demonstrated (*25*) by young rats fed a purified diet low in tryptophan, a niacin precursor, and deficient in niacin. This diet consisted of casein 9%, gelatin 3%, L-cystine 0.15%, carbohydrate 81%, corn oil 3%, salt mixture 4%, and substantially all the known vitamins except vitamin B_{12}. A comparison of the growth effects of fructose and certain other carbohydrates in the diet is given in Table III. In other data reported by Hundley (*25*), glucose gave about 4 times as much growth as sucrose and approximately 5 times as much as fructose. Also, when niacin was furnished, glucose and starch gave a higher growth maximum than either fructose or sucrose. Thus, there are unknown factors other than niacin that affect the utilization of fructose in this type of diet. Possibly this action is related to the rapid removal of fructose from the blood (*17*) and a consequent impairment of its value as a sparer of protein. In animals given adequate protein, there was no difference in growth rate between fructose and glucose (*14*).

9. D-MANNOSE

Relatively little is known regarding the metabolism and nutritional value of D-mannose, even though it is widely distributed in animal tissues as well as in plants and some microorganisms (*26*). There are indications of the direct utilization of mannose by higher animals. Rabbits utilized 96% of the sugar when it was administered orally or intraperitoneally (*26*). It increases the blood glucose level without any elevation of the fructose. Also, the concentration of liver glycogen is promptly raised to approximately the same levels that result from the administration of comparable amounts of glucose. Thus, it seems probable that a large proportion of ingested mannose is converted to glucose. (See also Chapter II.)

25. J. M. Hundley, *J. Biol. Chem.* **181,** 1 (1949).
26. W. H. Bailey, III, and J. H. Roe, *J. Biol. Chem.* **152,** 135 (1944).

10. D-GALACTOSE AND LACTOSE

The major source of absorbable D-galactose in the diet of man and many of the higher animals is lactose. The latter occurs only in milk as a product of the mammary gland; hence, these sugars are of special importance in the nutrition of all young mammals and older persons and animals that ingest appreciable amounts of milk.

The rate of absorption of galactose from the alimentary tract exceeds that of D-glucose, D-fructose, and D-mannose. In the rat, glycogen is formed more slowly from galactose than from glucose (*27*), and galactose differs from glucose in many respects.

Young rats on a mineralized skim milk diet excreted considerable amounts of a sugar which proved to be galactose (*28*). This surprising galactosuria did not occur when whole milk was fed. Thus, the idea arose that nature has put lactose and milk fat together as an optimum combination for the young animal. Most of the subsequent research has confirmed the conclusion that dietary fats promote lactose utilization, and that some vegetable fats are as effective as milk fat (*29*). The effect of the fat seems to be on the utilization of the galactose moiety, and not on the hydrolysis of lactose (*30*). Fat influences the excretion of galactose whether the diet contains free galactose or lactose. The rate of intestinal absorption of galactose varies inversely with the concentration of fat in the diet. The addition of glucose to skim milk lowers the galactose excretion but not to the same extent as does fat (*31*). It appears that fat acts largely, if not entirely, by delaying the gastric emptying and by reducing the rate of absorption of galactose. Rapid absorption of galactose results in increased galactosuria (*32*).

A. Lactose and the Microflora of the Digestive Tract

An important property of lactose is its ability to promote an aciduric microflora in the alimentary tract. *Lactobacillus acidophilus* is commonly regarded as the most responsive to the presence of lactose. However, the concentration of several other aciduric microorganisms is greatly increased when the milk sugar is ingested in considerable amounts regularly. Several days are required for the sugar to effect a change in the microflora. The

27. C. F. Cori, *Proc. Soc. Exptl. Biol. Med.* **23,** 459 (1926).

28. E. J. Schantz and C. A. Elvehjem, *J. Biol. Chem.* **122,** 381 (1938).

29. M. L. Nieft and H. J. Deuel, Jr., *J. Biol. Chem.* **167,** 521 (1947).

30. L. K. Riggs and A. Beaty, *J. Dairy Sci.* **30,** 939 (1947).

31. R. P. Geyer, R. K. Boutwell, C. A. Elvehjem, and E. B. Hart, *J. Biol. Chem.* **162,** 251 (1946).

32. V. H. Barki, P. Feigelson, R. A. Collins, and E. B. Hart, *J. Biol. Chem.* **181,** 565 (1949).

change is accompanied by a decrease in the pH of the intestinal contents. For example, when a cow's milk formula for young infants was supplemented with lactose, the extra milk sugar was sufficient to lower the fecal pH to approximately 5. This is in contrast to the pH of about 6.5 which is typical when cow's milk is fed with or without other added sugar (*33*). The lowered pH is due to lactic acid and other products of lactose fermentation.

Lactose has been used extensively in conjunction with *L. acidophilus* milk for the treatment of constipation, and as a general "health" food. The relation of lactose to the microflora of the intestines and to gastrointestinal mobility has been extensively reviewed (*34*).

B. α-Lactose vs. β-Lactose

Because β-lactose is initially more soluble than ordinary lactose (α-lactose), it may be supposed that the β-form is utilized more efficiently in nutrition, but the opposite appears to be true. Young rats on a low-fat diet fail to survive when the only source of carbohydrate in the diet is either α-lactose or β-lactose. Although alopecia occurs regardless of the form of lactose used, it occurs sooner and survival is shorter in rats fed β-lactose. Whether or not the greater deleterious effect of the β-lactose is due to a more rapid rate of hydrolysis and absorption does not seem to be known (*35*). An industrial demand for β-lactose has resulted in the development of practical processes for the manufacture of this sugar. (See Chapter IX, under Lactose.)

C. Influence of the Glycosidic Linkage on the Utilization of Lactose

Certain of the deleterious effects of lactose in large amounts are obviously related to an impairment in the ability to hydrolyze the glycosidic linkage which holds the galactose and glucose moieties together. For example, young rats on a low-fat diet grow less rapidly when the carbohydrate is lactose than in the case of animals given equivalent amounts of galactose and glucose. This is illustrated by the data of Riggs and Beaty (*30*) as given in Table IV. Intestinal disturbances, particularly diarrhea, which occur when the lactose intake is high, are minimal when equivalent amounts of the constituent monosaccharides are substituted. It has been concluded that impairment in the hydrolysis of lactose accounts for its laxative effects (*36*).

33. A. Primnig and M. Turkus, *Z. Kinderheilk.* **63,** 595 (1943).
34. J. E. Fischer and T. S. Sutton, *J. Dairy Sci.* **32,** 139 (1949).
35. B. H. Ershoff and H. J. Deuel, Jr., *J. Nutrition* **28,** 225 (1941).
36. H. S. Mitchell, G. M. Cook, and K. L. O'Brien, *J. Nutrition* **18,** 319 (1939).

TABLE IV

EFFECT OF GALACTOSE AND LACTOSE ON THE GROWTH OF RATS

Carbohydrate in diet	No. of rats	Av. initial weight (g.)	Av. weight at end of 12 wks. (g.)
7.5% Glucose plus 7.5% galactose	8	55	330
15% Lactose	8	53	332
15% Glucose plus 15% galactose	8	52	313
30% Lactose	8	51	292
25% Glucose plus 25% galactose	8	57	288
50% Lactose	8	53	219

D. Adaptation to Lactose Ingestion

Several investigations have shown that rats seem to become adapted to lactose feeding, as indicated by the eventual subsidence of diarrhea (*30*). It has been proposed that this effect is due to increased lactase (β-galactosidase) activity in the alimentary tract, but there seems to be little if any evidence in support of this suggestion (*34*, *37*).

In investigations of the effects of very large amounts of lactose in the diet (*36*), it was found by chance that a small amount of calcium gluconate or sodium gluconate in the diet caused extremely severe diarrhea and subsequent death of the animals. Such compounds have no known adverse effects when lactose is absent from the diet. It was suggested that the gluconate radical inhibits lactase, thus accounting for the apparent toxicity of lactose when gluconate is fed. This important question should be investigated further.

E. Laxative Action of Lactose

The laxative effect of large amounts of lactose in the diets of both mammals and birds has been widely observed. Farmers know that the feeding of large amounts of skim milk or whey to pigs and calves results in a purgative action. This seems to be due principally to the lactose in the milk products. When the lactose level of purified diets was 20, 25, and 30%, transitory symptoms of injury appeared. The symptoms were diarrhea and "pot bellies." However, at these levels, growth and food consumption were not affected (*30*).

Few reports are available on the amounts of lactose which will produce diarrhea in man although considerable use has been made of the sugar in connection with investigations of *L. acidophilus* milk in treating constipation. Pediatricians have considered lactose in connection with problems

37. J. E. Fischer, *Federation Proc.* **14**, 433 (1955).

of constipation in infants. Hurst (1919) commented on the fat and lactose of breast milk as the components which promote intestinal motility in babies. The common practice of diluting cow's milk to a protein concentration equal to that of breast milk greatly reduces the concentration of lactose below that of breast milk, because the initial concentration of lactose in cow's milk is only two-thirds as high. Some pediatricians recommend the addition of lactose when cow's milk is made to substitute for breast milk in feeding infants.

Various ideas have been considered by which lactose promotes its laxative effect. Perhaps the most probable one is that the sugar acts as a hydragog and, as such, results in a water purgation. Possibly this is due to slow hydrolysis and absorption of lactose, thus maintaining a high osmotic pressure in the lumen of the intestines. This increases the water content and distends the intestines which, in turn, stimulates peristaltic action. The subject has been extensively reviewed (*34*).

F. Cataractogenic Action of Lactose

The history of scientific discovery is replete with instances of significant findings made accidentally by observant investigators. As an example, the important results which have been reported concerning cataracts and lactose had their beginning in "The accidental observation of mature cataract in the first three rats which had received a 70 per cent lactose ration in connection with another experiment (*38*)." Various experimental investigations in different laboratories have extended these findings. It was soon learned that the effect of the lactose is due to its galactose moiety. Consequently most of the information on carbohydrate-induced cataracts centers about this monosaccharide.

Day and associates (*39*) extended the discovery that lactose and galactose are cataractogenic. In addition, the Day group found that D-xylose, a pentose, is cataractogenic in young rats. In some cases at a level of 35% of the diet, the cataracts developed in as little as 11 days. The progressive lens opacities may begin first as a zone of diffraction, which is a fine line in the lens around the periphery of the nucleus. This zone of diffraction increases in size, width, and density. Eventually it may outline the entire nucleus of the lens, followed by a complete opacity of the nucleus. At first the changes can be seen only with an ophthalmoscope, but later the opacity is evident even with casual inspection by the unaided eye.

As yet the reason for these changes has not been clarified, but some of the experimental data already available may furnish the basis of an explanation. Some attention has focused on the concentration of glucose and

38. H. S. Mitchell and W. M. Dodge, *J. Nutrition* **9,** 37 (1935).

39. W. J. Darby and P. L. Day, *J. Biol. Chem.* **133,** 503 (1940).

the cataractogenic sugar in the blood. The concentration of the sugar in the blood becomes much higher than that of glucose following the ingestion of equal amounts. For example, in the experiments of Darby and Day (*39*) the mean blood sugar level of rats fed galactose was 372 mg. per 100 ml. of blood, whereas in those given glucose it was 121 mg. per 100 ml. Rats fed D-xylose had a lower concentration of blood sugar than those given D-galactose. The cataractogenic nature of galactose and xylose led Darby and Day to suggest that the difference between these sugars and those which do not cause cataracts is related to stereochemical configuration. The known cataractogenic sugars are derivatives of D-threose and the known noncataractogenic sugars are derivatives of D-erythrose, as indicated by the following formulas:

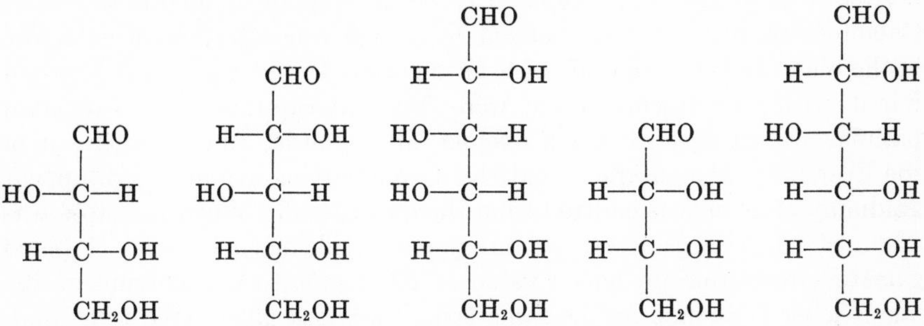

D-Threose D-Xylose D-Galactose D-Erythrose D-Glucose

That the apparent antagonistic effect is confined to the metabolic processes of the lens seems to be improbable. More likely the functional status of many tissues is affected. The question of biochemical antagonism in the sugar series ought to be more fully investigated. More information is especially needed concerning the intermediary metabolism of the cataractogenic sugars as compared with that of glucose. (See Chapter XIII.)

Other attempts to discover the nature of the biochemical defect due to lactose or galactose in the diet have revealed some facts which are of interest. In Handler's studies (*40*), rats fed large amounts of galactose or lactose underwent no specific changes which could be detected histologically. There was marked impairment in the skeletal mineralization of adolescent rats; this might be expected because of an elevation of serum calcium and an increase in the urinary excretion of calcium. The severe diarrhea, profound diuresis, and acidosis could hardly suffice to account for the severity of the symptoms and mortality. The information on changes in the carbohydrates of the tissues suggest that this is the primary biochemical defect. Moribund rats on both galactose and lactose diets had blood galactose level varying from 210 to 640 mg. per 100 ml., but the true blood

40. P. Handler, *J. Nutrition* **33**, 221 (1947).

glucose concentration varied from 26 to 73 mg. per 100 ml. The liver glycogen was almost nil. This suggests that the ability to synthesize glucose is greatly impaired and that the mechanism for the utilization of galactose is not adequate.

Some effects on protein metabolism are suggested by the finding that rats on a diet containing 70% galactose excrete peptides and amino acids in greater amount than in animals given glucose (*41*).

G. Galactosemia Associated with Cataracts in Humans

Although lactose is undoubtedly a desirable constituent of the dietary, within certain limitations, it is not surprising that there have been some unfortunate experiences from the ingestion of it by humans. These have been rare and they have apparently occurred only in infants (*42*, *43*). Galactosemia may be characterized by a high concentration of galactose in the blood and the excretion of it in the urine. In the case of a 7-week-old infant with galactosemia there were bilateral cataracts and associated pathological changes including anemia, albuminuria, and enlargement of the liver (*42*). The cataracts and the accompanying symptoms disappear gradually after milk is omitted from the diet (*42*, *43*). When galactose was administered to a galactosemic infant on a milk diet, the level of blood galactose rose from an initial value of 100 mg.% to a maximum of 297 mg.% after 1.5 hours. At the same time, the blood glucose fell to a minimum level of 30 to 40 mg.% in 2 hours. The galactose level fell after feeding glucose. This is additional evidence that the two sugars act in a competitive manner, and that galactosemia in infants is similar in its metabolic pattern to the condition induced in rats by feeding large amounts of lactose or galactose. Impairment in galactose utilization has been recognized only rarely. This fact and the fact that large amounts of lactose or galactose are necessary to induce the condition in rats suggests that most human beings are fully capable of metabolizing these sugars in the amounts which are normally ingested.

H. Lactose and Calcium Metabolism

Several different types of investigations have shown that lactose promotes the utilization of calcium and phosphorus. For example in chicks given a milk-grain rachitogenic diet containing 40% lactose, the lactose had a favorable effect on calcium utilization and it aided in preventing rickets (*44*). This effect has been repeatedly demonstrated in connection

41. J. M. Craig and C. E. Maddock, *Arch. Pathol.* **55,** 118 (1953).

42. F. A. Norman and G. J. Fachena, *Am. J. Diseases Children* **66,** 531 (1943).

43. E. Bruck and S. Rapaport, *Am. J. Diseases Children* **70,** 267 (1945).

44. O. L. Kline, J. A. Klemm, C. A. Elvehjem, and E. B. Hart, *J. Biol. Chem.* **98,** 121 (1932).

with the relief of tetany due to parathyroid deficiency. In these instances tetany was relieved by lactose and calcium salts, but calcium alone was useless. Particularly significant are the studies of Mills and co-workers (*45*), who showed that preschool boys had increased calcium retention when each received 36 g. of lactose per day, the equivalent of that quantity present in one quart of milk. Of the various dietary factors which have been studied, lactose appears to be second only to vitamin D in promoting the utilization of calcium and phosphorus.

The significance of lactose in nutrition has been extensively reviewed (*46*).

11. CELLOBIOSE

This β-D-glucopyranoside, unlike lactose, is not used in practical feeding, but it is of some interest. The disaccharide is derived from cellulose by partial acid hydrolysis or by the action of cellulase (p. 664). Experimental rats utilize it as completely as glucose (*47*). This indicates that cellobiose is hydrolyzed to D-glucose, but apparently little if anything has been reported on the nature of the enzyme of higher animals that catalyzes the reaction.

12. RARE SUGARS

The utilizability of carbohydrates is generally determined by estimating the concentration of glycogen in the liver of fasted animals a few hours after the administration of a carbohydrate to be tested. If the glycogen level is substantially elevated, it is concluded that the test substance is utilized and converted, in part at least, to glucose which then forms glycogen. On this basis it has been reported that sugars which are utilized in some degree by the rat include D-xylulose (*48*), melezitose (*49*), turanose (*49*), and trehalose (*49*). It is of interest that D-xylulose is utilized, by rats L-Xylulose, which is excreted in some forms of human pentosuria, is converted to glucose by the depancreatized dog (*50*). The status of D-arabinose and D-xylose is quite uncertain, but there is little if any evidence that either is utilized. Apparently all the D-arabinose and D-xylose absorbed from the digestive tract by man or dogs is excreted in the urine (*51*).

45. R. Mills, H. Breiter, E. Kempster, B. McKey, M. Pickens, and J. Outhouse, *J. Nutrition* **20,** 467 (1940).

46. E. O. Whittier, *J. Dairy Sci.* **27,** 505 (1944).

47. C. E. Vaniman and H. J. Deuel, Jr., *J. Biol. Chem.* **152,** 565 (1944).

48. H. W. Larson, N. R. Blatherwick, P. J. Bradshaw, M. E. Ewing, and S. D. Sawyer, *J. Biol. Chem.* **117,** 719 (1937).

49. F. Clarke, R. Solkot, and R. C. Corley, *J. Biol. Chem.* **131,** 135 (1939).

50. H. W. Larson, W. H. Chambers, N. R. Blatherwick, M. E. Ewing, and S. D. Sawyer, *J. Biol. Chem.* **129,** 701 (1939).

51. M. Rangier, P. M. de Traverse and M. Bonvallet, *Bull. soc. chim. biol.* **30,** 583 (1948).

D-Ribose is synthesized in the rat and presumably in all forms of higher life. However, it is utilized rather poorly. After the ingestion of 20 g. of D-ribose, 7.8% was excreted in the urine of one man and 16.6% in another (*52*). The low urinary excretion is probably due to low absorption from the intestine.

Among other sugars which are not utilized in the nutrition of the rat are: raffinose (*49*, *53*), melibiose (*49*), "mannoheptulose" (*54*), and L-rhamnose (*55*).

13. XYLOSE TOXICITY

Owing to its fairly sweet taste and abundance, D-xylose continues to be of interest as a possible "nonfattening" sugar for special uses such as in reducing diets. It is not utilized by monogastric animals (*51*, *56*), and it has laxative effects. However, the possible inclusion of xylose in foods immediately raises the question as to whether any health hazard would be involved. It has been pointed out that the continuous ingestion of xylose, like galactose or lactose, causes cataracts in rats (*39*). Diarrhea and abdominal distension occurs when rats are given considerable amounts of the pentose (*57*). (See also under D-xylose, Chapter II.)

A limited number of experiments have shown that xylose is toxic to rats. In weanling rats, xylose in the amount of 15% or more in the diet produces lens opacities, and rats made diabetic with alloxan develop more severe lens opacities when fed xylose than do diabetic controls (*58*). Thus, on the questionable basis that rats and humans would react in a comparable manner, it would appear that xylose could be more toxic for persons with a tendency toward cataract, as in diabetes, than for normal persons.

Like D-xylose, L-xylose is poorly absorbed by the rat and it does not appear to be glycogenic (*59*).

14. SUGAR ALCOHOLS (ALDITOLS)

The sugar alcohols of greatest interest are sorbitol and mannitol, and their derivatives (*60*). (See Chapter V.) Mannitol is the most abundant of

52. H. M. Wuest and U. V. Solmssen, *Arch. Biochem.* **11,** 199 (1946).
53. S. Kuriyama and L. B. Mendel, *J. Biol. Chem.* **31,** 125 (1917).
54. E. W. Cohn and J. H. Roe, *J. Lab. Clin. Med.* **29,** 106 (1944).
55. A. K. Silberman and H. B. Lewis, *J. Biol. Chem.* **101,** 741 (1933).
56. M. M. Miller and H. B. Lewis, *J. Biol. Chem.* **98,** 133 (1932).
57. N. R. Blatherwick, P. J. Bradshaw, O. S. Cullimore, M. E. Ewing, H. W. Larson, and S. D. Sawyer, *J. Biol. Chem.* **113,** 405 (1936).
58. A. N. Booth, R. H. Wilson, and F. DeEds, *J. Nutrition* **49,** 347 (1953).
59. H. W. Larson, N. R. Blatherwick, P. J. Bradshaw, M. E. Ewing, and S. D. Sawyer, *J. Biol. Chem.* **136,** 1 (1940).
60. C. J. Carr and J. C. Krantz, Jr., *Advances in Carbohydrate Chem.* **1,** 175 (1945).

all the naturally occurring sugar alcohols. In fungi, the amount may exceed the glucose content or in some it may displace glucose entirely. Sorbitol occurs in many fruits and berries, and it is an important industrial product. (See Chapter V.)

D-Mannitol is only slightly utilized if at all by higher animals and man (*60, 61*), and dulcitol (galactitol) is definitely inactive in the rat (*57*).

Unquestionably sorbitol (D-glucitol) is utilized by various higher animals as a source of energy (*60, 62*). When it is administered to dogs and to rabbits, there is only a moderate amount of sorbitol in the blood, but there is a prompt increase in blood reducing sugar. The sugar is D-fructose, and it is supposed that the ketose is formed directly from sorbitol (*62*).

Because mannitol and sorbitol are both moderately sweet and relatively inexpensive, they have been considered as special dietary constituents (*63*). The content of sorbitol in diabetic foods should be counted as available carbohydrate, and the label of foods containing sorbitol should indicate the amount present. Probably owing to the slow intestinal absorption of sorbitol, doses greater than 50 g. are laxative in humans, but smaller doses are well tolerated. Care needs to be exercised in determining more fully the possible harmful effect of ingesting considerable amounts of sugar alcohols, before their general use as food additives is accepted.

15. HEXOSAMINES

D-Glucosamine and D-galactosamine are the principal natural occurring sugar amines (Chapter VII). They are ingested almost entirely as components of mucoproteins and mucopolysaccharides. Quantitatively they are of little importance in nutrition, but they are of interest. It has been reported that glucosamine is not required in the nutrition of rats (*64*). Also, the synthesis of hexosamine in rats has been demonstrated by a method utilizing C^{14}-labeled glucose and glucosone (*65*). Thus, there is little doubt that hexosamines are dispensable components of the diet.

16. CELLULOSE AND RELATED SUBSTANCES

Cellulose is the main component of the cell walls of plants. The so-called hemicelluloses and other related polysaccharides constitute a considerable proportion of plants (Chapter XII). Therefore, these substances are present in nearly all dietaries. None of the higher forms of life appears to be

61. C. Johnston and H. J. Deuel, Jr., *J. Biol. Chem.* **149,** 117 (1943).

62. V. P. Seeberg, E. B. McQuarrie, and C. C. Secor, *Proc. Soc. Exptl. Biol. Med.* **89,** 303 (1955).

63. Anonymous, *Nutrition Revs.* **12,** 178 (1954).

64. W. C. Rose and S. S. Fierke, *J. Biol. Chem.* **143,** 115 (1942).

65. C. E. Becker and H. G. Day, *J. Biol. Chem.* **201,** 795 (1953).

capable of digesting these carbohydrates (*65a*). Even the termite which is widely recognized as a glutton for wood has no more ability alone to digest the cellulose than has man. However, the termite's alimentary tract, unlike that of man, is well stocked with protozoa which furnish the necessary digestive enzymes, thus benefiting the host as well as the parasites. Ruminants have a related symbiotic system in the form of bacteria and other microorganisms which digest cellulose, hemicellulose, etc., forming short-chain fatty acids and other products utilizable by the hosts (*66*).

The disappearance of crude fiber from the digestive tract is extremely variable and depends in part upon the proportion of cellulose and hemicelluloses, or pentosans, and also upon the presence of specific bacteria in the alimentary tract. The digestibility of the fibrous fraction appears to be inversely proportional to the lignin content of the foodstuff. Lignin does not appear to be digested.

The content of fibrous material affects the biological value of various dietary essentials (*67*). In studies on children, Macy and co-workers (*68*) found that the content of fibrous material influenced the nitrogen retention and also the acid-base and the mineral balances.

In dietaries particularly high in fibrous material, these facts must be given careful consideration in all quantitative determinations of nutritional value (*69*). Thus, the value that cellulose and related materials might have in human nutrition is concerned with their effect simply as bulk, which may be desirable in some instances (*70*).

It has been claimed that the growth of chickens is promoted by the presence of cellulose in amounts from 5 to 15% in complete but purified diets (*71*). Whether chickens have any ability to utilize cellulose, except through such microbiological activity as may occur in their alimentary tracts, has not been established. There is evidence that they can utilize sawmill wood waste when it is mixed with sugar molasses and fed in amounts up to 50% of the entire ration (*72*). There are numerous evidences that cattle, and to some extent other domestic animals, are able to utilize different sources of cellulose, especially when the sawdust or other product is mixed with molasses.

65a. W. W. Pigman, "The Enzymes" (J. B. Sumner and K. Myrbäck, eds.) Vol. I, p. 725. Academic Press, New York, 1951.

66. F. Baker, *Nature* **149,** 582 (1942).

67. E. W. Crampton and L. A. Maynard, *J. Nutrition* **15,** 383 (1938).

68. F. C. Hummel, M. L. Sheperd, and I. G. Macy, *J. Am. Dietet. Assoc.* **16,** 199 (1940).

69. L. C. Kung, *J. Nutrition* **28,** 407 (1944).

70. C. A. Hoppert and A. J. Clark, *J. Am. Dietet. Assoc.* **21,** 157 (1945).

71. F. Davis and G. M. Briggs, *J. Nutrition* **34,** 295 (1947).

72. J. McGinnis, H. I. MacGregor, and J. S. Carver, *Poultry Sci.* **27,** 459 (1948).

Wood saccharification and sulfite waste liquor utilization has been discussed extensively as a means of increasing the food resources (*73*). Substantial progress has been made in solving the technical aspects of such problems. It has been estimated that not more than half of the saw logs are converted to finished lumber. The sawmill waste alone is approximately one ton, dry basis, per thousand board feet of lumber produced. Such waste contains 50 to 65% carbohydrates as cellulose and hemicellulose. In large part, wood saccharification processes have been developed to furnish sugars for the growth of yeast, which may be used for food, and the microbiological production of ethanol, butanol, etc. However, production costs and other economic aspects of wood saccharification are usually not favorable.

Pectin and related substances occur in nearly all plant materials, especially in fruit and young tissues (Chapter XII). They are sometimes classed as hemicelluloses. On acid hydrolysis, crude pectins yield L-arabinose, D-galactose, D-galacturonic acid, and methanol. Investigation of the metabolic fate of pectin in normal persons has indicated that the polysaccharide may be broken down in the alimentary tract through the action of several groups of microorganisms. However, the galacturonic acid liberated by the bacteria is not absorbed. It has been concluded that the favorable effect of pectin in some forms of diarrhea is confined to the alimentary tract (*74*).

Alginic acid, which yields D-mannuronic acid upon hydrolysis, is a complex polysaccharide obtainable from seaweed and various other marine plants (Chapter XII). It is used in large amounts as a stabilizer by the food industry. Also, owing to its occurrence in *Chlorella*, the principal algae of potential value in human nutrition, knowledge of the nutritional effects of this material is of interest. Presumably alginic acid is not utilized by humans.

17. SWEETNESS AND FLAVORING CHARACTERISTICS OF SUGARS

From time immemorial the desire for sugars as sweetening agents has been great enough in many cases to cause highly damaging imbalances in diets. Nevertheless, the sweetness and flavor-enhancing qualities of sugars are greatly advantageous to humans when properly used. It appears that sugars are at least as valuable as monosodium glutamate as flavor enhancers and broadeners. The general subject has been reviewed (*75*).

It has been found that changes of sweetness will modify the impressions

73. E. E. Harris, *Advances in Carbohydrate Chem.* **4,** 153 (1949).

74. S. C. Werch, R. W. Jung, A. A. Day, T. E. Friedmann, and A. C. Ivy, *J. Infectious Diseases* **70,** 231 (1942).

75. L. B. Sjöström and S. E. Cairncross, *Advances in Chem. Ser.* **No. 12,** 108 (1955).

TABLE V

EFFECT OF VARIOUS FACTORS ON THE SWEETNESS OF SUCROSE

Taste factor	Concn. (%)	Additive	Concn. (%)	Effect
Sucrose	3–10	Salt	1	Sweetness reduced
Sucrose	5–7	Salt	0.5	Sweetness augmented
Acetic acid	0.04–0.06	Sucrose	1–10	Sourness reduced
Sucrose	1–5	Acetic acid	0.04–0.06	Sweetness not affected
Sucrose	6 and above	Acetic acid	0.04–0.06	Sweetness reduced

of saltiness, sourness, or bitterness and can be used frequently to make high levels of these factors tolerable (*75*). This property of sugar is widely used in the meat industry to minimize the harshness of salt used in curing. Some illustrations of the effect of certain basic taste factors on each other are given in Table V, which is taken from Sjöström and Cairncross' work (*75*).

A partial explanation of the flavor-enhancement properties of sucrose may be related to its ability to promote dissociation of weakly ionized compounds.

Sweetness is also markedly affected by temperature. For example, in one study (*76*) the sweetness of D-fructose was reported to be almost twice as great at 5°C. as at 60°C. The values were 143.7 at 5°, 128.5 at 18°, 100.0 at 40° and 79.0 at 60°. (See also under Fructose, Chapter II.)

The taste sense and the relative sweetness of sugars and other sweet substances have been critically reviewed (*77*). At certain concentrations mixtures of isosweet solutions of sucrose and corn sirup are slightly sweeter than either parent solution. α-D-Glucose is somewhat sweeter than β-D-glucose. Therefore, fresh α-D-glucose solutions are sweeter than those in which there is an equilibrium between the α- and β-forms. Because fructose is almost twice as sweet as glucose, it would seem that inversion of sucrose ought to increase its sweetness. This occurs, but it is not noticeable at concentrations below 10%.

18. APPETITE FOR CARBOHYDRATE

When laboratory animals are used under suitable conditions for experimentation in nutrition, interesting preferences are shown for different carbohydrates. Adult rats seem to have the greatest preference for solutions of the various common sugars when they are offered in concentrations near 10% (*78*). They show the greatest preference for maltose, next for glucose and sucrose, only a slight appetite for galactose, and none for lac-

76 Y. Tsuzuki and J. Yamazaki, *Biochem. Z.* **323,** 525 (1953).

77. A. T. Cameron, *Sugar Research Foundation, Sci. Rept. Ser.* **9,** (1947).

78. C. P. Richter and K. H. Campbell, *J. Nutrition* **20,** 31 (1940).

tose. This experience with lactose has been confirmed (*79*) with the observation that corn starch, dextrin, and sucrose are accepted to different extents, although the three materials are approximately equivalent nutritionally. The order of preference was starch > dextrin > sucrose. Although humans may have a stronger preference for sucrose than for starch, it is common experience that the desire for sugar becomes dulled by considerable amounts, and bland foods rich in starch are readily accepted day after day without satiation. Thus, the choices made by the animals are not surprising.

19. BLOOD GLUCOSE AND THE URGE TO EAT

Because D-glucose is the principal sugar in the body and it is a major source of energy, it is plausible to consider that its concentration in the blood may influence the urge to eat. However, the part played by the blood glucose concentration in actually conditioning the caloric intake has never been explained. It has been proposed (*80*) that gluco-receptors are located in the hypothalamic centers and that, through their great sensitivity to blood glucose, they affect the appetite for food.

One attempt to study the problem was based on the use of hypophysectomized alloxan-treated rats in which the blood glucose levels may be caused to fluctuate greatly through variations in the intake of sugar (*80*). A comparison was made on the effect of food intake of nutrients which were capable of exerting a direct influence on blood glucose, through the parenteral administration of glucose and fructose, with that of nutrient mixtures of similar caloric value which do not directly affect the concentration of blood glucose.

It was found that the procedures which induced hyperglycemia without appreciably decreasing the utilization of glucose were accompanied by substantial reductions in food intake. Whether the changes are due to definite cause-and-effect relationships has not been established. The observations suggest that normally the urge to eat may be controlled by the concentration of blood glucose.

The theory concerning gluco-receptors and the importance of blood glucose concentrations are attracting much attention for the control of human weight. Systems of dieting are based upon the deliberate inclusion of small amounts of sugar in the diet before meals. This procedure is supposed to raise quickly the level of blood sugar and, thus, promptly diminish the desire for food; some evidence suggests that this mechanism is operative (*80*), but further data are required. A further significance would relate to

79. E. M. Scott and E. L. Verney, *J. Nutrition* **34,** 401 (1947).

80. J. Mayer, *in* "Weight Control," Chapter 3. Iowa State College Press, Ames, Iowa, 1955.

the eating of candy or the use of soft drinks. An impairment of growth might be expected of normal children who are allowed to have sugar-rich food and drink without restraint.

20. SYNTHESIS OF VITAMINS BY THE INTESTINAL MICROFLORA

Since the early experiments of Fridericia in 1926 on refection (see p. 783), it has been recognized that the type of carbohydrate ingested is important in determining the activity of the intestinal microflora. Now it can be generalized that some carbohydrates in the diet have greater influence than others in determining the extent of synthesis of certain vitamins by microorganisms in the alimentary tract (*81*). The common carbohydrates may be arranged (*81*) in the following decreasing order as to their general effect on vitamin synthesis in the alimentary tract: dextrin, starch, lactose, glucose, and sucrose, but this varies with different vitamins. For example, lactose favors the production of riboflavin and vitamin B_6 (*81*), but it does not seem to promote biotin synthesis in the mature fowl (*82*). Dextrin causes the greatest synthesis of both niacin and folic acid. Although these effects are well established, vitamins synthesized through the changes in the microflora often do not become available in quantity in the nonruminant except through the feces.

The rapid development of awareness of the practical importance of certain antibiotics in animal nutrition has been accompanied by searches for the cause of the observed effects. The effects involve changes in the intestinal microflora, and these are influenced to a marked degree by the type of dietary carbohydrate (sucrose or dextrin) (*83*).

It has been already pointed out that, in general, starch and some dextrins appear to be superior to any of the sugars in promoting the growth of young animals on purified diets in which the content of certain vitamins may be suboptimal. In addition to the effect of the structure of these products on the microflora, they may be effective, in part, owing to the presence of one or more unrecognized nutritional factor (*84*). The choline content of corn starch is too low to account for its action in the prevention of the hemorrhagic kidney syndrome of choline deficiency (*85*). Possibly this effect is due to the same factor which seems to be necessary to promote growth and good feathering in ducks and prevent the development of acute

81. C. A. Elvehjem, *Federation Proc.* **7,** 410 (1948).

82. J. R. Couch, W. W. Cravens, C. A. Elvehjem, and J. G. Halpin, *J. Nutrition* **35,** 57 (1948).

83. G. E. Peterson, E. C. Dick, and K. R. Johansson, *J. Nutrition* **51,** 171 (1953).

84. O. N. Miller, *J. Nutrition* **50,** 13 (1953).

85. J. H. Baxter, *J. Nutrition* **34,** 333 (1947).

pancreatic fibrosis (*84*). Effort should be directed toward the isolation and identification of the factor.

21. PROTEIN SPARING ACTION

It is well established that carbohydrates are utilized in the synthesis of certain amino acids in the body and that the oxidation of amino acids is increased when the dietary source of carbohydrate or fat is inadequate to meet the caloric needs. Therefore, the differences between carbohydrates in promoting the efficient utilization of protein are of interest.

In the investigations by Harper and associates (*86*, *87*) it was shown that corn starch supports better growth of rats receiving 9% casein rations than does sucrose. The growth differences were eliminated by increasing either the level of casein or the level of five essential amino acids in the ration containing sucrose but were unchanged when liver extract and other sources of B vitamins were furnished. It seems probable that the beneficial effect of the corn starch is due to its action in reducing the rate of passage of food through the alimentary tract, thus promoting more efficient utilization of the low casein rations. This explanation is probably unsatisfactory in accounting for the superiority of starch and dextrin in diets containing suboptimal amounts of certain vitamins (*84*, *85*).

22. SUGAR IN CANDY AND CARBONATED BEVERAGES

The important and necessary function of carbohydrates in nutrition is to furnish energy. When the intake of sugar-rich foods such as candy and carbonated beverages is high in an individual, some imbalance in the diet might occur. The imbalance may well involve deficiencies in protein, mineral elements, various vitamins, and even possibly a deficiency of essential fatty acids. Conflicting strong convictions exist regarding the place of candy and carbonated beverages in the nutrition of persons of all ages, especially growing persons. Unyielding adherence to such opinions is justifiable only when relevant facts have been carefully assembled and objectively appraised.

It is estimated that in 1952 carbonated beverages accounted for approximately 2,122,000,000 lb. of sucrose and glucose used in the United States (*88*), and that the confectionery industry used about 2,225,000,000 lb. (*89*). Thus, the average consumption per capita is about 27 lb. per year, or approximately 130 cal. per person per day. This amount might be harmless

86. A. E. Harper and M. C. Katayama, *J. Nutrition* **49,** 261 (1953).

87. A. E. Harper, W. J. Monson, D. A. Arata, D. A. Benton, and C. A. Elvehjem, *J. Nutrition* **51,** 523 (1953).

88. C. Gortatowsky, *Advances in Chem. Ser.* **No. 12,** 70 (1955).

89. L. F. Martin, *Advances in Chem. Ser.* **No. 12,** 64 (1955).

or even beneficial depending upon the effect it would have on the consumption of foods furnishing the numerous dietary essentials. Since there is much variation between individuals and groups in the consumption of candy and carbonated beverages, a considerable percentage must consume far more than the average amount. These are the persons who may be most adversely affected.

Acting upon the basis of the facts and in the interests of good health, the American Dietetic Association, the American Medical Association, and the American Dental Association have each made public announcements of policy regarding candy and carbonated beverages. The statement of the American Dietetic Association is given herewith *(89a)*:

> "The American Dietetic Association does not accept advertising or exhibits for candy and soft drinks or carbonated beverages. This policy is established because our association is concerned professionally with the improvement of the nutritional status of human beings. We are concerned with the healthy individual as well as with the sick person and with children as well as adults and older people. And all of these groups must be considered when we recommend the use of any food or dietary supplement. A professional organization such as the American Dietetic Association must meet its responsibility to the general public on problems of food and nutrition, and particularly in regard to the nutrition of children, and not accept foods and drinks which may contribute to nutritional injury of children. . . ."

Candy and soft drinks are delightful developments of our civilization, but many persons use them in great excess and without suffcient regard for necessary foods which they may displace from the dietary. When used in moderation and with good oral hygiene, they may give pleasure without being appreciably harmful.

23. CARBOHYDRATES AND WEIGHT CONTROL

Problems of body weight control involve primarily the limitation of fat deposition or the removal of excess fat. Because carbohydrates may be converted to fat, systems of weight control invariably consider the carbohydrate intake as well as the fat intake. Both need to be controlled, but there are various interrelated factors involved in energy metabolism and the deposition or mobilization of fat.

When an effort is made to reduce the body weight, the diet must be planned to furnish less energy than is used by the body; thus, a net loss of

89a. Specific policy regarding candy and carbonated beverages, Dec. 15, 1952, Chicago, American Dietetic Association; Editorial in *J. Am. Dent. Assoc.* **47,** 222 (1953).

fat will occur. However, if the reducing diet tends to cause a decrease in the basal metabolic rate this will diminish the rate of fat mobilization and oxidation. In a series of investigations at Michigan State University, the importance of this relationship was emphasized (*90*). When the reducing diet was very low in fat, the basal metabolic rate decreased, thus necessitating a corresponding limitation of the caloric intake to achieve a given rate of weight reduction. A limited diet of moderate fat content, and furnishing some carbohydrate, resulted in a satisfactory loss of weight without causing excessive hunger and distress. (See also p. 801.)

24. CARBOHYDRATES IN PARENTERAL NUTRITION

Intravenous feeding involves many problems, some of which remain to be solved. The basic problem is the compounding of utilizable nutrients which can be dispersed in a suitable medium and administered without greatly disturbing the fluid distribution, acid-base balance, or metabolic status of the body. Because a major need in intravenous feeding is the provision of suitable energy-yielding food, carbohydrates are important.

Glucose has been used as the principal source of energy. However it cannot be administered in concentrations appreciably higher in osmotic pressure than the osmotic pressure of the blood. Thus, it cannot furnish more than a small proportion of the total energy requirements without flooding the body with water. Moreover, feeding which needs to be continued more than a day or two must furnish other nutrients. Good progress has been made in compounding mixtures containing fat and carbohydrate as the principal sources of energy, with other nutrients such as amino acids, inorganic salts, and vitamins being provided.

It would seem that fructose or invert sugar might have some advantages in intravenous feeding. Glucose utilization is temporarily inhibited following a prolonged fast, a condition which may lead to a need for parenteral nutrients. Fructose utilization shows little or no impairment in fasted rats (*91*). The evidence seems to be conflicting regarding the renal tolerance to invert sugar as compared with glucose and with fructose (*92*), but on the basis of the present evidence fructose or mixtures of fructose and glucose may prove to be preferable to glucose as the only carbohydrate in parenteral alimentation.

Owing to the high osmotic pressure of hexose solutions in comparison to that of equivalent amounts of carbohydrate as water-soluble polysac-

90. D. C. Cederquist, W. D. Brewer, R. M. Beegle, A. N. Wagoner, D. Dunsing, and M. A. Ohlson, *J. Am. Dietet. Assoc.* **28,** 113 (1952).

91. G. H. Wyshak and I. L. Chaikoff, *J. Biol. Chem.* **200,** 851 (1953).

92. Anonymous, *Nutrition Revs.* **11,** 299 (1953).

charide, consideration has been given to the effects of phytoglycogen (amylopectin) administered parenterally to rabbits (*93*, *94*). The polysaccharide causes an elevation of the blood sugar and appears to be converted into glucose in the body. More information needs to be obtained concerning the suitability of phytoglycogen for intravenous feeding.

93. D. L. Morris, *J. Biol. Chem.* **148,** 699 (1943).
94. E. Maywald, R. Christensen, and T. J. Schoch, *Agr. Food Chem.* **3,** 521 (1955).

Part II

Dental Aspects of Carbohydrates (95)

Teeth, as a part of a biological structure, are exposed to the same general metabolic influences of carbohydrates as the rest of the animal organism. These effects will be particularly important during the period of tooth formation. Formation occurs in the human in the prenatal period and before the age of about twelve years, at which time the permanent dentition has been completed, except for third molars. The erupted teeth, as shown by studies using radioactive tracer elements (*96*), are only slowly affected by general metabolic influences, much more slowly than the bones. The outer covering of the teeth, the enamel, is not capable of self-regeneration, and any changes which occur within the enamel are basically chemical exchanges with substances in the salivary secretions which bathe the teeth constantly. Human saliva, a mixed secretion exhibiting intrinsic variation, is also influenced in its composition by partial solution or emulsification of the foods entering the mouth. Since the saliva is in continuous contact with the teeth over many years, its composition and influence on the tooth surfaces obviously are of importance. The human mouth in common with the entire gastrointestinal tract as discussed earlier in this chapter also contains many types of microorganisms whose nature and distribution have not been adequately studied. The variable requirements of microorganisms for numerous growth factors indicate that the type and growth of microorganisms within the mouth may be extremely dependent upon the composition of the saliva. Although saliva contains many growth substances, the amounts are very small and variations in their amount could greatly influence the growth of microorganisms. Numerous organisms require minimal amounts of carbohydrates, and some will grow in proportion to the amount of carbohydrates present.

Strong evidence is available that the post-eruptive period may be divided into an early period of indefinite length, but perhaps lasting many years, during which the newly exposed surfaces mature. Before complete maturation, the teeth may be much more susceptible to attack and to exchange with components of saliva and blood than in the subsequent period.

Carbohydrates, then, are of dental interest through any general metabolic effect that they may exert, this effect being primarily operative during the pre-eruptive period of the tooth. Once the teeth are erupted, the

95. G. Toverud, S. B. Finn, G. J. Cox, C. F. Bodecker, and J. H. Shaw, "A Survey of the Literature of Dental Caries," Publ. 225, National Academy of Sciences, National Research Council, Washington, D. C., 1952.

96. O. Chievitz and G. Hevesy, *Kgl. Danske Vedenskab. Biol. Medd.* **13,** No. 9 (1937); J. F. Volker and R. F. Sognnaes, *Am. J. Physiol.* **133,** 112 (1941); R. F. Sognnaes and J. H. Shaw, *J. Am. Dental Assoc.* **44,** 489 (1952).

carbohydrates apparently exert their main influence through the medium of the saliva on the exposed surfaces of the enamel. This post-eruptive effect may also operate through an influence on the microbiological flora of the mouth.

1. PRE-ERUPTIVE EFFECTS

Any pre-eruptive or general metabolic effects of the carbohydrates on teeth have not been well established. The work of Sognnaes (*97*) with hamsters indicated possible prenatal and pre-eruptive effects of high carbohydrate diets. Teeth formed when the hamsters received high carbohydrate diets subsequently showed high rates of decay. Because of the difficulty in establishing controls for such experimentation, the validity of these interpretations is doubtful, and more recent experiments indicate that this supposed effect arises from differences in the inorganic portion of the diets (*98*).

Indirect evidence of a pre-eruptive effect has been described by Sognnaes and by Toverud as a result of considerations of the caries incidence among children in European countries during and subsequent to World War II (*99*). The consumption of purified carbohydrates was greatly reduced during the war period and increased subsequently. However, changes in the rate of dental decay required several years to become apparent and appeared to be correlated with the time of mineralization of the developing teeth.

2. POST-ERUPTIVE EFFECTS

Several important experimental procedures have been devised to study the factors influencing the development of caries during the post-eruptive period. Three general procedures are of special importance. These are the controlled studies of human nutrition, the use of experimental animals, and the *in vitro* studies of caries development in extracted teeth. Because of the difficulty of the direct control of human groups, studies on human beings are difficult to carry out and interpret. On the other hand, much information has been obtained by the use of experimental animals and by the *in vitro* studies.

A. Human Nutritional Studies

Numerous attempts have been made to demonstrate a relationship between the presence of carbohydrates in the diets of human beings and the

97. R. F. Sognnaes, *J. Am. Dental Assoc.* **37,** 676 (1948).

98. R. F. Sognnaes and J. H. Shaw, unpublished; see J. H. Shaw, *J. Dental Med.* **9,** 12 (1954).

99. R. F. Sognnaes, *Am. J. Diseases Children* **75,** 792 (1948); G. Toverud, reference *95*, page 34.

TABLE VI
ACCUMULATED DENTAL DECAY AS AVERAGE DMF RATES PER PERSON FOR 12,753 ADULTS ACCORDING TO AGE GROUP AND SEX (*100*)

Age	Male	Female	Age	Male	Female
17–19	11.95	12.77	45–49	21.25	23.72
20–24	15.72	15.84	50–54	21.18	24.65
25–29	17.70	18.59	55–59	23.25	25.62
30–34	20.08	20.34	60–64	23.59	22.69
35–39	19.53	21.60	65 and over	24.46	27.50
40–44	20.64	22.61			

incidence of dental decay. The results are influenced greatly by the criteria used for the initial lesions, by the methods of examination (in particular whether radiographic methods have been used), and by the method of expression of the data. The most common method of expressing the caries experience of the population is as the DMF value per mouth or per 100 teeth. The DMF is simply the number of decayed, missing, or filled teeth found in each individual or in 100 teeth examined.

The DMF rate is strongly dependent on the age of the individuals examined. A typical example of the dental decay experience of the adult American population is given by the data of Hollander and Dunning (*100*) (Table VI). From an examination of more than 12,000 adults, the DMF value per individual for the 30–34 year age group was found to be about 20 and thereafter increased only slowly, so that in the age group 60–64, the DMF value was about 24. No significant sex difference was observable.

Ancient man, as observed from the skeletons of past civilizations, and primitive tribes, such as Eskimos and African tribes when isolated from civilization, generally show relatively low rates of dental decay. When placed in contact with modern civilization, primitive tribes show a greatly intensified rate of dental decay, presumably as a result of a change in diets. An example of such observations are those reported by Price (*101*). Some 800 North American Indians and Eskimos were examined and classified according to their apparent contact with civilization. The Eskimos and Indians who had been completely isolated had very excellent teeth showing only one cavity per 1000 teeth. Those in close contact with civilization showed a much greater percentage of carious teeth, for the Eskimos, 13, and, for the Indians, 21.5 per 100 teeth. The isolated groups lived on meat and fish, primarily, whereas those in contact with trading posts included much flour, sugar, and other condensed foods.

100. F. Hollander and J. M. Dunning, *J. Dental Research*, **18,** 43 (1939).
101. W. A. Price, *J. Am. Dent. Assoc.* **23,** 417 (1936).

The enforced reduction in average consumption of purified carbohydrates during World War II has been used to explain the marked reduction of dental decay which occurred in the period subsequent to the war. Such studies assume that the only significant factor changing was the carbohydrate consumption. Actually, the delay in the appearance of a reduced caries rate, as indicated above, has been interpreted as signifying both pre-eruptive and post-eruptive effects of the diets.

In a broad sense, the above evidence has been deduced by studies of geographically isolated groups, and the normal population in civilized areas is taken as the control group. The same concept has been used directly to establish groups for which the diets could be assigned and controlled. Such groups include institutions such as orphan asylums and homes for the insane. Another type is composed of individuals with some medical disturbance requiring careful dietary control. Particularly suitable for the latter type are diabetics. Boyd (*102*) found that groups of diabetic children with carefully controlled consumptions of carbohydrates showed an incidence of dental decay much less than that of the average population. A very extensive comparison of institutionalized children on diets having variable amounts of carbohydrates was made by Mack and Urbach (*103*). Three orphan asylums were selected, and three standardized diets, differing in the amount of total carbohydrates and in many other nutritional factors, were used for the institutions. After two years, no correlation between the carbohydrate content of the diets and the caries incidence could be established.

In most dietary studies, the fluoride factor usually has not been given proper consideration. Since fluoride exerts a major influence, dietary effects ascribed to carbohydrates could in some instances be the results of varying amounts of fluoride. Also, as will be shown below, comparisons based on the crude establishment of total carbohydrate components of the diet is an undue oversimplification, since not only the amount but the type and the physical condition are important influences.

B. Studies Using Experimental Animals (*104*)

Although rats had been used earlier, the introduction of the Syrian hamster as an animal for caries research allowed animal experimentation to become important. The earlier lesions obtained with rats were not typical of human lesions, and factors such as the granule size of foods were of critical importance. More recently, suitable methods of using rats have

102. J. D. Boyd, *Am. J. Diseases Children* **66,** 349 (1943).

103. P. B. Mack and C. Urbach, *Soc. for Research in Child Development Monograph No. 46*, **13,** No. 1 (1948).

104. G. J. Cox, reference *95*, p. 55.

been developed. On the other hand, Syrian hamsters present the grave difficulty that hereditary and nutritional factors have not been established to the same extent as for experimental rats. By the use of hamsters, rats, and monkeys, it has been clearly shown by numerous investigators that diets rich in some types of carbohydrates will induce decay in the teeth. The experiments of Kite, Shaw, and Sognnaes demonstrated that the effect occurs directly in the mouth (*105*). The general metabolism is not involved because when the same diets were fed to rats by stomach tubes, the animals' teeth were unaffected. The necessity for bacteria in the decay process has been shown at the experimental "germ-free" laboratory at the University of Notre Dame (*106*). The existence of a period, following eruption, of enhanced susceptibility to attack has been established by a number of investigators who placed rats or hamsters on cariogenic carbohydrate diets, at various intervals after the teeth had erupted (*107*).

It must be noted, however, that hereditary influences exist, and caries-resistant and caries-susceptible strains of rats have been developed (*108*). Most dietary compositions used for experimentation have contained sucrose or starch as the principal carbohydrate material. But carbohydrates are not identical in their effects, and both chemical and physical differences may influence their cariogenicity (*109*).

C. In Vitro Caries Studies

Carious-like lesions can be produced in extracted human teeth by exposure to a nutrient medium suitable for bacterial growth and by innoculation of the solution with oral microorganisms. Lesions were produced in the early work of E. Magitot (around 1870) and later by W. D. Miller and many subsequent research workers (*110*). *In vitro* studies of this type have been greatly improved by the introduction of the "Artificial Mouth" in which many of the important oral conditions are reproduced. Under appropriate conditions, the entire tooth structure will be destroyed. In order to produce localized lesions, regular cleansing of the exposed tooth surfaces is required (*111*).

105. O. W. Kite, J. H. Shaw, and R. F. Sognnaes, *J. Nutrition* **42,** 89 (1950).

106. F. J. Orland, J. R. Blayney, R. W. Harrison, J. A. Reyniers, P. C. Trexler, M. Wagner, H. A. Gordon, and T. D. Luckey, *J. Dental Research* **33,** 147 (1954).

107. D. F. Mitchell and W. G. Shafer, *J. Dental Research* **28,** 424 (1949); F. J. McClure, *J. Nutrition* **43,** 303 (1951); J. C. Muhler, *J. Dental Research* **33,** 245 (1954).

108. See R. F. Keller, H. R. Hunt, and C. A. Hoppert, *J. Dental Research* **33,** 558 (1954).

109. See H. C. Elliott, Jr., and W. W. Pigman, *J. Dental Research* **33,** 27 (1954).

110. See W. Pigman, *J. Am. Dental Assoc.* **51,** 685 (1955).

111. W. Pigman, W. Hawkins, H. West, and C. Gaston, *Oral Surg. Oral Med. and Oral Pathol.* **7,** 427 (1954); W. Pigman, H. C. Elliott, and R. O. Laffre, *J. Dental Research* **31,** 627 (1952).

By the use of the Artificial Mouth, it has been demonstrated that two general types of attack on teeth can be distinguished. These, in turn, are dependent upon the amount of available carbohydrate in the nutrient medium. When glucose is present in the medium to an extent of about 100 mg. % or less, sound teeth are not attacked, but any previously decalcified matrix protein is rapidly destroyed. When glucose is present to an extent greater than about 300 mg. %, the inorganic portion of the tooth is rapidly removed, but the exposed matrix is attacked only slowly. At intermediate concentrations, probably 200 to 300 %, both types of attack proceed simultaneously, and the entire tooth substance is destroyed (*112*).

3. THE ORAL CLEARANCE FACTOR

Carbohydrates differ greatly in their rate of clearance from the oral cavity. Important factors in the rate of disappearance of foodstuffs from the mouth are the solubility, the physical consistency, and the chemical structure. Some enzymes, particularly salivary amylase, will quickly affect compounds of certain structures, such as starches.

Sticky carbohydrates or foods may cling to the oral structures and require long periods for their complete removal. Even soluble carbohydrates, however, require an appreciable period for their disappearance from the mouth. Ingestion of glucose will raise the apparent reducing sugar levels quickly, and the original reducing power of the saliva will be attained again only after 30 to 60 minutes (*113*). Individual foodstuffs differ greatly in the rate at which they leave the oral cavity (*114*).

Oral clearance in its relationship to dental health has been considered further by Lundqvist (*115*). In an extensive study, the values for the reducing sugar in the saliva were determined for a large group of persons at 15-minute intervals during the waking period. The subjects were divided into groups having the same basic diets, but with supplements of various types of carbohydrates. The control group without supplements exhibited an increased salivary reducing sugar value (as glucose) at meal times. The enhanced value lasted 30 to 60 minutes at each meal period and sometimes reached a peak of 2500 mg. % (Fig. 1). Individuals of other groups showed even higher peak reducing sugar values and a greater average period of duration. Persons consuming certain sticky candies at will had elevated reducing sugar values throughout the waking period (Fig. 1). A survey of

112. W. W. Pigman, W. Hawkins, J. Watson, R. Powell, and C. Gaston, *J. Dental Research* **34,** 537 (1955).

113. J. F. Volker and D. M. Pinkerton, *J. Dental Research* **26,** 225 (1947); G. W. Teuscher and L. S. Fosdick, *J. Dental Research* **16,** 354 (1937).

114. B. G. Bibby, H. J. V. Goldberg, and E. Chen, *J. Am. Dental Assoc.* **42,** 491 (1951).

115. See C. Lundqvist, *Odontologisk Revy* **3,** Suppl., 1–121 (1952).

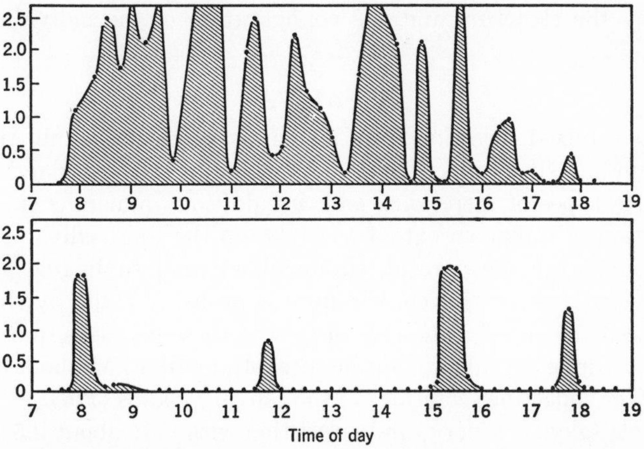
2.5
2.0
1.5
1.0
0.5
0
7
8
9
10
11
12
13
14
15
16
17
18
19
Time of day

FIG. 1. Reducing sugar values (as g. apparent glucose per 100 cc.) for salivas of two individuals during waking period. Upper curve, supplements of molasses candy. Lower, supplements of bread.

the caries incidence of the individuals on these various diets (made in conjunction with Gustafson) exhibited a marked degree of correlation between the average reducing sugar level of the salivas and the dental caries incidence of the various groups (Fig. 2).

All the factors involved in the rate of clearance of dietary carbohydrates from the oral cavity are not understood. The consistency, adhesiveness, and rate of solubility of the materials obviously are important. The chemical nature of the carbohydrates should influence the clearance time in relation to the ease of solubilization by the enzymes and microorganisms of the mouth. Both enzymes and microorganisms undoubtedly would be in

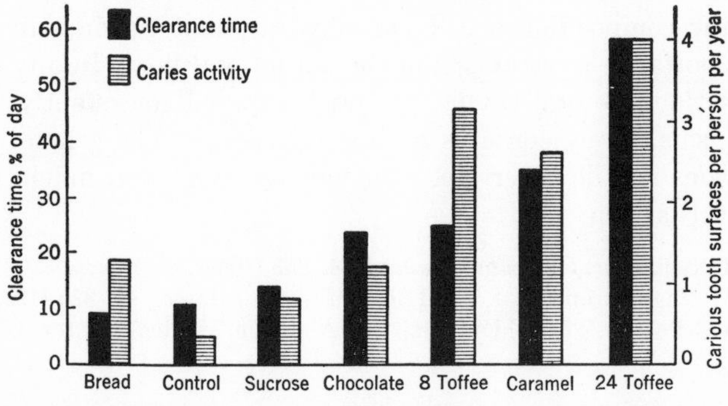
Clearance time
Caries activity
Clearance time, % of day
Carious tooth surfaces per person per year
Bread
Control
Sucrose
Chocolate
8 Toffee
Caramel
24 Toffee

FIG. 2. Group comparison between sugar clearance and caries activity. Shaded areas—mean values for clearance: all individuals studied. Dark areas—mean values for caries activity: all individuals in the groups.

fluenced by the structure and the configuration of the individual carbohydrates.

4. SALIVA

Saliva is a mixed secretion from a number of glands within the mouth and surrounding structures. Three pairs of major salivary glands contribute separate types of secretions, and, in addition, numerous small glands add a portion of unknown extent to make up the total saliva. The major salivary glands are the parotid, submaxillary, and sublingual glands. In most individuals the major contribution is probably made by the parotid and submaxillary glands. The rate of flow of these glands is quite variable and depends upon psychic and mechanical stimulation. Methods have been developed for collecting secretions of the salivary glands (*116*).

The whole saliva is a very dilute secretion with only about 0.5% of total solids. Of this, approximately one-half is composed of inorganic salts made up mainly of calcium, sodium, and potassium cations and chloride, phosphate, and thiocyanate anions. Many diverse organic materials are present in small amounts (*117*), but the major material is a "mucin". This "mucin" is a mixture whose composition is discussed in Chapter XII. The apparent reducing sugar level of whole saliva usually falls in the range of 10 to 30 mg.%, calculated as glucose. The actual level of endogenous free sugars including glucose is very low, probably less than 1 mg.% (*115*, *118*). Apparently, no direct relationship exists between blood sugar level and salivary reducing substance.

A portion of this reducing power arises from the mucin and the remainder from unknown substances, dialyzable and undialyzable. The blood-type polysaccharides are excreted in salivas.

Since microorganisms exhibit considerable difference in their ability to utilize specific carbohydrates and in their growth requirements for carbohydrates, the composition of the carbohydrate material in saliva may be of great importance in establishing the actual oral flora. In any case, it is remarkable that the oral cavity, although exposed consistently to foreign microorganisms, rarely contains pathogenic species. The general nature of the inhibitions is still uncertain, although lysozyme and mucin may contribute to this action.

116. See L. Schneyer, *J. Dental Research* **34,** 257 (1955).

117. See W. Pigman and A. J. Reid, *J. Am. Dental Assoc.*, **45,** 325 (1952).

118. J. Reid Patton, Thesis, University of Alabama, Medical Center, Birmingham, 1956.

XV. SOME GENERAL REFERENCES TO CARBOHYDRATE COMPILATIONS*

General and Sugars

"Advances in Carbohydrate Chemistry," Academic Press, New York, Vol. 1, 1945. Vol. 2, 1946. Vol. 3, 1948. Vol. 4, 1949. Vol. 5, 1950. Vol. 6, 1951. Vol. 7, 1952. Vol. 8, 1953. Vol. 9, 1954. Vol. 10, 1955. Vol. 11, 1956.

E. F. Armstrong and K. F. Armstrong, "The Carbohydrates." Longmans, Green, New York, 1934.

M. Cramer, "Les sucres et leurs derives." Gaston Doin, Paris, 1927.

N. Deerr, "The History of Sugar," 2 Vols. Chapman and Hall, London, 1949–50.

E. F. Degering, "An Outline of the Chemistry of the Carbohydrates." Swift, Cincinnati, 1943.

E. Fischer, "Untersuchungen über Kohlenhydrate und Fermente," 2 Vols. Springer, Berlin, 1922.

W. N. Haworth, "The Constitution of the Sugars." Edward Arnold, London, 1929.

J. Honeyman, "An Introduction to the Chemistry of the Carbohydrates." Oxford, New York, 1948.

C. S. Hudson, "Collected Papers," 2 Vols. Academic Press, New York, 1946–1948.

P. W. Kent and M. W. Whitehouse, "Biochemistry of the Amino Sugars." Academic Press, New York, 1953.

E. O. von Lippmann, "Chemie der Zuckerarten," 2 Vols. Vieweg, Braunschweig, 1904.

E. O. von Lippmann, "Geschichte des Zuckers," 2nd ed. Springer, Berlin 1929.

F. Micheel, "Chemie der Zucker und Polysaccharide." Springer, Berlin, 1939.

E. G. V. Percival, "Structural Carbohydrate Chemistry." Prentice-Hall, New York, 1950.

W. W. Pigman and R. M. Goepp, Jr., "Chemistry of the Carbohydrates." Academic Press, New York, 1948.

W. W. Pigman, ed., "The Carbohydrates." Academic Press, New York, 1957.

H. Pringsheim, "Zuckerchemie." Academische Verlagsges., Leipzig, 1925.

Scientific and Technical Report Series, Sugar Research Foundation, New York.

Tables, Handbooks, and Sugar Analysis

"Abderhalden's Handbuch der biologischen Arbeitsmethoden," Urban and Schwarzenberg, Berlin, 1922. G. Zemplén and F. F. Nord, Abt. I, Teil 5.

F. J. Bates, "Polarimetry, Saccharimetry and the Sugars," Nat'l Bur. Standards Circular 440, U. S. Gov't. Printing Office, Washington, D. C., 1942.

Beilsteins' "Handbuch der organischen Chemie," Vol. 31. Springer, Berlin, 1938.

C. A. Browne and F. W. Zerban, "Sugar Analysis." Wiley, New York, 1941.

E. Chargaff and J. N. Davidson, eds., "The Nucleic Acids," Vols. 1 and 2. Academic Press, New York, 1954.

H. Elsner, "Kurzes Handbuch der Kohlenhydrate." Tollens-Elsner, Barth, Leipzig, 1935.

*See also General Reference given by M. L. Wolfrom, A. L. Raymond and E. Heuser *in* "Organic Chemistry," (H. Gilman, ed.), Vol. 2. Wiley, New York, 1943.

A. W. van der Haar, "Anleitung zum Nachweis, zur Trennung und Bestimmung der Monosaccharide und Aldehydsauren." Borntraeger, Berlin, 1920.
G. Klein, "Handbuch der Pflanzenanalyse." Springer, Vienna, 1932.
K. Paech and M. V. Tracy, eds., "Moderne Methoden der Pflanzenanalyse," 4 Vols. Springer, Berlin, 1954.
H. Vogel and A. Georg, "Tabellen der Zucker und ihrer Derivate." Springer, Berlin, 1931.

Polysaccharides, Wood, and Glycosides

E. F. Armstrong and K. F. Armstrong, "The Glycosides." Longmans, Green, New York, 1931.
M. Burger, "Bacterial Polysaccharides." C. C. Thomas, Springfield, Ill., 1950.
E. Heuser, "Cellulose Chemistry." Wiley, New York, 1944.
P. Karrer, "Polymere Kohlenhydrate." Academische Verlagsges., Leipzig, 1925.
R. W. Kerr, ed., "Chemistry and Industry of Starch," 2nd ed. Academic Press, New York, 1950.
C. L. Mantell, "The Water Soluble Gums." Reinhold, New York, 1947.
R. J. McIlroy, "The Plant Glycosides." Longmans, Green, New York, 1951.
A. G. Norman, "The Biochemistry of Cellulose, the Polyuronides, Lignin, Etc." Oxford, New York, 1937.
E. Ott, H. M. Spurlin, and M. W. Grafflin, eds., "Cellulose and Cellulose Derivatives," 2nd ed. Interscience, New York, 1954.
H. Pringsheim, "Die Polysaccharide." Springer, Berlin, 1931.
J. A. Radley, "Starch and Its Derivatives," Vol. I, 3rd ed., Chapman and Hall, London, 1953.
A. Stoll, "The Cardiac Glycosides." Pharmaceutical Press, London, 1937.
A. C. Thaysen and H. J. Bunker, "The Microbiology of Cellulose, Hemicelluloses, Pectins and Gums." Oxford, New York, 1927.
R. L. Whistler and C. L. Smart, "Polysaccharide Chemistry." Academic Press, New York, 1953.
L. E. Wise and E. C. Jahn, eds., "Wood Chemistry," 2nd ed. Reinhold, New York, 1952.

Carbohydrate Nutrition (see also references in Chapter XIV)

D. J. Bell, "Introduction to Carbohydrate Biochemistry," 2nd ed. Univ. Tutorial Press, London, 1948.
G. H. Bourne and G. W. Kidder, eds., "Biochemistry and Physiology of Nutrition," Vols. I and II, Academic Press, New York, 1953.
Council on Foods and Nutrition of the American Medical Association, "Handbook of Nutrition," 2nd ed. Blakiston, New York, 1951.
L. B. Jensen, "Man's Foods." Garrard Press, Champaign, Ill., 1953.
D. W. Kent-Jones and A. J. Amos, "Modern Cereal Chemistry," 4th ed. Northern Publishing, Liverpool, 1947. Includes discussions on nutritive value of cereals.
J. S. McLester and W. J. Darby, "Nutrition and Diet in Health and Disease," 6th ed. Saunders, Philadelphia, 1952.
J. P. Peters and D. D. Van Slyke, "Quantitative Clinical Chemistry, Interpretations," Vol. I, 2nd ed. Williams and Wilkins, Baltimore, 1946. Includes 370 pages on energy metabolism, biochemistry, physiology, and clinical aspects of carbohydrates.
Symposium on Sugar and Dental Caries, *J. Calif. State Dental Assoc.* **26** (Suppl. to No. 3) (1950).

Photosynthesis and Metabolism
(see also references in Chapter XIII)

E. Rabinowitch, "Photosynthesis and Related Processes," Vol. I, 1945; Vol. II, Part 1, 1951; Vol. II, Part 2, 1956. Interscience, New York.

"Photosynthesis in Plants" (J. Franck and W. E. Loomis, eds.). Iowa State College Press, Ames, 1949.

"Carbon Dioxide Fixation and Photosynthesis," *Symposia Soc. Exptl. Biol.* **5,** Academic Press, New York (1951).

"CO_2 Assimilation Reactions in Biological Systems," Brookhaven Conference Report 70 (c-13) Brookhaven National Laboratory, Upton, New York.

J. S. Turner, *Revs. Pure and Appl. Chem.* (*Australia*) **1,** 214 (1951).

E. C. Wassink, *Advances in Enzymol.* **11,** 91 (1951).

C. P. Whittingham, *Botan. Rev.* **18,** 245 (1952).

R. Hill and C. P. Whittingham, "Photosynthesis." Wiley, New York, 1955.

AUTHOR INDEX

Numbers in parentheses are footnote numbers and are inserted to enable the reader to locate a cross reference when the author's name does not appear at the point of reference in the text.

C

D

E

G

H

I

J

L

N

O

Q

R

Y

Z

SUBJECT INDEX*

Italicized configurational prefixes (as *glycero-*) are used as main entries, whereas other italicized prefixes (as *scyllo-*) are listed under the stem name.

* Subject Index compiled by James W. Pratt.

D

G

I

M

Q

Y

Z

OC 1 2'65
Date Due
APR 6 1975
1975